①

欧洲藏汉籍目录丛编

Catalogues of
Ancient Chinese Classics
in Europe

张西平　主　编

谢　辉　林发钦　副主编

文化公所
Hall de Cultura

SPM
南方出版传媒
广东人民出版社
·广州·

图书在版编目（CIP）数据

欧洲藏汉籍目录丛编 1 / 张西平主编，谢辉、林发钦副主编. —澳门：文化公所；—广州：广东人民出版社，2020.1

ISBN 978–99981–36–62–5（中国澳门）

ISBN 978–7–218–13891–6（中国内地）

Ⅰ．①欧…　Ⅱ．①张…　②谢…　③林…　Ⅲ．①古籍—图书目录—汇编—欧洲　Ⅳ．①Z838

中国版本图书馆CIP数据核字（2019）第228770号

欧洲藏汉籍目录丛编 1

张西平　主编　　谢辉、林发钦　副主编

出 版 人：肖风华

策划编辑：梁　茵

编　　辑：赵香玲　王俊辉　李永新

出　　版：文化公所　广东人民出版社
发　　行：文化公所
　　　　　电　　邮：macau.publish@gmail.com
　　　　　网　　址：www.macau-publish.com
印　　刷：广东鹏腾宇文化创新有限公司
开　　本：787 毫米×1092 毫米　1/16
印　　张：256　　字　　数：4760千
版　　次：2020年1月第1版
印　　次：2020年1月第1次印刷
定　　价：MOP360.00

编委会

主　编：张西平

副主编：谢　辉　林发钦

编　委（按姓氏笔画为序）：
卢梦雅　张西平　杨慧玲　李　真　李　慧
阿日娜　林发钦　彭　萍　谢明光　谢　辉

项目支持单位：北京外国语大学比较文明与人文交流高等研究院
中国文化走出去协同创新中心
北京中外文化交流研究基地
澳门文化公所

本项目为北京外国语大学中国文化走出去协同创新中心、
北京中外文化交流研究基地资助项目

编者简介

张西平，北京外国语大学比较文明与人文交流高等研究院院长、教授，《国际汉学》主编，国际儒学联合会副会长，世界汉语教育史国际研究会会长。长期以现代西方文化、明清中西文化交流史、西方汉学史和中国基督教史为主要研究领域。出版专著十一部，发表论文一百余篇。

谢辉，北京外国语大学国际中国文化研究院助理研究员，历史学博士。主要从事明清之际西学汉籍、域外汉籍与中国古代学术思想史等方面的研究，发表相关论文五十余篇。

林发钦，澳门理工学院人文及社会科学高等学校代校长、教授，历史学博士。澳门特别行政区政府文化遗产委员会委员，澳门口述历史协会会长，澳门文教出版协会理事长。主要从事澳门历史文化、中国与荷兰关系史、文化遗产、口述历史等领域的研究工作。出版著作十余部，发表相关论文数十篇。

出版说明

　　本丛刊辑录十七世纪后期至二十世纪初，主要由西方学者编纂，著录欧洲各国公私机构收藏汉籍的目录30种。其中大部分为专门著录汉籍的目录，予以全文影印。少数为综合性目录，仅抽印其中汉籍部分。涉及国家包括英国、法国、德国、奥地利、意大利、俄罗斯、瑞典，文种涵盖英、法、德、意及拉丁文。现将各目录的基本情况作简要叙述。

　　《大英博物馆图书馆藏中文刻本、写本、绘本目录》（*Catalogue of Chinese Printed Books, Manuscripts and Drawings in the Library of the British Museum*），英国道格拉斯编。道格拉斯（Robert Kennaway Douglas，1838-1913），1838年8月23日生于德文郡，1858年来华，先后在广州、北京、天津、大沽领事馆供职，1864年返英后任职于大英博物馆，并成为1892年成立的东方写本与印本部的首任主任，直至1907年退休。本目录于1877年在伦敦出版，著录了大英博物馆当时收藏的汉籍约2500余种。目录主体的编纂方法为：以作者首字母为纲，无作者之书则按照书名中人名、地名或关键词首字母排列，另附书名索引。

　　《大英博物馆藏中文刻本写本目录续编》（*Supplementary Catalogue of Chinese Books and Manuscripts in the British Museum*），英国道格拉斯编，1903年伦敦出版。著录自1877年至1903年间，该馆新入藏的汉籍约1800种。其体例与前目大致相同。大英博物馆图书馆为英国国家图书馆前身，以上两种目录，可在很大程度上反映今英国国家图书馆收藏汉籍的情况。

　　《博德利图书馆藏中文典籍目录》（*A Catalogue of Chinese Works in the Bodleian Library*），英国艾约瑟（Joseph Edkins，1823-1905）编，1876年牛津大学出版。著录汉籍299部，仅将所收录的文献简单地编号排列，并无分类。

　　《博德利图书馆新入藏日文中文刻本与写本目录》（*A Catalogue of Japanese and Chinese Books and Manuscripts Lately Added to the Bodleian Library*），日本南条文雄（Nanjō Bunyū，1849-1927）编，1881年牛津大学出版。著录各类文献共计64部，其中前37部为伟烈亚力（Alexander Wylie，1815-1887）旧藏的佛教文献，分为汉译佛教经咒、梵文、悉昙文等八类，基本均为日本刊刻；第38至第44部为日本政府赠送给阿莫斯（S.Amos）的法律典籍，其中包括《唐律疏义》等5种中国法律典籍，与《类聚三代格》等2种日本法律典籍，但仅有《大清会典》与《大清律历刑案新纂集成》刻于中国，其余均为和刻本；第45至64部为麦克斯·缪勒（Max Müller，1823-1900）旧藏，大致亦均为梵文与佛教文献。

　　《剑桥大学图书馆威妥玛文库汉、满文书籍目录》（*A Catalogue of the Wade Collection of Chinese and Manchu Books in the Library of the University of Cambridge*），英国翟理思（Herbert Allen Giles，1845-1935）编，1898年剑桥大学出版。分8类收录汉籍883部4304卷。卷末附有人

名与书名索引。

《剑桥大学图书馆威妥玛文库汉、满文书籍目录续编》（*Supplementary Catalogue of the Wade Collection of Chinese and Manchu Books in the Library of the University of Cambridge*），英国翟理思编，1915年剑桥大学出版。收录1898年以来，剑桥大学通过购买与捐赠，新获得的汉籍1300卷，体例与前目大致相同。

《皇家亚洲学会中文文库目录》（*Catalogue of the Chinese Library of the Royal Asiatic Society*），英国基德（Samuel Kidd，1804–1843）编，1838年伦敦出版。分20余类，著录汉籍约200余种。其著录书名采用拼音，未用汉字，是其显著不足之处。

《皇家亚洲学会图书馆藏中文典籍目录》（*A Catalogue of the Chinese Manuscripts in the Library of the Royal Asiatic Society*），英国何为霖（Henry F. Holt）编，1890年发表于《皇家亚洲学会会刊》（*Journal of the Royal Asiatic Society of Great Britain and Ireland*）第22卷。出版时曾经翟理斯审定。共收录典籍559种，约5000卷。

《印度事务部图书馆藏中、日、满文典籍解题目录》（*Descriptive Catalogue of the Chinese, Japanese, and Manchu Books in the Library of the India Office*），英国岑马士（James Summers，1828–1891）编，1872年伦敦出版。著录典籍170部，其中尤以佛教典籍最为丰富，此外尚有《正卜考》等日本典籍，以及《御制增订清文鉴》等满文文献。另有少量欧洲印本，如《新约》满文译本即于1821至1836年印于俄国圣彼得堡。

《林赛文库中文印本及写本目录》（*Bibliotheca Lindesiana. Catalogue of Chinese Books and Manuscripts*），英国埃德蒙德（John Philip Edmond，1850–1906）编，1895年自印本。著录各类文献464部，约8000卷。目录编成后不久，该图书馆所收藏的汉籍，即于1901年售于今属曼彻斯特大学的约翰·莱兰兹图书馆（John Rylands Library），故本目录可在一定程度上反映出该馆目前收藏汉籍的情况。

《皇家图书馆写本目录》（*Catalogus Codicum Manuscriptorum Bibliothecae Regiae*），巴黎1739年出版。本目录为法国皇家图书馆所编综合目录，以拉丁文编成，其中汉籍部分为傅尔蒙（Étienne Fourmont，1683–1745）编。按照来源分6个部分，著录汉籍约400部。本次出版抽印其中汉籍部分。

《皇家图书馆藏中国图书目录》（*Catalgogus Librorum Bibliothecae Regiae Sinicorum*），法国傅尔蒙编。附于其所著《中国官话》（*Linguae Sinarum Mandarinicae Hieroglyphicae Grammatica Duplex*），1742年巴黎出版。该目录以《皇家图书馆写本目录》为基础，但不再按照来源进行划分，而是将其总体分为13类。此外添加了前目所无的中文书名，以便查找。

《国王图书馆的中文藏书和新目录规划》（*Mémoire sur les Livres Chinois de la Bibliothèque du Roi, et sur le Plan du Nouveau Catalogue*），法国雷慕沙（Jean Pierre Abel Rémusat，1788–1832）编。登载于1817年《百科年鉴》（*Annales Encyclopédiques*），次年于巴黎出版单行本。该书大体可分为两部分，前一部分为对法国国王图书馆藏汉籍的总体介绍，后一部分则主要订正傅尔蒙所编目录中的错误。据雷慕沙所言，当时国王图书馆所藏汉籍，除傅氏目录著录者外，尚有175种约2000卷，拟续编目录。但此工作似乎最终并未完成。

《中韩日文图书目录》（*Catalogue des Livres Chinois, Coréens, Japonais, etc*），法国古郎（Maurice Auguste Louis Marie Courant，1865—1935）编。全书三卷，第一卷为1—4423号，第二卷4424—6689号，第三卷6690—9080号，依次于1902、1910、1912年在巴黎出版。共分21大类，其下尚有二级类目。此目录为目前最为完备的法国国家图书馆藏汉籍目录，至今仍可利用，但亦未能囊括该馆藏全部汉籍。其后古郎仍有续编目录的计划，其目录手稿已编至10919号，但最终因病未能完成。

《国家图书馆中文藏书中的"伯希和藏品A"和"B"目录》（*Répertoire des "Collections Pelliot A" et "B" du Fonds Chinois de la Bibliothèque Nationale*），法国伯希和（Paul Pelliot，1878—1945）编。发表于《通报》（*T'oung Pao*）1913年第14卷第5期。1908年至1909年，伯希和在盗掠敦煌文书，并将其运回法国之后，又前往北京、上海等地，为法国国家图书馆采购大批汉籍，即本目录所著录者。全书分上下二卷，上卷收录书籍329部，下卷收录1743部，仅简单著录中文书名、译音与册数等基本信息。

《勒苏埃夫藏中文书籍与手稿目录》（*Catalogue des Livres et Manuscrits Chinois Collectionnés par A. Lesouëf*），法国勒苏埃夫（Alexandre-Auguste Lesouëf，1829—1906）藏，1886年荷兰莱顿布里尔（Brill）出版社出版。著录其所藏汉籍100部。卷末附刻书铺号目录，中、日年号及干支、公元纪年对照目录，以及四部分类法与二十四史目录。此批典籍后来亦归法国国家图书馆，故此目录实际也可视为该馆的早期汉籍目录之一。

《勒苏埃夫藏中日文卷轴目录》（*Catalogue des Kaké-Monos et des Maki-Monos Chinois et Japonais Collectionnés par A. Lesouëf*），法国勒苏埃夫藏，1900年布里尔出版社出版。共收录地图、绘本等41件。

《已故托奈利埃先生东方藏书目录》（*Catalogue de la Bibliothèque Orientale de Feu M. Jules Thonnelier*），1880年巴黎出版。其中3918—4037号为中文与满文典籍，本次出版抽印此部分。

《已故德理文先生中国图书目录》（*Catalogue de la Bibliothèque Chinoise de Feu M. le Marquis d'Hervey de Saint-Denys*），1894年巴黎出版。全书分三部分：中文藏书，与中国有关的作品，与考古学、钱币学等有关的作品。多数藏品为儒莲（Stanislas Aignan Julien，1797—1873）旧藏。

《已故雷慕沙先生藏印本与写本图书目录》（*Catalogue des Livres, Imprimés et Manuscrits, Composant la Bibliothèque de Feu M.J.-P. Abel-Rémusat*），1833年巴黎出版。其中1564—1673号为中文、日文等藏品，本次出版抽印此部分。

《已故皮埃尔·利奥波德·范·阿尔斯坦先生收藏书籍与写本目录》（*Catalogue des Livres et Manuscrits Formant la Bibliothèque de Feu Mr P.Léopold Van Alstein*），1863年根特（Gand）出版。其中2466—2814号、5410—5422号为中文文献。本次出版抽印此部分.

《勃兰登堡选帝侯藏中文书籍目录》（*Catalogus Librorum Sinicorum Bibliothecae Electoralis Brandenburgicae*），德国米勒（Andreas Müller，1630—1694）编，约于17世纪70年代末至80年代

初首次出版。著录汉籍20余种。

《中文书目的其它部分》（*Anderer Theil des Catalogi der Sinesischen Bücher*），德国米勒编，约1683年出版。为前目之续编。

《柏林皇家图书馆藏汉满文图书目录》（*Verzeichniss der Chinesischen und Mandshuischen Bücher und Handschriften der Königlichen Bibliothek zu Berlin*），德国克拉普洛特（Julius Klaproth, 1783-1835，一译"柯恒儒"）编，1822年巴黎出版。收录各类典籍约50种，每种均有较为详尽的解说。

《御书房满汉书广录》（*Verzeichniss der Chinesischen und Mandschu-Tungusischen Bücher und Handschriften der Königlichen Bibliothek zu Berlin*），德国硕特（Wilhelm Schott, 1802-1889）编，1840年柏林出版，著录《通鉴纲目》等各类典籍近200种。

《已故克拉普罗特先生藏中满日文书目》（*Catalogue des Livres Imprimés, des Manuscrits et des Ouvrages Chinois, Tartares, Japonais, etc., Composant la Bibliothèque de Feu M. Klaproth*），法国朗德雷斯（Ernest Clerc de Landresse, 1800-1862）编，1839年巴黎出版。共收录各类典籍290种。

《皇家图书馆藏汉、满、日、韩文书目》（*Übersicht der Chinesischen, Mandschouischen, Japanischen und Koreanischen Bücher der K.K. Hof.Bibliothek in Wien*），奥地利恩德利歇（Stephan Ladislaus Endlicher, 1804-1849）编，附于其所著《和汉钱志》（*Verzeichniss der Chinesischen und Japanischen Münzen des K.K Münz- und Antiken-Cabinets in Wien*），1837年维也纳出版。著录汉、满文典籍120余，既包括《钦定七经》、《通鉴纲目》等中国传统古籍，也收录了《赤道南北两总星图》、《天主降生出像经解》等传教士以中文撰写的西方科技、天主教类典籍。

《圣彼得堡皇家公共图书馆东方写本与刻本目录》（*Catalogue des Manuscrits et Xylographes Orientaux de la Bibliothèque Impériale Publique de St.Pétersbourg*），德国多恩（Bernhard Dorn, 1805-1881）等编，1852年圣彼得堡出版。其中第792-842号为中文文献，本次出版抽印此部分。

《灵采学院图书馆藏日文中文印本与写本目录》（*Catalogo delle Opere Giapponesi e Cinesi Manoscritte e Stampate Conservate nella Biblioteca della R. Accademia dei Lincei*），意大利华嘉（Giovanni Vacca, 1872-1953）编。发表于《灵采皇家学院论文集：道德科学、历史和语言学部分》（*Rendiconti della Reale Accademia dei Lincei, classe di scienze morali, storiche e filologiche*）1912年第21卷。著录中、日文典籍约40种。

《瑞典所藏中文书籍》（*Chinese Books in Swedish Collections*），瑞典高本汉（Klas Bernhard Johannes Karlgren, 1889-1978）编，1931年哥德堡（Göteborg）出版。著录瑞典多家公藏机构及高本汉自己的汉籍收藏约400部。

西文之中国文献学初议（代序）

一

做中国学问，文献学是其基础。"文献学"一词源于1920年梁启超在《清代学术概论》中所说的"全祖望亦私淑宗羲，言文献学者宗焉"，又在《近代三百年学术史》中说："明清之交各大师，大率都重视史学——或广义的史学，即文献学。"当代文献学大家张舜徽先生在谈到中国文献学时，总结历史，阐明近义，对中国文献学做了很好的表述，他说："我国古代，无所谓文献学，而有从事于研究、整理历史文献的学者，在过去称之为校雠学家。所以，校雠学无异成为文献学的别名。凡是有关整理、编纂、注释古典文献的工作，都由校雠学担负了起来。假若没有历代校雠学家们的辛勤劳动，尽管文献资料堆积成山，学者们也是无法去阅读、去探索的。我们今天，自然要很好地继承过去校雠学家们的方法和经验，对那些保存下来了的和已经发现了的图书、资料（包括甲骨、金石、竹简、帛书），进行整理、编纂、注释工作，使杂乱的资料条理化、系统化；古奥的文字通俗化、明朗化。并且进一步去粗取精，去伪存真，条别源流，甄论得失，替研究工作者们提供方便，节省时间，在研究、整理历史文献方面做出有益的贡献，这是文献学的基本要求和任务。"①

张舜徽先生所讲的中国文献学的范围是中文文献。但至晚明以后，中国的历史已经纳入到全球史之中，晚清之后，更是被拖入以西方世界为主导的世界历史之中。这样，来华的传教士，做生意的西方各国东印度公司，驻华的外交官和汉学家，留下了大批关于研究中国的历史文献，翻译了大批关于中国古代的历史典籍。由此，中国文化开始以西方语言的形态进入西方文化之中，关于中国近代历史的记载也再不仅仅是由中文文献组成。我们将其称为"中学西书"。很自然，这批"中学西书"是西方中国研究中的一个重要组成部分，是治西方汉学之基础。但对中国学术来说，这些"中学西书"也构成了研究中国近代历史的重要文献。

根据张舜徽的理解，我们可以说，在西方汉学的历史中也同样存在一个西方汉学文献学的研究领域，西方汉学文献学作为一个西方汉学研究的基础研究领域是完全存在的。进一步扩展来讲就是"西方语言的中国文献学"，简称之"中学西书"。金国平建议建立"西方语言中国史料学"，他认为："只要充分地利用在华传教士留下的这批宝贵历史遗产，比勘汉语史乘，从新的视角对已知史料进行新的诠释，披沙觅金，某些较具有争议的重大历史事件真相的发潜

---

① 张舜徽：《中国文献学》，上海世纪出版集团，2009年，第3页。

彰幽不无可能。"①

从全球史研究的新进展来看，如果打破欧洲中心主义的世界史写作，就必须将地域史的研究纳入全球化史研究的总体框架之中，这个进程不是东方被动地适应西方，而是一个互动的过程。迄今为止的世界史写作大都建立在单一地域史的写作基础上，对于文化与文明之间的互动关注不够。如果从全球化史的角度构建中国历史，中西之间的互动就成为关键，由此，传教史和贸易史就成为必须研究之材料。从东西互动的角度来构建中国史，就必须将"西学东渐"和"中学西传"作为一个整体来把握，中国近代历史就不仅仅是一个西化的历史，同时也是一个西方不断吸收东方，从而促进西方变化的历史，由此，西方汉学史的研究就不再仅仅属于西方东方学，它同时也是中国近代历史的一部分。中国近代的历史也不再仅仅局限于中文文献，这些"中学西书"就同样成为记载中国近代历史不可或缺的基本文献。如果确立这样的史观，西方语言的中国文献整理就成为基础性的工作，在这个意义上，"西方语言中国史料学"或者"中学西书"的梳理与整理就成为学术界的基础性工作。"西方语言的中国文献学"或者"中学西书"包括：凡是由西方文字出版的关于中国的书籍和藏于西方档案馆尚未出版的关于中国的档案、手稿、资料。

<h2 style="text-align:center">二</h2>

中国文献学作为一门学问包括目录、版本、校勘。同样西方语言中国文献学大体也包括这几个方面，不过呈现出不同的特点。

清代著名学者王鸣盛说："凡读书，最切要者，目录之学。目录明，方可读书。不明，终是乱读。""目录之学，学中第一紧要事，必从此问途，方能得其门而入。"②

治西方语言中国文献学亦是如此，西方关于中国的历史记载已经有几百年历史，关于中国的研究著作、中国游记同样浩如烟海，如果不从目录入手完全不知从何读起。考狄（Henri Cordier，1849–1924，Bibliotheca Sinica）书目、袁同礼书目是目前最基础的书目，各类专业书目也有多种，只有对这些书目都烂熟于心，方可摸到西方汉学发展之脉络。

版本学是文献学之基础之一，它主要研究各种中文版本的源流，比较刻本之优劣，鉴别各种版本之真伪。

西方的中国研究同样存在版本学的问题，十六至十八世纪关于中国的知识是一个剽窃流行的时代，海员的记载、传教士的著作在欧洲相互转抄、翻译出版，一部重要的著作很快就有各种语言的翻译。从十六到十九世纪，随着欧洲各国实力的变迁，关于中国记载的语言也在不断变化。因为，在十九世纪前中国典籍的翻译以传教士为主，传教士的这些中国典籍的译本在欧洲呈现出非常复杂的情况。十七世纪时传教士的一些译本是拉丁文本的，例如柏应理和一些耶

---

① 金国平：《构建"西方语言中国史料学"之初议》，载金国平、吴志良：《过十字门》，澳门成人教育学会出版，2004 年。

② 王鸣盛：《十七史商榷》卷二二，卷一。

稣会士联合翻译的《中国哲学家孔子》，这里包括了《论语》、《大学》、《中庸》，这本书的影响很大，很快就有了各种欧洲语言的译本，有些是节译，有些是改译，如果我们没有西方汉学文献学的知识，就搞不清这些译本之间的关系。

十八世纪时欧洲的流行语言是法语，会法语是上流社会的标志。恰好此时来华的传教士由意大利籍为主已经转变为法国耶稣会士为主。这些法国来华的传教士学问基础好，对中国典籍翻译极为勤奋。法国传教士的汉学著作中包含了大量的对中国古代文化典籍的介绍和翻译，例如来华耶稣会士李明返回法国后所写的《中国近事报道》（*Nouveaux mémoires sur L'état present de la Chine 1687–1692*），1696年在巴黎出版，他在书中介绍了中国古代重要的典籍《五经》，同时介绍了孔子的生平。该书所介绍的孔子生平在当时欧洲出版的来华耶稣会士的汉学著作中最为详细，因此出版后在四年内竟然重版五次，并开始有多种译本。如果我们对法文本和其他文本之间的关系不了解，就很难做好翻译研究。

十九世纪后英语逐步取得霸主地位，英文版的中国典籍著作逐渐增加，版本之间的关系也更为复杂。美国诗人庞德在翻译《论语》时既看早年由英国汉学家柯大伟（David Collie）翻译的第一本英文版《四书》，也参考理雅各的译本，如果只是从理雅各的译本来研究庞德的翻译肯定不全面。

因此，认真比较西方出版的关于中国的书籍的各种版本以及各种版本之间的关系，是做好西方汉学之必须，也是做好西方语言中国文献学之基础。

张舜徽认为，"校勘学是研究总结校勘工作的一般性方法和规律的专门学问"，"在雕版印刷术没有发明以前，书籍都是手写。在抄写过程中，有时不小心在字体上加了一笔或者减少了一笔，便成为另一个字，直接改换了文句原意，影响到内容的真实，甚至牵涉到古代制度的认识、说明和处理，以致引起许多混乱。"[1]这是指由稿本转写和抄写而导致的问题需要校勘。"至于古书在长期写、刻的过程中，有时无意识地掉一个字，或者添一个字；由于一个字的不同，便直接影响到内容的真相，带来许多不必要的争论和纠纷。对于做研究工作的人来说，关系尤大。"[2]这就提出中国文献学中校勘的重要性。

这在西方语言的中国文献学来说是同样存在的，只是在形态上有所不同。目前西方国家的档案馆中收藏着大量关于中国的手写档案，例如《耶稣会在亚洲》（Jesuí itas na Ásia）档案文献原藏于葡萄牙的阿儒达图书馆（Biblioteca da Ajuda），它是从1549年沙勿略到达日本后西方传教士在远东传教活动的真实原始记录。全部档案共61卷，均为手抄本，计三万页。文献是以拉丁文、葡萄牙文、西班牙文、意大利文及法文写成。这批文献最早是由葡萄牙耶稣会神父若瑟·门丹哈（José Montanda）和若奥·阿尔瓦雷斯（João Álvares）修士等于1742–1748年对保存在澳门的日本教省档案室的各个教区资料整理而成。在这些教区中包括中国的副省北京、广州、南京以及交趾支那、老挝、柬埔寨等地。这批档案是研究中国清代天主教史和明清中西文

---

① 张舜徽：《中国文献学》，第71–72页。

② 张舜徽：《中国文献学》，第75页。

化交流史及清代社会史最重要的一手文献，它包括向耶稣会总会的年报告表，教区内的通信，发生在康熙年间的"礼仪之争"的伦理学和神学的争论，宗座代牧与罗马传信部争论的报导，耶稣会殉难者列传，澳门、日本和中国教区的主教和各省会长记载，航行于澳门和日本之间的黑船所载运货的货物表，澳门及各省会修会的财产清单，传教士之间的通信等，为我们提供了清中前期的许多重要情况，都是中文文献所不记载的。

类似这样的档案文献在西方还很多，对于欧美所收藏的关于中国的外文文献，至今无论是欧美学术界还是中国学术界均无一个基本的书目介绍。这批文献的基本特点是以手稿为主，基本内容是原始的传教报告、贸易报告、外交档案等。

但如果使用这批文献就有一个对文献的校勘问题。对于西文文献的校勘来说，它有着悠久的传统，1933年胡适在为陈垣先生的《元典章校补释例》一书所写的序中对中西校勘学做了比较，他说："西洋印书术起于十五世纪，比中国晚了六七百年，所以西洋古书的古写本保存的多，有古本可供校勘，是一长。欧洲名著往往译成各国文字，古译本也可供校勘，是二长。欧洲很早就有大学和图书馆，古本的保存比较容易，校书的人借用古本也比较容易，所以校勘之学比较普及，只算是治学的人一种不可少的工具，而不成为一二杰出的人的专门事业，这是三长。在中国则刻印书流行以后，写本多被抛弃了；四方邻国偶有古本的流传，而无古书的古译本；大学与公家藏书又都不发达，私家学者收藏有限，故工具不够用，所以一千多年来，够得上科学的校勘学者，不过两三人而已。"[1]

对于西方语言的中国文献来说，在校勘上更有中西之共同特点，也是一个专门之学问。我们要学习西方校勘学的经验[2]，但这批文献又有其自身的特点，需要我们特别注意。

一是这批文献数量之大令人惊讶，超出一般学者之想象。英国东印度公司关于中国的手稿文献、荷兰东印度公司关于中国的手稿文献、梵蒂冈传信部关于中国的手稿文献等，这些文献加起来可以绕地球几圈。至今我国学术界对这批手稿文献没有一个基本的把握。

二是这批关于中国的西文手稿辨读困难。由于这些手稿文献大都是十六至十九世纪的欧洲各类语言的手稿，辨读十分困难。即便在西方，能辨读这些手稿也需要专门的训练。外语能力、历史知识、西方校勘学的训练都需要具备。目前，能辨认这些手写稿的中国学者不多，因此转写就是第一难事。笔者在国外看到这些手写稿时，如果转写只能求教于国外学者。

三是这些文献内容的核对困难。尽管是西方语言的文献，但其内容是关于中国的。如上文所说的《耶稣会在亚洲》文献，其中相当多的文献内容是对中国各地传教的记载。这样即便是一般的西方汉学家，如果不是专业的研究者，即便转写成现代西方语言，这些内容对他们来说也是陌生的，如果核对其中的内容更是要有专业的知识，尤其是涉及中国古代的地名、人名，正确理解极为困难。因为记载这些文献的西方人当时并未有统一的拼读中国文字的法则，加之许多人又生活在中国各地，方言、口音夹杂其中，使人完全不知所云。即便后来威妥玛汉语拼

---

① 胡适：《胡适文集》（5），北京大学出版社，1998年，第112页。

② 苏杰编译：《西方校勘学论著选》，上海人民出版社，2009年。

音系统出现后，也减轻不了多少核对的困难。

四是翻译更为复杂和困难。来华的传教士的报告、外交官的报告、东印度公司的报告大都是他们内部文件，其内容涉及到中西之间四百多年的历史，历史跨度大，内容繁杂，不了解历史背景，很难把握。他们对中国文化经典的翻译，也有着自己的文化立场。缺少了跨文化的视角，随之产生的"误译"和"误读"实为正常。

三

在笔者看来，西方语言之中国文献的研究整理比中国文献学和西方自身文献研究整理还要困难。

中国文献学的目的是为"辨章学术，考镜源流"，对学术之发展有一个宏观的了解和把握；西方语言之中国文献学亦是如此。尤其从事中国古代文化经典在西方的翻译和传播研究，一定要从文献学入手，从目录学入手，这样才能保证我们在翻译研究上对版本之间的复杂关系有一个清楚的了解，为研究打下坚实的基础。

另一方面，国家目前对汉籍外译投入了大量的费用，国内学术界也有相当一批学者在从事这项事业。但我们在开始这项工作时应该摸清西方汉学界已经做了哪些工作，哪些译本是受到欢迎的，哪些译本问题较大，哪些译本是节译，哪些译本是全译。只有清楚了这些以后，我们才能确定新的翻译政策。显然，由于目前我们在西方汉学的文献学上做得不够理想，对西方汉学界近四百年来对中国古代文化经典的翻译情况若明若暗，造成国内现在确立的一些翻译计划是重复的，这在学术上是一种浪费。即便国内学术界进行重译，也需要建立在前人的基础上展开。

因此，建立西方语言的中国文献学，或简而称之"中学西书文献学"，是展开西方汉学研究之基础，是做好中国典籍外译和流播研究之基础。同时，也是在全球范围内展开中国历史文化研究，将中国史放入全球史中加以研究的基础性工作。这里从文献学上对做好西方语言的中国文献研究的方法提出一个初步的设想，以期引起学界之重视，开启西方语言之中国文献之研究和整理，将其纳入中国学术发展的基础性工作。只有将这批西方语言的中国文献彻底掌握，我们才能真正写出全球史背景下的中国近代历史文化之研究，才能揭示出中国文化在西方的影响，才能在全球史的背景下说明中国文化之意义。

张西平

目录
contents

第五卷

第六卷

Catalogue of Chinese Printed Books, Manuscripts and Drawings in the Library of the British Museum

大英博物馆图书馆藏中文刻本、写本、绘本目录

CATALOGUE

OF

CHINESE PRINTED BOOKS,

MANUSCRIPTS AND DRAWINGS

IN THE

LIBRARY

OF THE

BRITISH MUSEUM.

BY

ROBERT KENNAWAY DOUGLAS.

PRINTED BY ORDER OF THE TRUSTEES OF THE BRITISH MUSEUM.

LONDON:

SOLD BY LONGMANS & CO., 39, PATERNOSTER ROW; B. M. PICKERING, 196, PICCADILLY; B. QUARITCH, 15, PICCADILLY; AND A. ASHER & CO., 13, BEDFORD STREET, COVENT GARDEN.

1877.

STEPHEN AUSTIN AND SONS,

PRINTERS, HERTFORD.

THE present Catalogue of Chinese books and MSS. in the British Museum, has been compiled by Mr. R. K. DOUGLAS, Senior Assistant in the Department of Printed Books and Professor of Chinese in King's College, London. It is believed to be the first Catalogue ever published in Europe of an extensive Chinese Library.

GEO. BULLEN.

KEEPER OF THE DEPARTMENT OF PRINTED BOOKS.

March, 1877.

PREFACE.

THE Chinese Books to which this Catalogue refers have been collected at different times and under various circumstances. The nucleus of the Library, apart from a few volumes contained in the Sloane, Harleian, Old Royal and Lansdowne bequests, was formed by a collection bequeathed to the Museum by Mr. Fowler Hull, of Sigaur in the East Indies, in 1825. In 1843 Her Majesty presented a number of Works which had been taken during the war in China of 1842, and in 1847 the collection of Chinese books belonging to Mr. Morrison the younger, amounting to 11,500 volumes, was purchased by the Government and presented to the Museum. Since that time, partly by purchase and partly by presentation, the library has reached its present very considerable dimensions, amounting in all to upwards of 20,000 Chinese volumes. On examining some of the less recently acquired books, many of which were presented by travellers and others, who regarded their volumes rather as isolated curiosities than as portions of works, it has been found, as might have been expected, that there exist imperfections among them. Many of these imperfections have been made good, but it has not as yet been possible to supply all the deficiencies.

In this Catalogue the Books are placed under the names of the authors, when these occur, in alphabetical order. When the author's name does not appear on the title, or in any other part of the book, the work is catalogued under the name of any person or country which may occur in the title. But if neither the name of a person nor that of a country occurs on the title of such work, the subject or the principal word in the title has been taken as a heading. As, however, even when the author's name appears, the titles of Chinese works are more readily remembered than the names of their authors, a complete Index has been added to the Catalogue from the titles to the headings under which the works are to be found in the body of the Catalogue.

As is well known, every Chinaman possesses, in addition to his surname, and, as we should say, Christian name, a literary appellation, frequently one or more pseudonyms, and in some instances a posthumous epithet. By any of these a Chinese author may be designated; and though in compiling this Catalogue I have endeavoured to reduce the various names applied to any author to a common form, yet doubtless instances have occurred in which I have been unable to recognize the different epithets owned and adopted by the same writer. As an instance of this difficulty I may quote the name of the celebrated scholar Maou Ke-ling, which sometimes appears thus, but quite as often as Maou Ta-ko, his literary appellation, or as Se-ho, his adopted pseudonym. Thus in one work he may appear on the title page as Maou Ke-ling, on another as Maou Ta-ko, and on a third as Se-ho, and the compiler of a Catalogue may have nothing before him to indicate that the three works are by the same author.

After much consideration it was decided to adopt in the Catalogue the Orthography employed by Morrison in his Dictionary, since it is the one most generally known amongst Chinese scholars, and also because it is the one best suited for English readers. It is much to be desired that a common system of transcribing Chinese characters should be adopted, and in any such system the vowels would, without question, have their continental values assigned to them. But until some such universal understanding be arrived at, the best course appears to be for each writer to use the orthography which most nearly represents the Chinese sounds to readers of his own nationality. We are accustomed to give to French, German, Italian and Russian transcriptions of Chinese characters the several sounds which we should give to words in those languages spelt in the same manner, and though the variations common to English vowel-sounds undoubtedly present difficulties in the way of transcribing Chinese words with exactness, they supply an easier medium for expressing them to the English reader than any system based on the value of the continental letters. As Chinese also is a language which forbids the idea that the most advanced scholar can dispense with the use of a Dictionary, it follows that the orthographies employed in the best Dictionaries will be those most generally known, and it was considered advisable, therefore, to let the orthography adopted harmonise with that used in the most authoritative work of the kind. This, at the time the decision was arrived at, was without doubt Morrison's.

It is customary for an Emperor when he ascends the throne to choose a *Neen haou* or title for his reign, much in the same way as the Popes of Rome adopt pontifical appellations on being called to the Chair of St. Peter, and when, therefore, it has been necessary to refer to an Emperor by name, I have designated him by his *Neen haou.*

The difficulty which, as every Librarian is aware, exists in describing the sizes of books generally, is aggravated in the case of Chinese volumes, in which the help towards settling the point, which is usually gained in European works by reckoning the number of pages into which the sheet is folded, is entirely wanting. The sizes therefore, as denoted in the present Catalogue, have been determined by comparison with European books.

In compiling this Catalogue I have received great assistance from Mr. Wylie's *Notes on Chinese Literature* and from the Prolegomena of Dr. Legge's Works on the Chinese Classics.

The Catalogue has been printed by Stephen Austin and Sons of Hertford, who obtained the necessary Chinese type from Shanghai for this express purpose.

ROBERT K. DOUGLAS.

BRITISH MUSEUM,
Feb. 17, 1877.

前　言

本《目录》著录的中国图书收藏的时间和条件各不相同。核心馆藏除少量来自斯隆（Sloane）、哈尔莱（Harleian）、旧皇室（Old Royal）和兰斯多恩（Lansdowne）的遗产外，主要由1825年东印度群岛西噶尔（Sigaur）的赫尔（Fowler Hull）先生遗赠给博物馆的藏品组成。1843年，女王陛下将1842年战争期间从中国所获的大量图书赠予博物馆。1847年，英国政府购买了小马礼逊（Morrison the younger）收藏的11500册中文图书赠送给大英博物馆。自那时起，通过购买和捐赠，博物馆的藏书逐渐达到了目前这样可观的规模，中文书籍超过两万册。较早收藏的不少图书来自旅行家和其他人的捐赠，他们将自己手里的书籍视为稀世珍宝，不单单是部分作品。翻阅这些书籍时，难免会发现其中存在一些瑕疵。这些瑕疵中有很多已得到修复，但到目前还不可能修复所有缺陷。

本《目录》中著录的书籍根据作者姓名归类，并按照字母排序。如果作者的姓名没有出现在书名或书籍中的其他任何部分，则该作品将按照书名中出现的任何人名或国名进行归类。如果该作品的书名中既无人名又无国名出现，则将书名中的主题词或主要词语作为分类条目。不过，即使出现了作者的姓名，中文著作的书名还是比作者的姓名更加容易记住，所以本《目录》添加了一份完整的索引，通过标题和条目可以在《目录》正文中找到这些著作。

众所周知，每个中国人除了姓名和"字"（正如我们所说的"洗礼名"），还会有一个或多个笔名，某些情况下还会在死后获得一个称号。对一位中国作者的称呼可能是以上的任何一个，因此尽管在编纂本《目录》时，我已尽力将同一作者的不同名字简化为常见形式，然而，毫无疑问，还是遇到了无法分辨同一作者不同称号的问题。例如，著名学者毛奇龄（Maou Ke-ling）有时以"毛奇龄"这个名字出现，又常常以他的字"毛大可（Maou Ta-ko）"，有时又以别人对他的称呼"西河先生（Se-ho）"出现。因此，他可能在一部著作的标题页是"毛奇龄"，在另一部著作的标题页可能是"毛大可"，在第三部著作的标题页又变成了"西河先生"，《目录》编纂人员可能完全不知道这三部著作出自同一位作者之手。

经过再三考虑，本《目录》决定采用马礼逊在其词典中所使用的拼字法，因为该方法最为中国学者所知晓，也最适合英语读者。很希望能够采用一种转译汉字的通用体系，且在这个体系中，元音能够毫无疑义地获得指定的欧洲大陆语言的音值。可是，在达成这种共识之前，最佳做法似乎是，每位作者在使用拼字法时应尽可能近似地向作者所在国的读者展示中文读音。通常，我们在为汉字的法语、德语、意大利语和俄语译文标音时，由于这几种语言使用了相同的拼写方式，因此采用给其本身的词汇注音的方法，而英语中由于经常存在元音的变化，用英语准确翻译汉语词汇不可避免会面临一些困难，但在向英语读者表达汉语词汇时，相比基于欧洲大陆语言字母音值的其他任何注音体系，英语仍是一种更为简单的手段。面对汉语，就连最出色的学者也不得不使用字典，因此，最好的字典中所用的拼字法就会成为最广为人知的一种方法，也正因为如此，明智的做法是，使用与最权威的字典相一致的拼字法。在决定这一事项时，马礼逊的字典毫无疑问是最佳选择。

通常，中国皇帝登基时，会选择一个"年号"，这与罗马教皇登基时选用新称号的做法相类似，因此，有必要提到中国皇帝的名字时，我一般会用"年号"来称呼这位皇帝。

每一位图书管理员都明白，很难笼统地描述书籍的开本，对中文图书而言，这种描述尤为困难。欧洲著作通常借助估算纸张折叠成的书页数量来解决这一问题，对中文图书来说，则完全没有办法。因此，本《目录》中所列书籍的开本是通过与欧洲书籍的比较来确定的。

在编纂本《目录》的过程中，伟烈亚力（Wylie）先生的《汉籍解题》（*Notes on Chinese Literature*）和理雅各博士（Dr. Legge）的《中国经典》（*Works on the Chinese Classics*）绪论都为我提供了很大帮助。

本《目录》由哈特福德郡的Stephen Austin and Sons公司印刷，该公司从上海购买了出版此《目录》所需的中文铅字。

罗伯特·K·道格拉斯（Robert K. Douglas）
于大英博物馆，
1877年2月17日

（管宇译，彭萍校）

ERRATA.

PAGE	COL.	LINE	
9	1	6	*for* Works *read* Writings.
15	2	13	„ Tables of Altitude etc. *read* Astronomical Tables.
15	2	16	„ A minute etc. *read* Minute Tables of Altitudes.
16	2	8	„ The Doubtful Passages of *read* Doubts on.
16	2	41	*dele* 存 . . . *Tsun.*
19	1	17	*for* Mǔh Leen-heen *read* Mew Leen-seen.
21	1	19	„ Amita Sutra *read* Amitâbha Sûtra.
23	2	26	„ Le Wǎn-keung *read* Le Wǎn-heung.
30	1	18	„ Mǔh *read* Mew.
34	1	38	„ Sing Ke-yun *read* Sung Ke-yuen.
35	2	23	„ Yaou *read* Chaou.
36	1	35	„ Fǔh *read* Foo.
48	2	11	„ *Ah* read *O.*
49	2	8	*dele* "Tablets in Ancestral."
51	2	2	for *wan* read *wǎn.*
52	2	41	*for* Mǔh *read* Mew.
53	1	13	„ *kang* read *kǎng.*
61	2	32	*dele* 塡 . . . Teen.
71	1	8	*for* Guṇadhadra *read* Guṇabhadra.
71	1	32 and 36	*for* Hambery *read* Hamberg.
74	2	1	*for* William Milne, D.D. *read* Leang Kung-fa.
81	1	32	„ *chǐh* read *shǐh.*
81	2	39	„ Mǔh *read* Mew.
87	1	10	*insert* 1801. *before* 8°.
101	2	4	*for* Seu *read* Yu.
108	2	12	*for* Heuen *read* Heung.
126	1	2	„ *wan* read *wǎn.*
128	2	23	„ 孟子 Mǎng tsze *read* 四書 Sze shoo.
129	1	22	„ Lǒ *read* Yǒ.
134	2	31	„ *yun* read *lun.*
156	2	37	*dele* See 學善 Heǒ-shen.
158	1	18	*for* Mow *read* Moo.
159	1	22	„ *Tseaou* read *Teaou.*
169	2	32	„ 語 *read* 詩.
172	1	34	„ *Leen* read *Seen.*
189	2	27	„ *Yen* read *Yin.*
191	2	2	„ *Kwan* read *Kwang.*
197	1	5	„ *che* read *choo.*
203	2	6	*insert* See *before* 求.
212	1	4	*dele* heading under 崔公.
221	2	20	*for* Fei *read* Pei.
225	2	22	„ Yěh *read* Yǐh.
227	1	2	„ 天 *read* 大.
227	1	25	„ *tsǔh* read *tseǐh.*
228	1	20	„ *yě* read *yay.*
237	2	30	„ *Kwan* read *Kwǎn.*
238	2		Transpose the third and fourth entries in second column.
239	1	31	*for* Gang *read* Gan.
240	1	38	*insert* See *before* 朱.
267	2	43	for *chǐh* read *shǐh.*
269	2	37	„ Yǔh Hwa-tsze *read* Yang Shing-kung.
282	1	29	*dele* entry beginning 行水 etc.
328	2	20	for *Shǔh* read *Tseaou.*
335	1	32	„ *neen* read *meen.*

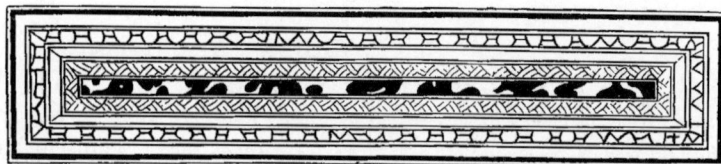

CATALOGUE,

ETC.

AQU

亞 伯 拉 罕 A-pǐh-la-han.
亞 伯 拉 罕 紀 畧 *A-pǐh-la-han ke leǒ.* "The Story of Abraham." [By James Legge?]
Hongkong, 1862. 8º.

ÆSOP, THE PHRYGIAN.
意 拾 秘 傳 *E-shǐh-pe chuen.* "Æsop's Fables." Translated into Chinese by Lo-pǐh Tan [*i.e.* Robert Thom]. 4 keuen. 1838. 8º.

阿 桂 AH-KWEI.
See CHINA, *Board of Revenue.* 欽 定 戶 部 軍 需 則 例 *Kin ting Hoo Poo keun seu tsǐh le.* "Regulations .. for the supply of Commissariat Stores." Compiled by .. Ah-kwei, &c. 1785. 8º.

ALENI (JULIO).
See 艾 儒 畧 GAE JOO-LEǑ.

APOSTLES' CREED.
信 式 *Sin shǐh.* "The Apostles' Creed," explained. [By the Preachers of the Chinese Union.] Tract 38. [1850?]. 8º.

—— 耶 穌 門 徒 信 經 *Yay-soo mun too sin king.* "The Apostles' Creed." To which are added the Ten Commandments. *Hongkong*, 1855. 8º.

Another copy.

AQUINAS (THOMAS) SAINT.
See 利 類 思 LE LUY-SZE. 超 性 學 要 *Chaou sing heǒ yaou.* "An Epitome of the Theology" of Thomas Aquinas, &c. 8º.

BIB

AUGSBURG CONFESSION.
皇 城 信 式 *Hwang ching sin shǐh.* "The Articles of Faith as established at Augsburg" in 1530. With a Catechism on the same. [1845?]. 8º.

BALL (ERNST FRIEDRICH).
See THIRZA. 金 屋 型 儀 *Kin ǔh hing e* . . . [Thirza . . . by E. F. Ball, translated into Chinese.] 8º.

BIBLE.
神 天 聖 書 *Shin teen shing shoo.* Translated into Chinese by R. Morrison and W. Milne. 21 vol. [*Malacca?*], 1823. 8º.

—— 新 增 聖 書 節 解 *Sin tsǎng Shing shoo tsëë keae.* With a commentary by Pǒ-gae-chay [*i.e.* William Milne]. 1825. 8º.
Imperfect, containing only the Epistle to the Ephesians.

Another copy.

—— 舊 約 全 書 (新 約 全 書) *Kew yŏ tseuen shoo* (*Sin yŏ tseuen shoo*). "The Old and New Testaments." The Delegates' version. 5 keuen.
Shanghae, 1854–55. 8º.
The Old Testament is in 3 keuen, the New Testament in 2.

Another copy.
Imperfect, containing only the 3rd keuen.

Another edition. *Shanghae*, 1855. 8º.

Another edition. 4 keuen. *Hongkong*, 1855. 8º.

Another edition. 9 keuen. *Hongkong*, 1864–66. 8º.
The Old Testament is in 7 keuen, the New Testament in 2.

Another edition. *Hongkong*, 1866–69. 8º.

1

BIBLE. (*Continued.*)

舊遺詔聖書 (救世主耶穌新遺詔書)
Kew e chaou shing shoo (*Kew she choo Yay-soo sin e chaou shoo*). " The Old and New Testaments."
Translated into Chinese by C. F. A. Gützlaff.
Published by the Chinese Evangelization Society.
[*Hongkong* ?], 1854–55. 8°.

BIBLE. OLD TESTAMENT.

舊遺詔聖書 *Kew e chaou shing shoo.* Published by order of the Tae-ping Teen Wang.
2 keuen. [*Nanking* ?], 1853. 8°.
Imperfect, containing only the Books of Genesis and Exodus.

Another copy.

—— 舊遺詔聖書 *Kew e chaou shing shoo.* Translated into Chinese by C. F. A Gützlaff.
[1855 ?]. 8°.

BIBLE. OLD TESTAMENT. *Genesis.*

創世傳註釋 *Chwang she chuen choo shih.*
" The Book of Genesis. With a Commentary "
by Wei-jin-chay [*i.e.* William Dean].
1851. 8°.

—— *Psalms.*

舊約詩篇 *Kew yŏ she peen.*
Hongkong, 1867. 8°.

—— *Proverbs.*

舊約箴言傳道 *Kew yŏ chin yen chuen taou.*
" The Books of Proverbs and Ecclesiastes."
Hongkong, 1868. 8°.

—— *Daniel.*

先知但依理書 *Seen che Tan-e-le shoo.* " The Book of the Prophet Daniel," followed by those of the twelve minor Prophets. [1850 ?]. 8°.

BIBLE. OLD TESTAMENT. *Miscellaneous Parts.*
(The Books of Job, the Psalms, the Proverbs, and Ecclesiastes.) [1840 ?]. 8°.
No head-title.

BIBLE. OLD TESTAMENT. *Appendix.*

舊約四字經 *Kew yŏ sze tsze king.* " The Old Testament versified, in lines of four characters."
[By F. Genaehr ?] *Hongkong*, 1866. 8°.

BIBLE. NEW TESTAMENT.

耶穌基利士督我主救者新遺詔書
Yay-soo Ke-le-sze-tŭh wo choo kew chay sin e chaou shoo. Translated into Chinese by Robert Morrison. [*Serampore* ?], 1813. 12°.

Another copy.

—— 救世主耶穌新遺詔書 *Kew she choo Yay-soo sin e chaou shoo.* [Translated into Chinese by C. F. A. Gützlaff, Dr. W. H. Medhurst, E. C. Bridgman, and R. Morrison.]
Singapore, [1836 ?]. 8°.

—— 救世主耶穌新遺詔書 *Kew she choo Yay-soo sin e chaou shoo.* [Published by the Chinese Union.] [1840 ?]. 8°.

—— 我等救世主耶穌新遺詔書 *Wo tăng kew she choo Yay-soo sin e chaou shoo.* [Translated into Chinese by R. Morrison ?] 4 keuen.
Malacca, [1845 ?]. 8°.

—— 新約全書 *Sin yŏ tseuen shoo.* The Delegates' version. 12 keuen. *Shanghae*, 1852. 12°.

Another edition. 10 keuen. *Shanghae*, 1861. 8°.

Another edition. *Hongkong*, 1862. 8°.

Another edition. *Shanghae*, 1866. 8°.

Another edition. *Hongkong*, 1866. 8°.

—— 新遺詔聖書 *Sin e chaou shing shoo.* Published by order of the Tae-ping Teen Wang.
[*Nanking* ?], 1853. 8°.
Imperfect, containing only St. Mark's Gospel.

—— 新約全書 *Sin yŏ tseuen shoo.* Translated into the Mandarin colloquial style. *Shanghae*, 1857. 8°.

Another edition. *Hongkong*, 1869. 8°.

—— 新約全書註解 *Sin yŏ tseuen shoo choo keae.* " The New Testament. With a Commentary."
[By Dr. W. H. Medhurst ?]
Shanghae, 1857–58. 8°.
Imperfect, containing only the Epistle to the Romans and the First Epistle to the Corinthians.

—— Ah-lah Kyiu-cü Yia-su Kyi-toh-go Sing Iah Shü: Peng-veng fan Nying-po T'u-wô. Feng p'in-tang-p'in: Yih-pin cü Siang-te-go Tsih-tsông. Pt. I., containing Gospels and Acts.
London, 1865. 8°.

Another edition. *London*, 1868. 8°.

BIBLE. NEW TESTAMENT. (*Continued.*)

The New Testament in the Colloquial of the Hakka Dialect. Sin, yok̲ s̆in̲ kin̲ tshen̲ s̆u̲. Hak̲ ka̲ syuk̲ wà. By some Missionaries of the Basel Evangelical Missionary Society.
Basel, 1866. 8º.

Imperfect, containing only the Gospels of St. Matthew and St. Luke.

Another copy.

Imperfect, containing only the Gospel of St. Matthew.

—— 新約全書註釋 *Sin yŏ tseuen shoo choo shĭh.* "The New Testament, with a Commentary."
Hongkong, 1868–70. 8º.

Imperfect, containing only the Gospels of St. Matthew and St. Mark, and the Epistles to the Romans and Corinthians.

—— 新約串珠 *Sin yŏ chuen choo.* "The New Testament, with references."
Fŭhchow Foo, 1869. 8º.

BIBLE. NEW TESTAMENT. *Matthew.*

山上宣道 *Shan shang seuen taou.* "The Sermon on the Mount."   [1855?]. 8º.

—— *Matthew.*

耶穌山上垂訓 *Yay-soo shan shang chuy heun.* "Christ's Sermon on the Mount." With a Commentary [by James Legge?].
Hongkong, 1869. 8º.

—— *Mark.*

哪勒 *Ma-lik.* Translated into Chinese by Dr. Marshman.   [*Serampore,* 1810?]. 8º.
No title-page.

Another copy.

Another copy.

—— *Luke.*

路加傳好新聞 *Loo-kea chuen haou sin wăn.* In the Shanghae dialect.
[*Shanghae?*], 1848. 8º.

—— *John, Gospel of.*

若翰傳福音之書 *Jŏ-han chuen fŭh yin che shoo.* Translated into Chinese by R. Morrison.
[1830?]. 8º.

BIBLE. NEW TESTAMENT. *John, Gospel of.*

約翰傳福音書 *Yŏ-han chuen fŭh yin shoo.* Translated into Chinese by C. F. A. Gützlaff, Dr. W. H. Medhurst, E. C. Bridgman, and R. Morrison.   *Singapore,* 1836. 8º.

—— *Romans.*

保羅寄羅馬人書第五章 *Paou-lo ke Lo-ma jin shoo te woo chang.* "The Fifth Chapter of St. Paul's Epistle to the Romans." With a Commentary. Tract 34. [By the Preachers of the Chinese Union.]   [1850?]. 8º.

—— *John, Epistle of.*

約翰上書第一章註解 *Yŏ-han shang shoo te yĭh chang choo keae.* "The First Chapter of the First Epistle of St. John. With a Commentary." Tract 33. [By the Preachers of the Chinese Union.]   [1850?]. 8º.

BIBLE. NEW TESTAMENT. *Miscellaneous Parts.*

新約聖書 *Sin yŏ shing shoo.* A selection of "the Books of the New Testament," including the Gospels of St. Matthew, St. Luke, and St. John, the Acts of the Apostles, the Epistles of St. Paul to Timothy, Titus, and Philemon, the Epistles of James, Peter, and John, and the Book of Revelations.   *Shanghae,* 1864. 8º.

BIBLE. NEW TESTAMENT. *Appendix.*

新約四字經 *Sin yŏ sze tsze king.* "The New Testament versified, in lines of four characters." [By F. Genaehr?]   *Hongkong,* 1863. 8º.

BIBLE. *Appendix.*

初學編 *Choo hŏ peen.* "Old Testament History for beginners." [By D. B. McCartee.] 2 keuen.
Ningpo, 1851. 8º.

—— 福音廣訓 *Fŭh yin kwang heun.* "The Teaching of the Gospel Explained."
Shanghae, 1854. 8º.

—— 救主耶穌開口教曰虛心者有福矣因得天國也 *Kew choo Yay-soo kae kow keaou yuĕ heu sin chay yew fŭh e yin tĭh Teen kwŏ yay.* "The Saviour Jesus opened his mouth and taught, saying, Blessed are the poor in spirit, for their's is the kingdom of Heaven." Tract 12. A Sermon [by the Preachers of the Chinese Union].   [1850?]. 8º.

BIBLE. *Appendix.* (*Continued.*)

古今聖史紀集 *Koo kin shing she ke tseĭh.* "Extracts from Bible History." By Pŏ-gae-chay [*i.e.* W. Milne]. From the *Chă she sŏ,* or 'Examiner.' 4 keuen.　　　　[1840 ?]. 8°.

—— 神經撮節 *Shin king tsŏ tsëë.* "An epitome of the Bible."　　　　[1850 ?]. 8°.

—— 聖經釋義 *Shing king shĭh e.* "Scripture Explained." By Chung-tĭh-chay [*i.e.* David Collie].　　　　*Singapore,* 1835. 8°.

—— 聖經之史 *Shing king che she.* "Bible History."　　　　[1840 ?]. 8°.

—— 聖經史記撮要 *Shing king she ke tsŏ yaou.* "A Compendium of Bible History." 2 keuen.　　　　[1850 ?]. 8°.

—— 聖經圖記 *Shing king too ke.* "Illustrated Bible Histories."　　　　[1850 ?]. 8°.

—— 聖經擇要 *Shing king chĭh yaou.* "Extracts from the Bible" in support of the Doctrines of Christianity. [By R. Lechler ?]　　　　*Hongkong,* 1869. 8°.

—— 聖書日課初學便用 *Shing shoo jĭh ko choo hcŏ peen yung.* "Scripture Lessons for the use of schools." 2 keuen.　　　　*British and Foreign School Society,* 1832. 8°.

—— 聖書勸言 *Shing shoo keuen yen.* "Words of admonition from the Bible."　　　　[1840 ?]. 8°.

—— 聖書曰爲義見害迫者有福矣因天國爲其所得也 *Shing shoo yuĕ wei e keen hae pĭh chay yew fŭh e yin Teen kwŏ wei ke so tĭh yay.* "The Bible says, Blessed are those who suffer for righteousness sake, for their's is the kingdom of Heaven." Tract 10. [By the Preachers of the Chinese Union.] [1850 ?]. 8°.

—— 聖書曰是以任肉慾者不能悅上帝矣 *Shing shoo yuĕ she e jin jow yŭh chay pŭh năng yuĕ Shang-te e.* "The Bible says : So that they that are in the flesh cannot please God." Tract 18. [By the Preachers of the Chinese Union.]　　　　[1850 ?]. 8°.

BIBLE. *Appendix.* (*Continued.*)

聖書曰止一上帝爲萬物之父超萬有通萬有又在爾眾者也 *Shing shoo yuĕ che yĭh Shang-te wei wan wŭh che foo chaou wan yew tung wan yew yew tsae urh tsung chay yay.* "The Bible says, One God and Father of all, who is above all, and through all, and in you all." Tract 29. [By the Preachers of the Chinese Union.]　　　　[1850 ?]. 8°.

—— 聖書曰信服耶穌者無見定罪 *Shing shoo yuĕ sin fŭh Yay-soo chay woo keen ting tsuy.* "The Bible says : He that believeth on Jesus is not condemned." Tract 20. [By the Preachers of the Chinese Union.]　　　　[1850 ?]. 8°.

—— 聖書曰行善勿倦倘若不廢屆期可穫也 *Shing shoo yuĕ hing shen wŭh keuen shang jŏ pŭh fei keae ke ko hwŏ yay.* "The Bible says : Let us not be weary in well doing : for in due season we shall reap if we faint not." Tract 19. [By the Preachers of the Chinese Union.]　　　　[1850 ?]. 8°.

—— 聖書曰蓋全律例以一言成也卽是愛他如己焉 *Shing shoo yuĕ kae tseuen leŭh le e yĭh yen ching yay tseĭh she gae ta joo ke yen.* "The Bible says, If there be any other commandment it is briefly comprehended in this saying, namely, Thou shalt love thy neighbour as thyself." Tract 28. [By the Preachers of the Chinese Union.]　　　　[1850 ?]. 8°.

—— 聖書曰有義人耶穌基督偕天父爲我保主 *Shing shoo yuĕ yew e jin Yay-soo Ke-tŭh keae Teen Foo wei wo paou choo.* "The Bible says, Jesus Christ the righteous who with the Heavenly Father is surety for us." Tract 16. [By the Preachers of the Chinese Union.]　　　　[1850 ?]. 8°.

This text appears to be a paraphrase of Heb. vii. 22.

—— 聖書曰但行眞理者就光以彰明所行者卽仰上帝而行之也 *Shing shoo yuĕ tan hing chin le chay tsew kwang e chang ming so hing chay tseĭh yang Shang-te urh hing che yay.* "The Bible says, He that doeth truth cometh to the light, that his deeds may be made manifest, that they are wrought of God." Tract 13. [By the Preachers of the Chinese Union.] [1850 ?]. 8°.

BIBLE. *Appendix.* (*Continued.*)

聖書曰設若我交通與上帝而自覆 暗地則說謊並不眞行 *Shing shoo yŭě she jŏ wo keaou tung yu Shang-te urh tsze fŭh gan te tsĭh shwŏ hwang ping pŭh chin hing.* "The Bible says, If we say we have fellowship with God and walk in darkness we lie, and do not the truth." Tract 26. [By the Preachers of the Chinese Union.] [1850 ?]. 8°.

—— 聖書曰造萬物者是上帝也 *Shing shoo yŭě tsaou wan wŭh chay she Shang-te yay.* "The Bible says, God is the Creator of all things." Tract 21. [By the Preachers of the Chinese Union.] [1850 ?]. 8°.

—— 聖書曰由之以信德進所立之恩地 且望上帝之榮而喜矣 *Shing shoo yŭě yew che e sin tĭh tsin so lĕ̆h che gău te tseay wang Shang-te che yung urh he e.* "The Bible says, By whom also we have access by faith into this grace wherein we stand, and rejoice in hope of the glory of God." Tract 30. [By the Preachers of the Chinese Union.] [1850 ?]. 8°.

—— 聖書曰爾勿勞爲可壞之口糧乃所 存及永生之口糧 *Shing shoo yŭě urh wŭh laou wei ko hwae che kow leang nae so tsun kĕh yung săng che kow leang.* "The Bible says, Labour not for the meat that perisheth, but for that meat which endureth unto everlasting life." Tract 24. [By the Preachers of the Chinese Union.] [1850 ?]. 8°.

—— 聖書曰眾敬神子如敬父焉 *Shing shoo yŭě tsung king shin tsze joo king Foo yen.* "The Bible says, That all men should honour the Son even as they honour the Father." Tract 22. [By the Preachers of the Chinese Union.] [1850 ?]. 8°.

—— 聖書要說析義 *Shing shoo yaou shwŏ sĕ̆h e.* "The meaning of important passages of Holy Writ." [By James Legge ?] *Hongkong,* [1860 ?]. 8°.

Another copy.

BIBLE. *Appendix.* (*Continued.*)

天主降生聖經直解 *Teen choo keang săng shing king chĭh keae.* "The Gospel of Christ, clearly explained," by Yang-ma-nŏ [*i.e.* Emmanuel Diaz]. 14 keuen. *Peking,* 1790. 8°.

—— 節錄聖經釋義 *Tsĕ̆ lŭh shing king shĭh e.* "Scripture explained." By Chung-tĭh-chay [*i.e.* David Collie]. [*Singapore,* 1836 ?]. 8°.

BOONE (WILLIAM JONES).

See LITURGIES. *England, Church of.* 週年早晨 禱告式 *Chow neen tsaou shin taou kaou shĭh.* "The Morning Service of the English Liturgy." Translated into the Shanghae dialect by W. J. Boone, &c. 1849. 8°.

—— See LITURGIES. *England, Church of.* 週年夜裡 禱告式 *Chow neen yay le taou kaou shĭh.* "The Evening Service of the English Liturgy." Translated into the Shanghae dialect by W. J. Boone, &c. 1849. 8°.

BRIDGMAN (ELIJAH COLEMAN).

See BIBLE. NEW TESTAMENT. 救世主耶穌 新遺詔書 *Kew she choo Yay-soo sin e chaou shoo.* Translated into Chinese by . . . E. C. Bridgman, &c. 1836. 8°.

BROWN (JOHN), *Minister of Haddington.*

See 後學者 HOW-HEŎ-CHAY. 節錄成章幼 學問答 *Tsĕ̆ lŭh ching chang yew heŏ wăn tă.* A translation of Brown's "Short Catechism for Young Children," &c. 1824. 8°.

BUDDHATALA.

See 佛陀多羅 FŬH-TO-TO-LO.

BUGLIO (LUIGI).

See 利類思 LE LUY-SZE.

BUNYAN (JOHN).

天路歷程 *Teen loo lĕ̆h ching.* "The Pilgrim's Progress," by J. Bunyan. Translated into Chinese by W. C. Burns. With Illustrations. 5 keuen. *Hongkong,* 1855. 8°.

BURNS (William Chalmers).

See BUNYAN (John). 天路歷程 *Teen loo leĭh ching.* "The Pilgrim's Progress." ... Translated into Chinese by W. C. Burns, &c. 1855. 8º.

—— See 厦 HEA. 厦腔養心神詩 *Hea keang yang sin shin she.* "Sacred Hymns." ... Translated into Chinese by W. C. Burns, &c. 1868. 8º.

CANTON.

粵海關額定欵項 *Yuĕ hae kwan gĭh ting kwan heang.* "A Return of the Establishment and fixed expenses of the Canton Customs." 1836. 8º.

Another copy.

—— 粵海關估計外洋船出口貨物價值 *Yuĕ hae kwan koo ke wae yang chuen chŭh kow hŏ wŭh kea chĭh.* "An Estimate of the Value of the different kinds of Merchandize exported from the Port of Canton in sea-going Ships." [1843 ?]. 8º.

Another copy.

—— 粵海關規例 *Yuĕ hae kwan kwei le.* "Customs Rules and Regulations for the Port of Canton." 1759. 8º.

Another copy.

Another copy.

—— 粵海關規例 *Yuĕ hae kwan kwei le.* "Customs Rules and Regulations for the Port of Canton." [1840 ?]. 8º.

—— 粵海關比例 *Yuĕ hae kwan pe le.* "Adjusted Customs Tariffs for the Port of Canton." 1809. 8º.

Another copy.

Another copy.

—— 粵海關稅例 *Yuĕ hae kwan shwuy le.* "Customs Tariffs for the Port of Canton." 1724. 8º.

—— 粵海關稅則 *Yuĕ hae kwan shwuy tsĭh.* "Customs Tariffs for the Port of Canton." 1789. 8º.

CANTON. 羅 Lo. *Prefect.*

[A Proclamation forbidding the Natives to abuse or illtreat Foreigners.] *Canton,* 1820. 8º.

Another copy.

CATALOGUES.

欽定四庫全書總目 *Kin ting sze koo tseuen shoo tsung mŭh.* "A descriptive Catalogue of the Imperial Library of the present Dynasty," drawn up by an Imperial Commission composed of Princes Yung Yung, Yung Seuen, Yung Sing, and others. The works in this Catalogue are classed under four headings, viz., Classics, History, Philosophy, and Belles-lettres. 200 keuen. 1790. 8º.

—— 欽定四庫全書簡明目錄 *Kin ting sze koo tseuen shoo keen ming mŭh lŭh.* An Abridgment of the Kin ting sze koo tseuen shoo tsung mŭh. ? keuen. [1800 ?]. 8º.
Imperfect, containing only keuen 6.

—— 天一閣書目 *Teen yĭh kŏ shoo mŭh.* "A Catalogue of the Library collected in the Teen-yĭh Pavilion" at Ningpo by Fan Sze-ma, under the Ming dynasty. Edited by Yuen Yuen. 8 keuen. 1808. 8º.
There are eight copies of this work.

—— 查送違碍書目 *Tsze sung wei gae shoo mŭh.* "A Catalogue of suspected and prohibited Books, furnished by Order." 1782. 8º.

—— 外省查查書目 *Wae sing tsze cha shoo mŭh.* "A Catalogue of Books published in the Provinces, furnished by Order." ? keuen. [1784 ?]. 8º.
Imperfect, containing only keuen 3.

查愼行 CHA SHIN-HING.

See 白潢 PĬH HWANG. 西江志 *Se keang che.* "A Topography of the Province of Keang se." Compiled by .. Cha Shin-hing, &c. 1720. 8º.

查爲仁 CHA WEI-JIN.

蓮坡詩話 *Leen po she hwa.* "Criticisms on Poetry." 3 keuen. 1741. 8º.

CHA   [7]   CHA

紫 紹 炳 CHAE SHAOU-PING.

戒 殺 篇 *Keae shă peen.* "Two tracts against destroying life." *See* 沈 培 木 CHIN PEI-MŬH.

慈 心 寶 鑑 *Tsze sin paou keen.* "A Collection of Tracts inculcating the virtue of Mercy," &c. 1771. 8°.

潛 然 CHAN-JEN.

禮 拜 觀 想 偈 畧 釋 *Le pae kwan seang kĕĕ leŏ shĭh.* "The Enigmas of Buddhist Worship and Devotion," by the Priest Chan-jen, of the Tang Dynasty; "briefly explained" by the Priest Che-heŭh, of the Ming Dynasty. A Reprint. *Canton,* 1803. Oblong.

長 城 CHANG CHING.

名 家 制 義 *Ming kea che e.* "Essays on Texts from the Four Books by celebrated Authors" of the Sung, Ming, and Tsing Dynasties. Compiled by Chang Ching. 119 Parts. 1699. 8°.

The works of each Author are preceded by a separate title-page and a preface.

長 白 CHANG PĬH.

勅 修 浙 江 通 志 *Chĭh sew Chĕ keang tung che.* "An authorized revised edition of the Complete Topography of the Province of Chĕ keang." Edited by Chang Pĭh. 280 keuen. 1812. 8°. Imperfect.

—— 飲 水 詩 集 *Yin shwuy she tseĭh.* "The Drinking-water-like Collection of Poetry." *See* 伍 崇 曜 Woo TSUNG-YAOU. 粵 雅 堂 叢 書 *Yuĕ ya Tang tsung shoo.* "The Yuĕ-ya Tang Collection of Reprints," &c. Series 7. 1853. 8°.

張 CHANG.

張 遠 兩 友 相 論 *Chang Yuen leang yew seang lun.* "Discussions [on Christianity] between the two Friends Chang and Yuen." [1830 ?]. 8°.

Another copy.

Another copy.

Another edition. 1831. 8°.

Another edition. *Hongkong,* 1844. 8°.

張 CHANG.

近 科 考 卷 湖 南 校 士 錄 *Kin ko kaou keuen Hoo-nan keaou sze lŭh.* "Collated Essays from Hoo-nan Examination Papers." Compiled by Chang. [1800 ?]. 8°.

張 CHANG.

玉 堂 雜 字 *Yŭh tang tsă tsze.* "A Literary Encyclopædia" for the use of Boys. By the Historiographer Chang. 3 kenen. [1750 ?]. 8°.

The first keuen is wanting.

張 湛 CHANG CHAN.

冲 虛 眞 經 *Chung heu chin king.* "The true Classic of the deep void." With a Commentary by Chang Chan, &c. *See* 黃 丕 烈 HWANG PEI-LĔĔ. 十 子 全 書 *Shĭh Tsze tseuen shoo.* "The complete Works of the Ten Philosophers," &c. 1804. 8°.

張 弨 CHANG CHAOU.

See 顧 炎 武 KOO YEN-WOO. 音 學 五 書 *Yin heŏ woo shoo.* "Five Works on the Science of the Sounds" .... Edited by Chang Chaou, &c. 1643. 8°.

張 璠 CHANG FAN.

周 易 集 解 *Chow Yĭh tseĭh keae.* "A Collection of Explanations of the Chow Changes." *See* 孫 堂 SUN TANG. 漢 魏 二 十 一 家 易 注 *Han Wei urh shĭh yĭh kea Yĭh choo.* "Commentaries on the Book of Changes," &c. 1799. 8°.

張 衡 CHANG HĂNG.

See 斌 倚 平 PIN E-PING. 文 選 集 腋 *Wăn seuen tseĭh yĭh.* "Selected Literary Expressions" ... from the Works of ... Chang Hăng, &c. 1813. 8°.

張 澩 CHANG HAOU.

雲 谷 雜 紀 *Yun yŭh tsă ke.* "The Cloudy Valley Miscellany." 5 keuen. *See* 葉 志 詵 YĔ CHE-SIN. 海 山 仙 館 叢 書 *Hae shan seen Kwan tsung shoo.* "The Hae-shan-seen Kwan Collection of Reprints," &c. Vol. 48. 1848. 8°.

—— 艮 嶽 記 *Kăn yŏ ke.* "An Account of Kăn-yŏ." *See* 說 SHWŎ. 說 纂 *Shwŏ tswan.* "Miscellaneous Records," &c. Tract 2. 8°.

張憲 CHANG HEEN.

玉笥集 *Yŭh-sze tseĭh.* "Collection of Songs and Odes." By Chang Heen, also called Yŭh-sze. 10 keuen. *See* 伍崇曜 Woo Tsung-yaou. 粵雅堂叢書 *Yŭĕ ya Tang tsung shoo.* "The Yŭĕ-ya Tang Collection of Reprints," &c. Series 2.　　　1853. 8º.

張華 CHANG HWA.

博物志 *Po wŭh che.* "Treatises on Diverse Matters." A Reprint. 10 keuen. [1750 ?]. 8º.

—— See 師曠 SZE KWANG. 禽經 *Kin king.* "A Book on Birds." With a Commentary by Chang Hwa, &c.　　　8º.

張機 CHANG KE.

金匱要畧 *Kin kwei yaou leŏ.* "An Epitome of the Golden Treasury of Medicine." [Also] 傷寒論 *Shang han lun.* "On Colds." *See* 吳謙 Woo Keen. 醫宗金鑑 *E tsung kin keen.* "The Golden Mirror of Medicine," &c. Keuen 1–25.　　　1740. 8º.

張芹 CHANG KIN.

靖難功臣錄 *Tsing nan kung Chin lŭh.* "Records of meritorious Ministers who restored peace to the Country." [Also] 備遺錄 *Pe wei lŭh.* "In memoriam Records." *See* 說 Shwŏ. 說纂 *Shwŏ tswan.* "Miscellaneous Records," &c. Tracts 22, 23.　　　8º.

張果 CHANG KO.

星宗大全 *Sing tsung ta tseuen.* "A complete Work on Astrology." Edited by Lŭh Wei. 8 keuen?　　　[1790 ?]. 8º.
Imperfect, containing only keuen 1–4, 7, 8.

張公 CHANG KUNG.

說林 *Shwŏ lin.* "A Forest of Treatises." *See* 沈津 Chin Tsin. 百家類纂 *Pih kea luy tswan.* "The Works of a hundred Authors," &c. keuen 12.　　　8º.

張瓦 CHANG LEANG.

陰符經 *Yin foo king.* "The Sutra of Secret Charms " [said to have been written by Hwang-te]. With the Commentaries of Tae kung, Fan Le, Kwei Kŭh-tsze, Choo-kŏ Leang, Le Tseuen, and of the Editor Chang Leang. A Reprint.　　　[1750 ?]. 8º.

張廛 CHANG LIN.

東隅錄 *Tung yu lŭh.* "The Records of the Eastern Corner." A Collection of Poetry. By the Editor Chang Lin and others.　　　1830. 8º.

張耒 CHANG LUY.

宛丘集 *Yuen kew tseĭh.* "A Collection of Yuen-kew's Poetry." *See* 吳孟舉 Woo Măng-keu, and 吳自牧 Woo Tsze-Mŭh. 宋詩鈔二集 *Sung she chaou urh tseĭh.* "Poetry of the Sung Dynasty," &c.　　　8º.

張穆 CHANG Mŭh.

顧亭林先生年譜 *Koo Ting-lin Seen săng neen poo.* "A Chronological Record of the Life of Koo Yen-woo." 4 keuen. [Also] 閻潛邱先生年譜 *Yen Tseen-kew Seen săng neen poo.* "A Chronological Record of the Life of Yen Jŏ-keu." 4 keuen. *See* 伍崇曜 Woo Tsung-yaou. 粵雅堂叢書 *Yŭĕ ya Tang tsung shoo.* "The Yŭĕ-ya Tang Collection of Reprints," &c. Series 18.　　　1853. 8º.

—— 俄羅斯事補輯 *Go-lo-sze sze poo tseĭh.* "A Further Treatise on Russian Affairs." *See* 何秋濤 Ho Tsew-taou. 北徼彙編 *Pih keaou wei peen.* "Treatises on the Countries beyond the Northern Frontier," &c. Keuen 2.　　　1865. 8º.

張楠 CHANG NAN.

神峰闢謬正宗 *Shin fung peĭh mew ching tsung.* "A Critical Examination into the Laws of Destiny." Edited by Chun Fang. 6 keuen.　　　[1750 ?]. 8º.

—— 神峰闢謬命理正宗 *Shin fung peĭh mew ming le ching tsung.* "A Critical Examination into the Laws of Destiny." 6 keuen. 1842. 8º.
Another edition of the above.

張寧 CHANG NING.

See 陸君弼 Lŭh Keun-peĭh. 江都志 *Keang too che.* "A Topography of the District of Keang-too" ... Edited by Chang Ning, &c.　　　1597. 8º.

張榜 CHANG PANG.

See 楊雄 Yang Heung. 法言 *Fă yen.* "A Discourse on Moral Laws." ... Edited by Chang Pang, &c.　　　8º.

張榜 CHANG PANG. (*Continued.*)

　　See 管 仲 KWAN CHUNG. 管 子 纂 *Kwan tsze tswan.* "The Works of Kwan Chung" ... Edited by Chang Pang, &c. 8º.

—— See 韓 非 HAN FEI. 韓 非 子 纂 *Han Fei tsze tswan.* "The Works of Han Fei" .... Edited by Chang Pang, &c. 8º.

張泌 CHANG PE.

　　妝 樓 記 *Chwang low ke.* "Scraps from a Painted Chamber." *See* 王 文 誥 WANG WĂN-KAOU. 唐 代 叢 書 *Tang tae tsung shoo.* "A Collection of Reprints of Works written during the Tang Dynasty," &c. Series 4. 1806. 8º.

—— 妝 樓 記 *Chwang low ke.* "Scraps from a Painted Chamber." By Chang Pe, of the Tang Dynasty. A Reprint. [1741?]. 8º.

張白 CHANG PĬH.

　　賈 氏 談 錄 *Kea She tan lŭh.* "Notes on Conversations of Kea She." *See* 說 SHWŎ. 說 郛 *Shwŏ foo.* "Odds and Ends," &c. 8º.

張溥 CHANG POO.

　　See 論 語 LUN YU. 論 語 註 疏 大 全 合 纂 *Lun yu choo soo ta tseuen hŏ tswan.* "The Confucian Analects" ... Compiled by Chang Poo, &c. 1836. 8º.

—— See 陳 祥 道 CHIN TSEANG-TAOU. 禮 書 *Le shoo.* "A History of Forms and Ceremonies" ... Edited by Chang Poo, &c. 8º.

張燮 CHANG SEĔ.

　　東 西 洋 考 *Tung se yang kaou.* "A Complete Account of those Countries in the Southern and Eastern Seas" which had commercial intercourse with China during the Ming Dynasty. Edited by Wang Ke-tsung, Sŭh Ke, Woo Peen, &c. 12 keuen. 1618. 8º.

張巽 CHANG SEUEN.

　　See 陳 珏 CHIN SĂNG. 常 山 縣 志 *Chang shan hëen che.* "A Topography of Chang-shan Heen," ... Compiled by ... Chang Seuen, &c. 1813. 8º.

張氏 CHANG SHE.

　　See 孔 丘 KUNG KEW. 春 秋 讀 本 *Chun Tsew tŭh pun.* "The Spring and Autumn Annals" .. Edited by Chang She, &c. [1800?]. 8º.

———————— [1818?]. 8º.

—— 春 秋 旁 訓 *Chun Tsew pang heun.* "The Spring and Autumn Annals" ... Edited by Chang She, &c. 8º.

—— 書 經 讀 本 *Shoo king tŭh pun.* "The Book of Historical Documents" ... Edited by Chang She, &c. 8º.

—— 書 經 旁 訓 讀 本 *Shoo king pang heun tŭh pun.* "The Book of Historical Documents" ... Edited by Chang She, &c. 1818. 8º.

—— See 禮 記 LE KE. 禮 記 讀 本 *Le ke tŭh pun.* "The Book of Rites" ... Edited by Chang She, &c. 8º.

—— See 詩 經 SHE KING. 詩 經 讀 本 *She king tŭh pun.* "The Book of Odes" ... Edited by Chang She, &c. 1785. 8º.

—— See 五 經 WOO KING. 五 經 句 解 *Woo king keu keae.* "The Five Classics" ... Edited by Chang She, &c. 1817. 8º.

—— See 易 經 YĬH KING. 易 經 增 訂 旁 訓 *Yĭh king tsăng ting pang heun.* "The Book of Changes" .... Edited by Chang She, &c. 8º.

張馭 CHANG SHE.

　　See 毛 奇 齡 MAOU KE-LING. 四 書 典 制 辨 正 *Sze shoo teen che peen ching.* "Explanatory Essays on Canonical Passages from the Four Books" ... Compiled by ... Chang She, &c. 8º.

張純 CHANG SHUN.

　　See 南 軒 NAN HEEN. 南 軒 先 生 文 集 *Nan Heen Seen săng wăn tseĭh.* "A Collection of the Works of Nan Heen Seen săng." Edited by Chang Shun, &c. 8º.

張說 CHANG SHWŏ.

虬髯客傳 *Kew jen kih chuen.* "The Story of the Dragon-bearded Guest." By Chang Shwŏ, of the Tang Dynasty. A Reprint.

[1741 ?]. 8°.

張岱 CHANG TAE.

陶菴夢憶 *Yaou gan mung yih.* "Dreamy Recollections of the Yaou Monastery." 8 keuen. *See* 伍崇曜 WOO TSUNG-YAOU. 粵雅堂叢書 *Yuĕ ya Tang tsung shoo.* "The Yue-ya Tang Collection of Reprints," &c. Series 2.

1853. 8°.

張濤 CHANG TAOU.

See 老君 LAOU KEUN. 感應篇註證 *Kan ying peen choo ching.* "The Book of Rewards and Punishments" .... Edited by Chang Taou, &c. 1792. 8°.

張載 CHANG TSAE.

See 四書 SZE SHOO. 四書遵註合講 *Sze shoo tsun choo hŏ keang.* "The Four Books ... With a Paraphrase and Notes" digested from the Works of ... Chang Tsae, &c. 1805. 8°.

—— 西銘 *Se ming.* "Western Records." [Also] 正蒙 *Ching mung.* "Corrected Obscurities." *See* 胡廣 HOO KWANG. 性理大全 *Sing le ta tseuen.* "A Complete Work on Mental Philosophy," &c. Keuen 4–6. 1414. 8°.

—— 西銘 *Se ming.* "Western Records." [Also] 正蒙 *Ching mung.* "Corrected Obscurities." *See* 李光地 LE KWANG-TE. 性理精義 *Sing le tsing e.* "The Essence of Works upon Mental Philosophy," &c. Keuen 2. 1715. 8°.

張鷟 CHANG TSŏ.

龍筋鳳髓判 *Lung kin fung suy pwan.* "The Dragon's Muscle and the Phœnix's Marrow Decisions." With a Commentary by Lew Yun-păng. 4 keuen. *See* 葉志詵 YĔ CHE-SIN. 海山仙館叢書 *Hae shan seen Kwan tsung shoo.* "The Hae shan seen Kwan Collection of Reprints," &c. Vol. 49–50. 1848. 8°.

張鷟 CHANG TSŏ. (*Continued.*)

朝野僉載 *Chaou yay tseen tsae.* "Tales" of the Tang Dynasty. [Also] 耳目記 *Urh muh ke.* "Things heard and seen." *See* 王文誥 WANG WĂN-KAOU. 唐代叢書 *Tang tae tsung shoo.* "A Collection of Reprints of Works written during the Tang Dynasty," &c. Series 1, 2. 1806. 8°.

—— 朝野僉載 *Chaou yay tseen tsae.* "Tales" of the Tang Dynasty. *See* 說 SHWŏ. 說畧 *Shwŏ leŏ.* Historical and other Tracts, &c. 8°.

張溥 CHANG TWAN.

大萬寶全書 *Ta wan paou tseuen shoo.* "An Encyclopædia." 32 keuen. 1757. 8°.

張謂 CHANG WEI.

宣室志 *Seuen chih che.* "Tales from an Imperial Mansion." *See* 王文誥 WANG WĂN-KAOU. 唐代叢書 *Tang tae tsung shoo.* "A Collection of Reprints of Works written during the Tang Dynasty," &c. Series 2. 1806. 8°.

張炎 CHANG YEN.

詞源 *Tsze yuen.* "The Fountain of Rhymes." A Work on the ancient Musical Notation, the Laws of Harmony, and the Mechanism and Principles of Song Writing. 2 keuen. *See* 伍崇曜 WOO TSUNG-YAOU. 粵雅堂叢書 *Yuĕ ya Tang tsung shoo.* "The Yuĕ-ya Tang Collection of Reprints," &c. Series 13.

1853. 8°.

張楫 CHANG YĬH.

廣雅 *Kwang Ya.* "An Extensive Dictionary." 10 keuen. *See* 郎奎金 LANG KWEI-KIN. 五雅 *Woo ya.* "The Five Dictionaries," &c. 1626. 8°.

—— 博雅 *Pŏ ya.* "A Glossary of Terms." A Reprint. 10 keuen. [1750 ?]. 8°.

Another copy.

張易 CHANG YĬH.

See 王通 WANG TUNG. 中說 *Chung shwŏ.* "Apposite Discourses" ... Edited by Chang Yĭh, &c. 8°.

CHA   [11]   CHA

張英 CHANG YING.

See 康熙 KANG-HE, *Emperor*. 御製文集
Yu che wăn tseih. "The Literary Works of ...
Kang-he." Edited by ... Chang Ying, &c.
1711. 8°.

—— See 易經 YĬH KING. 日講易經解義
Jĭh keang Yĭh king keae e. "The Book of
Changes, with a Paraphrase" ... Compiled by
... Chang Ying, &c. 1688. 8°.

—— 淵鑑類函 *Yuen keen luy han*. "An Encyclopædia. Arranged according to Subjects."
Compiled, by Imperial order, by Chang Ying,
Wang Sze-chin, Wang Yen, and others. 450
keuen. 1710. 8°.

Without title-page.

張志和 CHANG CHE-HO. 玄真子 *Heuen-chin-tsze*.
"On the Works of Heuen-chin-tsze." *See*
沈津 CHIN TSIN. 百家類纂 *Pĭh kea luy
tswan*. "The Works of a Hundred Authors,"
&c. Keuen 18. 8°.

張竹坡 CHANG CHŬH-PO. 金瓶梅 *Kin Ping
Mei*. "The Story of Kin, Ping, and Mei."
A Novel attributed to Wang She-ching. Edited
by Chang Chŭh-po. 100 Chapters. 1695. 8°.

張春波 CHANG CHUN-PO.

See 曹之升 TSAOU CHE-SHING. 典制文琳
註釋 *Teen che wăn lin choo shĭh*. "A Collection of Choice Essays" ... With Notes by
Chang Chun-po, &c. 1804. 8°.

—— See 曹之升 TSAOU CHE-SHING. 註釋典制
文琳 *Choo shĭh teen che wăn lin*. "A Collection
of Choice Essays" ... With Notes by Chang
Chun-po, &c. 1799–1808. 8°.

張方平 CHANG FANG-PING.

芻蕘奧論 *Tsoo yaou gaou lun*. "Rough and
Recondite Treatises" on Government, &c. 2
keuen. *See* 伍崇曜 WOO TSUNG-YAOU.
粵雅堂叢書 *Yuĕ ya Tang tsung shoo*.
"The Yuĕ-ya Tang Collection of Reprints,"
&c. Series 3. 1853. 8°.

張鳳孫 CHANG FUNG-SUN.

See 陳宏謀 CHIN HUNG-MOW. 在官法戒
錄摘鈔 *Tsae kwan fă keae lŭh tsĭh chaou*.
"The Mandarin's Instructor" ... Edited by
... Chang Fung-sun, &c. 1823. 8°.

張鳳翼 CHANG FUNG-YĬH.

瑞芝閣天崇名文枕中秘 *Shwuy che Kŏ
teen tsung ming wăn chin chung pe*. "The
Shwuy-che Kŏ Collection of Celebrated Essays"
on Texts from the Four Books. Compiled by
Chang Fung-yĭh. Edited by his pupils Woo
Ting-hwa and Woo Chin-peaou. 1790. 8°.

張海鵬 CHANG HAE-PĂNG.

See 戚繼光 TSEĬH KE-KWANG. 紀效新書
Ke heaou sin shoo. "A New Work on the
Stratagems of War" .... Edited by Chang
Hae-păng, &c. 1804. 8°.

張涵齋 CHANG HAN-CHAE.

See 吳穀人 WOO KŬH-JIN. 安定書院課藝
Gan ting shoo Yuen ko e, .. Essays from the
Gan-ting College. Edited by ... Chang Han-
chae, &c. 1803. 8°.

張翰純 CHANG HAN-SHUN.

See 姚培謙 YAOU PEI-KEEN. 類腋 *Luy yĭh*.
"A Thesaurus of Phrases" ... With a
Supplement by Chang Han-shun, &c.
1748. 8°.

張學畊 CHANG HEŎ-KĂNG.

See 胡曰從 HOO YUĔ-TSUNG. 十竹齋書
畫譜 *Shĭh chŭh chae shoo hwa poo*. "The
Ten-Bamboo Study Collection of Polychromatic
Prints" .... Edited by Chang Heŏ-kăng, &c.
1817. 8°.

張學蘇 CHANG HEŎ-SOO.

See 聶銑敏 SHĔ SEEN-MIN. 寄嶽雲齋試
體詩 *Ke yŏ yun chae she te she*. "A Collection of Poetical Essays from the Kĕ yo yun
Study" .. With Notes by Chang Heŏ-soo, &c.
1804. 8°.

張學士 CHANG HEŏ-SZE.

南華經 *Nan hwa king.* "The Nan hwa Classic." With Commentaries by .. Chang Heŏ-sze, &c. *See* 焦竑 TSEAOU HUNG. 老莊翼合刻 *Laou Chwang yih hŏ kih.* "The Works of Laou keun and Chwang Chow," &c. 1588. 8°.

張虹巢 CHANG HUNG-CHAOU.

See 張楳坪 CHANG MEI-PING. 金鈴集 *Kin ling tseĭh.* "The Kin-ling Collection" of Poetry. .. With Notes by Chang Hung-chaou, &c. 1822. 8°.

張惠言 CHANG HWUY-YEN.

周易虞氏義 *Chow Yih Yu She e.* "The Chow Changes with Yu Fan's Explanation." 9 keuen. [Also] 周易虞氏消息 *Chow Yih Yu She seaou seĭh.* "Yu Fan's Remarks on the Chow Changes." 2 keuen. [Also] 虞氏易禮 *Yu She Yih le.* "Yu Fan's Ceremonies of the Book of Changes." 2 keuen. [Also] 周易鄭氏義 *Chow Yih Ching She e.* "Ching's Explanation of the Chow Changes." 2 keuen. [Also] 周易荀氏九家義 *Chow Yih Seun She kew kea e.* "The Explanations of Seun She and nine other writers, of the Chow Changes." 易義別錄 *Yih e pĕĕ lŭh.* "Various Explanations of the Book of Changes." 14 keuen. *See* 嚴杰 YEN LĔĔ. 皇清經解 *Hwang Tsing king keae.* "The Classics Explained," &c. Keuen 1218–1247. 1829. 8°.

張忍齋 CHANG JIN-CHAE.

愛吾廬時文 *Gae woo leu she wăn.* "Occasional Essays from the Gae woo (Love myself) Cottage," on Texts from the Four Books. 1800. 8°.

Imperfect, four essays wanting.

張儒珍 CHANG JOO-CHIN.

See 高第丕 KAOU TE-PEI. 文學書官話 *Wăn hŏ shoo kwan hwa.* "A Mandarin Grammar." Compiled . . . with the assistance of Chang Joo-chin, &c. 1869. 8°.

張汝霖 CHANG JOO-LIN.

See 印光任 YIN KWANG-JIN, and CHANG JOO-LIN. 澳門記 *Gaou mun ke.* "A History of Macao," &c. 1800. 8°.

張季長 CHANG KE-CHANG.

See 蔡世遠 TSAE SHE-YUEN. 古文雅正 *Koo wăn ya ching.* "Elegant Extracts from Ancient Literature" .... Edited by ... Chang Ke-chang, &c. 1777. 8°.

張佳充 CHANG KEA-CHUNG.

江原常氏士女志 *Keang yuen Chang she sze neu che.* "A List of the Celebrities of the Chang Family." [1800?]. 8°.

張介賓 CHANG KEAE-PIN.

類經 *Luy king.* "Class Classics," being a Compilation of the Texts of the two ancient Medical Works entitled "Soo wăn" and "Ling choo king." Compiled and Annotated by Chang Keae-pin. A Reprint. 43 keuen. 1799. 8°.

—— 景岳全書 *King yŏ tseuen shoo.* Dr. Chang Keae-pin's, otherwise called King-yŏ, "Complete Medical System." A Reprint. 64 keuen. 1825. 8°.

張居正 CHANG KEU-CHING.

See 四書 SZE SHOO. 四書直解 *Sze shoo chĭh keae.* "The Four Books, clearly explained," by Chang Keu-ching, &c. 1766. 8°.

張瓈英 CHANG KEUNG-YING.

See 陳驦 CHIN SEANG. 鄱陽縣志 *Po yang heen che.* "A Topography of Po-yang Heen" ... Compiled by ... Chang Keung-ying, &c. 1824. 8°.

張九鉞 CHANG KEW-YUĔ.

鳴盛集 *Ming shing tseĭh.* "The Ming shing Collection" of Pentameter Poems. Compiled and Annotated by Chang Kew-yuĕ. 8 keuen. [1800?]. 8°.

Imperfect, wanting the first three keuen.

張經綸 CHANG KING-LUN.

從化縣新志 *Tsung hwa heen sin che.* "A New Topography of Tsung-hwa Heen," in the Province of Canton. Edited by Chang King-lun. 5 keuen. 1730. 8°.

Imperfect, wanting the first keuen.

張 景 星 CHANG KING-SING.

See 姚 培 謙 YAOU PEI-KEEN, and CHANG KING-SING. 通 鑑 綱 目 擘 要 *Tung keen kang mǔh lan yaou.* "An Epitome of Choo He's Condensations of the General .. History " ... Compiled by Yaou Pei-keen and Chang King-sing, &c.
1818. 8º.

張 卿 雲 CHANG KING-YUN.

See 姚 培 謙 YAOU PEI-KEEN. 類 腋 *Luy yǐh.* "A Thesaurus of Phrases " .. Compiled by .. Chang King-yun, &c. 1742, &c. 12º.

張 弸 先 CHANG KUNG-SEEN.

聖 門 禮 樂 統 *Shing mun le yǒ tung.* "The Sacred School of Confucius, its Ritual and its Music." Edited by Lew Yen. 24 keuen.
1701. 8º.

張 光 斗 CHANG KWANG-TOW.

藥 性 雷 公 炮 製 *Yǒ sing Luy kung paou che.* "On the Nature of Medicine, and Luy kung's System of Decocting Drugs." In two Parts. First Part, 8 keuen ; Second Part, 2 keuen.
1818. 8º.

張 貴 勝 CHANG KWEI-SHING.

遣 愁 集 *Keen tsew tseǐh.* "Anti-Melancholia." A series of Articles on the different Studies, etc., which the Author considers calculated to dispel Melancholy. Compiled by Chang Kwei-shing. Edited by Yu Saou and Koo Yew-heaou. 12 keuen, [1830 ?] 8º.

張 孟 遷 CHANG MǍNG-TSEEN.

傷 寒 世 驗 精 法 *Shang han she yen tsing fǎ.* "A Treatise on Fevers." Edited by Ke Chung. With Plates. A Reprint. 9 keuen.
1795. 12º.

張 楳 坪 CHANG MEI-PING.

金 鈴 集 *Kin ling tseǐh.* "The Kin-ling Collection" of Poetry. Compiled by Chang Mei-ping. With Notes by Chang Hung-chaou. 12 keuen.
1822. 8º.

張 鵬 翩 CHANG PǍNG-HǏH.

奉 使 俄 羅 斯 行 程 錄 *Fung she Go-lo-sze hing ching lǚh.* "The Journal of the Embassy sent overland from Peking to Russia " in the year 1688. See 何 秋 濤 HO TSEW-TAOU. 北 徼 彙 編 *Pǐh keaou wei peen.* "Treatises on the Countries beyond the Northern Frontier," &c. Keuen 4. 1865. 8º.

張 百 川 CHANG PǏH-CHUEN.

張 太 史 塾 課 *Chang Tae she shǔh ko.* "The Scholastic Essays of the Historiographer Chang Pǐh-chuen." 8 keuen. 1784 ? 8º.

Another copy.

Imperfect.

張 伯 端 CHANG PǏH-TWAN.

玉 清 金 笥 寶 籙 *Yǔh tsing kin sze paou lǚh.* "The Precious Talisman of the Precious, Pure, and Golden Casket." [Also] 金 丹 四 百 字 *Kin tan sze pǐh tsze.* "Four Hundred Words on the Elixir of Immortality." [Also] 石 橋 歌 *Shǐh keaou ko.* "The Song of the Stone Bridge." 悟 眞 篇 *Woo chin peen.* "On Understanding the Truth." See 彭 好 古 PǍNG HAOU-KOO. 道 言 內 外 秘 訣 全 書 *Taou yen nuy wae pé keuě tseuen shoo.* "A Complete Collection of Taouist Works," &c. 8º.

—— 悟 眞 篇 三 註 *Woo chin peen san choo.* "On Understanding the Truth." A Work on Alchemy. With Commentaries by Sěě Taou-kwang, Lǚh Yay, and Chin Che-heu. A Reprint. 3 keuen. 1809. 8º.
The third keuen wanting.

張 山 來 CHANG SHAN-LAE, and 張 進 也 CHANG TSIN-YAY.

昭 代 叢 書 *Chaou tae tsung shoo.* "A Collection of Reprints of Works by Authors under the present Dynasty." Compiled by Chang Shan-lae and Chang Tsin-yay. 50 keuen.
1703. 8º.

張 上 沖 CHANG SHANG-CHUNG.

See 吳 筠 WOO KEUN. 續 齊 諧 記 *Sǔh tse heae ke.* "A Supplementary Collection of Marvellous Tales " .... Edited by Chang Shang-chung, &c. 8º.

張世賢 CHANG SHE-HEEN.

See 王叔和 WANG SHŬH-HO. 圖註脈訣大全 *Too choo mǐh keuě ta tseuen.* "A Complete Work on the Pulse. With a Commentary and Plates" by Chang She-heen, &c.

1693. 8°.

—— See 王叔和 WANG SHŬH-HO. 圖註難經脈訣 *Too choo Nan king mǐh keue.* "The Nan king . . . and a Work on the Pulse," . . . With Commentaries and Plates by Chang She-heen, &c. 1800. 8°.

—— 圖註難經 *Too choo Nan king.* "The Nan king." A Medical Work. With a Commentary and Plates. Edited by Chang She-heen. A Reprint. [2 ?] keuen. [1800 ?]. 8°.

Imperfect, containing only the first keuen.

張聖度 CHANG SHING-TOO.

See 孔丘 KUNG KEW. 學源堂書經體註 *Heŏ yuen Tang Shoo king te choo.* " . . . The Book of Historical Documents" . . . Edited by . . . Chang Shing-too, &c. 1725. 8°.

張宋梅 CHANG SUNG-MEI.

方輿新鈔 *Fang yu sin chaou.* "A New Treatise on Geography." 12 keuen. 1747. 8°.

Title-page and some leaves at the end wanting.

張師誠 CHANG SZE-CHING.

御製全史詩 *Yu che tseuen she she.* "Historical Poetry." By the Emperor [Kang-he ?]. With Notes. Edited by Chang Sze-ching. 266 keuen. [1700 ?]. 8°.

Imperfect, containing only keuen 53, 54, 57–64.

張士範 CHANG SZE-FAN.

感應篇善過格 *Kan ying peen shen kwo kĭh.* "The Book of Rewards and Punishments," by Laou keun. Together with "The Adjustment of Merit and Blame," and other Taouist Tracts. With a Commentary. Edited by Chang Sze-fan. 1793. 8°.

張斯涵 CHANG SZE-HAN.

See 皇甫謐 HWANG FOO-MEĬH. 高士傳 *Kaou sze chuen.* "Biographies of Eminent Scholars." . . . . Edited by Chang Sze-han, &c. 8°.

張坦熊 CHANG TAN-HEUNG.

玉環志 *Yŭh hwan che.* "A Topography of Yŭh hwan," an Island on the Coast of Chĕkeang. Compiled by Chang Tan-heung. 4 keuen. 1732. 8°.

張唐英 CHANG TANG-YING.

九國志 *Kew kwŏ che.* "The History of the Nine States" . . . Supplemented by Chang Tang-ying, &c. See 伍崇曜 WOO TSUNG-YAOU. 粵雅堂叢書 *Yuě ya Tang tsung shoo.* "The Yuě-ya Tang Collection of Reprints," &c. Series 10. 1853. 8°.

張道緒 CHANG TAOU-SEU.

See 易經 YĬH KING. 周易義傳合訂 *Chow yĭh e chuen hŏ ting.* "The Book of Changes" . . With the sounds of doubtful Characters supplied by Chang Taou-seu, &c. 8°.

張鼎年 CHANG TING-NEEN.

See 文昌帝君 WĂN CHANG TE KEUN. 陰隲文註釋 *Yin chĭh wăn choo shĭh.* "A Treatise on Secret Rewards and Retributions. . . With a Commentary by Chang Ting-neen, &c.

1836. 8°.

張鼎思 CHANG TING-SZE.

See 李時珍 LE SHE-CHIN. 本草綱目全書 *Pun tsaou kang mǔh tseuen shoo.* "The Complete Materia Medica" . . . . Edited by Chang Ting-sze, &c. 1603. 8°.

—— 脈學奇經八脈 *Mǐh heŏ ke king pă mǐh.* "A Work on the Pulse," and also "On the Theory of the Eight Pulses." . . . Edited by Chang Ting-sze, &c. 1603. 8°.

—— 奇經八脈玫 *Ke king pă mǐh kaou.* "An Examination of the Theory of the Eight Pulses." . . . . Edited by Chang Ting-sze, &c. 12°.

張廷玉 CHANG TING-YŬH.

See CHINA. *Board of Office.* 欽定吏部則例 *Kin ting Le Poo tsĭh le.* "Regulations of the Board of Office" . . . . Compiled . . . by Chang Ting-yŭh, &c. 1741. 8°.

CHA [15] CHA

張 廷 玉 CHANG TING-YŬH. (*Continued.*)
See CHINA. 雍 正 YUNG-CHING. *Emperor.*
上 諭 *Shang yu.* "Imperial Edicts" . . .
Compiled by . . . Chang Ting-yŭh, &c.
1741. 8°.

—— See 孔 丘 KUNG KEW. 欽 定 春 秋 傳 說
彙 纂 *Kin ting Chun Tsew chuen shwŏ wei tswan.*
"The Spring and Autumn Annals" . . . . Compiled by . . Chang Ting-yŭh, &c. 1721. 8°.

———— 欽 定 書 經 傳 說 彙 纂 *Kin ting Shoo
king chuen shwŏ wei tswan.* "The Book of
Historical Documents" . . . Compiled by . .
Chang Ting-yŭh, &c. 1730. 8°.

—— See TSING DYNASTY. 大 清 會 典 *Ta Tsing
hwuy teen.* "A Comprehensive Description of
the System of Government under the Tsing
Dynasty." Compiled . . . by . . . Chang Ting-
yŭh, &c. 1732. 8°.

—— See 允 祿 YUN LŬH. 子 史 精 華 *Tsze she
tsing hwa.* "Choice Quotations" . . . Compiled
by . . . Chang Ting-yŭh, &c. 1727. 8°.

—— 分 類 字 錦 *Fun luy tsze kin.* "A Classified
Lexicon of Elegant Expressions." Compiled
by an Imperial Commission, consisting of Chang
Ting-yŭh, Tseang Ting-seĭh, Le Ting-e, and
others. 64 keuen. 1722. 8°.

—— 明 史 *Ming she.* "The History of the Ming
Dynasty." Compiled by Chang Ting-yŭh and
others. 332 keuen. [1742?]. 8°.
Containing only keuen 84, 85.

—— 御 撰 資 治 通 鑑 明 紀 綱 目 *Yu chuen tsze
che tung keen Ming ke kang muh.* "A Condensed
History of the Ming Dynasty for the Assistance
of Government." Compiled by an Imperial
Commission, consisting of Chang Ting-yŭh,
Wang Hwuy-fun, Chow Chang-fă, and others.
20 keuen. 1746. 8°.

Another copy.

張 曾 祉 CHANG TSĂNG-CHE.
See 葉 九 升 YĔ KEW-SHING. 地 理 山 法 全 書
Te le shan fă tseuen shoo. "The Laws of Mountains." . . . Fifth keuen is edited, with Notes,
by Chang Tsăng-che, &c. 8°.

張 曾 祉 CHANG TSĂNG-CHE.
See 葉 九 升 YĔ KEW-SHING. 地 理 山 法 全 書
Te le shan fă tseuen shoo. "The Laws of Moun-
tains." . . . Sixteenth keuen is edited, with
Notes, by Chang Tsăng-che, &c. 8°.

張 進 也 CHANG TSIN-YAY.
See 張 山 來 CHANG SHAN-LAE, and CHANG
TSIN-YAY. 昭 代 叢 書 *Chaou tae tsung shoo.*
"A Collection of Reprints of Works by Authors
under the present Dynasty." Compiled by
Chang Shan-lae and Chang Tsin-yay, &c.
1703. 8°.

張 作 楠 CHANG TSO-NAN.
欄 籌 續 錄 *Chuy yŏ sŭh lŭh.* "Tables of Altitude throughout the Year." Edited by Keang
Lin-tae. 3 keuen. [1820?]. 8°.

—— 高 弧 細 草 *Kaou hoo se tsaou.* "A Minute
Exposition of the Method of Calculating Arcs."
Edited by Keang Lin-tae. 1821. 8°.

—— 新 測 恒 星 圖 表 *Sin tsĭh hăng sing too peaou.*
"Newly Projected Celestial Charts, with a tabulated Catalogue of all the Stars." The Charts
are drawn by Keang Lin-tae. 1823. 8°.

張 遵 言 CHANG TSUN-YEN.
張 遵 言 傳 *Chang Tsun-yen chuen.* "The Story
of Chang Tsun-yen." See 說 SHWŎ. 說 淵
Shwŏ yuen. "A Collection of Tales," &c. 8°.

張 崇 懿 CHANG TSUNG-E.
錢 志 新 編 *Tseen che sin peen.* "An Illustrated
Treatise on the Currency" down to the end of
the Ming Dynasty, concluding with a Section
on Foreign Coins and another on unknown
Coins. 20 keuen. 1830. 8°.

Another edition. 20 keuen. 1830. 8°.

張 崇 烈 CHANG TSUNG-LĔĔ.
See 孫 汝 忠 SUN JOO-CHUNG. 金 丹 眞 傳
Kin tan chin chuen. "A Trustworthy Treatise
on the Philosopher's Stone." With a Commentary by Chang Tsung-lĕĕ, &c. 1615. 8°.

張 子 厚 CHANG TSZE-HOW.
See 汪 佑 WANG YEW. 五 子 近 思 錄 *Woo
tsze kin sze lŭh.* "Records of the Approximating
Thoughts of the Five Philosophers" . . . Chang
Tsze-how, &c. 1693. 8°.

張 自 烈 CHANG TSZE-LĔĔ.

See 梅 膺 祚 MEI YING-TSOO. 字 彙 *Tsze wei.* "A Dictionary" . . . Enlarged and Improved by Chang Tsze-lĕĕ, &c.   8°.

張 敦 仁 CHANG TUN-JIN.

See 老 君 LAOU KEUN. 感 應 篇 箋 註 *Kan ying peen tseen choo.* "The Book of Rewards and Punishments" . . . Edited by Chang Tun-jin, &c.   1827. 8°.

—— 撫 本 禮 記 鄭 注 考 異 *Foo pun Le ke Ching choo kaou e.* "The Different Readings of the Foo Chow Edition of the Book of Rites and of Ching's Commentary Examined." 2 keuen. *See* 嚴 杰 YEN LĔĔ. 皇 清 經 解 *Hwang Tsing king keae.* "The Classics Explained," &c. Keuen 1075, 1076.   1829. 8°.

張 爾 歧 CHANG URH-KE.

蒿 庵 閒 話 *Haou gan heen hwa.* "Occasional Jottings from the Southernwood Cottage." 2 keuen. *See* 伍 崇 曜 WOO TSUNG-YAOU. 粵 雅 堂 叢 書 *Yuĕ ya Tang tsung shoo.* "The Yuĕ-ya Tang Collection of Reprints," &c. Series 10.   1853. 8°.

CHANG WĂN-HOO.

See 利 瑪 竇 LE MA-TOW. 幾 何 原 本 *Ke ho yuen pun.* "Elements of the Science of Quantity" . . . Revised by . . . Chang Wăn-hoo, &c.   1857. 8°.

張 文 嘉 CHANG WĂN-KEA.

齊 家 寶 要 *Tse kea paou yaou.* "Valuable Hints for Domestic Rule." Compiled by Chang-Wăn-kea. Edited by Ho Kung. 2 keuen.

     [1790?]. 8°.

張 維 屏 CHANG WEI-PING.

國 朝 詩 人 徵 略 *Kwŏ chaou she jin ching lĕo.* "Short Biographical Notices of the Poets of the Tsing Dynasty." 60 keuen.   1819. 8°.

張 武 略 CHANG WOO-LĔŎ.

擬 易 *E yĭh.* "On Deciding on the Meaning of the Book of Changes." *See* 閔 景 賢 MIN KING-HEEN. 快 書 *Kwae shoo.* "A Book of Amusement," &c. Keuen 27.   1626. 8°.

張 無 頗 CHANG WOO-PO.

張 無 頗 傳 *Chang Woo-po chuen.* "The Story of Chang Woo-po." *See* 說 SHWŎ. 說 淵 *Shwŏ yuen.* "A Collection of Tales," &c. Vol. 4.   8°.

張 彥 陵 CHANG YEN-LING.

See 徐 在 漢 SEU TSAE-HAN. 易 或 *Yih hwŏ.* "The Doubtful Passages of the Book of Changes" Elucidated . . With Notes by Chang Yen-ling, &c.   1774. 8°.

張 延 世 CHANG YEN-SHE.

廣 錢 譜 *Kwang tseen poo.* "Historical References to Sums of Money." *See* 張 山 來 CHANG SHAN-LAE, and 張 進 也 CHANG TSIN-YAY. 昭 代 叢 書 *Chaou tae tsung shoo.* "A Collection of Reprints of Works by Authors under the present Dynasty," &c. Keuen 34.

     1703. 8°.

張 友 樵 CHANG YEW-TSEAOU.

See 吳 葉 桂 WOO YĔ-KWEI. 醫 效 秘 傳 *E heaou pe chuen.* "An Efficacious System of Medicine" . . . . Edited by Chang Yew-tseaou, &c.   1831. 8°.

張 營 塽 CHANG YING-HOW.

See 嚴 榮 YEN YUNG. 武 義 縣 志 *Woo e heen che.* "A Topography of Woo-e Heen." Compiled by . . Chang Ying-how, &c. 1804. 8°.

張 虞 庪 CHANG YU-HOW.

驚 筵 辨 *King yen peen.* "Discussions on Dangerous Subjects." *See* 閔 景 賢 MIN KING-HEEN. 快 書 *Kwae shoo.* "A Book of Amusement," &c.   Keuen 8. 1626. 8°.

張 元 幹 CHANG YUEN-WŎ.

蘆 川 歸 來 集 *Loo chuen kwei lae tseĭh.* "The Poetical Collection of the Return from Lao chuen." *See* 吳 孟 舉 WOO MĂNG-KEU, and 吳 自 牧 WOO TSZE-MŬH. 宋 詩 鈔 二 集 *Sung she chaou urh tseĭh.* "Poetry of the Sung Dynasty," &c.   8°.

張 玉 書 CHANG YŬH-SHOO.

存 稿 *Tsun kaou.* "Essays." *See* 長 城 CHANG CHING. 名 家 制 義 *Ming kea che e.* "Essays" on Texts from the Four Books, &c. Tsĭh 111.

     1699. 8°.

張 玉 書 Chang Yǔh-shoo. (*Continued.*)
See 康 熙 Kang-he. *Emperor.* 御 製 文 集 *Yu che wăn tseih.* "The Literary Works of .. Kang-he." Edited by .. Chang Yǔh-shoo, &c. 1711. 8°.

—— 康 熙 字 典 *Kang-he tsze teen.* "Kang-he's Dictionary," compiled . . . by Chang Yǔh-shoo, &c. 1716. 8°.

張 永 祺 Chang Yung-ke.
稿 *Kaou.* "Essays." See 長 城 Chang Ching. 名 家 制 義 *Ming kea che e.* "Essays" on Texts from the Four Books, &c. Tsǐh 107. 1699. 8°.

掌 Chang.
拊 掌 錄 *Foo chang lǔh.* "Records to cause Clapping of Hands." See 說 Shwŏ. 說 畧 *Shwŏ leŏ.* "Historical and other Tracts," &c. 8°.

常 沂 Chang E.
靈 鬼 志 *Ling kwei che.* "Ghost Stories." See 王 文 誥 Wang Wăn-kaou. 唐 代 叢 書 *Tang tae tsung shoo.* "A Collection of Reprints of Works written during the Tang Dynasty." Series 6. 1806. 8°.

—— 靈 鬼 志 *Ling kwei che.* "Ghost Stories." By Chang E, of the Tang Dynasty. A Reprint. [1741?]. 8°.

常 璩 Chang Keu.
漢 中 志 *Han chung che.* "An Account of Han-chung," an ancient State. A Reprint. [1800?]. 8°.

—— 漢 中 士 女 志 *Han chung Sze Neu che.* "Biographical Notices of Celebrated Scholars and Women of Han chung." A Reprint. [1800?]. 8°.

—— 後 賢 志 *How heen che.* "Biographical Notices of Worthies of a later date." A Reprint. [1800?]. 8°.

—— 公 孫 述 劉 牧 二 志 *Kung Sun-shǔh, Lew Mǔh urh che.* "The Biographies of Kung Sun-shǔh and Lew Mǔh," of the Han Dynasty. A Reprint. [1800?]. 8°.

—— 李 志 *Le che.* "A Biography of Le Tǐh," of the Han Dynasty. A Reprint. [1800?]. 8°.

常 璩 Chang Keu. (*Continued.*)
南 中 志 *Nan chung che.* "An Account of Nan-chung," an ancient State in the South of China. A Reprint. [1800?]. 8°.

—— 序 志 *Seu che.* "Serial Records" of Celebrities under the Han and Tsin Dynasties. [1800?]. 8°.

—— 蜀 志 *Shǔh che.* "An Account of Shǔh," an ancient State situated in the region of the modern Province of Sze-chuen. A Reprint. [1800?]. 8°.

—— 大 同 志 *Ta tung che.* "A Harmonized History" of the Western Tsin Dynasty. A Reprint. [1800?]. 8°.

章 Chang.
三 十 三 章 指 南 *San shǐh san chang che nan.* "A Guide to the Thirty-three Chapters" of the Chung Yung. 1822. 12°.
Imperfect, containing only the first twenty chapters.

章 懷 Chang-hwae.
See 范 曄 Fan Yě. 後 漢 書 *How Han shoo.* "The History of the later Han Dynasty." With Notes by Prince Chang-hwae, &c. 1643. 8°.

章 鈺 Chang Yǔh.
See 周 鼎 臣 Chow Ting-chin. 增 訂 敬 信 錄 *Tsăng ting king sin lǔh.* "Works on Reverence and Faith" . . . Edited by Chang Yǔh, &c. 1799. 8°.

章 香 艇 Chang Heang-ting.
二 論 題 備 *Urh lun te pe.* "Essays on the Confucian Analects." Edited by Chang Heang-ting. 1820. 12°.
Imperfect.

章 學 誠 Chang Heŏ-ching.
文 史 通 義 *Wăn she tung e.* "A Complete Review of Classical and Historical Literature." 8 keuen. [Also] 校 讐 通 義 *Keaou chow tung e.* "A Complete Review of the Collation of Books." 3 keuen. See 伍 崇 曜 Woo Tsung-yaou. 粵 雅 堂 叢 書 *Yuĕ ya Tang tsung shoo.* "The Yuĕ-ya Tang Collection of Reprints," &c. Series 5. 1853. 8°.

3

章金牧 CHANG KIN-MŬH.

稿 *Kaou.* "Essays." *See* 長城 CHANG CHING. 名家制義 *Ming kea che e.* "Essays" on Texts from the Four Books, &c. Tsĭh 114.

1699. 8°.

章世純 CHANG SHE-SHUN.

稿 *Kaou.* "Essays." *See* 長城 CHANG CHING. 名家制義 *Ming kea che e.* "Essays" on Texts from the Four Books, &c. Tsĭh 81.

1699. 8°.

漳州府 CHANG CHOW FOO.

漳州府志 *Chang chow Foo che.* "A Topography of Chang-chow Foo." 34 keuen.

[1750?]. 8°.

Imperfect, first keuen and preface wanting.

昌巖 CHANG YEN.

玉振 *Yŭh chin.* "Precious Rousings." *See* 閔景賢 MIN KING-HEEN. 快書 *Kwae shoo.* "A Book of Amusement," &c. Keuen 17.

1626. 8°.

兆毅 CHAOU E.

See CHINA. 乾隆 KEEN LUNG. *Emperor.* 欽定入旗則例 *Kin ting pă ke tsĭh le.* "Regulations for the Bannermen" .. Compiled by .. Chaou E, &c. 1742. 8°.

晁冲之 CHAOU CHUNG-CHE.

晁具茨詩集 *Chaou Keu-tsze she tseĭh.* "Chaou Chung-che's Poetry." 15 keuen. *See* 葉志詵 YĔ CHE-SIN. 海山仙館叢書 *Hae shan seen Kwan tsung shoo.* "The Hae shan seen Kwan Collection of Reprints," &c. Vol. 57. 1848. 8°.

—— 具茨集 *Keu tsze tseĭh.* "Chaou Chung-che's Poetry." *See* 吳孟舉 WOO MĂNG-KEU, and 吳自牧 WOO TSZE-MŬH. 宋詩鈔二集 *Sung she chaou urh tseĭh.* "Poetry of the Sung Dynasty," &c. 8°.

晁補之 CHAOU POO-CHE.

雞肋集 *Ke lĭh tseĭh.* "The Cock's Rib Collection of Poetry." *See* 吳孟舉 WOO MĂNG-KEU, and 吳自牧 WOO TSZE-MŬH. 宋詩鈔二集 *Sung she chaou urh tseĭh.* "Poetry of the Sung Dynasty," &c. 8°.

趙瑤 CHAOU FAN.

See CHINA. 嘉慶 KEA-KING. *Emperor.* 欽定軍器則例 *Kin ting keun ke tsĭh le.* "Military Store Regulations" .. Compiled by .. Chaou Fan, &c. 1801. 8°.

趙宏 CHAOU HUNG.

See 老君 LAOU-KEUN. 太上感應篇圖說 *Tae shang kan ying peen too shwŏ.* "The Book of Rewards and Punishments." Edited by Chaou Hung, &c. 1825. 8°.

趙均 CHAOU KEUN.

金石林時地攷 *Kin shĭh lin she te kaou.* "A Collection of Ancient Inscriptions, with their Dates and Localities." 2 keuen. *See* 伍崇曜 WOO TSUNG-YAOU. 粵雅堂叢書 *Yuĕ ya Tang tsung shoo.* "The Yuĕ-ya Tang Collection of Reprints," &c. Series 15.

1853. 8°.

趙葵 CHAOU KWEI.

行營雜錄 *Hing ying tsă lŭh.* "Camp Annals." *See* 說 SHWŎ. 說纂 *Shwŏ tswan.* "Miscellaneous Records," &c. 8°.

趙炳 CHAOU PING.

稿 *Kaou.* "Essays." *See* 長城 CHANG CHING. 名家制義 *Ming kea che e.* "Essays" on Texts from the Four Books, &c. Tsĭh 115.

1699. 8°.

趙坦 CHAOU TAN.

春秋異文箋 *Chun Tsew e wăn tseen.* "The Various Readings of the Spring and Autumn Annals, with Notes." [Also] 寶甓齋札記 *Paou peĭh chae chă ke.* "Literary Records from the Paou peĭh Study." [Also] 寶甓齋文集 *Paou peĭh chae wăn tseĭh.* "A Collection of Writings from the Paou peĭh Study." *See* 嚴杰 YEN LĔĔ. 皇清經解 *Hwang Tsing king keae.* "The Classics Explained," &c. Keuen 1303–1317.

1829. 8°.

趙瀗 CHAOU TSIN.

養疴漫筆 *Yang o mwan peĭh.* "Scraps for Invalids." *See* 說 SHWŎ. 說纂 *Shwŏ tswan.* "Miscellaneous Records," &c. 8°.

趙 曄 CHAOU YĔ.

吳越春秋 *Woo Yuĕ Chun Tsew.* "The History of the States of Woo and Yuĕ," corresponding to the modern Provinces of Keangnan and Chĕ-keang. A Reprint. 6 keuen.
[1800 ?]. 8°.

Another copy.

趙 佑 CHAOU YEW.

清獻堂稿 *Tsing heen Tang kaou.* "Essays from the Tsing heen Tang" on Texts from the Four Books. 1765. 8°.

趙 翼 CHAOU YĬH.

簷曝雜記 *Yen pŭh tsă ke.* "Miscellaneous Records from the Yen pŭh [Hall ?]." 6 keuen.
[1800 ?]. 8°.

趙 巢 阿 CHAOU CHAOU-AH.

See 繆 蓮 仙 MŬH LEEN-HEEN. 文章游戲 *Wăn chang yew he.* "Rambles in Polite Literature.".... Edited by .. Chaou Chaou-ah, &c.
1824. 8°.

趙 振 芳 CHAOU CHIN-FANG.

See 徐 在 漢 SEU TSAE-HAN. 易 或 *Yĭh hŭŏ.* "Doubts on the Book of Changes" elucidated. Edited by Chaou Chin-fang, &c. 1774. 8°.

—— 易原 *Yĭh yuen.* "The Source of the Book of Changes." Edited by Seu Tsae-han.
[1764 ?]. 8°.

趙 宜 崙 CHAOU E-LUN.

See 班 固 PAN KOO. 白虎通 *Pĭh hoo tung.* The Results of a "Convocation ... in the Pĭh hoo Kwan.".... Edited by Chaou E-lun, &c. 8°.

趙 飛 燕 CHAOU FEI-YEN.

飛燕遺事 *Fei yen wei sze.* "The Property left by the Empress Chaou Fei-yen." By an anonymous writer of the Tang Dynasty.
[1741 ?]. 8°.

趙 希 鵠 CHAOU HE-KŬH.

洞天清祿 *Tung teen tsing lŭh.* "Profound, Heavenly, and Pure Happiness." A Discussion of the merits and peculiarities of antique Vessels, Instruments, and Materials requisite for the Study. By Chaou He-kŭh. See 葉 志 詵 YĔ CHE-SIN. 海山仙館叢書 *Hae shan seen Kwan tsung shoo.* "The Hae shan seen Kwan Collection of Reprints," &c. Vol. 45. 1848. 8°.

趙 宦 光 CHAOU HWAN-KWANG.

護生品 *Hoo săng pin.* "On Preserving Life." See 沈 培 木 CHIN PEI-MŬH. 慈心寶鑑 *Tsze sin paou keen.* "The Precious Mirror of a Merciful Heart," &c. 1771. 8°.

趙 君 卿 CHAOU KEUN-KING.

周髀算經 *Chow pe swan king.* "A Work on Trigonometry and Astronomy," in three parts. Part 1 is a dialogue between Chow Kung and Shang Kaou on the properties of the right-angled triangle; Part 2 is a dialogue between Yung Fang and Chin-tsze on some of the rudimentary facts of astronomy; and the last part treats in detail of the elements of the *Kae teen* astronomy. Edited, with a Commentary, by Chaou Keun-king. Re-edited by Chin Lwan, with further elucidations by Le Chun-fung, and with MS. notes by J. F. Fonquet. A Reprint. 2 keuen. [1600 ?]. 8°.

趙 光 祧 CHAOU KWANG-YŬH.

See 趙 三 暘 CHAOU SAN-YANG. 武經標題正義 *Woo king peaou te ching E.* "The True Meaning of the ... Military Classic." With Notes by Chaou Kwang-yŭh, &c. 8°.

趙 靈 祐 CHAOU LING-YEW.

潙山警策 *Kwei shan king tsĭh.* "Religious Warnings from the Kwei shan Monastery" by Prior Chaou Ling-yew. With a Commentary by Hung-tsan. 2 keuen. *Canton,* 1660. 8°.

趙 南 星 CHAOU NAN-SING.

稿 *Kaou.* "Essays." See 長 城 CHANG CHING. 名家制義 *Ming hea che e.* "Essays" on Texts from the Four Books, &c. Tsĭh 58.
1699. 8°.

趙 秉 祧 CHAOU PING-YŬH.

See 楊 雄 YANG HEUNG. 方言 *Fang yen.* "Foreign Words" ...., Edited by Chaou Ping-yŭh, &c. 8°.

趙 三 暘 CHAOU SAN-YANG.

武經標題正義 *Woo king peaou te ching e.* "The True Meaning of the leading themes of the Military Classic." With Notes by Chaou Kwang-yŭh. Edited by Chaou San-yang and Lew Yew-kwang. 8 keuen. [1790 ?]. 8°.
Imperfect, containing only part of keuen 6 and keuen 7, 8.

趙 錫 禮 CHAOU SEÏH-LE.

See 爾 哈 善 URH-HŎ-SHEN. 蘇 州 府 志 *Soo chow foo che.* "A Topography of Soochow Foo." Compiled by ... Chaou Seïh-le, &c.
1748. 8°.

趙 松 一 CHAOU SUNG-YÏH.

丹 桂 籍 *Tan kwei tseïh.* "The Tan kwei Collection" of Taouist Works. With Notes by Yen Ching. Edited by Chaou Sung-yïh. 6 keuen. 1818. 8°.

Imperfect, wanting keuen 6.

趙 士 楨 CHAOU SZE-CHING.

See 朵 思 麻 To SZE-MA. 兵 錄 *Ping lŭh.* "A Treatise on Warlike Implements." Illustrated by Chaou Sze-ching, &c. 8°.

趙 士 麟 CHAOU SZE-LIN.

浙 江 通 志 *Chĕ keang tung che.* "A Topography of the Province of Chĕ-kĕang." Compiled by Chaou Sze-lin, She Wei han, Wang Kwŏ-gan, and others. 50 keuen. 1684. 8°.

趙 廷 健 CHAOU TING-KEEN.

崇 明 縣 志 *Tsung-ming heen che.* "A Topography of Tsung-ming Heen," at the mouth of the Yang-tsze keang. Compiled by Chaou Ting-keen. Edited by Han Yen-tsăng, Chung Hŏ-king, and others. 20 keuen. 1760. 8°.

趙 子 欽 CHAOU TSZE-KIN.

See 易 經 YÏH KING. 復 齋 易 說 *Fŭh chae Yïh shwŏ.* "A Commentary on the Book of Changes." By Chaou Tsze-kin, &c.
1676. 8°.

趙 萬 年 CHAOU WAN-NEEN.

襄 陽 守 城 錄 *Seang yang show ehing lŭh.* "The Defence of Seang-yang." See 伍 崇 曜 Woo TSUNG-YAOU. 粵 雅 堂 叢 書 *Yŭĕ ya Tang tsung shoo.* "The Yŭĕ-ya Tang Collection of Reprints," &c. Series 13. 1853. 8°.

趙 文 楷 CHAOU WĂN-KEAE.

槎 上 存 稿 *Cha shang tsun kaou.* "The Writings" of Chaou Wăn-keae. 1818. 8°.

—— 永 字 八 法 筆 陳 圖 *Yung tsze pă fă peïh chin too.* "Rules for Writing the Eight Strokes composing the Character 'Yung.'" 1810. 8°.

趙 聞 禮 CHAOU WĂN-LE.

陽 春 白 雪 *Yang chun pĭh seuĕ.* "The White Snow of Yang-chun." [Poems.] Compiled by Chaou Wăn-le. 9 keuen. See 伍 崇 曜 Woo TSUNG-YAOU. 粵 雅 堂 叢 書 *Yŭĕ ya Tang tsung shoo.* "The Yŭĕ-ya Tang Collection of Reprints," &c. Series 20. 1853. 8°.

趙 維 寰 CHAOU WEI-HWAN.

讀 史 快 編 *Tŭh she kwae peen.* "Pleasant Pages for Students of History." Compiled by Chaou Wei-hwan. 60 keuen. 1624. 8°.

趙 一 清 CHAOU YÏH-TSING.

See 桑 欽 SANG KIN. 水 經 注 釋 *Shwuy king choo shĭh.* "The Water Classic .... commented on and explained" by Chaou Yïh-tsing.
1786. 8°.

—— 水 經 注 箋 刊 誤 *Shwuy king choo tseen kan woo.* "Comments and Notes on the 'Water Classic,' calculated to annihilate erroneous views." Compiled by Chaou Yïh-tsing. 12 keuen. [1786?]. 8°.

趙 元 一 CHAOU YUEN-YÏH.

奉 天 錄 *Fung teen lŭh.* "Records of Fung teen." 4 keuen. See 伍 崇 曜 Woo TSUNG-YAOU. 粵 雅 堂 叢 書 *Yŭĕ ya Tang tsung shoo.* "The Yŭĕ-ya Tang Collection of Reprints," &c. Series 2. 1853. 8°.

朝 CHAOU.

朝 野 遺 紀 *Chaou yay e ke.* "Records of the Court." See 說 SHWŎ. 說 畧 *Shwŏ leŏ.* "Historical and other Tracts." 8°.

昭 君 CHAOU KEUN.

昭 君 傳 *Chaou keun chuen.* "The Story of Chaou keun," being an Account of his Adventures at the Court of Han wang. 8 keuen.
[1790?]. 8°.

Imperfect, containing only part of keuen 2 and 3–8.

哆 啉 哎 CHAY-LAN-LIN. *pseud.*

暎 咭 唎 國 新 種 痘 奇 書 *Ying-keïh-le kwŏ sin chung tow ke shoo.* "A Pamphlet on the English System of Vaccination." By Chay-lan-lin. Edited by Doctor Pe-chin, and translated into Chinese by Sze-tang-tung [*i.e.* Sir G. Stanton?] and Ching Tsung-keen. 1805. 8°.

CHE [21] CHE

車龍 CHAY LUNG.

繡像車龍公子花燈記 *Sew seang Chay lung kung tsze hwa tăng ke.* "The Story of Chay-lung's Ornamented Lamps." With an Illustration. [In verse.] 2 keuen.

[1850?]. 8°.

志 CHE.

一統志 *Yih tung che.* "A Geography of the whole Empire." Compiled by Imperial Order by Le Heen, Păng She, and Leu Yuen. 90 keuen. [1461?]. 8°.

Imperfect, wanting the first sixty keuen.

智旭 CHE-HEŬH.

See 湛然 CHAN-JEN. 禮拜觀想偈暑釋 *Le pae kwan seang kёё leŏ shih.* "The Enigmas of Buddhist Worship and Devotion" . . . . Explained by Che-heŭh, &c. 1803. Oblong.

—— 佛說阿彌陀經要解 *Fŭh shwŏ O-me-to king yaou keae.* "The Amita Sutra . . . Explained" by Che-heŭh. *See* 瀚益 Gow-yĭh. 淨土十要 *Tsing too shih yaou.* "Ten Requisites for the Attainment of the Pure Regions of Bliss," &c. 8°.

—— 慈悲水懺 *Tsze pe shwuy tsan.* "The Ritual of the Purifying Water of the Merciful" Tathâgata. By the Buddhist Che-hcuh. With a Preface by the Emperor Yung-lŏ. 3 keuen.

1415. 8°.

智祥 CHE-TSEANG.

禪林寶訓筆說 *Shen lin paou heun peĭh shwŏ.* "The Precious Teachings of Members of the Priesthood." Compiled by the Priest Che-tseang. 3 keuen. *Canton*, 1744. 8°.

智嚴共寶雲 CHE YEN HUNG PAOU YUN.

See 李嘉果 LE KEA-KWO. 天王經 *Teen wang king.* "The Sutra of the Four Heavenly Kings." . . . Translated by . . Che-yen-hung-paou-yun, &c. 1797 8°.

支中夫 CHE CHUNG-FOO.

十處士傳 *Shih choo sze chuen.* "Biographical Notices of the Ten Recluses." *See* 閔景賢 MIN KING-HEEN. 快書 *Kwae shoo.* "A Book of Amusement," &c. Keuen 45. 1626. 8°.

支華平 CHE HWA-PING.

九發 *Kew fă.* "The Nine Utterances." [Also] 錢罿 *Tseen le.* "The Reproach of Money." *See* 閔景賢 MIN KING-HEEN. 快書 *Kwae shoo.* "A Book of Amusement," &c. Keuen 38, 39. 1626. 8°.

浙江 CHĔ KEANG.

—— 浙海鈔關現行收稅則例 *Chĕ hae chaou kwan heen hing show shwuy tsih le.* "Customs Tariff for the Ports in the Province of Chĕ-kcang." 1729. 8°.

Another copy.

—— 浙海鈔關徵收稅銀則例 *Chĕ hae chaou kwan ching show shwuy yin tsih le.* "Customs Tariffs for the Ports in the Province of Chĕ-keang." 1724. 8°.

—— 浙江鄉試硃卷 *Chĕ keang heang shih choo keuen.* "The Red Book of Chĕ-keang Prize Examination Essays," written in the years 1771, 1786, 1788, 1792, 1800, 1804, 1819, 1821, 1834, and 1835. 1771–1835. 8°.

—— 浙江鄉試同年齒錄 *Chĕ keang heang shih tung neen che lŭh.* "A List of Successful Candidates at the Chĕ-keang Examinations" for the Year 1788. 1788. 8°.

—— 浙江試帖攬勝 *Chĕ keang she tёё lan shing.* "Successful Poetical Essays by Scholars of the Province of Chĕ-keang." 4 keuen.

[1800?]. 8°.

Imperfect, containing only keuen 3, 4.

—— 浙江省外海戰船則例 *Chĕ keang sing wae hae chen chuen tsih le.* "Naval Regulations for the Province of Chĕ-keang." 20 keuen.

[1800?]. 8°.

Imperfect, containing only keuen 4, 5, 8, 9, 15–19.

—— 治浙成規 *Che Chĕ ching kwei.* "Chĕ-keang Provincial Regulations" issued from the twenty-first year of the reign of the Emperor Keen-lung to the eighth year of the reign of the Emperor Kea-king. 1803. 8°.

浙 江 Chě keang. (Continued.)

———— From the twenty-first year of the Emperor Keen-lung [1756] to the twelfth year of Taou kwang [1832]. 4 keuen. 1832. 8°.

———— [1836?]. 8°.

Imperfect.

—— 浙 江 試 牘 Chě-keang she tŭh. "Chě-keang Examination Essays." [1810?]. 8°.

Imperfect.

—— 浙 江 圖 考 Chě keang too kaou. "A Geographical Survey of the Water Ways of the Province of Chě-keang." [1820?]. 8°.

皙 倣 Chě Fang.

舞 劍 集 Woo keen tseĭh. "Specimens of the Running-hand Forms of Characters." Compiled by Chě Fang. 5 keuen. [1700?]. 8°.

詹 詹 Chen Chen.

情 史 Tsing she. "Records of the Passions." 24 keuen. 1784. 8°.

詹 淮 Chen Hwae.

性 理 綜 要 Sing le tsung yaou. "An Epitome of Works on Mental Philosophy." By Chen Hwae. Edited by Chin Jin-seĭh. 22 keuen. 1632. 8°.

詹 承 誥 Chen Ching-kaou.

佛 門 定 制 Fŭh mun ting ehe. "The Established Laws and Formularies of the Disciples of Buddha." Compiled by Chen Ching-kaou. Edited by Ting She-ming. 8 keuen. Peking, [1840?]. 8°.

—— 道 門 定 制 Taou mun ting ehe. "The Established Laws and Formularies of the Disciples of Taouism." Compiled by Chen Ching-kaou. Edited by Ting She-ming. 10 keuen. [Peking, 1840?]. 8°.

Another copy.

詹 文 煥 Chen Wăn-hwan.

See 四 書 Sze shoo. 四 書 合 講 Sze shoo hŏ keang. "The Four Books" . . . Edited by Chen Wăn-hwan, &c. 8°.

織 Chĭh.

織 圖 Chĭh too. "Plates of the Operations employed in Weaving." With short Explanations. [1800?]. 4°.

尺 Chĭh.

增 補 尺 牘 達 衷 Tsăng poo chĭh tŭh tă chung. "A correct Letter Writer and Travelling Dictionary." [1750?]. 8°.

Imperfect, containing only part of keuen 1.

直 省 Chĭh săng.

直 省 考 卷 所 見 Chĭh săng kaou keuen so keen. "A Collection of Successful Provincial Examination Essays." Second Series. [1800?]. 8°.

Imperfect.

姪 端 石 Chĭh Twan-shĭh.

See 温 岐 山 Wăn Ke-shan. 分 韻 撮 要 Fun yun tsŏ yaou. "A Phonetic Dictionary" . . . . Edited by Chĭh Twan-shĭh, &c. 8°.

陳 Chin.

See 胡 本 淵 Hoo Pun-yuen. 子 史 輯 要 詩 賦 題 解 Tsze she tseĭh yaou she foo te keae. "A Collection of Themes" . . . Edited by . . Chin, &c. 1805. 8°.

陳 Chin, and 吳 Woo.

山 西 闈 墨 Shan se wei mĭh. "Shan-se Examination Essays." Edited by the Examiners Chin and Woo. 1821. 8°.

陳 檈 Chin E.

[Poetical Essays.] By Chin E and others. [A Fragment.] [1820?]. 8°.

陳 沆 Chin Hang, and 傅 綬 Foo Show.

廣 東 闈 墨 Kwang tung wei mĭh. "Kwang-tung Examination Essays." Edited by Chin Hang and Foo Show. 1821. 8°.

—— 簡 學 齋 詩 存 Keen heŏ chae she tsun. "Poems from the Keen heŏ Study." 1854. 8°.

—— 詩 比 興 箋 She pe hing tseen. "Notes on the Progressive Rise of Poetry." 4 keuen. 1854. 8°.

—— 簡 學 齋 館 課 試 律 存 Keen heŏ chae kwan ko she leŭh tsun. "Scholastic Poetical Essays from the Keen heŏ Study." 1857. 8°.

A MS. Index of Contents occupies the top margin of the first nine pages.

陳澔 CHIN HAOU.

See 禮記 LE KE. 禮記集說 Le ke tseih shwŏ. "The Book of Rites. With a Collection of Comments" compiled by Chin Haou, &c. 1322. 12°.

—— 全本禮記體註 Tseuen pun Le ke te choo. "The Book of Rites. With a Collection of Comments" compiled by Chin Haou, &c. 1766. 8°.

—— 芥子園重訂監本禮記 Keae tsze yuen chung ting keen pun Le ke. "The Keae-tsze yuen Revised Edition of the Book of Rites." With a Collection of Comments compiled by Chin Haou, &c. Nanking, 1790. 8°.

—— 監本禮記 Keen pun Le ke. "The Book of Rites." With a Collection of Comments compiled by Chin Haou, &c. 1796. 8°.

—— 禮記讀本 Le ke tŭh pun. "The Book of Rites." With an Interlinear Exposition by Chin Haou, &c. 1828. 8°.

陳熹 CHIN HE.

See 葉九升 YĔ KEW-SHING. 地理山法全書 Te le shan fă tseuen shoo. "The Laws of Mountains." ... Third keuen is edited, with notes, by Chin He, &c. 8°.

陳鴻 CHIN HUNG.

長恨歌傳 Chang hăn ko chuen. "The Story of the Song 'Lasting Grief.'" By Chin Hung, of the Tang Dynasty. A Reprint. [1741 ?]. 8°.

陳繼 CHIN KE.

酒顛補 Tsew teen poo. "A Repertory of Observations on Spirituous Liquors," collected from previous Writers. 3 keuen. [Also] 茶董補 Cha tung poo. "A Selection of Extracts from Ancient Authors respecting Tea." 2 keuen. See 葉志詵 YĔ CHE-SIN. 海山仙館叢書 Hae shan seen Kwan tsung shoo. "The Hae shan seen Kwan Collection of Reprints," &c. Vol. 88. 1848. 8°.

陳櫟 CHIN LŎ.

歷代蒙求 Leĭh tae mung kew. "A List of the Dynasties, for Beginners." In verse. See 陸清獻 LŬH TSING-HEEN. 小四書 Seaou Sze shoo. "The Lesser Four Books," &c. Keuen 3. 1845. 8°.

陳校 CHIN MEI.

See 顧鼎臣 KOO TING-CHIN. 狀元圖考 Chwang yuen too kaou. "Biographical Notices of Chwang-yuen." ... Edited by Chin Mei, &c. 1643. 8°.

陳楠 CHIN NAN.

羅浮翠虛吟 Lo fow Tsuy heu yin. "The Chant of Tsuy-heu of Lo-fow." See 彭好古 PĂNG HAOU-KOO. 道言內外秘訣全書 Taou yen nuy wae pe keuĕ tseuen shoo. "A Complete Collection of Taouist Works," &c. First Part. Keuen 3. 8°.

陳寳 CHIN PAOU.

See 李錫勳 LE SEĬH-HEUN. 成均課藝正續彙選 Ching keun ko e ching sŭh wei seuen. "A Collection of Essays." Compiled by ... Chin Paou, &c. 1802. 8°.

陳森 CHIN SAN.

See 揚甲 YANG KEĂ. 六經圖 Lŭh king too. "Illustrations to accompany the Six Classics." Edited by .. Chin San, &c. 1614. 4°.

陳甡 CHIN SĂNG.

常山縣志 Chang shan heen che. "A Topography of Chang-shan Heen," in the Province of Chĕ-keang. Compiled by Chin Săng, Le Wăn-keung, Chang Seuen, and others. 12 keuen. 1813. 8°.

陳驤 CHIN SEANG.

鄱陽縣志 Po yang heen che. "A Topography of Po-yang Heen," in the Province of Keang se. Compiled by Chin Seang, Hŏ Shoo-tsing, Chang Keung-ying, and others. 32 keuen. 1824. 8°.

陳選 CHIN SEUEN.

See 朱熹 CHOO HE. 小學體註大成 Seaou heŏ te choo ta ching. "A Complete Copy of the Youth's Instructor. With a Collection of Comments" compiled by Chin Seuen, &c. 8°.

陳璿 CHIN SEUEN.

普邨山志 Poo to shan che. "A Topography of the Island of Poo to," a renowned Seat of Buddhism, lying a few miles east of the Island of Chusan. Compiled by Chin Seuen, Kew Leen, Choo Kin, and others. 15 keuen. 1734. 8°.

陳 詩 CHIN SHE.

竹 書 紀 年 集 註 *Chŭh shoo ke neen tseĭh choo.* "The Annals of the Bamboo Books, with a Collection of Comments" compiled by Chin She. 2 keuen. 1801. 8°.

Imperfect, wanting preface and first page.

陳 善 CHIN SHEN.

See 周 兆 基 CHOW CHAOU-KE. 經 義 含 宻 *King e han tsze.* "A Collection of Essays explanatory of Texts from the Five Classics." ... Edited by Chin Shen, &c. 1810. 8°.

—— 萬 曆 杭 州 府 志 *Wan lĕĭh hang chow foo che.* "A Topography of Hang chow Foo," in the Province of Chĕ-keang. Compiled by Chin Shen. Edited by Seu Chĭh. 100 keuen. 1579. 8°.

陳 繩 CHIN SHING.

See 黃 任 HWANG JIN, and CHIN SHING. 惠 獻 貝 子 功 績 錄 *Hwuy heen Pei tsze kung tseĭh lŭh.* "A Record of the Meritorious Deeds of Hwuy-heen Pei-tsze." Compiled by Hwang Jin and Chin Shing, &c. 1741. 8°.

陳 壽 CHIN SHOW.

三 國 志 *San kwŏ che.* "The History of the Three Kingdoms." With a Commentary by Pei Yin. 65 keuen. See 毛 晋 MAOU TSIN. 十 七 史 *Shĭh tsĭh She.* "The Seventeen Histories," &c. 1656. 8°.

陳 第 CHIN TE.

讀 詩 拙 言 *Tŭh she chŭĕ yen.* "Stupid Remarks on the Study of the Book of Odes." See 葉 志 洗 YĔ CHE-SIN. 海 山 仙 館 叢 書 *Hae shan seen Kwan tsung shoo.* "The Hae shan seen Kwan Collection of Reprints," &c. Vol. 2. 1848. 8°.

陳 鼎 CHIN TING.

黃 山 史 槩 *Hwang shan she kae.* "A Resumé of the History of the Hwang Mountains." [Also] 滇 黔 土 司 婚 禮 記 *Teen keen too sze hwăn le ke.* "The Marriage Ceremonies of the Teen and Keen Tribes." See 張 山 來 CHANG SHAN-HAE, and 張 進 也 CHANG TSIN-YAY. 昭 代 叢 書 *Chaou tae tsung shoo.* A Collection of Reprints of Works by Authors under the present Dynasty, &c. Keuen 24, 28. 1703. 8°.

陳 造 CHIN TSAOU.

江 湖 長 翁 集 *Keang hoo Chang ung tseĭh.* "The Poetry of Chin Tsaou, nicknamed Chang Ung, of Keang hoo." See 吳 孟 舉 WOO MĂNG-KEU, and 吳 自 牧 WOO TSZE-MŬH. 宋 詩 鈔 二 集 *Sung she chaou urh tseĭh.* "Poetry of the Sung Dynasty," &c. 8°.

陳 鏳 CHIN TSUNG.

See 朱 熹 CHOO HE. 小 學 集 註 *Seaou heŏ tseĭh choo.* "The Youth's Instructor. With a Collection of Comments" compiled by Chin Tsung, &c. 1820. 8°.

陳 鍈 CHIN YING.

海 澄 縣 志 *Hae ching heen che.* "A Topography of Hae-ching Heen," in the Province of Fŭh-keen. Compiled by Chin Ying, Wang Tso-lin, Shĭh Kwŏ-kew, and others. 24 keuen. 1762. 8°.

陳 瑛 CHIN YING.

See 周 鼎 臣 CHOW TING-CHIN. 增 訂 敬 信 錄 *Tsăng ting king sin lŭh.* "Works on Reverence and Faith" ... Edited by Chin Ying, &c. 1795. 8°.

陳 郁 CHIN YŬH.

話 腴 *Hwa yu.* "Pithy Scraps." See 說 SHWŎ. 說 畧 *Shwŏ leŏ.* "Historical and other Tracts", &c. 8°.

陳 兆 崙 CHIN CHAOU-LUN.

紫 竹 山 房 文 集 *Tsze chŭh shan fang wăn tseĭh.* "A Collection of Literary Pieces from the House on Mount Tsze-chŭh." 20 keuen. 1756. 8°.

Imperfect, containing only keuen 1–3.

—— 紫 竹 山 房 詩 集 *Tsze chŭh shan fang she tseĭh.* "A Collection of Poetry from the House on Mount Tsze-chŭh." 12 keuen. 1771. 8°.

Imperfect, containing only keuen 1, 2, 4–8.

陳 致 虛 CHIN CHE-HEU.

判 惑 歌 *Pwan hwŏ ko.* "The Recitation of Settled Doubts." See 彭 好 古 PĂNG HAOU-KOO. 道 言 內 外 秘 訣 全 書 *Taou yen nuy wae pe keuĕ tseuen shoo.* "A Complete Collection of Taouist Works," &c. 8°.

陳 致 虛 CHIN CHE-HEU.   (*Continued.*)

See 張伯端 CHANG PĬH-TWAN. 悟 眞 篇 三 註 *Woo chin peen san choo.* " On Understanding the Truth ".. With Commentaries by.. Chin Che-heu, &c.   1809.   8°.

陳 之 綱 CHIN CHE-KANG.

四 明 古 蹟 詩 *Sze ming koo tseĭh she.* " Poetry on the Antiquities of Sze-ming." Compiled by Chin Che-kang. Edited by Le Kwŏ.   4 keuen.   1822.   12°.

陳 之 遴 CHIN CHE-LIN.

稿 *Kaou.* " Essays."   *See* 長 城 CHANG CHING. 名 家 制 義 *Ming kea che e.* " Essays " on Texts from the Four Books, &c.   Tsĭh 94.   1699.   8°.

陳 成 芳 CHIN CHING-FANG.

陳 春 園 稿 *Chin chun yuen kaou.* " Essays by Chin Ching-fang " on Texts from the Four Books.   3 keuen.   1835.   8°.

陳 貞 慧 CHIN CHING-HWUY.

秋 園 雜 佩 *Tsew yuen tsă pei.* " Miscellaneous Recollections of the Autumn Garden." *See* 伍 崇 曜 Woo TSUNG-YAOU. 粤 雅 堂 叢 書 *Yŭ ya Tang tsung shoo.* " The Yŭ-ya Tang Collection of Reprints," &c.   Series 19.   1853.   8°.

陳 宁 燮 CHIN CHOO-SËĔ.

沃 洲 古 蹟 *Yŭh chow koo tseĭh.* " The Antiquities of Yŭh-chow." With Illustrations.   [1830 ?].   8°.

—— 一 槳 舟 詩 課 *Yĭh yĕ chow she ko.* " Poetical Essays." By Chin Choo-sëĕ, the Editor, Chin Yung-sëĕ, Chin Leaou-sëĕ, and Chin Tse-sëĕ.   1832.   8°.

陳 鍾 麟 CHIN CHUNG-LIN.

聰 雨 軒 讀 本 *Ting yu heen tŭh pun.* " The Listening-to-the-Rain Study Reader." A Collection of Essays on the Four Books. Compiled by Chin Chung-lin. Edited by Sung Kwang-hăng and others. First and second Series.   1822.   8°.

Another edition. First Series.   1822.   8°.

陳 仲 微 CHIN CHUNG-WEI.

宋 季 三 朝 政 要 *Sung ke san chaou ching yaou.* " An Epitome of the Acts of the three Emperors Le-tsung, Too-tsung, and Kung-tsung, of the Sung Dynasty." With a supplementary chapter on the last two reigns. *See* 伍 崇 曜 Woo TSUNG-YAOU. 粤 雅 堂 叢 書 *Yŭ ya Tang tsung shoo.* " The Yŭ-ya Tang Collection of Reprints," &c.   Series 13.   1853.   8°.

陳 衷 一 CHIN CHUNG-YĬH.

See 徐 衢 SEU TAOU. 神 仙 鑑 *Shin seen keen.* " Biographies of Taouist Saints." .... Edited by Chin Chung-yĭh, &c.   8°.

陳 鍾 琛 CHIN CHUNG-YIN.

See 錢 大 昕 TSEEN TA-HIN. 鄞 縣 志 *Yin heen che.* " A Topography of Yin Heen." ... Edited by ... Chin Chung-yin, &c.   1788.   8°.

陳 芳 生 CHIN FANG-SĂNG.

捕 蝗 考 *Poo hwang kaou.* " On the Means of Getting Rid of Locusts." *See* 張 山 來 CHANG SHAN-LAE, and 張 進 也 CHANG TSIN-YAY. 昭 代 叢 書 *Chaou tae tsung shoo.* " A Collection of Reprints of Works by Authors under the present Dynasty," &c.   Keuen 40.   1703.   8°.

陳 傳 瓦 CHIN FOO-LEANG.

稿 *Kaou.* " Essays."   *See* 長 成 CHANG CHING. 名 家 制 義 *Ming kea che e.* " Essays " on Texts from the Four Books, &c.   Tsĭh 5.   1699.   8°.

陳 逢 衡 CHIN FUNG-HĂNG.

See 吳 寶 謨 Woo PAOU-MOO. 經 義 圖 說 *King e too shwŏ.* " The Meaning of the Classics Illustrated and Explained." Edited by Chin Fung-hăng, &c.   1819.   8°.

陳 希 祖 CHIN HE-TSOO.

See 賈 誼 KEA E. 新 書 *Sin shoo.* " The New Book." ... Edited by Chin He-tsoo, &c.   8°.

陳 香 泉 CHIN HEANG-TSEUEN.

See 呂 叟 LEU SOW. 女 仙 外 史 *Neu Seen wae she.* " Tales of Nymphs." With a Commentary by Chin Heang-tseuen, &c.   1711.   8°.

4

陳獻章 CHIN HEEN-CHANG.

稿 *Kaou.* "Essays." *See* 長城 CHANG CHING.

名家制義 *Ming kea che e.* "Essays" on Texts from the Four Books, &c. Tsǐh 11. 1699. 8°.

陳顯徵 CHIN HEEN-CHING.

參同契 *Tsan tung kĕĕ.* [A Work on Alchemy.] With a Commentary by Chin Heen-ching, &c. *See* 涵蟾子 HAN CHEN-TSZE. 金丹正理大要道書全集 *Kin tan ching le ta yaou taou shoo tseuen tseǐh.* "A Complete Collection of Important Taouist Works on the True Principle of the Elixir of Immortality," &c.
1538. 8°.

陳蔓齋 CHIN HŎ-CHAE.

東西晉演義 *Tung se Tsin yen e.* "The History of the Eastern and Western Tsin Dynasties." With Portraits. Edited by Chin Hŏ-chae. 12 keuen.
[1800 ?]. 8°.

Another edition. With Portraits. 12 keuen.
[1820 ?]. 8°.

陳宏謀 CHIN HUNG-MOW.

See 顧錫疇 KOO SEǏH-CHOW. 綱鑑正史約 *Kang keen ching she yŏ.* "A Compendium of History." . . Edited by Chin Hung-mow, &c.
1737. 8°.

—— See 四書 SZE SHOO. 四書考輯要 *Sze shoo kaou tseǐh yaou.* "A Collection of Important Researches on the Four Books." By Chin Hung-mow, &c. 1771. 8°.

—— 扣除添補說 *Kow choo teen poo shwŏ.* "A Tract illustrating the Principles which govern the Losses and Gains" in the Good Things of this Life. *Canton,* [1800 ?]. 8°.

—— 四種遺規摘鈔 *Sze chung wei kwei tsǐh chaou.* "Selections from Traditional Rules for Guidance on the four Subjects" of Education, Conduct, Government, and the Instruction of Females. Compiled by Chin Hung-mow. A Reprint.
1814. 8°.

—— 在官法戒錄摘鈔 *Tsae kwan fǎ keae lǔh tsǐh chaou.* "The Mandarin's Instructor." By Chin Hung-mow. Edited by Kŏ Ching-hwǔh, Chang Fung-sun, and Le Gan-min. 4 keuen.
1823. 8°.

陳竑願 CHIN HWANG-YUEN.

慈心功德錄 *Tsze sin kung tǐh lǔh.* "The Merit and Virtue of a Merciful Heart." *See* 沈培木 CHIN PEI-MǓH. 慈心寶鑑 *Tsze sin paou keen.* "A Collection of Tracts inculcating the Virtue of Mercy," &c.
1771. 8°.

陳仁錫 CHIN JIN-SEǏH.

See 薛應旂 SĔE YING-KE. 宋元通鑑 *Sung Yuen tung keen.* "A History of the Sung and Yuen Dynasties." . . . Edited by Chin Jin-seǐh, &c.
1626. 8°.

—— See 朱熹 CHOO HE. 通鑑綱目 *Tung keen kang mǔh.* "A Condensation of the 'Mirror of History.'" Edited by Chin Jin-seǐh, &c.
1630. 8°.

—— See 詹淮 CHEN HWAE. 性理綜要 *Sing le tsung yaou.* "An Epitome of Works on Mental Philosophy." . . Edited by Chin Jin-seǐh, &c.
1632. 8°.

—— See 班固 PAN KOO. 前漢書 *Tseen Han shoo.* "A History of the First Han Dynasty." . . . Edited by Chin Jin-seǐh, &c. 1632. 8°.

—— See 楊雄 YANG HEUNG. 太玄經 *Tae heuen king.* "The Great Deep Classic." . . . With Notes by Chin Jin-seǐh, &c. 8°.

—— 潛確類書 *Tseen keŏ luy shoo.* "An Encyclopædia." 120 keuen. 1632. 8°.
Imperfect, containing only keuen 29–62, 88–103.

陳繼昌 CHIN KE-CHANG.

新科三元文章 *Sin ko san yuen wǎn chang.* "Three Original Examination Essays." By Chin Ke-chang. 1820. 8°.
On title-page is a manuscript note in Chinese to the effect that this work is edited by a "Red-haired Englishman."

陳繼儒 CHIN KE-JOO.

See 陶朱公 TAOU CHOO-KUNG. 致富全書 *Che foo tseuen shoo.* "A Complete Guide to the Attainment of Wealth." Edited by Chin Ke-joo, &c. 1784. 8°.

—— 列國誌傳 *Leǐh kwŏ che chuen.* "The History of Leǐh kwŏ Period." With Illustrations. 8 keuen.
[1700 ?]. 8°.

陳 啓 源 CHIN KE-YUEN.

毛 詩 稽 古 編 *Maou she ke koo peen.* "The Views of the Old School on Maou Chang's Version of the Book of Odes." 30 keuen. *See* 嚴 杰 YEN LËË. 皇 清 經 解 *Hwang Tsing king keae.* "The Classics Explained," &c. Keuen 60–89.　　1829. 8º.

陳 階 平 CHIN KEAE-PING.

戎 政 芻 言 *Jung ching tsoo yen.* "Treatises on the Duties and Management of Soldiers."　　1820. 8º.

陳 瞿 石 CHIN KEU-SHǏH.

See 鄭 芷 畦 CHING CHE-HWUY. 廿 一 史 約 編 *Neen yǐh she yǒ peen.* "An Epitome of the Twenty-one Histories." ... Edited by Chin Keu-shǐh, &c.　　1697. 8º.

陳 君 擧 CHIN KEUN-KEU.

止 齋 詩 鈔 *Che chae she chaou.* "Poems from the Restful Study." *See* 吳 孟 擧 WOO MĂNG-KEU, and 吳 自 牧 WOO TSZE-MǓH. 宋 詩 鈔 二 集 *Sung she chaou urh tseǐh.* "Poetry of the Sung Dynasty," &c.　　8º.

—— 止 齋 文 集 *Che chae wǎn tseǐh.* "A Collection of Literary Pieces from the Restful Study." Edited by Chin Yung-kwang and Foo-ne-yang-ah. 25 keuen.　　1834. 8º.

陳 慶 槐 CHIN KING-HWAE.

借 樹 山 房 詩 鈔 *Tseay shoo shan fang she chaou.* "Poems from the House on Mount Tseay-shoo." 8 keuen.　　1803. 8º.

陳 景 雲 CHIN KING-YUN.

絳 雲 樓 書 目 *Keang yun low shoo mǔh.* "A Catalogue of Books." .. With Notes by Chin King-yun, &c. *See* 伍 崇 曜 WOO TSUNG-YAOU. 粵 雅 堂 叢 書 *Yuě ya Tang tsung shoo.* "The Yuě-ya Tang Collection of Reprints," &c. Series 9.　　1853. 8º.

陳 廓 寰 CHIN KŎ-HWAN.

See 四 書 SZE SHOO. 四 書 正 文 *Sze shoo ching wăn.* "The Le joo Tang edition of ... the Four Books." The Ta heǒ and Chung yung are edited by Chin Kŏ-hwan, &c.　　1816. 8º

陳 廓 寰 CHIN KŎ-HWAN. (*Continued.*)

See 四 書 SZE SHOO. 四 書 正 文 *Sze shoo ching wǎn.* "The Text of the Four Books." Edited by Chin Kŏ-hwan, &c.　　8º.

陳 崑 泉 CHIN KWĂN-TSEUEN.

氏 族 大 全 綱 目 *She tsǔh ta tseuen kang mǔh.* "An Epitomised Biographical Dictionary." Edited by Seu Tang.　　1573. 8º.

陳 觀 吾 CHIN KWAN-WOO.

道 德 經 轉 語 *Taou Tǐh king chuen yu.* "A Commentary on the Classic of Reason and Virtue." 2 keuen.　　1809. 8º.

Another copy.

陳 蘭 森 CHIN LAN-SAN.

See 樂 史 LŎ SHE. 太 平 寰 宇 記 *Tae ping hwan yu ke.* "A Geography of the Empire." ... Edited by Chin Lan-san, &c.　　1793. 8º.

陳 寮 爕 CHIN LEAOU-SËĚ.

See 陳 守 爕 CHIN CHOO-SËĚ. 一 葉 舟 詩 課 *Yǐh yě chow she ko.* "Poetical Essays." By .... Chin Leaou-sëě, &c.　　1832. 8º.

陳 倫 烱 CHIN LUN-KEUNG.

海 國 聞 見 錄 *Hae kwǒ wǎn keen lǔh.* "A Geographical Treatise," chiefly relating to the Islands in the Eastern and Southern Oceans. By Chin Lun-keung. Edited by Ma Tseun-leang. With Maps. 2 keuen.　　1793. 8º.

Another copy.

Another copy.

Imperfect.

陳 龍 標 CHIN LUNG-PEAOU.

See 周 禮 CHOW LE. 周 禮 精 華 *Chow le tsing hwa.* "The Essential Points of the Chow Ritual." ... Compiled by Chin Lung-peaou, &c.　　1814. 8º.

陳 明 卿 CHIN MING-KING.

See 薛 應 旂 SËĚ YING-KE. 四 書 人 物 備 考 *Sze shoo jin wǔh pe kaou.* "An Examination of the Men and Things mentioned in the Four Books." .. Edited by Chin Ming-king, &c. 8º.

陳明卿 CHIN MING-KING, and 鍾伯敬 CHUNG PĬH-KING.

國語國策詳注 *Kwŏ yu, kwŏ tsĭh, tseang choo.* "The Narratives of the States," by Tso Kew-ming, and "The Story of the Contending States," by Lew Heang. Edited, with explanatory notes, by Chin Ming-king and Chung Pĭh-king. Part I. 21 keuen. Part II. 12 keuen. 1724. 8°.

陳懋齡 CHIN MOW-LING.

經書算學天文考 *King shoo swan heŏ teen wăn kaou.* "An Elucidation of the various Mathematical and Astronomical Problems occurring in the Classical and Canonical Works." *See* 嚴杰 YEN LĔĔ. 皇清經解 *Hwang Tsing king keae.* "The Classics Explained," &c. Keuen 1328. 1829. 8°.

陳邦泰 CHIN PANG-TAE.

See 陳所聞 CHIN SO-WĂN. 北宮詞紀 *Pĭh kung tsze ke.* "Northern Songs" ... Edited by Chin Pang-tae, &c. 8°.

陳彭年 CHIN PĂNG-NEEN.

江南別錄 *Keang nan pĕĕ lŭh.* "Records from Keang-nan." *See* 說 SHWŎ. 說選 *Shwŏ seuen.* "A Collection of Records," &c. 8°.

陳伯廣 CHIN PĬH-KWANG.

三禮圖 *San le too.* "Illustrations of the Vessels, Ornaments, &c., referred to in the Three Rituals." With a Collection of Comments compiled by Nĕŏ Tsung-e. Edited by Chin Pĭh-kwang. A Reprint. 12 keuen. [1700 ?]. 8°.
Imperfect, keuen 1–4 wanting.

陳白沙 CHIN PĬH-SHA.

See 周興嗣 CHOW HING-TSZE. 千字文草法 *Tseen tsze wăn tsaou fă.* "The Thousand Character Classic" .... Edited by Chin Pĭh-sha. 12°.

陳世熙 CHIN SHE-HE.

霏屑軒尺牘類選 *Fei sĕĕ heen chĭh tŭh luy seuen.* "A Model Letter Writer." Compiled by Chin She-he. Edited by Sun Hwăn. 16 keuen. 1802. 8°.

陳世倌 CHIN SHE-KWAN.

See TSING DYNASTY. 大清通禮 *Ta Tsing tung le.* "A Complete Code of the Ceremonies of the Tsing Dynasty." Compiled by ... Chin She-kwan, &c. 1824. 8°.

陳樹芝 CHIN SHOO-CHE.

See 潘子聲 PWAN TSZE-SHING. 養蒙針度 *Yang mung chin too.* "The Student's Guide." ...... Edited by .... Chin Shoo-che, &c. 8°.

陳守詒 CHIN SHOW-E.

藏園九重曲 *Tsang yuen kew chung keŭh.* "The Nine Dramas of the Secret Garden." By "The Retired Scholar of the Secret Garden." Edited by Chin Show-e. 1774. 8°.

Another copy.

陳壽祺 CHIN SHOW-KE.

五經異義疏證 *Woo king e e soo ching.* "The Different Interpretations of the Five Classics, Commented on and Verified." 3 keuen. [Also] 左海經辨 *Tso hae king peen.* "The Classics Discussed." 2 keuen. [Also] 左海文集 *Tso hae wăn tseĭh.* "Writings on Classical Subjects." 2 keuen. *See* 嚴杰 YEN LĔĔ. 皇清經解 *Hwang Tsing king keae.* "The Classics Explained," &c. Keuen 1248–1254. 1829 8°.

陳新安 CHIN SIN-GAN.

See 四書 SZE SHOO. 論語註疏大全合纂 *Lun yu choo soo ta tseuen hŏ tswan.* "The Confucian Analects, with Commentaries and Explanations" by ... Chin Sin-gan, &c. 1636. 8°.

陳星齋 CHIN SING-CHAE.

文稿 *Wăn kaou.* "Essays" on Texts from the Four Books. With Notes by Tsae Seĭh-chow, Tsae Yu-tae, and Koo Ke-ching. 1803. 8°.

—— 陳星齋課孫草 *Chin Sing-chae ko sun tsaou.* "Rough Drafts of Essays." A new and enlarged edition. 1815. 8°.

陳所性 CHIN SO-SING.

See 高一志 KAOU-YĬH-CHE. 空際格致 *Kung tse kĭh che.* "A Work on the Chemical Composition of the Universe." ... Revised by Chin So-sing, &c. 8°.

陳 所 聞 CHIN SO-WĂN.

北宮詞紀 *Pĭh kung tsze ke*. "Northern Songs." Compiled by Chin So-wăn. Edited by Chin Pang-tae. 6 keuen.   [1790 ?]. 8°.

陳 師 顙 CHIN SZE-HAOU.

See 劉山英 LEW SHAN-YING. 信心應驗錄 *Sin sin ying yen lŭh*. "Convincing Records for Believing Hearts." . . . Edited by Chin Sze-haou, &c.   1794. 8°.

陳 師 濂 CHIN SZE-LEEN.

See 劉山英 LEW SHAN-YING. 信心應驗錄 *Sin sin ying yen lŭh*. "Convincing Records for Believing Hearts" . . . Edited by . . Chin Sze-leen, &c.   1794. 8°.

陳 師 道 CHIN SZE-TAOU.

後山集 *How shan tseĭh*. "The How shan Collection." *See* 吳孟舉 WOO MĂNG-KEU, and 吳自牧 WOO TSZE-MŬH. 宋詩鈔二集 *Sung she chaou urh tseĭh*. "Poetry of the Sung Dynasty," &c.   8°.

陳 大 士 CHIN TA-SZE.

五經讀 *Woo king tŭh*. "On the Study of the Five Classics." Edited by Hwang Chun-keu. 5 keuen.   1696. 8°.

     Imperfect, wanting keuen 5.

陳 泰 交 CHIN TAE-KEAOU.

倘書註考 *Shang shoo choo kaou*. "The Commentaries on the Book of Historical Documents examined." *See* 葉志詵 YĔ CHE-SIN. 海山仙館叢書 *Hae shan seen Kwan tsung shoo*. "The Hae shan seen Kwan Collection of Reprints," &c. Vol. 2.   1848. 8°.

陳 愿 華 CHIN TĬH-HWA.

See 弘晝 HUNG CHOW. 大清一統志 *Ta Tsing yĭh tung che*. "A Geography of the Empire, published under the Tsing Dynasty." Compiled by . . . Chin Tĭh-hwa, &c.   1744. 4°.

陳 廷 敬 CHIN TING-KING.

See 康熙 KANG-HE. *Emperor*. 御製文集 *Yu che wăn tseĭh*. "The Literary Works of . . Kang-he." Edited by . . . Chin Ting-king, &c.   1711. 8°.

陳 廷 敬 CHIN TING-KING. (*Continued*.)

See 康熙 KANG-HE. *Emperor*. 康熙字典 *Kang he tsze heen*. "Kang-he's Dictionary," compiled . . . by Chin Ting-king, &c. 1716. 8°.

陳 濟 生 CHIN TSE-SĂNG.

See 周克復 CHOW KĬH-FŬH. 金剛持驗紀 *Kin kang che yen ke*. "Records of the Effects of Studying the Diamond Classic." . . . Edited by Chin Tse-săng, &c.   1799. 8°.

陳 濟 燮 CHIN TSE-SĔĔ.

See 陳宁燮 CHIN CHOW-SĔĔ. 一葉舟詩課 *Yĭh ye chow she ko*. "Poetical Essays." By . . . . . . Chin Tse-sĕĕ, &c.   1832. 8°.

陳 際 泰 CHIN TSE-TAE.

稿 *Kaou*. "Essays." *See* 長城 CHANG CHING. 名家制義 *Ming kea che e*. "Essays" on Texts from the Four Books, &c. Tsĭh 93.   1699. 8°.

陳 祥 道 CHIN TSEANG-TAOU.

禮書 *Le shoo*. "A History of Forms and Ceremonies." By Chin Tseang-taou, of the Sung Dynasty. Edited by Chang Poo, of the Ming Dynasty. With Illustrations. 150 keuen.   [1600 ?]. 8°.

Another edition. 150 keuen.   1804. 8°.

     Imperfect, wanting keuen 1–11.

陳 資 齋 CHIN TSZE-CHAE.

天下沿海形勢錄 *Teen hea yuen hae hing she lŭh*. "On Coast Defences." *See* 水 SHWUY. 水陸戰守攻略方術秘書七種 *Shwuy lŭh chen show kung leo fang shŭh pe shoo tsĭh chung*. "A Military System for both Land and Sea," &c.   8°.

陳 子 龍 CHIN TSZE-LUNG.

稿 *Kaou*. "Essays." *See* 長城 CHANG CHING. 名家制義 *Ming kea che e*. "Essays" on Texts from the Four Books, &c. Tsĭh 96.   1699. 8°.

—— See 李雯 LE WĂN. 皇明詩選 *Hwang Ming she seuen*. "Selections from the Poetry of the Ming Dynasty." Compiled by . . . Chin Tsze-lung, &c.   8°.

陳子龍 CHIN TSZE-LUNG. (*Continued.*)

See 司馬遷 SZE-MA TSEEN. 史記 *Shc ke.* "The Historical Record." With a Commentary by .. Chin Tsze-lung, &c. 1806. 8º.

陳紫山 CHIN TSZE-SHAN.

See 熊應雄 HEUNG YING-HEUNG. 小兒推拿廣意 *Scaou urh chuy na kwang e.* "The Medical Examination of Children." ... Edited by Chin Tsze-shan, &c. 1832. 8º.

陳子性 CHIN TSZE-SING.

藏書 *Tsang shoo.* "A Hidden Book." A Work on Divination. 12 keuen. 1684. 8º.

陳子淵 CHIN TSZE-YUEN.

See 王元馭 WANG YUEN-YU. 諸史品節 *Choo she pin tsëë.* "Extracts from the Pages of History." .. Edited by Chin Tsze-yuen, &c. 1593. 8º.

陳韞石 CHIN WĂN-SHĬH.

See 繆蓮仙 MŬH LEEN-SEEN. 文章游戲 *Wăn chang yew he.* "Rambles in Polite Literature." ... Fourth Part is edited by Chin Wăn-shĭh, &c. 1824. 8º.

陳維崧 CHIN WEI-SUNG.

婦人集 *Foo jin tseĭh.* "A Collection of Women." See 葉志詵 YĔ CHE-SIN. 海山仙館叢書 *Hae shan seen Kwan tsung shoo.* "The Hae shan seen Kwan Collection of Reprints," &c. Vol. 65. 1848. 8º.

陳友恭 CHIN YEW-KUNG.

See 竇漢卿 TOW HAN-KING. 瘡瘍經驗全書 *Chwang yang king yen tseuen shoo.* "A Complete Work on the Treatment of Cutaneous Diseases." ... Edited by Chin Yew-kung, &c. 1750. 8º.

陳應魁 CHIN YING-KWEI.

See 黃任 HWANG JĬN. 香草齋詩註 *Heang tsaou chae she choo.* "Poetry from the Study of Fragrant Plants." With Notes by Chin Ying-kwei, &c. 1804. 8º.

陳與義 CHIN YU-E.

簡齋詩鈔 *Keen chae she chaou.* "The Poems of Chin Yu-e, otherwise known as Keen-chae." *See* 吳孟舉 WOO MĂNG-KEU, and 吳自牧 WOO TSZE-MŬH. 宋詩鈔二集 *Sung she chaou urh tseĭh.* "Poetry of the Sung Dynasty," &c. 8º.

陳元龍 CHIN YUEN-LUNG.

格致鏡原 *Kĭh che king yuen.* "An Encyclopædia of Arts and Sciences." Compiled from the Works of native Authors by Chin Yuen-lung. 100 keuen. 1735. 8º.

陳元祐 CHIN YUEN-YEW.

離魂記 *Le hwăn ke.* "A Ghost Story." By Chin Yuen-yew, of the Tang Dynasty. A Reprint. [1741 ?]. 8º.

陳毓靈 CHIN YŬH-LING.

知味軒啟事 *Che wei heen ke sze.* "The Model Letter Writer, from the 'Tasteful Study.'" 4 keuen. 1833. 8º.
Imperfect, wanting the third keuen.

—— 知味軒稟言 *Che wei heen pin yen.* "Model Petitions and Addresses from the 'Tasteful Study.'" 4 keuen. 1833. 8º.

Another copy,
Imperfect, containing only the second keuen.

陳允平 CHIN YUN-PING.

日湖漁唱 *Jĭh hoo yu chang.* "The Songs of the Fishermen of the Jĭh Lake." Compiled by Chin Yun-ping. *See* 伍崇曜 WOO TSUNG-YAOU. 粵雅堂叢書 *Yuĕ ya Tang tsung shoo.* "The Yuĕ-ya Tang Collection of Reprints," &c. Series 8. 1853. 8º.

陳榕軒 CHIN YUNG-HEEN.

直省鄉墨文淳 *Chĭh săng heang mĭh wăn shun.* "Provincial Examination Essays" for the year 1822. Compiled by Chin Yung-hëen. 1822. 8º.

陳用光 CHIN YUNG-KWANG.

See 劉向 LEW HEANG. 新序 *Sin seu.* "A New Arrangement" of Historical Incidents ... Edited by Chin Yung-kwang, &c. 8º.

—— See 陳君舉 CHIN KEUN-KEU. 正齋文集 *Che chae wăn tseĭh.* "A Collection of Literary Pieces from the 'Restful Study.'" Edited by Chin Yung-kwang, &c. 1834. 8º.

陳榮爕 CHIN YUNG-SËĔ.

See 陳宁爕 CHIN CHOO-SËĔ. 一業舟詩課 *Yĭh yĕ chow she ko.* "Poetical Essays." By ... Chin Yung-sëĕ, &c. 1832. 8º.

沈汾 CHIN FUN.

續仙傳 *Süh seen chuen.* "Supplementary Lives of the Saints." Edited by Hwang Sing-tsăng, &c. 1553. 8º.

沈潮 CHIN HOO.

See 唐惟懋 TANG WEI-MOW. 發蒙小品二集 *Fă mung seaou pin urh tseih.* "A Collection of Model Essays." . . . Edited by Chin Hoo, &c. 1743. 8º.

沈遘 CHIN KOW.

西溪集鈔 *Se ke tseih chaou.* "A Collection of Poetry from Se ke." See 吳孟舉 WOO MĂNG-KEU, and 吳自牧 WOO TSZE-MŬH. 宋詩鈔二集 *Sung she chaou urh tseih.* "Poetry of the Sung Dynasty," &c. 8º.

沈遼 CHIN LEAOU.

雲巢詩鈔 *Yun chaou she chaou.* "A Collection of Poetry from the 'Cloud Nest.'" See 吳孟舉 WOO MĂNG-KEU, and 吳自牧 WOO TSZE-MŬH. 宋詩鈔二集 *Sung she chaou urh tseih.* "Poetry of the Sung Dynasty," &c. 8º.

沈攀 CHIN PAN.

See 龔在升 KUNG TSAE-SHING. 三才彙編 *San tsae wei peen.* "An Encyclopædia." . . . . The fifth keuen . . edited by Chin Pan, &c. 8º.

沈俶 CHIN SHŬH.

諧史 *Heae she.* "Harmonious Records." See 說 SHWŎ. 說畧 *Shwŏ leŏ.* "Historical and other Tracts." 8º.

沈泰 CHIN TAE.

See 戴德 TAE TĬH. 大戴禮記 *Ta Tae le ke.* "The Ritual of the Elder Tae" . . . Edited by Chin Tae, &c. 1175. 8º.

沈潛 CHIN TSEEN.

See 沈李龍 CHIN LE-LUNG. 食物本草會纂 *Shih wüh pun tsaou hwuy tswan.* "A Medical Work on Edibles " . . . Edited by . . . Chin Tseen, &c. 1783. 8º.

沈津 CHIN TSIN.

百家類纂 *Pih kea luy tswan.* "The Works of a Hundred Authors." Compiled by Chin Tsin. 36 keuen. [1650 ?]. 8º.

Imperfect.

沈彤 CHIN TUNG.

周官祿田考 *Chow kwan lüh teen kaou.* "An Examination of the Emoluments of the Officers of the Chow Dynasty." 3 keuen. [Also] 尚書小疏 *Shang shoo seaou soo.* "A Short Exposition of the Book of Historical Documents." [Also] 儀禮小疏 *E le seaou soo.* "A Short Exposition of the Decorum Ritual." [Also] 春秋左傳小疏 *Chun Tsew Tso chuen seaou soo.* "A Short Exposition of the Spring and Autumn Annals, and Tso's Narrative." [Also] 果堂集 *Kwo Tang tseih.* "The Kwo Tang Collection." See 嚴杰 YEN LĔĔ. 皇清經解 *Hwang Tsing king keae.* "The Classics Explained," &c. Keuen 316–329. 1829. 8º.

沈渭 CHIN WEI.

See 沈李龍 CHIN LE-LUNG. 食物本草會纂 *Shih wüh pun tsaou hwuy tswan.* "A Medical Work on Edibles." . . . Edited by Chin Wei, &c. 1783. 8º.

沈約 CHIN YŎ.

宋書 *Sung shoo.* "The History of the Sung Dynasty." 100 keuen. See 毛晉 MAOU TSIN. 十七史 *Shih tsih she.* "The Seventeen Histories," &c. 1656. 8º.

—— See 王賢喈 WANG HEEN-KEAE. 竹書紀年 *Chüh shoo ke neen.* "The Bamboo Record." With a Commentary by Chin Yŏ, &c. 8º.

—— See 斌倚平 PIN E-PING. 文選集腋 *Wăn seuen tseih yih.* "Selected Literary Expressions" . . from the Works of . . . Chin Yŏ, &c. 1813. 8º.

沈亞之 CHIN A-CHE.

馮燕傳 *Fung Yen chuen.* "The Story of Fung Yen." By Chin A-che, of the Tang Dynasty. A Reprint. [1741 ?]. 8º.

—— 歌者葉志 *Ko chay Yĕ che.* "The Story of the Songstress Yĕ." See 王文誥 WANG WĂN-KAOU. 唐代叢書 *Tang tae tsung shoo.* "A Collection of Reprints of Works written during the Tang Dynasty," &c. Series 3. 1806. 8º.

沈 之 奇 CHIN CHE-KE.

See TSING DYNASTY. 大清律例重訂統纂集成 *Ta Tsing leŭh le chung ting tung tswan tseĭh ching.* "The Fundamental Laws and Subordinate Statutes of the Tsing Dynasty." With a Commentary by Chin Che-ke, &c. 1830. 8°.

沈 希 聲 CHIN HE-SHING.

大悲懺法 *Ta pei tsan fă.* "The Ritual of the Great Compassionate" Kwan yin. Edited by Chin He-shing. *Canton,* 1410. 8°.

沈 學 善 CHIN HEO-SHEN.

See 徐光燦 SEU KWANG-TSAN. 峰抱樓琴譜 *Fung paou low kin poo.* "The Music Book of the Fung-paou Pavilion." .. Edited by Chin Heŏ-shen, &c. 1826. 8°.

沈 旣 濟 CHIN KE-TSE.

任 氏 傳 *Jin she chuen.* "The Story of Jin she." By Chin Ke-tse, of the Tang Dynasty. A Reprint. [1741 ?]. 8°.

—— 雷民傳 *Luy min chuen.* "Popular Tales from Luy chow." By Chin Ke-tse, of the Tang Dynasty. A Reprint. [1741 ?]. 8°.

沈 起 潛 CHIN KE-TSEEN.

青雲梯 *Tsing yun te.* "A Ladder to the Azure Clouds," *i.e.* Literary Promotion. 1831. 8°.

沈 景 倩 CHIN KING-TSING.

野獲編 *Yay hwŏ peen.* "Fugitive Pieces." By Chin King-tsing, of the reign of Wan-leĭh. Edited by Tseen Fang. 30 keuen. Supplement, 4 keuen. 1827. 8°.

沈 李 龍 CHIN LE-LUNG.

食物本草會纂 *Shĭh wŭh pun tsaou hwuy tswan.* "A Medical Work on Edibles. With Illustrations." Compiled by Chin Le-lung. Edited by Chin Wei and Chin Tseen. 12 keuen. 1691. 8°.
Imperfect, containing only the first five keuen.

Another edition. 12 keuen. 1783. 8°.

沈 明 遠 CHIN MING-YUEN.

See 朱熹 CHOO HE. 小學體註大成 *Seaou heŏ te choo ta ching.* "A Complete Copy of the Youths' Instructor" ... Edited ... by .. Chin Ming-yuen, &c. 8°.

沈 業 富 CHIN NEĚ-FOO.

刪潤能與集 *Shan jun nǎng yu tseĭh.* "A Collection of able Essays." 1772. 8°.

沈 培 木 CHIN PEI-MŬH.

慈心寶鑑 *Tsze sin paou keen.* "The Precious Mirror of a Merciful Heart." A Collection of Tracts inculcating the Virtue of Mercy. Compiled by Chin Pei-mŭh. 4 keuen. 1771. 8°.

沈 品 華 CHIN PIN-HWA.

See 楊逢春 YANG FUNG-CHUN, and 蕭應辙 SEAOU YING-KWEI. 詳註分韻試帖青雲集 *Tseang choo fun yun she tĕĕ tsing yun tseĭh.* "The Tsing yun Collection of Poetical Essays" ... With Explanatory Notes by Chin Pin-hwa, &c. 1856. 8°.

沈 品 金 CHIN PIN-KIN.

See 楊逢春 YANG FUNG-CHUN, and 蕭應辙 SEAOU YING-KWEI. 詳註分韻試帖青雲集 *Tseang choo fun yun she tĕĕ tsing yun tseĭh.* "The Tsing yun Collection of Poetical Essays." .. With Explanatory Notes by Chin Pin-kin, &c. 1856. 8°.

沈 受 祺 CHIN SHOW-KE.

稿 *Kaou.* "Essays." See 長城 CHANG CHING. 名家制義 *Ming kea che e.* "Essays" on Texts from the Four Books," &c. Tsĭh 113. 1699. 8°.

沈 辛 田 CHIN SIN-TEEN.

名法指掌 *Ming fă che chang.* "A Digest of Ordinances." Compiled by Chin Sin-teen, and Tung Kung-chin. 4 keuen. [1800 ?]. 8°.

沈 思 倫 CHIN SZE-LUN.

學語雜篇 *Heŏ yu tsă peen.* "Notes for Learners." See 張山來 CHANG SHAN-LAE, and 張進也 CHANG TSIN-YAY. 昭代叢書 *Chaou tae tsung shoo.* "A Collection of Reprints of Works by Authors under the present Dynasty," &c. Keuen 20. 1703. 8°.

沈 德 潛 CHIN TĬH-TSEEN.

See 毛今培 MAOU KIN-PEI. 試體唐詩箋註 *She te Tang she tseen choo.* "Tang Dynasty Examination Poetry" .. Edited by Chin Tĭh-tseen, &c. 1757. 8°.

沈 德 潛 Chin Tĭh-tseen.   (*Continued.*)
欽 定 國 朝 詩 別 裁 集 *Kin ting kwŏ chaou she peĕ tsae tseĭh.* "A Separate Collection of the Poetry of the Tsing Dynasty." Compiled by Chin Tĭh-tseen. 32 keuen.   1761. 8º.

—— 唐 詩 別 裁 集 *Tang she peĕ tsae tseĭh.* "A Separate Collection of the Poetry of the Tang Dynasty." Compiled by Chin Tĭh-tseen. 20 keuen.   1763. 8º.

沈 鼎 新 Chin Ting-sin.
See 管 仲 Kwan Chung. 管 子 評 註 *Kwan tsze ping choo.* "Kwan Chung's Work on Legislation. With Critical Notes" by Chin Ting-sin, &c.   1804. 8º.

沈 清 塵 Chin Tsing-chin, and 周 遠 振 Chow Yuen-chin.
西 方 公 據 *Se fang kung keu.* "Evidences from the West." A Collection of Excerpta from Buddhist Works. Compiled by Chin Tsing-chin and Chow Yuen-chin. A Reprint.
Canton, 1804. 8º.
There are two other copies of this work.

沈 微 垣 Chin Wei-yuen.
See 王 叔 和 Wang Shŭh-ho. 圖 註 脈 訣 大 全 *Too choo mĭh keuĕ ta tseuen.* "A Complete Work on the Pulse." . . . Edited by Chin Wei-yuen, &c.   1693. 8º.

———— 圖 註 難 經 脈 訣 *Too choo Nan king mĭh keuĕ.* "The Nan king . . . and a Work on the Pulse," . . . Edited by Chin Wei-yuen, &c.
1800. 8º.

沈 與 求 Chin Yu-kew.
龜 谿 集 鈔 *Kwei ke tseĭh chaou.* "A Collection of Poetry from the Tortoise Valley." *See* 吳 孟 舉 Woo Măng-keu, and 吳 自 牧 Woo Tsze-mŭh. 宋 詩 鈔 二 集 *Sung she chaou urh tseĭh.* "Poetry of the Sung Dynasty," &c.
8º.

沈 玉 亮 Chin Yŭh-leang.
See 李 之 泖 Le Che-tung, and 汪 建 封 Wang Keen-fung. 叩 鉢 齋 纂 *Kow pŏ chae tswan.* "A Collection of Literary Pieces from the Kowpŏ Study." . . . With Notes by Chin Yŭh-leang, &c.   8º.

甄 鸞 Chin Lwan.
See 趙 君 卿 Chaou Keun-king. 周 髀 算 經 *Chow pe swan king.* "A Work on Trigonometry and Astronomy" . . . . Re-edited by Chin Lwan, &c.   8º.

震 澤 Chin Tsĭh.
震 澤 龍 女 傳 *Chin tsĭh lung neu chuen.* "The Story of the Dragon-woman of the Chin Marsh." *See* 說 Shwŏ. 說 淵 *Shwŏ yuen.* "A Collection of Tales," &c.   8º.

眞 理 Chin le.
眞 理 *Chin le.* "Truth." By C. F. A. Gützlaff.   [1840 ?]. 8º.

—— 眞 理 摘 要 *Chin le tsĭh yaou.* "Gleanings of Truth." By the Rev. Robert Cobbold.
Shanghae, 1856. 8º.

眞 道 Chin taou.
眞 道 入 門 *Chin taou jŭh mun.* "An Introduction to the True Doctrine." By William Milne.   Hongkong, 1856. 12º.

CHINA.
酌 修 條 例 *Chŏ sew teaou le.* "Amended Criminal Laws."   [1820 ?]. 8º.

—— 酌 增 常 例 *Chŏ tsăng chang le.* "Additional Regulations for the Purchase of Rank."
1828. 8º.

—— 現 行 常 例 *Heen hing chang le.* "Regulations for Promotion by Purchase."   [1827 ?]. 8º.

—— 刑 名 條 例 *Hing ming teaou le.* "Laws for the Adjustment of Punishments," issued during the reigns of the Emperors Kea king and Taou kwang, 1807–1826.   8º.
Imperfect.

—— 善 後 條 約 *Shen how teaou yŏ.* "An Additional Friendly Agreement," consisting of Seventeen Articles, regulating the Intercourse with Foreigners at the five Open Ports.
[1844 ?]. 8º.

—— 條 例 *Teaou le.* "Laws and Regulations," promulgated between the years 1753 and 1838.
1838. 8º.

5

CHINA. (*Continued.*)

條例總目 *Teaou le tsung müh*. "A Register of the Laws and Regulations" issued between the years 1751 and 1831. 6 Vol. 1831. 8°.

Another copy.

Extending to the year 1820.

Another copy.

Imperfect.

Another copy.

Extending to the year 1830.

—— 督捕則例 *Tüh poo tsih le*. "Regulations for the Capture" of Deserters. Compiled by an Imperial Commission consisting of Sö Gïh-too, Heung Tsze-le, Leang Tsing-peaou, and others. 1676. 8°.

—— 督捕則例 *Tüh poo tsih le*. "Regulations concerning the Capture" of Deserters. Compiled by an Imperial Commission consisting of Prince Hung Chow, Seu Pun, San Tae, &c. 2 keuen. 1743. 8°.

There are two other copies of this work.

—— 督捕則例 *Tüh poo tsih le*. "Regulations concerning the Capture" of Deserters. 2 keuen. [1800?]. 8°.

Wanting the first keuen.

—— 督捕則例附纂 *Tüh poo tsih le foo tswan*. "Supplementary Regulations concerning the Capture" of Deserters. 2 keuen. [1850?]. 8°.

Another copy.

—— 豫工事例 *Yu kung sze le*. "Regulations providing for the Performance of Public Works." [1800?]. 8°.

Title-page wanting.

—— BOARD OF CEREMONIES.

欽定禮部則例 *Kin ting Le Poo tsih le*. "Regulations of the Board of Ceremonies." Compiled by an Imperial Commission consisting of Sä Ying-ah, Soo Ching-gih, Sing Ke-yun, and others. 202 keuen. 1820. 8°.

Another copy.

Imperfect.

CHINA. BOARD OF OFFICE.

欽定吏部則例 *Kin ting Le Poo tsih le*. "Regulations of the Board of Office." Compiled by an Imperial Commission consisting of Prince Hung Chow, Chang Ting-yüh, Nüh Tsin, and others. 5 Parts. 1741. 8°.

—— 吏部修改則例 *Le Poo sew kae tsih le*. "Amended Regulations of the Board of Office." 1803. 8°.

—— BOARD OF PUNISHMENTS.

刑部則例 *Hing Poo tsih le*. "The Regulations of the Board of Punishments." Compiled by Hwang Ke, Shen Tä-hae, Fung Soo, and others. 2 keuen. *See* TSING DYNASTY. 大清律箋釋 *Ta Tsing leüh tseen shïh*. "The Laws of the Ta Tsing Dynasty," &c. 1725. 8°.

—— BOARD OF REVENUE.

戶部則例 *Hoo poo tsih le*. "Regulations of the Board of Revenue." Compiled by an Imperial Commission, consisting of Sung Neen, Keïh Tseang, Choo Lwan-ting, and others. 99 keuen. 1838. 8°.

—— 欽定戶部軍需則例 *King ting Hoo Poo keun seu tsih le*. "Regulations issued by the Board of Revenue for the Supply of Commissariat Stores." Compiled by an Imperial Commission consisting of Ah Kwei, Ho Shin, Leang Kwŏ-che, and others. 9 keuen. 1785. 8°.

There are four other copies of this work.

—— BOARD OF WAR.

欽定兵部處分則例 *Kin ting Ping Poo choo fun tsih le*. "Discriminating Regulations of the Board of War," for the Bannermen. [1800?]. 8°.

Imperfect, containing only keuen 3, 4, 12–21, 26, 30–32.

—— 欽定兵部處分則例 *Kin ting Ping Poo choo fun tsih le*. "Discriminating Regulations of the Board of War," for the Chinese Troops. [1800?]. 8°.

Imperfect, containing only keuen 1, 5–13, 16, 26, 31, 33–36.

CHINA. BOARD OF WAR. (*Continued.*)

欽定兵部續纂處分則例 *Kin ting Ping poo sǔh tswan choo fun tsǐh le.* "Supplamentary Discriminating Regulations of the Board of War." Compiled by an Imperial Commission consisting of King Yuen, Le Han, and others. 4 keuen.   1829. 8°.

Another copy.

———— 欽定較增處分則例 *Kin ting keaou tsǎng choo fun tsǐh le.* "Additional Discriminating Regulations" of the Board of War.   [1770 ?]. 8°.

———— 欽定兵部軍需則例 *Kin ting Ping Poo keun seu tsǐh le.* "Regulations of the Board of War for the Supply of Commissariat Stores." 5 keuen.   [1785.] 8°.
There are two other copies of this work.

———— 欽定中樞政考 *Kin ting chung choo ching kaou.* "An Examination into the Fundamental System" of governing the Army issued by the Emperors Yung-ching and Keen-lung. 16 keuen.   1742. 8°.

Another copy.
Imperfect, wanting keuen 7–10.

———— 欽定中樞政考 *Kin ting chung choo ching kaou.* "An Examination, &c." Compiled by a Commission consisting of Tsaou Ching, Tǐh Ching, Loo Tsung-mǔh, and others. 16 keuen.   1764. 8°.

———— 欽定中樞政考 *Kin ting chung choo ching kaou.* "An Examination, &c." Compiled by an Imperial Commission consisting of Pǐh King, Ke Ming, Pǒ Ming, and others. 15 keuen.   1785. 8°.

———— 欽定中樞政考 *Kin ting chung choo ching kaou.* "An Examination, &c." 16 keuen.   1807. 8°.

Imperfect, wanting keuen 1, 13–16.

CHINA. BOARD OF WAR. (*Continued.*)

欽定中樞政考 *Kin ting chung choo ching kaou.* "An Examination into the Fundamental System" of governing the Army issued by the Emperors Kea-king and Taou-kwang. Compiled by an Imperial Commission consisting of Nǎ-soo-tae, Ǒ-kǐh-tsing-yǐh, Foo-urh-tsung-ah, and others. 40 keuen.   1825. 8°.

———— Army Regulations issued by order of the Emperors Yung-ching and Keen-lung.
     1785. 8°.
No title-page or head title.

—— BOARD OF WORKS.

欽定工部軍需則例 *Kin ting kung Poo keun seu tsǐh le.* "Regulations issued by the Board of Works for the supply of Military Stores."   [1785 ?]. 8°.
There are two other copies of this work.

———— 欽定工部軍器則例 *Kin ting kung Poo keun ke tsǐh le.* "Regulations issued by the Board of Works for the supply of Military Stores." Compiled by an Imperial Commission consisting of Sung Taou-heun, Fǔh Yaou, Han-Yuen-shen, and others. 60 keuen. 1812. 8°.

Another edition. 60 keuen.   [1812 ?]. 8°.
Imperfect, containing only keuen 5–13, 29–37, 46–60.

—— HËEN-FUNG. *Emperor.*
See GREAT BRITAIN AND IRELAND. VICTORIA. *Queen.* 奏准天津新議通商條欵 *Tsou chun Teen tsin sin e tung shang teaou kwǎn.* "The New Commercial Treaties of Tientsin," contracted between Great Britain and China, France and China, the United States of America and China, and Russia and China, &c.
     1860. 8°.

—— 康熙 KANG-HE. *Emperor.*
上諭 *Shang yu.* "Imperial Edicts," issued during the sixty-first year of the reign of the Emperor Kang-he, and the first seven years of the reign of the Emperor Yung-ching. Compiled by Prince Yun-lǔh, and others.   1730. 8°.

Another copy.

CHINA. 嘉慶 KEA-KING. *Emperor.*

欽 定 軍 器 則 例 *Kin ting keun ke tsĭh le.* "Military Store Regulations" issued during the reign of the Emperor Kea-king. Compiled by an Imperial Commission consisting of Chaou Fan, Tsung-chĭh-wăn-keĭh, Tă-lĭh-ping-ah, and others. 2 keuen.   1801.   8º.

—— 乾隆 KEEN-LUNG. *Emperor.*

欽 定 入 旗 則 例 *Kin ting pă ke tsĭh le.* "Regulations for the Bannermen," issued during the earlier years of the reign of the Emperor Keen-lung. Compiled by an Imperial Commission consisting of Se Ching, Woo Ting, Chaou E, and others. 12 keuen.   1742.   8º.

———— 義 倉 圖 *E tsang too.* "Maps showing the disposition of the Public Granaries" in the Province of Chĭh-le, together with rules and regulations connected with the same. Compiled by order of the Emperor Keen-lung.   1753.   8º.

Title-page and first page wanting.

———— 交 代 例 冊 *Keaou tae le tsĭh.* "Regulations concerning the transfer of Military Commands," issued by order of the Emperor Keen-lung.   1775.   8º.

———— 行 軍 紀 律 *Hing keun ke leŭh.* "Regulations for Troops in the Field," issued by order of the Emperor Keen-lung.   1784.   8º.

Another copy.

———— 行 軍 紀 律 *Hing keun ke leŭh.* "Regulations for Troops," &c.   1785.   8º.

———— 欽 定 八 旗 則 例 *Kin ting pă ke tsĭh le.* "Regulations for the Bannermen," issued during the latter years of the reign of the Emperor Keen-lung. Compiled by an Imperial Commission consisting of Kwan Kwang, Fŭh Săn-poo, Tŭ-mŭh-tse-too, and others. 12 keuen.   1786.   8º.

—— 道光 TAOU-KWANG. *Emperor.*

Army Regulations.   1825.   8º.

Without either title-page or head title.

Another copy.

CHINA. 道光 TAOU-KWANG. *Emperor.* (*Continued.*)

酌 增 常 例 *Chŏ tsăng chang le.* "Additional Regulations for the Purchase of Rank," issued by order of the Emperor Taou-kwang.   1826.   8º.

—— 常 例 *Chang le.* "Laws and Regulations" on the subject of Promotions, &c.   1827.   8º.

———— 吏 部 兵 部 選 補 班 次 清 凖 *Le Poo Ping Poo seuen poo pan tsze tsing tan.* "Promotion Roster of the Boards of Office and War," issued by order of the Emperor Taou-kwang.   1827.   8º.

———— 現 行 常 例 *Heen hing chang le.* "Regulations for Promotion by Purchase," issued by order of the Emperor Taou-kwang.   1828.   8º.

———— 捐 輸 例 *Keuen shoo le.* "Regulations for the Purchase of Office," issued by order of the Emperor Taou-kwang.   1833.   8º.

———— 籌 備 經 費 事 例 *Chow pe king fe sze le.* "Regulations for providing for the current expenses" by the sale of offices, etc., issued by order of the Emperor Taou-kwang. 1833.   8º.

———— Regulations on Promotion by Purchase, issued by order of the Emperor Taou-kwang.   1837.   8º.

Without either title-page or head title.

———— Regulations against Opium Smoking.   1838.   8º.

Without either title-page or head title.

———— 欽 定 嚴 禁 鴉 片 章 程 *Kin ting yen kin Ya peen chang ching.* "Regulations for the Suppression of Opium Smoking," issued by order of the Emperor Taou-kwang.   1839.   8º.

———— 硝 磺 條 例 *Seaou Hwang teaou le.* Customs "Regulations concerning Nitre and Sulphur," issued by order of the Emperor Taou-kwang.   1841.   8º.

———— 豫 工 事 例 *Yu kung sze le.* "Regulations providing for the performance of Public Works," issued by order of the Emperor Taou-kwang.   1841.   8º.

CHINA. 道光 Taou-kwang. *Emperor.* (*Continued.*)
奏 定 通 商 章 程 稅 則 *Tsow ting tung shang chang ching shwuy tsĭh*. "Customs Regulations and Tariff" for English shipping at the five open Ports in China.　　1843.　8°.

—— 雍 正 Yung-ching. *Emperor.*
上 諭 *Shang yu.* "Imperial Edicts," published during the first seven years of the reign of the Emperor Yung-ching.　　1723–29.　8°.

———— During the second, third, sixth, and eleventh years of the reign of the Emperor Yung-ching.　　1733.　8°.

———— During the tenth, eleventh, and twelfth months of the fifth year of the reign of the Emperor Yung-ching.　　1727.　8°.

————　　　　　　　　　1728.　8°.
　　　Wanting title-page and first eight pages.

———— During the fifth to the seventh month of the fourth year, and during the first to the third month of the sixth year of the reign of the Emperor Yung-ching.　　1728.　8°.

———— During parts of the first, second, and fourth to the seventh years of the reign of the Emperor Yung-ching.　　1729.　8°.

———— During the first seven years of the reign of the Emperor Yung-ching. Compiled by Prince Yun-lŭh, and others.　　1730.　8°.
　　　Imperfect.

———— During the first four months of the eleventh year of the reign of the Emperor Yung-ching.　　1733.　8°.

Another copy.

———— During the reign of the Emperor Yung-ching. Compiled by an Imperial Commission consisting of Prince Hung chow, Gŏ Urh-tae, Chang Ting-yŭh, and others.　　1741.　8°.
Wanting the edicts issued during the first and part of the second year.

———— During the first seven, the ninth, the eleventh, and the thirteenth years of the reign of the Emperor Yung-ching. Compiled by Prince Hung chow and others.　　1741.　8°.

CHINESE UNION.
A Tract on the Bible, beginning 嘗 考 新 舊 遺 詔 *Chang kaou sin kew e chaou.* Tract 32. By the Preachers of the Chinese Union.
　　　　　　　[1850 ?].　8°

—— 行 善 *Hing shen.* "On Doing Good." Tract 50. By the Preachers of the Chinese Union.
　　　　　　　[1850 ?].　8°.

—— 悔 罪 之 理 *Hwuy tsuy che le.* "The Principle of Repentance." Tract 45. By the Preachers of the Chinese Union.　　8°.

—— 祈 禱 *Ke taou.* "On Prayer." Tract 48. By the Preachers of the Chinese Union.
　　　　　　　[1850 ?].　8°.

—— A Tract on Love, beginning 救 主 耶 穌 切 勸 庶 人 相 愛 *Kew choo Yay-soo tsëe keuen shoo jin seang gae.* Tract 52. By the Preachers of the Chinese Union.　　8°.
　　　　No title.

—— 摩 西 首 書 第 三 章 論 *Mo se show shoo te san chang lun.* "A Discourse on the third chapter of the first book of Moses." Tract 31. By the Preachers of the Chinese Union. [1850 ?].　8°.

—— 能 深 念 基 督 之 恩 者 其 罪 可 得 贖 矣 *Năng shin neen Ke-tŭh che găn chay ke tsuy ko tĭh shŭh e.* "He who is able deeply to ponder on the loving kindness of Christ shall have his sins forgiven." Tract 27. By the Preachers of the Chinese Union.　　[1850 ?].　8°.

—— 且 懇 籲 主 之 各 以 滌 去 爾 罪 也 *Tseay kăn yu Choo che ming e tĕih keu urh tsuy yay.* "And call upon the name of the Lord that he may wash away your sins." Tract 17. By the Preachers of the Chinese Union. [1850 ?].　8°.

—— A Tract on God, beginning 竊 以 末 有 天 地 以 前 *Tsëe e mŏ yew Teen Te e tseen.* Tract 42. By the Preachers of the Chinese Union.
　　　　　　　[1850 ?].　8°.
　　　　Without title.

—— 萬 人 復 生 *Wan jin fŭh săng.* "The Resurrection of all Men." Tract 44. By the Preachers of the Chinese Union.　　[1850 ?].　8°.

程川 CHING CHUEN.

See 孔丘 KUNG KEW. 尙書離句 *Shang shoo le keu*. "The Book of Historical Documents." . . Edited by Ching Chuen, &c. 8°.

程頤 CHING E.

See 汪佑 WANG YEW. 五子近思錄 *Woo tsze kin sze lŭh*. "Records of the Approximating Thoughts of the Five Philosophers," . . . Ching E, &c. 1693. 8°.

—— See 四書 SZE SHOO. 四書遵註合講 *Sze shoo tsun choo hŏ keang*. "The Four Books . . . With a Paraphrase and Notes digested from the Works" of . . Ching E, &c. 1805. 8°.

程顥 CHING HAOU.

See 汪佑 WANG YEW. 五子近思錄 *Woo tsze kin sze lŭh*. "Records of the Approximating Thoughts of the Five Philosophers," . . . Ching Haou, &c. 1693. 8°.

—— See 四書 SZE SHOO. 四書朱子異同條辨 *Sze shoo Choo tsze e tung teaou peen*. "The Four Books. With . . . the Commentaries" of . . . Ching Haou, &c. 1705. 8°.

—— 學類 *Heŏ luy*. "On Learning." 性命類 *Sing ming luy*. "On Life." 理氣類 *Le che luy*. "On Metaphysics." 治道類 *Che taou luy*. "On the Principles of Government." See 李光地 LE KWANG-TE. 御纂性理精義 *Yu tswan sing le tsing e*. "The Essence of Works on Mental Philosophy," &c. Keuen 7 to 12, &c. 1715. 8°.

—— See 易經 YĬH KING. 御纂周易折中 *Yu tswan Chow Yĭh chĕ chung*. "Decisions on the Book of Changes." With the Notes and Comments of . . Ching Haou, &c. 1715. 8°.

—— See 方鯤 FANG KWĂN. 易盪 *Yĭh tang*. "The Permutations of the Diagrams of the Book of Changes." . . . . . With Notes by . . . Ching Haou, &c. 1718. 8°.

—— See 孔丘 KUNG KEW. 書經大全 *Shoo king ta tseuen*. "A Complete Copy of the Book of Historical Documents." . . With Commentaries . . . . by Ching Haou, &c. 8°.

程顥 CHING HAOU. (*Continued.*)

See 四書 SZE SHOO. 四書典林 *Sze shoo teen lin*. "A Dictionary of Classical Expressions employed in the Four Books," illustrated and explained by . . Ching Haou, &c. 1795. 8°.

—— 四書蒙引 *Sze shoo mung yin*. "A Guide to the study of the Four Books." . . . . . with . . . Extracts from the Commentaries of Ching Haou, &c. 8°.

—— See 易經 YĬH KING. 周易義傳合訂 *Chow Yĭh e chuen hŏ ting*. "The Book of Changes. With the . . Commentary of Ching Haou," &c. 8°.

—— See 四書 SZE SHOO. 四書遵註合講 *Sze shoo tsun choo hŏ keang*. "The Four Books. . . . With a Paraphrase and Notes digested from the Works" of Ching Haou, &c. 1805. 8°.

—— —— 四書離句集註 *Sze shoo le keu tseĭh choo*. "The Four Books commented on " . . by . . Ching Haou, &c. 1818. 8°.

程俱 CHING KEU.

道德經 *Taou tĭh king*. "The Classic of Reason and Virtue." With a Commentary by Ching Keu. See 焦竑 TSEAOU HUNG. 老莊翼合刻 *Laou Chwang yĭh hŏ kĭh*. "The Works of Laou-keun and Chwang Chow," &c. 1588. 8°.

程本 CHING PUN.

子華子 *Tsze-hwa-tsze*. "The Philosophy of Tsze-hwa-tsze." See 沈津 CHIN TSIN. 百家類纂 *Pĭh kea luy tswan*. "The Works of a Hundred Authors," &c. Keuen 37. 8°.

程偉 CHING WEI.

See 曹雪芹 TSAOU SEUĔ-KIN. 紅樓夢 *Hung low mung*. "The Dream of the Red Chamber." . . Edited by Ching Wei, &c. 1811. 8°.

程正敏 CHING CHING-MIN.

剡溪野語 *Yen ke yay yu*. "Varieties from Yen ke." See 說 SHWŎ. 說郛 *Shwŏ foo*. "Odds and Ends," &c. 8°.

程 恩 澤 CHING GĂN-TSĬH.

國策地名考 *Kwŏ tsĭh te ming kaou.* "An Examination into the names of the Localities mentioned in the Story of the Contending States." 20 keuen. [Also] 程侍郞遺集 *Ching she lang wei tseĭh.* "The Literary Remains of Ching Găn-tsĭh, Vice-President" of the Board of Revenue. 10 keuen. *See* 伍崇曜 WOO TSUNG-YAOU. 粵雅堂叢書 *Yuĕ ya Tang tsung shoo.* "The Yuĕ-ya Tang Collection of Reprints," &c. Series 17, 19. 1853. 8º.

程 若 庸 CHING JŎ-YUNG.

性理子訓 *Sing le tsze heun.* "Instruction on the terms employed in Mental Philosophy." In verse. *See* 陸清獻 LŬH TSING-HEEN. 小四書 *Seaou sze shoo.* "The Lesser Four Books," &c. Keuen 2. 1845. 8º.

程 敬 承 CHING KING-CHING.

See 徐在漢 SEU TSAE-HAN. 易或 *Yĭh hwŏ.* "Doubts on the Book of Changes" elucidated. .. With Notes by Ching King-ching, &c. 1774. 8º.

程 國 彭 CHING KWŎ-PĂNG.

醫學心悟 *E heŏ sin woo.* "A Treatise on the Practice of Medicine." 6 keuen. [1790?]. 8º.

程 梅 庄 CHING MEI-CHWANG.

天賜花裙全本 *Teen tsze hwa keun tseuen pun.* "The Heaven-sent Flowery Petticoat." In verse. 4 keuen. [1850?]. 8º.

程 潘 基 CHING PWAN-KE.

老莊會解 *Laou Chwang hwuy keae.* "The Works of Laou-keun and Chwang Chow explained," by means of a collection of comments compiled by Ching Pwan-ke. [1800?]. 8º.

程 石 麟 CHING SHĬH-LIN.

鵪鶉譜 *Gan shun poo.* "A Work on Quails." *See* 張山來 CHANG SHAN-LAE, and 張進也 CHANG TSIN-YAY. 昭代叢書 *Chaou tae tsung shoo.* "A Collection of Reprints of Works by Authors under the present Dynasty," &c. Keuen 49. 1703. 8º.

程 大 昌 CHING TA-CHANG.

北邊備對 *Pĭh peen pe tuy.* "Answers on the Geography of the Northern Territories." *See* 說 SHWŏ. 說選 *Shwŏ seuen.* "A Collection of Historical Records," &c. Vol. 5. 8º.

程 大 中 CHING TA-CHUNG.

四書逸箋 *Sze shoo yĭh tseen.* "Occasional Notes on the Four Books." 6 keuen. *See* 葉志詵 YĔ CHE-SIN. 海山仙館叢書 *Hae shan seen Kwan tsung shoo.* "The Hae shan seen Kwan Collection of Reprints," &c. Vol. 5. 1848. 8º.

—— 四書逸牋 *Sze shoo yĭh tseen.* "Occasional Notes on the Four Books." 6 keuen. *See* 伍崇曜 WOO TSUNG-YAOU. 粵雅堂叢書 *Yuĕ ya Tang tsung shoo.* "The Yuĕ-ya Tang Collection of Reprints," &c. Series 4. 1853. 8º.

程 大 衡 CHING TA-HĂNG.

重訂綴白裘新集合編 *Chung ting chuĕ pĭh kew sin tseĭh hŏ peen.* "A new Collection of Dramatic Pieces." Compiled by Ching Ta-hăng. 12 Series. 1781. 8º.

Another edition. 12 Series. 1823. 8º.

程 大 位 CHING TA-WEI.

算法統宗全書 *Swan fă tung tsung tseuen shoo.* "A Complete Work on the Rules of Arithmetic," illustrating the principle of the Abacus. Edited by Woo Ke-show. 12 keuen. 1593. 8º.

—— 算法統宗 *Swan fă tung tsung.* "The Rules of Arithmetic," illustrating the principle of the Abacus. Edited by Woo Ke-show. 12 keuen. 1832. 8º.

Another edition of the above.

程 登 吉 CHING TĂNG-KEĬH.

See 丘濬 KEW SEUN. 幼學故事尋源 *Yew heŏ koo sze tsin yuen.* "A Search into Antiquities." . . Edited by Ching Tăng-keĭh, &c. 8º.

程 鶴 樵 CHING TSEAOU-TSEAOU.

See 文昌帝君 WĂN CHANG TE KEUN. 陰騭文詩牋 *Yin chĭh wăn she tseen.* "A Treatise on Secret Rewards and Retributions. With Poetical Essays thereon," by Ching Tseaou-tseaou, &c. 1812. 8º.

程 鶴 樵 CHING TSEAOU-TSEAOU. (*Continued*.)

陰 隲 文 詩 帖 *Yin chǐh wǎn she tëĕ*. "A Treatise on Secret Rewards and Retributions. With Poetical Essays thereon," by Ching Tseaou-tseaou, &c. 1812. 8°.

Another edition of the above.

程 遵 岳 CHING TSUN-Yŏ.

See 劉 勰 LEW HĔĔ. 新 論 *Sin lun*. "New Discourses." .. Edited by Ching Tsun-yŏ, &c. 8°.

程 宗 瑊 CHING TSUNG-TEEN.

See 王 WANG. 十 七 史 蒙 求 *Shǐh tsǐh she mung kew*. "The Student's Guide to the Seventeen Histories." . . . Edited by Ching Tsung-teen, &c. 8°.

程 瑤 田 CHING YAOU-TEEN.

宗 法 小 記 *Tsung fǎ seaou ke*. "The Laws of Kindred." [Also] 儀 禮 喪 服 足 徵 記 *E le sang fǔh tsǔh ching ke*. "The Funeral Clothes prescribed in the Decorum Ritual." 10 keuen. [Also] 釋 宮 小 記 *Shǐh kung seaou ke*. "On the Architecture of Palaces." [Also] 考 工 創 物 小 記 *Kaou kung chwang wǔh seaou ke*. "On the Manufacture of Weapons." 4 keuen. [Also] 聲 折 古 義 *King chě koo e*. "On the Ancient Meaning of King chě." [Also] 溝 洫 疆 理 小 記 *Kow heǔe keang le seaou ke*. "On Draining." [Also] 禹 貢 三 江 考 *Yu kung san keang kaou*. "The Three Rivers of the Tribute of Yu." 3 keuen. [Also] 水 地 小 記 *Shwuy te seaou ke*. "On Wet Land." [Also] 解 子 小 記 *Keae tsze seaou ke*. "On the Explanation of some Characters." [Also] 聲 律 小 記 *Shing leǔh seaou ke*. "On the Division of Sound." [Also] 九 穀 考 *Kew kǒ kaou*. "On the Nine Grains." [Also] 釋 草 小 記 *Shǐh tsaou seaou ke*. "On Grasses." [Also] 釋 蟲 小 記 *Shǐh chung seaou ke*. "On Insects." See 嚴 杰 YEN LĔĔ. 皇 清 經 解 *Hwang Tsing king keae*. "The Classics Explained," &c. Keuen 524–553. 1829. 8°.

程 元 章 CHING YUEN-CHANG.

See 李 衛 LE WEI. 西 湖 志 *Se hoo che*. "A Topography of the Western Lake." . . Compiled by . . . Ching Yuen-chang, &c. 1734. 8°.

程 允 升 CHING YUN-SHING.

幼 學 故 事 瓊 林 *Yew heŏ koo sze keung lin*. "An Encyclopædia of Antiquities for Beginners." Edited by Tsow Shing-mǐh. 4 keuen. 1760. 8°.

Another edition. 4 keuen. 1833. 8°.

—— 幼 學 須 知 句 解 *Yew heŏ seu che keu kcae*. "General Knowledge necessary for Beginners. With Explanations." Edited by Tseen Yuen-lung. 4 keuen. 1863. 8°.

程 永 培 CHING YUNG-PEI.

See 王 肯 堂 WANG KĂNG-TANG. 證 治 準 繩 *Ching che chun shing*. "A Manual of Medicine." . . . Re-edited by Ching Yung-pei, &c. 1791. 8°.

鄭 重 CHING CHUNG.

See 四 書 SZE SHOO. 四 書 直 解 *Sze shoo chǐh keae*. "The Four Books clearly explained." .... Edited by Ching Chung, &c. 1766. 8°.

鄭 贊 CHING FUN.

才 鬼 記 *Tsae kwei ke*. "Stories of Clever Devils." See 王 文 誥 WANG WĂN-KAOU. 唐 代 叢 書 *Tang tae tsung shoo*. "A Collection of Reprints of Works written during the Tang Dynasty," &c. Series 6. 1806. 8°.

—— 才 鬼 記 *Tsae kwei ke*. "Stories of Clever Devils." By Ching Fun, of the Tang Dynasty. [1741 ?]. 8°.

鄭 俠 CHING HĔĔ.

西 塘 集 *Se tang tseǐh*. "The Western Pond Collection." See 吳 孟 舉 WOO MĂNG-KEU, and 吳 自 牧 WOO TSZE-MǓH. 宋 詩 鈔 二 集 *Sung she chaou urh tseǐh*. "Poetry of the Sung Dynasty," &c. 8°.

鄭 玄 CHING HEUEN.

忠 經 *Chung king*. "The Classic on Patriotism." With a Commentary compiled by Ching Heuen. See 朱 熹 CHOO HE. 小 學 體 註 大 成 *Seaou heŏ te choo ta ching*. "A Complete Copy of the Youth's Instructor," &c. 8°.

鄭 環 CHING HWAN.

See 萬 之 薔 WAN CHE-HĂNG, and 吳 寳 彝 WOO PAOU-E. 漢 關 侯 事 蹟 彙 編 *Han Kwan how sze tseïh wei peen.* "A Memoir of Kwan Yu." ... Edited by Ching Hwan, &c. 8°.

鄭 棨 CHING KE.

開 天 傳 信 記 *Kae teen chuen sin ke.* "Truthful Records of the Reign of Yuen-tsung." *See* 王 文 誥 WANG WĂN-KAOU. 唐 代 叢 書 *Tang tae tsung shoo.* "A Collection of Reprints of Works written during the Tang Dynasty," &c. Series 1. 1806. 8°.

鄭 性 CHING SING.

See 黃 梨 洲 HWANG LE-CHOW. 南 雷 文 約 *Nan luy wăn yŏ.* "The Nan luy Collection of Literary Pieces." Edited by Ching Sing, &c. 8°.

鄭 樵 CHING TSEAOU.

通 志 *Tung che.* "A General History" of China. 200 keuen. 1749. Folio.

Another edition. 200 keuen. 1749. 8°.

鄭 澐 CHING YUN.

杭 州 府 志 *Hang chow foo che.* "A Topography of Hang chow Foo," in the Province of Chĕ-keang. Compiled by Ching Yun. 110 keuen. 1784. 8°.

鄭 之 僑 CHING CHE-KEAOU.

六 經 圖 *Lŭh king too.* "Illustrations to the Six Classics." Compiled by Ching Che-keaou. 24 keuen. 1744. 8°.

鄭 芷 畦 CHING CHE-HWUY.

廿 一 史 約 編 *Neen yĭh she yŏ peen.* "An Epitome of the Twenty-one Histories." Edited by Chin Keu-shĭh. 1697. 8°.

鄭 處 誨 CHING CHOO-HWUY.

明 皇 雜 錄 *Ming Hwang tsă lŭh.* "Miscellaneous Records of the Illustrious Emperor," Yuen-tsung. *See* 王 文 誥 WANG WĂN-KAOU. 唐 伐 叢 書 *Tang tae tsung shoo.* "A Collection of Reprints of Works written during the Tang Dynasty," &c. Series 1. 1806. 8°.

鄭 方 坤 CHING FANG-KWĂN.

五 代 詩 話 *Woo tae she hwa.* "Criticisms on the Poetry of the Five Dynasties." Enlarged by Ching Fang-kwăn, &c. *See* 伍 崇 曜 WOO TSUNG-YAOU. 粵 雅 堂 叢 書 *Yuĕ ya Tang tsung shoo.* "The Yuĕ-ya Tang Collection of Reprints," &c. Series 3. 1853. 8°.

鄭 還 古 CHING HWAN-KOO.

博 異 志 *Pŏ e che.* "Marvellous Tales." *See* 王 文 誥 WANG WĂN-KAOU. 唐 代 叢 書 *Tang tae tsung shoo.* "A Collection of Reprints of Works written during the Tang Dynasty," &c. Series 6. 1806. 8°.

—— 博 異 志 *Pŏ e che.* "Marvellous Tales." By Ching Hwan-koo, of the Tang Dynasty. A Reprint. [1741?]. 8°.

—— 杜 子 春 傳 *Too Tsze-chun chuen.* "The Story of Too Tsze-chun." By Ching Hwan-koo, of the Tang Dynasty. A Reprint. [1741?]. 8°.

鄭 康 成 CHING KANG-CHING.

See 周 禮 CHOW LE. 周 禮 註 疏 *Chow le choo soo.* "The Chow Ritual. With a Commentary" by Ching Kang-ching, &c. 8°.

—— See 儀 禮 E LE. 儀 禮 註 疏 *E le choo soo.* "The Decorum Ritual. With a Commentary" by Ching Kang-ching, &c. 8°.

—— See 禮 記 LE KE. 禮 記 註 疏 *Le ke choo soo.* "The Book of Rites. With a Commentary" by Ching Kang-ching, &c. [1750?]. 8°.

—— See 詩 經 SHE KING. 毛 詩 注 疏 *Maou she choo soo.* "Maou Chang's Version of the Book of Odes. With a Commentary" by Ching Kang-ching, &c. 1815. 8°.

—— 周 易 注 *Chow yĭh choo.* "A Commentary on the Chow Changes." 3 keuen. *See* 孫 堂 SUN TANG. 漢 魏 二 十 一 家 易 注 *Han Wei urh shĭh yĭh kea Yĭh choo.* "Commentaries on the Book of Changes," &c. 1799. 8°.

6

鄭 康 成 CHING KANG-CHING. *(Continued.)*

鄭 志 *Ching che.* "Records of Ching Kang-ching." A Catechism on Classical Subjects. &c. Compiled by Ching Seaou-tung, and edited by Tseen Tung-tan, and others. 4 keuen. *See* 伍 崇 曜 WOO TSUNG-YAOU. 粵 雅 堂 叢 書 *Yuĕ ya Tang tsung shoo.* "The Yuĕ-ya Tang Collection of Reprints," &c. Series 12. 1853. 8°.

鄭 兼 才 CHING KEEN-TSAE.

See 謝 金 鑾 SEAY KIN-LWAN. 續 修 臺 灣 縣 志 *Sŭh scw Tae wan heen che.* "A Revised Topography of Tae-wan Heen." Compiled by . . . Ching Keen-tsae, &c. 1807. 8°.

鄭 伯 壎 CHING PǏH-HEUEN.

See 蕭 應 槻 SEAOU YING-KWEI, and CHING PǏH-HEUEN. 律 賦 錦 標 初 集 箋 註 *Leŭh foo kin peaou choo tseĭh tseen choo.* "Elegant Odes." . . Compiled by Seaou Ying-kwei and Ching Pǐh-heuen. 1816. 8°.

鄭 小 同 CHING SEAOU-TUNG.

鄭 志 *Ching che.* "Records of Ching Kang-ching." . . Compiled by Ching Seaou-tung, &c. *See* 伍 崇 曜 WOO TSUNG-YAOU. 粵 雅 堂 叢 書 *Yuĕ ya Tang tsung shoo.* "The Yuĕ-ya Tang Collection of Reprints," &c. Series 12. 1853. 8°.

鄭 師 成 CHING SZE-CHING.

See 高 其 名 KAOU KE-MING, and CHING SZE-CHING. 四 書 左 國 輯 要 *Sze shoo Tso kwŏ tseĭh yaou.* "Extracts . . . . illustrating the Lives of Worthies mentioned in the Four Books," &c. 1789. 8°.

鄭 廷 獻 CHING TING-HEEN.

See 鄭 一 崧 CHING YǏH-SUNG. 永 春 州 志 *Yung chun chow che.* "A Topography of Yung-chun Chow." . . Compiled by . . Ching Ting-heen, &c. 1787. 8°.

鄭 崇 謙 CHING TSUNG-KEEN.

See 哆 啉 哖 CHAY-LAN-LIN. 嘆 咭 唎 國 新 種 痘 奇 書 *Ying-keĭh-le kwŏ sin chung tow ke shoo.* "A Pamphlet on the English System of Vaccination." . . . Translated into Chinese by . . Ching Tsung-keen, &c. 1805. 8°.

鄭 爾 齡 CHING URH-LING.

篆 江 樓 棑 律 詩 鈔 *Chuen keang low pae leŭh she chaou.* "Poems from the Chuen-keang Pavilion." Compiled by Ching Urh-ling. 4 keuen. [1800 ?]. 8°.

Imperfect, wanting first two keucn.

鄭 一 崧 CHING YǏH-SUNG.

永 春 州 志 *Yung chun chow che.* "A Topography of Yung-chun Chow," in the Province of Fŭh-kien. Compiled by Ching Yǐh-sung, Yen Show, Ching Ting-heen, and others. 16 keuen. 1787. 8°.

Imperfect, wanting keuen 12.

鄭 元 夫 CHING YUEN-FOO.

雙 門 調 *Shwang mun teaou.* "The Song of the Folding Doors." *See* 閔 景 賢 MIN KING-HEEN. 快 書 *Kwae shoo.* "A Book of Amusement," &c. Keuen 25. 1626. 8°.

鄭 元 慶 CHING YUEN-KING.

石 柱 記 *Shĭh choo ke.* "An Account of the Stone Monuments" in the Prefecture of Hoo-chow, in the Province of Chĕ-keang. 5 keuen. *See* 伍 崇 曜 WOO TSUNG-YAOU. 粵 雅 堂 叢 書 *Yuĕ ya Tang tsung shoo.* "The Yuĕ-ya Tang Collection of Reprints," &c. Series 9. 1853. 8°.

鄭 元 美 CHING YUEN-MEI.

See 孔 丘 KUNG KEW. 奎 壁 書 經 *Kwei peĭh Shoo king.* "The Kwei peĭh Edition of the Book of Historical Documents." . . Compiled by Ching Yuen-mei, &c. 8°.

鄭 元 祐 CHING YUEN-YEW.

遂 昌 山 樵 雜 錄 *Suy chang shan tseaou tsǎ lŭh.* "The Miscellaneous Records of the Woodman of the Suy chang Mountains." *See* 說 SHWŎ. 說 畧 *Shwŏ leŏ.* "Historical and other Tracts." 8°.

卓 瑤 CHǑ FAN.

See 葉 九 升 YĔ KEW-SHING. 地 理 山 法 全 書 *Te le shan fǎ tseuen shoo.* "The Laws of Mountains." . . Ninth keuen is edited, with notes, by Chǒ Fan, &c. 8°.

卓 長 齡 CHŏ CHANG-LING.

See 葉 九 升 YĕKEW-SHING. 地 理 山 法 全 書
Te le shan fǎ tseuen shoo. "The Laws of Mountains." . . . Seventh keuen is edited, with notes,
by Chŏ Chang-ling, &c. 8°.

卓 有 見 CHŏ YEW-KEEN. 答 論 神 丹 書 *Tǎ lun
Shen tan shoo.* "A Treatise on the Works on
the Wonderful Elixir." *See* 彭 好 古 PĂNG
HAOU-KOO. 道 言 內 外 秘 訣 全 書 *Taou
yen nuy wae pe keŭ tseuen shoo.* "A Complete
Collection of Taouist Works," &c. 8°.

朱 湜 CHOO CHĬH.
三 墳 *San fun.* "The Works of the Three
Emperors," Fuh-he, Shin-nung, and Hwang-te.
Edited by Choo Chĭh. With Notes by Yuen
Han, of the Tsin Dynasty. A Reprint.
[1800 ?]. 8°.

朱 熹 CHOO CHOW.
See 楊 慧 樓 YANG HWUY-LOW, and 王 惕 甫
WANG TEĬH-FOO. 國 朝 七 排 雲 襄 二 集
Kwŏ chaou tsĭh pae Yun seang urh tseĭh. "The
Yun-seang Collection of Heptameters by Authors
of the Tsing Dynasty." . . Edited by Choo
Chow, &c. 1807. 8°.

朱 輔 CHOO FOO.
溪 蠻 叢 笑 *Ke man tsung seaou.* "The Laughable Peculiarities of the Southern Barbarians."
See 說 SHWŏ. 說 選 *Shwŏ seuen.* "A Collection of Records," &c. Vol. 3. 8°.

朱 傳 CHOO FOO.
See 賴 太 素 LAE TAE-SOO. 催 官 解 *Tsuy
kwan keae.* "The Tsuy kwan . . . Explained"
by Choo Foo, &c. 1842. 8°.

朱 焞 CHOO FOW.
See 薛 應 旂 SĕĬh YING-KE. 四 書 人 物 備 考
Sze shoo jin wŭh pe kaou. "An Examination of
the Men and Things mentioned in the Four
Books." With Notes by Choo Fow, &c. 8°.

朱 熹 CHOO HE.
See 方 鯤 FANG KWĂN. 易 盪 *Yǐh tang.* "The
Permutations of the Diagrams of the Book of
Changes." . . . . With Notes by Choo He, &c.
1718. 8°.

—— See 邢 坤 元 HING KWĂN-YUEN. 朱 夫 子 家
訓 印 譜 *Choo Foo tsze kea heun yin poo.*
"Maxims from Choo He's Book of Domestic
Instructions," &c. 1750. 8°.

—— 易 學 啟 蒙 *Yǐh heŏ ke mnng.* "Instructions
for Students on the Book of Changes." [Also]
家 禮 *Kea le.* "Domestic Ceremonies." *See*
胡 廣 HOO KWANG. 性 理 大 全 *Sing le ta
tseuen.* "A Complete Work on Mental Philosophy," &c. Keuen 15-21. 1414. 8°.

—— See 屈 原 KEŬH YUEN. 楚 辭 集 註 *Tsoo
tsze tseĭh choo.* "The Elegies of Tsoo." With
the Commentary of Choo He, &c. 8°.

—— See 孔 丘 KUNG KEW. 書 經 大 全 *Shoo king
ta tseuen.* "The Book of Historical Documents."
. . With Comments . . . by Choo He, &c. 8°.

—— 易 學 啟 蒙 *Yǐh heo ke mung.* "Instructions
for Students on the Book of Changes." [Also]
家 禮 *Kea le.* "Domestic Ceremonies." *See* 李
光 地 LE KWANG-TE. 御 纂 性 理 精 義 *Yu
tswan sing le tsing e.* "The Essence of Works on
Mental Philosophy," &c. Keuen 4, 5. 1715. 8°.

—— See 禮 記 LE KE. 禮 記 棛 要 *Le ke kĕĕ yaou.*
"The Book of Rites. With an Abridgment"
of the Commentaries of Choo He, &c. 12°.

—— See 詩 經 SHE KING. 旁 訓 詩 經 體 註 衍 義
Pang heun She king te choo yen e. "The Book
of Odes." . . Containing the Commentary of
Choo He, &c. 1687. 8°.

—— —— 辨 志 堂 詩 經 說 約 集 解 *Peen che Tang
She king shwŏ yŏ tseĭh keae.* "The Peen-che Tang
Edition of the Book of Odes." . . With the
Commentary of Choo He, &c. 1688. 8°.

朱熹 Choo He. (*Continued.*)

See 詩經 She king. 聚錦堂詩經體註 *Tseu kin Tang She king te choo.* "The Tseu-kin Tang Edition of the Book of Odes," with ... the Commentary of Choo He, &c. 1711. 8°.

―――― 聚錦堂詩經 *Tseu kin Tang She king.* "The Tseu-kin Tang Edition of the Book of Odes." With the Commentary of Choo He, &c. 8°.

―――― 欽定詩經傳說彙纂 *Kin ting She king chuen shuŏ wei tswan.* "A Compilation and Digest of the Comments and Remarks" of Choo He "on the Book of Odes," &c. 1727. 8°.

―――― 詩經大全 *She king ta tseuen.* "The Book of Odes." With Extracts from the Commentaries of Choo He, &c. 8°.

―――― 詩經讀本 *She king tŭh pun.* "The Book of Odes." With Choo He's Commentary, &c. 1785. 8°.

―――― 詩經撮要 *She king kĕĕ yaou.* "The Book of Odes. With an Abridgment" of the Commentaries of Choo He, &c. 12°.

―――― 芥子園監本詩經 *Keae tsze yuen keen pun She king.* "The Keae-tsze Yuen Edition of the Book of Odes." With the Commentary of Choo He, &c. 1818. 8°.

――― See 四書 Sze shoo. 論語註疏大全合纂 *Lun yu choo soo ta tseuen ho tswan.* "The Confucian Analects." With Commentaries .. by Choo He, &c. 1636. 8°.

―――― 論語集註本義匯參 *Lun yu tseĭh choo pun e hwuy tsan.* "The Proper Meaning of the Confucian Analects," as determined by Choo He, &c. 8°.

―――― 論語 *Lun yu.* "The Confucian Analects." With Choo He's Commentary, &c. 8°.

―――― 論語集註 *Lun yu tseĭh choo.* "The Confucian Analects. With a Collection of Comments" compiled by Choo He, &c. 8°.

朱熹 Choo He. (*Continued.*)

See 四書 Sze shoo. 酈雅齋四書遵註合講 *Chŏ ya chae Sze shoo tsun choo ho keang.* "The Chŏ-ya Study Edition of the Four Books, according to the Commentary " of Choo He, &c. 8°.

―――― 四書朱子異同條辨 *Sze shoo Choo Tsze e tung teaou peen.* "The Four Books, with ... the Commentaries of Choo He," &c. 1705. 8°.

―――― 學源堂銅板四書發註 *Heŏ yuen Tang tung pan Sze shoo fă choo.* The Heŏ-yuen Tang Edition of the Four Books. With the Commentary " of Choo He, &c. 1723. 8°.

―――― 四書章句集注 *Sze shoo chang keu tseĭh choo.* "The Four Books," commented on .. by Choo He, &c. 8°.

―――― 四書便抄 *Sze shoo peen chaou.* "A Handy Copy of the Four Books," with Choo He's Commentary, &c. 1794. 8°.

―――― 四書典林 *Sze shoo teen lin.* "A Dictionary of Classical Phrases employed in the Four Books." Illustrated and Explained by .. Choo He, &c. 1795. 8°.

―――― 孟子 *Măng tsze.* "The Teachings of Mencius." With the Commentary of Choo He, &c. 8°.

――― 孟子集註 *Măng tsze tseĭh choo.* "The Teachings of Mencius. With a Collection of Comments " compiled by Choo He, etc. 8°.

―――― 四書蒙引 *Sze shoo mung yin.* "A Guide to the Study of the Four Books." ..... with ... Extracts from the Commentaries of Choo He, &c. 8°.

―――― 四書合講 *Sze shoo hŏ keang.* "The Four Books, according to the Commentary " of Choo He, &c. 8°.

―――― 四書遵註合講 *Sze shoo tsun choo hŏ keang.* "The Four Books, according to the Commentary " of Choo He, &c. 1805. 8°.

CHO [45] CHO

朱熹 CHOO HE. (*Continued.*)

小學體註大成 *Seaou heŏ te choo ta ching.* "A Complete Copy of the Youth's Instructor. With a Collection of Comments" compiled by Chin Seuen. Edited by Maou Sze-ching, Chin Ming-yuen, and Le Chang-mei. To which are added the Heaou king, "Book of Filial Piety," and the Chung king, "Classic on Patriotism." With a Collection of Comments, compiled by Ching Heuen. 6 keuen.

Fŭh shan, [1800 ?]. 8°.

Another copy.

Another copy.

Another edition. 6 keuen. [1810 ?]. 8°.

—— 小學集註 *Seaou heŏ tseĭh choo.* "The Youth's Instructor. With a Collection of Comments" compiled by Chin Tsung. 6 keuen. 1820. 8°.

—— 通鑑綱目 *Tung keen kang mŭh.* "A Condensation of the Mirror of History." By Choo He and his Disciples. Edited by Chin Jin-seĭh. Part I. 19 keuen, Part II. 59 keuen. 1630. 8°.

Another edition. Part I. 25 keuen, Part II. 59 keuen, Part III. 27 keuen. 1803. 8°.

朱釣 CHOO KEUN.

See TSING DYNASTY. 大清律例重訂統纂集成 *Ta Tsing leŭh le chung ting tung tswan tseĭh ching.* "The Fundamental Laws and Subordinate Statutes of the Tsing Dynasty." .... Revised and enlarged by Choo Keun, &c. 1830. 8°.

朱謹 CHOO KIN.

See 陳璿 CHIN SEUEN. 普陀山志 *Poo to shan che.* "A Topography of the Island of Poo-to." ... Compiled by ... Choo Kin, &c. 1734. 8°.

朱奎 CHOO KWEI.

See 嚴榮 YEN YUNG. 武義縣志 *Woo e heen che.* "A Topography of Woo-e Heen." Compiled by ... Choo Kwei, &c. 1804. 8°.

朱珪 CHOO KWEI.

See 王圻 WANG KE. 續文獻通考 *Sŭh wăn heen tung kaou.* "A Continuation of the Wăn heen tung kaou." Revised and edited by ... Choo Kwei, &c. 1784. 8°.

朱禮 CHOO LE.

漢唐事箋 *Han Tang sze tseen.* "Records of the Han and Tang Dynasties." In two parts. Part I. 12 keuen, Part II. 8 keuen. 1822. 8°.

朱淥 CHOO LŬH.

See 李式圃 LE SHĬH-POO. 嵊縣志 *Shing heen che.* "A Topography of Shing Heen." .. Compiled by .. Choo Lŭh, &c. 1828. 8°.

朱弁 CHOO PEEN.

曲洧舊聞 *Keŭh wei kew wăn.* "Old Tales of Keŭh wei." See 說 SHWŎ. 說郛 *Shwŏ foo.* "Odds and Ends," &c. 8°.

朱彬 CHOO PIN.

經傳攷證 *King chuen kaou ching.* "Commentaries on the Classics Examined and Verified." 8 keuen. See 嚴杰 YEN LĔĔ. 皇清經解 *Hwang Tsing king keae.* "The Classics Explained," &c. Keuen 1361–1368. 1829. 8°.

朱彖 CHOO SEANG.

See 桑世昌 SĂNG SHE-CHANG. 回文類聚 *Hwuy wăn luy tseu.* "A Collection of Literary Puzzles." .. Compiled by .. Choo Seang, &c. 8°.

朱氏 CHOO SHE.

See 禮記 LE KE. 監本禮記 *Keen pŭn Le ke.* "The Book of Rites." ... Edited by Choo she, &c. 1698. 8°.

朱軾 CHOO SHĬH.

駁呂留良四書講義 *Pŏ Leu Lew-leang sze shoo keang e.* "A Refutation of Leu Lew-leang's Commentary on the Four Books," by Choo Shĭh, Woo Seang, and others. Published by Imperial Authority. 6 vols. 1731. 8°.

朱棟 CHOO TUNG.

千巷志 *Kan-heang che.* "A Topography of the Village of Kan-heang." By Choo Tung. Edited by Wang Haou, and others. 6 keuen. 1801. 8°.

CHO [47] CHO

朱 兆 鳳 CHOO CHAOU-FUNG.

See 聶 銑 敏 SHĔ SĔEN-MIN. 寄 嶽 雲 齋 試 體 詩 *Ke yŏ yun chae she te she.* "A Collection of Poetical Essays from the Ke-yŏ-yun Study." Enlarged and revised by Choo Chaou-fung, &c. 1804. 8°.

朱 之 蕃 CHOO CHE-FAN.

金 陵 四 十 景 圖 考 *Kin-ling sze she king too kaou.* "Forty Views of Nanking. With Explanations." Compiled by Choo Che-fan. 1624. 8°.

朱 竹 咤 CHOO CHŬH-TSĬH.

朱 竹 咤 先 生 詩 鈔 *Choo Chŭh tsĭh seen săng she chaou.* "The Poems of Dr. Choo Chŭh-tsĭh." Compiled by Chow Jĭh-leen and Too Tĭh-sew. 6 keuen. [1800?]. 12°.

朱 彝 尊 CHOO E-TSUN.

詞 綜 *Tsze tsung.* "A Collection of Rhymes, arranged in chronological order." Compiled by Choo E-tsun. Edited, with additions, by Wang Săn. 30 keuen. 1678. 8°.

—— 曝 書 亭 集 *Paou shoo ting tseĭh.* "The Paou-shoo Ting Collection of the Writings of Choo E-tsun. 80 kenen. [1700?]. 8°.

朱 鳳 台 CHOO FUNG-E.

See 四 書 SZE SHOO. 四 書 直 解 *Sze shoo chĭh keae.* "The Four Books, clearly explained." .... Edited by Choo Fung-e, &c. 1766. 8°.

朱 楓 林 CHOO FUNG-LIN.

See 易 經 YĬH KING. 崇 道 堂 易 經 大 全 會 解 *Tsung taou Tang Yĭh king ta tseuen hwuy keae.* "The Tsung-taou Tang Edition of the Book of Changes. With Explanatory Comments" by .. Choo Fung-lin, &c. 1681. 8°.

朱 顯 祖 CHOO HEEN-TSOO.

瓊 花 志 *Keung hwa che.* "An Account of the Keung Flower." *See* 張 山 來 CHANG SHAN-LAE, and 張 進 也 CHANG TSIN-YAY. 昭 代 叢 書 *Chaou tae tsung shoo.* "A Collection of Reprints of Works by Authors under the present Dynasty," &c. Keuen 45. 1703. 8°.

朱 會 龍 CHOO HWUY-LUNG.

See 水 中 龍 SHWUY CHUNG-LUNG. 星 平 會 海 *Sing ping hwuy hae.* "The Junction of the Stars and the Sea." .. Edited by Choo Hwuy-lung, &c. 8°.

朱 奇 生 CHOO KE-SĂNG.

See 四 書 SZE SHOO. 學 源 堂 銅 板 四 書 發 註 *Heŏ-yuen Tang tung pan Sze shoo fă choo.* "The Heŏ-yuen Tang Edition of the Four Books." .. Compiled by Choo Ke-săng, &c. 1723. 8°.

朱 君 復 CHOO KEUN-FŬH.

諸 子 勘 淑 *Choo tsze chin shŭh.* "The Adjusted Merits of the Philosophers." See 閔 景 賢 MIN KING-HEEN. 快 書 *Kwae shoo.* "A Book of Amusement," &c. Keuen 32. 1626. 8°.

朱 景 固 CHOO KING-KOO.

See 劉 向 LEW HEANG. 古 列 女 傳 *Koo lĕĕ neu chuen.* "Biographies of Eminent Women." ... Edited by Choo King-koo, &c. 1551. 8°.

朱 鑾 廷 CHOO LWAN-TING.

See CHINA. BOARD OF REVENUE. 戶 部 則 例 *Hoo poo tsĭh le.* "Regulations of the Board of Revenue." Compiled by .... Choo Lwan-ting, &c. 1838. 8°.

朱 謀 㙔 CHOO MOW-WEI.

古 文 奇 字 *Koo wăn ke tsze.* "An Explanation of Curious Characters found in Ancient Literature." With an Index in manuscript. 12 keuen. 1612. 8°.

朱 錫 英 CHOO SEĬH-YING.

See 易 經 YĬH KING. 鹽 本 周 易 *Keen pun Chow Yĭh.* "The Book of Changes." Edited by Choo Seĭh-ying, &c. 1670. 8°.

朱 宷 諧 CHOO SHIN-KEAE.

See 薛 應 旂 SĔĔ YING-KE. 四 書 人 物 備 考 *Sze shoo jin wŭh pe kaou.* "An Examination of the Men and Things mentioned in the Four Books." .. With ... additions by Choo Shin-keae, &c. 8°.

朱 素 仙 CHOO SOO-SEEN.

玉 連 環 傳 *Yŭh leen hwan chuen.* "The Story of the Jade Ring." A Dramatic Tale. 8 keuen. 1805. 8°.

朱 思 本 Choo Sze-pun.

See 羅 洪 先 Lo Hung-seen. 廣 輿 圖 *Kwang yu too.* "An Atlas of the Chinese Empire." . . with the Maps of Choo Sze-pun, &c.
1579. Folio.

朱 鼎 臣 Choo Ting-chin.

全 像 觀 音 出 身 南 遊 記 傳 *Tscuen seang Kwan yin chŭh shin nan yew ke chuen.* "Records of a Journey to the South and of the Incarnation of the Goddess Kwan-yin. With Illustrations." Edited by Choo Ting-chin. 4 keuen. 1842. 8º.

朱 爲 弼 Choo Wei-pĭh.

See 屈 何 煥 Keŭh Ho-hwan. 萬 壽 恩 科 墨 卷 雅 正 *Wan show găn ko mĭh keuen ya ching.* "Elegant Essays, selected from those written for the Extra Examinations granted by Imperial favour in the year 1790." Edited by Choo Wei-pĭh," &c.
1790. 8º.

朱 惟 寅 Choo Wei-yin.

See 王 遜 齋 Wang Sun-chae. 註 釋 發 蒙 斜 度 初 集 *Choo shĭh fă mung chin too choo tseĭh.* "A Collection of Model Essays." . . Edited by Choo Wei-yin, &c. 1791. 8º.

朱 養 和 Choo Yang-ho.

See 管 仲 Kwan Chung. 管 子 評 註 *Kwan tsze ping choo.* "Kwan Chung's Work on Legislation." . . . Edited by Choo Yang-ho, &c.
1804. 8º.

朱 養 純 Choo Yang-tun.

See 管 仲 Kwan Chung. 管 子 評 註 *Kwan tsze ping choo.* "Kwan Chung's Work on Legislation. With Critical Notes" by . . . Choo Yang-tun, &c. 1804. 8º.

朱 元 寧 Choo Yuen-ning.

See 馮 李 驊 Fung Le-hwa, and Choo Yuen-ning. 初 學 小 題 明 文 鐏 *Choo heŏ seaou te ming wăn sew.* "Elegant Literary Essays." . . Compiled by Fung Le-hwa and Choo Yuen-ming, &c. 1730. 8º.

朱 雲 木 Choo Yun-mŭh.

粵 東 成 案 初 編 *Yuĕ tung ching gan choo peen.* "Judicial Record of Cases tried in the Province of Canton," between the years 1816 and 1828. Compiled by Choo Yun-mŭh. 38 keuen.
1832. 8º.

祿 宏 Choo Hung.

See 普 明 Poo Ming. 牧 牛 圖 *Mŭh new too.* "Tending the Cow. With Illustrations." . . Edited by Choo Hung, &c. 1609. 8º.

—— See 大 廣 智 Ta-kwang-che. 瑜 伽 集 要 施 食 儀 *Yu kea tseĭh yaou she shĭh e.* "The Yoga Rites of furnishing nourishment" to Hungry Ghosts. . . Edited by Choo Hung, &c.
Canton, 1737. 8º.

—— See 鳩 摩 羅 什 Kew-mo-lo-shĭh. 阿 彌 陀 經 疏 鈔 *Ah me to king soo chaou.* "The Amitabha Sûtra." . . Compiled by Choo Hung, &c. 1765. 8º.

—— 戒 殺 文 *Keae shă wăn.* "A Tract against Destroying Life." See 沈 培 木 Chin Pei-mŭh. 慈 心 寶 鑑 *Tsze sin paou keen.* "The Precious Mirror of a Merciful Heart," &c.
1771. 8º.

—— 瑜 伽 集 要 施 食 儀 *Yu kea tseĭh yaou she shĭh e.* "The Yoga Rites of furnishing nourishment" to Hungry Ghosts. Edited by Choo Hung. *Canton,* 1605. 8º.

—— 沙 彌 律 儀 要 略 *Sha me leŭh e yaou leŏ.* "An Epitome of Rules and Rites for Buddhist Novices." Compiled by Choo Hung.
[1760?]. 8º.

Another copy.

—— 沙 彌 律 儀 要 略 增 註 *Sha me leŭh e yaou leŏ tsăng choo.* "An Epitome of Rules and Rites for Buddhist Novices." Compiled by Choo Hung. With a Commentary by Hung Tsan. A Reprint. 2 keuen. *Canton,* 1762. 8º.

—— 諸 經 日 誦 集 要 *Choo king jĭh sung tseĭh yaou.* "A Collection of Daily Religious Exercises, taken from the various Sûtras." By the Priest Choo Hung. A Reprint. 2 keuen.
Canton, 1785. 8º.

—— 戒 殺 放 生 文 *Keae shă fang săng wăn.* "A Work against Destroying Life." By the Priest Choo Hung. *Canton,* [1790?]. 8º.

7

儲 欣 CHOO HIN. (*Continued.*)

西 漢 書 文 選 *Se Han shoo wăn seuen.* "Selections from the Literature of the Western Han Dynasty." Compiled by Choo Hin. 4 keuen.　　　　　　　　　1766. 8º.

—— 唐 宋 八 大 家 類 選 *Tang Sung pă ta kea luy seuen.* "Selections from the Works of Eight Scholars who flourished under the Tang and Sung Dynasties." Compiled by Choo Hin. Edited by Woo Chin-keen, Seu Yung-heun, Tung Nan-ke, &c. 14 keuen.　　1766. 8º.

Imperfect, wanting keuen 5 and 6.

駐 春 園 CHOO CHUN YUEN.

駐 春 園 小 史 *Choo chun yuen seaou she.* "The Tale of the Choo-chun-yuen" Pavilion. 6 keuen.　　　　　　　　　　　1783. 12º.

初 學 CHOO HEŎ.

初 學 作 文 意 路 *Choo heŏ tso wăn e loo.* "A Guide, for Beginners, to the Art of Literary Composition." A Collection of Model Essays.　　　　　　　　　　　[1800 ?]. 8º.

An odd volume.

周 CHOW.

佩 文 詩 韻 釋 要 *Pei wăn she yun shĭh yaou.* "An Epitomized Poetical Lexicon, arranged according to the Tones and Sounds of the Characters." Compiled by Chow. 5 keuen.　　　　　　　　　　　[1800 ?]. 8º.

Imperfect.

周 煇 CHOW CHEN.

北 轅 錄 *Pĭh yuen lŭh.* "An Account of a Journey to the North." See 說 SHWŎ. 說 選 *Shwŏ seuen.* "A Collection of Records," &c. 8º.

周 春 CHOW CHUN.

十 三 經 音 略 *Shĭh san king yin leŏ.* "A Treatise on the Original Sounds of the Thirteen Classics." 13 keuen. See 伍 崇 曜 WOO TSUNG-YAOU. 粤 雅 堂 叢 書 *Yuĕ ya Tang tsung shoo.* "The Yuĕ-ya Tang Collection of Reprints," &c. Series 11.　　1853. 8º.

周 煌 CHOW HWANG.

琉 球 國 志 略 *Lew kew kwŏ che leŏ.* "A Short Topography of the Lew kew Islands." 16 keuen.　　　　　　　　1759. 8º.

Another copy.

Imperfect.

周 暟 CHOW KAE.

黃 鶴 樓 *Hwang hŏ low.* "The Yellow Crane Pavilion." A Drama. 2 keuen.　　1795. 8º.

周 凱 CHOW KAE.

廈 門 志 *Hea mun che.* "A Topography of Amoy." Compiled by Chow Kae and others. 16 keuen.　　　　　　　　1839. 8º.

周 禮 CHOW LE.

周 禮 註 疏 *Chow le choo soo.* "The Chow Ritual. With Commentaries and Explanations." Compiled by Wang Ping-chung. Edited by Yĕ Pei-shoo. 30 keuen.　　　　　1639. 8º.

Imperfect, containing only keuen 1, 2, 20–26.

Another edition. 30 keuen.　　1792. 8º.

—— 周 禮 註 疏 *Chow le choo soo.* "The Chow Ritual. With a Commentary" by Ching Kang-ching, "and Expositions" made and collected by Kea Kung-yen. 21 keuen. [1792 ?]. 8º.

—— 周 禮 精 華 *Chow le tsing hwa.* "The Essential Points of the Chow Ritual." With a Commentary. Compiled by Chin Lung-peaou. Edited by Ke Heaou-lan. 6 keuen.　　1814. 8º.

周 密 CHOW MEĬH.

志 雅 堂 雜 鈔 *Che ya Tang tsă chaou.* "The Che-ya Tang Miscellany." 2 keuen. See 伍 崇 曜 WOO TSUNG-YAOU. 粤 雅 堂 叢 書 *Yuĕ ya Tang tsung shoo.* "The Yuĕ-ya Tang Collection of Reprints," &c. Series 1.　　　　　　　　　　　1853. 8º.

周 榤 CHOW YUN.

See 詩 經 SHE KING. 詩 序 廣 義 *She seu kwang e.* "The Book of Odes and its Preface fully explained." .. Edited by Chow Yun.　　　　　　　　　　　1815. 8º.

周 長 發 CHOW CHANG-FĂ.

See 張 廷 玉 CHANG TING-YŬH. 御 撰 資 治 通 鑑 明 紀 綱 目 *Yu chuen tsze che tung keen ming kĕ kang mŭh.* "A Condensed History of the Ming Dynasty." Compiled .... by Chow Chang-fă, &c.　　　1746. 8º.

周兆基 CHOW CHAOU-KE.

經義含睪 *King e han tsze.* "A Collection of Essays explanatory of Texts from the Five Classics." Compiled by Chow Chaou-ke, and edited by Chin Shen. 1810. 8°.

At the end of the work are a number of essays in manuscript. Title-page wanting.

周兆璧 CHOW CHAOU-PEĬH.

See 文昌帝君 WĂN CHANG TE KEUN. 陰隲 文圖說 *Yin chĭh wăn too shwŏ.* "A Treatise on Secret Rewards and Retributions . . . . Illustrated" by Chow Chaou-peĭh, &c. 8°.

周之炯 CHOW CHE-HING.

See 吳乘權 WOO SHING-KEUEN. 綱鑑易知錄 *Kang keen e che lŭh.* "The Mirror of History made easy." . . . By . . . Chow Che-hing, &c. 1711. 8°.

周之燦 CHOW CHE-TSAN.

See 吳乘權 WOO SHING-KEUEN. 綱鑑易知錄 *Kang keen e che lŭh.* "The Mirror of History made easy." . . . By . . . Chow Che-tsan, &c. 1711. 8°.

周之彥 CHOW CHE-YEN.

[Poetical Essays.] By Chow Che-yen and others. [1820 ?]. 8°.

A fragment.

周呈兆 CHOW CHING-CHAOU.

See 傅鸞祥 FOO LWAN-TSEANG. 六書分類 *Lŭh shoo fun luy.* "A Dictionary." . . Edited by Chow Ching-chaou, &c. 8°.

周仲箭 CHOW CHUNG-KEEN.

See 李兆洛 LE CHAOU-LŎ. 江陰縣志 *Keang yin heen che.* "A Topography of Keang-yin Heen." . . Compiled by . . . Chow Chung-keen, &c. 1840. 8°.

周𤪐巖 CHOW HEANG-YEN.

新墨鴻裁 *Sin mĭh hung tsae.* "A Choice Selection of Essays." Compiled by Chow Heang-yen. 1798. 8°.

周興嗣 CHOW HING-SZE.

千字文釋義 *Tseen tsze wan shĭh e.* "The Thousand-Character Classic Explained" by Sun Keen-yĭh. Edited by Wang Seaou-yin. [1800 ?]. 8°.

There are four copies of this work.

—— 會元千字文 *Hwuy yuen tseen tsze wăn.* "The Hwuy yuen's Thousand-Character Classic." [1800 ?]. 8°.

—— 千字文艸法 *Tseen tsze wăn tsaou fă.* "The Thousand-Character Classic in the Running Hand." Edited by Chin Pĭh-sha. [1800 ?]. 12°.

Another edition. [1800 ?]. 8°.

—— 千字文篆書 *Tseen tsze wăn chuen shoo.* "The Thousand-Character Classic in the Seal Character." Edited by Woo Chĭh-heen. 1803. 8°.

—— 千字文註釋 *Tseen tsze wăn choo shĭh.* "The Thousand-Character Classic, commented on and explained" by Hoo Yuen-chĭh. Edited by Chow Shĭh-foo. [1820 ?]. 8°.

—— 千字文隸法 *Tseen tsze wăn le fă.* "The Thousand-Character Classic, in the Abbreviated Form of Character," which was introduced by the Emperor Tsin. 1822. 8°.

周日澧 CHOW JĬH-LEEN.

See 朱竹垞 CHOO CHŬH-TSĬH. 朱竹垞先生 詩鈔 *Choo Chŭh-tsĭh seen săng she chaou.* "The Poems of Dr. Choo Chŭh-tsĭh." Compiled by Chow Jĭh-leen, &c. 12°.

周家棟 CHOW KEA-TUNG.

See 馮琦 FUNG KE. 經濟類編 *King tse luy peen.* "Aids to Classical Literature." . . Edited by . . . Chow Kea-tung, &c. 1604. 8°.

周克復 CHOW KĬH-FŬH.

金剛持驗紀 *Kin kang che neen ke.* "Records of the Effects of Studying the 'Diamond Classic,'" preceded by a copy of the *Kin kang pan jŏ po lo meĭh king.* Edited by Chin Tse-săng. 2 keuen. *Canton,* 1799. 8°.

周 桂 山 CHOW KWEI-SHAN.

 See 老君 LAOU KEUN. 感應篇 *Kan ying peen.* "The Book of Rewards and Punishments." . . Edited by Chow Kwei-shan, &c.
         1833. 8º.

周 蘭 九 CHOW LAN-KEW.

 See 吳遵程 WOO TSUN-CHING. 本草從新 *Pun tsaou tsung sin.* "A Newly-arranged Materia Medica." Edited by Chow Lan-kew, &c.
         1817. 8º.

周 亮 工 CHOW LEANG-KUNG.

 讀畫錄 *Tŭh hwa lŭh.* "Biographical Notices of Students of Painting." [Also] 尺牘新鈔 *Chĭh tŭh sin chaou.* "A New Letter-writer." Compiled by Chow Leang-kung. 12 keuen. *See* 葉志洗 YE CHE-SIN. 海山仙館叢書 *Hae shan seen kwan tsung shoo.* "The Hae shan seen Kwan Collection of Reprints," &c. Vol. 87, 89–92.
         1848. 8º.

—— 字觸 *Tsze chŭh.* "On the Analyses of Chinese Characters." 6 keuen. *See* 伍崇曤 WOO TSUNG-YAOU. 粵雅堂叢書 *Yuĕ ya Tang tsung shoo.* "The Yuĕ-ya Tang Collection of Reprints," etc. Series 7.
         1853. 8º.

周 亮 登 CHOW LEANG-TĂNG.

 See 龔雲林 KUNG YUN-LIN. 萬病回春 *Wan ping hwuy chun.* "The Ten Thousand Diseases which return with the Spring." . . . Edited by Chow Leang-tăng, &c. 1821. 8º

周 亮 節 CHOW LEANG-TSĔĔ.

 See 孫思邈 SUN SZE-MŎ. 銀海精微 *Yen hae tsing wei.* "The Essence and Delicacy of the Silver Seas." . . . Edited by Chow Leang-tsĕĕ, &c.   8º.

周 濂 溪 CHOW LEEN-KE.

 See 汪佑 WANG YEW. 五子近思錄 *Woo tsze kin sze lŭh.* "Records of the Approximating Thoughts of the Five Philosophers," Chow Leen-ke, &c.   1693. 8º.

周 目 藻 CHOW MŬH-TSAOU.

 四書詩題 *Sze shoo she te.* "Essays on Themes from the Four Books." Published by Authority. Compiled by Chow Mŭh-tsaou. Edited by Hwang Joo-tĭh, Koo Poo, &c. [1790?]. 8º.

周 夢 顏 CHOW MUNG-YEN.

 See 文昌帝君 WAN CHANG TE KEUN. 陰騭文廣義節錄 *Yin chĭh wăn kwang e tseĭh lŭh.* "The Full Meaning of . . . the Treatise on Secret Rewards and Retributions." By Chow Mung-yen, &c.   1828. 8º.

周 伯 琦 CHOW PĬH-KE.

 六書正譌 *Lŭh shoo ching go.* "Mistakes in the Use of the Six Kinds of Characters Corrected." 5 keuen. [1700?]. 8º.

周 世 緒 CHOW SHE-SEU.

 句東試帖 *Kow tung she tĕĕ.* "Kow-tung Examination Poetry." Compiled by Chow She-seu. 4 keuen.   1815. 8º.

—— 註釋句東試帖 *Choo shĭh kow tung she tĕĕ.* "Kow-tung Examination Poetry. With Explanatory Notes." Compiled by Chow She-seu. 8 keuen.   1824. 8º.

 Another edition of the above. Imperfect, containing only keuen 1–5.

周 世 樟 CHOW SHE-CHANG.

 五經類編 *Woo king luy peen.* "Quotations from the Five Classics, arranged according to their subjects." With Notes. By Chow She-chang. 28 keuen.   1724. 8º.

A new edition. 28 keuen.   1773. 8º.

周 石 帆 CHOW SHĬH-FAN.

 See 周大樞 CHOW TA-CHOO. 應試排律精選鯨鏗集 *Ying she pae leŭh tsing seuen king kăng tseĭh.* "The King-kăng Collection of Successful Poetical Examination Essays." Edited by . . . . . Chow-Shĭh-fan, &c. 1758. 8º.

周 實 夫 CHOW SHĬH-FOO.

 See 周興嗣 CHOW HING-SZE. 千字文註釋 *Tseen tsze wăn choo shĭh.* "The Thousand-Character Classic." . . Edited by Chow Shĭh-foo, &c.   8º.

周 聖 化 CHOW SHING-HWA.

 定海縣志 *Ting hae heen che.* "A Topography of Tinghae Heen" in Chusan. Compiled by Chow Shing-hwa. Edited by Mŭh Suy. 8 keuen.
         1715. 8º.

Another copy.

 Imperfect, containing only keuen 1, 4–8.

CHO [53] CHO

周 守 忠 CHOW SHOW-CHUNG.
姝 聯 *Choo leen.* "A String of Beauties." *See* 閔 景 賢 MIN KING-HEEN. 快 書 *Kwae shoo.* "A Book of Amusement," &c. Keuen 23.
1626. 8°.

周 思 兼 CHOW SZE-KEEN.
稿 *Kaou.* "Essays." *See* 長 城 CHANG CHING. 名 家 制 義 *Ming kea che e.* "Essays" on Texts from the Four Books, &c. Tsih 47.
1699. 8°.

周 大 樞 CHOW TA-CHOO.
應 試 枇 律 精 選 鯨 鏗 集 *Ying she pae leŭh tsing seuen king kang tseĭh.* "The King-kăng Collection of Successful Poetical Examination Essays." By Authors of the Tang and later Dynasties. Compiled by Chow Ta-choo. Edited by Kew Man-sze and Chow Shĭh-fan. With Notes by Teĭh Che-woo and Shin Tsan-hwuy. 6 keuen.
1758. 8°.

—— 應 試 五 枇 精 選 *Ying she woo pae tsing seuen.* "A Collection of Model Poetical Essays in Pentameter Verses." Compiled and Annotated by Chow Ta-choo. Edited by Kew Mwan-sze and Shin Hwŭh-shan. 5 keuen. [1758 ?]. 8°. Imperfect, containing only keuen 2–5.

周 達 觀 CHOW TĂ-KWAN.
誠 齋 雜 記 *Ching chae tsă ke.* "Miscellaneous Records from the Study of Truth." *See* 說 SHWŏ. 說 郛 *Shwŏ foo.* "Odds and Ends," &c.
8°.

—— 眞 臘 風 士 記 *Chin lă fung too che.* "An Account of Cambodia." *See* 說 SHWŏ. 說 選 *Shwŏ seuen.* "A Collection of Records," &c. 8°.

周 旦 林 CHOW TAN-LIN.
See 孔 丘 KUNG KEW. 春 秋 體 註 大 全 合 參 *Chun Tsew te choo ta tseuen hŏ tsan.* "The Spring and Autumn Annals." . . Compiled by Chow Tan-lin, &c.
1711. 8°.

—— See 禮 記 LE KE. 禮 記 體 註 大 全 合 參 *Le ke te choo ta tseuen hŏ tsan.* "The Book of Rites." . . Edited by Chow Tan-lin, &c.
1711. 8°.

周 鼎 臣 CHOW TING-CHIN.
增 訂 敬 信 錄 *Tsăng ting king sin lŭh.* "Works on Reverence and Faith." Compiled by Chow Ting-chin. Edited by Yin Ke-shen. 1769. 8°.

Another edition. 1786. 8°.

Another edition. *Ningpo,* 1795. 8°. There are eleven copies of this edition.

Another edition. *Canton,* 1799. 8°.

Another copy.
Imperfect.

Another edition. *Canton,* 1818. 8°. There are three copies of this edition.

Another edition. 1820. 8°.
Imperfect.

Another edition. *Tae chow,* [1820 ?]. 8°.

Another edition. *Keang-ning,* 1827. 8°. There are five copies of this edition.

Another edition. 1837. 8°.

周 祥 鈺 CHOW TSEANG-YŬH.
九 宮 大 成 南 北 詞 宮 譜 *Kew kung ta ching nan pĭh tsze kung poo.* "A Collection of Southern and Northern Rhymes, with their appropriate Airs." Compiled by Chow Tseang-yŭh and Tsow Kin-săng; and arranged by Seu Hing-hwa, Wang Wăn-lŭh, and others. 61 keuen.
[1800 ?]. 8°.
Imperfect, containing only keuen 42–61.

周 清 原 CHOW TSING-YUEN.
游 雁 蕩 山 記 *Yew yen tang shan ke.* "Rambles in the Yen-tang Mountains." *See* 鈴 LING. 說 鈴 *Shwŏ ling.* "Miscellaneous Records," &c. 8°.

周 子 安 CHOW TSZE-GAN.
五 知 齋 琴 譜 *Woo che chae Kin poo.* "The Music Book for the Kin, or Chinese Lyre, from the Study of the Five Intelligencies." Edited by Seu Ki. 8 keuen. 1746. 8°.

周 敦 頤 CHOW TUN-E.

太 極 圖 *Tae keǐh too.* "On the First Cause. With Illustrations." [Also] 通 書 *Tung shoo.* "The Complete Book" on Philosophy. *See* 李 光 地 LE KWANG-TE. 性 理 精 義 *Sing le tsing e.* "The Essence of Works on Mental Philosophy," &c. Keuen 1. 1715. 8º.

周 統 學 CHOW TUNG-HEŎ.

See 孔 丘 KUNG KEW. 春 秋 三 傳 通 經 合 纂 *Chun tsew san chuen tung king hŏ tswan.* "The Spring and Autumn Annals." . . Compiled by Chow Tung-heŏ, &c. 8º.

周 揚 熙 CHOW YANG-HE.

See 甘 馭 麟 KAN YU-LIN. 四 書 類 典 賦 *Sze shoo luy teen foo.* "Odes on Subjects from the Four Books." . . . . . Edited by . . Chow Yang-he, &c. 1777. 8º.

周 瀛 橋 CHOW YING-KEAOU.

See 曹 之 升 TSAOU CHE-SHING. 典 制 文 琳 註 釋 *Teen che wǎn lin choo shǐh.* "A Collection of Choice Essays." . . With Notes by Chow Ying-keaou, &c. 1804. 8º.

周 羽 沖 CHOW YU-CHUNG.

三 楚 新 錄 *San Tsoo sin lǔh.* "A New Record of the three Tsoo Provinces." 3 keuen. *See* 說 SHWŎ. 說 選 *Shwŏ seuen.* "A Collection of Records," &c. 8º.

周 愚 峰 CHOW YU-FUNG.

古 人 說 畧 *Koo jin shwŏ leŏ.* "Minor Works by Ancient Authors." Compiled by Chow Yu-fung. 1673. 8º.

周 遠 振 CHOW YUEN-CHIN.

See 沈 清 塵 CHIN TSING-CHIN, and CHOW YUEN-CHIN. 西 方 公 據 *Se fang kung keu.* "A Collection of Excerpta." . . Compiled by Chin Tsing-chin and Chow Yuen-chin, &c. 1804. 8º.

周 允 振 CHOW YUN-CHIN.

See 葉 九 升 YE KEW-SHING. 地 理 山 法 全 書 *Te le shan fǎ tseuen shoo.* "The Laws of Mountains." . . The twelfth keuen is edited, with notes, by Chow Yun-chin, &c. 8º.

CHRISTIANITY.

[An Outline of Christianity. In verse. 1840?] 8º.

傳 晟 CHUEN-SHING.

See 鳩 摩 羅 什 KEW-MO-LO-SHǏH. 菩 薩 戒 疏 義 *Poo să keae soo e.* "The Precepts of Buddha, with an Explanation of their Meaning." . . . Edited by Chuen-shing. 8º.

—— See 般 刺 密 諦 PWAN-LĂ-MEǏH-TE. 楞 嚴 經 集 註 *Lăng yen king tseǐh choo.* "The Certain and Firm Sutra . . with a Collection of Comments," compiled by Chuen-shing. 1735. 8º.

—— 心 經 直 指 *Sin king chǐh che.* "A Guide to the Heart Sutra." A Buddhist tract. By Chuen-shing. [1800?]. 8º.

傳 晟 CHUEN-YEN.

比 丘 戒 本 疏 義 *Pe kew keae pun soo e.* "A Code of Rules for Buddhist Bhikshus, with full explanations." Compiled by the Priest Chuen-yen. 2 keuen. 1735. 8º.

Another copy.

傳 檀 越 度 CHUEN-TAN-YUĔ-TOO.

See 一 鷟 靈 峻 YǏH-TSEW-LING-TSEUN. 經 懺 直 音 *King tsan chǐh yin.* "The Correct Sounds of Characters used in the Buddhist Sutras and Liturgical Works." . . Edited by . . Chuen-tan-yuĕ-too, &c. 1745. 8º.

船 CHUEN.

安 船 醮 科 *Gan chuen tseaou ko.* "A Sacrificial Form of Prayer for the Safety of Vessels," and other Taouist Rituals. [1780?]. 8º.

竹 CHǓH.

竹 譜 *Chǔh poo.* "Sketches of Bamboos." [1800?]. 8º.

竹 莊 CHǓH CHWANG.

晚 笑 堂 畫 傳 *Wan seaou Tang hwa chuen.* "The Evening-laughter Hall Collection of Illustrated Biographies." 3 keuen. 1743. 8º.

丛 法 蘭 CHŬH-FĂ-LAN.

See 迦 葉 摩 騰 KEA-YĔ-MO-TĂNG, and CHŬH-
FĂ-LAN [*i.e.* Kasyapa Matanga and Chufalan].
佛 說 四 十 二 章 經 *Fŭh shwŏ sze shĭh urh
chang king.* "The Sutra of Forty-two Sections,"
&c. 1727. 8º.

祝 子 CHŬH TSZE.

環 碧 齋 小 言 *Hwan peĭh chae seaou yen.*
"Jottings from the Hwan peĭh Study." *See*
閔 景 賢 MIN KING-HEEN. 快 書 *Kwae shoo.*
"A Book of Amusement," &c. Keuen 16.
1626. 8º.

鬻 熊 CHŬH HEUNG.

鬻 子 *Chŭh tsze.* "The Writings of the Philosopher Chŭh." *See* 沈 津 CHIN TSIN. 百 家
類 纂 *Pĭh kea luy tswan.* "The Works of a
Hundred Authors," &c. Keuen 28. 8º.

春 芳 CHUN FANG.

See 張 楠 CHANG NAN. 神 岸 闢 謬 正 宗
Shin fung peĭh mew ching tsung. "A Critical
Examination in the Laws of Destiny." . . Edited
by Chun Fang, &c. 8º.

春 溪 居 士 CHUN-KE KEU-SZE.

See 闈 WEI. 棘 闈 勸 戒 錄 *Keĭh wei keuen
keae lŭh.* "Admonitory Records." . . By the
Retired Scholar of Chun ke, &c. 1809. 8º.

春 秋 CHUN TSEW.

春 秋 文 苞 *Chun tsew wăn paou.* "Literary
Husks to Texts from the Spring and Autumn
Annals." Being a Collection of Essays.
[1700 ?]. 12º.

—— 春 秋 擬 題 類 典 *Chun Tsew e te luy teen.*
"Classified Essays on Texts from the Spring and
Autumn Annals" [1790 ?]. 24º.

春 燕 CHUN WOO.

春 燕 記 *Chun woo ke.* "The Story of the Chun
woo." *See* 曲 KEŬH. 六 十 種 曲 *Lŭh shĭh
chung keŭh.* Sixty Plays, &c. Taou 3. 8º.

鍾 嶸 CHUNG HĂNG.

詩 品 *She pin.* "Poetry Classified." By Chung
Hăng, of the Leang Dynasty. A Reprint. 3
keuen. [1750 ?]. 8º.

鍾 輅 CHUNG LOO.

前 定 錄 *Tseen ting lŭh.* "A Record of Pre-
ordained Events." *See* 王 文 誥 WANG WĂN-
KAOU. 唐 代 叢 書 *Tang tae tsung shoo.* "A
Collection of Reprints of Works written during
the Tang Dynasty, &c. Series 5. 1806. 8º.

鍾 惺 CHUNG SING.

See 面 MEEN. 如 面 談 *Joo meen tan.* "Conversations." By Chung Sing. 8º.

鍾 英 CHUNG YING.

See 端 木 賜 TWAN MŬH-SZE. 詩 傳 *She chuen.*
"A Commentary on the Book of Odes." . . Edited
by Chung Ying, &c. 8º.

鍾 離 權 CHUNG-LE KEUEN.

傳 道 集 *Chuen taou tseĭh.* "The Opinions of
Leu Yen, and Chung-le Keuen, collected for the
Promulgation of Taou." [Also] 靈 寶 畢 法
Ling paou peĭh fă. "The Spiritual, Precious,
and Final Law." [Also] 破 迷 正 道 歌
Po me ching taou ko. "The Chant of the true
Taou for breaking through the Trammels of
Sensuality." *See* 彭 好 古 PĂNG HAOU-KOO.
道 言 內 外 秘 訣 全 書 *Taou yen nuy wae
pe keuĕ tseuen shoo.* "A Complete Collection of
Taouist Works," &c. Part I. Keuen 2, 3. 8º.

鍾 伯 敬 CHUNG PĬH-KING.

See 陳 明 卿 CHIN MING-KING, and CHUNG PĬH-
KING. 國 語 國 策 詳 注 *Kwŏ yu kwŏ tsĭh
tseang choo.* "Narrative of the States . . . and
the Story of the Contending States," &c.
1724. 8º.

—— 封 神 演 義 *Fung shin yen e.* "The Story of
the Appointed Genii." A Tale regarding the
adventures of Woo Wang, the founder of the
Chow Dynasty, in his contest with Chow Wang,
the last of the House of Shang. 1695. 8º.

Another edition. 20 keuen. 1813. 8º.

—— 東 西 漢 全 傳 *Tung se Han tseuen chuen.*
"The Story of the Eastern and Western Han
Dynasties." An Historical Novel. With Illustrations. Edited by Chung Pĭh-king. 8 keuen.
[1820 ?]. 12º.

鍾泰華 CHUNG TAE-HWA.

文苑四史 *Wăn yuen sze she.* "The Four Historians of the Literary Garden." *See* 閔景賢 MIN KING-HEEN. 快書 *Kwae shoo.* "A Book of Amusement," &c. Keuen 48.
1626. 8°.

種崇伃 CHUNG TSUNG-KWAN.

See 馬融 MA-YUNG. 忠經 *Chung king.* "The Classic on Patriotism." .. Edited by Chung Tsung-kwan, &c. 8°.

種崇保 CHUNG TSUNG-PAOU.

See 陶潛 TAOU TSEEN. 孝傳 *Heaou chuen.* "Stories of Filial Piety." .. Edited by Chung Tsung-paou, &c. 8°.

種于序 CHUNG YU-SEU.

宗規 *Tsung kwei.* "Family Customs." *See* 張山來 CHANG SHAN-LAE, and 張進也 CHANG TSIN-YAY. 昭代叢書 *Chaou tae tsung shoo.* "A Collection of Reprints of Works by Authors under the present Dynasty," &c. Keuen 18.
1703. 8°.

種德者 CHUNG-TĬH-CHAY. *pseud.* [*i.e.* Rev. David Collie.]

See BIBLE. *Appendix.* 聖經釋義 *Shing king shĭh e.* "Scripture Explained." By Chung-tĭh-chay, &c. 1835. 8°.

—— *See* BIBLE. *Appendix.* 節錄聖經釋義 *Tsëĕ lŭh shing king shĭh e.* "Scripture Explained." By Chung-tĭh-chay, &c. 8°.

—— 天鏡明鑑 *Teen king ming heen.* "The Bright Reflection of Heaven's Mirror." 2 keuen.
1826. 8°.
Another copy.

—— 耶穌言行總論 *Yay soo yen hing tsung lun.* "The Life of Christ." In verse. 1826. 8°.

中興 CHUNG HING.

中興禦侮錄 *Chung hing yu woo lŭh.* "An Account of an Insurrection" which broke out during the Sung Dynasty. 2 keuen. *See* 伍崇曜 WOO TSUNG-YAOU. 粤雅堂叢書 *Yuĕ ya Tang tsung shoo.* "The Yuĕ-ya Tang Collection of Reprints." Series 13. 1853. 8°.

中山 CHUNG SHAN.

中山狼傳 *Chung shan Lang chuen.* "A Story of the Chung shan Wolves." *See* 說 SHWŏ. 說淵 *Shwŏ yuen.* "A Collection of Tales," &c. 8°.

仲鶴慶 CHUNG HŏKING.

See 趙廷健 CHAOU TING-KEEN. 崇明縣志 *Tsung-ming heen che.* "A Topography of Tsung-ming Heen." .. Edited by Chung Hŏ-king, &c.
1760. 8°.

忠 CHUNG.

昭忠錄 *Chaou chung lŭh.* "Records of Illustrious Patriots" under the Sung Dynasty. *See* 伍崇曜 WOO TSUNG-YAOU. 粤雅堂叢書 *Yuĕ ya Tang tsung shoo.* "The Yuĕ-ya Tang Collection of Reprints, &c. Series 2. 1853. 8°.

蟲 CHUNG.

禳災載蟲保卉科儀 *Jang tsae tsze chung paou hwuy ko e.* "A Ritual to be employed at the Sacrifices for dispelling Insects destructive to Trees and Shrubs." Taouist work. 1849. 8°.

贅言改 CHUY YEN-KAE.

螢燈 *Yung tăng.* "Glowworm Lamps." *See* 閔景賢 MIN KING-HEEN. 快書 *Kwae shoo.* "A Book of Amusement," &c. Keuen 4.
1626. 8°.

瑞蘭 CHUY-LAN.

瑞蘭分別搶傘全本 *Chuy-lan fun pĕĕ tsang san tseuen pun.* "The Story of the Separation of Chuy-lan" from her mother. 4 keuen.
[1850?]. 8°.

莊周 CHWANG CHOW.

南華眞經 *Nan hwa chin king.* "The Nan hwa Classic." *See* 沈津 CHIN TSIN. 百家類纂 *Pĭh kea luy tswan.* "The Works of a Hundred Authors," &c. Keuen 14, 15. 8°.

—— 南華經 *Nan kwa king.* "The Nan hwa Classic." *See* 程潘基 CHING PWAN-KE. 老莊會解 *Laou Chwang hwuy keae.* "The Works of Laou keun and Chwang chow," &c. 8°.

莊周 CHWANG CHOW.

南華眞經 *Nan hwa chin king.* "The Nan hwa Classic." *See* 黃海岸 HWANG HAE-GAN. 周秦十一子 *Chow Tsin shǐh yǐh tsze.* "The Works of the Eleven Philosophers of the Chow and Tsin Dynasties," &c.   8º.

—— 南華眞經 *Nan hwa chin king.* "The Nan hwa Classic." With a Commentary by Kŏ Seang. *See* 黃丕烈 HWANG PEI-LĔĔ. 九子全書 *Kew tsze tseuen shoo.* "The Complete Works of the Nine Philosophers," &c. Keuen 8, 9.   1804. 8º.

—— *See* 黃丕烈 HWANG PEI-LĔĔ. 十子全書 *Shǐh tsze tseuen shoo.* "The Complete Works of the Ten Philosophers," &c.   1804. 8º.

—— 南華經 *Nan hwa king.* "The Nan hwa Classic." With Commentaries by Kŏ Seang and others. *See* 焦竑 TSEAOU HUNG. 老莊翼合刻 *Laou Chwang yǐh hŏ kǐh.* "The Works of Laou keun and Chwang Chow," &c. Keuen 1–8.   1588. 8º.

—— 莊子註釋評林 *Chwang tsze choo shǐh ping lin.* "The Nan hwa Classic by Chwang Chow, commented upon and explained by Tseaou Hung, with a Collection of Criticisms" by Ung Ching-chun. 10 keuen.   [1750?]. 8º.
    Imperfect, containing only keuen 1.

—— 南華眞經副墨 *Nan hwa chin king foo mǐh.* "A Guide to the Nan hwa king." By Lǔh Se-sing, Le Tse-fang, and others. 4 keuen.   1578. 8º.

—— 南華經 *Nan hwa king.* "The Nan hwa Classic." With notes by Kŏ Seang and Heang Sew of the Tsin Dynasty. A Reprint. 5 keuen. 1716. 8º.

—— 南華內篇別解 *Nan hwa nuy peen pĕĕ keae.* "The First Part of the Nan hwa Classic explained" by Tseǐh Shan-tsew. Edited by Wang Chow-san and others. 7 sections. 1721. 8º.

—— 齊物論 *Tse wǔh lun.* "A Discussion on Regulated Matter." A Part of the Nan hwa king. With manuscript notes by J. F. Fouquet.   [1750?]. 8º.

狀元 CHWANG YUEN.

狀元幼學詩 *Chwang yuen yew hŏ she.* "The "Chwang Yuen's Poetry for Young Students."   [1830?]. 8º.

莊逵吉 CHWANG KWEI-KEǏH.

See 劉安 LEW GAN. 淮南子箋釋 *Hwae nan tsze tseen shǐh.* "The Treatise of .. the Prince of Hwae nan on the Doctrine of Taou.". Edited by Chwang Kwei-keǐh, &c. 1804. 8º.

莊存與 CHWANG TSUN-YU.

春秋正辭 *Chun Tsew ching tsze.* "The Language of the Spring and Autumn Annals Determined and Regulated." 13 keuen. *See* 嚴杰 YEN LĔĔ. 皇清經解 *Hwang Tsing king keae.* "The Classics Explained," &c. Keuen 375–387.   1829. 8º.

莊有恭 CHWANG YEW-KUNG.

See 尹繼善 YIN KE-SHEN. 直隸通州志 *Chǐh le Tung chow che.* "A Topography of Tung Chow.".. Compiled by ... Chwang Yew-kung, &c.   1755. 8º.

莊元臣 CHWANG YUEN-CHIN.

叔苴子 *Shǔh tseu tsze.* "Gathering Hemp Seeds." A Work on Metaphysics. 8 keuen. *See* 伍崇曜 WOO TSUNG-YAOU. 粵雅堂叢書 *Yuĕ ya Tang tsung shoo.* "The Yuĕ-ya Tang Collection of Reprints," &c. Series 3.   1853. 8º.

ÇIKSHÂNANDA.

See 實叉難陀 SHǏH-CHA-NAN-TO.

COBBOLD (ROBERT HENRY).

See 眞理 CHIN LE. 眞理摘要 *Chin le teǐh yaou.* "Gleanings of Truth." By Rev. R. H. Cobbold, &c.   1856. 8º.

—— *See* 編 PEEN. 指迷編 *Che me peen.* "Directions for the Misguided." By Rev. R. H. Cobbold.   1857. 8º.

COLLIE (DAVID).

See 種德者 CHUNG-TǏH-CHAY.

CONDIT (IRA MILLER).

See 地理 TE LE. 地理問答 *Te le wǎn tă.* "A Catechism on Geography." By I. M. Condit, &c.   1865. 8º.

8

COOKERY.

Foreign Cookery in Chinese, with a Preface and Index in English. Chinese. *Shanghae*, 1866. 8º.

Has also a Chinese title, viz.: Tsaou yang fan shoo.

CRAWFORD (TARLETON P   ).

See 高 第 丕 KAOU TE PEI.

—— 臼 伊 木 扣 *Sung kiung tsĭh loh.* "Bible Stories." Written in the Shanghai dialect, and printed in a new phonetic character. *Shanghae*, 1857. 8º.

DANIEL. THE PROPHET.

See 善 德 者 SHEN-TĬH-CHAY. 但 耶 利 言 行 全 傳 *Tan-yay-le yen hing tseuen chuen.* "The Life of the Prophet Daniel," &c. 1837. 8º.

DEAN, WILLIAM.

See BIBLE. OLD TESTAMENT. *Genesis.* 創 世 傳 註 釋 *Chwang she chuen choo shĭh.* "The Book of Genesis. With a Commentary" by . . . [William Dean]. 1851. 8º.

DIAZ (P. EMMANUEL).

See 陽 瑪 諾 YANG-MA-NŎ.

DICTIONARIES.

繡 刻 圖 像 雜 字 *Sew kĭh too seang tsă tsze.* "A Pictorial Vocabulary." [1800?]. 8º.

Another copy.

Another copy.

DIVÂKARA.

See 地 婆 訶 羅 TE-PO-HO-LO.

DYER (SAMUEL).

See 福 音 FŬH YIN. 福 音 總 論 *Fŭh yin tsung lun.* "A Discourse on the Gospel." . . By S. Dyer. 1839. 12º.

宣 E.

宣 政 雜 錄 *E Ching tsă lŭh.* "Miscellaneous Records of the Reigns of E-ho and Ching-ho." *See* 說 SHWŏ. 說 畧 *Shwŏ leŏ.* "Historical and other Tracts," &c. 8º.

醫 E.

古 今 醫 鑑 *Koo kin e keen.* "A Mirror of Ancient and Modern Medicine." [1790?]. 8º.

A Fragment.

醫 方 E FANG.

醫 方 考 *E fang kaou.* "Medical Prescriptions Examined." 4 keuen. [1700?]. 8º.

Imperfect, containing only keuen 4.

八 厂 E HAN.

鵪 鶉 論 *Gan shun lun.* "A Treatise on the Quail." 1775. 12º.

—— 畫 眉 譜 *Hwa mei poo.* "A Work on the Singing Thrush." 1753. 12º.

—— 黃 頭 誌 *Hwang tow che.* "An Account of the Yellow-head" Bird. 1776. 12º.

—— 促 織 經 *Tsŭh chĭh king.* "The Classic of the Cricket." 1775. 12º.

伊 齡 阿 E LING-AH.

See 杜 琳 TOO LIN. 淮 關 統 志 *Hwae kwan tung che.* "A Topography of the Hwae Custom-house Districts." . . Recast by E Ling-ah, &c. 1806. 8º.

伊 把 漢 E PA-HAN.

盛 京 通 志 *Shing king tung che.* "A Topography of the Metropolitan Province of Moukden." Compiled by E Pa-han, Mŭh Tae, Tung Paou, &c. 32 keuen. 1684. 8º.

倪 勖 E MAE.

彭 姥 詩 蒐 *Păng moo she sow.* "A Collection of Poetry," by Authors under the Sung, Yuen, Ming, and Tsing Dynasties. Compiled by E Mae. Edited by E Tsung-fŭh and E Tsung-tae. 12 keuen. 1827. 8º.

倪 晉 E TSIN.

See 龔 在 升 KUNG TSAE-SHING. 三 才 彙 編 *San tsae wei peen.* "An Encyclopædia." . . The second keuen . . is edited by E Tsin, &c. 8º.

倪 會 鼎 E HWUY-TING.

倪 文 正 公 年 譜 *E Wăn ching kung neen poo.* "A Chronological Record of the Life of E Wăn ching kung." By his son E Hwuy-ting. 4 keuen. See 伍 崇 曜 WOO TSUNG-YAOU. 粵 雅 堂 叢 書 *Yuĕ ya Tang tsung shoo.* "The Yuĕ-ya Tang Collection of Reprints," &c. Series 19. 1853. 8º.

倪魯玉 E Loo-yŭh.

See 庾子山 Yu Tsze-shan. 庾開府全集 箋注 Yu kae foo tseuen tseĭh tseen choo. "The .. Works of Yu Tsze-shan. With Notes" by E Loo-yŭh, &c. 8°.

倪宗澓 E Tsung-fŭh.

See 倪勵 E Mae. 彭城詩覽 Păng moo she sow. "A Collection of Poetry." . . . Edited by E Tsung-fŭh, &c. 1827. 8°.

倪宗泰 E Tsung-tae.

See 倪勵 E Mae. 彭城詩覽 Păng moo she sow. "A Collection of Poetry." . . . Edited by . . . . E Tsung-tae, &c. 1827. 8°.

倪允昌 E Yun-chang.

光明藏 Kwang ming tsang. "The Luminous and Bright Pitaka." See 閔景賢 Min King-heen. 快書 Kwae shoo. "A Book of Amusement," &c. Keuen 2. 1626. 8°.

儀禮 E le.

儀禮章句 E le chang keu. "The Decorum Ritual explained sentence by sentence" by Woo Ting-hwa. Edited by Fang Ling-kaou and Le Keu-lae. 17 keuen. 1757. 8°.
Imperfect, containing only keuen 1–5.

—— 儀禮註疏 E le choo soo. "The Decorum Ritual. With a Commentary" by Ching Kang-ching, "and Expositions" made and collected by Kea Yung-yen. 17 keuen. [1800?]. 8°.

EDKINS (Joseph).

See 艾約瑟 Gae Yŏ-sĭh.

—— See 艾約瑟迪謹 Gae Yŏ-sĭh Teĭh kin. 1857. 8°.

ENGLAND, Church of. Homilies.

勸讀聖錄諭知文 Keuen tŭh shing lŭh shŭh che wăn. "Exhortations to the Study of the Bible." The two first Homilies of the Church of England, translated into Chinese by Dr. Morrison. [1820?]. 8°.

Another copy.

Another copy.
Imperfect, containing only the first Homily.

EPHEMERIDES.

[An Astrological Almanac. Very imperfect, without either title-page or date.] [1800?]. 8°.

—— 中外通書 Chung wae tung shoo. "A Chinese and Foreign Almanac" for the Year 1858. Compiled by J. T. Points. To which are added three Tracts on Scriptural Subjects. 1858. 8°.

—— 和合通書 Ho hŏ tung shoo. "A Harmonized Almanac." An Illustrated Magazine, containing an English and Chinese Calendar, also short treatises on geography, natural history, &c. [Edited by J. B. French.] 2 Numbers. 1855–56. 8°.

—— 日書 Jih shoo. An Astrological "Almanac" for the Year 1798. 8°.

—— 康熙二十九年庚午日用集福通書 Kang he urh shĭh kew neen kăng woo jih yung tseĭh fŭh tung shoo. "An Astrological Almanac for the twenty-ninth year of the reign of the Emperor Kang-he [i.e. 1690]. 1690. 8°.

—— 欽定協紀辨方書日月表合鈔 Kin ting hĕĕ ke peen fang shoo jih yuĕ peaou hŏ chaou. "An Astrological Almanac, published under Imperial Patronage." Edited by Tan Tsuy. 1787. 8°.

—— 欽定選擇曆書 Kin ting seuen chĭh leĭh shoo. "A Select Astrological Almanac for the Cycle ending 1803 (?). 10 keuen (?). 8°.
Imperfect, containing only keuen 7, 8.

—— 欽定七政四餘萬年書 Kin ting tseĭh ching sze yu wan neen shoo. "An Ephemeris of the Sun, Moon, and Five Planets, with the places of the Moon's Perigee, Apogee, and Nodes," for the Years 1746 to 1775. Published by the Astronomical Board. [Peking], 1775. 8°.

—— For the Years 1735 to 1795. Published by the Astronomical Board. [Peking?], 1795. 8°.

EPHEMERIDES.　(*Continued.*)

大明中與永曆二十五年大統曆 *Ta Ming chung hing Yung leĭh urh shĭh woo neen ta tung leĭh.* "An Almanac for the twenty-fifth year of the reign of the Emperor Yung-leĭh, of the Ming Dynasty," *i.e.* 1671.　　1671.　8°.

Another copy.

—— 大全通書 *Ta tseuen tung shoo.* "A Complete Astrological Almanac" for the Year 1836.
　　　1836.　8°.

—— 大清康熙四十一年便民通書 *Ta Tsing Kang he sze shĭh yĭh neen peen min tung shoo.* "An Almanac for the forty-first year of the reign of the Emperor Kang-he," *i.e.* 1702.
　　　1702.　8°.

—— 大清康熙四十二年時憲曆 *Ta Tsing Kang he sze shĭh urh neen she heen leĭh.* "An Almanac for the forty-second year of the reign of the Emperor Kang-he," *i.e.* 1703.
　　　[*Peking* ?], 1703.　8°.

—— 大清乾隆四十七年時憲曆 *Ta Tsing Keen lung sze shĭh tseĭh neen she heen shoo.* "An Almanac for the forty-seventh year of the reign of the Emperor Keen-lung," *i.e.* 1782.
　　　[*Peking* ?], 1782.　8°.

—— 大清嘉慶二十五年時憲書 *Ta Tsing Kea king urh shĭh woo neen she heen shoo.* "An Almanac for the twenty-fifth year of the reign of the Emperor Kea-king," *i.e.* 1820.
　　　[*Peking* ?], 1820.　8°.

—— 大清道光六年時憲書 *Ta Tsing Taou kwang lüh neen she heen shoo.* "An Almanac for the sixth year of the reign of the Emperor Taou-kwang," *i.e.* 1826. [*Peking* ?], 1826. 8°.

—— 大清道光八年時憲書 *Ta Tsing Taou kwang pă neen she heen shoo.* "An Almanac for the eighth year of the reign of the Emperor Taou-kwang," *i.e.* 1828. [*Peking* ?], 1828. 8°.

—— 大清道光十一年時憲書 *Ta Tsing Taou kwang shĭh yĭh neen she heen shoo.* "An Almanac for the eleventh year of the reign of the Emperor Taou-kwang," *i.e.* 1831.
　　　[*Peking* ?], 1831.　8°.

EPHEMERIDES.　(*Continued.*)

大清道光二十年時憲書 *Ta Tsing Taou kwang urh shĭh neen she heen shoo.* "An Almanac for the twentieth year of the reign of the Emperor Taou-kwang," *i.e.* 1840.
　　　[*Peking* ?], 1840.　8°.

—— 大清道光二十一年時憲書 *Ta Tsing Taou kwang urh shĭh yĭh neen she heen shoo.* "An Almanac for the twenty-first year of the reign of the Emperor Taou-kwang," *i.e.* 1841.
　　　[*Peking* ?], 1841.　8°.

Another edition.　　　1841.　8°.

Another edition.　　　1841.　8°.

Another copy.

—— 大清咸豐二年時憲書 *Ta Tsing Heen fung urh neen she heen shoo.* "An Almanac for the second year of the reign of the Emperor Heen-fung," *i.e.* 1852.　　1852.　8°.

—— 大清同治六年時憲書 *Ta Tsing Tung che lüh neen she heen shoo.* "An Almanac for the sixth year of the reign of the Emperor Tung-che," *i.e.* 1867.　　1867.　8°.

—— 太平天國癸好三年新曆 *Tae ping Teen kwŏ kwei haou san neen sin leĭh.* "A New Calendar for the Kwei haou, or third year of the Tae-ping Dynasty," *i.e.* 1853.　*Nanking*, 1853.　8°.

Another edition.　　　*Nanking*, 1853.　8°.

—— 天主聖教瞻禮齋期表 *Teen choo shing keaou chen le chue ke peaou.* "A Calendar of the Festivals and Fasts of the Roman Catholic Church" for the Year 1736.　1736.　A Sheet.

—— 七政臺曆 *Tseĭh ching tae leĭh.* "An Ephemeris of the Sun, Moon, and Five Planets."
　　　[1750 ?].　8°.
　　　Imperfect.

———— For the Years 1776–82.　　1782.　8°.
　　　Imperfect.

———— For the Years 1804–13.　　1813.　8°.
　　　Imperfect.

EPHEMERIDES.　(*Continued.*)

諏吉便覽 *Tseu keĭh peen lan.* "A Handbook for choosing Lucky Days." A divinatory Almanac. Arranged by Fei Ta-sze-ma.
1818. 8º.

—— 趨避通書 *Tseu pe tung shoo.* "A divinatory Almanac" for the Year 1815.
Tseuen Chow, 1815. 8º.

Another copy.

——— For the Year 1824.　　　1824. 8º.

—— 御定七政四餘萬年書 *Yu ting tseĭh ching sze yuĕ wan neen shoo.* "An Ephemeris of the Sun, Moon, and Five Planets" for the Years 1775–95, 1821–40. Published by the Astronomical Board.　　[*Peking* ?], 1840. 8º.

EUCLID.

幾何原本 *Ke ho yuen pun.* Euclid's "Elements of Geometry." Translated into Chinese by Mathew Ricci. Edited by Rev. J. W. Quarterman.　　*Ningpo*, 1852. 8º.

法 FǍ.

法語 *Fă yu.* "Discourses on the Law." A Buddhist work. By the Priest of Chung fung.
Canton, 1751. 8º.

法 FǍ.

法筆駑天雷 *Fă peĭh king teen luy.* "The Pencil of the Law fears the Thunder of Heaven." A handbook to criminal procedure. 2 keuen.　　　[1800 ?]. 8º.
Imperfect, containing only part of keuen 1.

法顯 FǍ-HEEN.

佛國記 *Fŭh kwŏ ke.* "An Account of Buddhist Countries." A narrative of the travels of Fă-heen in Central Asia [where he went to obtain information and documents regarding the Buddhist religion]. Edited by Heu Heŭh-kung.
[1800 ?]. 8º.

法家 FǍ KEA.

法家駑天雷 *Fă kea king teen luy.* "Lawyers fear the Thunder of Heaven." A handbook of criminal procedure. 2 keuen.　[1800 ?]. 8º.

法藏 FǍ-TSANG.

大乘起信論直解 *Ta shing ke sin lun chĭh keae.* "A Treatise for promulgating the Faith of the Mahâyâna." Compiled by Fă-tsang. With a Commentary by Tĭh-tsing. 2 keuen.
1620. 8º.

法式善 FǍ SHĬH-SHEN.

See 洪瑩 HUNG YING, and FǍ SHĬH-SHEN. 同館試律 *Tung kwan shĭh leŭh.* "Examination Odes." ... Compiled by Hung Ying and Fă Shĭh-shen.　　　8º.

—— See 毛履謙 MAOU LE-KEEN, and 吳涵一 WOO HAN-YĬH. 十家詩詳註 *Shĭh kea she tseang choo.* "The Poetical Works of Ten Authors," viz.: . . . Fă Shĭh-shen, &c.
1813. 8º.

范攄 FAN CHOO.

雲溪友議 *Yun ke yew e.* "Friendly Discussions at Yun ke." See 王文誥 WANG WĂN-KAOU. 唐代叢書 *Tang tae tsung shoo.* "A Collection of Reprints of Works written during the Tang Dynasty," &c. Series 2.　　1806. 8º.

—— 雲溪友議 *Yun ke yew e.* "Friendly Discussions" at Yun ke. By Fan Choo, of the Tang Dynasty.　A Reprint. [1741 ?]. 8º.

范甯 FAN NING.

See 孔丘 KUNG KEW. 春秋穀梁傳註疏 *Chun tsew Kŏ-leang chuen choo soo.* "The Spring and Autumn Annals." With . . . a Collection of Comments compiled by Fan Ning, &c.　　8º.

范梧 FAN WOO.

See 李凱塡 LE KAE-TEEN. 寒香亭傳奇 *Han heang ting chuen ke.* "The Story of the Cool and Fragrant Pavilion." . . . Edited by Fan Woo, &c.　　　1797. 8º.

范曄 FAN YĔ.

後漢書 *How Han shoo.* "History of the Later Han Dynasty." With a Commentary by Lew Chaou. 120 keuen. See 毛晉 MAOU TSIN. 十七史 *Shĭh tseĭh she.* "The Seventeen Histories," &c.　　　1656. 8º.

范曄 FAN YĔ. (*Continued.*)

後漢書 *How Han shoo.* "The History of the Later Han Dynasty." With Notes by Prince Chang-hwae and Lew Chaou. 80 keuen.

1643. 8°.

Another copy.

Imperfect.

范昌治 FAN CHANG-CHE.

See 劉良璧 LEW LEANG-PEĬH. 臺灣府志 *Tae wan foo che.* "A Topography of Tae-wan Foo .... Compiled .. by ... Fan Chang-che, &c. 1741. 8°.

范長生 FAN CHANG-SĂNG.

蜀才周易注 *Shŭh tsae Chow Yĭh choo.* "Fan Shŭh-tsae's Notes on the Chow Changes." *See* 孫堂 SUN TANG. 漢魏二十一家易注 *Han Wei urh shĭh yĭh kea Yĭh choo.* "Commentaries on the Book of Changes," &c. 1799. 8°.

范成大 FAN CHING-TA.

桂海虞衡志 *Kwei hae yu hăng che.* "History of the Productions of the Rivers and Mountains of Kwei-lin." *See* 說 SHWŎ. 說選 *Shwŏ seuen.* "A Collection of Records," &c. Vol. 6. 8°.

范橫或 FAN HWANG-HWŎ.

元寶媒 *Yuen paou mei.* "The Fifty Tael Match-maker." [A Drama.] By Fan Hwang-hwŏ. The Lyrical Parts being by Ko seaou jin, 'the Laughable Man.' 2 keuen. [1700?]. 8°.

范稼軒 FAN KEA-HEEN.

See 詩經 SHE KING. 詩經說約集解 *She king shwŏ yŏ tseĭh keae.* "The Book of Odes" .. Edited by Fan Kea-heen, &c. 1688. 8°.

范世勳 FAN SHE-HEUN.

桃花泉碁譜 *Taou hwa tseuen ke poo.* "The Peach-Blossom-Spring Chess Book." 2 keuen.

1765. 8°.

Imperfect, containing only keuen 1.

范司馬 FAN SZE-MA.

See CATALOGUES. 天一閣書目 *Teen yĭh kŏ shoo mŭh.* "A Catalogue of the Library" collected ... by Fan Sze-ma, &c. 1808. 8°.

范題名 FAN TE-MING.

五經題解集要 *Woo king te keae tseĭh yaou.* "A Collection of Essays explanatory of Texts from the Five Classics." By Fan Te-ming, Tseen Tsing-seuen, Tseang Hing-maou, and Yang Shing-ho. [1750?]. 12°.

Imperfect, containing only essays on texts from the Shoo king and the She king.

—— 袖珍五經題旨 *Sew chin Woo king te che.* "Essays on Texts from the Five Classics. Pocket Edition." By Fan Te-ming, Tseen Tsing-seuen, Tseang Hing-maou, &c.

1850. 24°.

Another edition of the above. Imperfect, wanting essays on texts from the She king.

范清洪 FAN TSING-HUNG.

See 史鳴臯 SHE MING-KAOU. 象山縣志 *Seang shan heen che.* "A Topography of Seang-shan Heen" ... Compiled by .. Fan Tsing-hung, &c. 1756. 8°.

范紫登 FAN TSZE-TĂNG.

See 孔丘 KUNG KEW. 春秋體註大全合參 *Chun Tsew te choo ta tseuen hŏ tsan.* "The Spring and Autumn Annals." .. Edited by Fan Tsze-tăng, &c. 1711. 8°.

——— 學源堂書經體註 *Heŏ yuen tang Shoo king te choo.* "The .. Book of Historical Documents." ... Edited .. by Fan Tsze-tăng, &c.

1725. 8°.

——— 書經瑯環體註 *Shoo king lang hwan te choo.* "The Book of Historical Documents." .. Edited by Fan Tsze-tăng, &c. 1789. 8°.

——— 書經體註 *Shoo king te choo.* "The Book of Historical Documents." .. Edited by Fan Tsze-tăng, &c. 1815. 8°.

—— See 禮記 LE KE. 禮記體註大全合參 *Le ke te choo ta tseuen hŏ tsan.* "The Book of Rites." .. Edited by Fan Tsze-tăng, &c.

1711. 8°.

——— 禮記體註大全 *Le ke te choo ta tseuen.* "The Book of Rites." .... Edited by Fan Tsze-tăng, &c. 1713. 8°.

FAN [63] FAN

范紫登 FAN TSZE-TĂNG. (*Continued.*)
See 禮記 LE KE. 全本禮記體註 *Tseuen pun Le ke te choo.* "The Book of Rites." .. Edited by Fan Tsze-tăng, &c. 1766. 8º.

范文安 FAN WĂN-GAN.
See 彭人傑 PĂNG JIN-KĔĔ. 東莞縣志 *Tung kwan heen che.* "A Topography of Tung-kwan Heen." .. Compiled by ... Fan Wăn-gan, &c. 1797. 8º.

樊廷枚 FAN TING-MEI.
See 閻若璩 YEN JŎ-KEU. 四書釋地補註 *Sze shoo shĭh te poo choo.* "The Topography of the Four Books. .. With additional Notes" by Fan Ting-mei, &c. 1816. 8º.

方回 FANG HWUY.
盧谷閒抄 *Heu kŭh heen chaou.* "Occasional Tales by Fang Hwuy, Heu-kŭh." *See* 說 SHWŎ. 說纂 *Shwŏ tswan.* "Miscellaneous Records," &c. Vol. 5. 8º.

方鯤 FANG KWĂN.
易盪 *Yih tang.* "The Permutations of the Diagrams of the Book of Changes." With Notes by Choo He, Ching Haou, Kew Keen-gan, and others. Edited by Yaou Wăn-jen and Yaou Wăn-sĕĕ. 2 keuen. 1718. 8º.

方春池 FANG CHUN-CHE.
See 閻其淵 YEN KE-YUEN. 四書典制類聯音註 *Sze shoo teen che luy leen yin choo.* "Essays on Canonical Passages from the Four Books." .. Edited by Fang Chun-che, &c. 1799. 8º.

方中履 FANG CHUNG-LE.
切字釋疑 *Tsёĕ tsze shĭh e.* "An Explanation of Doubtful Points in the System of Dividing two Characters to give the Sound of a Third." *See* 張山來 CHANG SHAN-LAE, and 張進也 CHANG TSIN-YAY. 昭代叢書 *Chaou tae tsung shoo.* "A Collection of Reprints of Works by Authors under the present Dynasty," &c. Keuen 30. 1703. 8º.

方以智 FANG E-CHE.
通雅 *Tung ya.* "A Perspicuous and Learned" Encyclopædia. Edited by Yaou Wăn-sĕĕ. 52 keuen. 1666. 8º.

方逢辰 FANG FUNG-SHIN.
名物蒙求 *Ming wŭh mung keu.* "The Beginner's Book on Common Things." In verse. By Fang Fung-shin. *See* 陸清獻 LŬH TSING-HEEN. 小四書 *Seaou Sze shoo.* "The lesser Four Books," &c. Keuen 1. 1845. 8º.

方拱乾 FANG KUNG-KEEN.
寧古塔志 *Ning koo tă che.* "An Account of Ninguta." *See* 張山來 CHANG SHAN-LAE, and 張進也 CHANG TSIN-YAY. 昭代叢書 *Chaou tae tsung shoo.* "A Collection of Reprints of Works by Authors under the present Dynasty," &c. Keuen 26. 1703. 8º.

方觀旭 FANG KWAN-HEŬH.
論語偶記 *Lun yu gow ke.* "Harmonious Records on the Confucian Analects." *See* 嚴杰 YEN LĔĔ. 皇清經解 *Hwang Tsing king keae.* "The Classics Explained," &c. Keuen 1327. 1829. 8º.

方靈皋 FANG LING-KAOU.
See 儀禮 E LE. 儀禮章句 *E le chang keu.* "The Decorum Ritual explained sentence by sentence." .... Edited by Fang Ling-kaou, &c. 1757. 8º.

方濬頤 FANG SEUN-E.
二知軒詩鈔 *Urh che heen she chaou.* "Poetry from the Study of Dual Intelligencies." 14 keuen. 1866. 8º.

方士俊 FANG SZE-TSEUN.
楊芬集 *Yang fun tseĭh.* "The Fragrance-spreading Collection" of Poems in memory of Tsow Ching-koo. Compiled by Fang Sze-tseun. 2 keuen. 1836. 8º.

方引彥 FANG YIN-YEN.
遂安縣志 *Suy gan heen che.* "A Topography of Suy-gan Heen," in the Province of Chĕ-keang. Compiled by Fang Yin-yen, Keang Sze-lun, and others. 10 keuen. 1767. 8º. Imperfect, wanting keuen 10.

方應祥 FANG YING-TSEANG.
稿 *Kaou.* "Essays." *See* 長城 CHANG CHING. 名家制義 *Ming kea che e.* "Essays" on Texts from the Four Books, &c. Tsĭh 77. 1699. 8º.

方于魯 FANG YU-LOO.

方氏墨譜 *Fang she mih poo.* "Specimens of Engravings on Cakes of Ink as manufactured by Fang Yu-loo." 6 keuen. 1588. 8º.

房祺 FANG KE.

河汾諸老詩集 *Ho fun choo laou she tseih.* "A Collection of Poetry by the Elders of the 'River's Eddies.'" Compiled by Fang Ke. 8 keuen. *See* 伍崇曜 WOO TSUNG-YAOU. 粤雅堂叢書 *Yuĕ ya Tang tsung shoo.* "The Yuĕ-ya Tang Collection of Reprints," &c. Series 2. 1853. 8º.

房玄齡 FANG HEUEN-LING.

管子 *Kwan tsze.* "Kwan Chung's Work" on Legislation. With a Commentary by Fang Heuen-ling. *See* 黄丕烈 HWANG PEI-LĔĔ. 九子全書 *Kew tsze tseuen shoo.* "The Complete Works of the Nine Philosophers," &c. 1804. 8º.

—— *See* 管仲 KWAN CHUNG. 管子評註 *Kwan tsze ping choo.* "Kwan Chung's Work on Legislation. With . . . Commentaries" by Fang Heuen-ling, &c. 1804. 8º.

房循媛 FANG SEUN-HWŎ.

See 王朝佐 WANG CHAOU-TSO. 安州誌 *Gan chow che.* "A Topography of Gan Chow." . . Compiled by . . Fang Seun-hwŏ, &c. 1680. 8º.

房千里 FANG TSEEN-LE.

楊娟傳 *Yang Chang chuen.* "The Story of Yang Chang." By Fang Tseen-le, of the Tang Dynasty. A Reprint. [1741 ?]. 8º.

FEER (LÉON).

Le Sûtra en Quarante-deux Articles. Textes Chinois, Tibétain et Mongol, autographiés par Léon Feer. *Paris*, 1868. 8º.

費 FEI.

[A Proclamation issued by the Canton Customs officer Fei, and sent to the captain of the ship Loo-kea-la, in which the people at Whampoa are forbidden to go on board the ship to make a disturbance, and the sailors are prohibited from going on shore.] 1701. A Sheet.

費信 FEI SIN.

星槎勝覽 *Sing cha shing lan.* "A Minute Inspection of Foreign Countries." *See* 說 SHWŎ. 說選 *Shwŏ seuen.* "A Collection of Records," &c. Vol. 10. 8º.

費奇規 FEI KE-KWEI.

See 艾儒畧 GAE JOO-LEŎ. 三山論學紀 *San shan lun heŏ ke.* "A Dialogue . . . on God as the Creator and Governor of the Universe." . . . Edited by Fei Ke-kwei, &c. 8º.

—— *See* 郭居靜 KŎ KEU-TSING. 天主聖教日課 *Teen choo shing keaou jĭh ko.* "Daily Christian Religious Exercises." Compiled by . . Fei Ke-kwei, &c. 8º.

費樂德 FEI LŎ-TĬH.

See 艾儒畧 GAE JOO-LEŎ. 萬物眞原 *Wan wŭh chin yuen.* "The True Origin of all Things." . . Edited by . . . Fei Lŏ-tĭh, &c. 8º.

—— *See* 艾儒畧 GAE JOO-LEŎ. 三山論學紀 *San shan lun heŏ ke.* "A Dialogue . . . on God as the Creator and Governor of the Universe." . . . Edited by . . . Fei Lŏ-tĭh, &c. 8º.

—— *See* 郭居靜 KŎ KEU-TSING. 天主聖教日課 *Teen choo shing keaou jĭh ko.* "Daily Christian Religious Exercises." Compiled by . . Fei Lŏ-tĭh, &c. 8º.

費錫章 FEI SEĬH-CHANG.

See 齊鯤 TSE KWĂN, and FEI SEĬH-CHANG. 續琉球國志畧 *Sŭh Lew kew kwŏ che leŏ.* "A Supplementary Account of the Lew chew Islands," &c. 1774. 8º.

費泰升 FEI TAE-SHING.

See 王子音 WANG TSZE-YIN. 今古地理述 *Kin koo te le shŭh.* "Modern and Ancient Geography." . . . With Notes by Fei Tae-shing, &c. 1807. 8º.

費大司馬 FEI TA-SZE-MA.

See EPHEMERIDES. 諏吉便覽 *Tseu keĭh peen lan.* "A Handbook for choosing Lucky Days." . . . Arranged by Fei Ta-sze-ma. 1818. 8º.

裴仙先 FEI CHOW-SEEN.

裴仙先別傳 *Fei Chow-seen peǐh chuen.* "The Story of Fei Chow-seen." *See* 說 SHWǑ. 說淵 *Shwǒ yuen.* "A Collection of Tales," &c. Vol. 3.   8°.

費孝源 FEI HEAOU-YUEN.

公私畫史 *Kung sze hwa she.* "A Catalogue of Public and Private Illustrated Records." *See* 王文誥 WANG WĂN-KAOU. 唐代叢書 *Tang tae tsung shoo.* "A Collection of Reprints of Works written during the Tang Dynasty," &c. Series 3.   1806. 8°.

飛濤培 FEI TAOU-PEI.

See 姒倚平 PIN E-PING. 文選集腋 *Wăn seuen tseǐh yǐh.* "Selected Literary Expressions." .. Compiled by ... Fei Taou-pei, &c. 1813. 8°.

傅椿 FOO CHUN.

See 爾哈善 URH-HǑ-SHEN. 蘇州府志 *Soo chow Foo che.* "A Topography of Soo-chow Foo." Compiled by ... Foo Chun, &c.   1748. 8°.

傅恒 FOO HĂNG.

See 乾隆 KEEN-LUNG. *Emperor.* 御製盛京賦 *Yu che Shing king foo.* "A Poetical Eulogium on the City of Moukden." ... Edited by .. Foo Hăng, &c.   1748. 4°.

—— *See* 允祿 YUN LǓH. 欽定同文韻統 *Kin ting tung wăn yun tung.* "A Sanskrit, Thibetan, and Manchoo Syllabary." Compiled by ... Foo Hăng, &c.   1750. 8°.

傅山 FOO SHAN.

女科 *Neu ko.* "A Treatise on the Diseases common to Women." 2 keuen. [Also] 產後編 *Chan how peen.* "A Treatise on the Medical Treatment of Women after Childbirth." 2 keuen. *See* 藥志洗 YĚ CHE-SIN. 海山仙館叢書 *Hae shan seen Kwan tsung shoo.* "The Hae shan seen Kwan Collection of Reprints," &c. Vol. 111–112.   1848. 8°.

傅泛際 FOO FAN-TSE.

See 艾儒略 GAE JOO-LEǑ. 萬物眞原 *Wan wǔh chin yuen.* "The True Origin of All Things." .. Edited by Foo Fan-tse, &c. 8°.

傅汎際 FOO FAN-TSE.

See 郭居靜 KǑ KEU-TSING. 天主聖教日課 *Teen choo shing keaou jǐh ko.* "Daily Christian Religious Exercises." Compiled by .. Foo Fan-tse, &c.   8°.

傅仁宇 FOO JIN-YU.

眼科大全 *Yen ko ta tseuen.* "A Complete Work on the Eye." Enlarged and edited by Lin Chang-săng. 6 keuen.   1819. 8°.

傅鸞祥 FOO LWAN-TSEANG.

六書分類 *Lǔh shoo fun luy.* "A Dictionary of the Ancient Forms of Characters arranged" according to the radicals. Compiled by Foo Lwan-tseang. Edited by Chow Ching-chaou.   [1800?]. 8°.

Imperfect, containing only keuen 3.

傅遠度 FOO YUEN-TOO.

七幅菴 *Tseǐh fǔh gan.* "The Seven-Scroll Cell." *See* 閔景賢 MIN KING-HEEN. 快書 *Kwae shoo.* "A Book of Amusement," &c. Keuen 37.   1626. 8°.

夫 FOO.

謀夫害子 *Mow foo hae tsze.* "The Boy illused by a designing Stepmother." In verse. 2 keuen.   [1850?]. 8°.

富春 FOO CHUN.

See 高晉 KAOU TSIN. 南巡盛典 *Nan seun shing teen.* "An Account of .. Progresses ... in the South." .. Compiled by .. Foo Chun, &c.   1771. 8°

富森布 FOO SĂN-POO.

See CHINA. 乾隆 KEEN-LUNG. *Emperor.* 欽定八旗則例 *Kin ting pǎ ke tsǐh le.* "Regulations for the Bannermen." .. Compiled by .. Foo Săn-poo, &c.   1786. 8°.

富兜揚阿 FOO-NE-YANG-AH.

See 陳君擧 CHIN KEUN-KEU. 止齋文集 *Che chae wăn tseǐh.* "A Collection of Literary Pieces from the Restful Study." Edited by .... Foo-ne-yang-ah, &c.   1834. 8°.

9

FOUQUET (Jean François).

See 趙君卿 Chaou Keun-king. 周髀算經 *Chow pe swan king.* "A Work on Trigonometry and Astronomy." . . . With MS. Notes by J. F. F., &c.　　　　8º.

—— See 莊周 Chwang Chow. 齊物論 *Tse wǔh lun.* "A Discussion on Regulated Matter." . . With MS. Notes by J. F. F., &c.　　　　8º.

—— See 孔丘 Kung Kew. 奎壁書經 *Kwei peǐh Shoo king.* "The Kwei peǐh Edition of the Book of Historical Documents." . . With MS. Notes by J. F. F., &c.　　　　8º.

FRANCE. Napoleon III. *Emperor.*

See Great Britain and Ireland. Victoria. Queen. 奏准天津新議通商條欵 *Tsow chun Teen tsin sin e tung shang teaou kwǎn.* "The New Commercial Treaties of Tientsin," contracted between . . France and China, &c.　　　　1860. 8º.

FRENCH (John Booth).

See Ephemerides. 和合通書 *Ho hŏ tung shoo.* "A Harmonized Almanac." . . [Edited by J. B. F.], &c.　　　　1855–56. 8º.

福兆 Fŭh Chaou.

See China. Board of Works. 欽定工部軍器則例 *Kin ting kung poo keun ke tsǐh le.* "Regulations issued by the Board of Works for the supply of Military Stores." Compiled by Fŭh Chaou, &c.　　　　1812. 8º.

福建 Fŭh-keen.

福建通志 *Fŭh keen tung che.* "A Complete Topography of the Province of Fŭh-keen."　　　　[1750 ?]. 8º.

Imperfect, containing only keuen 6–10, 24–38, 52–66, and 69–75

Another edition.　　　　[1790 ?]. 8º.

Imperfect, containing only keuen 1–78 ; wanting title-page and preface.

—— 省例 *Sing le.* "Provincial Regulations" for the Province of Fŭh-keen.　　　　1826. 8º.

FŬH KEEN. 雙 Shwang. *General.*

A Proclamation urging the necessity of vigilance and preparation to oppose the Ying [English] rebels.　　　　1841. 8º.

福音 Fŭh yin.

福音總論 *Fŭh yin tsung lun.* "A Discourse on the Gospel." In verse. [By Samuel Dyer.]　　　　1839. 12º.

Another copy.

—— 福音大旨 *Fŭh yin ta ehe.* "The Cardinal Truth of the Gospel." A Sermon on John iii. 16. By Dr. Medhurst (?).　　　　*Hongkong,* 1869. 8.

佛 Fŭh.

晋勸念佛 *Poo keuen neen Fŭh.* "Exhortations to the Study of Buddha."　　　　1797. 8º.

佛山 Fŭh-shan.

佛山街畧 *Fŭh shan keae leŏ.* "A Sketch of the Streets of Fŭh-shan," a Town near Canton.　　　　1830. 8º.

佛陀多羅 Fŭh-to-to-lo. *pseud.* [*i.e.* Buddhatala.]

大方廣圓覺經畧疏 *Ta fang kwang yuen keaou king leŏ soo.* "The Sûtra of Complete Perception." Translated into Chinese by Fŭh-to-to-lo. With a Commentary by Tsung-meǐh. 6 keuen.　　　　1573. 8º.

—— 大方廣圓覺經直解 *Ta fang kwang yuen keaou king chǐh keae.* "The Sûtra of Complete Perception, with a true Exposition" by Tǐh-tsing. 2 keuen.　　　　*Canton,* 1623. 8º.

—— 大方廣圓覺經 *Ta fang kwang yuen keaou king.* "The Sûtra of Complete Perception." A Reprint.　　　　*Canton,* 1680. 8º.

伏勝 Fŭh Shing.

See 孔丘 Kung Kew. 欽定書經傳說彙纂 *Kin ting Shoo king chuen shwŏ wei tswan.* "The Book of Historical Documents . . . with Comments and Remarks" thereon by . . Fŭh Shing, &c.　　　　1730. 8º.

FUN [67] FUN

伏 若 望 FŬH JǑ-WANG.

耶 穌 受 難 禱 文 *Yay soo show nan taou wăn.* "Prayers on the Sufferings of Jesus." Translated into Chinese by Fŭh Jǒ-wang. *See* 郭 居 靜 Kǒ KEU-TSING. 天 主 聖 敎 日 課 *Teen choo shing keaou jih ko.* "Daily Christian Religious Exercises," &c. Keuen 2. 8°.

粉 粧 樓 FUN CHWANG LOW.

粉 粧 樓 全 傳 *Fun chwang low tseuen chuen.* "The Story of the Painted Pavilion." With Illustrations. An Historical Novel, in continuation of the *Shwǒ Tang che chuen.* By the Man of the Chŭh-ke Mountain. 80 chapters. 1806. 12°.

馮 琦 FUNG KE.

經 濟 類 編 *King tse luy peen.* "Aids to Classical Literature." Compiled by Fung Ke. Edited by Fung Yuen, Chow Kea-tung, and Woo Kwang-e. 100 keuen. 1604. 8° Imperfect, wanting keuen 9–51.

馮 甦 FUNG SOO.

刑 部 則 例 *Hing poo tsĭh le.* "The Regulations of the Board of Punishments." Compiled by . . Fung Soo, &c. *See* TSING DYNASTY. 大 淸 律 箋 釋 *Ta Tsing leŭh tseen shĭh.* "The Laws of the Tsing Dynasty," &c. 1725. 8°.

馮 舠 FUNG YĬH.

桂 苑 叢 談 *Kwei yuen tsung tan.* "Conversations from the Cassia Garden." *See* 王 文 誥 WANG WĂN-KAOU. 唐 代 叢 書 *Tang tae tsung shoo.* "A Collection of Reprints of Works written during the Tang Dynasty," &c. Series 1. 1806. 8°.

馮 瑗 FUNG YUEN.

See 馮 琦 FUNG KE. 經 濟 類 編 *King tse luy peen.* "Aids to Classical Literature." . . Edited by Fung Yuen, &c. 1604. 8°.

馮 鴻 模 FUNG HUNG-MOO.

慈 谿 縣 志 *Tsze ke heen che.* "A Topography of Tsze-ke Heen," in the Province of Chě keang. Compiled by Fung Hung-moo. Edited by Yang Ching-seun. 16 keuen. 1738. 8°.

馮 起 鳳 FUNG KE-FUNG.

長 生 殿 曲 譜 *Chang săng teen keŭh poo.* "The Song-book of the Hall of Longevity." With the appropriate Airs. 2 keuen. 1789. 8°.

馮 經 景 FUNG KING-KING.

解 春 集 *Keae chung tsĕh.* "A Collection of Explanations and 'Poundings'" on Classical Subjects. 2 keuen. *See* 嚴 杰 YEN LĔĔ. 皇 淸 經 解 *Hwang Tsing king keae.* "The Classics Explained," &c. Keuen 205–206. 1829. 8°.

馮 李 驊 FUNG LE-HWA.

See 孔 丘 KUNG KEW. 春 秋 經 傳 集 解 *Chun tsew king chuen tsĕh keae.* "The Spring and Autumn Annals." . . . Edited by Fung Le-hwa, etc. 8°.

—— and 朱 元 寧 CHOO YUEN-NING.

初 學 小 題 明 文 鑰 *Choo heŏ seaou te ming wăn sew.* "Elegant Literary Essays as Models for Students." Compiled by Fung Le-hwa and Choo Yuen-ning. Edited by Fung Nëen-e and Fung Sze-yen. 1730. 8°. Imperfect.

馮 鷺 庭 FUNG LOO-TING.

See 吳 穀 人 WOO KŬH-JIN. 安 定 書 院 課 藝 *Gan ting shoo yuen ko e.* "Examination Essays from the Gan-ting College." Edited by . . . Fung Loo-ting, &c. 1803. 8°.

馮 夢 禎 FUNG MUNG-CHING.

稿 *Kaou.* "Essays." *See* 長 城 CHANG CHING. 名 家 制 義 *Ming kea che e.* "Essays" on Texts from the Four Books, &c. Tsĭh 59. 1699. 8°.

—— *See* 孔 丘 KUNG KEW. 古 本 官 板 書 經 大 全 *Koo pun kwan pan Shoo king ta tseuen.* "The Original Official Text of the Book of Historical Documents." . . Compiled by Fung Mung-ching, &c. 8°.

馮 夢 龍 FUNG MUNG-LUNG.

See 孔 丘 KUNG KEW. 春 秋 大 全 *Chun tsew ta tseuen.* "A Complete Copy of the Spring and Autumn Annals" . . Edited by Fung Mung-lung, &c. 1625. 8°.

馮夢龍 Fung Mung-lung. (*Continued.*)

列國始末 *Lĕĕ kwŏ che mŏ.* "The Rise and Fall of the Kingdoms that existed about the Chun Tsew period." *See* 孔丘 Kung Kew. 春秋指掌 *Chun tsew che chang.* "A Guide to the Spring and Autumn Annals," &c.
1688. 8º.

馮念詒 Fung Nëen-e.

See 馮李驊 Fung Le-hwa, and 朱元寧 Choo Yuen-ning. 初學小題明文讟 *Choo heŏ seaou te ming wăn sew.* "Elegant Literary Essays." . . Edited by Fung Nëen-e, &c.
1730. 8º.

馮秉正 Fung Ping-ching. *pseud.*

聖心規程 *Shing sin kwei ching.* "The Rules of the Sacred Heart." *See* 郭居靜 Kŏ Keu-tsing. 天主聖敎日課 *Teen choo shing keaou jĭh ko.* "Daily Christian Religious Exercises," &c. Keuen 4.
8º.

—— 盛世芻蕘 *Shing she tsow yaou.* "A General Discourse on the Christian Religion." By Fung Ping-ching.
[*Peking* ?], 1796. 8º.

—— 聖年廣益 *Shing neen kwang yĭh.* "Lives of Saints, with Reflections for every Day in the Year." A new Edition.
1815. 8º.

馮思燕 Fung Sze-yen.

See 馮李驊 Fung Le-hwa, and 朱元寧 Choo Yuen-ning. 初學小題明文讟 *Choo heŏ seaou te ming wăn sew.* "Elegant Literary Essays." . . Edited by . . Fung Sze-yen, &c.
1730. 8º.

馮登府 Fung Tăng-foo.

象山縣志 *Seang shan heen che.* "A Topography of Seang-shan Heen," in the Province of Chĕ-keang. Compiled by Fung Tăng-foo, Tung Leĭh-ching, Woo Seĭh-chow, and others. 21 keuen. Appendix, 2 keuen.
1834. 8º.

馮應京 Fung Ying-king.

月令廣義 *Yuĕ ling kwang e.* "The Seasons fully Explained." By Fung Ying-king. With additional explanatory matter by Tae Jin. 24 keuen.
1602. 8º.

風箏 Fung tsăng.

風箏誤傳 *Fung tsăng woo chuen.* "The Intrigue of the Paper Kite." A Drama. 8 keuen.
1811. 8º.

鳳 Fung.

酒樓戲鳳 *Tsew low he Fung.* "The Sportive Le Fung of the Wine Tavern." A Drama.
[1800 ?]. 8º.

鳳林 Fung Lin.

元草堂詩餘 *Yuen tsaou tang she yu.* "Additional Poetry from the Yuen-tsaou Tang." Compiled by Fung Lin. 3 keuen. *See* 伍崇曜 Woo Tsung-yaou. 粵雅堂叢書 *Yuĕ ya Tang tsung shoo.* "The Yuĕ-ya Tang Collection of Reprints," &c. Series 13. 1853. 8º.

鳳蟬 Fung Pe.

鳳蟬告狀 *Fung Pe kaou chwang.* "Fung Pe's Petition." A Drama.
[1800 ?]. 8º.

愛漢者 Gae-han-chay. *pseud.* [*i.e.* Carl F. A. Guetzlaff.]

See Periodical Publications. *China.* 東西洋考每月統記傳 *Tung se yang kaou mei yuĕ tung ke chuen.* "A Monthly Periodical." . . Edited by Gae-han-chay, &c. 1833–37. 8º.

—— 誠崇拜類函 *Ching tsung pae luy han.* "Faithful Letters." [*Singapore*, 1834 ?]. 8º.

—— 正敎安慰 *Ching keaou gan wei.* "The Comfort of True Religion." 4 keuen.
Singapore, 1836. 8º.

—— 求世主耶穌之聖訓 *Kew she choo Yay-soo che shing heun.* "The Teachings of Jesus."
Singapore, 1836. 8º.

—— 贖罪之道傳 *Shŭh tsuy che taou chuen.* "A Story illustrating the Doctrine of the Redemption." 2 keuen. [*Singapore* ?], 1836. 8º.

—— 全人矩矱 *Tseuen jin keu hwŏ.* "The Perfect Man's Model." 5 keuen. *Singapore*, 1836. 8º.

Another edition. 5 keuen. *Singapore*, 1836. 8º.

愛 漢 者 GAE-HAN-CHAY. *pseud.* [*i.e.* Carl F. A. Guetzlaff.] (*Continued.*)

   耶 穌 降 世 之 傳 *Yay-soo keang she che chuen.* "The Nativity of Jesus Christ."

         Singapore, 1836. 8º.

—— 耶 穌 神 蹟 之 傳 *Yay-soo shin tseĭh che chuen.* "The Miracles of Jesus." *Singapore,* 1836. 8º.

艾 儒 畧 GAE JOO-LEŎ. *pseud.* [*i.e.* Julio Aleni.]

   耶 穌 聖 體 禱 文 *Yay-soo shing te taou wǎn.* "Prayers of the Holy Body of Jesus." *See* 郭 居 靜 KŎ KEU-TSING. 天 主 聖 敎 日 課 *Teen choo shing keaou jĭh ko.* "Daily Christian Religious Exercises," &c. Keuen 2.   8º.

—— 三 山 論 學 紀 *San shan lun heŏ ke.* "A Dialogue between J. Aleni and a Native Dignitary, on God as the Creator and Governor of the Universe." Edited by Fei Ke-kwei, Yang-ma-nŏ, and Fei Lŏ-tĭh.   [1630 ?]. 8º.

—— 天 主 降 生 言 行 紀 像 *Teen choo keang sǎng yen hing ke seang.* "An Illustrated Life of Christ." Edited by Keu Se-mwan, Yang-ma-nŏ [*i.e.* Emmanuel Diaz], and Nëё Pĭh-to.   [1630 ?]. 8º.

—— 萬 物 眞 原 *Wan wǔh chin yuen.* "The True Origin of All Things." Edited by Foo Fan-tse, Lung Hwa-min, and Fei Lŏ-tĭh. [1628 ?]. 8º.

艾 南 英 GAE NAN-YING.

   稿 *Kaou.* "Essays." *See* 長 城 CHANG CHING. 名 家 制 義 *Ming kea che e.* "Essays" on Texts from the Four Books, &c. Tsĭh 84. 1699. 8º.

艾 鈞 瑟 GAE YŎ-SĬH. *pseud.* [*i.e.* Rev. Joseph Edkins.]

  See 麥 都 思 MĬH-TOO-SZE [*i.e.* W. H. Medhurst]. 耶 穌 敎 畧 *Yay-soo keaou leŏ.* "An Outline of the Christian Religion." Edited by . . Gae Yŏ-sĭh, &c.   1858. 8º.

—— See 韋 廉 臣 WEI-LEEN-CHIN [*i.e.* Rev. A. Williamson]. 植 物 學 *Chĭh wŭh heŏ.* "A Work on Botany." Completed by Gae Yŏ-sĭh, &c.   1858. 8º.

艾 約 瑟 迪 謹 GAE YŎ SĬH TEĬH KIN. [*i.e.* Rev. Joseph Edkins].

   釋 敎 正 謠 *Shĭh keaou ching meu.* "The Errors of the Buddhist Religion Corrected."

         Shanghae, 1857. 8º.

GAMBLE (WILLIAM).

  Two Lists of Selected Characters, containing all in the Bible and Twenty-seven other Books. With Introductory Remarks. By W. Gamble.

         Shanghae, 1865. 8º.

安 念 祖 GAN NEEN-TSOO, and 華 湛 恩 HWA CHAN-GĂN.

   古 韻 溯 原 *Koo yun soo yuen.* "Ancient Sounds traced to their Source." By Gan Neen-tsoo and Hwa Chan-gǎn. 8 keuen.

         1838. 4º.

安 文 思 GAN WĂN-SZE. *pseud.* [*i.e.* P. Gabriel Megalhaens.]

  See 康 熙 KANG-HE. *Emperor.* 上 諭 *Shang yu.* "An Imperial Edict" . . . expressing regret at the death of Gan Wǎn-sze, &c.   1677. 8º.

晏 嬰 GAN YING.

   晏 子 春 秋 *Gan tsze Chun Tsew.* "The Spring and Autumn Annals [*i.e.* the Biography] of the Philosopher Gan Ying." *See* 沈 津 CHIN TSIN. 百 家 纇 纂 *Pĭh kea luy tswan.* "The Works of a Hundred Authors," &c. Keuen 3. 8º.

恩 成 GĂN CHING.

   夔 州 府 志 *Kwei chow foo che.* "A Topography of Kwei-chow Foo," in the Province of Sze chuen. Compiled by Gǎn Ching and others, from the Materials supplied by Lew Tĭh-tseuen and others. 19 keuen.   1827. 8º.

恩 士 GĂN-SZE [*i.e.* JOHN INCE].

   聖 書 敎 問 答 *Shing shoo keaou wǎn tǎ.* "A Bible Catechism."   1823. 8º.

敖 淸 江 GAOU TSING-KEANG.

   綠 雪 亭 雜 言 *Lǔh seuĕ ting tsǎ yen.* "Miscellanies from the Green-snow Pavilion." *See* 閔 景 賢 MIN KING-HEEN. 快 書 *Kwae shoo.* "A Book of Amusement," &c. Keuen 11.   1626. 8º.

GENAEHR (Ferdinand).

See 堪 輿 Kan yu. 堪 輿 問 答 *Kan yu wăn tă.* "A Conversation on Geomancy." By F. Genaehr, &c.　　　1868.　8°.

—— See London. Chinese Evangelization Society. 廟 祝 問 答 *Meaou chŭh wăn tă.* "A Conversation with a Buddhist Priest." By F. G., &c.　　　1859.　8°.

—— See 葉 納 淸 Yĕ-nă Tsing.

咢 爾 泰 Gŏ Urh-tae.

See China. 雍 正 Yung-ching. *Emperor.* 上 諭 *Shang yu.* "Imperial Edicts." .. Compiled by ... Gŏ Urh-tae, &c.　　　1741.　8°.

漢 益 Gow-yĭh.

淨 土 十 要 *Tsing too shĭh yaou.* "Ten Requisites for the Attainment of the Pure Regions of Bliss." Compiled by the Priest Gow-yĭh.　　　1848.　8°.

歐 陽 修 Gow-yang Sew.

歐 文 *Gow wan.* Selections from "the Writings of Gow-yang Sew." *See* 儲 欣 Choo Hin. 唐 宋 八 大 家 類 選 *Tang Sung pa ta kea luy seuen.* "Selections from the Works of Eight Scholars who flourished under the Tang and Sung Dynasties," &c.　　　1766.　8°.

—— 歐 文 *Gow wan.* "The Writings of Gow-yang Sew." 32 keuen. *See* 茅 坤 Maou Kwăn. 唐 宋 八 大 家 文 鈔 *Tang Sung pă ta kea wăn chaou.* "The Works of Eight Scholars who flourished under the Tang and Sung Dynasties," &c.　　　1631.　8°.

—— 唐 書 *Tang shoo.* "The History of the Tang Dynasty." 225 keuen. *See* 毛 晉 Maou Tsin. 十 七 史 *Shĭh tseĭh she.* "The Seventeen Histories," &c.　　　1656.　8°.

GREAT BRITAIN AND IRELAND. Victoria. *Queen.*

奏 准 天 津 新 議 通 商 條 欵 *Tsow chun Teen tsin sin e tung shang teaou kwăn.* "The New Commercial Treaties of Tientsin," contracted between Great Britain and China, France and China, the United States of America and China, and Russia and China.　　　*Peking,* 1860.　8°.

GUETZLAFF (Carl Friedrich August).

See Bible. 舊 遺 詔 聖 書（救 世 主 耶 穌 新 遺 詔 書）*Kew e chaou shing shoo (Kew she choo Yay-soo sin e chaou shoo).* "The Old and New Testaments." Translated into Chinese by C. F. A. Guetzlaff, &c.　　　1855.　8°.

——— New Testament. 救 世 主 耶 穌 新 遺 詔 書 *Kew she choo Yay-soo sin e chaou shoo.* Translated into Chinese by C. F. A. G., &c.　　　1836.　8°.

—— See 眞 理 Chin le. 眞 理 *Chin le.* "Truth." By C. F. A. G., &c.　　　8°.

—— See 愛 漢 者 Gae-han-chay.

—— See 悔 罪 Hwuy tsuy. 悔 罪 之 大 畧 *Hwuy tsuy che ta leŏ.* "The Great Scheme of Repentance." By C. F. A. G., &c.　　　8°.

—— See Jesus Christ. 救 世 主 言 行 全 傳 *Kew she choo yen hing tseuen chuen.* "The Life of Christ." By C. F. A. G., &c.　　　8°.

——— 救 世 耶 穌 受 死 全 傳 *Kew she Yay-soo show sze tseuen chuen.* "The Narrative of the Death of Our Saviour Jesus Christ." By C. F. A. G., &c.　　　1843.　8°.

—— See 人 Jin. 招 人 獲 救 *Chaou jin hwŏ kew.* An Invitation to obtain Salvation." By C. F. A. G., &c.　　　8°.

—— See 敎 Keaou. 敎 條 *Keaou teaou.* "The Principles of the Protestant Faith." By C. F. A. G., &c.　　　8°.

—— See 善 德 Shen-tĭh.

—— See 善 德 者 Shen-tĭh-chay.

—— See 聖 會 Shing hwuy. 聖 會 之 史 *Shing hwuy che she.* "The History of the Church of Christ." By C. F. A. G., &c.　　　8°.

—— See 道 Taou. 誨 謨 訓 道 *Hwuy moo heun taou.* "Instructive Doctrines." By C. F. A. G., &c.　　　8°.

—— See 萬 國 Wan kwŏ. 萬 國 史 傳 *Wan kwŏ she chuen.* "The History of the World." .. By C. F. A. G., &c.　　　8°.

GUETZLAFF (CARL FRIEDRICH AUGUST). (*Continued.*)
See 萬 國 WAN KWŏ. 萬 國 地 理 全 集 *Wan kwŏ te le tseuen tseĭh.* "A Complete Geography of the World." By C. F. A. G., &c.   8°.

—— See 問 答 WĂN TĂ. 緊 要 問 答 *Kin yaou wăn tă.* "A Catechism on Important Doctrines." .. By C. F. A. G., &c.   8°.

GUNADHADRA.
See 求 那 跋 陀 羅 KEW-NA-Pŏ-TO-LO.

海 HAE.
淵 海 *Yuen hae.* "A Deep Sea" of Divinatory Lore.   [1750?]. 8°.
Imperfect, containing only keuen 3–5.

海 陵 HAE LING.
海 陵 三 仙 傳 *Hae ling san Seen chuen.* "The Story of the Three Genii of Hae-ling." See 說 SHWŏ. 說 淵 *Shwŏ yuen.* "A Collection of Tales," &c.   Vol. 10.   8°.

HAEMMERLEIN (THOMAS), *à Kempis.*
See 天 鏡 TEEN KING. 天 鏡 衡 人 *Teen king hăng jin.* ... Extracts from Thomas à Kempis' "Christian Pattern," &c.   1866. 8°.

海 瑞 HAE SHWUY.
稿 *Kaou.* "Essays." *See* 長 城 CHANG CHING. 名 家 制 義 *Ming kea che e.* "Essays" on Texts from the Four Books, &c.   Tsĭh 49.   1699. 8°.

HAK KA.
Hak ka syuk wa pho hok. First Lessons in Reading and Writing the Hakka Colloquial.   *Basel*, 1869. 8°.

HAMBERY (THEODORE).
See 耶 穌 信 徒 YAY-SOO SIN TOO. 耶 穌 信 徒 受 苦 總 論 *Yay-soo sin too show koo tsung lun.* "A History of the Early Christian Martyrs." By T. Hambery.   1855. 8°.

韓 非 HAN FEI.
韓 非 子 *Han Fei-tsze.* "The Writings of Han Fei." *See* 沈 津 CHIN TSIN. 百 家 類 纂 *Pĭh kea luy tswan.* "The Works of a Hundred Authors," &c.   Keuen 22.   8°.

韓 非 HAN FEI.   (*Continued.*)
韓 子 *Han tsze.* "The Writings of Han Fei." *See* 黃 海 岸 HWANG HAE-GAN. 周 秦 十 一 子 *Chow Tsin shĭh yĭh tsze.* "The Works of the Eleven Philosophers of the Chow and Tsin Dynasties," &c.   8°.

—— 韓 非 子 *Han Fei-tsze.* "The Writings of Han Fei." With a Commentary by Kŏ Seang.   20 keuen. *See* 黃 丕 烈 HWANG PEI-LĔĔ. 十 子 全 書 *Shĭh tsze tseuen shoo.* "The Complete Works of the Ten Philosophers," &c.   1804. 8°.

—— See 廣 圻 KWANG KE. 韓 非 子 識 誤 *Han Fei tsze shĭh woo.* "Errors in the Text of the Writings of Han Fei pointed out," &c.   1816. 8°.

—— 韓 非 子 *Han Fei tsze.* "The Writings of Han Fei" on Legislation. Edited by Woo Tsze.   20 keuen.   1845. 8°.

—— 韓 非 子 纂 *Han Fei tsze tswan.* "The Writings of Han Fei" on Legislation, &c. Edited by Chang Pang. With Notes by Woo Kwang-tsze.   2 keuen.   [1750?]. 8°.

韓 休 HAN HEW.
監 本 九 度 *Keen pun kew too.* "The Nine Rules" of Han Hew. A Dramatised Tale.   3 keuen.   1791. 8°.

韓 駒 HAN KEU.
陵 陽 詩 鈔 *Ling yang she chaou.* "The Ling-yang Collection of Poetry." *See* 吳 孟 舉 WOO MĂNG-KEU, and 吳 自 牧 WOO TSZE-MŭH. 宋 詩 鈔 二 集 *Sung she chaou urh tseĭh.* "Poetry of the Sung Dynasty," &c.   8°.

韓 霖 HAN LIN.
慎 守 要 錄 *Shin show yaou lŭh.* "An Important Work on the Art of Defence." 9 keuen. *See* 葉 志 詵 YĔ CHE-SIN. 海 山 仙 館 叢 書 *Hae shan seen Kwan tsung shoo.* "The Hae-shan-seen Kwan Collection of Reprints," &c.   Vol. 36, 37.   1848. 8°.

韓 氏 HAN SHE.
可 楣 摩 *Ko chuy mo.* A Collection of Essays "Worthy of Study" on Texts from the Four Books. Compiled by Han she.   1812. 8°.

咸淳 HAN-SHUN.

咸淳遺事 *Han-shun wei sze.* "A Memoir of the Reign of Han-shun." 2 keuen. *See* 伍崇曜 Woo Tsung-yaou. 粵雅堂叢書 *Yuĕ ya Tang tsung shoo.* "The Yuĕ-ya Tang Collection of Reprints," &c. Series 2. 1853. 8°.

邯鄲 HAN-TAN.

邯鄲記 *Han tan ke.* "A Record of Han-tan." *See* 曲 Keŭh. 六十種曲 *Lŭh shĭh chung keŭh.* "Sixty Plays," &c. Taou 2. 8°.

涵蟾子 HAN CHEN-TSZE.

金丹正理大要道書全集 *Kin tan ching le ta yaou taou shoo tseuen tseĭh.* "A Complete Collection of Important Taouist Works on the True Principle of the Elixir of Immortality." Compiled by Han Chen-tsze. With Commentaries by Wang Taou, Păng Heaou, Chin Heen-ching, Shang Yang-tsze, Ung Paou-kwan, Hwang Tsze-joo. 1538. 8°.

杭世駿 HANG SHE-TSEUN.

質疑 *Chĭh e.* "Doubts Examined." *See* 嚴杰 Yen Lĕĕ. 皇清經解 *Hwang Tsing king keae.* "The Classics Explained," &c. Keuen 309. 1829. 8°.

杭資能 HANG TSZE-NĂNG.

古文快筆貫通解 *Koo wăn kwae peĭh kwan tung keae.* "Brilliant Passages from Ancient Literature Explained." A New Edition. 8 keuen. 1693. 8°.

杏壇 HĂNG TAN.

杏壇聖蹟 *Hăng tan shing tseĭh.* "The Sacred Footprints of the School of Confucius." [1750?]. 8°.

Containing only five illustrations belonging to the above-named work.

希夷 HE-E.

希夷夢 *He-e mung.* "The Dreams" of the Taouist Doctor "of He-e." A Novel. 40 keuen. 1809. 8°.

希喇 HE-LĂ.

[A Petition addressed to the Custom House authorities at Canton by the English merchant He-lă, asking to be allowed to repair his vessel.] 1702. Oblong.

廈 HEA.

廈腔養心神詩 *Hea keang yang sin shin she.* "Sacred Hymns in the Amoy Dialect." Translated into Chinese by Rev. W. C. Burns. *Amoy*, 1868. 8°.

夏象秉 HEA SEANG-PING.

少有園二十四小照圖 *Shaou yew yuen urh shĭh sze seaou chaou too.* "Twenty-four Views in the Shaou-yew Gardens." With short descriptive pieces of Poetry. Edited by Hea Seang-ping. 1815. 8°.

夏浸之 HEA TSIN-CHE.

書史紀原 *Shoo she ke yuen.* "The History and Origin of the Characters." *See* 閔景賢 Min King-heen. 快書 *Kwae shoo.* "A Book of Amusement," &c. Keuen 42. 1626. 8°.

夏禹鑄 HEA YU-CHOO.

幼科鋳鏡 *Yew ko tĕĕ king.* "A Durable Mirror of Medicine for the Young." 6 keuen. 1695. 8°.

霞箋 HEA TSEEN.

霞箋記 *Hea tseen ke.* "The Variegated Note Paper." *See* 曲 Keŭh. 六十種曲 *Lŭh shĭh chung keŭh.* "Sixty Plays," &c. Taou 1. 8°.

香 HEANG.

焚香記 *Fun heang ke.* "Burning Incense." *See* 曲 Keŭh. 六十種曲 *Lŭh shĭh chung keŭh.* "Sixty Plays," &c. Taou 1. 8°.

香囊 HEANG NANG.

香囊記 *Heang nang ke.* "The Scent Bag." *See* 曲 Keŭh. 六十種曲 *Lŭh shĭh chung keŭh.* "Sixty Plays," &c. Taou 6. 8°.

向秀 HEANG SEW.

See 莊周 Chwang Chow. 南華經 *Nan hwa king.* "The Nan-hwa Classic." With Notes by Heang Sew, &c. 1716. 8°.

—— 周易義 *Chow Yĭh e.* "The Meaning of the Chow Changes." *See* 孫堂 Sun Tang. 漢魏二十一家易注 *Han Wei urh shĭh yĭh kea Yĭh choo.* "Commentaries on the Book of Changes," &c. 1799. 8°.

10

向 日 貞 HEANG JĬH-CHING.

註 釋 向 太 史 全 稿 *Choo shĭh Heang tae she tseuen kaou.* "A Complete Collection of the Essays of Heang Jĭh-ching, the Historian." With Comments and Explanations. Edited by Hwang Tse-fei, and Annotated by Tso She and Loo Chĭh. 1771. 8°.

鄉 墨 HEANG MĬH.

乙 末 鄉 墨 *Yĭh we heang mĭh.* "District Essays for the Year 1835 (?)." 1835 (?). 8°.
Imperfect.

鄉 試 HEANG SHE.

鄉 試 硃 卷 *Heang she choo keuen.* "The Red Book of District Examination Essays" for the Years 1794, 1819, 1822. 1794–1822. 8°.

孝 經 HEAOU KING.

孝 經 衍 義 *Heaou king yen e.* "The Book of Filial Piety Explained and Illustrated." 72 keuen. [1750 ?]. 8°.
Imperfect, wanting keuen 1–33.

俠 HËĔ.

義 俠 記 *E hëĕ ke.* "The Story of a Patriotic Hero." *See* 曲 KEŬH. 六 十 種 曲 *Lŭh shĭh chung keŭh.* "Sixty Plays," &c. Taou 5. 8°.

賢 HEEN.

四 賢 記 *Sze Heen ke.* "The Story of the Four Sages." *See* 曲 KEŬH. 六 十 種 曲 *Lŭh shĭh chung keŭh.* "Sixty Plays," &c. Taou 6. 8°.

軒 轅 黃 帝 HEEN-YUEN HWANG-TE.

龍 虎 上 經 *Lung hoo shang king.* "The Sûtra of the Dragon and the Tiger." *See* 彭 好 古 PĂNG HAOU-KOO. 道 言 內 外 秘 訣 全 書 *Taou yen nuy wae pe keŭ tseuen shoo.* "A Complete Collection of Taouist Works," &c. Part II. Keuen 1. 8°.

現 聞 HEEN-WĂN.

See 地 婆 訶 羅 TE-PO-HO-LO. 陀 羅 尼 經 *To lo ne king.* "The To-lo-ne Sûtra." … With a Commentary by Heen-wăn, &c. 1812. 8°.

學 HEŎ.

勸 學 初 編 *Keuen heŏ choo peen.* Essays for "the Encouragement of Learning. First Series." [1750 ?]. 8°.
Very imperfect.

學 善 HEŎ-SHEN. *pseud.* [*i.e.* William Milne, D.D.]

揀 選 勸 世 要 言 *Keen seuen keuen she yaou yen.* "A Selection of Important Discourses to Admonish the Age." *Singapore*, [1828 ?]. 8°.

—— 融 學 聖 理 略 論 *Shŭh heŏ shing le leŏ lun.* "A Tract on the Intimate Study of the Holy Doctrine." [*Canton*], 1828. 8°.

HERSCHEL (SIR JOHN FREDERICK WILLIAM), *Bart.*

談 天 *Tan teen.* "Herschel's "Outlines of Astronomy." Translated into Chinese by A. Wylie, and transcribed by Le Shen-lan. With a Preface in English. 18 keuen. 1859. 8°.

許 辮 HEU KEAE.

稿 *Kaou.* "Essays." *See* 長 城 CHANG CHING. 名 家 制 義 *Ming kea che e.* "Essays" on Texts from the Four Books, &c. Tsĭh 75. 1699. 8°.

許 慎 HEU SHIN.

說 文 *Shwŏ wăn.* "A Dictionary" of the Seal Character. Edited by Seu Heuen and others. 12 keuen. 1627. 8°.

Another copy.

Another edition. 15 keuen. 1807. 8°.

許 錢 HEU TSEEN.

See 紀 昀 KE YUN. 館 課 賦 註 *Kwan ko foo choo.* "College Poems. With Notes" by Heu Tseen, &c. 1802. 8°.

許 洞 HEU TUNG.

虎 鈐 經 *Hoo keen king.* "The Classic of the Tiger's Spear." A Work on the Art of War. 20 keuen. *See* 伍 崇 曜 WOO TSUNG-YAOU. 粵 雅 堂 叢 書 *Yuĕ ya Tang tsung shoo.* "The Yuĕ-ya Tang Collection of Reprints," &c. Series 7. 1853. 8°.

許 琰 HEU YEN.

普 陀 山 志 *Poo to shan che.* "A Topography of the Island of Poo-to." Compiled by Heu Yen. Edited by Hwang Ying-heung. A New Edition. 20 keuen. 1740. 8°.

Another copy.
Imperfect, containing only keuen 1–6.

許孚遠 HEU FOO-YUEN.

稿 *Kaou.* "Essays." *See* 長城 CHANG CHING. 名家制義 *Ming kea che e.* "Essays" on Texts from the Four Books, &c.   Tsǐh 52.
             1699.   8°.

許旭惠 HEU HEǓH-HWUY.

See 桑欽 SANG KIN. 水經 *Shwuy king.* "The Water Classic." . . . Edited by Heu Heǔh-hwuy, &c.   8°.

許旭恭 HEU HEǓH-KUNG.

See 法顯 FǍ-HEEN. 佛國記 *Fǔh kwŏ ke.* "An Account of Buddhist Countries." . . . Edited by Heu Heǔh-kung, &c.   8°.

許喬林 HEU KEAOU-LIN.

See 李松石 LE SUNG-SHǏH. 鏡花緣繡像 *King hwa yuen sew seang.* "The Mysterious Influences of Bright Flowers." . . Edited by Heu Keaou-lin, &c.   1832.   8°.

許敬宗 HEU KING-TSUNG.

文館詞林 *Wǎn kwan tsze lin.* "A Collection of Rhymes from the College of Literature." Compiled by Heu King-tsung. 4 keuen. *See* 伍崇曜 WOO TSUNG-YAOU. 粵雅堂叢書 *Yuě ya Tang tsung shoo.* "The Yuě-ya Tang Collection of Reprints, &c.   Series 12.
             1853.   8°.

許桂林 HEU KWEI-LIN.

春秋穀梁傳時月日書法釋例 *Chun Tsew kǔh leang chuen she yuě jǐh shoo fǎ shǐh le.* "The Dates of the Spring and Autumn Annals, as laid down in Kǔh leang's Commentary, Explained and Adjusted." *See* 伍崇曜 WOO TSUNG-YAOU. 粵雅堂叢書 *Yuě ya Tang tsung shoo.* "The Yuě-ya Tang Collection of Reprints," &c.   Series 16.   1853.   8°.

許賓善 HEU PAOU-SHEN.

See 孔丘 KUNG KEW. 書經楬要 *Shoo king kěě yaou.* "The Book of Historical Documents." . . Edited by Heu Paou-shen, &c.   12°.

—— *See* 禮記 LE KE. 禮記楬要 *Le ke kěě yaou.* "The Book of Rites." . . Edited by Heu Paou-shen.   12°.

許賓善 HEU PAOU-SHEN.   (*Continued.*)

See 詩經 SHE KING. 詩經楬要 *She king kěě yaou.* "The Book of Odes." . . Edited by Heu Paou-shen, &c.   12°.

—— *See* 易經 YǏH KING. 周易楬要 *Chow Yǐh kěě yaou.* "The Book of Changes." . . Edited by Heu Paou-shen, &c.   1789.   12°.

許壽門 HEU SHOW-MUN.

See 曹之升 TSAOU CHE-SHING. 註釋典制文琳 *Choo shǐh teen che wǎn lin.* "A Collection of Choice Essays." . . With Notes by . . Heu Show-mun, &c.   1799–1808.   8°.

—————— 典制文琳註釋 *Teen che wǎn lin choo shǐh.* "A Collection of Choice Essays." . . With Notes by Heu Show-mun, &c.   1804.   8°.

許騰驤 HEU TǍNG-SEANG.

明聖桃園經 *Mung shing Taou yuen king.* "The Sûtra of the Bright and Holy Peach Garden." A Taouist Work. Edited by Heu Tǎng-seang.   1850.   8°.

許旌陽 HEU TSING-YANG.

醉思仙歌 *Tsuy sze seen ko.* "The Chant of Deeply-Contemplative Genii." [Also] 石函記 *Shǐh han ke.* "A Record of the Stone Letter." *See* 彭好古 PǍNG HAOU-KOO. 道言內外秘訣全書 *Taou yen nuy wae pe keuě tseuen shoo.* "A Complete Collection of Taouist Works," &c. Part I. keuen 3.   Part II. keuen 2.   8°.

—— 玉匣記通書 *Yǔh heǎ ke tung shoo.* "The Record of the Jewelled Casket." A Work on Divination. 6 keuen.   1684.   8°.

Another edition.   6 keuen.   1827.   8°.

許宗彥 HEU TSUNG-YEN.

鑑止水齋集 *Keen che shwuy chae tsǐh.* "A Collection of Literary Productions from the Overlooking-still-waters Study." *See* 嚴杰 YEN-LĚĚ. 皇清經解 *Hwang Tsing king keae.* "The Classics Explained," &c. Keuen 1255, 1256.   1829.   8°.

訴纉曾 HEU TSWAN-TSANG.
See 老君 LAOU KEUN. 太上感應篇圖說
Tae shang kan ying peen too shwŏ. "The Book
of Rewards and Punishments. With a Commentary" by Heu Tswan-tsăng, &c. 1825. 8°.

訴堯佐 HEU YAOU-TSO.
章臺柳傳 *Chang tae Lew chuen.* "The Story
of Lew of Chang tae." By Heu Yaou-tso, of
the Tang Dynasty. A Reprint [1741?]. 8°.

玄覺 HEUEN-KEŎ. *pseud.* (*i.e.* 戴氏 Tae she.)
永嘉集 YUNG KEA TSEĬH. "The Yung kea
Collection" of the Writings of Prior Heuen-
keŏ. Edited by Wei Tsing. A Reprint.
Canton, 1801. 8°.

玄奘 HEUEN-TSANG.
See 竭誠 KĔĔ-CHING. 藥師瑠璃光如來
本願功德經 *Yŏ sze lew le kwang Joo-lae
pun yuen kung tĭh king.* "The Ârya Bhagavatî
Bhêshaja guru pûrva pranidhâna nâma mahâyâna sûtra." Translated from the Sanskrit by
Heuen-tsang, &c. 1805. Oblong.

—— 大唐西域記 *Ta Tang se yĭh ke.* "An Account of the Western Frontiers of the Empire
during the Tang Dynasty." Principally Translated from the Sanskrit by the Priest Heuen-
tsang. Together with an account of the countries
through which he himself passed in his travels.
Edited by the Priest Peen-ke. 10 keuen. 8°.

玄黄齋 HEUEN HWANG-CHAE.
印龍譜 *Yin lung poo.* "A Book of Engravings."
Edited by Heuen Hwang-chae. [1800?]. 8°.

熏沐 HEUN SHŬH.
觀世音菩薩普門品經 *Kwan she yin Poo-
sa poo mun pin king.* "The Avalôkitêsvara
Bôdhisattva Sûtra." Edited by Heun Shŭh.
Canton, 1795. Oblong.

訓 HEUN.
寶訓合編 *Paou heun hŏ peen.* "Precious
Teachings, harmoniously arranged." Taouist
Tracts. 4 keuen. [1790?]. 8°.
Imperfect.

熊朋來 HEUNG PĂNG-LAE.
瑟譜 *Sĭh poo.* "A Music Book for the Sĭh," a
stringed instrument. 4 keuen. See 伍崇曜
WOO TSUNG-YAOU. 粵雅堂叢書 *Yuĕ ya
Tang tsung shoo.* "The Yuĕ-ya Tang Collection
of Reprints," &c. Series 8. 1853. 8°.

熊伯龍 HEUNG PĬH-LUNG.
稿 *Kaou.* "Essays." See 長城 CHANG CHING.
名家制義 *Ming kea che e.* "Essays" on
Texts from the Four Books, &c. Tsĭh 103.
1699. 8°.

熊賜履 HEUNG TSZE-LE.
See CHINA. 督捕則例 *Tŭh poo tsĭh le.*
"Regulations for the Capture" of Deserters.
Compiled by ... Heung Tsze-le, &c. 1676. 8°.

—— See 朱熹 CHOO HE. 朱子全書 *Choo tsze
tseuen shoo.* "The Complete Works of Choo
He." Compiled .. by Heung Tsze-le, &c.
1713. 8°.

—— 學統 *Heŏ tung.* "The Founders of Learning."
Biographies of Sages and Scholars. Compiled
by Heung Tsze-le. 56 keuen. 1685. 8°.

熊應雄 HEUNG YING-HEUNG.
小兒推拿廣意 *Seaou urh chuy na kwang e.*
"The Medical Examination of Children." Compiled by Heung Ying-heung. Edited by Chin
Tsze-shan. 3 keuen. 1832. 8°.

兄大生 HEUNG TA-SĂNG.
See 潘長吉 PWAN CHANG-KEĬH. 宋稗類鈔
Sung pae luy chaou. "Miscellanies of the History
of the Sung Dynasty." .. Edited by Heung
Ta-săng, &c. 1669. 8°.

HILLIER (C   B   ).
See PERIODICAL PUBLICATIONS. 遐邇貫珍 *Hea
urh kwan chin.* "A Serial of Foreign and
Domestic News." [Edited by .. C. B. H.] &c.
1853–55. 8°.

行道 HING TAOU.
行道信主以免後日之刑論 *Hing taou
sin choo e meen how jĭh che hing lun.* "A Discourse on the Conduct and Faith necessary to
avoid Future Punishment." [By W. H. Medhurst.] [1850?]. 8°.

邢昺 HING PING.

See 孔丘 KUNG KEW. 孝經註疏 *Heaou king choo soo*. "The Book of Filial Piety. . . . With a Commentary and Paraphrase" by Hing Ping, &c.   8°.

—— See 四書 SZE SHOO. 論語註疏大全合纂 *Lun yu choo soo ta tseuen hŏ tswan*. "The Confucian Analects." . . . . Edited by Hing Ping, &c.   1636. 8°.

—— 爾雅註疏 *Urh ya choo soo*. "The Literary Expositor. With Kŏ Pŏ's Commentary, and a Paraphrase" by the Editor, Hing Ping. 11 keuen.   1778. 8°.

邢坤元 HING KWĂN-YUEN.

朱夫子家訓印譜 *Choo Foo tsze kea heun yin poo*. "Maxims from Choo He's Book of Domestic Instructions, transcribed in the form of Seals."   1750. 8°.

何 HO, and 王 WANG.

浙江闈墨 *Chĕ keang wei mĭh*. "Chĕ-keang Examination Essays." Edited by Ho and Wang.   1831. 8°.

何休 HO HEW.

See 孔丘 KUNG KEW. 春秋公羊傳註疏 *Chun Tsew Kung-yang chuen choo soo*. "The Spring and Autumn Annals and Kung-yang Kaou's Narrative." . . Compiled by Ho Hew, &c.   1634. 8°.

何遑 HO HWAN.

春渚紀聞 *Chun choo ke wăn*. "Records from Chun choo. *See* 說 SHWŏ. 說郛 *Shwŏ foo*. "Odds and Ends," &c.   8°.

何公 HO KUNG.

家規 *Kea kwei*. "Family Rules." *See* 張文嘉 CHANG WĂN-KEA. 齊家寶要 *Tse kea paou yaou*. "Valuable Hints for Domestic Rule," &c. Keuen 1.   8°.

何游 HO YEW.

因果實錄 *Yin ko shĭh lŭh*. "True Records of the Cause and Effect" of Studying the Buddhist Scriptures.   *Canton*, 1819. 8°.

何漢 HO YING.

See 衛廷璞 WEI TING-Pŏ. 建平縣志 *Keen-ping heen che*. "A Topography of Keen-ping Heen." . . . Edited by Ho Ying, &c. 1731. 8°.

何詠 HO YUNG.

史學提要補 *She hŏ te yaou poo*. "A Supplement to Hwang Ke-shen's Epitome of History." . . With Notes by Ho Yung. *See* 陸清獻 LŬH TSING-HEEN. 小四書 *Seaou Sze shoo*. "The Lesser Four Books." Keuen 6. 1845. 8°.

何承鋙 HO CHING-KWĂN.

See 華綱 HWA KANG. 字類標韻 *Tsze luy peaou yun*. "A Dictionary," in which are added the Tonic Finals. . . . Edited by Ho Ching-kwăn, &c.   1793. 8°.

何屺瞻 HO KE-CHEN.

See 王應麟 WANG YING-LIN. 困學紀聞 *Kwăn hŏ ke wăn*. "Criticisms on Literature and Science." With Notes by . . Ho Ke-chen, &c.   1742. 8°.

—— 義門讀書記 *E mun tŭh shoo ke*. "Records of the Studies of Ho Ke-chen." Comments on Classical, Historical, and Polite Literature.   1769. 8°.

何喬遠 HO KEAOU-YUEN.

皇明文徵 *Hwang ming wăn ching*. "A Collection of the Literature of the Ming Dynasty." Compiled by Ho Keaou-yuen. 28 keuen.   [1700 ?]. 8°.

何國宗 HO KWŏ-TSUNG.

See 李光地 LE KWANG-TE. 性理精義 *Sing le tsing e*. "The Essence of Works on Mental Philosophy." Compiled by . . . Ho Kwŏ-tsung, &c.   1715. 8°.

—— See 易經 YĬH KING. 御纂周易折中 *Yu tswan Chow Yĭh chĕ chung*. "Decisions on the Book of Changes." . . . . Compiled by . . Ho Kwŏ-tsung, &c.   1715. 8°.

何平叔 HO PING-SHŬH.

景福殿賦 *King fŭh Teen foo*. "The Poem of the Hall of Great Happiness." *See* 蕭統 SEAOU TUNG. 文選 *Wăn seuen*. "Elegant Extracts," &c. Keuen 11.   1772. 8°.

何 仙 郎 Ho Seen-lang.
花 案 *Hwa gan.* "A Table of Flowers." *See*
閔 景 賢 Min King-heen. 快 書 *Kwae shoo.*
"A Book of Amusement," &c. Keuen 44.
1626. 8°.

何 蜀 川 Ho Shŭh-chuen.
See 陶 篁 村 Taou Hwang-tsun. 文 選 編 珠
Wăn seuen peen choo. "A Selection of Literary
Gems." ... Edited by Ho Shŭh-chuen, &c.
1802. 8°.

何 士 祁 Ho Sze-ke.
川 沙 撫 民 廳 志 *Chuen sha foo min ting che.* "A
Topography of the Borough of Chuen-sha," in
the Province of Keang-soo. Compiled by Ho
Sze-ke. Edited by Wang Hŏ-neen and others.
12 keuen. 1837. 8°.

何 臺 山 Ho Tae-shan.
盤 珠 算 法 *Pwan choo swan fǎ.* "Rules for the
Use of the Abacus." To which are appended
Rules for the Measurement of Land. Compiled
by Ho Tae-shan. 2 keuen. *Canton,* [1800?]. 8°.

何 道 生 Ho Taou-săng.
See 毛 履 謙 Maou Le-keen, and 吳 涵 一
Woo Han-yǐh. 十 家 詩 詳 註 *Shǐh kea she
tseang choo.* "The Poetical Works of Ten
Authors," viz.: ... Ho Taou-săng, &c. 1813. 8°.

何 秋 濤 Ho Tsew-taou.
北 徼 彙 編 *Pĭh keaou wei peen.* "Treatises on
the Countries beyond the Northern Frontier."
Compiled by Ho Tsew-taou. 6 keuen.
Peking, 1865. 8°.

何 進 善 Ho Tsin-shen.
聖 經 證 據 *Shing king ching keu.* "Evidences
of the Truth of the Bible." *Hongkong,* 1867. 8°.

何 偉 然 Ho Wei-jen.
See 閔 景 賢 Min King-heen. 快 書 *Kwae
shoo.* "A Book of Amusement." ... Edited
by Ho Wei-jen, &c. 50 keuen. 1626. 8°.

何 元 烺 Ho Yuen-lang.
See 毛 履 謙 Maou Le-keen, and 吳 涵 一
Woo Han-yǐh. 十 家 詩 詳 註 *Shǐh kea she
tseang choo.* "The Poetical Works of Ten
Authors," viz.: ... Ho Yuen-lang, &c.
1813. 8°.

河 Ho.
河 下 解 心 *Ho hea keae sin.* "River-side Reflections." [1800?]. 8°.

河 南 Ho nan.
河 南 闈 墨 *Ho nan wei mǐh.* "Honan Examination Essays." [1790?]. 8°.
A fragment.

河 源 Ho yuen.
探 河 源 傳 *Tan ho yuen chuen.* "The Search
for the River's Springs." A Drama. 59 keuen.
1813. 8°.

河 上 公 Ho Shang-kung.
道 德 經 評 註 *Taou tǐh king ping choo.* "The
Classic of Reason and Virtue." .. With a Commentary by Ho Shang-kung, &c. *See* 黃 丕 烈
Hwang Pei-lěě. 九 子 全 書 *Kew Tsze tseuen
shoo.* "The Complete Works of the Nine
Philosophers," &c. 1804. 8°.

和 畾 Ho fan.
"Ho-fan," the Name of a District in the North.
A Dramatic Tale. [1800?]. 8°.

和 珅 Ho Shin.
See China. Board of Revenue. 欽 定 戶 部
軍 需 則 例 *Kin ting Hoo Poo keun seu tsǐh le.*
"Regulations .. for the Supply of Commissariat
Stores." Compiled by .. Ho Shin, &c.
1785. 8°.

賀 世 駿 Ho She-tseun.
長 樂 縣 志 *Chang lŏ heen che.* "A Topography
of Chang-lŏ Heen," in the Province of Shan-
tung. 10 keuen. [1750?]. 8°.
Imperfect, title-page and preface wanting.

合 信 Hŏ-sin [*i.e.* Benjamin Hobson].
全 體 新 論 *Tseuen te sin lun.* "A Work on
Physiology." 10 keuen. *See* 葉 志 詵 Yě
Che-sin. 海 山 仙 館 叢 書 *Hae shan seen
kwan tsung shoo* "The Hae shan seen Kwan Collection of Reprints," &c. Vol. 120. 1848. 8°.

—— 婦 嬰 新 說 *Foo ying sin shwŏ.* "A New
Treatise on Midwifery and the Diseases of
Children." Edited by Kwan Mow-tsun.
Shanghae, 1858. 8°.

合信 Hŏ-sin [*i.e.* Benjamin Hobson]. (*Continued.*)

內科新說 *Nuy ko sin shwŏ.* "A New Treatise on the Practice of Medicine." Edited by Kwan Mow-tsun. 2 keuen.   *Shanghae,* 1858. 8°.

—— 博物新編 *Pŏ wŭh sin peen.* "A New Treatise on the Natural Sciences." Parts I. and III.   *Shanghae,* 1855. 8°.

Part III. of this work is part of an edition which was published at Canton in 1854. Part II. is represented by a work entitled *Teen wǎn leŏ lun,* which was in the first instance published separately at Canton in 1849.

鶡冠子 Hŏ Kwan-tsze.

鶡冠子 *Hŏ Kwan-tsze.* "The Writings of Hŏ Kwan-tsze." *See* 沈津 Chin Tsin. 百家類纂 *Pĭh kea luy tswan.* "The Works of a Hundred Authors," &c. Keuen 17.   8°.

———— "The Writings of Hŏ Kwan-tsze." With a Commentary by Lŭh Teen. 3 keuen. *See* 黃丕烈 Hwang Pei-lĕĕ. 十子全書 *Shĭh Tsze tseuen shoo.* "The Complete Works of the Ten Philosophers," &c.   1804. 8°.

鶴臞子 Hŏ Keu-tsze.

唱道眞言 *Chang taou chin yen.* "True Words on Reciting Taou." 5 keuen. *Canton,* 1813. 8°.

郝碩 Hŏ Chĭh.

即墨縣志 *Tseĭh-mĭh heen che.* "A Topography of Tseĭh-mĭh Heen," in the Province of Shantung. Compiled, from Materials supplied in the former Histories, by Hŏ Chĭh, Wang Ke, Tsae Ying-peaou and others. 12 keuen.   1763. 8°.

郝敬 Hŏ King.

稿 *Kaou.* "Essays." *See* 長城 Chang Ching. 名家制義 *Ming kea che e.* "Essays" on Texts from the Four Books, &c. Tsĭh 70.   1699. 8°.

—— *See* 易經 Yĭh king. 周易正解 *Chow Yĭh ching keae.* "The Chow Changes correctly explained" by Hŏ King, &c.   8°.

郝象周 Hŏ Seang-chow.

初學指掌 *Choo heŏ che chang.* "A Guide to Beginners." Essays annotated. 4 Vol.   1820. 8°.

Imperfect, vol. 2 wanting.

郝天挺 Hŏ Teen-ting.

唐詩鼓吹註解 *Tang she koo chuy choo keae.* "Poetry of the Tang Dynasty. With a Laudatory Commentary" by Hŏ Teen-ting, "and Explanatory Notes" by Leaou Wǎn-ping. 10 keuen.   [1800 ?]. 8°.

郝懿行 Hŏ Yĭh-hing.

爾雅義疏 *Urh Ya e soo.* "A Paraphrase of the Meaning of the 'Literary Expositor.'" *See* 嚴杰 Yen Lĕĕ. 皇清經解 *Hwang Tsing king keae.* "The Classics Explained," &c. Keuen 1257–76.   1829. 8°.

郝玉麟 Hŏ Yŭh-lin.

See 稽曾筠 Ke Tsǎng-yun. 浙江通志 *Chĕ keang tung che.* "A Topography of the Province of Chĕ-keang." Compiled by . . . Hŏ Yŭh-lin, &c.   1736. 8°.

霍樹淸 Hŏ Shoo-tsing.

See 陳驤 Chin Seang. 鄱陽縣志 *Po yang heen che.* "A Topography of Po-yang Heen." . . Compiled by . . Hŏ Shoo-tsing, &c.   1824. 8°.

HOBSON (Benjamin).

See 天文 Teen wǎn. 天文畧論 *Teen wǎn leŏ lun.* "A Digest of Astronomy." [By B. H.], &c.   1849. 8°.

—— *See* 合信 Hŏ-sin.

—— 西醫畧論 *Se e leŏ lun.* "A Short Practical Work on European Surgery." Written in Chinese by Dr. Hobson under his Chinese name of Ho-sin, with the assistance of Kwan Mow-tsun. With Plates and a Chinese and English Vocabulary. 3 keuen.   *Shanghae,* 1857. 8°

Has an introductory preface in English.

胡直 Hoo Chĭh.

戒殺生論 *Keae shǎ sǎng lun.* "A Discourse against destroying Life." *See* 沈培木 Chin Pei-mŭh. 慈心寶鑑 *Tsze sin paou keen.* "The Precious Mirror of a Merciful Heart," &c.   1771. 8°.

胡 宏 Hoo Hung.

胡 子 知 言 *Hoo tsze che yen.* " The Wise Sayings of Hoo Hung. 8 keuen. *See* 伍 崇 曜 Woo Tsung-yaou. 粵 雅 堂 叢 書 *Yuĕ ya Tang tsung shoo.* " The Yuĕ-ya Tang Collection of Reprints," &c. Series 10. 1853. 8°.

胡 廣 Hoo Kwang.

性 理 大 全 *Sing le ta tseuen.* " A Complete Work on Mental Philosophy." Being a Compilation of the Works of Chow Leen-ke, Chang Tsae, Shaou Yung, Choo He, Tsae Yuen-ting, and others. Compiled by Hoo Kwang, Yang yung, Kin Yew-tsze, and others. With a Preface by the Emperor Yung-lo. 70 keuen. 1597. 8°.

Another edition. Edited by Le Kew-wo. 70 keuen. 1597. 8°.

胡 南 Hoo Nan.

胡 南 闈 墨 *Hoo nan wei mǐh.* " Hoo-nan Examination Essays." [1821 ?]. 8°.
A fragment.

胡 北 Hoo Pǐh.

胡 北 闈 墨 *Hoo pǐh wei mǐh.* " Hoo-pǐh Examination Essays." [1800 ?]. 8°.
A fragment.

胡 璇 Hoo Seuen.

See 葉 九 升 Yĕ Kew-shing. 地 理 山 法 全 書 *Te le shan fǎ tseuen shoo.* " The Laws of Mountains " . . . the Eleventh Keuen is edited, with Notes, by Hoo Seuen, &c. 8°.

胡 澄 Hoo Tang.

東 軒 詩 鈔 *Tung heen she chaou.* " Poems from the Eastern Study." 1803. 8°.

胡 定 Hoo Ting.

稿 *Kaou.* " Essays." *See* 長 城 Chang Ching. 名 家 制 義 *Ming kea che e.* " Essays " on Texts from the Four Books, &c. Tsǐh 50. 1699. 8°.

胡 仔 Hoo Tsun.

茗 溪 漁 隱 叢 話 *Teaou ke yu yin tsung hwa.* " A Collection of Criticisms on Poetry." Compiled by Hoo Tsun. Series I. 60 keuen. Series II. 40 keuen. *See* 葉 志 洗 Yĕ Che-sin. 海 山 仙 館 叢 書 *Hae shan seen Kwan tsung shoo.* " The Hae-shan-seen Kwan Collection of Reprints," &c. Vol. 66-75. 1848. 8°.

胡 渭 Hoo Wei.

易 圖 明 辨 *Yǐh too ming peen.* " The Diagrams of the Book of Changes plainly discussed." 10 keuen. *See* 伍 崇 曜 Woo Tsung-yaou. 粵 雅 堂 叢 書 *Yuĕ ya Tang tsung shoo.* " The Yuĕ-ya Tang Collection of Reprints," &c. Series 4. 1853. 8°.

—— 禹 貢 錐 指 *Yu kung chuy che.* " The Needle Touch applied to the Tribute of Yu." 21 keuen. *See* 嚴 杰 Yen Lëĕ. 皇 清 經 解 *Hwang Tsing king keae.* " The Classics Explained," &c. Keuen 27-47. 1829. 8°.

胡 寅 Hoo Yin.

敍 古 千 文 *Seu koo tseen wăn.* " An Ancient ' Thousand-character Classic.' " With a Commentary by Hwang Haou. *See* 伍 崇 曜 Woo Tsung-yaou. 粵 雅 堂 叢 書 *Yuĕ ya Tang tsung shoo.* " The Yuĕ-ya Tang Collection of Reprints," &c. Series 7. 1853. 8°.

胡 鳳 藻 Hoo Fung-tsaou.

See 王 嘉 Wang Kea. 拾 遺 記 *Shǐh e ke.* " Lost Pages of History." . . . Edited by Hoo Fung-tsaou, &c. 8°.

胡 安 國 Hoo Gan-kwǒ.

See 孔 丘 Kung Kew. 春 秋 大 全 *Chun Tsew ta tseuen.* " A Complete Copy of the Spring and Autumn Annals." With Commentaries by Hoo Gan-kwǒ, &c. 1625. 8°.

—— 春 秋 指 掌 *Chun Tsew che chang.* " A Guide to the Spring and Autumn Annals." . . . Containing Extracts from the Commentaries of . . . Hoo Gan-kwǒ, &c. 1688. 8°.

—— 春 秋 體 註 大 全 合 參 *Chun Tsew te choo ta tseuen hŏ tsan.* " The Spring and Autumn Annals." . . With the Commentary of Hoo Gan-kwǒ, &c. 1711. 8°.

—— 芥 子 園 重 訂 監 本 春 秋 *Keae tsze yuen chung ting keen pun Chun Tsew.* " The Spring and Autumn Annals." With the Commentary of Hoo Gan-kwo, &c. 1790. 8°.

胡 安 定 Hoo GAN-TING.

See 四 書 SZE SHOO. 四 書 朱 子 異 同 條 辨 *Sze shoo Choo tsze e tung teaou peen.* "The Four Books." With . . . the Commentaries of . . . Hoo Gan-ting, &c.   1705. 8°.

—— See 易 經 YIH KING. 周 易 口 義 *Chow Yih kow e.* "The Chow Changes. With an Oral Explanation of the Meaning" by Hoo Gan-ting, &c.   1687. 8°.

胡 金 杖 Hoo KIN-CHIH.

See 孫 理 SUN LE. 國 朝 律 賦 新 機 *Kwŏ chaou leŭh foo sin ke.* "Odes by Authors of the Present Dynasty." . . . With Notes by Hoo Kin-chĭh, &c.   8°.

———— 國 朝 七 桝 詩 鈔 *Kwŏ chaou tseĭh pae she chaou.* "A Selection of Odes by Authors of the Present Dynasty in Verses of Seven Characters each." . . . Edited by Hoo Kin-chĭh, &c.   1807. 8°.

胡 匡 夷 Hoo KWANG-CHUNG.

儀 禮 釋 官 *E le shĭh kwan.* "An Explanation of the Officers mentioned in the Decorum Ritual." 9 keuen. *See* 嚴 杰 YEN LĔĔ. 皇 清 經 解 *Hwang Tsing king keae.* "The Classics Explained," &c. Keuen 775–783. 1829. 8°.

胡 瀾 洪 Hoo LAN-HUNG.

雲 間 孝 糯 錄 *Yun heen heaou te lŭh.* "Records of Dutiful Conduct." Compiled by Hoo Lan-hung.   1833. 8°.

胡 培 翬 Hoo PEI-KWEI.

燕 寢 考 *Yen tsin kaou.* "An Examination of the Yen Chambers" of the Palace. [Also] 研 六 室 雜 著 *Yen lŭh chĭh tsŏ choo.* "Various Investigations into the Six Apartments." *See* 嚴 杰 YEN LĔĔ. 皇 清 經 解 *Hwang Tsing king keae.* "The Classics Explained," &c. Keuen 1299–1302. 1829. 8°.

胡 本 淵 Hoo PUN-YUEN.

子 史 輯 要 詩 賦 題 解 *Tsze She tseĭh yaou she foo te keae.* "A Collection of Themes gathered from the Works of Philosophers and Historians." With Explanatory Notes. Compiled by Hoo Pun-yuen. Edited by the Historian Chin. 2 keuen.   1805. 8°.

胡 本 淵 Hoo PUN-YUEN. (*Continued.*)

Another edition. Edited by Loo Wăn-shaou. 4 keuen. Supplement, 4 keuen.   1810. 8°.

Another edition. 4 keuen. Supplement, 4 keuen.   1812. 8°.

胡 三 省 Hoo SAN-SING.

See 司 馬 光 SZE-MA KWANG. 資 治 通 鑑 *Tsze che tung keen.* "A History of China." . . With a Commentary by Hoo San-sing, who also wrote the *Tsze che tung keen shĭh wăn peen woo,* &c.   1067. 8°.

胡 廷 訓 Hoo TING-HEUN.

See 龔 雲 林 KUNG YUN-LIN. 萬 病 回 春 *Wan ping hwuy chun.* "The Ten Thousand Diseases which return with the Spring." . . . Edited by Hoo Ting-heun, &c.   1589. 8°.

胡 宗 憲 Hoo TSUNG-HEEN.

籌 海 圖 編 *Chow hae too peen.* "A Detailed Work on the Seaboard Districts of China, illustrated by an Extensive Series of Maps." By Hoo Tsung-heen. Edited by Maou Kwăn. 13 keuen.   1562. 8°.

胡 文 清 Hoo WĂN-TSING.

廣 東 鄉 試 硃 卷 *Kwang tung heang she choo keuen.* "Essays written by Hoo Wăn-tsing at the Canton Examination" for the Year 1822.   1822. 8°.

胡 瑤 光 Hoo YAOU-KWANG.

See 禮 記 LE KE. 禮 記 心 典 傳 本 *Le ke sin teen chuen pun.* "The Central Canons of the Book of Rites. With a Commentary" . . . Compiled by Hoo Yaou-kwang, &c. 1693. 8°.

胡 友 信 Hoo YEW-SIN.

稿 *Kaou.* "Essays." *See* 長 城 CHANG CHING. 名 家 制 義 *Ming kea che e.* "Essays" on Texts from the Four Books, &c. Tsĭh 54.   1699. 8°.

胡 叉 邨 Hoo YEW-TSUN.

See 繆 蓮 仙 MŬH LEEN-SEEN. 文 章 游 戲 *Wăn chang yew he.* "Rambles in Polite Literature." Edited by Hoo Yew-tsun, &c.   1824. 8°.

11

胡 曰 從 Hoo Yuĕ-tsung.

十 竹 齋 書 畫 譜 *Shĭh chŭh chae shoo hwa poo.* "The Ten-Bamboo Study Collection of Polychromatic Prints." By Hoo Yuĕ-tsung. Edited by Chang Heŏ-kăng.　　1817.　8°.

胡 元 質 Hoo Yuen-chĭh.

See 周 與 嗣 Chow Hing-sze. 千 字 文 註 釋 *Tseen tsze wăn choo shĭh.* "The Thousand-character Classic, commented on and explained" by Hoo Yuen-chĭh, &c.　　　8°.

胡 玉 樹 Hoo Yŭh-shoo.

See 孫 理 Sun Le. 國 朝 律 賦 新 機 *Kwŏ chaou leŭh foo sin ke.* "Odes by Authors of the Present Dynasty." ... With Notes by ... Hoo Yŭh-shoo, &c.　　　8°.

―――― 國 朝 七 排 詩 鈔 *Kwŏ chaou tseĭh pae she chaou.* "A Selection of Odes by Authors of the Present Dynasty in Verses of Seven Characters each." ... Edited by Hoo Yŭh-shoo, &c.　　1807.　8°.

胡 雲 峰 Hoo Yun-fung.

See 徐 在 漢 Seu Tsae-han. 易 或 *Yĭh hwŏ.* "Doubts on the Book of Changes" Elucidated. .. With Notes by Hoo Yun-fung, &c.　　1774.　8°.

―――― See 四 書 Sze shoo. 論 語 註 疏 大 全 合 纂 *Lun yu choo soo ta tseuen hŏ tswan.* "The Confucian Analects, with Commentaries and Explanations" by Hoo Yun-fung, &c. 1636. 8°.

蔖 學 稼 Hoo Heŏ-kea.

堅 瓠 集 *Keen koo tseĭh.* "The Hard Calabash [*i.e.* valueless] Collection" of Tales. Compiled by Hoo Heŏ-kea. 15 Series.　1690.　12°.

呼 Hoo.

呼 家 后 代 全 本 *Hoo kea how tae tseuen pun.* "The Story of the Descendants of the Hoo Family." In Verse. 5 keuen. [1850?]. 8°.

後 學 者 How-heŏ-chay. *pseud.*

節 錄 成 章 幼 學 問 答 *Tsĕĕ lŭh ching chang yew heŏ wăn tă.* A Translation of Brown's "Short Catechism for Young Children." Translated by How-heŏ-chay.　　1824.　8°.

侯 矢 勒 How-shĭh-lĭh.

See Herschel (Sir John Frederick William), *Bart.*

HUMPHREYS (James).

See 宏 富 禮 Hung-foo-le [*i.e.* James Humphreys]. 敬 信 洗 心 篇 *King sin se sin peen.* "A Tract on Regeneration by Faith."　　1823.　8°.

紅 拂 Hung-fŭh.

紅 拂 記 *Hung fŭh ke.* "The Story of the Red Duster." See 曲 Keŭh. 六 十 種 曲 *Lŭh shĭh chung keŭh.* "Sixty Plays," &c. Taou 2.　8°.

紅 梨 Hung le.

紅 梨 記 *Hung le ke.* "The Red Pear." See 曲 Keŭh. 六 十 種 曲 *Lŭh shĭh chung keŭh.* "Sixty Plays," &c. Taou 4.　8°.

紅 樓 Hung low.

續 紅 樓 夢 *Sŭh Hung low mung.* "A Sequel to the Dream of the Red Chamber." By "The Master of the Marine Garden." [1800?]. 8°.

Imperfect.

紅 毛 Hung maou.

紅 毛 通 用 番 話 *Hung maou tung yung fan hwa.* "A Vocabulary of the Common Words of the Language of the Red-haired Foreigners" [*i.e.* the English].　　[1850?]. 8°.

Another copy.

紅 藕 山 Hung gow shan.

紅 藕 山 莊 尺 牘 *Hung gow shan chwang chĭh tŭh.* "A Complete Letter Writer." By "The Dissipated Man of Yay-yin." 12 kenen.　　1813. 8°.

Another copy.

Imperfect, containing only keuen 8, 10, 12.

弘晝 HUNG CHOW.

See CHINA. 督捕則例 *Tŭh poo tsĭh le.* "Regulations concerning the Capture" of Deserters. Compiled by .. Prince Hung Chow, &c.   1743. 8º.

———— BOARD OF OFFICE. 欽定吏部則例 *Kin ting Le Poo tsĭh le.* "Regulations of the Board of Office." Compiled by .. Prince Hung Chow, &c.   1741. 8º.

———— 雍正 YUNG-CHING. *Emperor.* 上諭 *Shang yu.* "Imperial Edicts." .. Compiled by ... Prince Hung Chow, &c.   1741. 8º.

—— See 杜佑 TOO YEW. 通典 *Tung Teen.* "A Complete Treatise" on the Political Constitution of China. Edited by .. Prince Hung Chow, &c.   1747. 8º.

—— See TSING DYNASTY. 大清律例 *Ta Tsing leŭh le.* "The Fundamental Laws and Subordinate Statutes of the Tsing Dynasty." Compiled by Prince Hung Chow, &c.   1768. 8º.

—— See 吳謙 WOO KEEN. 御纂醫宗金鑑 *Yu tswan e tsung kin keen.* "The Golden Mirror of Medecine." . . . Compiled . . . under the supervision of Prince Hung Chow, &c.   1740. 8º.

———— 欽定授時通考全書 *Kin ting show she tung kaou tseuen shoo.* "An Exhaustive Treatise on Agriculture, Horticulture, and the various Collateral Branches of Industrial Science." Compiled by an Imperial Commission consisting of Prince Hung Chow and others. A Reprint. 78 keuen.   1826. 8º.

———— 大清一統志 *Ta Tsing yĭh tung che.* "A Geography of the Empire, published under the Tsing Dynasty." Compiled by an Imperial Commission consisting of Prince Hung Chow, Tseang Ting-seĭh, Chin Tĭh-hwa, and others. 356 keuen.   1744. 4º.

弘禮 HUNG LE.

See 瞿汝稷 KEU JOO-TSEĬH. 指月錄 *Che yuĕ lŭh.* [A Thesaurus of Buddhist Biography.] .. Edited by Hung Le, &c.   8º.

弘贊 HUNG TSAN.

See 趙靈祐 CHAOU LING-YEW. 溈山警策 *Kwei shan king tsĭh.* "Religious Warnings." ... With a Commentary by the Priest Hung Tsan, &c.   1660. 8º.

—— See 袾宏 CHOO HUNG. 沙彌律儀要略增註 *Sha me leŭh e yaou leŏ tsăng choo.* "An Epitome of Rules and Rites for Buddhist Novices." .. With a Commentary by the Priest Hung Tsan, &c.   1762. 8º.

—— 解惑編 *Keae hwŏ peen.* "Doubts on Buddhism Dispelled." By Hung Tsan. 2 keuen.   1808. 8º.

—— 六道集 *Lŭh taou tseĭh.* "The Six Paths." A Buddhist Work. By the Priest Hung Tsan. A Reprint. 5 keuen.   1795. 8º.

宏富禮 HUNG-FOO-LE [*i.e.* James Humphreys]. 敬信洗心篇 *King sin se sin peen.* "A Tract on Regeneration by Faith."   1823. 8º.

洪邁 HUNG MAE.

夷堅志 *E keen che.* "An Established Collection of Tales." Compiled by Hung Mae, of the Sung Dynasty. 10 Parts.   1778. 8º.

洪昇 HUNG SHING.

長生殿 *Chang săng teen.* "The Palace of Longevity." A Drama. 4 keuen.   [1750 ?]. 12º.

洪遵 HUNG TSUN.

泉志 *Tseuen che.* "A History of the Coinage" from the Earliest Times to the Middle of the Tenth Century. A Reprint. 15 keuen.   [1814 ?]. 8º.

洪瑩 HUNG YING, and 法式善 FĂ SHĬH-SHEN.

同館試律 *Tung kwan shĭh leŭh.* "Examination Odes by Fellow Students." Compiled by Hung Ying and Fă Shĭh-shen.   [1809 ?]. 8º.

洪震煊 HUNG CHIN-HEUEN.

夏小正疏義 *Hea seaou ching soo e.* "The Meaning of the Calendar of the Hea Dynasty Explained." See 嚴杰 YEN LĔĔ. 皇清經解 *Hwang Tsing king keae.* "The Classics Explained," &c. Keuen 1318–1321.   1829. 8º.

洪 正 治 Hung Ching-che.
See 劉 宗 周 Lew Tsung-chow 人 譜 *Jin poo.*
"A Book on Man." . . Edited by Hung Ching-
che, &c. 1811. 8º.

洪 亮 吉 Hung Leang-keĭh.
北 江 詩 話 *Pĭh keang she hwa.* "Critiques on
Poetry." 4 keuen. *See* 伍 崇 曜 Woo Tsung-
yaou. 粵 雅 堂 叢 書 *Yuĕ ya Tang tsung shoo.*
"The Yuĕ-ya Tang Collection of Reprints," &c.
Series 6. 1853. 8º.

—— 附 鮚 軒 詩 *Foo keĭh heen she.* "Poetry from
the Bivalve Study." 8 keuen. 1795. 8º.

—— 漢 魏 音 *Han Wei yin.* "The Pronunciation
of Chinese during the Han and Wei Dynasties."
4 keuen. 1785. 8º.

Another copy.

—— 更 生 齋 集 *Kăng săng chae tseĭh.* "A Collection of Literary Pieces from the Study of an
Altered Life." 8 keuen. 1802. 8º.

—— 更 生 齋 詩 *Kăng săng chae she.* "Poetry from
the Study of an Altered Life." 10 keuen.
1802. 8º.

—— 乾 隆 府 廳 州 縣 圖 志 *Keen lung foo ting
chow heen too che.* "A Topography of the Prefectures, Boroughs, Sub-Prefectures, and Districts
of the Empire during the reign of Keen-lung"
[*i.e.* A.D. 1735–95]. 50 keuen. 1789. 8º.

Another copy.
Imperfect, containing only keuen 41–50.

—— 卷 施 閣 詩 *Keuen she kŏ she.* "Poetry from
the Rolling-up-and-spreading-out Pavilion." 20
keuen. 1794. 8º.

—— 卷 施 閣 文 集 *Keuen she kŏ wăn tseĭh.*
"The Literary Collection from the Rolling-up-
and-spreading-out Pavilion." In two Series.
Series I. 10 keuen. Series II. 10 keuen.
1795. 8º.
Imperfect, wanting keuen 9 and 10 of Series II.

洪 亮 吉 Hung Leang-keĭh. (*Continued.*)
補 三 國 疆 域 志 *Poo San kwŏ keang yĭh che.*
"An Enlarged Topography of the Frontier
Districts during the Period of the Three Kingdoms." 2 keuen. 1781. 8º.

Another copy.

—— 十 六 國 疆 域 志 *Shĭh lŭh kwŏ keang yĭh che.*
"A Topography of the Frontier Districts during
the Period of the Sixteen Kingdoms." 16
keuen. *Peking,* 1798. 8º.

Another copy.

Another copy.

—— 東 晉 疆 域 志 *Tung Tsin keang yĭh che.* "A
Topography of the Frontier Districts during the
Eastern Tsin Dynasty" [*i.e.* A.D. 319 to 416].
4 keuen. *Peking,* 1796. 8º.

Another copy.

Another copy.

洪 德 元 Hung Tĭh-yuen.
See 文 昌 帝 君 Wăn chang te keun. 陰 騭
文 勸 戒 編 *Yin chĭh wăn keuen keae peen.*
"A Treatise on Secret Rewards and Retributions." . . With a Commentary by Hung Tĭh-
yuen, &c. 1819. 8º.

洪 洋 洞 Hung Yang Tung.
洪 洋 洞 盜 骨 *Hung yang tung taou kŭh.* "The
Stolen Bones from the Hung-yang Cave." A
Dramatic Tale. [1800?]. 8º.

鴻 臚 寺 Hung Seu-sze.
奏 鴉 片 條 例 *Tsow Ya peen teaou le.* "Memorials on the Subject of Opium Regulations."
[1858?]. 8º.

花 Hwa.
曇 花 記 *Tan hwa ke.* "The Story of the En-
shrouded Flowers." *See* 曲 Keuh. 六 十 種 曲
Lŭh shĭh chung keŭh. "Sixty Plays," &c.
Taou 6. 8º.

華 綱 Hwa Kang.
字 類 標 韻 *Tsze luy peaou yun.* "A Dictionary,"
in which are added the Tonic Finals. By Hwa
Kang. Edited by Ho Ching-kwăn. 6 keuen.
1793. 8º.

華淞 Hwa Sung.

See 顧棟高 Koo Tung-kaou. 春秋輿圖 *Chun tsew yu too.* "The Geography of China during the Chun tsew Period." . . . Edited by Hwa Sung.   1749. 8°.

華陀 Hwa to.

華陀靈籤 *Hwa to ling tseen.* "The Inspired Lots of Hwa to."   *Canton,* [1830 ?]. 8°.

華湛恩 Hwa Chan-gän.

See 安念祖 Gan Neen-tsoo, and Hwa Chan-gän. 古韻瀏原 *Koo yun soo yuen.* "Ancient Sounds traced to their Source," &c.   1838. 4°.

華希閎 Hwa He-hung.

See 華希閎 Hwa He-min. 廣事類賦 *Kwang sze luy foo.* "An Encyclopædia." . . . . . Edited by . . . . . Hwa He-hung.   1788. 8°.

華希閎 Hwa He-min.

廣事類賦 *Kwang sze luy foo.* "An Encyclopædia. In Verse." With Notes. By Hwa He-min. Edited by Tsow Shing-häng and Hwa He-hung. 40 keuen.   1788. 8°.

華麟祥 Hwa Lin-tseang.

See 吳淑 Woo Shŭh. 事類賦 *Sze luy foo.* "A Literary Encyclopædia. In Verse." Edited by Hwa Lin-tseang, &c.   1810. 8°.

懷香 Hwae heang.

懷香記 *Hwae heang ke.* "The Cherished Perfume." See 曲 Keŭh. 六十種曲 *Lŭh shĭh chung keŭh.* "Sixty Plays," &c. Taou 3. 8°.

懷素 Hwae soo.

四分比丘尼戒本 *Sze fun Pe kew ne keae pun.* "General Precepts for the Bhikshus of the Four Divisions." Compiled by the Priest Hwae-soo.   [1800 ?]. 8°.

幻 Hwan.

糾幻首集 *Tow hwan show tseĭh.* "An Exposure of Popular Beliefs. First Part." By Rev. John Chalmers.   *Hongkong,* 1863. 8°.

桓寬 Hwan Kwan.

鹽鐵論 *Yen tëë lun.* "Discourses on Salt and Iron." See 沈津 Chin Tsin. 百家類纂 *Pĭh kea luy tswan.* "The Works of a Hundred Authors," &c. Keuen 8.   8°.

—— 鹽鐵論 *Yen tëë lun.* "Discourses on Salt and Iron." Edited by Wan Ting-sin. 12 keuen.   1553. 8°.

丸 Hwan.

飛丸記 *Fei hwan ke.* "The Story of the Flying Ball." See 曲 Keŭh. 六十種曲 *Lŭh shĭh chung keŭh.* "Sixty Plays," &c. Taou 4.   [1800 ?]. 8°.

還魂 Hwan hwăn.

還魂記 *Hwan hwăn ke.* "The Returned Ghost." See 曲 Keŭh. 六十種曲 *Lŭh shĭh chung keŭh.* "Sixty Plays," &c. Taou 2.   8°.

黃 Hwang.

See 苪 Joo, and Hwang. 江南闈墨 *Keang nan wei mĭh.* "A Collection of Keang-nan Examination Essays." . . . Edited by the Examiners Joo and Hwang, &c.   1813. 8°.

黃易 Hwang E.

嵩洛訪碑日記 *Sung Lŏ fang pae jĭh ke.* "A Journal of a Tour through the Districts of Sung and Lŏ [yang] in Search of Tablets." See 伍崇曜 Woo Tsung-yaou. 粵雅堂叢書 *Yuĕ ya Tang tsung shoo.* "The Yuĕ-ya Tang Collection of Reprints," &c. Series 15.   1853. 8°.

黃巘 Hwang Haou.

敍古千文 *Seu koo tseen wăn.* "An Ancient 'Thousand-Character Classic.'" With a Commentary by Hwang Haou. See 伍崇曜 Woo Tsung-yaou. 粵雅堂叢書 *Yuĕ ya Tang tsung shoo.* "The Yuĕ-ya Tang Collection of Reprints," &c. Series 7.   1853. 8°.

黃憲 Hwang Heen.

外史 *Wae she.* "Unorthodox History." By Hwang Heen, of the Han Dynasty. A Reprint. 8 keuen.   [1800 ?]. 8°.

黃 惠 HWANG HWUY, and 李 疇 LE CHOW.

龍溪縣志 *Lung ke heen che.* "A Topography of Lung-ke Heen," in the Province of Fŭh-keen. Compiled by Hwang Hwuy and Le Chow. Edited by Woo E-sëĕ. 24 keuen.

1762. 8º.

Title-page and first page of Preface are wanting.

黃 任 HWANG JIN.

香草齋詩註 *Heang tsaou chae she choo.* "Poetry from the Study of Fragrant Plants." With Notes by Chin Ying-kwei. 6 keuen.

1804. 8º.

—— and 陳 繩 CHIN SHING.

惠獻貝子功績錄 *Hwuy heen Pei tsze kung tseïh lŭh.* "A Record of the Meritorious Deeds of Hwuy-heen Pei-Tsze." Compiled by Hwang Jin and Chin Shing. 6 keuen, 1741. 8º.

黃 機 HWANG KE.

刑部則例 *Hing poo tsĭh le.* "The Regulations of the Board of Punishments." Compiled by Hwang Ke, &c. *See* TSING DYNASTY. 大淸律箋釋 *Ta Tsing leŭh tseen shĭh.* "The Laws of the Tsing Dynasty," &c. 1725. 8º.

黃 堦 HWANG KEAE.

See 葉九升 YE KEW-SHING. 地理山法全書 *Te le shan fă tseuen shoo.* "The Laws of Mountains." ... The First Kenen is Edited, with Notes, by Hwang Keae, &c. 8º.

黃 卷 HWANG KEUEN.

See 萬年茂 WAN NEEN-mow, and 戴第元 TAE TE-yuen. 策學纂要 *Tsĭh heŏ tswan yaou.* "The Student's Manual." ... Edited by Hwang Keuen, &c. 1766. 8º.

黃 梅 HWANG MEI.

See 吳鏞 WOO YUNG. 同安縣志 *Tung gan heen che.* "A Topography of Tung-gan Heen." Compiled by ... Hwang Mei, &c. 1767. 8º.

黃 標 HWANG PEAOU.

平夏錄 *Ping Hea lŭh.* "The History of the Pacification of Hea." *See* 說 SHWŏ. 說選 *Shwŏ seuen.* "A Collection of Records," &c. 8º.

黃 帝 HWANG TE.

陰符經 *Yin foo king.* "The Sûtra of Secret Charms." *See* 沈津 CHIN TSIN. 百家類纂 *Pĭh kea luy tswan.* "The Works of a Hundred Authors," &c. Keuen 17. 8º.

—— 內經註證 *Nuy king choo ching.* "The Two Medical Treatises, the Soo wăn and the Ling choo, by the Emperor Hwang-te. With Notes and Comments" by Ma Yuen-tae. A Reprint. Part I. 9 keuen. Part II. 10 keuen. 1805. 8º.

—— 陰符經 *Yin foo king.* "The Sûtra of Secret Charms." The oldest Taouist record in existence, said to have been written by Hwang-te. With a Commentary by Tăng Taou-shun.

[1750 ?]. 8º.

Another edition. With a Commentary by Shĭh Ho-yang. Edited by Le Ming-chĕ. 1793. 8º.

黃 佐 HWANG TSO.

翰林記 *Han lin ke.* "Records of the Han lin College." 20 keuen. [1800 ?]. 8º.

—— 廣州人物 *Kwang chow jin wŭh.* "Men and Things of Kwang chow." 24 keuen.

[1800 ?]. 8º.

黃 越 HWANG YUĕ.

See 劉豫庵 LEW YU-GAN. 詳訂古文評註 *Tseang ting koo wăn ping choo.* "Extracts from Ancient Literature. .. With Critical Notes and Comments," by .. Hwang-yuĕ, &c. 1823. 8º.

黃掌綸 HWANG CHANG-LUN.

See 徐衜 SEU TAOU. 神仙鑑 *Shin seen keen.* "Biographical Notices of Taouist Saints." ... Edited by Hwang Chang-lun, &c. 8º.

黃振瘦 HWANG CHIN-SOW.

石榴記 *Shĭh lew ke.* "The Story of the Pomegranate." By "The Husbandman of the Tsze wan Village." Edited by Hwang Chin-sow. A Drama. 4 keuen. 1799. 8º.

黃徵乂 HWANG CHING-E.

瑞安縣志 *Suy gan heen che.* "A Topography of Suy-gan Heen," in the Province of Chĕ-keang. Compiled by Hwang Ching-e, Wang Teen-kin, and others. 10 keuen. 1808. 8º.

Imperfect, wanting keuen 2.

黃正綱 HWANG CHING-KANG.

See 文昌帝君 WĂN CHANG TE KEUN. 陰騭
文圖說 *Yin chĭh wăn too shwŏ*. "A Treatise
on Secret Rewards and Retributions." . . . . .
Compiled by Hwang Ching-kang, &c.   8°.

黃正元 HWANG CHING-YUEN.

See 文昌帝君 WĂN CHANG TE KEUN. 陰騭
文圖說 *Yin chĭh wăn too shwŏ*. "A Treatise
on Secret Rewards and Retributions." . . . . .
Compiled by Hwang Ching-yuen, &c.   8°.

—— See 文昌帝君 WĂN CHANG TE KEUN. 寶訓
Paou heun. "The Precious Teachings" of Wăn
chang te keun. . . With Illustrative Stories by
Hwang Ching-yuen, &c.   1820. 8°.

—— 性天眞境 *Sing teen chin king*. "The True
Limits of Human and Divine Nature." Com-
piled by Hwang Ching-yuen. Edited by Keang
Loo-chae and Wang Han-chung. 1737. 8°.

Another edition. To which is appended a Tract entitled *Gŏ yin shĭh chin*, or Ten Prohibitions
against Lewdness, by Tsin Chan-keĭh. Edited
by Lew Kwŏ-fung.   1805. 8°.

黃柱坪 HWANG CHOO PING.

See 尹方橋 YIN FANG-KEOAU. 德潤書院
課藝 *Tĭh jun shoo yuen ko e*. "Literary
Exercises from the Tĭh-jun College." . . . Edited
by Hwang Choo-ping, &c.   1821. 8°.

黃春槳 HWANG CHUN-KEU.

See 陳大士 CHIN TA-SZE. 五經讀 *Woo king
tŭh*. "On the Study of the Five Classics."
Edited by Hwang Chun-keu, &c.   1696. 8°.

黃鳳翔 HWANG FUNG-TSEANG.

泉州府志 *Tseuen chow foo che*. "A Topography
of Tseuen-chow Foo," in the Province of Fŭh
keen. Compiled by Hwang Fung-tseang, Lin
Heŏ-tsăng, and others. 24 keuen. 1612. 8°.

黃海岸 HWANG HAE-GAN.

周秦十一子 *Chow Tsin shĭh yĭh tsze*. "The
Works of the Eleven Philosophers of the Chow
and Tsin Dynasties," namely, Laou-keun, Kwan
Chung, Sun Woo, Lëĕ Yu-kow, Chwang Chow,
Ho-kwan-tsze, Shang-tsze, Kung-sun Lung,
Seun Hwang, Han Fei, and Leu Lan. Edited
by Hwang Hae-gan. 8 keuen. [1758?]. 8°.

黃漢章 HWANG HAN-CHANG.

閩海律賦同音 *Min hae leŭh foo tung yin*.
"A Collection of Odes by Scholars of the Pro-
vince of Fŭh-keen, and others." Compiled by
Hwang Han-chang. 4 keuen. 1801. 8°.

黃曉峰 HWANG HEAOU-FUNG.

See 孔丘 KUNG KEW. 袖珍書經 *Sew chin
shoo king*. . . . "The Book of Historical Documents." . . . Edited by Hwang Heaou-fung,
&c.   1750. 8°.

—— See 李昉 LE FANG. 太平廣記 *Tae ping
kwang ke*. "Extensive Records, Compiled during
the Reign of the Emperor Tae-tsung." . . .
Edited by Hwang Heaou-fung, &c. 1806. 8°.

—— See 王黼 WANG FOO. 博古圖 *Pŏ koo too*.
"An Illustrated Collection of Antiquities." . .
Edited by Hwang Heaou-fung, &c. 1752. 8°.

黃休復 HWANG HEW-FŬH.

茅亭客話 *Maou ting kĭh hwa*. "Narrations
by Guests of the Maou Pavilion." See 說
SHWŎ. 說郛 *Shwŏ foo*. "Odds and Ends,"
&c.   8°.

黃洪憲 HWANG HUNG-HEEN.

稿 *Kaou*. "Essays." See 長城 CHANG CHING.
名家制義 *Ming kea che e*. "Essays" on
Texts from the Four Books, &c. Tsĭh 56.
    1699. 8°.

黃汝亨 HWANG JOO-HĂNG.

稿 *Kaou*. "Essays." See 長城 CHANG CHING.
名家制義 *Ming kea che e*. "Essays" on
Texts from the Four Books, &c. Tsĭh 74.
    1699. 8°.

黃汝德 HWANG JOO-TĬH.

See 周目藻 CHOW MŬH-TSAOU. 四書詩題
Sze shoo she te. "Essays on Themes from the
Four Books." . . Edited by Hwang Joo-tĭh, &c.
    8°.

黃淦綺 HWANG KAN-KE.

新墨正軌 *Sin mĭh ching kwei*. "New and
Correct Essays." Compiled by Hwang Kan-ke.
    1816. 8°.

黄淦緯 HWANG KAN-WEI.

書經精義 *Shoo king tsing e.* "The Essential Meaning of the Book of Historical Documents." 2 keuen. 1804. 8º.

黄繼善 HWANG KE-SHEN.

史學提要 *She heŏ te yaou.* "An Epitome of History." In verse. By Hwang Ke-shen. *See* 陸清獻 LǓH TSING-HEEN. 小四書 *Seaou Sze shoo.* "The Lesser Four Books," &c. Keuen 4, 5. 1845. 8ᵘ.

黄嘉惠 HWANG KEA-HWUY.

See 王符 WANG FOO. 潛夫論 *Tseen foo lun.* "The Discourses of an Unknown Scholar." ... Edited by Hwang Kea-hwuy, &c. 8º.

黄九石 HWANG KEW-SHǏH.

See 易經 YǏH KING. 易經備旨眞本 *Yih king pe che chin pun.* "A Correct Copy of the Book of Changes." ... Compiled by Hwang Kew-shǐh, &c. 1707. 8º.

黄梨洲 HWANG LE-CHOW.

南雷文定 *Nan luy wăn ting.* "The Nan luy Collection of Literary Pieces." In three parts. 18 keuen. *See* 伍崇曜 WOO TSUNG-YAOU. 粤雅堂叢書 *Yuĕ ya Tang tsung shoo.* "The Yuĕ-ya Tang Collection of Reprints," &c. Series 19. 1853. 8º.

—— 明夷待訪錄 *Ming e tae fang lŭh.* "An Inquiry into the Means of Preserving National Peace." *See* 葉志詵 YĔ CHE-SIN. 海山仙館叢書 *Hae shan seen Kwan tsung shoo.* "The Hae-shan-seen Kwan Collection of Reprints," &c. Vol. 38. 1848. 8º.

—— 南雷文約 *Nan luy wăn yŏ.* "The Nan-luy Collection of Literary Pieces." Edited by Ching Sing. 4 keuen. [1750?]. 8º.

黄孟威 HWANG MĂNG-WEI.

雅俗辨 *Ya sŭh peen.* "On the Manners of the Learned and the Vulgar." *See* 閔景賢 MIN KING-HEEN. 快書 *Kwae shoo.* "A Book of Amusement," &c. Keuen 41. 1626. 8º.

黄培芳 HWANG PEI-FANG.

See 鄧淳 TĂNG SHUN. 嶺南叢述 *Ling nan tsung shŭh.* "An Account of the Provinces of Kwang-tung and Kwang-se." .. Edited by Hwang Pei-fang. 1830. 8º.

黄丕烈 HWANG PEI-LĔĔ.

戰國策札記 *Chen kwŏ tsĭh chă ke.* "Critical Observations on the Text of the Story of the Contending States." Compiled by Hwang Pei-lĕĕ. 3 keuen. 1803. 8º.

—— 九子全書 *Kew tsze tseuen shoo.* "The Complete Works of the Nine Philosophers." Compiled by Hwang Pei-lĕĕ. 1804. 8º.

This copy is imperfect, containing only the Works of Laou-keun, Chwang Chow, Seun Hwang, Lĕĕ Yu-kow, and Kwan Chung. Judging from these books, this work would appear to be another edition of the following.

—— 十子全書 *Shĭh tsze tseuen shoo.* "The Complete Works of the Ten Philosophers," namely, Laou-keun, Chwang Chow, Seun Hwang, Lĕĕ Yu-kow, Kwan Chung, Han Fei, Lew Gan, Yang Heung, Wang Tung, and Hŏ-kwan-tsze. Compiled by Hwang Pei-lĕĕ. 1804. 8º.

黄百家 HWANG PǏH-KEA.

內家拳法 *Nuy kea keuen fă.* "The Art of Boxing." *See* 張山來 CHANG SHAN-LAE, and 張進也 CHANG TSIN-YAY. 昭代叢書 *Chaou tae tsung shoo.* "A Collection of Reprints of Works by Authors under the Present Dynasty," &c. Keuen 38. 1703. 8º.

黄錫禧 HWANG SEǏH-HE.

See 劉安 LEW GAN. 淮南鴻烈解 *Hwae nan hung lĕĕ heae.* "The Treatise of ... the Prince of Hwae nan. .. Comprehensively Explained." Edited by Hwang Seǐh-he, &c. 8º.

黄錫禔 HWANG SEǏH-YUEN.

See 韓嬰 HAN YING. 韓詩外傳 *Han She wae chuen.* "Han Ying's Illustrations of the Book of Odes from External Sources." .. Edited by Hwang Seǐh-yuen, &c. 8º.

黃紹聖 HWANG SHAOU-SHING.

See 呂嵒 LEU YEN. 呂祖全書 *Leu Tsoo tseuen shoo.* "The Complete Works of Leu Yen." ... Edited by Hwang Shaou-shing, &c. 1744. 8°.

黃峕沛 HWANG SHE-POO.

See 彭人傑 PĂNG JIN-KĔĔ. 東莞縣志 *Tung kwan heen che.* "A Topography of Tung-kwan Heen." .. Compiled by Hwang She-poo, &c. 1797. 8°.

黃石公 HWANG SHÏH-KUNG.

素書 *Soo shoo.* [A Work on Military Matters.] *See* 沈津 CHIN TSIN. 百家類纂 *Pĭh kea luy tswan.* "The Works of a Hundred Authors," &c. Keuen 18. 8°.

—— 素書 *Soo shoo.* [A Work on Military Matters.] A Reprint. [1750 ?]. 8°.

黃叔琳 HWANG SHŬH-LIN.

See 劉勰 LEW HĔĔ. 文心雕龍輯註 *Wăn sin teaou lung tsĕĭh choo.* "Lew Hĕĕ's Critique on Poetry and Literature. With an ... Exegesis" by Hwang Shŭh-lin, &c. 1738. 8°.

黃淳耀 HWANG SHUN-YAOU.

稿 *Kaou.* "Essays." *See* 長城 CHANG CHING. 名家制義 *Ming kea che e.* "Essays" on Texts from the Four Books, &c. Tsĭh 98. 1699. 8°.

黃省曾 HWANG SING-TSĂNG.

See 沈汾 CHIN FUN. 續仙傳 *Sŭh seen chuen.* "Supplementary Lives of Saints." Edited by Hwang Sing-tsăng, &c. 1553. 8°.

—— See 皇甫謐 HWANG FOO-MEĬH. 高士傳 *Kaou sze chuen.* "Biographies of Eminent Scholars." Edited by Hwang Sing-tsăng, &c. 1533. 8°.

—— 西洋朝貢典錄 *Se yang chaou kung teen lŭh.* "An Account of the Tributary States of the Southern Ocean." 3 keuen. *See* 伍崇曜 WOO TSUNG-YAOU. 粵雅堂叢書 *Yuĕ ya Tang tsung shoo.* "The Yuĕ-ya Tang Collection of Reprints," &c. Series 3. 1853. 8°.

黃思湖 HWANG SZE-HOO.

居官福惠全書 *Keu kwan fŭh hwuy tseuen shoo.* "The Officials' Guide to Happy and Considerate Rule." 32 keuen. 1694. 8°.

黃道周 HWANG TAOU-CHOW.

稿 *Kaou.* "Essays." *See* 長城 CHANG CHING. 名家制義 *Ming kea che e.* "Essays" on Texts from the Four Books, &c. Tsĭh 83. 1699. 8°.

—— 廣名將傳 *Kwang ming tseang chuen.* "Lives of Celebrated Commanders" from the Chow to the Ming Dynasties. 20 keuen. *See* 葉志詵 YĔ CHE-SIN. 海山仙館叢書 *Hae shan seen kwan tsung shoo.* "The Hae shan seen Kwan Collection of Reprints," &c. Vol. 21–26. 1848. 8°.

黃道煥 HWANG TAOU-HWĂN.

北涼錄 *Pĭh Leang lŭh.* "Records of the Northern Leang Dynasty." Edited by Hwang Taou-hwăn. *See* 崔鴻 TSUY HUNG. 十六國春秋 *Shĭh lŭh kwŏ chun tsew.* "The Annals of the Sixteen Dynasties," &c. 8°.

黃體端 HWANG TE-TWAN.

See 老君 LAOU KEUN. 感應篇直講 *Kan ying peen chĭh keang.* "The Book of Rewards and Punishments," .. clearly explained by Hwang Te-twan, &c. 1831. 8°.

黃庭堅 HWANG TING-KEEN.

山谷集 *Shan kŭh tsĕĭh.* "The Hill and Valley Collection." *See* 吳孟舉 WOO MĂNG-KEU, and 牧自吳 WOO TSZE-MUH. 宋詩鈔二集 *Sung she chaou urh tsĕĭh.* "Poetry of the Sung Dynasty," &c. 8°.

黃際飛 HWANG TSE-FEI.

See 向日貞 HEANG JĬH-CHING. 註釋向太史全稿 *Choo shĭh Heang tae she tseuen kaou.* "A Complete Collection of the Essays of Heang Jĭh-ching, the Historian." .. Edited by Hwang Tse-fei, &c. 1771. 8°.

黃宗聖 HWANG TSUNG-SHING.

百中經 *Pĭh chung king.* "The Book of a Hundred Hits." *Canton*, [1830 ?]. 8°.

Another edition. *Canton*, [1840 ?]. 8°.

黃 自 如 Hwang Tsze-joo.

See 涵蠾子 Han Chen-tsze. 金丹正理大要道書全集 *Kin tan ching le ta yaou taou shoo tseuen tseĭh.* "A Complete Collection of Important Taouist Works on the True Principle of the Elixir of Immortality." .. With Commentaries by Hwang Tsze-joo, &c.
1538. 8°.

黃 應 熊 Hwang Ying-heung.

See 許琰 Heu Yen. 普陀山志 *Poo to shan che.* "A Topography of the Island of Poo-to." ... Edited by Hwang Ying-heung, &c.
1740. 8°.

黃 應 澄 Hwang Ying-tăng.

See 顧鼎臣 Koo Ting-chin. 狀元圖考 *Chwang yuen too kaou.* "Biographical Notices of Chwang yuen. With Illustrations" by Hwang Ying-tăng, &c. 1643. 8°.

黃 雨 泉 Hwang Yu-tseuen.

See 尹方橋 Yin Fang-keaou. 德潤書院課藝 *Tĭh jun shoo yuen ko e.* "Literary Exercises from the Tĭh-jun School." ... Edited by Hwang Yu-tseuen, &c. 1821. 8°.

黃 俞 言 Hwang Yu-yen.

黃辭 *Hwang tsze.* "Hwang's Phraseology." See 閔景賢 Min King-heen. 快書 *Kwae shoo.* "A Book of Amusement," &c. Keuen 10.
1626. 8°.

皇 明 Hwang ming.

皇明英烈志傳 *Hwang Ming ying lëe che chuen.* "Biographical Notices of Heroes of the Ming Dynasty." With Illustrations. 4 keuen.
[1750?]. 8°.

皇 甫 枝 Hwang Foo-che.

三水小牘 *San shwuy seaou tŭh.* "A Small Collection of Anecdotes from San shwuy." See 說 Shwŏ. 說畧 *Shwŏ lĕŏ.* "Historical and other Tracts," &c. 8°.

皇 甫 枚 Hwang Foo-mei.

非烟傳 *Fei yin chuen.* "The Story of Poo Fei-yin." By Hwang Foo-mei, of the Tang Dynasty. A Reprint. [1741?]. 8°.

皇 甫 謐 Hwang Foo-meĭh.

高士傳 *Kaou sze chuen.* "Biographies of Eminent Scholars." Edited by Hwang Sing-tsăng. 3 keuen. 1533. 8°.

Another edition. Edited by Chang Sze-han. 3 keuen.
[1700?]. 8°.

惠 棟 Hwuy Tung.

See 老君 Laou keun. 感應篇箋註 *Kan ying peen tseen choo.* "The Book of Rewards and Punishments. . . With a Commentary" by Hwuy Tung, &c. 1827. 8°.

—— 後漢書補註 *How Han shoo poo choo.* "Supplementary Comments on the History of the Later Han Dynasty." Compiled by Hwuy Tung. 24 keuen. [Also] 感應篇註 *Kan ying peen choo.* "The Book of Rewards and Punishments." ... With a Commentary by Hwuy Tung. See 伍崇曜 Woo Tsung-yaou. 粵雅堂叢書 *Yuĕ ya Tang tsung shoo.* "The Yuĕ-ya Tang Collection of Reprints," &c. Series 10, 12. 1853. 8°.

—— 易大義 *Yĭh ta e.* "The Principal Meaning of the Book of Changes." See 葉志洗 Yĕ Che-sin. 海山仙館叢書 *Hae shan seen Kwan tsung shoo.* "The Hae-shan-seen Kwan Collection of Reprints," &c. Vol. 2. 1848. 8°.

—— 周易述 *Chow Yĭh shŭh.* "The Book of Changes, with a Collection of Notes and Explanations." 21 keuen. [Also] 古文尚書考 *Koo wăn Shang shoo kaou.* "An Examination of the Ancient Text of the Book of Historical Documents." [Also] 春秋左傳補注 *Chun Tsew Tso chuen poo choo.* "Supplementary Comments on the Chun Tsew and Tso chuen." 6 keuen. [Also] 九經古義 *Kew king koo e.* "The Ancient Meaning of the Nine Classics." 16 keuen. See 嚴杰 Yen Lĕĕ. 皇清經解 *Hwang Tsing king keae.* "The Classics Explained," &c. Keuen 330-374. 1829. 8°.

惠 周 惕 Hwuy Chow-teĭh.

詩說 *She shwŏ.* "Discourses on the Book of Odes." 4 keuen. See 嚴杰 Yen Lĕĕ. 皇清經解 *Hwang Tsing king keae.* "The Classics Explained," &c. Keuen 190-93. 1829. 8°.

惠士奇 Hwuy Sze-ke.

易說 *Yih shwŏ.* "Discourses on the Book of Changes." 6 keuen. [Also] 禮說 *Le shwŏ.* "Discourses on the Book of Rites." 14 keuen. [Also] 春秋說 *Chun Tsew shwŏ.* "Discourses on the Spring and Autumn Annals." 15 keuen. *See* 嚴杰 Yen Lĕĕ. 皇清經解 *Hwang Tsing king keae.* "The Classics Explained," &c. Keuen 208–242. 1829. 8º.

慧皎 Hwuy Keaou.

高僧傳 *Kaou Tsăng chuen.* "Lives of Celebrated Buddhist Priests." By Hwuy Keaou. 10 keuen. *See* 葉志詵 Yĕ Che-sin. 海山仙館叢書 *Hae shan seen Kwan tsung shoo.* "The Hae-shan-seen Kwan Collection of Reprints," &c. Vol. 27–30. 1848. 8º.

慧苑 Hwuy Yuen.

華嚴經音義 *Hwa yen king yin e.* "The Meaning and Sounds of the Chinese Version of the Buddha purana Sûtra." 4 keuen. *See* 伍崇曜 Woo Tsung-yaou. 粵雅堂叢書 *Yuĕ ya Tang tsung shoo.* "The Yuĕ-ya Tang Collection of Reprints," &c. Series 12. 1853. 8º.

會試 Hwuy she.

會試硃卷 *Hwuy she choo keuen.* "The Red Book of Examination Essays," containing Essays for the Years 1733, 1790, 1808, 1817, 1819, 1822, 1837, and 1838. 1733–1838. 8º.
Imperfect.

悔罪 Hwuy tsuy.

悔罪之大畧 *Hwuy tsuy che ta lĕŏ.* "The Great Scheme of Repentance." [By C. F. A. Gützlaff.] [*Singapore,* 1839 ?]. 8º.

INCE ( ).

See 聖錄 Shing lŭh. 聖錄名人問答 *Shing lŭh ming jin wăn tă.* ... A Translation of Ince's Catechism, &c. 1822. 8º.

JESUS CHRIST.

救世主言行全傳 *Kew she choo yen hing tseuen chuen.* "The Life of Christ." [By C. F. A. Gützlaff.] 11 keuen. [1820 ?]. 8º.

JESUS CHRIST. (*Continued.*)

救世主耶穌言行畧傳 *Kew she choo Yay-soo yen hing lĕŏ chuen.* "A Short Narrative of the Life of Jesus Christ." Published by the Chinese Evangelization Society. 1855. 8º.

—— 救世耶穌受死全傳 *Kew she Yay-soo show sze tseuen chuen.* "The Narrative of the Death of Our Saviour Jesus Christ. [By C. F. A. Gützlaff.] 1843. 8º.

—— 總論耶穌之榮 *Tsung lun Yay-soo che yung.* "A Discourse on the Glory of Jesus Christ." [By A. Stronach.] *Hongkong,* 1868. 8º.

—— 耶穌復生傳 *Yay-soo fŭh săng chuen.* "The Story of the Resurrection of Jesus Christ." 1843. 8º.

—— 耶穌基督降世傳 *Yay-soo Ke-tŭh keang she chuen.* "The Life of Jesus Christ." [By B. Hobson (?).] [*Shanghae,* 1860 ?]. 8º.

—— 耶穌受苦尋源 *Yay-soo show koo tsin yuen.* "A Search into the Causes of the Sufferings of Jesus Christ." [By P. Winnes.] *Hongkong,* 1868. 8º.

人 Jin.

招人獲救 *Chaou jin hwŏ kew.* "An Invitation to Obtain Salvation." [By C. F. A. Gützlaff.] [1830 ?]. 8º.

—— 正人明堂圖 *Ching jin ming tang too.* "An Anatomical Plate of the Front of the Human Body." [1800 ?]. A sheet.

—— 伏人明堂圖 *Fŭh jin ming tang too.* "An Anatomical Plate of the Back of the Human Body." [1800 ?]. A sheet.
There are three copies of this Plate.

—— 側人明堂圖 *Tsĭh jin ming tang too.* "An Anatomical Plate of the Side of the Human Body." [1800 ?]. A sheet.
There are three copies of this Plate.

—— 人當自省以食晚饔論 *Jin tang tsze sing e shĭh wan tsan lun.* "On the Necessity of Self-Examination before Partaking of the Lord's Supper." [By Dr. W. H. Medhurst.] [*Shanghae,* 1857 ?]. 8º.

人 JIN. (*Continued.*)

人子須知資孝書 *Jin tsze seu che tsze heaou shoo.* "A Book for the Instruction of Men in Matters to which they should yield Obedience." A Work on Geomancy.   [1750?].   8°.
Very imperfect and much torn.

—— 論善惡人死 *Lun shen gŏ jin sze.* "The Death of the Good and Bad." [By Dr. W. H. Medhurst.]   *Hongkong*, 1844.   8°

人虎 JIN HOO.

人虎傳 *Jin hoo chuen.* "The Story of the Man-Tiger." *See* 說 SHWŎ. 說淵 *Shwŏ yuen.* "A Collection of Tales," &c.   Vol. 9   8°.

仁潮 JIN CHAOU.

法界安立圖 *Fă keae gan leĭh too.* "The Buddhist Kosmos. With Illustrations." Compiled by the Priest Jin Chaou. A Reprint. 6 keuen.   *Canton*, 1679.   8°.

仁岠 JIN KEU.

人天眼目 *Jin teen yen mŭh.* "The Eyes of Men and of Heaven." A Buddhist Work. By the Priest Jin Keu. A Reprint. 2 keuen.   1745.   8°.

仁賣 JIN-KWEI.

仁賣回家 *Jin-kwei hwuy kea.* "The Return of General Sëĕ Jin-kwei." A Drama.   [1800?].   8°.

仁愛者 JIN-GAE-CHAY. *pseud.* [*i.e.* Ira Tracey.]

鴉片速改文 *Ya peen sŭh kae wăn.* "A Tract for the Speedy Reformation of Opium Smokers."   *Singapore*, 1835.   8°.

仁愛會 JIN GAE HWUY. *pseud.*

醒世要言 *Sing she yaou yen.* "Important Words to Arouse the World." A Christian Tract. By Jin-gae-hwuy.   1838.   8°.

仁和龔 JIN HO-KUNG.

See 諸暨蔣 CHOO KE-TSEANG, and JIN HO-KUNG. 文廟彙考 *Wăn meaou wei kaou.* "An Examination of Literary Temples." By Choo Ke-tseang and Jin Ho-kung, &c.   1827.   8°.

任蕃 JIN FAN.

夢遊錄 *Mung yew lŭh.* "Wanderings in Dreamland." *See* 王文誥 WANG WĂN-KAOU. 唐代叢書 *Tang tae tsung shoo.* "A Collection of Reprints of Works written during the Tang Dynasty," &c.   Series 4.   1806.   8°.

—— 夢遊錄 *Mung yew lŭh.* "Wanderings in Dreamland." By Jin Fan, of the Tang Dynasty. A Reprint.   [1741?].   8°.

任昉 JIN FANG.

述異記 *Shŭh e ke.* "Notes on Curious Facts and Phenomena." By Jin Fang. Edited by Wang Yĭh-keun. 2 keuen.   1750.   8°.

任之全 JIN CHE-TSEUEN.

See 李錫勛 LE SEĬH-HEUN. 成均課藝正續彙選 *Ching keun ko e ching sŭh wei seuen.* "A Collection of Essays." Compiled by ... Jin Che-tseuen, &c.   1802.   8°.

任以治 JIN E-CHE.

See 甘芳谷 KAN FANG-KŬH. 詩韻含英題解辨同合訂 *She yun han ying te keae peen tung hŏ ting.* "A Copious Tonic Dictionary of Poetical Expressions." ... Edited by Jin E-che, &c.   1775.   8°.

任如堂 JIN JOO-TANG.

越絕書 *Yuĕ tseuĕ shoo.* "An Account of the Extinction of the Kingdom of Yuĕ." Edited by Jin Joo-tang. 15 keuen.   1552.   8°.

任階平 JIN KEAE-PING.

直省鄉墨 *Chĭh shing heăng mĭh.* "A Collection of Essays" from the Hoo-pĭh, Hoo-nan, Ho-nan, and Shan-tung Examination Papers for the Year 1832. Edited by Jin Keae-ping.   1832.   8°.

—— 直省鄉墨珠林 *Chĭh shing heang mĭh choo lin.* "A Valuable Collection of Essays by Authors of Various Provinces." Compiled by Jin Keae-ping.   1834.   8°.
Imperfect.

任大椿 JIN TA-CHUN.

弁服釋例 *Peen fŭh shĭh le.* "The Rules on the Subject of Dress Explained." 8 keuen. [Also] 釋繪 *Shĭh hwuy.* "Dress Ornaments Explained." *See* 嚴杰 YEN LĔĔ. 皇清經解 *Hwang tsing king keae.* "The Classics Explained," &c. Keuen 495–503. 1829. 8°.

若亞敬公 JŎ-A-KING-KUNG. *pseud.*

See 陽瑪諾 YANG-MA-NŎ. 輕世金書 *King she kin shoo.* A Translation of the "Imitation of Christ" by Thomas à Kempis. . . . Published with the approval of Jŏ-a-king-kung, &c. 1815. 8°.

如蓮 JOO LEEN.

仁貴征西 *Jin-kwei ching se.* "A History of the Conquest of the West by General Sëë Jin-kwei," during the Tang Dynasty. By Joo Leen. 10 keuen. 1807. 8°.

Another edition. 10 keuen. 1828. 8°.

—— 薛仁貴征東全傳 *Sëë Jin-kwei ching tung tseuen chuen.* "A Complete History of the Conquest of the East by General Sëë Jin-kwei." By Joo Leen. 6 keuen. 1838. 8°.

如氐亞 JOO-TE-A.

古時如氐亞國歷代略傳 *Koo she Joo-te-a kwŏ leĭh tae leŏ chuen.* "A Short History of Ancient Judæa." [By R. Morrison.] [1815?]. 8°.

茹 JOO, and 黃 HWANG.

江南闈墨 *Këang-nan wei mĭh.* "A Collection of Këang-nan Examination Essays." Edited by the Examiners Joo and Hwang. 1813. 8°.

儒 JOO.

儒林外史 *Joo lin wae she.* "Tales of Scholars." By "The Old Man of the Lounger's Study." 1803. 8°.

Another copy.

Imperfect.

襦 JOO.

繡襦記 *Sew joo ke.* "The Story of the Embroidered Jacket." *See* 曲 KEŬH. 六十種曲 *Lŭh shĭh chung keŭh.* "Sixty Plays," &c. Taou 4. 8°.

JOSEPH, *Poor.*

貧人約瑟 *Pin jin Yŏ-sĭh.* "An Account of the Conversion and Death of Poor Joseph." Translated into Chinese by G. Piercy. [*Hongkong*, 1860?]. 12°.

入泮 JŬH PWAN.

八泮探芹集 *Jŭh pwan tsae kin tseĭh.* "A Select Collection of the Essays of Graduates." 2 keuen (?). [1780?]. 8°.

Imperfect, containing only keuen 2.

JULIEN (STANISLAS AIGNAN).

日常口頭話 *Ji-tch'ang-k'eou-t'eou-hoa.* Dialogues Chinois. . . Publiés avec une traduction et un Vocabulaire Chinois-Français de tous les mots. Par S. J. 1re Partie : Texte Chinois. [With an Italian Title-page as follows, Dialoghi Cinesi. Partie prima, &c.] *Paris*, 1863. 8°.

KALAYAÇAS.

See 疊瓦那舍 KEANG-LEANG-YAY-SHAY.

甘公 KAN KUNG, and 石申 SHĬH SHIN.

星經 *Sing king.* "A Work on Astronomy." By Kan Kung and Shĭh Shin. A Reprint. 2 keuen. [1750?]. 8°.

甘芳谷 KAN FANG-KŬH.

詩韻含英題解辨同合訂 *She yun han ying te keae peen tung hŏ ting.* "A Copious Tonic Dictionary of Poetical Expressions Explained and Discussed." Compiled by Kan Fang-kŭh. Edited by Jin E-che and Tsae Ying-seang. 10 keuen. 1775. 8°.

甘臤麟 KAN YU-LIN.

四書類典賦 *Sze shoo luy teen foo.* "Odes on Subjects from the Four Books." With a Vocabulary of phrases at the end of each poem. Edited by Seay Fung-tae and Chow Yang-he. 24 keuen. 1777. 8°.

干寶 KAN PAOU.

周易注 *Chow Yĭh choo.* "A Commentary on the Chow Changes." *See* 孫堂 SUN TANG. 漢魏二十一家易注 *Han Wei urh shĭh yĭh kea Yĭh choo.* "Commentaries on the Book of Changes," &c. 1799. 8°.

干寶 KAN PAOU. (*Continued.*)

搜神記 *Sow shin ke.* "Marvellous Tales." By Kan Paou, of the Tsin Dynasty. Edited by Yang Kwang-lĕŭ. [1750?]. 8°.

堪輿 KAN YU.

堪輿問答 *Kan yu wăn tă.* "A Conversation on Geomancy." [By F. Genaehr.]
Hongkong, 1868. 8°.

康熙 KANG-HE. *Emperor.*

See 朱熹 CHOO HE. 朱子全書 *Choo tsze tseuen shoo.* "The Complete Works of Choo He." Compiled under the direction of the Emperor Kang-he, &c. 1713. 8°.

—— 康熙字典 *Kang-he tsze teen.* "Kang-he's Dictionary." Compiled under the direction and by the orders of that Emperor by Chang Yŭh-shoo, Chin Ting-king, Ling Shaou-wăn, and other Scholars. In 12 Parts. 1716. 8°.

Another edition. In 12 Parts. 1716. 8°.

Another edition. In 12 Parts. 1716. 8°.

Another edition. In 12 Parts. 1716. 8°.
Imperfect, characters under the radicals 167–214 being wanting.

Another edition. In 12 Parts. [1716?]. 4°.
An interleaved copy. With illustrations and MS. notes. Title-page and preface wanting.

Another edition. In 12 Parts. [1716?]. 8°.
Imperfect, containing only characters under radicals 72 to 94.

Another edition. In 12 Parts. 1716. 8°.

Another edition. In 12 Parts. 1716. 8°.

Another edition. In 12 Parts. 1716. 8°.
Imperfect, title-page and preface wanting.

—— 上論 *Shang yu.* "An Imperial Edict," published by the Emperor Kang-he, expressing his regret at the death of Gan Wăn-sze, *i.e.* P Gabriel de Magalhaens. 1677. 8°.

康熙 KANG-HE. *Emperor.* (*Continued.*)

聖諭廣訓 *Shing yu kwang heun.* "The Maxims of the Emperor Kang-he, amplified" by his successor Yung-ching. 1724. 8°.

Another edition. 1724. 8°.

Another edition. 2 keuen. [1730?]. 8°.

Another edition. [1740?]. 8°.
Imperfect.

Another edition. [1800?]. 8°.

Another edition. 1808. 8°.

Another edition. 1815. 8°.

—— 御製文集 *Yu che wăn tseĭh.* "The Literary Works of the Emperor Kang-he." Edited by Chang Yŭh-shoo, Chang Ying, Chin Ting-king, and others. 40 keuen. 1711. 8°.

—— 御製文第二集 *Yu che wăn te urh tseĭh.* "A Second Collection of the Works of the Emperor Kang-he." Edited by Chang Yŭh-shoo, Chang Ying, Chin Ting-king, and others. 50 keuen. 1712. 8°.

—— 御製文第三集 *Yu che wăn te san tseĭh.* "A Third Collection of the Works of the Emperor Kang-he." Edited by Chang Yŭh-shoo, Chin Ting-king, and Wang Yen. 50 keuen. 1714. 8°.

—— 御選古文淵鑒 *Yu seuen koo wăn yuen keen.* "A Deep Mirror of Ancient Literature." Compiled by the Emperor Kang-he. Edited by Seu Keen-heŭ. This Collection begins with the Narrative of Tso Kew-ming, and is continued down to the Works of Authors under the Sung Dynasty. With Notes. 64 keuen. 1685. 8°.

Another copy.

Another edition. 1685. 8°.
Imperfect, containing only the first twenty-two keuen.

康駢 KANG PEEN.

劇談錄 *Keĭh tan lŭh.* "Trivial Conversations." *See* 王文誥 WANG WĂN-KAOU. 唐代叢書 *Tang tae tsung shoo.* "A Collection of Reprints of Works written during the Tang Dynasty," &c. Series 2. 1806. 8°.

KAO [95] KAO

康 紹 鏞 KANG SHAOU-YUNG.

See 嘉慶 KEA-KING. *Emperor.* 大行皇帝
遺詔 *Ta hing hwang te e chaou.* "The Last
Testament of the Emepror Kea-king." Prepared
by Kang Shaou-yung, &c. 1820. 8º.

—— See 阮元 YUEN YUEN. 廣東通志 *Kwang
tung tung che.* "A Topography of the Province
of Kwang-tung." Compiled by . . . Kang
Shaou-yung, &c. 1822. 8º.

康 譽 之 KANG YU-CHE.

昨夢錄 *Tsŏ mung lùh.* "A Record of Dreams."
See 說 SHWŏ. 說畧 *Shwŏ leŏ.* "Historical
and other Tracts," &c. 8º.

庚 肩 吾 KĂNG KEEN-WOO.

書品 *Shoo pin.* "On Calligraphers." By Kăng
Keen-woo, of the Leang Dynasty. A Reprint.
[1750?]. 8º.

庚 桑 楚 KĂNG SANG-TSOO.

亢倉子 *Kang tsang tsze.* "The Writings of
Kăng Sang-tsoo." *See* 沈津 CHIN TSIN. 百
家類纂 *Pĭh kea luy tswan.* "The Works of
a Hundred Authors," &c. Keuen 16. 8º.

高 平 KAOU PING.

高平關取級 *Kaou ping kwan tseu keĭh.*
"Gaining Promotion at Kaou ping." A Drama.
[1800?]. 8º.

高 晉 KAOU TSIN.

南巡盛典 *Nan seun shing teen.* "An Account
of Four Royal Progresses made by the Emperor
Keen-lung in the South," between the Years
1751 and 1765. Compiled by Kaou Tsin, Foo
Chun, Yung Paou, and others. This Work
gives a minute description of the various routes,
with plans, and views of all the interesting
objects on the way. 120 keuen. 1771. 8º.

Another copy.

Imperfect, containing only keuen 11–15, 18–23, 34–39,
43–48, 54–56, 60–62, 68–84, 87–91, 106–117.

Another copy.

Imperfect, containing only keuen 54–56, 106–108, 114,
115.

高 誘 KAOU YEW.

國策 *Kwŏ tsĭh.* "The Story of the Contending
States." With a Commentary by Kaou Yew.
See 陳明卿 CHIN MING-KING, and 鍾伯敬
CHUNG PĬH-KING. 國語國策詳注 *Kwŏ
yu kwŏ tsĭh tseang choo.* "The Narratives of the
States . . . and the Story of the Contending
States," &c. Part II. 1724. 8º.

—— 淮南子 *Hwae nan tsze.* "The Treatise of the
Prince of Hwae nan." With a Commentary by
Kaou Yew, &c. *See* 黃丕烈 HWANG PEI-
LĔĔ. 十子全書 *Shĭh tsze tseuen shoo.* "The
Complete Works of the Ten Philosophers," &c.
1804. 8º.

—— See 呂不韋 LEU PŬH-WEI. 呂氏春秋 *Leu
she Chun Tsew.* "The Spring and Autumn
Annals of Leu Pŭh-wei." With a Commentary
by Kaou Yew, &c. 1579. 8º.

—— See 劉安 LEW GAN. 淮南子箋釋 *Hwae
nan tsze tseen shĭh.* "The Treatise of the Prince
of Hwae nan." With a Commentary by Kaou
Yew, &c. 1804. 8º.

—— See 劉向 LEW HEANG. 戰國策 *Chen kwŏ
tsĭh.* "The Story of the Contending States."
. . . With a Commentary by Kaou Yew, &c.
1803. 8º.

高 朝 瓔 KAOU CHAOU-YING.

See 詩經 SHE KING. 詩經體註 *She king te
choo.* "The Book of Odes." . . Edited by Kaou
Chaou-ying, &c. 1711. 8º.

高 陳 謨 KAOU CHIN-MOO.

雲襄集 *Yun yang tseĭh.* "The Yun-yang Collection" of Poetry. Compiled by Kaou Chin-
moo. 8 keuen. 1803. 8º.

高 學 濂 KAOU HEŎ-LEEN.

江安縣志 *Keang gan heen che.* "A Topography
of Keang-gan Heen." Compiled by Kaou Heŏ-
leen. 2 keuen. 1829. 8º.

高 其 倬 KAOU KE-CHŎ.

See 尹繼善 YIN KE-SHEN. 江南通志
Keang nan tung che. "A Topography of the
Province of Keang-nan." Compiled by . . . Kaou
Ke-chŏ, &c. 1737. 8º.

高其名 KAOU KE-MING, and 鄭師成 CHING SZE-CHING.

四書左國輯要 Sze shoo Tso kwŏ tseĭh yaou. "Extracts from Tso Kew-ming's Narrative, The Story of the Contending States, and other Works, illustrating the Lives of Worthies mentioned in the Four Books." Compiled by Kaou Ke-ming and Ching Sze-ching. An enlarged edition. 4 keuen. 1789. 8°.

Another edition. 4 keuen. 1806. 8°.

高鼓峰 KAOU KOO-FUNG.

己任編 E jin peen. "A Treatise which has proved itself to be Trustworthy." A Medical Work. Keuen 1 to 5 are by Kaou Koo-fung, and keuen 6 to 8 by Tung Fei-ung. A Reprint. 8 keuen. 1830. 8°.

高伯揚 KAOU PĬH-YANG.

續琵琶 Sŭh Pe pa. "A Sequel to the Tale of the Pe pa." A Drama. By Kaou Pĭh-yang. A Reprint. 2 keuen. 1799. 8°.

高象先 KAOU SEANG-SEEN.

金丹歌 Kin tan ko. "The Recitation of the Elixir of Immortality." See 彭好古 PĂNG HAOU-KOO. 道言內外秘訣全書 Taou yen nuy wae pe keŭ tseuen shoo. "A Complete Collection of Taouist Works," &c. 8°.

高雪君 KAOU SEUĔ-KEUN.

See 易經 YĬH KING. 易經來註圖解 Yĭh king Lae choo too keae. "The Book of Changes." ... Edited by Kaou Seuĕ-keun, &c. 1598. 8°.

高士奇 KAOU SZE-KE.

松亭行紀 Sung ting hing ke. "Notes of an Imperial Progress to Sung ting." [Also] 扈從西巡日錄 Hoo tsung se seun jĭh lŭh. "A Diary of an Imperial Journey towards the West." [Also] 塞北小鈔 Sĭh pĭh seaou chaou. "An Account of an Imperial Journey to the North." See 張山來 CHANG SHAN-LAE, and 張進也 CHANG TSIN-YAY. 昭代叢書 Chaou tae tsung shoo. "A Collection of Reprints of Works by Authors under the present Dynasty," &c. Keuen 10-12. 1703. 8°.

高第丕 KAOU TE PEI. pseud. [i.e. T. P. Crawford.]

文學書官話 Wăn heŏ shoo kwan hwa. "A Mandarin Grammar." Compiled by Kaou Te Pei, with the assistance of Chang Joo-chin, a Chinaman. With Preface and Index in English. 1869. 8°.

高廷㮥 KAOU TING-TSAN.

See 屈何煥 KEŬH HO-HWAN. 萬壽恩科墨卷雅正 Wan show găn ko mĭh keuen ya ching. "Elegant Essays, selected from those written for the extra Examinations granted by Imperial Favour" in the Year 1780.... Edited by ... Kaou Ting-tsan, &c. 1790. 8°.

高文虎 KAOU WĂN-HOO.

蓼花洲間錄 Leaou hwa chow heen lŭh. "Tales from Leaou hwa chow." See 說 SHWŎ. 纂說 Shwŏ tswan. "Miscellaneous Records." Vol. 5. 8°.

高一志 KAOU YĬH-CHE. pseud. [i.e. Alphonsus Vagnoni.]

空際格致 Kung tse kĭh che. "A Work on the Chemical Composition of the Universe." By Kaou Yĭh-che. Edited by Han Yun, and revised by Chin So-sing. 2 keuen. [1610?]. 8°.

Another copy.
Imperfect.

高應斗 KAOU YING-WOO.

小農塾課 Seaou nung shŭh ko... "Essays from the Seaou-nung School." By Kaou Ying-woo. Second edition. 1817. 8°.

考卷 KAOU KEUEN.

考卷清雅 Kaou keuen tsing ya. "Elegant Essays from Examination Papers." Third Series. [1790?]. 8°.
An odd vol.

稽曾筠 KE TSĂNG-YUN.

浙江通志 Chĕ keang tung che. "A Topography of the Province of Chĕ-keang." Compiled by Ke Tsăng-yun, Le Wei, Hŏ Yŭh-lin, and others. 280 keuen. 1736. 8°.
Imperfect, containing only keuen 1-21.

紀鎔 KE CHUNG.

See 張孟遷 CHANG MĂNG-TSEEN. 傷寒世聡精法 Shang han she neen tsing fă. "A Treatise on Fevers." ... Edited by Ke Chung, &c. 1795. 8°.

第一卷

紀鑑 KE KEEN.

貫虱心傳 *Kwan sǐh sin chuen.* "On Archery." See 張山來 CHANG SHAN-LAE, and 張進也 CHANG TSIN-YAY. 昭代叢書 *Chaou tae tsung shoo.* "A Collection of Reprints of Works by Authors under the present Dynasty," &c. Keuen 39.   1703.   8º.

紀氏 KE SHE.

灤陽消夏錄 *Lwan yang seaou hea lǔh.* "Summer Tales from Lwan-yang." 6 keuen.   1789.   8º.

紀昀 KE YUN.

See 桑欽 SANG KIN. 水經注 *Shwuy king choo.* "The Water Classic." . . . Edited by Ke Keun, &c.   1744.   8º.

—— See 衛宏 WEI HUNG. 漢官舊儀 *Han kwan kew e.* "The Ancient Ceremonies of the Officials of the Han Dynasty." . . . Edited by Ke Yun, &c.   1774.   8º.

—— See 易經 YĬH KING. 傳家易說 *Chuen kea yǐh shwǒ.* "The Book of Changes." . . . Edited by Ke Yun, &c.   1775.   8º.

—— 欽定歷代職官表 *Kin ting leǐh tae chǐh kwan peaou.* "A Series of Tables exhibiting the Changes which have taken place in the Names and Duties of the Officers in the several Departments of Government from the Earliest Times down to the present Dynasty." Compiled by an Imperial Commission consisting of Ke Yun, Lǚh Seǐh-heung, Sun Sze-e, and others. 72 keuen.   1783.   8º.

—— 欽定勝朝殉節諸臣錄 *Kin ting shing chaou seun tsëë choo chin lǔh.* "Biographical Notices of Officials of the Ming Dynasty who lost their Lives in the Service of their Country." Compiled by Imperial order by Ke Yun, Lǚh Seǐh-heung, Sun Sze-e, and others. 12 keuen.   1797.   8º.

—— 館課賦註 *Kwan ko foo choo.* "College Poems. With Notes" by Heu Tseen and Le Tsung-le.   1802.   8º.

紀昀 KE YUN.   (*Continued.*)

續通志 *Sǔh tung che.* "A Supplement to the 'Tung che.'" Embracing also the Annals of the Sung, Leaou, Kin, Yuen, and Ming Dynasties. Compiled by Imperial order by Ke Yun and others. 640 keuen.   1785.

—— 續通典 *Sǔh Tung teen.* "A Supplement to the 'Tung Teen.'" Compiled by Imperial order by Ke Yun and others. 150 keuen.   1783.

紀曉嵐 KE HEAOU-LAN.

See 周禮 CHOW LE. 周禮精華 *Chow le tsing hwa.* "The Essential Points of the Chow Ritual." . . . Edited by Ke Heaou-lan, &c.   1814.   8º.

奇明 KE MING.

See CHINA. BOARD OF WAR. 欽定中樞政考 *Kin ting chung choo ching kaou.* "An Examination into the Fundamental System" of Governing the Army. Compiled by . . Ke Ming, &c.   1785.   8º.

寄瓢子 KE PEAOU-TSZE.

溫熱贅言 *Wǎn jě chuy yen.* "A Treatise on Warmth and Heat."   1834.   8º.

綺樓 KE LOW.

綺樓重夢 *Ke low chung mung.* "The Dreams of the Painted Chamber." 28 Chapters.   1816.   8º.

季本 KE PUN.

稿 *Kaou.* "Essays." *See* 長城 CHANG CHING. 名家制義 *Ming kea che e.* "Essays" on Texts from the Four Books, &c. Tsǐh 33.   1699.   8º.

稽含 KE HAN.

南方草木狀 *Nan fang tsaou mǔh chwang.* "The Botany of the South," *i.e.* the Regions of Kwang tung and Kwang se. By Ke Han, of the Tsin Dynasty. A Reprint. 3 keuen. [1750?].   8º.

稽世臣 KE SHE-CHIN.

稿 *Kaou.* "Essays." *See* 長城 CHANG CHING. 名家制義 *Ming kea che e.* "Essays" on Texts from the Four Books, &c. Tsǐh 40.   1699.   8º.

13

祁 韻 士 KE YUN-SZE.

See 松 筠 SUNG YUN. 伊犂總統事畧 *E le tsung tung sze leŏ.* "A Short Account of Affairs in E-le." ... Compiled by ... Ke Yun-sze, &c. 1809. 8º.

祁 秀 昌 KE SEW-CHANG.

三 合 明 珠 *San hŏ ming choo.* "The Three United Bright Gems." A Tale in Verse. 4 keuen. [1850 ?]. 8º.

家 KEA.

千家詩選 *Tseen kea she seuen.* "Selections from the Poetical Pieces of a Thousand Authors." With Illustrations. [1750 ?]. 8º.

Another edition. [1800 ?]. 8º.

迦葉摩騰 KEA-YĔ-MO-TĂNG, and 竺法蘭 CHŬH-FA-LAN [*i.e.* Kasyapa Matanga and Chufalan].

佛說四十二章經 *Fŭh shwŏ sze shĭh urh chang king.* "The Sûtra of Forty-two Sections." Translated from the Sanskrit by Kea-yĕ-mo-tăng and Chŭh-fă-lan. *Canton,* 1727. 8º.

嘉慶 KEA-KING. *Emperor.*

大行皇帝遺詔 *Ta hing hwang te e chaou.* "The Last Testament of the Emperor Kea-king." Prepared by Yuen Yuen, the Governor-General of the Two Kwangs, and Kang Shaou-yung, the Governor of Kwang-tung. [*Peking*], 1820. 8º.

嘉約翰 KEA YŏHAN.

See KERR (JOHN GLASGOW), *M.D.*

賈 誼 KEA E.

新 書 *Sin shoo.* "The New Book." *See* 沈 津 CHIN TSIN 百家類纂 *Pĭh kea luy tswan.* "The Works of a Hundred Authors," &c. Keuen 5. 8º.

—— 新 書 *Sin shoo.* "The New Book." A Series of Essays on the Confucian Doctrine. By Kea E. Edited by Chin He-tsoo. 10 keuen. [1800 ?]. 8º.

Another edition. Edited by Loo Wăn-chaou. 10 keuen. [1825 ?]. 8º.

賈 棠 KEA TANG.

See 老君 LAOU KEUN. 感應篇圖說 *Kan ying peen too shwŏ.* "The Book of Rewards and Punishments." ... Edited by Kea Tang, &c. 1709. 8º.

賈昌朝 KEA CHANG-CHAOU.

羣經音辨 *Keun king yin peen.* "The Sounds of the Classics Discussed." *See* 伍崇曜 WOO TSUNG-YAOU. 粤雅堂叢書 *Yuĕ ya Tang tsung shoo.* "The Yuĕ-ya Tang Collection of Reprints," &c. Series 17. 1853. 8º.

賈公彦 KEA KUNG-YEN.

See 周禮 CHOW LE. 周禮註疏 *Chow le choo soo.* "The Chow Ritual. With .. Expositions" made and collected by Kea Kung-yen, &c. 8º.

—— See 儀禮 E LE. 儀禮註疏 *E le choo soo.* "The Decorum Ritual. With .. Expositions" made and collected by Kea Kung-yen. 8º.

甲 KEĂ.

甲乙二友論述 *Keă Yĭh urh yew lun shŭh.* "A Discussion between the Friends Keă and Yĭh." By William Milne. Edited by A. Wylie. *Shanghae,* 1858. 8º.

姜魯齋 KEANG LOO-CHAE.

See 黃正元 HWANG CHING-YUEN. 性天眞境 *Sing teen chin king.* "The True Limits of Human and Divine Nature." ... Edited by Keang Loo-chae, &c. 1737. 8º.

姜炳璋 KEANG PING-CHANG.

See 詩經 SHE KING. 詩序廣義 *She seu kwang e.* "The Book of Odes and its Preface, fully explained" by Keang Ping-chang, &c. 1815. 8º.

—— See 左丘明 TSO KEW-MING. 讀左補義 *Tŭh Tso poo e.* "Aids to Reading Tso Kew-ming's Narrative." .... By Keang Ping-chang, &c. 1772. 8º.

姜宸英 KEANG SHIN-YING.

湛園札記 *Chan yuen chă ke.* "Notes [on the Classics] from the Still Garden." *See* 嚴杰 YEN LĔĔ. 皇清經解 *Hwang Tsing king keae.* "The Classics Explained," &c. Keuen 194. 1829. 8º.

—— 湛園札記 *Chan yuen chă ke.* "Notes [on the Classics] from the Still Garden." 4 keuen. 1787. 8º.

姜士崙 KEANG SZE-LUN.

See 方引彥 FANG YIN-YEN. 遂安縣志 *Suy gan heen che.* "A Topography of Suy-gan Heen." .. Compiled by .. Keang Sze-lun, &c.
1767. 8°.

江藩 KEANG FAN.

隸經文 *Le king wăn.* "On the Texts of the Classics." 4 keuen. [Also] 樂縣考 *Yŏ heen kaou.* "An Examination of the Office of Music." 2 keuen. [Also] 國朝漢學師承記 *Kwŏ chaou Han heŏ sze ching ke.* "Biographical Notices of Scholars of the present Dynasty who were Versed in the Literature of the Han Dynasty." 9 keuen. [Also] 國朝宋學淵源記 *Kwŏ chaou Sung heŏ yuen yuen ke.* "Biographical Notices of Scholars of the present Dynasty who were Deeply Versed in the Literature of the Sung Dynasty." 3 keuen. *See* 伍崇曜 WOO TSUNG-YAOU. 粵雅堂叢書 *Yuĕ ya Tang tsung shoo.* "The Yuĕ-ya Tang Collection of Reprints," &c. Series 18.
1853. 8°.

—— 周易述補 *Chow Yĭh shŭh poo.* "A Supplement to the Chow Yĭh shŭh." *See* 嚴杰 YEN LĔĔ. 皇清經解 *Hwang Tsing king keae.* "The Classics Explained," &c. Keuen 1166–1169.
1829. 8°.

江南 KEANG NAN.

江南闈墨 *Keang nan wei mĭh.* "Keang-nan Examination Essays."
1825–1832. 8°.

江西 KEANG-SE.

江西試帖 *Keang se she tĕĕ.* "Keang-se Examination Essays."
[1810?]. 8°.
A Fragment.

—— 江西闈墨 *Keang se wei mĭh.* "Keang-se Examination Essays."
1821. 8°.

江聲 KEANG SHING.

尚書集注音疏 *Shang shoo tseĭh choo yin soo.* "A Collection of Comments on the Book of Historical Documents, and on the Pronunciation of the Characters." 14 keuen. *See* 嚴杰 YEN LĔĔ. 皇清經解 *Hwang Tsing king keae.* "The Classics Explained," &c. Keuen 390–403.
1829. 8°.

江永 KEANG YUNG.

See 四書 SZE SHOO. 四書典林 *Sze shoo teen lin.* "A Dictionary of Classical Phrases employed in the Four Books." .. Compiled by Keang Yung, &c.
1795. 8°.

—— 古韻標準 *Koo yun peaou chun.* "An Adjustment of Ancient Sounds." 4 keuen. [Also] 四聲切韻表 *Sze shing tsĕĕ yun peaou.* "A Dictionary of the Sounds tabulated in accordance with the Four Tones under the Thirty-six Initials." *See* 伍崇曜 WOO TSUNG-YAOU. 粵雅堂叢書 *Yuĕ ya Tang tsung shoo.* "The Yuĕ-ya Tang Collection of Reprints," &c. Series 4.
1853. 8°.

—— 翼梅 *Yĭh mei.* "Treatises on Mei Wŭh-gan's" Works on Astronomy. 9 keuen. *See* 葉志詵 YĔ CHE-SIN. 海山仙館叢書 *Hae shan seen Kwan tsung shoo.* "The Hae-shan-seen Kwan Collection of Reprints," &c. Vol. 108–110.
1848. 8°.

—— 周禮疑義舉要 *Chow Le e e keu yaou.* "On the Meaning of Doubtful Passages in the Chow Ritual." 7 keuen. [Also] 深衣考誤 *Shin e kaou woo.* "An Examination in Mistakes concerning 'Deep Garments.'" [Also] 春秋地理考實 *Chun Tsew te le kaou shĭh.* "The Geography of the Spring and Autumn Annals Examined and Verified." 4 keuen. [Also] 羣經補義 *Keun king poo e.* "A Supplementary Explanation of the Classics." 10 keuen. [Also] 鄉黨圖考 *Heang tang too kaou.* "An Examination of the Tenth Book of the Confucian Analects. With Plates." 10 keuen. *See* 嚴杰 YEN LĔĔ. 皇清經解 *Hwang Tsing king keae.* "The Classics Explained," &c. Keuen 244–270.
1829. 8°.

—— 周禮疑義舉要 *Chow Le e e keu yaou.* "On the Meaning of Doubtful Passages in the Chow Ritual." 7 keuen.
[1790?]. 8°.
Imperfect, keuen 5–7 being wanting.

—— 鄉黨圖考 *Heang tang too kaou.* "An Examination of the Tenth Book of the Confucian Analects. With Plates." 10 keuen. 1793. 8°.

江 永 KEANG YUNG. (*Continued.*)

禮書綱目 *Le shoo kang mŭh.* "A Condensation of the History of Forms and Ceremonies." A Reprint. 88 keuen.   1810. 8°.

—— 四書古人典林 *Sze shoo koo jĭn teen lin.* "A Biographical Dictionary of the Characters of Antiquity mentioned in the Four Books." 12 keuen.   1774. 8°.

Another edition. 12 keuen.   1802. 8°.

—— 四書典林轂 *Sze shoo teen lin kŏ.* "A Crust to the Canons of the Four Books." A collection of extracts from the Classics and the works of celebrated authors on subjects mentioned in the Four Books. 20 keuen.   [1800?]. 12°.
Imperfect, keuen 15–20 being wanting.

江 臨 泰 KEANG LIN-TAE.

See 張作楠 CHANG TSO-NAN. 楕篿續錄 *Chuy yŏ sŭh lŭh.* "Tables of Altitude." ... Edited by Keang Lin-tae.   8°.

—— 高弧細草 *Kaou hoo se tsaou.* "A Minute Exposition of the Method of Calculating Arcs." .... Edited by Keang Lin-tae, &c. 1821. 8°.

—— 新測恒星圖表 *Sin tsĭh hăng sing too peaou.* "Newly Projected Celestial Charts." .. Drawn by Keang Lin-tae, &c. 1823. 8°.

江 幼 光 KEANG YEW-KWANG.

蓮社高賢傳 *Leen shay kaou heen chuen.* "Biographies of the Saints of the Lily Society." Edited by Keang Yew-kwang. [1790?]. 8°.

江 陰 六 KEANG YIN-LŬH.

皇朝輿地略 *Hwang chaou yu te leŏ.* "An Epitomized Gazetteer of the Empire of China under the Tsing Dynasty."   1831. 8°.

疊㕧那舍 KEANG-LEANG-YAY-SHAY [*i.e.* Kalayaças].

佛說觀無量壽佛經 *Fŭh shwŏ kwan woo leang show Fŭh king.* "The Gazing on the Eternal Buddha Sûtra." Translated into Chinese by Kalayaças. See 彭際清 PĂNG TSE-TSING. 淨土三經 *Tsing too san king.* "The Three Sûtras of the Pure Regions of Bliss," &c.
     1797. Oblong.

疊㕧那舍 KEANG-LEANG-YAY-SHAY [*i.e.* Kalayaças]. (*Continued.*)

過去莊嚴劫千佛名經 *Kwŏ keu chwang yen kĕĕ tseen Fŭh ming king.* "The Celebrated Sûtra of the Thousand Buddhas of the past Solemn Kalpa." Translated into Chinese by Kalayaças.   [1790?]. Oblong.

交 光 眞 鑑 KEAOU-KWANG-CHIN-KEEN.

See 般剌密諦 PAN-LĂ-MEĬH-TE. 楞嚴正脈 *Lăng yen ching mĭh.* "The Correct Pulse of the Lăng yen king." ..... By Keaou-kwang-chin-keen, &c.   1633. 8°.

敎 KEAOU.

敎條 *Keaou teaou.* "The Principles of the Protestant Faith." [By C. F. A. Gützlaff.] 2 keuen.   [1849?]. 8°.
Imperfect, title-page wanting.

竭 誠 KĔĔ-CHING.

千手千眼大悲心咒懺法 *Tseen show tseen yen ta pei sin chow tsan fă.* "The Confessional Services of the Great Compassionate Kwan-yin, possessing a Thousand Hands and a Thousand Eyes." Edited by the Priest Kĕĕ-ching. With a Preface by the Emperor Yung-lŏ. A Reprint.   1801. Oblong.

—— 藥師瑠璃光如來本願功德經 *Yŏ sze lew le kwang Joo-lae pun yuen kung tĭh king.* "The Ârya Bhagavatî Bhêshaja guru pûrva praṇidhâna nâma mahâyâna sûtra." Translated into Chinese by Heuen-tsang. Edited by Kĕĕ-ching.   *Canton,* 1805. Oblong.

揭 曼 碩 KĔĔ MAN-SHĬH.

揭文安公文粹 *Kĕĕ wăn gan kung wăn suy.* "Literary Fragments by Kĕĕ Man-shĭh." 2 keuen. *See* 伍崇曜 WOO TSUNG-YAOU. 粵雅堂叢書 *Yuĕ ya Tang tsung shoo.* "The Yuĕ-ya Tang Collection of Reprints," &c. Series 2.   1853. 8°.

—— 揭曼碩詩 *Kĕĕ Man-shĭh she.* "The Poetry of Kĕĕ Man-shĭh." Edited by Maou Tsin. 3 keuen. *See* 葉志詵 YĔ CHE-SIN. 海山仙館叢書 *Hae shan seen Kwan tsung shoo.* "The Hae-shan-seen Kwan Collection of Reprints," &c. Vol. 58.   1848. 8°.

乾隆 KEEN-LUNG. *Emperor.*
See CHINA. BOARD OF WAR. 欽定中樞政考 *Kin ting chung choo ching kaou.* "An Examination into the Fundamental System" of Governing the Army issued by order of the Emperors Yung-ching and Keen-lung, &c. 1807. 8°.

—— 御製盛京賦 *Yu che Shing king foo.* "A Poetical Eulogium on the City of Moukden." By the Emperor Keen-lung. This edition, which was brought out under the superintendence of Foo Hăng, Wang Yew-tun, and other officials, is printed in thirty-two different kinds of Chinese characters, and in the same number of varieties of the Manchoo letters. 1748. 4°.

Another edition. [1748?]. 8°.

簡履謙 KEEN LE-KEEN.
See 老君 LAOU KEUN. 太上感應篇緖言 *Tae shang Kan ying peen seu yen.* "The Book of Rewards and Punishments." . . . Edited by Keen Le-keen, &c. 8°.

諫 KEEN.
五諫妻 *Woo keen tse.* "Five Reproofs to a Wife." [1800?]. 8°.

吉慶 KEĬH KING.
廣西通志 *Kwang se tung che.* "A Topography of the Province of Kwang-se." Compiled by a Commission consisting of Keĭh King, Seay Kehwăn, Tseen Keae, and others. 279 keuen.
Kwei-lin Foo, 1800. 8°.
Imperfect, wanting keuen 9–12, 70–73, 90–93, 241–244.

吉祥 KEĬH TSEANG.
See CHINA. BOARD OF REVENUE. 戸部則例 *Hoo poo tsĭh le.* "Regulations of the Board of Revenue." Compiled by . . . Keĭh Tseang, &c. 1838. 8°.

覺世 KEŎ-SHE.
今古奇觀續編十二樓 *Kin koo ke kwan sŭh peen shĭh urh low.* "The Twelve Chambers. A Sequel to the Wondrous Tales of Ancient and Modern Times." By the Taouist Keŏ-she. 12 keuen. 1658. 8°.

覺羅四明 KEŎ-LO-SZE-MING.
續脩臺灣府志 *Sŭh sew Tae-wan foo che.* "A Revised Topography of Tae-wan Foo." Compiled by Keŏ-lo-sze-ming, Seu Wăn-e, and others. 26 keuen. [1800?]. 8°.

KERR (JOHN GLASGOW), *M.D.*
See WELLS. 化學初階 *Hwa heŏ choo keae.* "Wells' Principles of Chemistry,—Inorganic Part." Translated into Chinese by J. G. Kerr, &c. 1871. 8°.

區大相 KEU TA-SEANG.
區太史詩集 *Keu tae she she tseĭh.* "Poems. By the Historiographer Keu Ta-seang." 27 keuen. 1643. 8°.

瞿佑 KEU YEW.
歸田詩話 *Kwei teen she hwa.* "Criticisms on Poetry." By Keu Yew. A Reprint. 3 keuen. [1741?]. 8°.

瞿汝稷 KEU JOO-TSEĬH.
指月錄 CHE YUĚ LŬH. [A Thesaurns of Buddhist Biography.] Compiled by Keu Joo-tseĭh. Revised by Yen Ching-taou. Edited by Hung Le. 32 keuen. [1750?]. 8°.

瞿景淳 KEU KING-SHUN.
稿 *Kaou.* "Essays." See 長城 CHANG CHING. 名家制義 *Ming kea che e.* "Essays" on Texts from the Four Books, &c. Tsĭh 43. 1699. 8°.

瞿西滿 KEU SE-MWAN.
See 艾儒畧 GAE JOO-LEŎ. 天主降生言行紀像 *Teen choo keang săng yen hing ke seang.* "An Illustrated Life of Christ." . . . Edited by Keu Se-mwan, &c. 8°.

瞿天潢 KEU TEEN-HWANG.
雙忠廟 *Shwang chung meaou.* "The Temple of the Two Patriots." A Drama. By Keu Teenhwang. The Lyrical Parts being by Ko seaou jin, or the Laughable Man. 2 keuen. [1700?]. 8°.

瞿曾輯 KEU TSĂNG-TSEĬH.
See 馬賷與 MA KWEI-YU. 策海全書 *Tsĭh hae tseuen shoo.* "An Encyclopædia." . . . . Edited by Keu Tsăng-tseĭh, &c. 12°.

瞿曇法智 KEU-TAN-FĂ-CHE.

業報差別經 *Nĕĕ paou cha pĕĕ king.* "A Sûtra on the various Requitals attaching to different Occupations." Translated into Chinese by Keu-tan-fă-che. Edited by Le Fŭh. A Buddhist Work. *Canton,* 1811. 8º.

玦 KEUĔ.

珊瑚玦 *Shen hoo keuĕ.* "The Coral Ring." A Drama. The Lyrical Parts are by Ko seaou jin, or the Laughable Man. 2 keuen.
[1700 ?]. 8º.

卷 KEUEN.

魁卷 *Kwei keuen.* "A Volume of Examination Essays." [1800 ?]. 8º.
A Fragment.

權衡 KEUEN HĂNG.

庚申外史 *Kăng shin wae she.* "A History of Events between the Years 1333 and 1368." By Keuen Hăng. 2 keuen. *See* 葉志詵 YĔ CHE-SIN. 海山仙館叢書 *Hae shan seen Kwan tsung shoo.* "The Hae-shan-seen Kwan Collection of Reprints," &c. Vol. 19. 1848. 8º.

橘 KEŬH.

橘中秘歌括 *Keŭh chung pe ko kwŏ.* "A Bundle of Rhymes on the Art of Chess." With Diagrams. 4 keuen. [1790 ?]. 8º.
Imperfect, containing only keuen 3, 4.

曲 KEŬH.

六十種曲 *Lŭh shĭh chung keŭh.* "Sixty Plays." 6 Taou. [1800 ?]. 8º.

屈原 KEŬH YUEN.

離騷經 *Le saou king.* "The Classic of the Exiled Mourner." *See* 蕭統 SEAOU TUNG. 文選 *Wăn seuen.* "Elegant Extracts from Polite Literature," &c. Keuen 32. 1772. 8º.

—— 離騷經 *Le saou king.* "The Classic of the Exiled Mourner." A Poem in Justification of the Author's Public Character. By Keŭh Yuen. With Notes by Yang Shin. [1750 ?]. 8º.

—— 楚辭集註 *Tsoo tsze tseĭh choo.* "The Elegies of Tsoo." With a Commentary by Choo He. 8 keuen. [1800 ?]. 8º.
An odd volume, containing only keuen 2 and 3.

屈成霖 KEŬH CHING-LIN.

習是編 *Seĭh she peen.* "On Practising what is Right." By Keŭh Ching-lin. Edited by Seay Ying-taou. 12 keuen. *Leen-ching,* 1824. 8º.

屈何煥 KEŬH HO-HWAN.

萬壽恩科墨卷雅正 *Wan show găn ko mĭh keuen ya ching.* "Elegant Essays, selected from those written for the Extra Examinations granted by Imperial Favour" in the Year 1790. Compiled by Keŭh Ho-hwan. Edited by Choo Wei-pĭh, Kaou Ting-tsan, and Keŭh Shang-keen. 1790. 8º.

屈上謙 KEŬH SHANG-KEEN.

See 屈何煥 KEŬH HO-HWAN. 萬壽恩科墨卷雅正 *Wan show găn ko mĭh keuen ya ching.* "Elegant Essays, selected from those written for the Extra Examinations granted by Imperial Favour" in the Year 1790. . . . Edited by . . . Keŭh Shang-keen, &c. 1790. 8º.

屈宗談 KEUH TSUNG-TAN.

子史試帖彙鈔 *Tsze she she tĕĕ wei chaou.* "Essays on Themes from the Works of Philosophers and Historians." Compiled by Keŭh Tsung-tan. 10 keuen. With a Supplement. 1813. 8º.

丘濬 KEW SEUN.

稿 *Kaou.* "Essays." *See* 長城 CHANG CHING. 名家制義 *Ming kea che e.* "Essays" on Texts from the Four Books, &c. Tsĭh 14. 1699. 8º.

—— See 朱熹 CHOO HE. 朱子家禮 *Choo-tsze kea le.* "Domestic Ceremonies as taught by Choo He." Compiled by Kew Seun, &c. 1701. 8º.

—— See 文昌帝君 WĂN-CHANG TE KEUN. 文昌孝經 *Wăn-chang heaou king.* "Wăn-chang's Classic on Filial Piety." Edited by Kew Seun, &c. 1811. 8º.

—— 幼學故事尋源 *Yew heŏ koo sze tsin yuen.* "A Search into Antiquities. A Book for Beginners." With a Collection of Comments, compiled by Yang Ying-seang. 10 keuen. [1750 ?]. 8º.
Imperfect, the first two keuen are wanting.

Another edition. Edited by Ching Tăng-keĭh. 10 keuen. [1800 ?]. 8º.

丘 建 安 KEW KEEN-GAN.

See 方 鯤 FANG KWĂN. 易 盥 *Yih tang.* "The Permutations of the Diagrams of the Book of Changes." . . . . . With Notes by . . . Kew Keen-gan, &c. 1718. 8°.

丘 毛 伯 KEW MAOU-PĬH.

史 遺 *She wei.* "Scraps from History." *See* 閔 景 賢 MIN KING-HEEN. 快 書 *Kwae shoo.* "A Book of Amusement," &c. Keuen 29. 1626. 8°.

邱 文 KEW WĂN.

成 語 考 *Ching yu kaou.* "Correct Phraseology." For the Young. [1820 ?]. 8°.

邱 長 春 KEW CHANG-CHUN.

西 遊 眞 詮 *Se yew chin tseuen.* "A Complete Narrative of Travels in the West" in Search of the Sacred Books. By Kew Chang-chun. Edited by Kin Shing-tan. With Illustrations. 20 keuen. 1696. 8°.

求 那 跋 陀 羅 KEW-NA-PŎ-TO-LO [*i.e.* Guṇabhadra].

觀 楞 伽 阿 跋 多 羅 寶 經 記 *Kwan Lăng-kea a-po-to-lo paou king ke.* "The Lankávatara Maháyána Sûtra." Translated into Chinese by Guṇabhadra. With a Commentary by Tĭh-tsing. A Reprint. 4 keuen. 1724. 8°.

—— 楞 伽 阿 跋 多 羅 寶 經 心 印 *Lăng-kea a-po-to-lo paou king sin yin.* "The Lankávatara Maháyána Sûtra." Translated into Chinese by Guṇabhadra. "With Explanations" by Han-she. 4 keuen. 1723. 8°.

裴 建 KEW LEEN.

See 陳 璿 CHIN SEUEN. 普 陀 山 志 *Poo to shan che.* "A Topography of the Island of Poo to.". . Compiled by . . . Kew Leen, &c. 1734. 8°.

裴 漫 士 KEW MWAN-SZE.

See 周 大 樞 CHOW TA-CHOO. 應 試 五 排 精 選 *Ying she woo pae tsing seuen.* "A Collection of Model Poetical Essays." . . Edited by Kew Mwan-sze, &c. 8°.

———— 應 試 排 律 精 選 鯨 鏗 集 *Ying she pae leŭh tsing seuen king kăng tseĭh.* "The King Kăng Collection of Successful Poetical Examination Essays." . . . Edited by Kew Man-sze, &c. 1758. 8°.

裴 紹 謨 KEW SHAOU-MOW.

See 孔 鮒 KUNG FOO. 孔 叢 *Kung tsung.* "Confucian Miscellanies." . . Edited by Kew Shaou-mow, &c. 1817. 8°.

逑 KEW.

好 逑 傳 *Haou kew chuen.* "The Fortunate Union." 4 keuen. 1787. 8°.

Imperfect, containing only keuen 1.

Another edition. 6 keuen. 1806. 8°.

Another copy.

Another edition. 4 keuen. 1814. 8°.

Another edition. 6 keuen. 1822. 8°.

Another edition. Edited by T. F. Wade. 4 keuen. 1863. 8°.

仇 池 石 KEW CHE-SHĬH.

羊 城 古 鈔 *Yang ching koo chaou.* "Ancient Records of the City of Rams" [*i.e.* Canton]. Compiled by Kew Che-shĭh. 8 keuen. 1806. 8°.

仇 天 一 KEW TEEN-YĬH.

See 翁 仲 仁 UNG CHUNG-JIN. 痘 疹 玉 髓 金 鏡 錄 *Tow chin yŭh suy kin king lŭh.* "A Searching Treatise on Smallpox." . . . Edited by Kew Teen-yĭh, &c. 1768. 8°.

仇 滄 柱 KEW TSANG-CHOO.

See 四 書 SZE SHOO. 四 書 補 註 附 考 備 旨 *Sze shoo poo choo foo kaou pe che.* "The Four Books." . . . A New Edition. With Additions by Kew Tsang-choo, &c. 1829. 8°.

—— See 易 經 YĬH KING. 易 經 備 旨 眞 本 *Yih king pe che chin pun.* "A Correct Copy of the Book of Changes." . . . . Edited by Kew Tsang-choo, &c. 1707. 8°.

鳩 摩 羅 什 KEW-MO-LO-SHĬH [*i.e.* Kumâragîva].

佛 說 阿 彌 陀 經 要 解 *Fŭh shwŏ O-me-to king yaou keae.* "The Amitâbha Sûtra," translated into Chinese by Kumâragîva, and explained by Che-heŭh. *See* 漃 益 GOW-YĬH. 淨 土 十 要 *Tsing too shĭh yaou.* "Ten Requisites for the Attainment of the Pure Regions of Bliss," &c. 8°.

鳩 摩 羅 什 KEW-MO-LO-SHĬH [*i.e.* Kumâragîva].
(*Continued.*)

佛 說 阿 彌 陀 經 *Fŭh shwŏ O-me-to king.*
"The Amitâbha Sûtra," translated into Chinese
by Kumâragîva. *See* 彭 際 清 PĂNG TSE-
TSING. 淨 土 三 經 *Tsing too san king.* "The
Three Sûtras of the Pure Regions of Bliss, &c.
1797. Oblong.

—— 佛 遺 敎 經 *Fŭh e keaou king.* "The Bequeathed Teachings of Buddha." Translated
iuto Chinese by Kumâragîva.
Canton, 1727. 8°.

—— 金 剛 直 說 *Kin kang chĭh shwŏ.* "The Diamond
Classic," being a Translation made by Kumâragîva of the Vajra Prajnâpâramita Sûtra, "clearly
explained" by Tseĭh Shan-tsew. [1800?]. 8°.

—— 金 剛 經 直 解 *Kin kang king chĭh keae.* "The
Diamond Classic clearly explained" by Leu Yen.
Edited by Yu Mei. 1813. 8°.

—— 金 剛 經 解 義 *Kin kang king keae e.* "The
Diamond Classic explained."
Canton, [1800?]. 8°.

—— 金 剛 經 集 註 *Kin kang king tseĭh choo.* "The
Diamond Classic. With a Collection of Com-
ments." To which is added, *Kin kang king
yin kwŏ shĭh lŭh,* or The Cause and Effect of
Studying the Diamond Classic.
Keang-ning, 1835. 8°.

Another copy.

Another copy.

—— 金 剛 般 若 波 羅 密 經 *Kin kang Pan-jŏ po-
lo-meĭh king.* "The Diamond Classic."
[1730?]. 8°.
The title and first page are wanting.

Another edition. Edited by the Priest Mĭh-yin.
1795. Oblong.

—— 金 剛 般 若 波 羅 密 經 如 義 *Kin kang
Pan-jŏ po-lo-meĭh king joo e.* "The Diamond
Classic Explained." Edited by Yuen-hae.
1787. 8°.

鳩 摩 羅 什 KEW-MO-LO-SHĬH [*i.e.* Kumâragîva].
(*Continued.*)

金 剛 般 若 波 羅 密 經 宗 通 *Kin kang Pan-
jŏ po-lo-meĭh king tsung tung.* "The Diamond
Classic throughly elucidated" by Tsăng Fung-e.
2 keuen. 1810. 8°.

—— 妙 法 蓮 華 經 *Meaou fă leen hwa king.* "The
Lotus of the Excellent Law." Translated into
Chinese by Kumâragîva. Edited by the Priest
Taou-seuen. 7 keuen. 1764. 8°.

Another copy.

Another edition. 7 keuen. 1842.

—— 阿 彌 陀 經 *O-me-to king.* "The Amitâbha
Sûtra." Translated into Chinese by Kumâragîva. 1795. 8°.

—— 阿 彌 陀 經 疏 鈔 *O-me-to king soo chaou.*
"The Amitâbha Sûtra," translated into Chinese
by Kumâragîva, "with Explanatory Comments."
Compiled by Choo Hung. 4 keuen.
Canton, 1765. 8°.

—— 菩 薩 戒 疏 義 *Poo să keae soo e.* "The Precepts of Buddha, with an Explanation of their
Meaning." Translated into Chinese by Kumâragîva. Edited by Chuen-shing. 2 keuen.
[1800?]. 8°.

—— 維 摩 詰 所 說 經 註 *Wei-mo-keĭh so shwŏ king
choo.* "The Sûtra delivered by Wei-mo-keĭh."
Translated into Chinese by Kumâragîva. With
a Commentary by Tsăng-shaou. A Reprint.
10 keuen. [1790?]. 8°.

Another edition. *Canton*, 1835. 8°.

金 KIN.
千 金 記 *Tseen kin ke.* "The Story of a Thousand
Pieces of Gold." *See* 曲 KEŬH. 六 十 種 曲
Lŭh shĭh chung keŭh. "Sixty Plays," &c. Taou
6. 8°.

金 蓮 KIN LEEN.
金 蓮 記 *Kin leen ke.* "The Story of the Golden
Water Lilies." *See* 曲 KEŬH. 六 十 種 曲
Lŭh shĭh chung keŭh. "Sixty Plays," &c. Taou
3. 8°.

金 陵 KIN LING.

金 陵 救 生 局 *Kin ling kew săng keu.* "The Reports of the Kin-ling [*i.e.* Nanking] Society for the Preservation of Life for the Years 1838, 1839, 1840." Being the 24th, 25th, and 26th Reports of the Society. This Society, which was founded in the year 1803, also provides for the burial of bodies found. 1838–1840. 8º.

There are five other copies of the Report for the year 1840, and one of that for 1839.

—— 金 陵 述 畧 *Kin-ling shŭh leŏ.* "A Short Account of the Nanking" Rebels. 1853. 8º.

With manuscript notes.

金 榜 KIN PANG.

禮 箋 *Le tseen.* "Notes on Ceremonies." 3 keuen. *See* 嚴 杰 YEN LĔĔ. 皇 清 經 解 *Hwang Tsing king keae.* "The Classics Explained," &c. Keuen 554–556. 1829. 8º.

金 堡 KIN PAOU.

稿 *Kaou.* "Essays." *See* 長 城 CHANG CHING. 名 家 制 義 *Ming kea che e.* "Essays" on Texts from the Four Books, &c. Tsĭh 97. 1699. 8º.

金 生 KIN-SĂNG.

金 生 挑 盒 *Kin săng teaou hŏ.* "Kin-săng carries away her boxes." A Dramatic Tale. [1800?]. 8º.

金 聲 KIN SHING.

稿 *Kaou.* "Essays." *See* 長 城 CHANG CHING. 名 家 制 義 *Ming kea che e.* "Essays" on Texts from the Four Books, &c. Tsĭh 89. 1699. 8º.

金 山 KIN SHAN.

往 金 山 要 訣 *Wang Kin shan yaou keuĕ.* "Important Advice to Emigrants to the Goldfields." [By Dr. James Legge.] *Hongkong,* 1869. 8º.

金 牲 KIN SIN.

See 劉 勰 LEW HĔĔ. 文 心 雕 龍 輯 註 *Wăn sin teaou lung tseĭh choo.* "Lew Hĕĕ's Critique on Poetry and Literature." .. Edited by ... Kin Sin, &c. 1738. 8º.

金 雀 KIN TSEŎ.

金 雀 記 *Kin tseŏ ke.* "The Story of the Golden Tseŏ." *See* 曲 KEŬH. 六 十 種 曲 *Lŭh shĭh chung 'keŭh.* "Sixty Plays," &c. Taou 1. 8º.

金 溪 甫 KIN KE-FOO.

說 帖 類 編 *Shwŏ tĕĕ luy peen.* "Judicial Decisions. Arranged and Classified" by Kin Ke-foo. 36 keuen. 1835. 8º.

金 居 敬 KIN KEU-KING.

稿 *Kaou.* "Essays." *See* 長 城 CHANG CHING. 名 家 制 義 *Ming kea che e.* "Essays" on Texts from the Four Books, &c. Tsĭh 119. 1699. 8º.

金 古 良 KIN KOO-LEANG.

無 雙 譜 *Woo shwang poo.* "Biographical Notices of Peerless Worthies." *See* 顏 希 源 YEN HE-YUEN. 百 美 新 詠 圖 傳 *Pĭh mei sin yung too chuen.* "A New Collection of Sonnets to the Hundred Beauties," &c. 1790. 8º.

—— 無 雙 譜 *Woo shwang poo.* "Biographical Notices of Peerless Worthies." 1690. 8º.

Another edition. 1743. 8º.

金 匱 秦 KIN KWEI-TSIN.

五 禮 通 考 *Woo le tung kaou.* "A Thorough Investigation into the Five Ceremonies," viz.: those of Joy, Marriage, Hospitality, the Camp, and Calamity. Compiled by Kin Kwei-tsin. [1750?]. 8º.

Imperfect, containing only keuen 27–56, 63–69, 71–81, 85–116, 120–150, 157–189, 193–213, 215, 216, 225–230, 234–249, 254–262.

金 彌 格 KIN ME-KĬH. *pseud.* A Jesuit.

聖 宗 徒 禱 文 *Shing tsung too taou wăn.* "Prayers to the Holy Disciples." *See* 郭 居 靜 KŎ KEU-TSING. 天 主 聖 教 日 課 *Teen choo shing keaou jĭh ko.* "Daily Christian Religious Exercises," &c. Keuen 4. 8º.

金 聖 嘆 KIN SHING-TAN.

See 邱 長 春 KEW CHANG-CHUN. 西 遊 眞 詮 *Se yew chin tseuen.* "A Complete Narrative of Travels in the West." ... Edited by Kin Shing-tan, &c. 1696. 8º.

—— *See* 羅 貫 中 LO KWAN-CHUNG. 三 國 志 *San kwŏ che.* "The History of the Three Kingdoms." .... Edited by Kin Shing-tan, &c. 1644. 8º.

14

金聖嘆 KIN SHING-TAN. (*Continued.*)

See 賞心 SHANG-SIN. 征四冦傳 *Ching sze kow chuen.* "The Four Banditti Subdued." ... Edited by Kin Shing-tan, &c. 1792. 8º.

—— See 施耐菴 SHE NAE-GAN. 水滸傳 *Shwuy hoo chuen.* "The Story of the River's Bank." .. Edited by Kin Shing-tan, &c. 1734. 8º.

—— 花箋記 *Hwa tseen ke.* "The Story of the Flowery Note-paper." A Novel. Edited, with Notes, by Kin Shing-tan. 6 keuen.
[1820?]. 8º.

—— 西廂記 *Se seang ke.* "The Story of the Western Chamber," or The Book of the Scholar of the Sixth Degree. Edited by Kin Shing-tan. 6 keuen (?). [1800?]. 8º.
Imperfect, containing only the third keuen.

Another edition. 8 keuen. [1800?]. 8º.
Imperfect, containing only keuen 4–8.

—— 西遊後傳 *Se yew how chuen.* "A Later Narrative of Travels in the West." Edited by Kin Shing-tan. 40 Chapters. [1750?]. 8º.

金幼孜 KIN YEW-TSZE.

See 胡廣 HOO KWANG. 性理大全 *Sing le tu tseuen.* "A Complete Work on Mental Philosophy." ... Compiled by ... Kin Yew-tsze, &c. 1414. 8º.

—— 北征錄 *Pih ching lüh.* "The History of the Northern Conquest." With a Supplement. See 說 SHWŎ. 說選 *Shwŏ seuen.* "A Collection of Records," &c. Vol. 1. 8º.

靳治荊 KIN CHE-KING.

思舊錄 *Sze kew lüh.* "Records of the Past." See 張山來 CHANG SHAN-LAE, and 張進也 CHANG TSIN-YAY. 昭代叢書 *Chaou tae tsung shoo.* "A Collection of Reprints of Works by Authors under the Present Dynasty," &c. Keuen 43. 1703. 8º.

靳榮藩 KIN YUNG-FAN.

See 吳梅村 WOO MEI-TSUN. 吳詩集覽 *Woo she tseih lan.* "A Collective View of Woo Mei-tsun's Poetry." Compiled by Kin Yung-fan, &c. 1781. 8º.

琴 KIN.

琴心記 *Kin sin ke.* "Love for the Lute." See 曲 KEŬH. 六十種曲 *Lüh shih chung keŭh.* "Sixty Plays," &c. Taou 3. 8º.

慶桂 KING KWEI.

See 王圻 WANG KE. 續文獻通考 *Süh wăn heen tung kaou.* "A Continuation of the 'Wăn heen tung kaou.'" ... Edited and Revised by ... King Kwei, &c. 1784. 8º.

慶源 KING YUEN.

See CHINA. BOARD OF WAR. 欽定兵部續纂處分則例 *Kin ting Ping Poo süh tswan choo fun tsih le.* "Supplementary .. Regulations of the Board of War." Compiled by .. King Yuen, &c. 1829. 8º.

京房 KING FANG.

周易章句 *Chow Yih chang keu.* "The Chow Changes explained by Paragraphs and by Sentences." See 孫堂 SUN TANG. 漢魏二十一家易注 *Han Wei urh shih yih kca yih choo.* "Commentaries on the Book of Changes," &c. 1799. 8º.

—— 易傳 *Yih chuen.* "A Commentary on the Book of Changes." By King Fang. Edited by Leu Lin-yih. 2 keuen. [1800?]. 8º.

荊釵 KING CHAE.

荊釵記 *King chae ke.* "The Story of the King Bodkin." See 曲 KEŬH. 六十種曲 *Lüh shih chung keŭh.* "Sixty Plays," &c. Taou 1. 8º.

可笑人 KO SEAOU JIN. *pseud.*

See 范續彧 FAN HWANG-HWŎ. 元寶媒 *Yuen paou mei.* "The Fifty Tael Match-maker." ... The Lyrical Parts being by Ko seaou jin, &c. 8º.

科 KO.

乙酉科 *Yih yew ko.* "Examination Essays of the Year 1825." 1825. 8º.
Imperfect.

郭湜 KŎ CHIH.

高力士傳 *Kaou Leih-sze chuen.* "The Story of Kaou Leih-sze." See 王文誥 WANG WĂN-KAOU. 唐代叢書 *Tang tae tsung shoo.* "A Collection of Reprints of Works written during the Tang Dynasty," &c. Series 4. 1806. 8º.

郭湜 KŎ Chĭh.　(*Continued.*)

高力士傳 *Kaou Leĭh-sze chuen.* "The Story of Kaou Leĭh-sze." By Kŏ Chĭh, of the Tang Dynasty. A Reprint.　　　[1741 ?]. 8°.

郭憲 KŎ Heen.

洞冥記 *Tung ming ke.* "Mysterious Records." By Kŏ Heen, of the Han Dynasty. A Reprint. 4 keuen.　　　[1800 ?]. 8°.

郭璞 KŎ Pŏ.

See 邢昺 Hing Ping. 爾雅註疏 *Urh ya choo soo.* "The Literary Expositor. With Kŏ Pŏ's Commentary," &c.　　　1778. 8°.

—— 爾雅 *Urh ya.* "The Literary Expositor." With a Commentary by Kŏ Pŏ, &c. *See* 郎奎金 Lang Kwei-kin. 五雅 *Woo ya.* "The Five Dictionaries," &c.　1626. 8°.

—— See 畢沅 Peĭh Yuen. 山海經 *Shan hae king.* "The Hill and River Classic." With Kŏ Pŏ's Commentary, &c.　1783. 8°.

—— See 荀勗 Seun Heŭh. 穆天子傳 *Mŭh Teen tsze chuen.* "A Narrative of the Adventures of the Emperor Mŭh." . . With Notes by Kŏ Pŏ, &c.　　　8°.

—— See 爾雅 Urh ya. 爾雅音圖 *Urh ya yin too.* "The Literary Expositor." . . With a Commentary by Kŏ Pŏ, &c.　1801. 4°.

—— See 吳中珩 Woo Chung-hăng. 山海經 *Shan hae king.* "The Hill and River Classic." With Kŏ Pŏ's Commentary, &c.　　　8°.

—— See 吳任臣 Woo Jin-chin. 山海經 *Shan hae king.* "The Hill and River Classic." With Kŏ Pŏ's Commentary, &c.　1667. 8°.

—— See 楊雄 Yang Heung. 方言 *Fang yen.* On Dialects. With Notes by Kŏ Pŏ, &c.　　　8°.

郭象 KŎ Seang.

See 莊周 Chwang Chow. 南華經 *Nan hwa king.* "The Nan hwa Classic." With Notes by Kŏ Seang, &c.　　　1716. 8°.

郭象 KŎ Seang.　(*Continued.*)

南華眞經 *Nan hwa chin king.* "The Nan hwa Classic." With a Commentary by Kŏ Seang, &c. *See* 黃丕烈 Hwang Pei-lĕĕ. 十子全書 *Shih tsze tseuen shoo.* "The Complete Works of the Ten Philosophers," &c. 1804. 8°.

—— 韓非子 *Han Fei tsze.* "The Works of Han Fei." With a Commentary by Kŏ Seang, &c. *See* 黃丕烈 Hwang Pei-lĕĕ. 十子全書 *Shih tsze tseuen shoo.* "The Complete Works of the Ten Philosophers," &c.　1804. 8°.

—— 南華經 *Nan hwa king.* "The Nan hwa Classic." With Commentaries by Kŏ Seang, &c. *See* 焦竑 Tseaou Hung. 老莊翼合刻 *Laou Chwang yĭh hŏ kĭh.* "The Works of Laou keun and Chwang Chow," &c.　1588. 8°.

郭雍 KŎ Yung.

See 易經 Yĭh king. 傳家易說 *Chuen kea yĭh shwŏ.* "The Book of Changes." . . . Compiled by Kŏ Yung, &c.　1775. 8°.

郭溶 KŎ Yung.

稿 *Kaou.* "Essays." *See* 長城 Chang Ching. 名家制義 *Ming kea che e.* "Essays" on Texts from the Four Books, &c. Tsĭh 112.
　　　1699. 8°.

郭居靜 KŎ Keu-tsing.

天主聖敎日課 *Teen choo shing keaou jĭh ko.* "Daily Christian Religious Exercises." Compiled by the Jesuits Kŏ Keu-tsing, Fei Ke-kwei, Yang Ma-no, Foo Fan-tse, Fei Lŏ-tĭh. Edited in the present form by the Jesuits Luigi Buglio and Ferdinand Verbiest, under the Chinese names of Le Luy-sze and Nan Hwae-jin. 4 keuen.　　　[1690 ?]. 8°.

郭景純 KŎ King-shun.

江賦 *Keang foo.* "River Odes." *See* 蕭統 Seaou Tung. 文選 *Wăn seuen.* "Elegant Extracts from Polite Literature," &c. Keuen 12.
　　　1772. 8°.

郭廷彥 KŎ Ting-yen.

See 葉九升 Yĕ Kew-shing. 地理山法全書 *Te le shan fă tseuen shoo.* "The Laws of Mountains." . . . The Second Keuen is edited, with Notes, by Kŏ Ting-yen, &c.　　　8°.

郭 存 會 Kǒ Tsun-hwuy.

聖 節 會 約 *Shing tsëě hwuy yǒ.* "Periods in the Life of Confucius. With Corroborative Passages." *See* 張 山 來 Chang Shan-lae, and 張 進 也 Chang Tsin-yay. 昭 代 叢 書 *Chaou tae tsung shoo.* "A Collection of Reprints of Works written under the Present Dynasty," &c. Keuen 14. 1703. 8°.

葛 洪 Kǒ Hung.

抱 朴 子 *Paou pǒ tsze.* "The Writings of Kǒ Hung, *alias* Paou pǒ tsze." *See* 沈 津 Chin Tsin. 百 家 類 纂 *Pih kea luy tswan.* "The Works of a Hundred Authors," &c. Keuen 16. 8°.

—— 枕 中 書 *Chin chung shoo.* "The Inside of a Pillow." By Kǒ Hung, of the Tsin Dynasty. A Reprint. [1800?]. 8°.

—— 抱 朴 子 *Paou pǒ tsze.* "The Writings of Paou pǒ tsze" on Taouistic Alchemy, &c. In Two Parts. Part I. 20 keuen. Part II. 50 keuen. 1813. 8°.

—— 神 仙 傳 *Shin seen chuen.* "Biographical Notices of Ninety-two Immortals." A New Edition. 10 keuen. [1800?]. 8°.

葛 窠 Kǒ Meïh.

See 李 中 立 Le Chung-leïh. 本 草 原 始 *Pun tsaou yuen che.* "The Natural Condition of the Substances mentioned in the Materia Medica." ... Edited by Kǒ Meïh, &c. 8°.

葛 正 笏 Kǒ Ching-hwǔh.

See 陳 宏 謀 Chin Hung-mow. 在 官 法 戒 錄 摘 鈔 *Tsae kwan fǎ keae lǔh tsǐh chaou.* "The Mandarins' Instructor." .... Edited by Kǒ Ching-hwǔh, &c. 1823. 8°.

葛 見 堯 Kǒ Keen-yaou.

含 少 論 略 *Han shaou lun leǒ.* "A Disquisition on Self-restraint." *See* 閔 景 賢 Min King-Heen. 快 書 *Kwae shoo.* "A Book of Amusement," &c. Keuen 26. 1626. 8°.

古 德 Koo-tǐh. *pseud.*

眞 心 直 說 *Chin sin chǐh shwǒ.* "Moral Discourses on a Sincere Heart." A Buddhist Tract by Koo-tǐh. *Canton,* [1830?]. 8°.

古 雲 Koo-yun. *pseud.*

沙 門 日 用 錄 *Sha mun jǐh yung lǔh.* "The Priest's Daily Exercises." Compiled by Koo-yun. A Buddhist Work. *Canton,* [1830?]. 8°.

Another copy.

庫 勒 納 Koo Lǐh-nǎ.

日 講 書 經 解 義 *Jǐh keang Shoo king keae e.* "Daily Lectures on the Meaning of the Shoo king." Compiled by an Imperial Commission consisting of Koo Lǐh-nǎ, Yě Fang-gae, and others. 13 keuen. 1680. 8°.

顧 嶫 Koo Heuen.

袁 氏 傳 *Yuen she chuen.* "The Story of Yuen she." By Koo Heuen, of the Tang Dynasty. A Reprint. [1741?]. 8°.

顧 錦 Koo Kin.

See 文 昌 帝 君 Wǎn chang te keun. 陰 隲 文 圖 說 *Yin chǐh wǎn too shwǒ.* "A Treatise on Secret Rewards and Retributions." .. Illustrated by Koo Kin, &c. 1801. 8°.

顧 浦 Koo Poo.

See 周 目 藻 Chow Mǔh-tsaou. 四 書 詩 題 *Sze shoo she te.* "Essays on Themes from the Four Books." ... Edited by .. Koo Poo, &c. 8°.

顧 氏 Koo she.

救 急 篇 *Kew keǐh peen.* "Prescriptions for Cases of Extreme Peril." A Medical Work by the Retired Scholar of San kin. Edited by Koo she. 1846. 8°.

顧 辰 Koo Shin.

See 管 靜 山 Kwan Tsing-shan. 管 靜 山 全 稿 *Kwan Tsing-shan tseuen kaou.* "The Essays of Kwan Tsing-shan." With a Third Supplementary Collection. ... Edited by Koo Shin, &c. 1817. 1819. 8°.

顧 進 Koo Tsin.

See 劉 勰 Lew Hëě. 文 心 雕 龍 輯 註 *Wǎn sin teaou lung tsěǐh choo.* "Lew Hëě's Critique on Poetry and Literature." .. Edited by Koo Tsin, &c. 1738. 8°.

顧 清 Koo Tsing.

稿 *Kaou.* "Essays." *See* 長 城 Chang Ching. 名 家 制 義 *Ming kea che e.* "Essays" on Texts from the Four Books, &c.　Tsǐh 22.
1699.　8°.

顧 沅 Koo Yuen.

古 聖 賢 像 傳 畧 *Koo shing heen seang chuen leŏ.* "Short Illustrated Biographies of Ancient Sages." Compiled by Koo Yuen.　16 keuen.
1830.　8°.

—— 聖 廟 祀 典 圖 考 *Shing meaou sze teen too kaou.* "Sacrificial Canon of Confucian Temples. With Portraits." By Koo Yuen. This work is a very painstaking account of all the Names sacrificed to in the Temples of Confucius, the dates of their attaining to that honour, &c.; and to it is added a Volume entitled *Shing tseǐh too,* *i.e.* "The Footsteps of the Sages," being records of the most remarkable Events in the Lives of Confucius and Mencius.　5 keuen and appendix.
1826.　8°.

Another copy.
Imperfect, wanting the first keuen.

—— 焦 山 志 *Tseaou shan che.* "A Topography of Tseaou shan or Silver Island," an Island in the Yang tsze keang.　28 keuen.　1839.　8°.

—— 吳 郡 名 賢 圖 傳 贊 *Woo keun ming heen too chuen tsan.* "Illustrated Biographies of the Eminent Heroes of the Principality of Woo," *i.e.* the Region around Soochow Foo.　20 keuen.
1829.　8°.

顧 非 熊 Koo Fěi-heung.

妙 女 傳 *Meaou-neu chuen.* "The Story of Meaou-neu." By Koo Fei-heung, of the Tang Dynasty. A Reprint.　[1741 ?].　8°.

顧 奉 璋 Koo Fung-chang.

壽 世 編 *Show she peen.* "The Book of Long Life." A Short Disquisition on Parturition and the Rearing of Children. Enlarged and edited by Koo Fung-chang.　1846.　8°.

顧 憲 成 Koo Heen-ching.

稿 *Kaou.* "Essays." *See* 長 城 Chang Ching. 名 家 制 義 *Ming kea che e.* "Essays" on Texts from the Four Books, &c.　Tsǐh 61.
1699.　8°.

顧 汝 璉 Koo Joo-leen.

See 王 充 Wang Chung. 論 衡 *Lun hǎng.* "Discussions by Means of Comparisons." ... Edited by Koo Joo-leen, &c.　8°.

顧 凱 之 Koo Kae-che.

See 劉 向 Lew Heang. 古 列 女 傳 *Koo lĕĕ neu chuen.* "Biographies of Eminent Women." ... Illustrated by Koo Kae-che, &c. 1825.　8°.

顧 繼 成 Koo Ke-ching.

See 陳 星 齋 Chin Sing-chae. 文 稿 *Wǎn kaou.* "Essays." .. With Notes by Koo Ke-ching, &c.　1803.　8°.

顧 嘉 瑞 Koo Kea-shwuy.

See 蕭 應 榴 Seaou Ying-kwei, and 顧 德 罄 Koo Tǐh-hing. 律 賦 菰 珠 新 編 *Leǔh foo juy choo sin peen.* "Elegant Odes." ... Edited by Koo Kea-shwuy, &c.　1815.　8°.

Koo Kwan-kwang.

See 利 瑪 竇 Le Ma-tow. 幾 何 原 本 *Ke ho yuen pun.* "Elements of the Science of Quantity." ... Revised by Koo Kwan-kwang, &c.
1857.　8°.

顧 錫 疇 Koo Seǐh-chow.

稿 *Kaou.* "Essays." *See* 長 城 Chang Ching. 名 家 制 義 *Ming kea che e.* "Essays" on Texts from the Four Books, &c.　Tsǐh 78.
1699.　8°.

—— 綱 鑑 正 史 約 *Kang keen ching she yŏ.* "A Compendium of History," from the Reigns of the Three Emperors to the End of the Yuen Dynasty. Compiled by Koo Seǐh-chow. Edited by Chin Hung-mow.　36 keuen.　1737.　8°.

顧 天 埈 Koo Teen-tseun.

稿 *Kaou.* "Essays." *See* 長 城 Chang Ching. 名 家 制 義 *Ming kea che e.* "Essays" on Texts from the Four Books, &c.　Tsǐh 72.
1699.　8°.

顧 德 罄 Koo Tǐh-hing.

See 蕭 應 榴 Seaou Ying-kwei, and Koo Tǐh-hing. 律 賦 菰 珠 新 編 *Leǔh foo juy choo sin peen.* "Elegant Odes." .. Compiled by Seaou Ying-kwei and Koo Tǐh-hing, &c.
1815.　8°.

顧 鼎 臣 Koo Ting-chin.

稿 *Kaou.* "Essays." *See* 長 城 Chang Ching. 名 家 制 義 *Ming kea che e.* "Essays" on Texts from the Four Books, &c. Tsih 28. 1699. 8º.

—— 狀 元 圖 考 *Chwang yuen too kaou.* "Biographical Notices of Chwang yuen" [*i.e.* Literati of the Highest Rank]. By Koo Ting-chin. Edited by Chin Mei. With Illustrations by Hwang Ying-tăng. And with a Collection of Poetry in the Fifteenth Keuen by Members of the Third Rank of Chwang yuen. Compiled by Woo Leih-sing, and edited by Woo Ching-găn. 6 keuen. 1643. 8º.

顧 且 巷 Koo Tseay-gan.

See 孔 丘 Kung Kew. 書 經 體 註 *Shoo king te choo.* "The Book of Historical Documents." . . Edited by . . Koo Tseay-gan, &c. 1815. 8º.

—— *See* 詩 經 She king. 詩 經 體 註 衍 義 合 參 *She king te choo yen e hŏ tsan.* "The Book of Odes." . . Edited by Koo Tseay-gan, &c. 1689. 8º.

—— *See* 王 修 玉 Wang Sew-yŭh. 歷 朝 賦 楷 *Leih chaou foo keae.* "Pattern Odes by Authors of Successive Dynasties." . . . Edited by Koo Tseay-gan, &c. 8º.

顧 棟 高 Koo Tung-kaou.

春 秋 輿 圖 *Chun tsew yu too.* "The Geography of China during the Chun tsew Period," *i.e.* about the Sixth and Seventh Centuries B.C. By Koo Tung-kaou. Edited by Hwa Sung. 1749. 8º.

顧 野 王 Koo Yay-wang.

玉 篇 *Yŭh peen.* An Ancient Dictionary. By Koo Yay-wang. A Reprint. 30 keuen. 1704. 8º.

顧 炎 武 Koo Yen-woo.

菰 中 隨 筆 *Koo chung suy peih.* "Jottings from amidst the Ku," *i.e.* a Water-vegetable. *See* 葉 志 詵 Yĕ Che-sin. 海 山 仙 館 叢 書 *Hae shan seen Kwan tsung shoo.* "The Hae-shan-seen Kwan Collection of Reprints," &c. Vol. 47. 1848. 8º.

顧 炎 武 Koo Yen-woo. (*Continued.*)

左 傳 杜 解 補 正 *Tso chuen Too keae poo ching.* "A Supplement, with Corrections, to Too Yu's Explanations of the Tso chuen." 3 keuen. [Also] 音 論 *Yin lun.* "Disquisitions on the Sounds." [Also] 易 音 *Yĭh yin.* "The Sounds of the Book of Changes." 3 keuen. [Also] 詩 本 音 *She pun yin.* "The Original Sounds of the Book of Odes." 10 keuen. [Also] 日 知 錄 *Jĭh che lŭh.* "The Fruits of Daily Acquisitions." 2 keuen. *See* 嚴 杰 Yen Lĕĕ. 皇 清 經 解 *Hwang Tsing king keae.* "The Classics Explained," &c. Keuen 1–19. 1829. 8º.

—— 音 學 五 書 *Yin hĕŏ woo shoo.* "Five Works on the Science of the Sounds," consisting of the *Yin lun,* "Disquisitions on the Sounds"; 3 keuen. The *She pun yin,* "The Original Sounds of the Book of Odes"; 10 keuen. The *Yĭh yin,* "The Sounds of the Book of Changes"; 3 keuen. The *Tang yun ching,* "A Rectification of the Tang Dynasty Finals"; 20 keuen. And the *Koo yin peaou,* "Ancient Sounds Tabulated"; 2 keuen. By Koo Yen-woo. Edited by Chang Chaou. 1643. 8º.

Imperfect, the *Koo yin peaou* being wanting.

Another copy.

Imperfect.

顧 有 孝 Koo Yew-heaou.

See 張 貴 勝 Chang Kwei-shing. 遣 愁 集 *Keen tsew tseih.* "Anti-Melancholia." . . . . . Edited by Koo Yew-heaou, &c. 8º.

句 東 Kow tung.

句 東 律 賦 *Kow tung leŭh foo.* "Kow tung Odes." 4 keuen (?). [1800?]. 8º.

Imperfect, containing only keuen 2 and 4.

狗 Kow.

殺 狗 記 *Shă kow ke.* "The Story of Killing a Dog." *See* 曲 Keŭh. 六 十 種 曲 *Lŭh shĭh chung keŭh.* "Sixty Plays," &c. Taou 6. 8º.

寇 Kow.

綏 寇 紀 畧 *Suy kow ke leŏ.* "Short Records of the Suppression of Banditti." [By Woo Wei-nĕĕ.] 12 keuen. [1652.] 8º.

Imperfect, containing only keuen 9 and 10.

穀 梁 赤 KŬH-LEANG CHĬH.

See 孔 丘 KUNG KEW. 春 秋 穀 梁 傳 註 疏 *Chun Tsew Kŭh-leang chuen choo soo.* "The Spring and Autumn Annals, and Kŭh-leang Chĭh's Narrative," &c.   8°.

——— 春 秋 三 傳 楬 要 *Chun Tsew san chuen kĕĕ yǎou.* "The Spring and Autumn Annals, with Extracts from the Three Narratives" of . . . Kŭh-leang Chĭh, &c.   12°.

——— 春 秋 三 傳 通 經 合 纂 *Chun Tsew san chuen tung king hŏ tswan.* "The Spring and Autumn Annals." With the Three Narratives of Kŭh-leang Chĭh, &c.   8°.

—— See 公 羊 高 KUNG-YANG KAOU. 公 穀 選 *Kung Kŭh seuen.* "Selections from the Works of . . Kŭh-leang Chĭh," &c.   1766. 8°.

KUMÂRAGÎVA.

See 鳩 摩 羅 什 KEW-MO-LO-SHĬH.

孔 冕 KUNG CHAOU.

See 嚴 作 哲 YEN TSŏ-CHĚ. 汲 冢 周 書 *Keĭh mung Chow shoo.* "A History of the Chow Dynasty." . . With Notes by Kung Chaou, &c.   [1800 ?]. 8°.

孔 鮒 KUNG FOO.

孔 叢 子 *Kung tsung tsze.* "Confucian Miscellanies." See 沈 津 CHIN TSIN. 百 家 類 纂 *Pĭh kea luy tswan.* "The Works of a Hundred Authors," &c.   Keuen 3.   8°.

—— 小 爾 雅 *Seaou Urh ya.* "The Lesser Literary Expositor." See 郎 奎 金 LANG KWEI-KIN. 五 雅 *Woo ya.* "The Five Dictionaries," &c.   1626. 8°.

——— See 汪 士 漢 WANG SZE-HAN. 祕 書 廿 八 種 *Pe shoo neen pǎ chung.* "A Collection of Twenty-eight Reprints," &c.   1808. 8°.

—— 詰 墨 *Keĭh Mĭh.* "Criticisms on the Writings of the Philosopher Mĭh Teĭh." By Kung Foo, of the Han Dynasty. A Reprint.   [1800 ?]. 8°.

孔 鮒 KUNG FOO.   (*Continued*)

孔 叢 子 *Kung tsung tsze.* "Confucian Miscellanies." 3 keuen.   [1750 ?]. 8°.

—— 孔 叢 *Kung tsung.* "Confucian Miscellanies." By Kung Foo, of the Han Dynasty. Edited by Kew Shaou-mow. 2 keuen.   1817 (?). 8°.
      Another edition of the above.

—— 小 爾 雅 *Seaou Urh ya.* "The Lesser Literary Expositor." A Reprint.   [1800 ?]. 8°.

—— 小 爾 雅 疏 *Seaou Urh ya soo.* "The Lesser Literary Expositor. With a Commentary." Edited by Wang Heu.   1800. 8°.

孔 丘 KUNG KEW.

尚 書 *Shang shoo.* "The Book of Historical Documents." [Also] 春 秋 *Chun Tsew.* "The Spring and Autumn Annals." See 毛 鳳 苞 MAOU FUNG-PAOU. 十 三 經 注 疏 *Shih san king choo soo.* "The Thirteen Classics. With Commentaries and Expositions," &c.   1813. 8°.

—— 學 春 秋 隨 筆 *Heŏ Chun Tsew suy peĭh.* "A Help to the Study of the Spring and Autumn Annals," &c. See 嚴 杰 YEN LĕĔ. 皇 清 經 解 *Hwang Tsing king kcae.* "The Classics Explained," &c.   Keuen 50–59.   1829. 8°.

—— 春 秋 大 全 *Chun Tsew ta tseuen.* "A Complete Copy of the Spring and Autumn Annals." With Commentaries by Tso Kew-ming, Hoo Gan-kwo, Kung-yang Kaou, and others. Edited by Fung Mung-lung. To which is added the *Lĕĕ kwŏ che mŏ,* or "The Rise and Fall of the Kingdoms which co-existed with Loo," by the Editor. 30 keuen.   1625. 8°.

—— 春 秋 劈 訓 *Chun Tsew pang heun.* "The Spring and Autumn Annals. With an Interlinear Exposition." Edited by Chang She. 4 keuen.   [1818 ?]. 8°.

Another edition. 4 keuen.   [1820 ?]. 8°.

孔 丘 KUNG KEW. (*Continued.*)

春秋 讀本 *Chun Tsew tŭh pun.* "The Original Text of the Spring and Autumn Annals." With an Interlinear Exposition. Edited by Chang She. 4 keuen.   [1800 ?]. 8°.

Imperfect, wanting the first two pages of the text.

Another edition. 12 keuen.   1806. 8°.

Another edition. 4 keuen.   [1818 ?]. 8°.

Another edition. Edited by Seu Leïh-kang. 4 keuen.   [1820 ?]. 8°.

—— 春 秋 詳 解 *Chun Tsew tseang keae.* "The Spring and Autumn Annals Explained" by Hoo Gan-kwŏ. Edited by Woo Han-ke. 2 keuen.   1103. 12°.

—— 春 秋 指 掌 *Chun Tsew che chang.* "A Guide to the Spring and Autumn Annals." Compiled by Choo Hin and Tseang King-ke. Containing extracts from the Commentaries of Tso Kew-ming, Hoo Gan-kwŏ, Kung-yang Kaou, &c. With a Prefatory Work, by Fung Mung-lung, entitled *Lëë kwŏ che mŏ*, or "The Rise and Fall of the Kingdoms which Co-existed with Loo." 30 keuen.   1688. 8°.

With an Appendix.

—— 春 秋 體 註 大 全 合 參 *Chun Tsew te choo ta tseuen hŏ tsan.* "The Spring and Autumn Annals. With a Body of Comments," and with the Commentary of Hoo Gan-kwŏ. Compiled by Chow Tan-lin, and edited by Fan Tsze-tăng. 4 keuen.   1711. 8°.

Another copy.

Imperfect, containing only keuen 1–3.

—— 春 秋 四 傳 讀 本 *Chun Tsew sze chuen tŭh pun.* "The Spring and Autumn Annals. With Extracts from the Four Narratives" of Tso Kew-ming, Kŭh-leang Chïh, Hoo Gan-kwŏ, and Kung-yang Kaou. 4 keuen.   [1790 ?]. 8°.

Another copy.

—— 春 秋 三 傳 揭 要 *Chun Tsew san chuen këë yaou.* "The Spring and Autumn Annals. With Extracts from the Three Narratives" of Tso Kew-ming, Kung-yang Kaou, and Kŭh-leang Chïh. 6 keuen.   [1750 ?]. 12°.

孔 丘 KUNG KEW. (*Continued.*)

春秋 三 傳 通 經 合 纂 *Chun Tsew san chuen tung king hŏ tswan.* "The Spring and Autumn Annals. With the Three Narratives" of Tso Kew-ming, Kŭh-leang Chïh, and Kung-yang Kaou. Compiled by Chow Tung-heŏ. 12 keuen.   8°.

Imperfect, containing only keuen 10–12.

—— 春 秋 穀 梁 傳 註 疏 *Chun Tsew Kŭh-leang chuen choo soo.* "The Spring and Autumn Annals, and Kŭh-leang Chïh's Narrative," with a Collection of Comments compiled by Fan Ning, and with Explanations by Yang Sze-heun. 20 keuen.   [1800 ?]. 8°.

—— 春 秋 公 羊 傳 註 疏 *Chun Tsew Kung-yang chuen choo soo.* "The Spring and Autumn Annals, and Kung-yang Kaou's Narrative. With a Commentary and Explanations." Compiled by Ho Hew. 28 keuen.   1634. 8°.

—— 春 秋 左 傳 杜 林 合 註 *Chun Tsew Tso chuen Too Lin hŏ choo.* "The Spring and Autumn Annals, and Tso Kew-ming's Narrative. With the Commentaries of Too Yu and Lin Yaou-sow." Edited by Sun Yuĕ-fung, Han Yew-yïh, and others. 50 keuen.   [1780 ?]. 8°.

Another copy.

—— 春 秋 經 傳 集 解 *Chun Tsew king chuen tseïh keae.* "The Spring and Autumn Annals, and Tso Kew-ming's Narrative. With a Collection of Comments." With Notes by Lin Yaou-sow, and with Remarks on the Sounds of the Characters by Lŭh Yuen-lang. Compiled by Too Yu. Edited by Fung Le-hwa. 30 keuen.   [1790 ?]. 8°.

Imperfect, containing only keuen 2, 7–23, 26–28.

Another edition. 30 keuen.   [1790 ?]. 8°.

Imperfect, containing only keuen 29, 30.

—— 孝 經 註 疏 *Heaou king choo soo.* "The Book of Filial Piety," being a Conversation between Kung Kew and his Disciple Tsang Tsan on the Subject. With a Commentary and Paraphrase by Hing Ping. A Reprint. 9 keuen.   [1750 ?]. 8°.

孔 丘 KUNG KEW. (*Continued.*)

孝 經 註 *Heaou king choo.* "The Book of Filial Piety." With a Commentary by Le Kwang-te. A Reprint. 1801. 8°.

—— 學 源 堂 書 經 體 註 *Heŏ yuen tang Shoo king te choo.* "The Heŏ-yuen Tang Edition of the Book of Historical Documents." With a Body of Comments. Edited by Fan Tsze-tăng, Chang Shing-too, and Tseen He-tseang. 6 keuen. 1725. 8°.

The sixth keuen is wanting.

—— 洪 範 説 *Hung Fan shwŏ.* "The Great Plan." With a Commentary by Le Kwang-te. 1708. 8°.

—— 芥 子 園 重 訂 監 本 春 秋 *Keae tsze yuen chung ting keen pun Chun Tsew.* "The Spring and Autumn Annals." With the Commentary of Hoo Gan-kwŏ, and with Notes on the Sounds of the Characters by Lin Yaou-sow. Edited by Le she. The Keae-tsze-yuen Edition. 30 keuen. *Nanking*, 1790. 8°.

Another copy.

—— 芥 子 園 重 訂 監 本 書 經 *Keae tsze yuen chung ting keen pun Shoo king.* "The Book of Historical Documents." With Tsae Chin's Commentary. The Keae-tsze yuen Edition. 6 keuen. *Nanking*, 1790. 8°.

Another edition. 6 keuen. *Nanking*, 1818. 8°.

—— 欽 定 春 秋 傳 説 彙 纂 *Kin ting Chun Tsew chuen shwŏ wei tswan.* "The Spring and Autumn Annals. With a Compilation and Digest of Comments and Remarks" thereon by Tso Kew-ming, Kung-yang Kaou, Too Yu, and others. Compiled by an Imperial Commission consisting of Wang Yen, Chang Ting-yŭh, Tseang Ting-seĭh, and others. With a Preface by the Emperor Kang-he. 38 keuen. 1721. 8°.

Another copy.
Imperfect, containing only keuen 15, 16, 21, 22, 25, 26, 31–34, 36–38.

Another copy.

孔 丘 KUNG KEW. (*Continued.*)

欽 定 書 經 傳 説 彙 纂 *Kin ting Shoo king chuen shwŏ wei tswan.* "The Book of Historical Documents, with a Compilation and Digest of Comments and Remarks" thereon by Tsae Chin, Fŭh Shing, Kung Gan-kwŏ, and others. Compiled by an Imperial Commission consisting of Wang Heŭh-ling, Chang Ting-yŭh, Tseang Ting-seĭh, and others. With a Preface by the Emperor Yung-ching. 21 keuen. 1730. 8°.

Another copy.
Imperfect, containing only keuen 3, 4, 11, 12.

—— 古 本 官 板 書 經 大 全 *Koo pun kwan pan Shoo king ta tseuen.* "The Original Official Text of the Book of Historical Documents." With a Collection of Comments. Compiled by Shin She-hing, Fung Mung-ching, and Yang She. With MS. Notes by J. F. Fouquet. 10 keuen. [1700 ?]. 8°.

—— 奎 壁 書 經 *Kwei pei̇̆h Shoo king.* "The Kwei pei̇̆h Edition of the Book of Historical Documents." With the Commentary of Tsae Chin. Compiled by Ching Yuen-mei. With MS. Notes by J. F. Fouquet. 6 keuen. *Nanking*, [1780 ?]. 8°.

—— 袖 珍 書 經 *Sew chin Shoo king.* "A Pocket Edition of the Book of Historical Documents." With Tsae Chin's Commentary. Edited by Hwang Heaou-fung. 6 keuen. 1750. 8°.
Imperfect, wanting keuen 3–6.

—— 尚 書 讀 本 *Shang shoo tŭh pun.* "The Book of Historical Documents." Edited by Seu Leĭh-kang. 4 keuen. [1800 ?]. 8°.

Another edition. 4 keuen. 1806. 8°.

—— 尚 書 離 句 *Shang shoo le keu.* "The Book of Historical Documents, explained Sentence by Sentence" by Tseen Tsae-pei. Edited by Ching Chuen. 6 keuen. [1750 ?]. 8°.
With copious manuscript notes.

—— 尚 書 註 疏 *Shang shoo choo soo.* "The Book of Historical Documents, with the Commentary" of Kung Gan-kwŏ, "and with Expositions" collected by Kung Ying-tă. 20 keuen. [1800?]. 8°.

15

孔 丘 Kung Kew. (*Continued.*)

尚書七篇解義 *Shang shoo tseĭh peen keae e.* "The First Six Sections of the Book of Historical Documents, together with the Hung Fan, explained" by Le Kwang-te. 2 keuen.
　　　　　　　　　　　　[1710 ?]. 8°.

—— 書 經 *Shoo king.* "The Book of Historical Documents." Chinese and Manchoo. 6 keuen.
　　　　　　　　　　　　[1790 ?]. 8°.

—— 書 經 *Shoo king.* "The Book of Historical Documents." With Notes. 4 keuen.
　　　　　　　　　　　　[1800 ?]. 8°.
Imperfect, containing only part of second, third, and fourth keuen.

—— 書 經 讀 本 *Shoo king tŭh pun.* "The Book of Historical Documents." With an Interlineal Exposition. Edited by Chang she. 4 keuen.
　　　　　　　　　　　　[1800 ?]. 8°.
Another copy.

Another edition. 4 keuen. 　　[1820 ?]. 8°.

—— 書 經 大 全 *Shoo king ta tseuen.* "A Complete Copy of the Book of Historical Documents." With Comments by Tsae Chin, Choo He, Ching Haou, and others. Edited by Seu Kew-yĭh. With Plates. 10 keuen. 　[1750 ?]. 8°.

—— 書 經 體 註 *Shoo king te choo.* "The Book of Historical Documents. With a Body of Comments."　　　　　　[1800 ?]. 8°.
Imperfect, containing only keuen 4 and 6.

Another edition. Edited by Fan Tsze-tăng and Koo Tseay-gan. 6 keuen. 　　　1806. 8°.

Another edition. Edited by Fan Tsze-tang and Koo Tseay-gan. 6 keuen. 　　　1815. 8°.

—— 書 經 詳 解 *Shoo king tseang keae.* "The Book of Historical Documents Explained." Edited by Woo Han-ke. 3 keuen. 　　1209. 12°.

—— 書 經 楬 要 *Shoo king kĕĕ yaou.* "The Book of Historical Documents. With an Abridgment" of the Commentaries of Tsae Chin and others. Edited by Heu Paou-shen. 6 keuen.
　　　　　　　　　　　　[1800 ?]. 12°.
Another copy.

Another copy.

孔 丘 Kung Kew. (*Continued.*)

書 經 旁 訓 讀 本 *Shoo king pang heun tŭh pun.* "The Book of Historical Documents. With an Interlineal Exposition." Edited by Chang she. 4 keuen. 　　　1818. 8°.

—— 書 經 補 註 備 旨 *Shoo king poo choo pe che.* "The Book of Historical Documents. With an Enlarged Commentary, and with Explanations." Compiled by Wang Yew-hăng. Edited by Ma Ta-yew. 6 keuen. 　　1822. 8°.

—— 書 經 瑯 環 體 註 *Shoo king lang hwan te choo.* "The Book of Historical Documents. With a Valuable Body of Comments." Compiled by Tseen He-tseang. Edited by Fan Tsze-tăng. 6 keuen. 　　　　　1789. 8°.

孔 明 Kung-ming.

孔 明 借 壽 *Kung ming tseay show.* "Choo Kung-ming Borrows Longevity." A Dramatic Tale.
　　　　　　　　　　　　[1800 ?]. 8°.

孔 貞 瑄 Kung Ching-seuen.

泰 山 紀 勝 *Tae shan ke shing.* "Notes on Tae shan." *See* 說 Shwŏ. 說 鈴 *Shwŏ ling.* "Miscellaneous Records," &c. 　　　8°.

孔 安 國 Kung Gan-kwŏ.

See 孔 丘 Kung Kew. 欽定書經傳說彙纂 *Kin ting Shoo king chuen shwŏ wei tswan.* "The Book of Historical Documents. . . With Comments and Remarks thereon" by . . . Kung Gan-kwŏ, &c. 　　　1730. 8°.

——— 尚 書 註 疏 *Shang shoo choo soo.* "The Book of Historical Documents, with the Commentary" of Kung Gan-kwŏ, &c. 　　8°.

—— See 禮 記 Le ke. 欽定禮記義疏 *Kin ting Le ke e soo.* "The Meaning of the Book of Rites. With Explanations" by . . Kung Gan-kwŏ, &c. 　　　　8°.

—— See 詩 經 She king. 欽定詩經傳說彙纂 *Kin ting She king chuen shwŏ wei tswan.* "The Book of Odes. With Comments and Remarks" thereon by . . Kung Gan-kwŏ. . . 1727. 8°.

孔 安 國 KUNG GAN-KWŎ. (*Continued.*)

See 易 經 YĬH KING. 御 纂 周 易 折 中 *Yu tswan Chow Yĭh che chung.* "Decisions on the Book of Changes." With the Notes and Comments of .. Kung Gan-kwŏ, &c.　　1715.　8°.

孔 繼 光 KUNG KE-KWANG.

See 文 昌 帝 君 WĂN CHANG TE KEUN. 陰 隲 文 勸 戒 編 *Yin chĭh wăn keuen keae peen.* "A Treatise on Secret Rewards and Retributions." ..... Edited by Kung Ke-kwang, &c.　　1819.　8°.

孔 稼 部 KUNG KEA-POO.

桃 花 扇 傳 奇 *Taou hwa shen chuen ke.* "The Story of the Peach-Blossom Fan." A Drama by Kung Kea-poo. 4 keuen. [1800?]. 8°.
Imperfect, wanting keuen 1.

孔 廣 森 KUNG KWANG-SĂN.

春 秋 公 羊 通 義 *Chun Tsew Kung-yang tung e.* "The Complete Meaning of the Spring and Autumn Annals and of the Narrative of Kung-yang Kaou." 13 keuen. [Also] 禮 學 卮 言 *Le heŏ che yen.* "Measured Remarks on the Teachings of the Rituals." 6 keuen. [Also] 大 戴 禮 記 補 註 *Ta tae Le ke poo choo.* "An Additional Commentary on the Ta Tae Le ke." 13 keuen. [Also] 經 學 卮 言 *King heŏ che yen.* "Measured Remarks on the Teachings of the Classics." 6 keuen. *See* 嚴 杰 YEN LĔĔ. 皇 清 經 解 *Hwang Tsing king keae.* "The Classics Explained," &c. Keuen 679–716.　　1829.　8°.

孔 平 仲 KUNG PING-CHUNG.

孔 氏 雜 說 *Kung she tsă shwŏ.* "Miscellanies" by Kung Ping-chung, &c. *See* 說 SHWŎ. 說 畧 *Shwŏ leŏ.* "Historical and other Tracts," &c.　　8°.

孔 穎 達 KUNG YING-TĂ.

See 孔 丘 KUNG KEW. 尙 書 註 疏 *Shang shoo choo soo.* "The Book of Historical Documents. ... With Expositions" collected by Kung Ying-tă, &c.　　8°.

—— See 禮 記 LE KE. 禮 記 註 疏 *Le ke choo soo.* "The Book of Rites. With .. Expositions" collected by Kung Ying-tă, &c.　　8°.

孔 穎 達 KUNG YING-TĂ. (*Continued.*)

See 詩 經 SHE KING. 毛 詩 注 疏 *Maou she choo soo.* "Maou Chang's Version of the Book of Odes. With .. Expositions" collected by Kung Ying-tă, &c.　　1815.　8°.

—— See 四 書 SZE SHOO. 四 書 朱 子 異 同 條 辨 *Sze shoo Choo tsze e tung teaou peen.* "The Four Books," with ... the Commentaries of ... Kung Ying-tă, &c.　　1705.　8°.

公 孫 龍 KUNG-SUN LUNG.

公 孫 龍 子 *Kung-sun Lung tsze.* "The Writings of Kung-sun Lung." *See* 沈 津 CHIN TSIN. 百 家 類 纂 *Pĭh kea luy tswan.* "The Works of a Hundred Authors," &c. Keuen 24. 8°.

—— See 黃 海 岸 HWANG HAE-GAN. 周 秦 十 一 子 *Chow Tsin shĭh yĭh tsze.* "The Works of the Eleven Philosophers of the Chow and Tsin Dynasties," &c.　　8°.

公 羊 高 KUNG-YANG KAOU.

See 孔 丘 KUNG KEW. 春 秋 大 全 *Chun Tsew ta tseuen.* "A Complete Copy of the Spring and Autumn Annals." With Commentaries by Kung-yang Kaou, &c.　　1625.　8°.

—— 春 秋 三 傳 揭 要 *Chun Tsew san chuen kĕĕ yaou.* "The Spring and Autumn Annals. With Extracts from the Three Narratives" of ... Kung-yang Kaou, &c.　　12°.

—— 春 秋 三 傳 通 經 合 纂 *Chun Tsew san chuen tung king hŏ tswan.* "The Spring and Autumn Annals. With the Three Explanatory Narratives" of .. Kung-yang Kaou, &c.　　8°.

—— 春 秋 公 羊 傳 註 疏 *Chun Tsew kung yang chuen choo soo.* "The Spring and Autumn Annals, and Kung-yang Kaou's Narrative," &c.　　1634.　8°.

—— 欽 定 春 秋 傳 說 彙 纂 *Kin ting Chun Tsew chuen shwŏ wei tswan.* "The Spring and Autumn Annals. ..... With .... Comments and Remarks" thereon by Kung-yang Kaou, &c.　　1721.　8°.

—— 公 穀 選 *Kung kŭh seuen.* "Selections from the Works of Kung-yang Kaou and Kŭh-leang Chĭh." Compiled by Choo Hin.　1766.　8°.

宮 門 Kung mun.

宮門掛帶 *Kung mun kwa tae.* "Hanging the Girdle at the Palace Gate." A Drama.
[1800 ?]. 8°.

宮夢仁 Kung Mung-jin.

松風閣 *Sung fung kŏ.* "The Sung-fung Pavilion" Music Book. Edited by Kung Mung-jin. 2 keuen. [1790 ?]. 8°.
Title-page and part of Preface are wanting.

龔 Kung, and 吳 Woo.

山右闈墨 *Shan yew wei mĭh.* "Shan-se Examination Essays." Compiled by the Examiners Kung and Woo. 1822. 8°.

龔明之 Kung Ming-che.

中吳紀聞 *Chung Woo ke wăn.* "Records of Soochow." *See* 伍崇曜 Woo Tsung-yaou. 粵雅堂叢書 *Yuĕ ya Tang tsung shoo.* "The Yuĕ-ya Tang Collection of Reprints," &c. Series 1. 1853. 8°.

龔在升 Kung Tsae-shing.

三才彙編 *San tsae wei peen.* "An Encyclopædia." Compiled by Kung Tsae-shing. Keuen (?). [1750 ?]. 8°.
Imperfect, containing only keuen 2, 3, 5, 6.

龔雲林 Kung Yun-lin.

萬病回春 *Wan ping hwuy chun.* "The Ten Thousand Diseases which Return with the Spring." Edited by Hoo Ting-heun and others. 8 keuen. 1589. 8°.
Imperfect, containing only keuen 1–3.

Another edition. Edited by Chow Leang-tăng. With Plates. 8 keuen. 1821. 8°.

關朗 Kwan Lang.

關氏易傳 *Kwan she Yĭh chuen.* "Kwan Lang's Commentary on the Book of Changes." Edited by Woo Shaou-tae. [1800 ?]. 8°.

關帝 Kwan te. *The God of War.*

忠義經文 *Chung e king wăn.* "Canonical Works on Patriotism and Uprightness," and other Tracts, namely, the *Keŏ she king,* or "The Sûtra for Arousing the World"; the *Ling yen kŏ,* "The Proofs of the Spiritual Efficacy of Virtue," and a short Medical Tract. Edited by Pwan Shaou-ke. A Reprint. 1839. 8°.
There are four other copies of this work.

關帝 Kwan te. *The God of War.* (*Continued.*)

覺世經詩鈔 *Keŏ she king she chaou.* "Poetry on the Sûtra for Arousing the World." With Notes. 1820. 8°.

—— 警世新文 *King she sin wăn.* "A New Warning to the World." 1835. 8°.

—— 關帝日省編 *Kwan te jĭh sing peen.* "Pages on Daily Self-scrutiny." 1834. 8°.

關尹喜 Kwan Yin-he.

關尹子 *Kwan Yin tsze.* "The Writings of Kwan Yin-he." *See* 沈津 Chin Tsin. 百家類纂 *Pĭh kea luy tswan.* "The Works of a Hundred Authors," &c. Keuen 16. 8°.

官子 Kwan tsze.

官子譜 *Kwan tsze poo.* "Chess Diagrams." [1800 ?]. 8°.

管仲 Kwan Chung.

管子 *Kwan tsze.* "Kwan Chung's Work on Legislation." *See* 沈津 Chin Tsin. 百家類纂 *Pĭh kea luy tswan.* "The Works of a Hundred Authors," &c. Keuen 20, 21. 8°.

—— *See* 黃海岸 Hwang Hae-gan. 周秦十一子 *Chow Tsin shĭh yĭh tsze.* "The Works of the Eleven Philosophers of the Chow and Tsin Dynasties," &c. 8°.

—— With a Commentary by Fang Heuen-ling. 24 keuen. *See* 黃丕烈 Hwang Pei-lĕĕ. 十子全書 *Shĭh tsze tseuen shoo.* "The Complete Works of the Ten Philosophers," &c. 1804. 8°.

—— 管子纂 *Kwan tsze tswan.* "The Work of Kwan Chung on Legislation." Compiled by Chang Pang. With Explanations by Woo Kwang-tsze. 2 keuen. [1750 ?]. 8°.

—— 管子評註 *Kwan tsze ping choo.* "Kwan Chung's Work on Legislation. With Critical Notes" by Chin Ting-sin and Choo Yang-tun, "and Commentaries" by Fang Heuen-ling and Lew Tseĭh. Edited by Choo Yang-ho. 24 keuen. 1804. 8°.

管 茂 村 KWAN MOW-TSUN.

See HOBSON (BENJAMIN). 西醫略論 *Se e leŏ lun.* "A Short Practical Work on European Surgery." Written in Chinese by Dr. Hobson, ... with the assistance of ... Kwan Mow-tsun, &c.   1857. 8°.

—— See 合 信 HŎ-SIN [*i.e.* Benjamin Hobson]. 婦嬰新說 *Foo ying sin shwŏ.* "A New Treatise on Midwifery and the Diseases of Children." Edited by Kwan Mow-tsun, &c.   1858. 8°.

———— 內 科 新 說 *Nuy ko sin shwŏ.* "A New Treatise on the Practice of Medicine." Edited by Kwan Mow-tsun, &c.   1858. 8°.

管 世 銘 KWAN SHE-MING.

管 緅 若 時 文 *Kwan Keen-jŏ she wăn.* "The Occasional Essays of Kwan She-ming" on Texts from the Four Books. In Three Series. 4 Vol. 1781. 1786. 1793. 8°.

管 靜 山 KWAN TSING-SHAN.

管 靜 山 全 稿 *Kwan Tsing-shan tseuen kaou.* "The Essays of Kwan Tsing-shan." With a Third Supplementary Collection, edited by Koo Shin.   1817. 1819. 8°.

觀 光 KWAN KWANG.

See CHINA. 乾 隆 KEEN-LUNG. *Emperor.* 欽 定 八 旗 則 例 *Kin ting pă ke tsĭh le.* "Regulations for the Bannermen." .. Compiled by .. Kwan Kwang, &c.   1786. 8°.

觀 世 音 KWAN-SHE-YIN.

高 王 觀 世 音 經 *Kaou wang Kwan-she-yin king.* "The Sûtra of the Lofty Goddess Kwan-she-yin."   *Canton,* 1838. 8°.

—— 觀 音 籤 *Kwan yin tseen.* "Votary Charms used in the Worship of the Goddess Kwan-she-yin." [1800?]. 8°.

—— 觀 世 音 菩 薩 普 門 品 經 *Kwan-she-yin Poo-să poo mun pin king.* "The Avalôkitêsvara Bodhisattva Sûtra." *Canton,* [1795?]. Oblong.

—— 妙 法 蓮 華 經 觀 世 音 菩 薩 普 門 品 *Meaou fă leen hwa king kwan-she-yin Poo-să poo mun pin.* "The Avalôkitêsvara Bodhisattva Sûtra, from the 'Lotus of the Excellent Law.'" 1705. 8°.

廣 圻 KWANG KE.

韓 非 子 識 誤 *Han Fei tsze shĭh woo.* "Errors in the Text of the Writings of Han Fei pointed out." By Kwang Ke. 3 keuen. 1816. 8°.

廣 錄 KWANG-LŬH.

金 剛 略 義 *Kin kang leŏ e.* "A Short Explanation of the Diamond Classic." By the Priest Kwang-lüh.   *Canton,* [1800?]. 8°.

廣 東 KWANG TUNG.

廣 東 名 人 故 事 *Kwang tung ming jin koo sze.* "An Account of Canton and of Celebrated Cantonese."   *Canton,* [1850?]. 8°.

—— 廣 東 省 外 海 戰 船 做 法 *Kwang tung sing wae hae chen chuen tso fă.* "Instructions for the Construction of Ships of War for the Canton Waters." 40 keuen.   [1800?]. 8°.

—— 廣 東 闈 墨 *Kwang tung wei mĭh.* "Canton Provincial Examination Essays." [1820?]. 8°.
A Fragment.

KWANG-TUNG, PROVINCE OF.

內 河 則 例 *Nuy ho tsĭh le.* "Regulations for the Navy of the Inland Waters of the Province of Kwang-tung." 58 keuen.   [1800?]. 8°.

廣 成 子 KWANG CHING-TSZE.

陰 符 經 *Yin foo king.* "On the Sûtra of Secret Charms." [Also] 金 藥 秘 訣 *Kin yŏ pe keuĕ.* "The Secret of the Golden Medicine." See 彭 好 古 PĂNG HAOU-KOO. 道 言 內 外 秘 訣 全 書 *Taou yen nuy wae pe keuĕ tseuen shoo.* "A Complete Collection of Taouist Works," &c. Part I. keuen 1. Part II. keuen 1.   8°.

桂 枝 KWEI-CHE.

桂 枝 寫 狀 全 本 *Kwei che seay chwang tseuen pun.* "Kwei-che writes a Petition." A Tale in Verse. 2 keuen.   *Canton,* [1850?]. 8°.

桂 馥 KWEI FŬH.

續 三 十 五 舉 *Sŭh san shĭh woo keu.* "A Supplement to the First Part of the *Heŏ koo peen,* on the Seal Character." Compiled by Kwei Fŭh. *See* 葉 志 詵 YĔ CHE-SIN. 海 山 仙 館 叢 書 *Hae shan seen kwan tsung shoo.* "The Hae-shan-seen Kwan Collection of Reprints," &c. Vol. 87.   1848. 8°.

貴 州 KWEI-CHOW.

貴州闈墨 *Kwei chow wei mih.* "Kwei-chow Examination Essays" for the Years 1819 and 1821.   1819–1821.   8°.

      A Fragment.

貴 中 孚 KWEI CHUNG-FOO, and 萬 承 紀 WAN CHING-KE.

丹徒縣志 *Tan too heen che.* "A Topography of Tan-too Heen," in the Province of Keang-soo.   47 keuen.   1805.   8°.

Another copy.

      Imperfect, containing only keuen 28–31, 35–47.

揆 敘 KWEI SEU.

See 詩 經 SHE KING. 欽定詩經傳說彙纂 *Kin ting she king chuen shwŏ wei tswan.* "The Book of Odes." . . . Compiled by . . Kwei Seu, &c.   1727.   8°.

鬼 KWEI.

鬼神傳 *Kwei shin chuen.* "Tales of Gods and Demons."   4 keuen.   1859.   8°.

—— 平鬼傳 *Ping kwei chuen.* "The Story of the Pacification of the Demons." A Romance of the Tang Dynasty. By the Man of the Yang-chih-tseaou-yun Mountain. 4 keuen. 1720. 8°.

Another copy.

      Imperfect, containing only the first keuen.

鬼 谷 子 KWEI-KŬH-TSZE.

鬼谷子 *Kwei-kŭh-tsze.* "The Writings of Kwei-kŭh-tsze." *See* 沈津 CHIN TSIN. 百家類纂 *Pĭh kea luy tswan.* "The Works of a Hundred Authors," &c.   Keuen 26.   8°.

歸 有 光 KWEI YEW-KWANG.

稿 *Kaou.* "Essays." *See* 長城 CHANG CHING. 名家制義 *Ming kea che e.* "Essays" on Texts from the Four Books, &c.   Tsĭh 53.   1699.   8°.

—— 震川先生全集 *Chin chuen Seen-săng tseuen tseih.* "A Complete Collection of the Writings of Kwei Yew-kwang." In Two Parts. Part I. 30 keuen. Part II. 10 keuen.   1675.   8°.

Another copy.

歸 有 光 KWEI YEW-KWANG. *(Continued).*

諸子彙函 *Choo tsze wei han.* "Extracts from the Writings of all the Philosophers" from the Time of the Chow to that of the Ming Dynasty. Compiled by Kwei Yew-kwang. Edited by Wăn Chin-mang.   26 keuen.   1625.   8°.

過 琪 KWŎ HUNG.

See 劉豫庵 LEW YU-GAN. 詳訂古文評註 *Tseang ting koo wăn ping choo.* "Extracts from Ancient Literature. . . With Critical Notes and Comments," by Kwŏ Kung, &c.   1847.   8°.

來 保 LAE PAOU.

See TSING DYNASTY. 大清通禮 *Ta Tsing tung le.* "A Complete Code of the Ceremonies of the Ta Tsing Dynasty." Compiled by . . . Lae Paou, &c.   1824.   8°.

來 瞿 唐 LAE KEU-TANG.

See 易經 YĬH KING. 易經來註圖解 *Yĭh king Lae choo too keae.* "The Book of Changes. With a Commentary by Lae Keu-tang," &c.   1598.   8°.

來 木 臣 LAE MŬH-CHIN.

See 易經 YĬH KING. 易經大全會解 *Yĭh king ta tseuen hwuy keae.* "The Book of Changes." . . Compiled by Lae Mŭh-chin, &c.   1681.   8°.

賴 太 素 LAE TAE-SOO.

催官解 *Tsuy kwan keae.* "The Tsuy kwan," a Work on Geomancy by Lae Tae-soo, "explained" by Choo Foo.   1842.   8°.

蘭 簃 LAN E.

靖逆記 *Tsing nĕih ke.* "An Account of the Suppression of Banditti" in Shen-se and other parts. By Lan E, the Historian.   6 keuen.   1821.   8°.

Another copy.

郎 奎 金 LANG KWEI-KIN.

五 雅 *Woo ya.* "The Five Dictionaries," viz.: The Urh ya; the Kwang ya, by Chang Yĭh; the Seaou Urh ya, by Kung Foo; the Yĭh ya, by Lew He; and the Pe ya, by Lŭh Teen. Compiled by Lang Kwei-kin.   1626.   8°.

郎 廷 極 LANG TING-KĔIH.

勝 飮 編 *Shing yin peen.* "A Treatise on Overcoming the Love of Drinking." 18 keuen. *See* 伍 崇 曜 WOO TSUNG-YAOU. 粵 雅 堂 叢 書 *Yuĕ ya Tang tsung shoo.* "The Yuĕ-ya Tang Collection of Reprints," &c. Series 15. 1853. 8°.

浪 子 LANG TSZE.

浪 子 悔 改 *Lang tsze hwuy kae.* "The Parable of the Prodigal Son." [By Dr. James Legge?.] *Hongkong,* [1868?]. 8°.

老 君 LAOU KEUN.

道 德 經 *Taou tĭh king.* "The Classic of Reason and Virtue." *See* 沈 津 CHIN TSIN. 百 家 類 纂 *Pĭh kea luy tswan.* "The Works of a Hundred Authors," &c. Keuen 13.   8°.

—— See 程 潘 基 CHING PWAN-KE. 老 莊 會 解 *Laou Chwang hwuy keae.* "The Works of Laou keun and Chwang Chow," &c.   8°.

—— 感 應 篇 *Kan ying peen.* "The Book of Rewards and Punishments." *See* 周 鼎 臣 CHOW TING-CHIN. 增 訂 敬 信 錄 *Tsĕng ting king sin lŭh.* "Works on Reverence and Faith," &c.   1827. 8°.

—— 道 德 經 *Taou tĭh king.* "The Classic of Reason and Virtue." *See* 黃 海 岸 HWANG HAE-GAN. 周 秦 十 一 子 *Chow Tsin shĭh yĭh tsze.* "The Works of the Eleven Philosophers of the Chow and Tsin Dynasties," &c.   8°.

—— With a Commentary by Ho Shang-kung. 2 keuen. *See* 黃 丕 烈 HWANG PEI-LĔĚ. 十 子 全 書 *Shĭh tsze tseuen shoo.* "The Complete Works of the Ten Philosophers," &c. 1804. 8°.

—— With a Commentary by Ching Keu, &c. *See* 焦 竑 TSEAOU HUNG. 老 莊 翼 合 刻 *Laou Chwang yĭh hŏ kĭh.* "The Works of Laou keun and Chwang Chow," &c. Keuen 1-3. 1588. 8°.

—— 道 德 眞 經 註 *Taou tĭh chin king choo.* "The True Classic of Reason and Virtue." With a Commentary by Woo Ching. 4 keuen. [Also] 感 應 篇 註 *Kan ying peen choo.* "The Book of Rewards and Punishments. With a Commentary" by Hwuy Tung. 2 keuen. *See* 伍 崇 曜 WOO TSUNG-YAOU. 粵 雅 堂 叢 書 *Yuĕ ya Tang tsung shoo.* "The Yuĕ-ya Tang Collection of Reprints," &c. Series 12. 1853. 8°.

老 君 LAOU KEUN. (*Continued.*)

黃 庭 經 註 *Hwang ting king choo.* "A Work on the Government of the Inner Man." With a Commentary by Shĭh Ho-yang. Edited by Le Ming-chĕ. 3 keuen.   1793. 8°.

—— 感 應 篇 圖 說 *Kan ying peen too shwŏ.* "The Book of Rewards and Punishments. With Illustrations and Expositions." Edited by Kea Tang. 4 keuen.   *Canton,* 1709. 8°.

—— 感 應 篇 註 證 *Kan ying peen choo ching.* "The Book of Rewards and Punishments. With Comments and Illustrative Stories." Edited by Chang Taou and others. 4 keuen. 1792. 8°.

Another copy.

—— 感 應 篇 圖 說 *Kan ying peen too shwŏ.* "The Book of Rewards and Punishments. With Illustrations and Expositions." 4 keuen.
     [1800 ?]. 8°.
Wanting the first and fourth keuen.

Another copy.
Wanting the third and fourth keuen.

—— 感 應 篇 註 *Kan ying peen choo.* "The Book of Rewards and Punishments. With a Commentary " by Tĕĕ Tseaou. A Reprint.
     Canton, 1805. 8°.

Another copy.

—— 感 應 篇 箋 註 *Kan ying peen tseen choo.* "The Book of Rewards and Punishments." With a Commentary by Hwuy Tung. Edited by Chang Tun-jin.   *Keang-ning,* 1827. 8°.

—— 感 應 篇 直 講 *Kan ying peen chĭh keang.* "The Book of Rewards and Punishments," clearly explained by Hwang Te-twan. A Reprint.
     Keang-ning, 1831. 8°.
There are three copies of this work.

—— 感 應 篇 *Kan ying peen.* "The Book of Rewards and Punishments." Edited by Chow Kwei-shan. To which are appended six other Taouist tracts.   *Canton,* 1833. 8°.

老君 Laou keun. (*Continued.*)

太上感應篇圖說 *Tae shang Kan ying peen too shwŏ.* "The Book of Rewards and Punishments." With a Commentary by Heu Tswan-tsăng. Edited by Chaou Hung. A Reprint. With Illustrations. 4 keuen. 1825. 8°.

—— 太上感應篇緒言 *Tae shang Kan ying peen seu yen.* "The Book of Rewards and Punishments. With a Collection of Comments." Edited by Keen Le-keen. 8 keuen. 1865. 8°.

—— 三官經 *San kwan king.* "The Sûtra of the Three Celestial Magnates." A Reprint. *Canton,* 1818. 8°.

—— 三官寶經 *San kwan paou king.* "The Precious Sûtra of the Three Celestial Magnates." A Reprint. *Canton,* 1816. 8°.

—— 太上說三官經 *Tae shang shwŏ san kwan king.* "The Sûtra of the Three Celestial Magnates delivered by Laou keun." [1750 ?]. 8°. Mutilated.

—— 道德經考正 *Taou Tĭh king kaou ching.* "A Critical Work on the Classic of Reason and Virtue." By Shun-yang-chin-jin, *i.e.* Leu Yen. 2 keuen. 1809. 8°.

Auother copy.

—— 道德經解 *Taou tĭh king keae.* "The Classic of Reason and Virtue, explained" by Shun-yang Te keun, *i.e.* Leu Yen. Edited by Loo She. In Two Parts. [1809.] 8°.

—— 道德經釋義 *Taou Tĭh king shĭh e.* "The Classic of Reason and Virtue, explained" by Shun-yang-chin-jin, *i.e.* Leu Yen. Edited by Mow Mŭh-yuen. 2 keuen. 1809. 8°.

Another copy.

—— 道德經 Le *Tao-Te-king,* ou Le livre révéré de la raison suprême et de la vertu. Traduit en François ... avec une version latine et le texte Chinois en regard, accompagné du commentaire complet de Sie-Hoéï, d'origine occidentale, et des notes tirées de divers autres commentateurs Chinois, par G. Pauthier. 1re Livraison. *Paris,* [printed] *Leipzig,* 1838. 8°.

老君 Laou keun. (*Continued.*)

老子道德經 *Lao tseu Tao te king.* Le livre de la voie et de la vertu. .... Traduit en Français et publié avec le texte Chinois et un commentaire perpétuel par Stanislas Julien. *Paris,* 1842. 8°.

勞之辨 Laou che-peen.

詩經 *She king.* Essays on Texts from "The Book of Odes," by Laou Che-peen and others. [1800 ?]. 12°. Imperfect.

勞大與 Laou ta-yu.

甌江逸志 *Gow keang yĭh che.* "Miscellanies from Gow-keang." *See* 說 Shwŏ. 說鈴 *Shwŏ ling.* "Miscellaneous Records," &c. 8°.

黎醽亭 Le Gae-ting.

尺·牘壽源書札要覽 *Chĭh tŭh sin yuen shoo chă yaou lan.* "A Complete Letter Writer." 4 keuen. 1860. 8°.

黎照樓 Le-chaou low.

黎照樓智燈難字 *Le chaou low che tăng nan tsze.* "The Lamp of Knowledge applied for the Elucidation of Difficult Characters." The Le-chaou Low Edition. 2 keuen. 8°.

理 Le.

中外理辨 *Chung wae le peen.* "A Discussion on Orthodox [*i.e.* Christian] and Heretical [*i.e.* Confucian] Principles." [By Rev. Thomas McClatchie.] *Shanghae,* [1847]. 8°.

厲鶚 Le Gŏ.

東城雜記 *Tung ching tsă ke.* "Miscellaneous Records of the Antiquities in the Eastern Quarter of the City of Hang Chow." 2 keuen. *See* 伍崇曜 Woo Tsung-yaou. 粵雅堂叢書 *Yuĕ ya Tang tsung shoo.* "The Yuĕ-ya Tang Collection of Reprints," &c. Series 1. 1853. 8°.

—— 遼史拾遺 *Leaou she shĭh wei.* "A Supplement to the History of the Leaou Dynasty." 24 keuen. 1821. 8°.

勵廷儀 Le Ting-e.

See 張廷玉 Chang Ting-yŭh. 分類字錦 *Fun luy tsze kin.* "A Classified Lexicon of Elegant Expressions." Edited ... by ... Le Ting-e, &c. 1722. 8°.

LE [121] LE

鄺 道 元 Le Taou-yuen.

See 桑 欽 Sang Kin. 冰 經 注 Shwuy king choo. "The Water Classic." With a Commentary by Le Taou-yuen, &c. 1774. 8º.

梨 園 Le yuen.

梨 園 雅 韻 Le yuen ya yun. "Elegant Rhymes from the Pear Orchard." A Play. [1840 ?]. 8º.

禮 記 Le ke.

See 毛 鳳 苞 Maou Fung-paou. 十 三 經 注 疏 Shih san king choo soo. "The Thirteen Classics, with Commentaries and Expositions," &c. 1813. 8º.

—— 滿 漢 禮 記 Mwan han Le ke. "The Book of Rites in Manchoo and Chinese." With a Preface by the Emperor Keen-lung. 30 keuen. 1783. 8º.

—— 禮 記 讀 本 Le ke tŭh pun. "The Original Text of the Book of Rites." With a Commentary by Ching Kang-ching. 6 keuen. [1790 ?]. 8º.

Another edition. Edited by Chang she. 6 keuen. [1800 ?]. 8º.

Another copy.

Another edition. 10 keuen. 1806. 8º.

Another edition. 6 keuen. 1828. 8º.

—— 監 本 禮 記 Keen pun Le ke. "The Book of Rites." With a Collection of Comments compiled by Chin Haou. Edited by Choo she. 30 keuen. 1698. 8º.

Another edition. 10 keuen. 1792. 8º.

Another edition. 10 keuen. 1796. 8º.

—— 芥 子 園 重 訂 監 本 禮 記 Keae tsze yuen chung ting keen pun Le ke. "The Keae-tsze Yuen Edition of the Book of Rites." With a Collection of Comments compiled by Chin Haou. Edited by Le she. 10 keuen.
Nanking, 1790. 8º.

Another copy.

—— 禮 記 增 訂 旁 訓 Le ke tsăng ting pang heun. "The Book of Rites. With an Enlarged Interlinear Commentary." 6 keuen. [1800 ?]. 8º.
Imperfect, containing only the third keuen.

禮 記 Le ke. (*Continued.*)

禮 記 註 疏 Le ke choo soo. "The Book of Rites. With a Commentary" by Ching Kang-ching, "and Expositions" collected by Kung Ying-tă. 28 keuen. [1750 ?]. 8º.

—— 欽 定 禮 記 義 疏 Kin ting Le ke e soo. "The Meaning of the Book of Rites. With Explanations" by Seun Hwang, Sze-ma Tseen, Kung Gan-kwŏ, and others." 82 keuen. [1700 ?]. 8º.

Another copy.
Imperfect, wanting keuen 1–3, 77–82.

—— 全 本 禮 記 體 註 Tseuen pun Le ke te choo. "The Book of Rites, with a Collection of Comments" compiled by Chin Haou. Edited by Fan Tsze-tăng. 10 keuen. 1766. 8º

Another copy.
Imperfect, wanting keuen 1.

—— 禮 記 體 註 大 全 Le ke te choo ta tseuen. "The Book of Rites, with a Body of Comments." Edited by Fan Tsze-tăng. 4 keuen. 1713. 8º.

—— 禮 記 體 註 大 全 合 參 Le ke te choo ta tseuen ho tsan. "The Book of Rites, with a Body of Comments." Compiled by Fan Tsze-tăng. Edited by Chow Tan-lin. 4 keuen. 1711. 8º.

—— 全 文 禮 記 疏 意 體 註 Tseuen wăn Le ke soo e te choo. "The Complete Text of the Book of Rites. With Explanations and a Body of Comments." Compiled by Tsin Ke-tsung and Seu Wăn-choo. 28 keuen. 1632. 8º.

—— 禮 記 楬 要 Le ke kĕĕ yaou. "The Book of Rites. With an Abridgment" of the Commentaries of Choo He and others. Edited by Heu Paou-shen. 6 keuen. [1789 ?]. 12º

—— 禮 記 集 說 Le ke tseĭh shwŏ. "The Book of Rites. With a Collection of Comments" compiled by Chin Haou. The Keae-tsze Yuen Edition. 10 keuen. 1322. 12º.
Imperfect, wanting keuen 8.

—— 禮 記 心 典 傳 本 Le ke sin teen chuen pun. "The Central Canons of the Book of Rites." With a Commentary. Compiled by Hoo Yaou-kwang. 3 keuen. 1693. 8º.

16

利類思 LE LUY-SZE [*i.e.* Luigi Buglio].

     See 郭居靜 Kǒ KEU-TSING. 天主聖敎日課 *Teen choo shing keaou jǐh ko.* "Daily Christian Religious Exercises." Edited .. by .. Le Luy-sze, &c.   8°.

—— 超性學要 *Chaou sing heǒ yaou.* "An Epitome of the Theology" of Thomas Aquinas. By Le Luy-sze. Edited by Pǐh Ying-le and Min Ming-wo. 22 keuen.   *Peking,* [1730 ?]. 8°.

Another copy.

     Imperfeet, containing only the sixteeuth keuen.

利瑪竇 LE MA-TOW [*i.e.* Matteo Ricci].

     幾何原本 *Ke ho yuen pun.* "Elements of the Science of Quantity" (being a Translation of the first six books of Euclid's Elements of Geometry), orally translated into Chinese by Matteo Ricci, and written out by Seu Kwang-ke. 6 keuen. [Also] 圜容較義 *Yuen yung keaou e.* "A Geometrical Treatise" .. Written .. from the Dictation of Le Ma-tow. [Also] 測量法義 *Tsǐh leang fǎ e.* "An Explanation of the Theory of Astronomical Measurement" by means of the Right-angled Triangle. Translated by Le Ma-tow. *See* 葉志詵 YĚ CHE-SIN. 海山仙館叢書 *Hae shan seen Kwan tsung shoo.* "The Hae-shan-seen Kwan Collection of Reprints," &c. Vol. 98–101, 107.   1848. 8°.

—— 幾何原本 *Ke ho yuen pun.* "The Elements of the Science of Quantity," being a Translation of Euclid. Commenced by Matteo Ricci, who with the assistance of Seu Kwang-ke translated the first six Books, and completed by Wei-lěǐ Ah-leǐh, *i.e.* A. Wylie, assisted by Le Shen-lan, and revised by Koo Kwan-kwang and Chang Wǎn-hoo. 15 keuen.   1857. 8°.

—— 天主實義 *Teen choo shǐh e.* "A Treatise on the Character and Attributes of God." 2 keuen.   1602. 8°.

     Wanting the second keuen.

Another edition.

     Wanting the second keuen.

李 LE.

     See 顧 Koo, and LE. 浙江魁卷 *Chě keang kwei keuen.* "A Volume of Chě keang Examination Essays." Compiled by ... Koo and Le, &c.   1816. 8°.

—— 李衛公別傳 *Le Wei kung pěǐh chuen.* "The Story of Le Duke of Wei." *See* 說 SHWǑ. 說淵 *Shwǒ yuen.* "A Collection of Tales," &c. Vol. 6.   8°.

李禎 LE CHING.

     See 四書 SZE SHOO. 四書朱子異同條辨 *Sze shoo Choo tsze e tung teaou peen.* "The Four Books." ... Edited by .. Le Ching, &c.   1705. 8°.

李綽 LE CHǑ.

     尚書故實 *Shang shoo koo shǐh.* "Causes and Effects." *See* 王文誥 WANG WǍN-KAOU. 唐代叢書 *Tang tae tsung shoo.* "A Collection of Reprints of Works written during the Tang Dynasty," &c. Series 1. 1806. 8°.

李疇 LE CHOW.

     See 黃惠 HWANG HWUY, and LE CHOW. 龍溪縣志 *Lung ke heen che.* "A Topography of Lung-ke Heen." .. Compiled by Hwang Hwuy and Le Chow, &c.   1762. 8°.

李蘩 LE FAN.

     李泌傳 *Le Pe chuen.* "The Story of Le Pe." *See* 王文誥 WANG WǍN-KAOU. 唐代叢書 *Tang tae tsung shoo.* "A Collection of Reprints of Works written during the Tang Dynasty," &c. Series 4.   1806. 8°.

—— 李泌傳 *Le Pe chuen.* "The Story of Le Pe." By Le Fan, of the Tang Dynasty. A Reprint.   [1741 ?]. 8°.

李昉 LE FANG.

     太平廣記 *Tae ping kwang ke.* "Extensive Records compiled during the Reign of the Emperor Tae-tsung," by Le Fang. Edited by Hwang Heaou-fung. Containing Mythological and other Tales. 500 keuen.   1806. 8°.

     Imperfect, wanting keuen 269–283.

Another copy.

     Imperfect, wanting keuen 1–239.

李福 Le Fŭh.

See 瞿曇法智 Keu-tan-fă-che. 業報差別經 Něĕ paou cha pĕĕ king. "A Sûtra on the various Requitals attaching to different Occupations." . . . Edited by Le Fŭh, &c. 1811. 8°.

李翱 Le Gaou.

卓異記 Chŏ e ke. "A Record of Strange Phenomena and Events." See 王文誥 Wang Wăn-kaou. 唐代叢書 Tang tae tsung shoo. "A Collection of Reprints of Works written during the Tang Dynasty," &c. Series 5.

1806. 8°.

李涵 Le Han.

See China. Board of War. 欽定兵部續纂處分則例 Kin ting Ping poo sŭh tswan choo fun tsĭh le. "Supplementary . . Regulations of the Board of War." Compiled by . . . Le Han, &c. 1829. 8°.

李賢 Le Heen.

一統志 Yĭh tung che. "A Geography of the Empire." Compiled by an Imperial Commission consisting of Le Heen, Păng She, Leu Yuen, and others. 90 keuen. 1461. 8°.

Another copy.

李翮 Le Hĭh.

See 魏晉錫 Wei Tsin-seĭh. 欽定學政全書 Kin ting heŏ ching tseuen shoo. "A Complete Collection of Educational Statutes." . . Compiled by . . . Le Hĭh, &c. 1781. 8°.

李湟 Le Hwang.

See 毛奇齡 Maou Ke-ling. 四書典制辨正 Sze shoo teen che peen ching. "Explanatory Essays on Canonical Passages from the Four Books." . . . Edited by Le Hwang, &c. 8°.

李凱 Le Kae.

寒香亭傳奇 Han heang ting chuen ke. "The Story of the Cool and Fragrant Pavilion." A Drama. Edited by Fan Woo. 4 keuen.

1797. 8°.

李堪 Le Kan.

See 孫汝忠 Sun Joo-chung. 金丹眞傳 Kin tan chin chuen. "A Trustworthy Treatise on the Philosopher's Stone." With . . a Paraphrase by Le Kan, &c. 1615. 8°.

李綱 Le Kang.

靖康傳信錄 Tsing kang chuen sin lŭh. "A True Account of the Reign of the Emperor Tsing-kang" [A.D. 1125–1127]. 3 keuen. See 葉志詵 Yĕ Che-sin. 海山仙館叢書 Hae shan seen Kwan tsung shoo. "The Hae-shan-seen Kwan Collection of Reprints," &c. Vol. 18. 1848. 8°.

李介 Le Keae.

天香閣隨筆 Teen heang kŏ suy pĕĭh. "Occasional Pieces of Poetry from the Pavilion of Heavenly Fragrance." 3 keuen. See 伍崇曜 Woo Tsung-yaou. 粵雅堂叢書 Yuĕ ya Tang tsung shoo. "The Yuĕ-ya Tang Collection of Reprints," &c. Series 2. 1853. 8°.

李碻 Le Keŏ.

乍浦九山補誌 Cha poo kew shan poo che. "A Supplementary Topography of the Nine Mountains of Cha-poo," in the Province of Chĕ-keang. 2 keuen. 1831. 8°.

李秬 Le Keu.

安徽試牘存眞約選 Gan hwuy she tŭh tsun chin yŏ seuen. "Select Essays from the Gan-hwuy Examinations." Compiled by Le Keu.

1812. 8°.

李覯 Le Kow.

旴江集鈔 Heu keang tseĭh chaou. "The Heu keang Collection of Poetry." See 吳孟舉 Woo Măng-keu, and 吳自牧 Woo Tsze-mŭh. 宋詩鈔二集 Sung she chaou urh tseĭh. "Poetry of the Sung Dynasty," &c.

[1800 ?]. 8°.

李觀 Le Kwan.

李元賓集 Le Yuen-pin tseĭh. "The Writings of Le Kwan." Compiled by Lŭh He-shing. 6 keuen. See 伍崇曜 Woo Tsung-yaou. 粵雅堂叢書 Yuĕ ya Tang tsung shoo. "The Yuĕ-ya Tang Collection of Reprints," &c. Series 20. 1853. 8°.

李軌 Le Kwei.

See 揚雄 Yang Heung. 法言 Fă yen. "A Discourse on Moral Laws." . . With a Commentary by Le Kwei, &c. 1818. 8°.

李國 LE KWŎ.

See 陳之綱 CHIN CHE-KANG. 四明古蹟詩 *Sze ming koo tseĭh she.* "Poetry on the Antiquities of Sze-ming." ... Edited by Le Kwŏ, &c.   1822. 12°.

李理 LE LE.

See 徐衜 SEU TAOU. 佛祖傳燈 *Fŭh tsoo chuen tăng.* "A Lamp applied to the Lives of Buddhist Saints." ... Edited by Le Le, &c. 8°.

———— 神仙鑑 *Shin seen keen.* "Biographical Notices of Taouist Saints." By Seu Taou, assisted by Le Le, &c.   8°.

李泌 LE PE.

枕中記 *Chin chung ke.* "The Story of the Inside of a Pillow." See 王文誥 WANG WĂN-KAOU. 唐代叢書 *Tang tae tsung shoo.* "A Collection of Reprints of Works written during the Tang Dynasty," &c. Series 5.   1806. 8°.

—— 枕中記 *Chin chung ke.* "The Story of the Inside of a Pillow." By Le Pe, of the Tang Dynasty. A Reprint.   [1741?]. 8°.

李盤 LE PWAN.

金湯十二籌 *Kin tang shĭh urh chow.* "Twelve Devices in the Art of War." See 水 SHWUY. 水陸戰守攻略方術秘書七種 *Shwuy lŭh chen show kung leŏ fang shŭh pe shoo tseĭh chung.* "A Military System for both Land and Sea," &c.   [1800?]. 8°.

李游 LE SEUN.

摭異記 *Chĭh e ke.* "Wondrous Tales taken down from Hearsay." See 王文誥 WANG WĂN-KAOU. 唐代叢書 *Tang tae tsung shoo.* "A Collection of Reprints of Works written during the Tang Dynasty," &c. Series 5.   1806. 8°.

李肇 LE SHAOU.

國史補 *Kwŏ she poo.* "A Supplement to History." See 王文誥 WANG WĂN-KAOU. 唐代叢書 *Tang tae tsung shoo.* "A Collection of Reprints of Works written during the Tang Dynasty," &c. Series 2.   1806. 8°.

李氏 LE SHE.

See 孔丘 KUNG KEW. 芥子園重訂監本春秋 *Keae tsze yuen chung ting keen pun Chun Tsew.* "The Spring and Autumn Annals." ... Edited by Le She, &c.   1790. 8°.

—— See 禮記 LE KE. 芥子園重訂監本禮記 *Keae tsze yuen chung ting keen pun Le ke.* "The ... Book of Rites." .. Edited by Le She, &c.   *Nanking,* 1790. 8°.

—— See 余象斗 YU SEANG-TOW. 華光天王南遊志傳 *Hwa kwang Teen wang nan yew che chuen.* "An Account of a Journey to the South made by the Deity Hwa-kwang." Edited by Le She, &c.   8°.

—— 觀世音菩薩普門品經 *Kwan she yin Poo-să poo mun pin king.* "The Avalôkitêsvara Bodhisattva Sûtra." Edited by Le She.   1686. Oblong.

李善 LE SHEN.

See 蕭統 SEAOU TUNG. 文選 *Wăn seuen.* "Elegant Extracts from Polite Literature," .. With a Commentary by Le Shen, &c. 1772. 8°.

李芨 LE TAN.

See 萬玉卿 WAN YŬH-KING. 紅樓夢傳奇 *Hung low mung chuen ke.* "The Dream of the Red Chamber" Dramatized. ... Edited by Le Tan, &c.   1800. 8°.

李坦 LE TAN.

增刪卜易 *Tsăng shan poo yĭh.* "A Work on Divination." By the Old Man of Yay-hŏ. Enlarged and revised by Le Wăn-hwuy. Edited by Le Tan. First Series. 12 keuen. 1714. 8°.

Another edition. 12 keuen.   [1800?]. 8°.
     Wanting keuen 1, 4, 5.

李清 LE TSING.

See 馬驌 MA SŬH. 繹史 *Yĭh she.* "History Arranged." ... Edited by Le Tsing, &c.   1670. 8°.

—— 李清傳 *Te tsing chuen.* "The Story of Le-tsing." See 說 SHWŎ. 說淵 *Shwŏ yuen.* "A Collection of Tales," &c. Vol. 8.   8°.

李惇 LE TUN.

羣經識小 *Keun king shih seaou.* "Explanations of Minor Points in the Classics." 8 keuen. *See* 嚴杰 YEN LËË. 皇清經解 *Hwang Tsing king keae.* "The Classics Explained," &c. Keuen 719–726.　　　　1829.　8°.

李雯 LE WĂN.

皇明詩選 *Hwang Ming she seuen.* "Selections from the Poetry of the Ming Dynasty." Compiled by Le Wăn, Chin Tsze-lung, and Sung Ching-yu. 13 keuen.　　[1800 ?].　8°.

李衛 LE WEI.

See 稽曾筠 KE TSĂNG-YUN. 浙江通志 *Chě keang tung che.* "A Topography of the Province of Chě keang." Compiled by ... Le Wei, &c.　　　　1736.　8°.

—— 西湖志 *Se hoo che.* "A Topography of the Western Lake" in Chě keang. Compiled by Le Wei, Ching Yuen-chang, and others. 48 keuen.　　　　1734.　8°.

李冶 LE YAY.

敬齋古今註 *King-chae koo kin tow.* "The Independent Criticisms of Le Yay on Ancient and Modern" Literature. 8 keuen. *See* 葉志詵 YĚ CHE-SIN. 海山仙館叢書 *Hae shan seen Kwan tsung shoo.* "The Hae-shan-seen Kwan Collection of Reprints," &c. Vol. 55, 56.　　　　1848.　8°.

李梲 LE YEN.

See TSING DYNASTY. 大清律箋釋 *Ta Tsing leŭh tseen shih.* "The Laws of the Ta Tsing Dynasty elucidated and explained." Compiled by Le Yen, &c.　　　　1725.　8°.

李有 LE YEW.

古杭雜記 *Koo Hang tsă ke.* "Miscellaneous Records from Koo Hang." *See* 說 SHWŎ. 說畧 *Shwŏ leŏ.* "Historical and other Tracts," &c.　　　　8°.

李隱 LE YIN.

瀟湘錄 *Seaou seang lŭh.* "Records from Seaou seang." *See* 說 SHWŎ. 說畧 *Shwŏ leŏ.* "Historical and other Tracts," &c.　　　　8°.

李隱 LE YIN. (*Continued.*)

瀟湘錄 *Seaou seang lŭh.* "Records from Seaou seang." *See* 王文誥 WANG WĂN-KAOU. 唐代叢書 *Tang tae tsung shoo.* "A Collection of Reprints of Works written during the Tang Dynasty," &c. Series 2.　　1806.　8°.

李章美 LE CHANG-MEI.

See 朱熹 CHOO HE. 小學體註大成 *Seaou heŏ te choo ta ching.* "The Youth's Instructor." ... Edited ... by ... Le Chang-mei, &c. 8°.

李章武 LE CHANG-WOO.

李章武傳 *Le Chang-woo chuen.* "The Story of Le Chang-woo." *See* 說 SHWŎ. 說淵 *Shwŏ yuen.* "A Collection of Tales," &c. Vol. 2. 8°.

李兆洛 LE CHAOU-LŎ.

紀元編 *Ke yuen peen.* "A Chronological List" of the Emperors of China from the Han to the beginning of the Tsing Dynasty. 3 keuen. *See* 伍崇曜 WOO TSUNG-YAOU. 粤雅堂叢書 *Yuĕ ya Tang tsung shoo.* "The Yuĕ-ya Tang Collection of Reprints," &c. Series 12. 1853. 8°.

—— 歷代地理志韻編今釋 *Leih tae te le che yun peen kin shih.* "A Gazetteer, giving the Topographical Changes which have taken place in the Empire through succeeding ages down to the present time. The Names of Places are arranged under the Tonic Finals." Compiled by Le Chaou-lŏ. Edited by Lŭh Yen, Lŭh Ching-joo, Sung King-chang, and others. 20 keuen.　　　　1837.　8°.

—— 江陰縣志 *Keang yin heen che.* "A Topography of Keang-yin Heen," in the Province of Keang-soo. Compiled by Le Chaou-lo, Yang King-tsăng, Chow Chung-keen, and others. 28 keuen.　　　　1840.　8°.

李朝威 LE CHAOU-WEI.

柳毅傳 *Lew E chuen.* "The Story of Lew E." *See* 王文誥 WANG WĂN-KAOU. 唐代叢書 *Tang tae tsung shoo.* "A Collection of Reprints of Works written during the Tang Dynasty," &c. Series 4.　　　1806.　8°.

—— 柳毅傳 *Lew E chuen.* "The Story of Lew E." By Le Chaou-wei, of the Tang Dynasty. A Reprint.　　　　[1741 ?].　8°.

李之藻 LE CHE-TSAOU.

同文算指 *Tung wan swan che.* "A Treatise
on Arithmetic" by Le Che-tsaou, being a Digest
of the Science communicated to him by Matteo
Ricci in the year 1614. 10 keuen. [Also]
圜容較義 *Yuen yung keaou e.* "A Geometrical Treatise on the Proportional Capacities of
Various Figures and Bodies." Written by Le
Che-tsaou, from the Dictation of Le Ma-tow, *i.e.*
Matteo Ricci. *See* 葉志詵 YĚ CHE-SIN.
海山仙館叢書 *Hae shan seen kwan tsung
shoo.* "The Hae-shan-seen Kwan Collection of
Reprints," &c. Vol. 102–107. 1848. 8º.

李之泍 LE CHE-TUNG, and 汪建封 WANG KEEN-
FUNG.

叩鉢齋纂 *Kow pŏ chae tswan.* "A Collection
of Literary Pieces from the Kow-pŏ Study."
Compiled by Le Che-tung and Wang Keen-
fung. With Notes by Chin Yŭh-leang and
Wang Tso-pin. 13 keuen. [1790 ?]. 8º.
Imperfect, containing only keuen 2, 3, 13.

李振裕 LE CHIN-YU.

See 易經 YĬH KING. 周易口義 *Chow Yĭh
kow e.* "The Chow Changes." ... Edited by
... Le Chin-yu, &c. 1687. 8º.

李承祖 LE CHING-TSOO.

文苑聯珠 *Wăn yuen leen choo.* "Pearls from
the Garden of Literature, classified and arranged" by Le Ching-tsoo. 8 keuen. 1770. 8º.
Imperfect, wanting keuen 4–8.

李卓吾 LE CHŎ-WOO.

See 羅貫中 LO KWAN-CHUNG. 三國志傳
San kwŏ che chuen. "The History of the Three
Kingdoms." Edited by Le Chŏ-woo, &c. 8º.

李淳風 LE CHUN-FUNG.

See 趙君卿 CHAOU KEUN-KING. 周髀算經
Chow pe swan king. "A Work on Trigonometry
and Astronomy." ..With further Elucidations
by Le Chun-fung. 8º.

李中立 LE CHUNG-LEĬH.

本草原始 *Pun tsaou yuen che.* "The Natural
Conditions of the Substances mentioned in the
Materia Medica of Le She-chin." By Le Chung-
leĭh. Edited by Kŏ Meĭh. [1700 ?]. 8º.
Imperfect, containing only keuen 8 and 9.

李中梓 LE CHUNG-TSZE.

醫宗必讀 *E tsung pe tŭh.* "A Brief Summary
of Medical Practice." 10 keuen. [1650 ?]. 8º.
Imperfect, containing only keuen 5 and 6.

李義山 LE E-SHAN.

雜纂 *Tsă tswan.* "Aphorisms." *See* 說 SHWŎ.
說纂 *Shwŏ tswan.* "Miscellaneous Records,"
&c. Vol. 8. 8º.

—— 義山雜纂 *E shan tsă tswan.* "Le E-shan's
Aphorisms." *See* 王文誥 WANG WĂN-KAOU.
唐代叢書 *Tang tae tsung shoo.* "A Collection of Reprints of Works written during the
Tang Dynasty," &c. Series 2. 1806. 8º.

李黼平 LE FOO-PING.

毛詩紬義 *Maou She chow e.* "The Meaning
of the Book of Odes." *See* 嚴杰 YEN LĔĔ.
皇清經解 *Hwang Tsing king keae.* "The
Classics Explained," &c. Keuen 1331–1354.
1829. 8º.

李復言 LE FŬH-YEN.

續幽怪錄 *Sŭh yew kwae lŭh.* "A Supplementary Record of Wonders." By Le Fŭh-yen,
of the Tang Dynasty. A Reprint. [1741?]. 8º.

李安民 LE GAN-MIN.

See 陳宏謀 CHIN HUNG-MOW. 在官法戒
錄摘鈔 *Tsae kwan fă keae lŭh tsĭh chaou.*
"The Mandarin's Instructor." .... Edited by
...... Le Gan-min, &c. 1823. 8º.

李何事 LE HO-SZE.

白雲梯 *Pĭh yun te.* "The White Cloud Ladder."
See 閔景賢 MIN KING-HEEN. 快書 *Kwae
shoo.* "A Book of Amusement," &c. Keuen 7.
1626. 8º.

李弘植 LE HUNG-CHĬH.

See 王朝佐 WANG CHAOU-TSO. 安州誌 *Gan
chow che.* "A Topography of Gan chow." ...
Compiled by .. Le Hung-chĭh, &c. 1680. 8º.

李宏甫 LE HUNG-FOO.

道德經 *Taou tĭh king.* "The Classic of Reason
and Virtue." With a Commentary by Le
Hung-foo. *See* 焦竑 TSEAOU HUNG. 老莊
翼合刻 *Laou Chwang yĭh hŏ kĭh.* "The
Works of Laou keun and Chwang Chow," &c.
1588. 8º.

第一卷

李 鴻 賓 LE HUNG-PIN.

See 阮 元 YUEN YUEN. 廣 東 通 志 *Kwang tung tung che.* "A Topography of the Province of Kwang-tung." Compiled by ... Le Hung-pin, &c. 1822. 8º.

李 如 枚 LE JOO-MEI.

See 杜 琳 TOO LIN. 淮 關 統 志 *Hwae kwan tung che.* "A Topography of the Hwae Custom-house District." ... Edited by Le Joo-mei, &c. 1806. 8º.

李 如 筠 LE JOO-YUN.

See 毛 履 謙 MAOU LE-KEEN, and 吳 涵 一 WOO HAN-YIH. 十 家 詩 詳 註 *Shih kea she tseang choo.* "The Poetical Works of Ten Authors," viz. : ... Le Joo-yun, &c. 1813. 8º.

李 嘉 果 LE KEA-KWO.

八 師 經 *Pa sze king.* "The Sûtra of the Eight Teachers." Edited by Le Kea-kwo. Translated into Chinese by Yew-po-sih-che-keen. 1797. 8º.

—— 天 王 經 *Teen wang king.* "The Sûtra of the Four Heavenly Kings." Edited by Le Kea-kwo. Translated into Chinese by the Priest Che-yen-hung-paou-yun. 1797. 8º.

李 秬 香 LE KEU-HEANG.

墨 卷 脫 穎 *Mih keuèn tŏ ying.* "A Collection of Superior Examination Essays" for the Years 1825 and 1828. Second and Third Supplementary Series. Compiled by Le Keu-heang. 1828. 8º.

李 秬 薌 LE KEU-HEANG.

制 義 約 選 *Che e yŏ seuen.* "Selected Essays" on Texts from the Four Books. Compiled and Arranged by Le Keu-heang, in Two Series. 1826. 1829. 8º.

李 巨 來 LE KEU-LAE.

See 儀 禮 E LE. 儀 禮 章 句 *E le chang keu.* "The Decorum Ritual." ... Edited by Le Keu-lae, &c. 1757. 8º.

李 九 我 LE KEW-WO.

See 胡 廣 HOO KWANG. 性 理 大 全 *Sing le ta tseuen.* "A Complete Work on Mental Philosophy." .. Edited by Le Kew-wo, &c. 1597. 8º.

李 格 非 LE KIH-FEI.

洛 陽 名 園 記 *Lŏ yang ming yuen ke.* "An Account of the Nineteen Celebrated Gardens of Lŏ-yang." *See* 葉 志 詵 YĚ CHE-SIN. 海 山 仙 館 叢 書 *Hae shan seen Kwan tsung shoo.* "The Hae-shan-seen Kwan Collection of Reprints," &c. Vol. 18. 1848. 8º.

李 公 佐 LE KUNG-TSO.

南 柯 記 *Nan ko ke.* "An Account of the Kingdom of Nan-ko." *See* 王 文 誥 WANG WĂN-KAOU. 唐 代 叢 書 *Tang tae tsung shoo.* "A Collection of Reprints of Works written during the Tang Dynasty," &c. Series 5. 1806. 8º.

—— 南 柯 記 *Nan ko ke.* "An Account of the Kingdom of Nan-ko." By Le Kung-tso, of the Tang Dynasty. A Reprint. [1741 ?]. 8º.

—— 謝 小 娥 傳 *Seay Seaou-go chuen.* "The Story of Seay Seaou-go." By Le Kung-tso, of the Tang Dynasty. A Reprint. [1741 ?]. 8º.

李 觀 瀾 LE KWAN-LAN.

See 宋 慈 SUNG TSZE. 洗 寃 錄 集 證 *Se yuen lŭh tseih ching.* "Records of the Washing Away of Injuries," ... with additions by Le Kwan-lan, &c. 1796. 8º.

李 光 地 LE KWANG-TE.

稿 *Kaou.* "Essays." *See* 長 城 CHANG CHING. 名 家 制 義 *Ming kea che e.* "Essays" on Texts from the Four Books, &c. Tsih 117. 1699.

—— See 朱 熹 CHOO HE. 朱 子 全 書 *Choo tsze tseuen shoo.* "The Complete Works of Choo He." Compiled .. by Le Kwang-te, &c. 1713. 8º.

—— See 孔 丘 KUNG KEW. 孝 經 註 *Heaou king choo.* "The Classic on Filial Piety." With a Commentary by Le Kwang-te, &c. 1801. 8º.

—— —— 洪 範 說 *Hung fan shŭŏ.* "The Great Plan. With a Commentary" by Le Kwang-te, &c. 1708. 8º.

—— —— 尙 書 七 篇 解 義 *Shang shoo tseih peen keae e.* "The First Six Sections of the Book of Historical Documents, together with the Hung Fan, explained" by Le Kwang-te, &c. 8º.

李 光 地 LE KWANG-TE. *(Continued.)*
　　See 詩 經 SHE KING. 詩 所 *She so.* "The Correct Meaning and Order of the Book of Odes." ... By Le Kwang-te, &c.　1718. 8º.

—— See 易 經 YĬH KING. 御纂周易折中 *Yu tswan Chow Yĭh che chung.* "Decisions on the Book of Changes." .. Compiled by .. Le Kwang-te, &c.　　　　1715. 8º.

—— 中 庸 章 段 *Chung yung chang twan.* "The 'Doctrine of the Mean' explained Paragraph by Paragraph" by Le Kwang-te. 1720. 8º.

—— 中 庸 餘 論 *Chung yung yu lun.* "A Further Consideration of the 'Doctrine of the Mean.'" By Le Kwang-te.　　　　1720. 8º.

—— 古 文 精 藻 *Koo wăn tsing tsaou.* "Elegant Pieces of Ancient Literature." Compiled by Le Kwang-te. 2 keuen.　　1713. 8º.

—— 性 理 精 義 *Sing le tsing e.* "The Essence of Works on Mental Philosophy." Compiled by order of the Emperor Kang-he, by a Commission consisting of Le Kwang-te, Wei Ting-chin, Ho Kwŏ-tsung, and others. 12 keuen. 1715. 8º.

—— 大 學 古 本 說 *Ta heŏ koo pun shwŏ.* "The Original Text of the 'Great Learning.' With a Commentary" by Le Kwang-te. 1720. 8º.

—— 讀 論 語 劄 記 *Tŭh Lun yu tă ke.* "Memoranda for Students of the Confucian Analects." By Le Kwang-te.　　　　1720. 8º.

—— 讀 孟 子 劄 記 *Tŭh Măng tsze tă ke.* "Memoranda for Students of the Works of Mencius." By Le Kwang-te.　　　　1720. 8º.

李 來 泰 LE LAE-TAE.
　　稿 *Kaou.* "Essays." *See* 長 城 CHANG CHING. 名 家 制 義 *Ming kea che e.* "Essays" on Texts from the Four Books, &c. Tsĭh 106.　　　　　　　　1699. 8º.

李 良 壽 LE LEANG-SHOW.
　　[A Notice announcing the Death of Pope Innocent XIII. ?] Written by Le Leang-show.
　　　　　　　　[1724 ?]. A Sheet.

李 兩 堂 LE LEANG-TANG.
　　萬 花 樓 傳 *Wan hwa low chuen.* "A Tale from the Gallery of Ten Thousand Flowers." Edited by Le Leang-tang. 14 keuen. 1836. 8º.

李 立 庚 LE LEĬH-HOW.
　　See 蔡 世 遠 TSAE SHE-YUEN. 古 文 雅 正 *Koo wăn ya ching.* "Elegant Extracts from Ancient Literature." ... Edited by Le Leĭh-how, &c.　　　　1777. 8º.

李 笠 翁 LE LEĬH-UNG.
　　芥 子 園 畫 傳 *Keae tsze yuen hwa chuen.* "The Keae-tsze Yuen Drawing Book." Illustrated by Drawings taken from Ancient Models, by Wang Gan-tsëĕ, Wang Sze-chĭh, and Wang Meĭh-tsaou. Compiled by Le Leĭh-ung. In Four Parts.　　　　1679–1818. 8º.
　　There are three imperfect copies of this work.

李 林 甫 LE LIN-FOO.
　　李 林 甫 外 傳 *Le Lin-foo wae chuen.* "The Story of Le Lin-foo." *See* 說 SHWŏ. 說 淵 *Shwŏ yuen.* "A Collection of Tales," &c. Vol. 3.　　　　　　　　8º.

李 龍 雲 LE LUNG-YUN.
　　See 孟 子 MĂNG TSZE. 蘇 老 泉 批 評 孟 子 眞 本 *Soo Laou-tseuen pe ping Măng tsze chĭn pun.* "Soo Seun's Edition of the Works of Mencius." Edited by Le Lung-yun. 1803. 8º.

李 明 徹 LE MING-CHĔ.
　　See 黃 帝 HWANG TE. 陰 符 經 *Yin foo king.* "The Sûtra of Secret Charms." ... Edited by Le Ming-chĕ, &c.　　　　1793. 8º.

—— See 老 君 LAOU KEUN. 黃 庭 經 註 *Hwang ting king choo.* "A Work on the Government of the Inner Man." ... Edited by Le Ming-chĕ, &c.　　　　1793. 8º.

—— 圜 天 圖 說 *Yuen teen too shwŏ.* "A Treatise on Astronomy." By Le Ming-chĕ, a Taouist Priest. Edited by Yuen Yuen. With Illustrations. 3 keuen.　　　　1819. 8º.

—— 圜 天 圖 說 續 編 *Yuen teen too shwŏ sŭh peen.* "A Supplement to the *Yuen teen too shwŏ,* or Treatise on Astronomy." By Le Ming-chĕ. Edited by Yuen Yuen. With Illustrations. 2 keuen.　　　　1821. 8º.
　　Another copy.

LE [129] LE

李夢陽 LE MUNG-YANG.

稿 *Kaou.* "Essays." *See* 長城 CHANG CHING. 名家制義 *Ming kea che e.* "Essays" on Texts from the Four Books, &c. Tsĭh 23. 1699. 8°.

李念莪 LE NEEN-GO.

內經知要 *Nuy king che yaou.* "A Selection of Passages from the Soo wăn and Ling choo [Medical Works]. With a Commentary" by Le Neen-go. Edited by Sëĕ Săng-pĭh. 2 keuen. 1764. 8°.

Imperfect, containing only kcuen 1.

李扱式 LE PĂ-SHĬH.

爾雅蒙求 *Urh Ya mung kew.* "The Literary Expositor, arranged for Beginners." 2 keuen. 1798. 8°.

李沛霖 LE PEI-LIN.

See 四書 SZE SHOO. 四書朱子異同條辨 *Sze shoo Choo tsze e tung teaou peen.* "The Four Books." ... Edited by Le Pei-lin, &c. 1705. 8°.

李百藥 LE PĬH-LŎ.

北齊書 *Pĭh Tse shoo.* "The History of the Northern Tse Dynasty." *See* 毛晉 MAOU TSIN. 十七史 *Shĭh tseĭh She.* "The Seventeen Histories," &c. 1656. 8°.

李本固 LE PUN-KOO.

See 易經 YĬH KING. 古易彙編 *Koo Yĭh wei peen.* "The Ancient Text of the Book of Changes." .... Compiled by Le Pun-koo, &c. 1612. 8°.

李息齋 LE SEĬH-CHAE.

道德經 *Taou tĭh king.* "The Classic of Reason and Virtue." With a Commentary by Le Seĭh-chae. *See* 焦竑 TSEAOU HUNG. 老莊翼合刻 *Laou Chwang yĭh hŏ kĭh.* "The Works of Laou keun and Chwang Chow," &c. 1588. 8°.

李錫勛 LE SEĬH-HEUN.

成均課藝正續彙選 *Ching keun ko e ching sŭh wei seuen.* "A Collection of Essays on Texts from the Four Books by Eminent Scholars." Compiled by Le Seĭh-heun, Jin Che-tseuen, and Chin Paou. 1802. 8°.

李錫隮 LE SEĬH-TSAN.

近科考卷脫頴集 *Kin ko kaou keuen tŏ ying tseĭh.* "A Collection of Superior Examination Essays," on Texts from the Four Books. Edited by Le Seĭh-tsan. 1815. 8°.

李時珍 LE SHE-CHIN.

奇經八脈玫 *Ke king pa mĭh kaou.* "An Examination of the Theory of the Eight Pulses." By Le She-chin. Edited by Chang Ting-sze. 1603. 12°.

—— 脈學 *Mĭh heŏ.* "A Work on the Pulse." 1603. 12°.

—— 脈學奇經八脈 *Mĭh heŏ Ke king pă mĭh.* "A Work on the Pulse, and, The Theory of the Eight Pulses." Edited by Chang Ting-sze. 1603. 8°.

—— 本草綱目全書 *Pun tsaou kang mŭh tseuen shoo.* "The Complete Materia Medica" of Le She-chin, who spent thirty years on the Work, and extracted from the Works of 800 Authors 1518 different Medicaments and added 374 new ones. These are arranged in sixty-two classes, under sixteen divisions. Edited by Chang Ting-sze. 52 keuen. 1603. 8°.

—— 本草綱目 *Pun tsaou kang mŭh.* "The Materia Medica" of Le She-chin. Edited by Woo Yŭh-chang. 52 keuen. 1655. 8°.

—— The Keae-tsze yuen Edition of the Materia Medica of Le She-chin. 52 keuen. *Nanking,* 1657. 8°.

There are three other imperfect copies of this work.

李善蘭 LE SHEN-LAN.

See HERSCHEL (SIR JOHN FREDERICK WILLIAM), *Bart.* 談天 *Tan teen.* Herschel's "Outlines of Astronomy" ... transcribed by Le Shen-lan, &c. 1859. 8°.

—— See 利瑪竇 LE MA-TOW. 幾何原本 *Ke ho yuen pun.* "The Elements of the Science of Quantity." .. Completed by Wei-lëĕ Ah-leĭh, assisted by Le Shen-lan, &c. 1857. 8°.

17

李 善 蘭 LE SHEN-LAN. (*Continued.*)

See 羅 密 士 LO-MEĬH-SZE. 代 微 積 拾 級 *Tae wei tseĭh shĭh keĭh.* "Analytical Geometry." ... Transcribed by Le Shen-lan, &c.

1855? 8°.

—— See 韋 廉 臣 WEI-LEEN-CHIN. 植 物 學 *Chĭh wŭh heŏ.* "A Work on Botany." .... With the Chinese Text revised by Le Shen-lan, &c.

1858. 8°.

李 式 圖 LE SHĬH-POO.

嵊 縣 志 *Shing heen che.* "A Topography of Shing Heen," in the Province of Keang-se. Compiled by Le Shĭh-poo, Choo Lŭh, and others. 14 keuen and Appendix. 1828. 8°.

李 淳 風 LE SHUN-FUNG.

See 劉 徽 LEW HWUY. 海 島 算 經 *Hae taou swan king.* "The Art of Measuring the Height of Islands." .. With a Commentary by Le Shun-fang, &c. 1775. 8°.

李 惺 菴 LE SING-GAN.

證 治 彙 補 *Ching che wei poo.* "A Supplementary Medical Treatise." [1691?]. 8°. Imperfect, containing only keuen 6–8.

李 松 石 LE SUNG-SHĬH.

鏡 花 綠 繡 像 *King hwa yuen sew seang.* "The Mysterious Influences of Bright Flowers." A Mythological Work. Edited by Heu Keaou-lin. 20 keuen. *Nanking,* 1832. 8°.

李 太 白 LE TAE-PĬH.

太 白 詩 話 *Tae pĭh she hwa.* "An Account of Le Tae-pĭh and his Poems." [1830?]. 8°.

李 鐵 垣 LE TĔĔ-YUEN.

讀 雅 筆 記 *Tŭh ya peĭh kc.* "Memoranda for Students of Polite Literature." 3 keuen.

1804. 8°.

李 鼎 祚 LE TING-TSOO.

See 易 經 YĬH KING. 易 傳 *Yĭh chuen.* "The Book of Changes. With a Commentary" by Le Ting-tsoo, &c. 1756. 8°.

李 鼎 元 LE TING-YUEN.

See 戴 侗 TAE TUNG. 六 書 故 *Lŭh shoo koo.* "The Origin of the Six Kinds of Characters." .. Edited by Le Ting-yuen, &c. 1784. 8°.

李 齊 芳 LE TSE-FANG.

See 莊 周 CHWANG CHOW. 南 華 眞 經 副 墨 *Nan hwa chin king foo mĭh.* "A Guide to the Nan hwa king." ... By Le Tse-fang, &c.

1578. 8°.

李 清 照 LE TSING-CHAOU.

打 馬 圖 經 *Ta ma too king.* "A Work on the Ancient Game of 'Striking the Horses,' with Plans." See 伍 崇 曜 WOO TSUNG-YAOU. 粵 雅 堂 叢 書 *Yuĕ ya Tang tsung shoo.* "The Yuĕ-ya Tang Collection of Reprints," &c. Series 7. 1853. 8°.

李 宗 昉 LE TSUNG-FANG.

立 誠 編 試 牘 合 鈔 *Leĭh ching peen shĭh tŭh ho chaou.* "Examination Essays" from the Provinces of Gan-hwuy, Keang-se, Chĕ-keang, and Kwei-chow. Edited by Le Tsung-fang.

1817. 8°.

Imperfect.

李 崇 禮 LE TSUNG-LE.

See 紀 昀 KE YUN. 館 課 賦 註 *Kwan ko foo choo.* "College Poems. With Notes" by .. Le Tsung-le, &c. 1802. 8°.

李 紫 庭 LE TSZE-TING.

See 孫 上 登 SUN SHANG-TĂNG. 初 學 行 文 語 類 *Choo heŏ hing wăn yu luy.* "Notes on Behaviour and Literature for Beginners." ... Edited by Le Tsze-ting, &c. 1800. 8°.

李 東 陽 LE TUNG-YANG.

稿 *Kaou.* "Essays." See 長 城 CHANG CHING. 名 家 制 義 *Ming kea che e.* "Essays" on Texts from the Four Books, &c. Tsĭh 15.

1699. 8°.

李 文 熊 LE WĂN-HEUNG.

See 陳 埭 CHIN SĂNG. 常 山 縣 志 *Chang shan heen che.* "A Topography of Chang-shan Heen." ... Compiled by .. Le Wăn-heung, &c.

1813. 8°.

李 文 輝 LE WĂN-HWUY.

See 李 坦 LE TAN. 增 刪 卜 易 *Tsăng shan pŭh yĭh.* "A Work on Divination." .. Enlarged and Revised by Le Wăn-hwuy, &c. 8°.

李 文 山 LE Wăn-shan.
See 吳 懋 政 Woo Mow-ching. 八 銘 塾 鈔
Pă ming shŭh chaou. "A Copy of Essays from
the Pă ming College." With Notes by Le Wăn-
shan, &c. 1781. 1782. 8°.

李 文 耀 LE Wăn-yaou.
上 海 縣 志 Shang hae heen che. "A Topography
of Shang-hae Heen." Compiled, on the basis of
former Histories, by Le Wăn-yaou, Tan Ke-
hing, Yĕ Ching, and others. 12 keuen.
1750. 8°.

李 維 楨 LE Wei-ching.
續 藏 書 Sŭh tsang shoo. "A Sequel to the 'Book
of Biographical Treasures.'" 27 keuen.
[1750 ?]. 8°.

李 彥 貴 LE Yen-kwei.
生 祭 李 彥 貴 全 本 Săng tse Le yen-kwei tseuen
pun. "The Story of Le Yen-kwei." In Verse.
2 keuen. 1840. 8°.

李 延 壽 LE Yen-show.
南 史 Nan she. "The History of the South."
80 keuen. [Also] 北 史 Pĭh she. "The
History of the North." 100 keuen. See 毛 晉
Maou Tsin. 十 七 史 Shĭh tsĕih she. "The
Seventeen Histories," &c. 1656. 8°.

—— 南 史 Nan she. "The History of the South."
Compiled by Le Yen-show; revised by Ling-
hoo Tĭh-fun. This Work includes also the
abbreviated History of the Sung, Southern Tse,
Leang, and Chin Dynasties. 80 keuen.
[1750 ?]. 8°.

—— 北 史 Pĭh she. "The History of the North."
This Work includes also the Histories of the
Northern Wei, the Northern Tse, the Chow,
and the Suy Dynasties. 100 keuen.
[1750 ?]. 8°.

Imperfect, wanting the first forty-five keuen.

李 叉 存 LE Yew-tsun.
See 唐 虒 Tang Shing. 范 縣 志 Fan heen che.
"A Topography of Fan Heen." ... Edited by
Le Yew-tsun, &c. 1813. 8°.

李 因 培 LE Yin-pei.
See 尹 繼 善 Yin Ke-shen. 直 隷 通 州 志
Chĭh le Tung chow che. "A Topography of Tung
Chow." .. Compiled by ... Le Yin-pei, &c.
1755. 8°.

李 月 桂 LE Yuĕ-kwei.
See 陽 靳 賢 Yang Kin-heen. 鍼 灸 大 成
Chin kew ta ching. "A Complete System of
Acupuncture." ... Edited by Le Yuĕ-kwei, &c.
1798. 8°.

李 雲 翔 LE Yun-seang.
See 潘 海 虞 Pwan Hae-yu. 與 圖 備 攷 Yu
too pe kaou. "A Treatise on Geography." ..
Edited by Le Yun-seang, &c. 1650. 8°.

李 永 壽 LE Yung-show.
See 馬 伯 瓦 Ma Pĭh-leang. 敎 欵 捷 要
Keaou kwan tsĕĕ yaou. "An Exposition of the
Mohammedan Law." ... Edited by Le Yung-
show, &c. 1817. 8°.

梁 Leang.
抓 字 意 Chĭh tsze e. "The Meanings of Characters traced out." By Leang. 1801. 8°.

梁 揆 長 Leang Kwei-chang.
See 易 經 Yĭh king. 易 經 備 旨 眞 本 Yĭh
king pe che chin pun. "A Correct Copy of the
Book of Changes." ... Compiled by Leang
Kwei-chang, &c. 1707. 8°.

梁 國 治 Leang Kwŏ-che.
See China. Board of Revenue. 欽 定 戶 部
軍 需 則 例 Kin ting Hoo Poo keun seu tsĭh le.
"Regulations .. for the Supply of Commissariat
Stores." Compiled by .. Leang Kwŏ-che, &c.
1785. 8°.

梁 上 國 Leang Shang-kwŏ.
See 毛 履 謙 Maou Le-keen, and 吳 涵 一
Woo Han-yĭh. 十 家 詩 詳 註 Shĭh kea she
tseang choo. "The Poetical Works of Ten
Authors," viz.: ... Leang Shang-kwŏ, &c.
1813. 8°.

梁 紹 仁 Leang Shaou-jin.
陰 陽 扇 全 本 Yin yang shen tseuen pun. "The
Story of the Yin and Yang Fans." In Eight
Parts. In Verse. 80 keuen. [1850 ?]. 8°.

梁 詩 正 LEANG SHE-CHING.

錢 錄 *Tseen lŭh.* "A Record of Coins," compiled by .. Leang She-ching, &c. *See* 西 清 SE TSING. 西 清 古 鑑 *Se tsing koo keen.* "Antiquities [from the Palace?] of Western Purity," &c. Folio.

梁 天 來 LEANG TEEN-LAE.

警 富 新 書 *King foo sin shoo.* "Warning to the Rich." With Illustrations. 4 keuen. 1809. 8°.

梁 清 標 LEANG TSING-PEAOU.

See CHINA. 督 捕 則 例 *Tŭh poo tsǐh le.* "Regulations for the Capture" of Deserters. Compiled by ... Leang Tsing-peaou, &c. 1676. 8°.

梁 文 煜 LEANG WĂN-YŬH.

鳳 山 縣 志 *Fung shan heen che.* "A Topography of Fung shan Heen," in Formosa. Compiled by Leang Wăn-yŭh and others. Edited by Keŏ-lo-sze-ming and others. 12 keuen. 1764. 8°.

梁 玉 繩 LEANG YŬH-SHING.

瞥 記 *Pĕĕ ke.* "Hasty Notes" on Classical Subjects. *See* 嚴 杰 YEN LĔĔ. 皇 清 經 解 *Hwang Tsing king keae.* "The Classics Explained," &c. Keuen 1179. 1829. 8°.

廖 文 炳 LEAOU WĂN-PING.

See 祁 天 挺 HŎ TEEN-TING. 唐 詩 鼓 吹 註 解 *Tang she koo chuy choo keae.* "Poetry of the Tang Dynasty. ... With ... Explanatory Notes" by Leaou Wăn-ping, &c. 8°.

廖 文 英 LEAOU WĂN-YING.

正 字 通 *Ching tsze tung.* "A Chinese Dictionary." Compiled by Leaou Wăn-ying. [1800 ?]. 8°.

廖 瑩 中 LEAOU YUNG-CHUNG.

江 行 雜 錄 *Keang hing tsǎ lŭh.* "River Miscellanies." *See* 說 SHWŎ. 說 纂 *Shwo tswan.* "Miscellaneous Records," &c. Vol. 3. 8°.

廖 用 賢 LEAOU YUNG-HEEN.

尚 友 錄 *Shang yew lŭh.* "A Biographical Dictionary of Eminent Characters." A New Edition. 22 keuen. 1666. 8°. Imperfect.

列 國 LĔĔ KWŎ.

列 國 誌 傳 *Lĕĕ kwŏ che chuen.* "The History of the Lĕĕ kwŏ Period." With Illustrations. 8 keuen ? [1700 ?] 8°. Imperfect, containing only keuen 4 and 7.

列 仙 LĔĔ SEEN.

列 仙 傳 *Lĕĕ seen chuen.* "Lives of Eminent Taouist Saints." To which is appended a Work entitled, *Chang săng tseuen,* or "Helps to Obtaining Longevity," by Tsze-ching-she. 4 keuen. [1800 ?]. 8°. Imperfect, wanting the first keuen.

列 禦 寇 LĔĔ YU-KOW.

沖 虛 眞 經 *Chung heu chin king.* "The True Classic of the Deep Void." *See* 沈 津 CHIN TSIN. 百 家 類 纂 *Pĭh kea luy tswan.* "The Works of a Hundred Authors," &c. Keuen 14. 8°.

———— See 黃 海 岸 HWANG HAE-GAN. 周 秦 十 一 子 *Chow Tsin shǐh yĭh tsze.* "The Works of the Eleven Philosophers of the Chow and Tsin Dynasties," &c. 8°.

———— With a Commentary by Chang Chan. 8 keuen. *See* 黃 丕 烈 HWANG PEI-LĔĔ. 十 子 全 書 *Shǐh tsze tseuen shoo.* "The Complete Works of the Ten Philosophers," &c. 1804. 8°.

烈 LĔĔ.

雙 烈 記 *Shwang lĕĕ ke.* "A Pair of Heroes." *See* 曲 KEŬH. 六 十 種 曲 *Lŭh shǐh chung keŭh.* "Sixty Plays," &c. Taou 5. 8°.

連 斗 山 LEEN TOW-SHAN.

周 官 精 義 *Chow kwan tsing e.* "The Essential Meaning of the 'Officers of the Chow.'" 12 ? keuen. [1790 ?]. 8°. Imperfect, containing only keuen 10–12.

LEGGE (JAMES), *D.D.*

See 亞 伯 拉 罕 A-PĬH-LA-HAN. 亞 伯 拉 罕 紀 畧 *A-pĭh-la-han ke leŏ.* "The Story of Abraham." [By Dr. J. L.], &c. 1862. 8°.

—— See 金 山 KIN SHAN. 往 金 山 要 訣 *Wang Kin shan yaou keŭ.* "Important Advice to Emigrants to the Gold-fields." [By Dr. J. L.], &c. 1869. 8°.

第一卷

LEGGE (James), *D.D.* (*Continued.*)

See 浪子 Lang tsze. 浪子悔改 *Lang tsze hwuy kae.* "The Parable of the Prodigal Son." [By Dr. J. L.], &c. 8º.

— See 爐 Loo. 落爐不燬 *Lŏ loo pŭh shaou.* "They fell into the furnace, and were not burned." .. [By Dr. J. L.], &c. 8º.

— See Periodical Publications. 遐邇貫珍 *Hea urh kwan chin.* "A Serial of Foreign and Domestic News." [Edited by .. Dr. J. L.], &c. 1853–55. 8º.

— See 聖會 Shing hwuy. 聖會準繩 *Shing hwuy chun shing.* "The Faith and Practice of a Christian Church." .. [By Dr. J. L.], &c. 1856. 8º.

— See 心 Sin. 養心神詩 *Yang sin shin she.* "Hymns." .. [By Dr. J. L.], &c. 1842. 8º.

— 約瑟 Yŏ-sĭh. 約瑟紀畧 *Yŏ-sĭh ke leŏ.* "The History of Joseph." [By Dr. J. L.], &c. 1870. 8º.

笠翁 Leĭh Ung.

廻文傳 *Hwuy wăn chuen.* "The Story of a Literary Puzzle." 16 keuen. 1798. 8º.

— 巧團圓傳奇 *Keaou twan yuen chuen ke.* "The Secret Affectionate Union." A Drama. 4 keuen. [1750 ?]. 12º.

— 十種曲 *Shĭh chung keŭh.* "Ten Plays." Compiled by Leĭh Ung. 1818. 8º.

— 十二種曲 *Shĭh urh chung keŭh.* "Twelve Plays." Compiled by Leĭh Ung. 1785. 12º. The eighth and ninth Plays are wanting.

呂叟 Leu Sow.

女仙外史 *Neu Sëen wae she.* "Tales of Nymphs." With Commentaries by Lew Tsae-yuen, Chin Heang-tseuen, and others. 1711. 8º.

呂溫 Leu Wăn.

呂衡州集 *Leu Hang-chow tseĭh.* "The Literary Productions of Leu Wăn." 10 keuen. See 伍崇曜 Woo Tsung-yaou. 粵雅堂叢書 *Yuĕ ya Tang tsung shoo.* "The Yuĕ-ya Tang Collection of Reprints," &c. Series 20. 1853. 8º.

呂嵒 Leu Yen.

See 鳩摩羅什 Kew-mo-lo-shĭh. 金剛經直解 *Kin kang king chĭh keae.* "The Diamond Classic clearly explained" by Leu Yen, &c. 1813. 8º.

— See 老君 Laou keun. 道德經解 *Taou tĭh king keae.* "The Classic of Reason and Virtue explained" by Leu Yen, &c. 8º.

— 道德經考正 *Taou tĭh king kaou ching.* "A Critical Work on the Classic of Reason and Virtue" ... By Leu Yen, &c. 1809. 8º.

— 道德經釋義 *Taou tĭh king shĭh e.* "The Classic of Reason and Virtue explained" by .. Leu Yen, &c. 1809. 8º.

— 瑤頭坏歌 *Yaou tow pei ko.* "The Yaou tow pei and other Recitations," &c. See 彭好古 Păng Haou-koo. 道言內外秘訣全書 *Taou yen nuy wae pe keuĕ tseuen shoo.* "A Complete Collection of Taouist Works," &c. Part I. keuen 3. 8º.

— 金玉經 *Kin yŭh king.* "The Golden Jade Classic." Edited by Mow Mŭh-yuen. 1809. 8º.

Another copy.

— 呂祖全書 *Leu Tsoo tseuen shoo.* "The Complete Works of Leu Yen." Compiled by Lew Tseaou. Edited by Hwang Shaou-shing. 32 keuen. 1744. 8º.

呂原 Leu Yuen.

See 李賢 Le Heen. 一統志 *Yĭh tung che.* "A Geography of the Empire." Compiled by .... Leu Yuen, &c. 1461. 8º.

呂吉甫 Leu Keĭh-foo.

道德經 *Taou tĭh king.* "The Classic of Reason and Virtue." With a Commentary by Leu Keĭh-foo. See 焦竑 Tseaou Hung. 老莊翼合刻 *Laou Chwang yĭh hŏ kĭh.* "The Works of Laou keun and Chwang Chow," &c. 1588. 8º.

呂國祚 Leu Kwŏ-tsoo.

See 龍圖耀 Lung Too-yŏ. 高唐州志 *Kaou-tang Chow che.* "A Topography of Kaou-tang Chow." ... Edited by Leu Kwŏ-tsoo, &c. 1712. 8º.

呂留瓦 LEU LEW-LEANG.

See 朱軾 CHOO SHĬH. 駁呂留瓦四書講義 *Pŏ Leu Lew-leang sze shoo keang e.* "A Refutation of Leu Lew-leang's Commentary on the Four Books," &c.　　　　1731.　8°.

呂林育 LEU LIN-YŬH.

See 京房 KING FANG. 易傳 *Yĭh chuen.* "A Commentary on the Book of Changes." . . . Edited by Leu Lin-yŭh, &c.　　　　8°.

呂不韋 LEU PŬH-WEI.

呂氏春秋 *Leu she chun tsew.* "The Spring and Autumn Annals of Leu Pŭh-wei." *See* 沈津 CHIN TSIN. 百家類纂 *Pĭh kea luy tswan.* "The Works of a Hundred Authors," &c. Keuen 28, 29.　　　　8°.

———— See 黃海岸 HWANG HAE-GAN. 周秦 十一子 *Chow Tsin shĭh yĭh tsze.* "The Works of the Eleven Philosophers of the Chow and Tsin Dynasties," &c.　　　　8°.

—— 呂氏春秋 *Leu she chun tsew.* "The Spring and Autumn Annals of Leu Pŭh-wei." A Miscellaneous Treatise, embodying a great number of Historical Facts regarding the early History of China. With a Commentary by Kaou Yew. 26 keuen.　　　　1579.　8°.

Another edition. Edited by Wan Kwŏ-kin. 6 keuen. *Nanking*, 1581.　8°.

呂耀曾 LEU YAOU-TSĂNG.

盛京通志 *Shing king tung che.* "A Topography of the Metropolitan Province of Shing king." Compiled by Leu Yaou-tsăng, Sung Yun, Wang Ho, and others. 48 keuen.　　　　1736.　8°.

呂燕昭 LEU YEN-CHAOU.

新修江寧府志 *Sin sew Keang ning foo che.* "A Topography of Keang-ning Foo," *i.e.* Nanking. Compiled by Leu Yen-chaou, Yaou Nae, and others. A New Edition. 56 keuen.　　　　1811.　8°.

Another copy.

Imperfect, containing only keuen 6–31.

呂元臣 LEU YUEN-CHIN.

初學問津集 *Choo heŏ wăn tsin tseĭh.* "A Collection of Model Essays for Beginners." Edited by Wang Pĭh-seuĕ.　　[1830?].　8°.

LEVASSEUR (J. C. V.).

Ju-kiao-li, Roman Chinois, traduit par M. A. Rémusat. Texte autographié et publié par J. C. V. L. Edition dans laquelle on donne la forme régulière des Caractères vulgaires et des variantes.　　　*Paris*, 1829.　8°.

劉 LEW.

山東考卷 *Shan-tung kaou keuen.* "Shantung Examination Essays." Compiled by Lew and Edited by Tĕĕ. 2 Parts.

　　　　Tse-nan Foo, 1803.　8°.

劉昭 LEW CHAOU.

See 范曄 FAN YĔ. 後漢書 *How Han shoo.* "The History of the later Han Dynasty." With a Commentary by Lew Chaou, &c.　1643.　8°.

—— 後漢書 *How Han shoo.* "The History of the later Han Dynasty." With a Commentary by Lew Chaou. *See* 毛晉 MAOU TSIN. 十七史 *Shĭh tseĭh She.* "The Seventeen Histories," &c.　　　　1656.　8°.

劉晝 LEW CHOW.

劉子 *Lew tsze.* "The Writings of Lew Chow." *See* 沈津 CHIN TSIN. 百家類纂 *Pĭh kea luy tswan.* "The Works of a Hundred Authors," Keuen 36.　　　　8°.

劉忠 LEW CHUNG.

二論啟幼引端 *Urh yun ke yew yin twan.* "The Beginner's Guide to the Confucian Analects." 4 keuen.　　　　1795.　8°.

　　　Imperfect, wanting keuen 4.

劉安 LEW GAN.

淮南子 *Hwae nan tsze.* "The Treatise of Lew Gan, the Prince of Hwae nan." *See* 沈津 CHIN TSIN. 百家類纂 *Pĭh kea luy tswan.* "The Works of a Hundred Authors," &c. Keuen 30.　　　　8°.

———— With a Commentary by Kaou Yew. *See* 黃 丕烈 HWANG PEI-LĔĔ. 十子全書 *Shĭh tsze tseuen shoo.* "The Complete Works of the Ten Philosophers," &c.　　1804.　8°.

劉 安 Lew Gan.　(*Continued.*)

火 蓮 經 *Ho leen king.* "The Sûtra of the Fire Lily." *See* 彭 好 古 Păng Haou-koo.

道 言 內 外 秘 訣 全 書 *Taou yen nuy wae pe keuĕ tseuen shoo.* "A Complete Collection of Taouist Works," &c.　　　　　8º.

—— 淮 南 鴻 烈 解 *Hwae nan hung lĕĕ keae.* "The Treatise of Lew Gan, the Prince of Hwae nan, on the Doctrines of Taou comprehensively explained." Edited by Hwang Seĭh-he. 21 keuen. [1750 ?]. 8º.

—— 淮 南 子 箋 釋 *Hwae nan tsze tseen shĭh.* "The Treatise of Lew Gan, the Prince of Hwae nan. With a Commentary" by Kaou Yew. Edited by Chwang Kwei-keĭh. 21 keuen. 1804. 8º.

劉 熙 Lew He.

逸 雅 *Yĭh ya.* "The Occasional Expositor." 8 keuen. *See* 郎 奎 金 Lang Kwei-kin. 五 雅 *Woo ya.* "The Five Dictionaries," &c. 1626. 8º.

—— 釋 名 *Shĭh ming.* "Phrases Explained." By Lew He, of the Han Dynasty. A Reprint. 4 keuen. [1750 ?]. 8º.

Another edition. Edited by She Wei-ching. 4 keuen. [1800 ?]. 8º.

劉 向 Lew Heang.

新 序 *Sin seu.* "A New Arrangement" of Historical Incidents. [Also] 說 苑 *Shwŏ yuen.* "A Garden of Discourses." [Also] 戰 國 策 *Chen kwŏ tsĭh.* "The Story of the Contending States." *See* 沈 津 Chin Tsin. 百 家 類 纂 *Pĭh kea luy tswan.* "The Works of a Hundred Authors," &c. Keuen 7, 26, 27. 8º.

—— 戰 國 策 *Chen kwŏ tsĭh.* "The Story of the Contending States." Arranged by Lew Heang. With a Commentary by Kaou Yew. Edited by Yaou Hung. 33 keuen. 1803. 8º.

—— 戰 國 策 選 *Chen kwŏ tsĭh seuen.* "Selections from the Story of the Contending States" [by Lew Heang. Edited by Choo Hin]. [1766 ?]. 8º.

Imperfect, the first part wanting.

劉 向 Lew Heang.　(*Continued.*)

古 列 女 傳 *Koo lĕĕ neu chuen.* "Lives of Eminent Women." Edited by Choo King-koo. 8 keuen. 1551. 8º.

Another edition. Illustrated by Koo Kae-che. 8 keuen. 1825. 8º.

—— 列 仙 傳 *Lĕĕ sĕen chuen.* "The Lives of Seventy-one Mortals who are said to have attained to a State of Immortality." 2 keuen. 1553. 8º.

—— 說 苑 *Shwŏ yuen.* "A Garden of Discourses" on the Principles of Government, and the relative Duties devolving on the several Members of the State. By Lew Heang, of the Han Dynasty. A Reprint. 20 keuen. [1800 ?]. 8º.

Another edition. 20 keuen. 8º.

—— 新 序 *Sin seu.* "A New Arrangement" of Historical Incidents, supplementary to the Regular Histories. By Lew Heang, of the Han Dynasty. A Reprint. 10 keuen. [1750 ?]. 8º.

Another edition. Edited by Chin Yung-kwang. 10 keuen. [1800 ?]. 8º.

劉 勰 Lew Hĕĕ.

新 論 *Sin lun.* "New Discourses," on Moral Duties, &c. Edited by Ching Tsun-yŏ. 10 keuen. [1700 ?]. 8º.

—— 文 心 雕 龍 *Wăn sin teaou lung.* "A Critique on Poetry and Literature," Ancient and Modern. By Lew Hĕĕ, of the Leang Dynasty. A Reprint. 10 keuen. [1700 ?]. 8º.

—— 文 心 雕 龍 輯 註 *Wăn sin teaou lung tseĭh choo.* "Lew Hĕĕ's Critique on Poetry and Literature, with an Extended and Critical Exegesis" by Hwang Shŭh-lin. Edited by Koo Tsin and Kin Sin. 10 keuen. 1738. 8º.

劉 壎 Lew Heun.

隱 居 通 議 *Yin keu tung e.* "Searching Deliberations on Literary Subjects from the Obscure Dwelling." 31 keuen. *See* 葉 志 詵 Yĕ Che-sin. 海 山 仙 館 叢 書 *Hae shan seen Kwan tsung shoo.* "The Hae-shan-seen Kwan Collection of Reprints," &c. Vol. 40-44. 1848. 8º.

劉歆 LEW HIN.

西京雜記 *Se king tsă ke.* "The Miscellaneous Records of Chang-gan, the Western Capital," the modern Kae-fung Foo. 6 keuen. 8°.

劉瓛 LEW HWAN.

周易義疏 *Chow yih e soo.* "The Meaning of the Chow Changes. With Notes." *See* 孫堂 SUN TANG. 漢魏二十一家易注 *Han Wei urh shih yih kea yih choo.* "Commentaries on the Book of Changes," &c. 1799. 8°.

劉徽 LEW HWUY.

海島算經 *Hae taou swan king.* "The Art of Measuring the Height of Islands," consisting of Nine Problems in Practical Trigonometry. By Lew Hwuy. With a Commentary by Le Shun-fung. A Reprint. 1775. 8°.

劉基 LEW KE.

郁離子 *Yŭh le tsze.* "The Writings of Yŭh-le-tsze." *See* 沈津 CHIN TSIN. 百家類纂 *Pih kea luy tswan.* "The Works of a Hundred Authors," &c. Keuen 11. 8°.

劉誵 LEW KĔĔ.

See 陶潛 TAOU TSEEN. 搜神後記 *Sow shin how ke.* "A Sequel to the *Sow shin ke.*" . . . . Edited by Lew Kĕĕ, &c. 8°.

劉健 LEW KEEN.

庭聞錄 *Ting wan lŭh.* "Records of the Court." An Account of Political Outbreaks during the Reign of the Emperor Kang-he. 5 keuen ? 1733. 8°.

Imperfect, wanting keuen 1–4.

劉恂 LEW SEUN.

嶺表錄異 *Ling peaou lŭh e.* "Marvels of Ling-peaou." *See* 王文誥 WANG WĂN-KAOU. 唐代叢書 *Tang tae tsung shoo.* "A Collection of Reprints of Works written under the Tang Dynasty," &c. Series 3. 1806. 8°.

劉邵 LEW SHAOU.

人物志 *Jin wŭh che.* "A Philosophical Treatise on Mankind." By Lew Shaou, of the Wei Dynasty. A Reprint. 3 keuen. [1750 ?]. 8°.

劉肅 LEW SŬH.

大唐新語 *Ta Tang sin yu.* "New Records of the Tang Dynasty." *See* 王文誥 WANG WĂN-KAOU. 唐代叢書 *Tang tae tsung shoo.* "A Collection of Reprints of Works written during the Tang Dynasty," &c. Series 1. 1806. 8°.

劉餗 LEW SŬH.

隋唐嘉話 *Suy Tang kea hwa.* "Happy Sayings of the Suy and Tang Dynasties." *See* 王文誥 WANG WĂN-KAOU. 唐代叢書 *Tang tae tsung shoo.* "A Collection of Reprints of Works written during the Tang Dynasty," &c. Series 1. 1806. 8°.

劉燦 LEW TSAN.

嚴氏詩緝補義 *Yen she she tseĭh poo e.* "A Supplement to Yen Tsan's Commentary on the Book of Odes." Edited by Wang Sĭh-gan. 8 keuen. 1811. 8°.

劉樵 LEW TSEAOU.

See 呂嵒 LEU YEN. 呂祖全書 *Leu Tsoo tseuen shoo.* "The Complete Works of Leu Yen." . . Compiled by Lew Tseaou, &c. 1744. 8°.

劉績 LEW TSEĬH.

See 管仲 KWAN CHUNG. 管子評註 *Kwan tsze ping choo.* "Kwan Chung's Work on Legislation. With . . . Commentaries" by . . Lew Tseĭh, &c. 1804. 8°.

劉琰 LEW YEN.

See 張�先 CHANG KUNG-SEEN. 聖門禮樂統 *Shing mun le yŏ tung.* "The Sacred School of Confucius, its Ritual and its Music." Edited by Lew Yen, &c. 1710. 8°.

劉郁 LEW YŬH.

酉使記 *Se she ke.* "An Account of an Embassy to the West." *See* 說 SHWŎ. 說選 *Shwŏ seuen.* "A Collection of Historical Records," &c. Vol. 8. 8°.

劉拙軒 LEW CHUĔ-HEEN.

See 陶中洋 TAOU CHUNG-YANG. 堪輿理氣青天白日 *Kan yu le ke tsing teen pih jih.* "The Principles of the Fung shwuy Art made plain." . . Edited by Lew Chuĕ-heen, &c. 1761. 8°.

劉 台 拱 Lew E-kung.

劉 氏 遺 書 *Lew she wei shoo.* "The Posthumous Writings of Lew E-kung." *See* 嚴 杰 Yen Lĕĕ. 皇 淸 經 解 *Hwang Tsing king keae.* "The Classics Explained," &c. Keuen 789.
1829. 8º.

劉 方 璿 Lew Fang-seuen.

周 官 說 約 *Chow kwan shwŏ yŏ.* "The Officers of Chow, with a Compendium of Notes." Compiled by Lew Fang-seuen. Edited by Loo Yun-kin and others. 6 keuen.　　1812. 8º.

劉 若 愚 Lew Jŏ-yu.

酌 中 志 *Chŏ chung che.* "Records of the Council Chamber." 24 keuen. *See* 葉 志 詵 Yĕ Che-sin. 海 山 仙 館 叢 書 *Hae shan seen Kwan tsung shoo.* "The Hae-shan-seen Kwan Collection of Reprints," &c. Vol. 31–34.
1848. 8º.

劉 季 然 Lew Ke-jen.

See 王 黼 Wang Foo. 博 古 圖 *Pŏ koo too.* "A Large Illustrated Collection of Antiquities," &c. . . . Edited by Lew Ke-jen, &c. 1588. 8º.

劉 光 斗 Lew Kwang-tow.

See 王 充 Wang Chung. 論 衡 *Lun hăng.* "Discussions by Means of Comparisons." . . . Edited by Lew Kwang-tow, &c.　　8º.

劉 國 鳳 Lew Kwŏ-fung.

See 黃 正 元 Hwang Ching-yuen. 性 天 眞 境 *Sing teen chin king.* "The True Limits of Human and Divine Nature." Edited by Lew Kwŏ-fung, &c.　　1805. 8º.

劉 履 徇 Lew Le-seun.

秋 槎 雜 記 *Tsew cha tsă ke.* "Autumn-cutting Miscellanies." *See* 嚴 杰 Yen Lĕĕ. 皇 淸 經 解 *Hwang Tsing king keae.* "The Classics Explained," &c. Keuen 1322.　　1829. 8º.

劉 瓦 璧 Lew Leang-peĭh.

臺 灣 府 志 *Tae wan foo che.* "A Topography of Tae-wan Foo," in Formosa. With Maps. Compiled from older editions by Lew Leang-peĭh, Tseen Choo, Fan Chang-che, and others. 20 keuen.　　1741. 8º.

劉 豹 君 Lew Paou-keun.

唐 詩 合 選 詳 解 *Tang she hŏ seuen tseang keae.* "A Collection of the Poetry of the Tang Dynasty, with Explanatory Comments." Compiled by Lew Paou-keun. 12 keuen. 1831. 8º.

劉 伯 溫 Lew Pĭh-wăn.

兵 法 心 要 *Ping fă sin yaou.* "The Essentials of the Military Art." [Also] 百 戰 奇 略 *Pĭh chen ke leŏ.* "A Hundred Modes of Fighting." *See* 水 Shwuy. 水 陸 戰 守 攻 略 方 術 秘 書 七 種 *Shwuy lŭh chen show kung leŏ fang shŭh pe shoo tseĭh chung.* "A Military System for both Land and Sea," &c.　　8º.

劉 山 英 Lew Shan-ying.

信 心 應 聰 錄 *Sin sin ying yen lŭh.* "Convincing Records for Believing Hearts." A Taouist Work. By Lew Shan-ying. Edited by Chin Sze-haou and Chin Sze-leen. 8 keuen.
1794. 8º.

Imperfect, containing only keuen 1 and 8.

劉 石 芝 Lew Shĭh-che.

See 易 經 Yĭh king. 周 易 廣 義 *Chow Yĭh kwang e.* "The Chow Changes." . . Edited by Lew Shĭh-che, &c.　　1672. 8º.

劉 石 閭 Lew Shĭh-leu.

See 徐 在 漢 Seu Tsae-han. 易 或 *Yĭh hwŏ.* "Doubts on the Book of Changes." . . With Notes by Lew Shĭh-leu, &c.　　1774. 8º.

劉 師 峻 Lew Sze-tseun.

北 嶽 歷 祀 考 *Pĭh yŏ leĭh sze kaou.* "An Examination of the Successive Sacrifices in Pĭh yŏ." *See* 張 山 來 Chang Shan-lae, and 張 進 也 Chang Tsin-yay. 昭 代 叢 書 *Chaou tae tsung shoo.* "A Collection of Reprints of Works by Authors under the present Dynasty," &c. Keuen 13.　　1703. 8º.

劉 思 敬 Lew Sze-king.

稿 *Kaou.* "Essays." *See* 長 城 Chang Ching. 名 家 制 義 *Ming kea che e.* "Essays" on Texts from the Four Books, &c. Tsĭh 101.
1699. 8º.

18

劉坦之 Lew Tan-che.
近科直省試策法程 *Kin ko chih săng she tsĭh fă ching.* "Model Examination Essays." Compiled by Lew Tan-che. 1786. 8°.

Another copy.

劉德銓 Lew Tĭh-tseuen.
See 恩成 Găn Ching. 夔州府志 *Kwei chow foo che.* "A Topography of Kwei-chow Foo." ... Compiled ... from Materials supplied by Lew Tĭh-tseuen, &c. 1827. 8°.

劉在園 Lew Tsae-yuen.
See 呂叟 Leu Sow. 女仙外史 *Neu sëen wae she.* "Tales of Nymphs." With Commentaries by Lew Tsae-yuen, &c. 1711. 8°.

劉作樑 Lew Tso-leang.
新昌縣志 *Sin chang heen che.* "A Topography of Sin-chang Heen," in the Province of Chĕ-keang. Compiled by Lew Tso-leang. [1800 ?]. 8°.
Imperfect, containing only keuen 11–16.

劉祖煥 Lew Tsoo-hwan.
山西鄉試 *Shan se heang she.* "Shan-se District Examination Essays for the Year 1819." Compiled by Lew Tsoo-hwan. 1819. 8°.

劉宗周 Lew Tsung-chow.
人譜 *Jin poo.* "A Book on Man," illustrating the Virtues and Vices by Biographical Instances. Compiled by Lew Tsung-chow, of the Ming Dynasty. Edited by Hung Ching-che. 2 keuen. 1811. 8°.

劉子壯 Lew Tsze-chwang.
稿 *Kaou.* "Essays." *See* 長城 Chang Ching. 名家制義 *Ming kea che e.* "Essays" on Texts from the Four Books, &c. Tsĭh 102. 1699. 8°.

劉統勳 Lew Tung-heun.
See 蔣溥 Tseang Poo. 御覽經史講義 *Yu lan king she keang e.* "The Meaning of the Classics and the Histories Explained." Edited ... by Lew Tung-heun, &c. 1758. 8°.

劉堯思 Lew Yaou-sze.
See 龍圖躍 Lung Too-yŏ. 高唐州志 *Kaou-tang Chow che.* "A Topography of Kaou-tang Chow." ... Edited by Lew Yaou-sze, &c. 1712. 8°.

劉有光 Lew Yew-kwang.
See 趙三暘 Chaou San-yang. 武經標題正義 *Woo king peaou te ching e.* "The True Meaning of the ... Military Classic." ... Edited by ... Lew Yew-kwang, &c. 8°.

劉裕鐸 Lew Yu-tŏ.
See 吳謙 Woo-keen. 御纂醫宗金鑑 *Yu tswan e tsung kin keen.* "The Golden Mirror of Medicine." ..... Compiled .... by .. Lew Yu-tŏ, &c. 1740. 8°.

劉豫庵 Lew Yu-gan.
詳訂古文評註 *Tseang ting koo wăn ping choo.* "Extracts from Ancient Literature." Compiled by Lew Yu-gan. "With Critical Notes and Comments" by Kwŏ Kung and Hwang Yuĕ. A Reprint. This Collection begins with Extracts from the Narrative of Tso Kew-ming and is continued down to the Works by Authors under the Tsing Dynasty. 10 keuen. 1823. 8°.

Another edition. 10 keuen. 1847. 8°.
Imperfect, wanting keuen 9.

劉玉麐 Lew Yŭh-lin.
甓齋遺稿 *Pcih chae wei kaou.* "Posthumous Papers from the Brick Study." *See* 嚴杰 Yen Lëĕ. 皇清經解 *Hwang Tsing king keae.* "The Classics Explained," &c. Keuen 1369. 1829. 8°.

劉玉坡 Lew Yŭh-po.
See 徐繼畬 Seu Ke-yu. 瀛環志畧 *Ying hwan che leŏ.* "A Geographical Treatise on all within the Circuit of the Seas." Edited by .. Lew Yŭh-po, &c. 1848. 8°.

劉允鵬 Lew Yun-păng.
龍觔鳳髓判 *Lung kin Fung suy pwan.* "The Dragon's Muscle and the Phœnix Marrow's Decisions." With a Commentary by Lew Yun-păng, &c. *See* 葉志詵 Yĕ Che-sin. 海山仙館叢書 *Hae shan seen Kwan tsung shoo.* "The Hae-shan-seen Kwan Collection of Reprints," &c. 1848. 8°.

柳 Lew.

柳參軍傳 *Lew Tsan keun chuen.* "The Story of General Lew." *See* 說 Shwŏ. 說淵 *Shwŏ yuen.* "A Collection of Tales," &c. Vol. 8. 8°.

柳華陽 Lew Hwa-yang.

金仙証論 *Kin seen ching lun.* "The Golden Genii Substantiated and Discussed" by Lew Hwa-yang. Edited by Ting Yang-tsae. A Work on Alchemy. 1811. 8°.

柳歸舜 Lew Kwei-shun.

柳歸舜傳 *Lew Kwei-shun chuen.* "The Story of Lew Kwei-shun." *See* 說 Shwŏ. 說淵 *Shwŏ yuen.* "A Collection of Tales," &c. Vol. 9. 8°.

柳宗元 Lew Tsung-yuen.

柳文 *Lew wăn.* "The Writings of Lew Tsung-yuen." 12 keuen. *See* 茅坤 Maou Kwăn. 唐宋八大家文鈔 *Tang Sung pă ta kea wăn chaou.* "The Works of Eight Scholars . . . under the Tang and Sung Dynasties," &c. 1631. 8°.

—— 龍城錄 *Lung ching lüh.* "Records of the Dragon City." *See* 王文誥 Wang Wăn-kaou. 唐代叢書 *Tang tae tsung shoo.* "A Collection of Reprints of Works written during the Tang Dynasty," &c. Series 2. 1806. 8°.

鎦績 Lew Tseĭh.

霏雪錄 *Fe seŭh lŭh.* "Sleet and Snow [*i.e.* Miscellaneous] Records." *See* 說 Shwŏ. 說畧 *Shwŏ leŏ.* "Historical and other Tracts," &c. 8°.

林 Lin.

墨林金玉 *Mĭh lin kin yŭh.* "Gems from the Literary Forest." Essays. [1750?]. 8°.
Imperfect.

—— 東潘林氏園族遵 *Tung fan Lin she hŏ tsŭh tsun.* "Records of the Family of Lin of Tung-fan." 1815. 8°.

林蘆 Lin Fun.

僊遊縣志 *Seen yew heen che.* "A Topography of Seen-yew Heen," in the Province of Fŭh-keen. Compiled by Lin Fun, Woo Ke, Wang Nan, &c. 53 keuen. 1771. 8°.

林瀚 Lin Han.

稿 *Kaou.* "Essays." *See* 長城 Chang Ching.

名家制義 *Ming kea che e.* "Essays" on Texts from the Four Books, &c. Tsĭh 17. 1699. 8°.

—— 隋唐演義 *Suy Tang yen e.* "A History of the Suy and Tang Dynasties." With Illustrations. By Lin Han. Edited by Woo Hŏ-tseaou. 20 keuen. 1805. 8°.

林子 Lin Tsze.

感溺供 *Hwŏ neĭh hung.* "The Depravity of Creating Doubts in the Minds of Men, proved." *See* 閔景賢 Min King-heen. 快書 *Kwae shoo.* "A Book of Amusement," &c. Keuen 24. 1626. 8°.

林昌彝 Lin Chang-e.

三禮通釋 *San Le tung shĭh.* "The Three Rituals (viz.: the Chow Ritual, the Decorum Ritual, and the Book of Rites) thoroughly explained." 280 keuen. *Canton,* 1863. 8°.

林長生 Lin Chang-săng.

See 傅仁宇 Foo Jin-yu. 眼科大全 *Yen ko ta tseuen.* "A Complete Work on the Eye." Edited by Lin Chang-săng, &c. 1819. 8°.

林希元 Lin He-yuen.

See 蔡清 Tsae Tsing. 四書蒙引 *Sze shoo mung yin.* "A Guide to the Study of the Four Books." . . . . Edited by . . . Lin He-yuen, &c. 8°.

林學曾 Lin Heŏ-tsăng.

See 黃鳳翔 Hwang Fung-tseang. 泉州府志 *Tseuen chow foo che.* "A Topography of Tseuen chow Foo." . . . Compiled by . . . Lin Heŏ-tsăng, &c. 1612. 8°.

林謙光 Lin Keen-kwang.

臺灣紀畧 *Tae wan ke leŏ.* "A Short Account of Formosa." *See* 說 Shwŏ. 說鈴 *Shwŏ ling.* "Miscellaneous Records," &c. 8°.

林碧山 Lin Peĭh-shan.

See 戚 Tseĭh, and Lin Peĭh-shan. 八音合訂 *Pă yin hŏ ting.* "A Dictionary of the Fŭh-keen Dialect, arranged under the Eight Tones," &c. 1841. 8°.

林 西 仲 LIN SE-CHUNG.

古 文 析 義 合 編 *Koo wăn seĭh e hŏ peen.*
"Ancient Compositions, with Notes on their
Meaning." This Collection begins with Extracts
from the Tso chuen and Kwŏ yu by Tso Kew-
ming, and is continued down to Works of
Authors under the Ming Dynasty. 16 keuen.
1716. 8º.

林 慎 巷 LIN SHIN-GAN.

四 診 抉 微 *Sze chin keuĕ we.* "The Abstruse
Question of the Four Modes of Medical Examination." 8 keuen.   1723. 8º.

林 大 謵 LIN TA-GŎ.

繭 齋 詩 賦 稿 *Kĕen chae she foo kaou.* "Poems
from the Silkworm's Cocoon Study." With
Notes by Soo Wei and others. 3 keuen.
1820. 8º.

Another copy.
Imperfect, containing only the first keuen.

林 天 如 LIN TEEN-JOO.

淨 土 或 問 *Tsing too hŭŏ wăn.* "Enquiries
respecting the Pure Regions of Bliss in the
West." By the Priest Lin Teen-joo. 1756. 8º.

林 則 徐 LIN TSĬH-SEU.

俄 羅 斯 國 總 記 *Go-lo-sze kŭŏ tsung ke.* "A
General Account of Russia." *See* 何 秋 濤
HO TSEW-TAOU. 北 徼 彙 編 *Pih keaou wei
peen.* "Treatises on the Countries beyond the
Northern Frontier," &c. Keuen 2. 1865. 8º.

林 堯 叟 LIN YAOU-SOW.

See 孔 丘 KUNG KEW. 春 秋 左 傳 杜 林 合 註
Chun Tsew Tso chuen Too Lin hŏ choo. "The
Spring and Autumn Annals. . . With the Com-
mentaries of Lin Yaou-sow," &c.   8º.

—— 春 秋 經 傳 集 解 *Chun Tsew king chuen
tseĭh keae.* "The Spring and Autumn Annals."
. . With Notes by Lin Yaou-sow, &c.   8º.

—— 芥 子 園 重 訂 監 本 春 秋 *Keae tsze yuen
chung ting keen pun Chun Tsew.* "The Spring
and Autumn Annals." . . . With Notes on the
Sounds of the Characters by Lin Yaou-sow, &c.
1790. 8º.

麟 慶 LIN KING.

河 工 器 具 圖 說 *Ho kung ke keu too shwŏ.* "A
Description of the Machinery and Implements
employed on Rivers. With Illustrations." 4
keuen.   1836. 8º.
The last two keuen are wanting.

靈 LING.

救 靈 先 路 *Kew ling sëen loo.* "The Road to
Salvation." [By W. Muirhead.]
[*Hongkong* ?], 1857. 8º.

靈 芝 LING CHE.

拗 碎 靈 芝 記 *Yaou suy ling che ke.* "The
Story of the Broken Ling che." In Verse. 4
keuen.   [*Canton*, 1850 ?]. 8º.

靈 魂 LING HWĂN.

葆 靈 魂 以 升 天 國 論 *Paou ling hwăn e
shing teen kwŏ lun.* "Guard your Soul that you
may enter into the Kingdom of Heaven." A
Tract [by Dr. W. H. Medhurst].
[*Shanghae*, 1857 ?]. 8º.

靈 應 LING YING.

靈 應 傳 *Ling ying chuen.* "The Story of the
Prayer-answering Deity." *See* 說 SHWŎ. 說
淵 *Shwŏ yuen.* "A Collection of Tales," &c.
Vol. 1.   8º.

—— 靈 應 傳 *Ling ying chuen.* "The Story of the
Prayer-answering Deity." By an Anonymous
Writer of the Tang Dynasty. A Reprint.
[1741 ?]. 8º.

凌 曙 LING SHOO.

公 羊 禮 說 *Kung yang le shwŏ.* "On Kung-
yang Kaou's Ceremonies." [Also] 禮 說 *Le
shwŏ.* "On Ceremonies." *See* 嚴 杰 YEN LÉE.
皇 清 經 解 *Hwang Tsing king keae.* "The
Classics Explained," &c. Keuen 1355–1359.
1829. 8º.

凌 義 渠 LING E-KEU.

稿 *Kaou.* "Essays." *See* 長 城 CHANG CHING.
名 家 制 義 *Ming kea che e.* "Essays" on
Texts from the Four Books, &c. Tsĭh 85.
1699. 8º.

凌 厚 子 LING HOW-TSZE.

See 易 經 YĬH KING. 易 經 來 註 圖 解 *Yĭh
king Lae choo too keae.* "The Book of Changes."
. . . Edited by Ling How-tsze, &c. 1598. 8º.

淩瓅王 Ling Seuen-wang.
See 左丘明 Tso Kew-ming. 春秋分國左傳
Chun Tsew fun kwŏ Tso chuen. "Extracts from
the Tso chuen." ... Compiled by Ling Seuen-
wang, &c. 1761. 8º.

淩紹雯 Ling Shaou-wǎn.
See 康熙 Kang-he. Emperor. 康熙字典
Kang-he tsze teen. "Kang-he's Dictionary."
... Compiled ... by Ling Shaou-wǎn, &c.
1716. 8º.

淩述知 Ling Shŭh-che.
See 淩迪知 Ling Teĭh-che. 萬姓統譜
Wan sing tung poo. "A General Biographical
Dictionary." ... Edited by ... Ling Shŭh-
che, &c. 1579. 8º.

淩迪知 Ling Teĭh-che.
萬姓統譜 Wan sing tung poo. "A General
Biographical Dictionary." By Ling Teĭh-che.
Edited by Woo King and Ling Shŭh-che. 38
keuen. 1579. 8º.

淩廷堪 Ling Ting-kan.
燕樂考原 Yen yŏ kaou yuen. "The Origin
of the Yen Music." 6 keuen. See 伍崇曜
Woo Tsung-yaou. 粵雅堂叢書 Yuĕ ya
Tang tsung shoo. "The Yuĕ-ya Tang Collection
of Reprints," &c. Series 8. 1853. 8º.

—— 禮經釋例 Le king shĭh le. "An Explanation
of the Laws laid down in the Rituals." 13
keuen. [Also] 挍禮堂文集 Keaou le Tang
wǎn tseĭh. "The Literary Collection of the
Keaou-le Hall." See 嚴杰 Yen Lĕĕ. 皇清
經解 Hwang Tsing king keae. "The Classics
Explained," &c. Keuen 784-797. 1829. 8º.

仒狐德棻 Ling-hoo Tĭh-fun.
See 李延壽 Le Yen-show. 南史 Nan she.
"The History of the South." .. Revised by
Ling-hoo Tĭh-fun, &c. 8º.

—— 後周書 How Chow shoo. "History of the
later Chow Dynasty." See 毛晉 Maou Tsin.
十七史 Shĭh tseĭh she. "The Seventeen
Histories," &c. 8º.

伶元 Ling Yuen.
飛燕外傳 Fei-yen wae chuen. "The Story of
Chaou Fei-yen, the Empress of Ching-te of the
Han Dynasty." [1800?]. 8º.

LITTLE (Sophia).
See 馬典 Ma-teen.

LITURGIES. England, Church of.
週年早晨禱告式 Chow neen tsaou shin taou
kaou shĭh. "The Morning Service of the English
Liturgy" translated into the Shanghae Dialect
[by Dr. W. J. Boone?]. [Shanghae?], 1849. 8º.

—— 週年夜裡禱告式 Chow neen yay le taou
kaou shĭh. "The Evening Service of the English
Liturgy" translated into the Shanghae Dialect
[by Dr. W. J. Boone?]. [Shanghae?], 1849. 8º.

—— 年中每日早晚祈禱敍式 Neen chung mei
jĭh tsaou wan ke taou seu shĭh. "The Morning
and Evening Prayers of the Liturgy of the
Church of England." Translated into Chinese
by Dr. R. Morrison. Published by the Prayer
Book and Homily Society. [1818?]. 8º.

—— 聖會禱詞 Shing hwuy taou sze. "The Liturgy
of the Holy Church" of England. 6 keuen.
[1830?]. 8º.

—— 英吉利國神會祈禱文大概翻譯漢字
Ying-keĭh-le kwŏ shin hwuy ke taou wǎn ta kae fan
yĭh Han tsze. "The United Prayers and Supplications to God of the English Nation, translated into Chinese." A Compendium of the
Book of Common Prayer. By Ma, i.e. Dr. R.
Morrison. 1829. 8º.

羅成 Lo Ching.
羅成寫書 Lo Ching seay shoo. "Lo Ching
writes a Letter." A Drama. [1800?]. 8º.

羅倫 Lo Lun.
稿 Kaou. "Essays." See 長城 Chang Ching.
名家制義 Ming kea che e. "Essays" on
Texts from the Four Books, &c. Tsĭh 16.
1699. 8º.

羅 阅 Lo LIWAN.

比 紅 兒 詩 *Pe hung urh she*. "Poems instituting Comparisons with Hung urh." *See* 王 文 誥 WANG WĂN-KAOU. 唐 代 叢 書 *Tang tae tsung shoo*. "A Collection of Reprints of Works written during the Tang Dynasty," &c. Series 3. 1806. 8°.

羅 鄴 Lo NĚĚ.

蔣 子 文 傳 *Tseang Tsze-wăn chuen*. "The Story of Tseang Tsze-wăn." By Lo Nëë, of the Tang Dynasty. A Reprint. [1741?]. 8°.

羅 訥 Lŏ NŬH.

金 光 斗 臨 經 *Kin kwang tow lin king*. "The Sûtra of the Golden, Bright North Star." A Work on Divination. 1857. 8°.

羅 泌 Lo PE.

路 史 *Loo she*. "A History of the Nation's Course" from the Earliest Period down to the Beginning of the Shang Dynasty, about the Eighteenth Century B.C. To which are added "Geographical Records," "Disquisitions," and "Extra Discourses." By Lo Pe. With Notes by Lo Ping. Edited by Lo Ta-chin. 47 keuen. [1700?]. 8°.

羅 苹 Lo PING.

See 羅 泌 Lo PE. 路 史 *Loo she*. "A History of the Nation's Course." .. With Notes by Lo Ping, &c. 8°.

羅 隱 Lo YIN.

廣 陵 妖 亂 志 *Kwang-ling Yaou lwan che*. "Fairy Tales from Kwang-ling." *See* 王 文 誥 WANG WĂN-KAOU. 唐 代 叢 書 *Tang tae tsung shoo*. "A Collection of Reprints of Works written during the Tang Dynasty," &c. Series 4. 1806. 8°.

羅 願 Lo YUEN.

鄂 州 小 集 *Gŏ-chow seaou tseih*. "A Small Collection of Lo Yuen's Literary Pieces." 6 keuen. *See* 伍 崇 曜 WOO TSUNG-YAOU. 粤 雅 堂 叢 書 *Yuĕ ya Tang tsung shoo*. "The Yuĕ-ya Tang Collection of Reprints," &c. Series 20. 1853. 8°.

羅 傳 烈 Lo CHUEN-LĚĚ.

羅 傳 烈 選 *Lo Chuen-lëë seuen*. "Selections from the Writings of Lo Chuen-lëë" on Divination. [1800?]. 8°.

羅 傳 炳 Lo CHUEN-PING.

通 書 *Tung shoo*. "A Thorough Work" on Divination. 1842. 8°.

羅 含 章 Lo HAN-CHANG.

嶺 南 集 *Ling nan tseih*. "A Collection of the Writings of Lo Han-chang." 7 keuen. 1814. 8°.

羅 洪 先 Lo HUNG-SEEN.

稿 *Kaou*. "Essays." *See* 長 城 CHANG CHING. 名 家 制 義 *Ming kea che e*. "Essays" on Texts from the Four Books, &c. Tsïh 37. 1699. 8°.

—— 廣 輿 圖 *Kwang yu too*. "An Atlas of the Chinese Empire." Compiled by Lo Hung-seen, with the Maps of Choo Sze-pun. 2 keuen. 1579. Folio.

羅 貫 中 Lo KWAN-CHUNG.

三 國 志 *San kwŏ che*. "The History of the Three Kingdoms." By Lo Kwan-chung. Edited by Yu Yang-che. 20 keuen. 1592. 8°.
Imperfect, wanting keuen 1–18.

Another edition. Edited by Kin Shing-tan. Revised by Maou Shing-shan. 19 keuen. 1644. 8°.

Another copy.
Imperfect, wanting keuen 2–5.

Another edition. [1700?]. 8°.
Imperfect, wanting keuen 12–15.

Another edition. 20 keuen. [1700?]. 8°.
Imperfect, containing only keuen 8–13.

Another edition. 20 keuen. [1750?]. 8°.
Imperfect, wanting title-page, preface and keuen 6–8 and 12–15.

Another edition. Edited by Le Chŏ-woo. 20 keuen. [1800?]. 8°.

Another edition. [1800?]. 8°.

Another edition. Edited by King Shing-tan. A Reprint. 60 keuen. 1820. 8°.

Another copy.

Another edition. 60 keuen. 1824. 8°.

羅 密 士 Lo-MEĬH-SZE (*i.e.* Elias Loomis).

代 微 積 拾 級 *Tae wei tseĭh shĭh keĭh.* "Analytical Geometry and Differential and Integral Calculus." By Lo-meĭh-sze. Translated into Chinese by Wei-lĕĕ-a-leĭh, *i.e.* A. Wylie, and transcribed by Le Shen-lan. 18 keuen.

1855 ? 8°.

Imperfect, contains only keuen 10–16.

羅 明 堅 Lo MING-KEEN.

天 主 聖 敎 實 錄 *Teen choo shing keaou shĭh lŭh.* "A True Account of the Christian Religion." By Lo Ming-keen, a Jesuit. 1685. 8°.

羅 懋 登 Lo MOW-TĂNG.

西 洋 記 *Se yang ke.* "An Account of the Western Ocean." An apocryphal account of the expedition of the Eunuch Ching Ho to subdue the refractory nations of the Southern Ocean at the commencement of the fifteenth century. With Illustrations. 20 keuen.

1597. 8°.

Another copy.

Imperfect, containing only keuen 11 and 13.

羅 伯 聃 Lo-PĬH TAN [*i.e.* Robert Thom].

See ÆSOP, THE PHRYGIAN. 意 拾 秘 傳 *E shĭh-pe chuen.* "Æsop's Fables." Translated into Chinese by Lo-pĭh Tan, &c. 1838. 8°.

—— 華 英 通 用 雜 話 *Hwa Ying tung yung tsă hwa.* "A Chinese and English Vocabulary." Part I. 1843. 8°.

羅 大 振 Lo TA-CHIN.

See 羅 泌 Lo PE. 路 史 *Loo she.* "A History of the Nation's Course." . . Edited by Lo Ta-chin, &c. 8°.

羅 前 蔭 Lo TSEEN-YIN.

See 吳 鏞 Woo YUNG. 同 安 縣 志 *Tung gan heen che.* "A Topography of Tung-gan Heen." . . Compiled by . . . Lo Tseen-yin, &c.

1767. 8°.

羅 萬 藻 Lo WAN-TSAOU.

稿 *Kaou.* "Essays." *See* 長 城 CHANG CHING. 名 家 制 義 *Ming kea che e.* "Essays" on Texts from the Four Books, &c. Tsĭh 86.

1699. 8°.

羅 尹 孚 Lo YIN-FOO.

嘉 善 縣 災 賑 徵 信 錄 *Kea shen heen tsae chang ching sin lŭh.* "A Report of Charitable Contributions to the Relief of the Distress caused by Floods in the District of Kea-shen," in Che-keang. Compiled by Lo Yin-foo. 1824. 8°.

Another copy.

洛 京 Lŏ KING.

洛 京 獵 記 *Lŏ king lĕĕ ke.* "A Hunting Adventure at Lŏ king." *See* 說 SHWŎ. 說 淵 *Shwŏ yuen.* "A Collection of Tales," &c. Vol. 5. 8°.

洛 神 Lŏ SHIN.

洛 神 傳 *Lŏ shin chuen.* "The Story of the Deity of Lŏ." *See* 說 SHWŎ. 說 淵 *Shwŏ yuen.* "A Collection of Tales," &c. Vol. 1. 8°.

樂 史 Lŏ SHE.

楊 太 眞 外 傳 *Yang Tae-chin wae chuen.* "The Story of Yang Tae-chin." *See* 王 文 誥 WANG WĂN-KAOU. 唐 代 叢 書 *Tang tae tsung shoo.* "A Collection of Reprints of Works written during the Tang Dynasty," &c. Series 4. 1806. 8°.

—— 楊 太 眞 外 傳 *Yang Tae chin wae chuen.* "The Story of Yang Tae-chin." By Lo She, of the Tang Dynasty. A Reprint. 2 keuen.

[1741 ?]. 8°.

—— 太 平 寰 宇 記 *Tae ping hwan yu ke.* "A Geography of the Empire during the Reign of Tae-ping-hing-kwŏ." By Lo She. Edited by Chin Lan-san. 200 keuen. 1793. 8°.

LOBSCHEID (WILHELM).

See LONDON. *Chinese Evangelization Society.* 福 世 津 梁 *Fŭh she tsin leang.* "A Bridge to the World of Happiness." . . [By W. L.], &c.

1855. 8°.

—— 誡 妄 行 錄 *Keae wang hing lŭh.* "A Warning against Depraved Conduct." [By W. L.], &c. 8°.

LONDON.   *Chinese Evangelization Society.*

See BIBLE. 舊遺詔聖書（求世主耶穌新遺詔書）*Kew e chaou shing shoo* (*Kew she choo Yay-soo sin e chaou shoo*). "The Old and New Testaments." . . Published by the Chinese Evangelization Society, &c.   1854–1855. 8°.

—— 福世津梁 *Fŭh she tsin leang.* "A Bridge to the World of Happiness." [By W. Lobscheid.] Published by the Chinese Evangelization Society.   1855. 8°.

—— 誡妄行錄 *Keae wang hing lŭh.* "A Warning against Depraved Conduct." [By W. Lobscheid.] Published by the Chinese Evangelization Society.   [1855 ?]. 8°.

—— 廟祝問答 *Meaou chŭh wăn tă.* "A Conversation with a Buddhist Priest." [By F. Genaehr.]   *Hongkong,* 1859. 8°.

Another copy.

盧坤 Loo KWĂN.

信驗方 *Sin yen fang.* "Trustworthy Prescriptions." Compiled by Loo Kwăn. A Reprint. 2 keuen.   *Canton,* 1858. 8°.

盧燦 Loo TSAN.

龍游縣誌 *Lung yew hĕen che.* "A Topography of Lung-yew Heen," in the Province of Ché-keang. Compiled by Loo Tsan and others. 12 keuen.   1681. 8°.

盧文弨 Loo WĂN-CHAOU.

See 胡本淵 Hoo PUN-YUEN. 子史輯要詩賦題解 *Tsze she tseĭh yaou she foo te keae.* "A Collection of Themes." . . . Edited by Loo Wăn-chaou, &c.   1810. 8°.

—— See 賈誼 KEA E. 新書 *Sin shoo.* "The New Book." . . . Edited by Loo Wăn-chaou, &c.   8°.

—— See 陸德明 LŬH TĬH-MING. 經典釋文 *King teen shĭh wăn.* "An Explanation of Phrases and Expressions used in the Classics." . . Edited by Loo Wăn-chaou, &c.   1791. 8°.

盧文弨 Loo WĂN-CHAOU. (*Continued.*)

鍾山札記 *Chung shan chă ke.* "Notes [on the Classics] from Mount Chung." [Also] 龍城札記 *Lung ching chă ke.* "Notes [on the Classics] from the Dragon City." *See* 嚴杰 YEN LĔĔ. 皇清經解 *Hwang tsing king keae.* "The Classics Explained," &c. Keuen 388–89.   1829. 8°.

—— 經典釋文考證 *King teen shĭh wăn kaou ching.* "Lŭh Tĭh-ming's Explanation of Phrases and Expressions used in the Classics examined and verified." 2 keuen.   [1791 ?]. 8°.

盧文子 Loo WĂN-TSZE.

See 左丘明 Tso KEW-MING. 春秋分國左傳 *Chun Tsew fun kwŏ Tso chuen.* "Extracts from the Tso chuen." . . Edited by Loo Wăn-tsze, &c.   1761. 8°.

盧雲錦 Loo YUN-KIN.

See 劉方璿 LEW FANG-SEUEN. 周官說約 *Chow kwan shwŏ yŏ.* "The Officers of Chow." . . . Edited by Loo Yun-kin, &c.   1812. 8°.

魯質 Loo CHĬH.

See 向日貞 HEANG JĬH-CHING. 註釋向太史全稿 *Choo shĭh Heang tae she tseuen kaou.* "A Complete Collection of the Essays of Heang Jĭh-ching, the Historian." . . Annotated by Loo Chĭh, &c.   1771. 8°.

魯班 Loo PAN.

破煞神訣 *Po shă shin keuĕ.* "Rules for Exorcising Baneful Spirits." With Explanatory Notes.   [1800 ?]. 8°.

魯賓 Loo PIN.

魯賓之文鈔 *Loo Pin che wăn chaou.* "Literary Essays by Loo Pin." Edited by Yaou Ke-chuen.   1800. 8°.

魯習 Loo SEĬH.

魯習之文鈔 *Loo Seĭh che wăn chaou.* "Literary Essays by Loo Seĭh." Edited by Yaou Ke-chuen.   1800. 8°.

魯史 Loo SHE.

See 老君 LAOU KEUN. 道德經解 *Taou tĭh king keae.* "The Classic of Reason and Virtue." . . Edited by Loo She, &c.   8°.

第一卷

魯絜非 Loo Këě-fei.

魯山木先生文集 *Loo Shan-muh Seen-săng wăn tseĭh.* "A Collection of the Writings of Loo Këě-fei." Edited by Yaou Ke-chuen. 12 keuen. 1831. 8°.

—— 魯山木先生外集 *Loo Shan-muh Seen-săng wae tseĭh.* "An Additional Collection of the Writings of Loo Këě-fei." Edited by Yaou Ke-chuen. 2 keuen. 1798. 8°.

魯宗穆 Loo Tsung-muh.

See CHINA. BOARD OF WAR. 欽定中樞政考 *Kin ting chung choo ching kaou.* "An Examination into the Fundamental System" of Governing the Army. Compiled by .. Loo Tsung-muh, &c. 1764. 8°.

爐 Loo.

落爐不燬 *Lŏ loo pŭh shaou.* "They fell into the Furnace and were not burned." The Story of Shadrach, Meshach, and Abednego. [By Dr. James Legge.] [*Hongkong,* 1870 ?]. 8°.

路振 Loo Chin.

九國志 *Kew kwŏ che.* "The History of the Nine States." Supplemented by Chang Tang-ying. 12 keuen. *See* 伍崇曜 Woo Tsung-yaou. 粵雅堂叢書 *Yuĕ ya Tang tsung shoo.* "The Yuĕ-ya Tang Collection of Reprints," &c. Series 10. 1853. 8°.

————— See 葉志詵 Yĕ Che-sin. 海山仙館叢書 *Hae shan seen Kwan tsung shoo.* "The Hae-shan-seen Kwan Collection of Reprints," &c. Vol. 16, 17. 1848. 8°.

LOOMIS (Elias).

See 羅密士 Lo-meĭh-sze.

LORD'S PRAYER.

祈禱眞法註解 *Ke taou chin fă choo keae.* "The True Model of Prayer [*i.e.* The Lord's Prayer]. Commented on and Explained" by Pŏ-găe-chay. [1835 ?]. 8°.

樓 Low.

望兒樓 *Wang urh low.* "The Watching-for-Son's-return Tower." A Drama. [1800 ?]. 8°.

樓冷 Low-lang.

See PERIODICAL PUBLICATIONS. 英吉利每月雜記傳的通報 *Ying-keĭh-le mei yuĕ tsă ke chuen teĭh tung paou.* "An English Monthly Magazine." Written in Chinese by Low-lang, &c. [1750 ?]. A sheet.

六壬 Lŭh jin.

大六壬大全 *Ta lŭh jin ta tseuen.* A Work on Divination. 10 keuen. [1800 ?]. 8°.

Imperfect, containing only keuen 7–10.

六姑 Lŭh koo.

六姑回門新發財全本 *Lŭh koo hwuy mun sin fă tsae tseuen pun.* "The Story of Lew-koo's Return and Newly-acquired Wealth." In verse. 3 keuen. [1850 ?]. 8°.

六嚴 Lŭh yen.

See 李兆洛 Le Chaou-lŏ. 歷代地理志韻編今釋 *Leĭh tae te le che yun peen kin shĭh.* "A Gazetteer." ... Edited by Lŭh Yen, &c. 1837. 8°.

六承如 Lŭh Ching-joo.

See 李兆洛 Le Chaou-lŏ. 歷代地理志韻編今釋 *Leĭh tae te le che yun peen kin shĭh.* "A Gazetteer." ... Edited by Lŭh Ching-joo, &c. 1837. 8°.

陸贄 Lŭh Che.

陸宣公全集 *Lŭh Seuen kung tseuen tseĭh.* "A Complete Collection of the Writings of Lŭh Che." With a Portrait. 22 keuen. 1824. 8°.

陸貽 Lŭh E.

See 焦延壽 Tseaou Yen-show. 焦氏易林 *Tseaou she Yĭh lin.* "A Forest of Changes," ... Edited by Lŭh E, &c. 1808. 8°.

陸璣 Lŭh Ke.

毛詩草木鳥獸蟲魚疏 *Maou She tsaou muh neaou show chung yu soo.* "The Botany and Zoology of the Book of Odes." By Lŭh Ke. Edited by Shĭh Yung-ling. A Reprint. 2 keuen. [1800 ?]. 8°.

19

陸賈 LŬH KEA.

新語 *Sin yu.* "New Discourses" on Philosophical and other Subjects. *See* 沈津 CHIN TSIN. 百家類纂 *Pih kea luy tswan.* "The Works of a Hundred Authors," &c. Keuen 3. 8°.

—— 新語 *Sin yu.* "New Discourses." By Lŭh Kea, of the Han Dynasty. A Reprint. 2 keuen. [1800?]. 8°.

陸師 LŬH SZE.

儀徵縣志 *E ching heen che.* "A Topography of E-ching Heen," in the Prefecture of Yang-chow. Compiled by Lŭh Sze. 22 keuen. 1718. 8°.

陸佃 LŬH TEEN.

鶡冠子 *Hŏ kwan-tsze.* "The Writings of Hŏ Kwan-tsze." With a Commentary by Lŭh Teen, &c. *See* 黄丕烈 HWANG PEI-LËĔ. 十子全書 *Shih tsze tseuen shoo.* "The Complete Works of the Ten Philosophers," &c. 1804. 8°.

—— 埤雅 *Pe Ya.* "A Supplementary Expositor." 20 keuen. *See* 郎奎金 LANG KWEI-KIN. 五雅 *Woo Ya.* "The Five Dictionaries," &c. 1626. 8°.

—— 爾雅新義 *Urh ya sin e.* "A New Interpretation of the 'Literary Expositor.'" 20 keuen. *See* 伍崇曜 WOO TSUNG-YAOU. 粤雅堂叢書 *Yuĕ ya Tang tsung shoo.* "The Yuĕ-ya Tang Collection of Reprints," &c. Series 16. 1853. 8°.

陸燦 LŬH TSAN.

稿 *Kaou.* "Essays." *See* 長城 CHANG CHING. 名家制義 *Ming kea che e.* "Essays" on Texts from the Four Books, &c. Tsĭh 109. 1699. 8°.

陸績 LŬH TSEĬH.

周易述 *Chow Yih shŭh.* "Notes on the Chow Changes." *See* 孫堂 SUN TANG. 漢魏二十一家易注 *Han Wei urh shih yih kea Yih choo.* "Commentaries on the Book of Changes," &c. 1799. 8°.

陸偉 LŬH WEI.

暌車志 *Kwei chay che.* "Tales." *See* 說 SHWŎ. 說畧 *Shwŏ leŏ.* "Historical and other Tracts," &c. 8°.

陸位 LŬH WEI.

See 張果 CHANG KO. 星宗大全 *Sing tsung ta tseuen.* "A Complete Work on Astrology." . . . Edited by Lŭh Wei, &c. 8°.

陸埜 LŬH YAY.

See 張伯端 CHANG PĬH-TWAN. 悟眞篇三註 *Woo chin peen san choo.* "On Understanding the Truth." With Commentaries by Lŭh Yay, &c. 1809. 8°.

陸游 LŬH YEW.

劍南詩鈔 *Keen nan she chaou.* "The Keen-nan Collection of Poetry" by Lŭh Yew. Edited by Yang Ta-hŏ. 1685. 8°.

—— 南唐書 *Nan Tang shoo.* "A History of the Southern Tang Dynasty." With a Supplementary Keuen by Tseĭh Kwang, in which is given the Pronunciation and Elucidation of uncommon Terms in the original Work. 19 keuen. 1813. 8°.

陸釴 LŬH YĬH.

稿 *Kaou.* "Essays." *See* 長城 CHANG CHING. 名家制義 *Ming kea che e.* "Essays" on Texts from the Four Books, &c. Tsĭh 35. 1699. 8°.

陸羽 LŬH YU.

茶經 *Cha king.* "A Treatise on the Tea Plant." *See* 王文誥 WANG WĂN-KAOU. 唐代叢書 *Tang tae tsung shoo.* "A Collection of Reprints of Works written during the Tang Dynasty," &c. Series 3. 1806. 8°.

陸顒 LŬH YUNG.

陸顒傳 *Lŭh Yung chuen.* "The Story of Lŭh Yung." *See* 說 SHWŎ. 說淵 *Shwŏ yuen.* "A Collection of Tales," &c. Vol. 6. 8°.

陸以莊 LŬH E-CHWANG.

會試硃卷 *Hwuy she choo keuen.* "Examination Essays." 1796. 8°.

—— 小書巢詩課偶存 *Seaou shoo chaou she ko gow tsun.* "Poetical Exercises from the Nest of Minor Works." 4 keuen. [1800?]. 8°.

陸法言 LŬH FĂ-YEN.

廣韻 *Kwang yun.* "An Ancient Tonic Dictionary." A Reprint. 5 keuen. 1702. 8°.

陸 希 聲 LŬH HE-SHING.

李 元 賓 集 *Le Yuen-pin tseĭh.* "The Writings of Le Kwan." Compiled by Lŭh He-shing, &c. *See* 伍 崇 曜 WOO TSUNG-YAOU. 粵 雅 堂 叢 書 *Yuĕ ya Tang tsung shoo.* "The Yuĕ-ya Tang Collection of Reprints," &c. 1853. 8°.

陸 稼 書 LŬH KEA-SHOO.

See 葉 文 康 YĔ WĂN-KANG. 禮 經 會 元 *Le king hwuy yuen.* "On the Ritual Classics." ... Edited by Lŭh Kea-shoo, &c. 1189. 8°.

陸 君 弼 LŬH KEUN-PEĬH.

江 都 志 *Keang too che.* "A Topography of the District of Keang-too," in the Province of Keang-soo. Compiled by Lŭh Keun-peĭh. Edited by Chang Ming. 1597. 8°.

陸 九 淵 LŬH KEW-YUEN.

稿 *Kaou.* "Essays." *See* 長 城 CHANG CHING. 名 家 制 義 *Ming kea che e.* "Essays" on Texts from the Four Books, &c. Tsĭh 4. 1699. 8°.

陸 金 麗 LŬH KIN-LE.

堪 輿 一 貫 *Kan yu yĭh kwan.* "A Work on Geomancy." [1800?]. 8°.
Imperfect.

陸 廣 微 LŬH KWANG-WEI.

吳 地 記 *Woo te ke.* "An Account of the Principality of Woo." *See* 王 文 誥 WANG WĂN-KAOU. 唐 代 叢 書 *Tang tae tsung shoo.* "A Collection of Reprints of Works written during the Tang Dynasty," &c. Series 3. 1806. 8°.

陸 奎 勳 LŬH KWEI-HEUN.

See 白 潢 PĬH HWANG. 西 江 志 *Se keang che.* "A Topography of the Province of Keang-se." Compiled by .. Lŭh Kwei-heun, &c. 1720. 8°.

陸 龜 蒙 LŬH KWEI-MUNG.

小 名 錄 *Seaou ming lŭh.* "A Record of Nicknames." *See* 王 文 誥 WANG WĂN-KAOU. 唐 代 叢 書 *Tang tae tsung shoo.* "A Collection of Reprints of Works written during the Tang Dynasty," &c. Series 4. 1806. 8°.

陸 伯 焜 LŬH PĬH-HWĂN, and 屠 德 修 TOO TĬH-SEW.

愚 山 詩 鈔 *Yu shan she chaou.* "Poetry from Yu-shan." Compiled by Lŭh Pĭh-hwăn and Too Tĭh-sew. 5 keuen. [1750?]. 12°.

陸 西 星 LŬH SE-SING.

See 莊 周 CHWANG CHOW. 南 華 眞 經 副 墨 *Nan hwa chin king foo mĭh.* "A Guide to the Nan hwa king." .... By Lŭh Se-sing, &c. 1578. 8°.

陸 錫 熊 LŬH SEĬH-HEUNG.

See 紀 昀 KE YUN. 欽 定 歷 代 職 官 表 *Kin ting leĭh tae chĭh kwan peaou.* "A Series of Tables exhibiting the Changes which have taken place in the Names and Duties of the Officers in the several Departments of Government." .. Compiled by .. Lŭh Seĭh-heung, &c. 1783. 8°.

—————— 欽 定 勝 朝 殉 節 諸 臣 錄 *Kin ting shing chaou seun tsëë choo chin lŭh.* "Biographical Notices of Officials ... who lost their Lives in the Service of their Country." Compiled by ... Lŭh Seĭh-heung, &c. 1797. 8°.

—— See 謝 庭 薰 SEAY TING-HEUN. 冀 縣 志 *Low heen che.* "A Topography of Low Heen." ... Edited by Lŭh Seĭh-heung, &c. 1786. 8°.

陸 心 源 LŬH SIN-YUEN.

儀 顧 堂 集 *E koo Tang tseĭh.* "The E koo Hall Collection of Literary Pieces." 8 keuen. 1862. 8°.

陸 德 明 LŬH TĬH-MING.

經 典 釋 文 *King teen shĭh wăn.* "An Explanation of Phrases and Expressions used in the Classics." By Lŭh Tĭh-ming, of the Tang Dynasty. A Reprint. 30 keuen. [1750?]. 8°.
Imperfect, wanting keuen 15–30.

Another edition. Edited by Loo Wăn-chaou. 30 keuen. 1791. 8°.

陸 蒼 霖 LŬH TSANG-LIN.

See 魏 晉 錫 WEI TSIN-SEĬH. 欽 定 學 政 全 書 *Kin ting heŏ ching tseuen shoo.* "A Complete Collection of Educational Statutes." ... Compiled by ... Lŭh Tsang-lin, &c. 1781. 4°.

陸 清 獻 LŬH TSING-HEEN.

小 四 書 *Seaou Sze shoo.* "The Lesser Four Books." Consisting of *Ming wăh mung kew,* by Fang Fung-shin; *Sing le tsze heun,* by Ching Jŏ-yung; *Leĭh tae mung kew,* by Chin Lŏ; *She heŏ te yaou,* by Hwang Ke-shen; and *She heŏ te yaou poo,* by Tso Hwuy-chun, with Notes by Ho Yung. 6 keuen. 1845. 8°.

陸 次 雲 LǓH TSZE-YUN.

峒 谿 纖 志 志 餘 *Tung ke sëen che che yu.* "Songs of the Caves and Valleys." *See* 張 山 來 CHANG SHAN-LAE, and 張 進 也 CHANG TSIN-YAY. 昭 代 叢 書 *Chaou tae tsung shoo.* "A Collection of Reprints of Works by Authors under the present Dynasty," &c. Keuen 27.

1703. 8°.

—— 峒 谿 纖 志 *Tung ke sëen che.* "Songs of the Caves and Valleys." *See* 說 SHWŎ. 說 鈴 *Shwŏ ling.* "Miscellaneous Records," &c. 8°.

陸 應 陽 LǓH YING-YANG.

廣 興 記 *Kwang yu ke.* "A Geography of the Empire." Compiled by Lǔh Ying-yang. Edited by Tsae Fang-ping. 24 keuen. [1750?]. 8°.
Imperfect, containing only the second keuen.

Another edition. 24 keuen.   1802. 8°.

Another edition. 24 keuen.   1824. 8°.

陸 元 朗 LǓH YUEN-LANG.

See 孔 丘 KUNG KEW. 春 秋 經 傳 集 解 *Chun tsew king chuen tseǐh keae.* "The Spring and Autumn Annals," .. with Remarks on the Sounds of the Characters by Lǔh Yuen-lang, &c. 8°.

綠 窗 LǓH CHWANG.

綠 窗 人 物 花 譜 *Lǔh chwang jin wǔh hwa poo.* "The Drawing Book of the Green Window." [1800?]. 8°.

綠 牡 丹 LǓH MOW-TAN.

綠 牡 丹 全 傳 *Lǔh mow-tan tseuen chuen.* "The Complete Story of the Green Peony." 12? keuen. [1750?]. 8°.
Imperfect, containing only keuen 10 and 11.

茶 斐 軒 LǓH FE-HEEN.

詞 林 韻 釋 *Tsze lin yun shǐh.* "A Rhyming Dictionary." 2 keuen. *See* 伍 崇 曜 WOO TSUNG-YAOU. 粵 雅 堂 叢 書 *Yuě ya Tang tsung shoo.* "The Yuě-ya Tang Collection of Reprints," &c. Series 17. 1853. 8°.

錄 LǓH.

不 可 不 可 錄 *Pǔh ko pǔh ko lǔh.* "On the Value of Moral Restraint." 2 keuen.
Chang-chow, [1800?]. 8°.

錄 LǓH. (*Continued.*)

精 華 錄 *Tsing hwa lǔh.* "Elegant Poetical Pieces." By the Man of Mount Yu-yang. 12 keuen. 1704. 12°.
Imperfect, containing only keuen 1, 2, 5, 8–12.

倫 文 敍 LUN WĂN-SEU.

稿 *Kaou.* "Essays." *See* 長 城 CHANG CHING. 名 家 制 義 *Ming kea che e.* "Essays" on Texts from the Four Books, &c. Tsǐh 25.
1699. 8°.

龍 LUNG.

龍 虎 圞 *Lung Hoo tow.* "The Fight of the Dragon and the Tiger." A Drama.
[1800?]. 8°.

龍 膏 LUNG KAOU.

龍 膏 記 *Lung kaou ke.* "The Story of the Dragon's Fat." *See* 曲 KEÙH. 六 十 種 曲 *Lǔh shǐh chung keǔh.* "Sixty Plays," &c. Taou 6. 8°.

龍 圖 LUNG-TOO.

龍 圖 公 案 *Lung too kung gan.* "The Just Tribunal of Lung-too." 10 keuen. 1816. 8°.

龍 華 民 LUNG HWA-MIN.

See 艾 儒 略 GAE JOO-LEŎ. 萬 物 眞 原 *Wan wǔh chin yuen.* "The True Origin of all Things." .. Edited by ... Lung Hwa-min, &c. 8°.

—— 聖 敎 日 課 *Shing keaou jǐh ko.* "Daily Religious Exercises." [*Also*] 聖 母 德 敍 禱 文 *Shing moo tǐh seu taou wǎn.* "Prayers to the Holy Mother." [*Also*] 吾 主 念 珠 默 想 規 條 引 *Woo Choo neen choo teen seang kwei teaou yin.* "Directions for Studying the Beads." [*Also*] 聖 人 列 品 壽 文 *Shing jin lëĕ pin taou wǎn.* "Prayers to the Saints." *See* 郭 居 靜 KŎ KEU-TSING. 天 主 聖 敎 日 課 *Teen choo shing keaou jǐh ko.* "Daily Religious Exercises," &c. Keuen 1, 2. 8°.

龍 圖 躍 LUNG TOO-YŎ.

高 唐 州 志 *Kaou tang chow che.* "A Topography of Kaou-tang Chow." Compiled from materials supplied in former histories by Lung Too-yŏ. Edited by Lew Yaou-sze, Leu Kwŏ-tsoo, and others. 12 keuen.
1712. 8°.

雷公 LUY KUNG.

See 張光斗 CHANG KWANG-TOW. 藥性雷公炮製 Yŏ sing Luy Kung paou che. "On the Nature of Medicines, and Luy Kung's System of Decocting Drugs," &c. 1818. 8°.

雷琳 LUY LIN.

經餘必讀 King yu pĕih tŭh. "A Series of Elegant Extracts from Ancient Works exclusive of the Classics." Compiled by Luy Lin, Tseen Shoo-tang, and Tseen Shoo-lĕih. 8 keuen. 1805. 8°.

—— 經餘必讀續編 King yu pĕih tŭh sŭh peen. "A Supplementary Collection of Elegant Extracts from Ancient Works exclusive of the Classics." Compiled by Luy Lin, Tseen Shoo-chang, and Tseen Shoo-lĕih. 8 keuen. 1807. 8°. Wanting keuen 3–8.

雷霆 LUY TING.

雷霆解懺科 Luy-ting keae tsan ko. "The Luy-ting Ritual." A Taouist Work. 1821. 8°.

雷峰塔 LUY FUNG TĂ.

雷峰塔 Luy fung tă. "The Story of the Luy-fung Pagoda," otherwise known as the "History of the White Serpent." 5 keuen. 1806. 8°.

雷維霶 LUY WEI-PEI.

See 毛履謙 MAOU LE-KEEN, and 吳涵一 WOO HAN-YĬH. 十家詩詳註 Shih kea she tseang choo. "The Poetical Works of Ten Authors," viz... Luy Wei-pei, &c. 1813. 8°.

雷玉樞 LUY-YŬH-CHOO.

高上神雷玉樞雷霆寶經符篆 Kaou shang shin Luy yŭh choo Luy ting paou king fŭh chuen. "The Sûtra of the Lofty Deities Luy-yŭh-choo and Luy ting." [1800?]. Oblong.

鸞鎞 LWAN PE.

鸞鎞記 Lwan pe ke. "The Story of the Lwan pe." See 曲 KEŬH. 六十種曲 Lŭh shih chung keŭh. "Sixty Plays," &c. Taou 3. 8°.

馬 MA [i.e. Dr. R. Morrison].

See LITURGIES. England, Church of. 英吉利國神會祈禱文大概翻譯漢字 Ying-kĕih-le kwŏ shin hwuy ke taou wăn ta kae fan yĭh Han tsze. "The United Prayers and Supplications to God of the English Nation. Translated into Chinese." ... By Ma, &c. 1829. 8°.

馬志 MA CHE.

天寧寺石刻五百大阿羅漢 Teen-ning sze shih kĭh woo pĭh ta Ah Lo-han. "Drawings of the Stone Images of the Five Hundred Disciples of Buddha in the Teen-ning Temple." Edited by Ma Che. 10 keuen. 1799. Oblong. Imperfect, containing only Volumes 1, 2, 4, 8.

馬縞 MA KAOU.

中華古今注 Chung hwa koo kin choo. "A Record of Historical Antiquities." Being an Amplification and Elucidation of the Koo kin choo. 8°.

馬令 MA LING.

南唐書 Nan Tang shoo. "The History of the Southern Tang Dynasty." By Ma Ling, of the Sung Dynasty. A Reprint. 30 keuen. 1813. 8°.

馬驌 MA SŬH.

繹史 Yĭh sze. "History Arranged." By Ma Sŭh. Edited by Le Tsing. The body of this work consists of a compilation of quotations from old authors, arranged chronologically under the several heads, with disquisitions at the end of each keuen by Ma Sŭh. 160 keuen. 1670. 8°.

Another copy.

馬典 MA-TEEN [i.e. Sophia Martin, afterwards Little].

訓女三字經 Hcun neu san tsze king. "A Three-Character Classic for the Instruction of Females." 1832. 8°.

馬沅 MA YUEN.

駐颿閣文鈔 Choo fan kŏ wăn chaou. "Literary Papers from the Choo-fan Pavilion." [1830?]. 8°.

—— 湘帆試帖 Seang fan she tĕĕ. "Poetical Essays." [1800?]. 8°.

馬融 MA YUNG.

周易傳 Chow Yĭh chuen. "A Commentary on the Chow Changes." See 孫堂 SUN TANG. 漢魏二十一家易注 Han Wei urh shĭh yĭh kea Yĭh choo. "Commentaries on the Book of Changes," &c. 1799. 8°.

—— 忠經 Chung king. "The Classic on Patriotism." By Ma Yung, of the Han Dynasty. Edited by Chung Tsung-kwan. A Reprint. [1750?]. 8°.

Another edition. [1800?]. 8°.

馬 如 龍 MA JOO-LUNG.

See 易經 YĬH KING. 周易圖說述 *Chow Yĭh too shwŏ shŭh.* "Dissertations and Commentaries on the Diagrams of the Book of Changes.". . Edited by Ma Joo-lung. 1687. 8°.

馬 季 長 MA KE-CHANG.

長笛賦 *Chang teĭh foo.* "An Ode on the Flute." *See* 蕭統 SEAOU TUNG. 文選 *Wăn seuen.* "Elegant Extracts from Polite Literature," &c. Keuen 18. 1772. 8°.

馬 區 那 MA-KEU-NA.

See PERIODICAL PUBLICATIONS. 英吉利每月雜記傳的通報 *Ying-keĭh-le mei yuĕ tsă ke ehuen teĭh tung paou.* "An English Monthly Magazine." Written in Chinese by .. Ma-keuna, &c. [1750?]. A sheet.

馬 貴 與 MA KWEI-YU.

策海全書 *Tsĭh hae tseuen shoo.* "An Encyclopædia." 6 keuen. By Ma Kwei-yu. Edited by Keu Tsăng-tseĭh. 1814. 12°.

馬 伯 良 MA PĬH-LEANG.

教欵捷要 *Keaou kwan tsĕĕ yaou.* "An Exposition of the more important Points of the Mahommedan Law," the Technical Terms being all given in the Arabic Character. By Ma Pĭh-leang. Edited by Le Yung-show. *Canton,* 1817. 8°.

Another copy.

馬 伯 樂 MA PĬH-LŎ.

浙江鄉試硃卷 *Chĕ keang heang she choo keuen.* "The Red Book of Chĕ-keang District Examination Essays" for the Year 1821. Compiled by the Examiner Ma Pĭh-lŏ. 1821. 8°.

馬 少 雲 MA SHAOU-YUN, and 盛梅溪 SHING MEI-KE.

衛藏圖識 *Wei tsang too shĭh.* "An Itinerary of Tibet, with an Account of the Inhabitants, their Customs and Institutions. With Maps and Illustrations." Compiled by Ma Shaou-yun and Shing Mei-ke. 4 keuen. 1792. 8°.

馬 大 猷 MA TA-YEW.

See 孔丘 KUNG KEW. 書經補註備旨 *Shoo king poo choo pe ehe.* "The Book of Historical Documents.". . Edited by Ma Ta-yew, &c. 1822. 8°.

馬 天 君 MA TEEN-KEUN.

See 文昌帝君 WĂN-CHANG TE KEUN. 大洞經詮註 *Ta tung king tseuen choo.* "The Great, Profound Sûtra, ... With a Complete Commentary" by Ma Teen-keun, &c. 1819. 8°.

馬 俊 良 MA TSEUN-LEANG.

See 陳倫烱 CHIN LUN-KEUNG. 海國聞見錄 *Hae kwŏ wăn keen lŭh.* "A Geographical Treatise.". . Edited by Ma Tseun-leang, &c. 1793. 8°.

—— 本朝律賦集服 *Pun chaou leŭh foo tseĭh yĭh.* "Lyrical Poems by Authors of the Present Dynasty. A Pocket Edition." Compiled by Ma Tseun-leang. 1789. 8°.

—— 禹貢圖說 *Yu kung too shwŏ.* "The Geography of the Tribute of Yu." [1790?]. 8°.

馬 宗 璉 MA TSUNG-LEEN.

春秋左傳補注 *Chun Tsew Tso chuen poo choo.* "Supplementary Comments on the Spring and Autumn Annals and Tso Kew-ming's Narrative." *See* 嚴杰 YEN LĔĔ. 皇清經解 *Hwang Tsing king keae.* "The Classics Explained," &c. Keuen 1277–1279. 1829. 8°.

馬 自 然 MA TSZE-JEN.

馬自然傳 *Ma Tsze-jen chuen.* "The Story of Ma Tsze-jen." *See* 說 SHWŎ. 說淵 *Shwŏ yuen.* "A Collection of Tales," &c. Vol. 9. 8°.

馬 端 臨 MA TWAN-LIN.

See 嚴思菴 YEN SZE-GAN. 文獻通考詳節 *Wăn heen tung kaou tseang tsĕĕ.* "Explanatory Chapters on Ma Twan-lin's 'Wăn heen tung kaou.'" 1764. 8°.

—— 文獻通考 *Wăn heen tung kaou.* "A General Examination of Records and Scholars" by Ma Twan-lin. Being a Research into every Subject connected with the Government, History, Literature, Religion, &c., of the Empire of China. Edited by She E-mow and others. A New Edition. 348 keuen. 1748. 8°.

Another copy.

Another edition. 348 keuen. [1750?]. 8°.
Wanting Preface and Index.

第一卷

馬曰琯 MA Yuĕ-kwan.

林屋唱酬錄 Lin ŭh chang chow lŭh. "Festive Songs from the 'Forest Dwelling.'" Compiled by Ma Yuĕ-kwan. [Also] 焦山紀游集 Tseaou shan ke yew tseĭh. "Pieces of Poetry commemorative of Wanderings on the Tseaou Mountains." Compiled by Ma Yuĕ-kwan and others. [Also] 沙河逸老小稿 Sha ho yĭh laou seaou kaou. "Poetry by the Retired Old Man of Sha-ho." 7 keuen. See 伍崇曜 Woo Tsung-yaou. 粵雅堂叢書 Yuĕ ya Tang tsung shoo. "The Yuĕ-ya Tang Collection of Reprints," &c. Series 9.   1853. 8°.

馬曰璐 MA Yuĕ-loo.

南齋集 Nan chae tseĭh. "A Collection o Poems from the Southern Study." 8 keuen. [Also] 韓柳年譜 Han Lew neen poo. "A Chronological Record of the Events in the Lives of Han Yu and Lew Tsung-yen." Edited by Ma Yuĕ-loo. 8 keuen. See 伍崇曜 Woo Tsung-yaou. 粵雅堂叢書 Yuĕ ya Tang tsung shoo. "The Yuĕ-ya Tang Collection of Reprints," &c. Series 9, 14.   1853. 8°.

馬元臺 MA Yuen-tae.

See 黃帝 Hwang-te. 內經註證 Nuy king choo ching. "The Two Medical Treatises, the Soo wăn and the Ling choo. . . With Notes and Comments" by Ma Yuen-tae, &c.   1805. 8°.

瑪吉士 MA Keĭh-sze [i.e.   Marques].

外國地理備考 Wae kwŏ te le pe kaou. "A Treatise on the Geography of Foreign Countries." 10 keuen. See 葉志兖 Yĕ Che-sin. 海山仙館叢書 Hae shan seen kwan tsung shoo. "The Hae-shan-seen Kwan Collection of Reprints," &c. Vol. 114–119.   1848. 8°.

MACGOWAN (D. J.), M.D.

航海金針 Hang hae kin chin. "The Navigator's Golden Needle." A Work based on the Chapter on Typhoons of the China Seas in Col. Reid's Work.   Ningpo, 1853. 8°.
This work has also the following English title, "The Law of Storms in Chinese."

Another copy.

MAGALHAENS (Gabriel de).

See 康熙 Kang-he. 上諭 Shang yu. "An Imperial Edict" . . . expressing Regret at the Death of . . . P. Gabriel de Magalhaens, &c.   1677. 8°.

孟喜 Măng He.

周易章句 Chow Yĭh chang keu. "The Chow Changes explained by Paragraphs and Sentences." See 孫堂 Sun Tang. 漢魏二十一家易注 Han Wei urh shĭh yĭh kca Yĭh choo. "Commentaries on the Book of Changes," &c.   1799. 8°.

孟琪 Măng Hung.

蒙鞬備錄 Mung Tă pe lŭh. "An Account of the Mongol Tartars." See 說 Shwŏ. 說選 Shwŏ seuen. "A Selection of Historical Records," &c. Vol. 5.   8°.

孟啓 Măng Ke.

本事詩 Pun sze she. "Poems by Able Writers." See 王文誥 Wang Wăn-kaou. 唐代叢書 Tang tae tsung shoo. "A Collection of Reprints of Works written during the Tang Dynasty," &c. Series 3.   1806. 8°.

—— 本事詩 Pun sze she. "Poems by Able Writers." Compiled by Măng Ke, of the Tang Dynasty. A Reprint.   [1741 ?]. 8°.

孟子 Măng tsze.

孟子 Măng tsze. "The Works of Mencius." See 毛鳳苞 Maou Fung-paou. 十三經注疏 Shĭh san king choo soo. "The Thirteen Classics, with Commentaries and Expositions," &c.   1813. 8°.

孟儒望 Măng Joo-wang.

耶穌聖號禱文 Yay-soo shing haou taou wăn. "Prayers in the Holy Name of Jesus." [Also] 煉獄禱文 Leen yŏ taou wăn. "Prayers for Souls in Purgatory." See 郭居靜 Kŏ Keu-tsing. 天主聖敎日課 Teen choo shing keaou yĭh ko. "Daily Christian Religious Exercises," &c. Keuen 2.   8°.

毛萇 Maou Chang.

See 詩經 She king. 毛詩注疏 Maou she choo soo. "Maou Chang's Version of the Book of Odes," &c.   1815. 8°.

毛萇 MAOU CHANG. (*Continued.*)

毛詩稽古編 *Maou She ke koo peen.* "The Views of the Old School on Maou Chang's Version of the Book of Odes," &c. *See* 嚴杰 YEN LËË. 皇清經解 *Hwang Tsing king keae.* "The Classics Explained," &c. Keuen 60–89. 1829. 8º.

毛蕃 MAOU FAN.

See 龔在升 KUNG TSAE-SHING. 三才彙編 *San tsae wei peen.* "An Encyclopædia." . . . . . The Third Keuen . . . was enlarged by Maou Fan, &c. 8º.

—— See 楊廉 YANG LEEN. 嘉善縣志 *Kea-shen heen che.* "A Topography of Kea-shen Heen." . . Edited by Maou Fan, &c. 1677. 8º.

毛晃 MAOU HWANG.

禹貢指南 *Yu kung che nan.* "The Compass applied to the Tribute of Yu." By Maou Hwang, of the Sung Dynasty. A New Edition. 4 keuen. 1773. 8º.

毛晉 MAOU TSIN.

See 司馬遷 SZE-MA TSEEN. 史記 *She ke.* "The Historical Record." . . . Edited by Maou Tsin, &c. 1640. 8º.

—— 柯邕碩詩 *Këĕ Man-shĭh she.* "The Poetry of Këĕ Man-shĭh." Edited by Maou Tsin, &c. *See* 葉志詵 YĔ CHE-SIN. 海山仙館叢書 *Hae shan seen Kwan tsung shoo.* "The Hae-shan-seen Kwan Collection of Reprints," &c. Vol. 58. 1848. 8º.

—— 十七史 *Shĭh tseĭh she.* "The Seventeen Histories." With Supplementary Histories of the Sung, Leaou, Kin, Yuen, and Ming Dynasties. Compiled by Maou Tsin. 1656. 8º.

毛鳳苞 MAOU FUNG-PAOU.

See 王象晉 WANG SEANG-TSIN. 羣芳譜 *Keun fang poo.* "A Herbarium." Edited by Maou Fung-paou, &c. 1621. 8º.

—— 十三經注疏 *Shĭh san king choo soo.* "The Thirteen Classics, with Commentaries and Expositions." Edited by Maou Fung-paou. 1813. 8º.
Imperfect.

毛煥文 MAOU HWAN-WĂN.

萬寶全書 *Wan paou tseuen shoo.* "An Encyclopædia." An Enlarged Edition. Edited by Maou Hwan-wăn. 20 keuen. 1739. 8º.
Imperfect, containing only keuen 1–9, 14–20.

毛奇齡 MAOU KE-LING.

聖諭樂本解說 *Shing yu yŏ pun keae shwŏ.* "Imperial Edicts on Music Explained." [Also] 檀弓訂悮 *Tan kung ting woo.* "The Errors of the Second Section of the Book of Rites." [Also] 三年服制考 *San neen fŭh che kaou.* "An Examination of the Regulations for Three Years' Mourning." 西河詩話 *Se ho she hwa.* "Se-ho's Criticisms on Poetry." *See* 張山來 CHANG SHAN-LAE, and 張進也 CHANG TSIN-YAY. 昭代叢書 *Chaou tae tsung shoo.* "A Collection of Reprints of Works by Authors under the present Dynasty," &c. Keuen 4, 6, 7, 31. 1703. 8º.

—— 仲氏易 *Chung she Yĭh.* "Chung's Edition of the Book of Changes." 30 keuen. [Also] 春秋毛氏傳 *Chun tsew Maou she chuen.* "Maou's Commentary on the Spring and Autumn Annals." 36 keuen. [Also] 春秋簡書刊悮 *Chun tsew keen shoo kan woo.* "The Misprints in the Spring and Autumn Annals." 2 keuen. [Also] 春秋屬比事記 *Chun tsew shŭh pe sze ke.* "An Exhibition of the Style of the Spring and Autumn Annals according to the Analogies of the Subject Matter." 4 keuen. [Also] 經問 *King wăn.* "Questions on the Classics." 15 keuen. [Also] 論語稽求篇 *Lun yu ke kew peen.* "Examinations and Searchings into the Confucian Analects." 7 keuen. [Also] 四書賸言 *Sze shoo ying yen.* "Additional Remarks on the Four Books." 6 keuen. *See* 嚴杰 YEN LËË. 皇清經解 *Hwang Tsing king keae.* "The Classics Explained," &c. Keuen 90–189. 1829. 8º.

—— 四書典制辨正 *Sze shoo teen che peen ching.* "Explanatory Essays on Canonical Passages from the Four Books." By Maou Ke-ling. Revised by Han Tae-tsing. Edited by Le Hwang, and Compiled by Chang She. 4 keuen. [1830 ?]. 8º.

MAO   [153]   McC

毛 今 培 Maou Kin-pei.

試 體 唐 詩 箋 註 *She te Tang she tseen choo.*
"Tang Dynasty Examination Poetry. With Explanatory Notes." Compiled by Maou Kin-pei.
Edited by Chin Tǐh-tseen. 4 keuen. 1757. 8°.

毛 履 謙 Maou Le-keen, and 吳 涵 一 Woo Han-
yǐh.

十 家 詩 詳 註 *Shǐh kea she tseang choo.* "The
Poetical Works of Ten Authors," viz. Woo Seǐh-
ke, Wang Soo, Wang Joo-yang, Leang Shang-
kwǒ, Luy Wei-pei, Ho Taou-săng, Ho Yuen-
lang, Fǎ Shǐh-shen, Wang Ke-sun, and Le Joo-
yun. Edited with Explanatory Notes by Maou
Le-keen and Woo Han-yǐh. 7 keuen.

1813. 8°.

毛 邦 翰 Maou Pang-han.

See 揚 甲 Yang Keǎ. 六 經 圖 *Lǔh king too.*
"Illustrations to the Six Classics." Edited by
Maou Pang-han, &c.   1614. Folio.

毛 先 舒 Maou Seen-shoo.

諺 說 *Yen shwǒ.* "On Proverbs." *See* 張 山 來
Chang Shan-lae, and 張 進 也 Chang Tsin-
yay. 昭 代 叢 書 *Chaou tae tsung shoo.* "A
Collection of Reprints of Works by Authors
under the present Dynasty," &c. Keuen 35.

1703. 8°.

毛 聲 山 Maou Shing-shan.

See 羅 貫 中 Lo Kwan-chung. 三 國 志 *San
kwǒ che.* "The History of the Three Kingdoms."
. . . . Revised by Maou Shing-shan, &c.

1644. 8°.

毛 師 鄭 Maou Sze-ching.

See 朱 熹 Choo He. 小 學 體 註 大 成 *Seaou
heǒ te choo ta ching.* ". . . The Youth's Instructor." . . Edited by Maou Sze-ching, &c. 8°.

茅 坤 Maou Kwăn.

稿 *Kaou.* "Essays." *See* 長 城 Chang Ching.
名 家 制 義 *Ming kea che e.* "Essays" on
Texts from the Four Books, &c. Tsǐh 42.

1699. 8°.

—— See 胡 宗 憲 Hoo Tsung-heen. 籌 海 圖 編
Chow hae too peen. "A Detailed Work on the
Seaboard Districts of China." . . . Edited by
Maou Kwăn, &c.   1562. 8°.

茅 坤 Maou Kwăn. (*Continued.*)

See 左 丘 明 Tso Kew-ming. 春 秋 左 傳
解 要 *Chun Tsew Tso chuen keae yaou.* "The
Essential Portions of Tso Kew-ming's Narrative
. . Explained" by Maou Kwăn, &c. 1817. 8°.

—— 唐 宋 八 大 家 文 鈔 *Tang Sung pǎ ta kea wǎn
chaou.* "The Works of Eight Scholars who
flourished under the Tang and Sung Dynasties,"
viz. the Han wǎn, by Han Yu; the Lew wǎn,
by Lew Tsung-yuen; the Tsăng wǎn, by Tsăng
Kung; the Gow wǎn, by Gow-yang Sew;
the Wang wǎn, by Wang Gan-shǐh; and the
Soo wǎn, by Soo Seun, Soo Shǐh, and Soo Chě.
Edited by Maou Kwăn.   1631. 8°.

茅 元 儀 Maou Yuen-e.

武 備 志 *Woo pe che.* "The Art of War." With
Maps and Illustrations. 240 keuen. 1621. 8°.

Imperfect, containing only keuen 1–84, 86–89, 92–168,
179, 180, 187–238. There are three other imperfect copies
of this work.

MARQUES.

See 瑪 吉 士 Ma-keǐh-sze.

MARSHMAN (Joshua).

See Bible. New Testament. *Mark.* 唷 勒
Ma-lik. [Translated into Chinese by Dr. Marsh-
man], &c.   8°.

MARTIN (Sophia).

See 馬 典 Ma-teen.

MARTIN (William A. P.), *D.D.*

See Bible. New Testament. *John, Gospel of.*
官 話 約 翰 福 音 書 *Kwan hwa Yǒ-han fǔh
yin shoo.* "The Gospel of St. John, translated
into the Mandarin Dialect" [by W. A. P. M.],
&c.   1864. 8°.

—— See Wheaton (Henry). Wheaton's International Law, translated into Chinese by W. A.
P. M., &c.   *Peking,* 1864. 8°.

McCARTEE (D. B.).

See Bible. *Appendix.* 初 學 編 *Choo heǒ peen.*
"Old Testament History." . . . [By D. B. McC.],
&c.   1851. 8°.

20

McCLATCHIE (THOMAS).

See 理 LE. 中外理辨 *Chung wae le peen.*
"A Discussion on Orthodox and Heretical Principles." By Rev. T. McC., &c. [1847.] 8º.

米 黻 ME FŬH.

襄陽集 *Seang yang tseïh.* "The Seang-yang Collection." *See* 吳孟舉 Woo MĂNG-KEU, and 吳自牧 Woo TSZE-MŬH. 宋詩鈔二集 *Sung she chaou urh tseïh.* "Poetry of the Sung Dynasty. Second Collection," &c. 8º.

彌伽釋迦 ME-KEA-SHĬH-KEA [*i.e.* Meghasikha].

See 般剌密帝 PAN-LĂ-MEĬH-TE. 楞嚴經 *Lăng yen king.* "The Certain and Firm Sûtra." .. With Interpretorial Notes by Me-kea-shĭh-kea, &c. 1800. 8º.

———— 楞嚴經集註 *Lăng yen king tseïh choo.* "The Certain and Firm Sûtra." ... With Interpretorial Notes by Me-kea-shĭh-kea, &c. 1735. 8º.

妙峰福登 MEAOU-FUNG-FŬH-TĂNG.

See 般剌密帝 PAN-LĂ-MEĬH-TE. 楞嚴正脈 *Lăng yen ching mĭh.* "The Correct Pulse of the Certain and Firm Sûtra." .... Edited by Meaou-fung-fŭh-tăng, &c. 1633. 8º.

MEDHURST (WALTER HENRY), D.D., the Elder.

See BIBLE. NEW TESTAMENT. 救世主耶穌新遺詔書 *Kew she choo Yay-soo sin e chaou shoo.* [Translated into Chinese by ... W. H. Medhurst], &c. 1836. 8º.

———— 新約全書註解 *Sin yŏ tseuen shoo choo keae.* "The New Testament. With a Commentary" by W. H. M., &c. 1857. 8º.

—— 行道 HING TAOU. 行道信主以免後日之刑論 *Hing taou sin choo e meen how jĭh che hing lun.* "A Discourse on the Conduct and Faith necessary to avoid Future Punishment." [By W. H. M.], &c. 8º.

MEDHURST (WALTER HENRY) D.D., the Elder. (Continued.)

See 人 JIN. 人當自省以食晚餐論 *Jin tang tsze săng e shĭh wan tsan lun.* "On the Necessity of Self-examination before Partaking of the Lord's Supper." [By W. H. M.] 8º.

———— 論善惡人死 *Lun shen gŏ jin sze.* "The Death of the Good and Bad." [By W. H. M.], &c. 1844. 8º.

—— See 靈魂 LING HWĂN. 葆靈魂以升天國論 *Paou ling hwăn e Shing Teen kwŏ lun.* "Guard your Soul that you may enter into the Kingdom of Heaven." A Tract [by W. H. M.]. 8º.

—— See PERIODICAL PUBLICATIONS. 遐邇貫珍 *Hea urh kwan chin.* "A Serial of Foreign and Domestic News." [Edited by W. H. M.], &c. 1853–55. 8º.

—— See 小子 SEAOU TSZE. 小子初讀易識之書課 *Seaou tsze choo tŭh e shĭh che shoo ko.* "Easy Reading Exercises for Children." [By W. H. M.], &c. 8º.

—— See 尚德 SHANG-TĬH.

—— See 尚德者 SHANG-TĬH-CHAY.

—— See 善德者 SHEN-TĬH-CHAY.

—— See 地理 TE LE. 地理便童畧傳 *Te le peen tung leŏ chuen.* "A Short Catechism on Geography." [By W. H. M.] &c. 8º.

—— See 天 TEEN. 天地人論 *Teen te jin lun.* "Discourses on Heaven, Earth, and Man." [By W. H. M.], &c. 1869. 8º.

—— See 宗主 TSUNG CHOO. 宗主詩章 *Tsung choo she chang.* "Hymns." .. [By W. H. M.], &c. 1855. 8º.

—— See 野客 YAY KĬH. 野客問難記 *Yay kĭh wăn nan ke.* "A Rustic's Inquiries on Difficult Subjects." [By W. H. M.], &c. 1870. 8º.

—— See 耶穌教 YAY-SOO KEAOU. 耶穌教畧 *Yay-soo keaou leŏ.* "An Outline of the Christian Religion." [By W. H. M.], &c. 1855. 8º.

面 MEEN.

如 面 談 *Joo meen tan.* Conversations." [By Chung Sing.]   [1750 ?]. 8º.

Very imperfect.

MEGHASIKHA.

See 彌 伽 釋 迦 ME-KEA-SHĬH-KEA.

梅 MEI.

二 度 梅 傳 *Urh too Mei chuen.* "The Story of Mei of the Two Schemes." By 'The Master of Seïh yin Hall.' 6 keuen.   1800. 8º.

梅 庚 MEI KĂNG.

知 我 錄 *Che wo lŭh.* "Records of my Acquaintances." *See* 張 山 來 CHANG SHAN-LAE, and 張 湻 也 CHANG TSIN-YAY. 昭 代 叢 書 *Chaou tae tsung shoo.* "A Collection of Reprints of Works by Authors under the present Dynasty," &c. Keuen 44.   1703. 8º.

梅 純 MEI SHUN.

損 齋 備 忘 錄 *Sun chae pe wang lŭh.* "Memoirs." *See* 說 SHWŎ. 說 纂 *Shwŏ tswan.* "Miscellaneous Records," &c. Vol. 8.   8º.

梅 文 鼎 MEI WĂN-TING.

叢 書 輯 要 *Tsung shoo tseïh yaou.* "An Epitome of Astronomy."   [1750 ?]. 8º.

Imperfect, containing only keuen 51–54.

梅 膺 祚 MEI YING-TSOO.

字 彙 *Tsze wei.* "A Dictionary." By Mei Ying-tsoo.   1615. 8º.

The Title-page is wanting.

Another edition. This edition bears on the Title-page the title 醫 金 字 彙 *Heuen kin tsze wei.*   1690. 8º.

Another edition. Edited by Han Tan. 1705. 8º.

Another edition. This edition bears on the Title-page the title 關 西 字 彙 *Kwan se tsze wei.*   1724. 8º.

An odd Vol., containing only the Prefatory part.

Another edition. Enlarged and Improved by Chang Tsze-lĕč.   [1750 ?]. 8º.

Another copy.

Title-page and Preface wanting.

梅 膺 祚 MEI YING-TSOO. (*Continued.*)

Another edition. Edited by Han Tan. This edition bears on the Title-page the title 增 補 醫 金 字 彙 *Tsang poo heuen kin tsze wei.* 1786. 8º.

Another copy.

An odd Vol., containing only the characters under the first sixty radicals.

—— 玉 堂 字 彙 *Yŭh Tang tsze wei.* "The Jade Hall Dictionary." Compiled by Mei Ying-tsoo.   1665. 12º.

Imperfect, containing only the preliminary keuen.

梅 禹 金 MEI YU-KIN.

才 鬼 記 *Tsae kwei ke.* "Stories of Clever Devils." *See* 閔 景 賢 MIN KING-HEEN. 快 書 *Kwae shoo.* "A Book of Amusement," &c. Keuen 50.   1626. 8º.

美 MEI.

四 美 同 心 金 鈪 記 *Sze mei tung sin Kin ak ke.* "The Four Beauties of One Mind, or The Story of the Golden Bracelet." 6 keuen. 1842. 8º.

校 叔 MEI SHŬH.

七 發 *Tseïh fă.* "The Seven Declarations." *See* 蕭 統 SEAOU TUNG. 文 選 *Wăn seuen.* "Elegant Extracts from Polite Literature," &c. Keuen 34.   1772. 8º.

密 如 椿 MEĬH JOO-CHUN.

帖 體 詩 存 註 釋 *Tĕe te she tsun choo shĭh.* "Poems. With a Commentary and Notes" by Woo Chuen-keae. 6 keuen.   1817. 8º.

—— 燕 山 制 義 *Yen shan che e.* "Essays" on Texts from the Four Books by Meĭh Joo-chun. Edited with Notes by Yu Fung-che and others.   1813. 8º.

Another copy.

繆 襲 MEW SHĬH.

尤 射 *Yew shay.* "Strange Archery." By Mew Shĭh, of the Wei Dynasty. A Reprint.   [1750 ?]. 8º.

繆 燧 MEW SUY.

See 周 聖 化 CHOW SHING-HWA. 定 海 縣 志 *Ting hae heen che.* "A Topography of Tinghae Heen." ... Edited by Mew Suy, &c.   1715. 8º.

繆 宜 亭 MEW E-TING.
See 吳 金 壽 WOO KIN-SHOW. 三 家 醫 案 合 刻 *San kea E gan hŏ kĭh*. "The Medical Practice of the Three Physicians," ...... Mew E-ting, &c. 1831. 8°.

繆 蓮 仙 MEW LEEN-SEEN.
文 章 游 戲 *Wăn chang yew he*. "Rambles in Polite Literature." Compiled by Mew Leen-seen. In Four Parts. Edited by Hoo Yew-Tsun, Tang Seaou-mei, Chaou Chaou-ah, and Chin Wăn-shĭh. 4 Parts. 1824. 8°.

脈 MĬH.
脈 訣 攷 證 *Mĭh keuĕ kaou ching*. "A Critical Examination of the *Mĭh keuĕ*," or "Secrets of the Pulse." [1783 ?]. 12°.

默 持 MĬH-CHE.
禪 門 日 誦 *Shen mun jĭh sung*. "Buddhist Daily Liturgies." Compiled by the Priest Mĭh-che. 1792. 8°.

默 印 MĬH-YIN.
See 鳩 摩 羅 什 KEW-MO-LO-SHĬH. 金 剛 般 若 波 羅 密 經 *Kin kang pan jŏ po lo meĭh king*. "The Diamond Classic." .. Edited by the Priest Mĭh-yin, &c. 1795. Oblong.

墨 MĬH.
會 墨 *Hwuy mĭh*. "Examination Essays." [1820 ?]. 8°.
A Fragment.

—— 會 墨 鴻 裁 *Hwuy mĭh hung tsae*. "A Select Collection of Examination Essays" for the Year 1803. 1803. 8°.
A Fragment.

—— 會 墨 金 聲 *Hwuy mĭh kin shing*. "The Golden Sound of Examination Essays." [1815 ?]. 8°.
A Fragment.

—— 會 試 魁 墨 *Hwuy she kwei mĭh*. "A Collection of Superior Examination Essays." 1814. 8°.

—— 會 試 墨 卷 *Hwuy she mĭh keuen*. "A Volume of Examination Essays" of the Year 1836. 1836. 8°.

—— 墨 卷 鴻 裁 *Mĭh keuen hung tsae*. "A Choice Collection of Examination Essays." [1820 ?]. 8°.
Imperfect.

墨 MĬH. (*Continued*.)
墨 卷 脫 穎 *Mĭh keuen tŏ ying*. "A Collection of Superior Examination Essays," for the Years 1819–1821. 1821. 8°.
Imperfect.

—— 闈 墨 *Wei mĭh*. "Examination Essays." [1800 ?]. 8°.
A Fragment.

墨 客 MĬH KĬH.
墨 客 揮 犀 *Mĭh kĭh hwuy che*. "The Pencillings of a Student." See 說 SHWŎ. 說 畧 *Shwŏ leŏ*. "Historical and other Tracts," &c. 8°.

墨 翟 MĬH TEĬH.
墨 子 *Mĭh tsze*. "The Writings of Mĭh Teĭh." See 沈 津 CHIN TSIN. 百 家 類 纂 *Pĭh kea huy tswan*. "The Works of a Hundred Authors," &c. Keuen 25. 8°.

—— See 孔 鮒 KUNG FOO. 詰 墨 *Keĭh Mĭh*. "Criticisms on the Writings of the Philosopher Mĭh Teĭh," &c. 8°.

麥 氏 MĬH SHE [*i.e.* Dr. W. H. Medhurst].
三 字 經 *San tsze king*. "A Three-Character Classic," containing an Outline of the Christian Religion. With Six Plates at the End of the Volume. *Hongkong*, 1854. 12°.

Another edition. *Shanghae*, 1856. 8°.

Another edition. *Hongkong*, 1856. 8°.

麥 都 思 MĬH-TOO SZE [*i.e.* Dr. W. H. Medhurst].
耶 穌 敎 畧 *Yay-soo keaou leŏ*. "An Outline of the Christian Religion." Edited by Joseph Edkins under his Chinese name of Gae Yŏ-sĭh. *Shanghae*, 1858. 8°.

MILNE (WILLIAM), *D.D.*
See 眞 道 CHIN TAOU. 眞 道 入 門 *Chin taou jŭh mun*. "An Introduction to the True Doctrine." ... [by W. M.], &c. 1856. 8°.

—— See 學 善 HEŎ-SHEN.

—— See 甲 KEĂ. 甲 乙 二 友 論 述 *Keă Yĭh urh yew lun shŭh*. "A Discussion between the Two Friends Keă and Yĭh." [By W. M.], &c. 1858. 8°.

MILNE (WILLIAM), *D.D.* (*Continued.*)

See 靈魂 LING HWĂN. 靈魂篇 *Ling hwăn peen.* "A Treatise on the Soul." [By W. M.], &c.　　　　　　　　　　　8°.

―― 博愛者 Pŏ-GAE-CHAY.

―― See 心 SIN. 新增養心神詩 *Sin tsăng yang sin shin she.* "Hymns." . . [. . Compiled by W. M.], &c.　　　　　　　　　8°.

MILNER (THOMAS), *M.A.*

大英國志 *Ta Ying kwŏ che.* "The History of England." With a Chapter on the English Constitution from 'Chambers' Information for the People.' Translated into Chinese by Moo Wei-leen [*i.e.* William Muirhead]. 8 keuen.
　　　　　　　　　Shanghae, 1856. 8°.

閔承詔 MIN CHING-CHAOU.

See 王肯堂 WANG KĂNG-TANG. 女科證治準繩 *New ko ching che chun shing.* "A Treatise on the Cure of Diseases peculiar to Females." . . Edited by Min Ching-chaou, &c.　1607. 8°.

閔景賢 MIN KING-HEEN.

快書 *Kwae shoo.* "A Book of Amusement." A Collection of Fifty Short Works by as many Authors. Compiled by Min King-heen. Edited by Ho Wei-jen. 50 keuen.　1626. 8°.

閔麟嗣 MIN LIN-SZE.

古國都今郡縣合考 *Koo kwŏ too kin keun heen hŏ kaou.* "An Examination of the Ancient and Modern Names of Districts and Cities." [Also] 周末列國有今郡縣考 *Chow wei Lĕĕ kwŏ yew kin keun heen kaou.* "An Examination of the Names of Districts and Cities during the Chow and Lĕĕ kwŏ Periods and of the Names at the Present Time." *See* 張山來 CHANG SHAN-LAE, and 張進也 CHANG TSIN-YAY. 昭代叢書 *Chaou tae tsung shoo.* "A Collection of Reprints of Works written by Authors under the present Dynasty," &c. Keuen 22, 23.　　　　1703. 8°.

閔明我 MIN MING-WO.

See 利類思 LE LUY-SZE. 超性學要 *Chaou sing heŏ yaou.* "An Epitome of the Theology" of Thomas Aquinas. . . . Edited by Min Ming-wo, &c.　　　　　　　　8°.

命 MING.

知命錄 *Che ming lüh.* "A Glance into Fate." *See* 說 SHWŎ. 說淵 *Shwŏ yuen.* "A Collection of Tales," &c. Vol. 9.　　8°.

―― 三命通會 *San ming tung hwuy.* "A Complete Work on the Three Fates." By the 'Man of the Yŭh-woo Mountain.' ? keuen.
　　　　　　　　　[1750 ?]. 8°.
Imperfect, containing only keuen 2, 4–9.

名臣 MING CHIN.

欽定名臣傳 *Kin ting ming chin chuen.* "A Biographical Dictionary of Celebrated Ministers. Published by Imperial Order." In Two Parts, the first of which relates to Mantchoo, and the second to Chinese Ministers. Part I. 48 keuen. Part II. 32 keuen.　　[1750 ?]. 8°.

明珠 MING CHOO.

明珠記 *Ming choo ke.* "The Story of Sparkling Pearls." *See* 曲 KEŬH. 六十種曲 *Lŭh shĭh chung keŭh.* "Sixty Plays," &c. Taou 2. 8°.

MING DYNASTY.

大明會典 *Ta Ming hwuy teen.* "A Comprehensive View of the System of Government under the Ming Dynasty." Compiled by Imperial Order. 228 keuen.　　1585. 8°.

Another copy.

鳴鳳 MING FUNG.

鳴鳳記 *Ming Fung ke.* "The Story of the Singing Fung." *See* 曲 KEŬH. 六十種曲 *Lŭh shĭh chung keŭh.* "Sixty Plays," &c. Taou 4.　　　　　　　　　　　8°.

莫晉 Mŏ TSIN.

See 宋如林 SUNG JOO-LIN. 松江府志 *Sung-keang foo che.* "A Topography of Sung-keang Foo." Compiled by . . Mŏ Tsin, &c. 1817. 8°.

―― 江蘇試牘存眞 *Keang-soo she tŭh tsun chin.* "Keang-soo Examination Essays." Edited by Mŏ Tsin.　　　　　　1806. 8°.

―― 試牘存眞續編 *Shĭh tŭh tsun chin sŭh peen.* "A Supplementary Collection of Examination Essays." Edited by Mŏ Tsin. [1810 ?]. 8°.

Another copy.

MONCRIEFF (EDWARD T. R.).

A Treatise on Arithmetic in the Chinese Language. By the Rev. E. T. R. M. *Hongkong*, 1853. 8°.

The work has also the following Chinese title, 算法全書 *Swan fä tseuen shoo.* "A Complete Work on Arithmetic."

聶維廉 Moo WEI-LEEN [*i.e.* Rev. William Muirhead].

See MILNER (THOMAS), *M.A.* 大英國志 *Ta Ying kwŏ che.* "The History of England." Translated into Chinese by Moo Wei-leen, &c. 8°.

—— 地理全志 *Te le tseuen che.* "An Universal Geography." 10 keuen. *Shanghae*, 1854. 8°.

With Table of Contents in English.

聶益生 Moo YÏH-SÄNG.

See 孫端人 SUN TWAN-JIN. 昭明選詩初學讀本 *Chaou ming seuen she choo heŏ tŭh pun.* "A Selection of Brilliant Poems for the Instruction of Students." ... Edited by Mow Yĭh-säng, &c. 8°.

母 Moo.

母諫心田 *Moo keen sin teen.* "A Mother's Advice to her Daughters." [1850?]. 8°.

MORRISON (ROBERT), *D.D.*

See BIBLE. NEW TESTAMENT. 救世主耶穌新遺詔書 *Kew she choo Yay-soo sin e chaou shoo.* [Translated into Chinese by R. M.], &c. 1836. 8°.

—— 我等救世主耶穌新遺詔書 *Wo tăng kew she choo Yay-soo sin e chaou shoo.* [Translated into Chinese by R. M.] *Malacca.* 8°.

—— *John, Gospel of.* 若翰傳福音之書 *Jŏ-han chuen fŭh yin che shoo.* [Translated into Chinese by R. M.] 8°.

—— See ENGLAND, CHURCH OF. *Homilies.* 勸讀聖錄勸知文 *Keuen tŭh shing lŭh jĕ che wăn.* ... "The First Homily of the Church of England," translated into Chinese by R. M. 8°.

—— See 如氐亞 JOO TE A. 古時如氐亞國歷代畧傳 *Koo she Joo te a kwŏ lcĭh tae leŏ chuen.* "A Short History of Ancient Judea." [By R. M.], &c. 8°.

MORRISON (ROBERT), *D.D.* (*Continued.*)

See LITURGIES. *England, Church of.* 年中每日早晚祈禱敍式 *Neen chung mei jĭh tsaou wan ke taou seu shĭh.* "The Morning and Evening Prayers." ... Translated into Chinese by R. M., &c. 8°.

—— 英吉利國神會祈禱文大概翻譯漢子 *Ying-keĭh-le kwŏ shin hwuy ke taou wăn ta kae fan yĭh Han tsze.* "The United Prayers and Supplications to God of the English Nation." .. By ... R. M., &c. 1829. 8°.

—— See 馬 MA.

—— See 神天 SHIN TEEN. 神天道碎集傳 *Shin teen taou suy tseĭh chuen.* "Short Dissertations on the Heavenly Doctrine." [By R. M.], &c. 8°.

—— See 心 SIN. 養心神詩 *Yang sin shin she.* "Hymns." .. [By R. M.], &c. 8°.

—— See 地球 TE KEW. 西遊地球聞見畧傳 *Se yew te kew wăn keen leŏ chuen.* "A Short Account of a Tour round the World." [By R. M.], &c. 8°.

—— See 耶穌教 YAY-SOO KEAOU. 問答淺註耶穌教法 *Wăn tă tseen choo Yay-soo keaou fă.* "A Catechism explanatory of the Doctrines of the Christian Religion." [By R. M.], &c. 8°.

牡丹亭 Mow TAN TING.

牡丹亭 *Mow tan ting.* "The Story of the Pæania Moutan Portico." See 曲 KEŬH. 六十種曲 *Lŭh shĭh chung keŭh.* "Sixty Plays," &c. Taou 4. 8°.

牟目源 Mow MŬH-YUEN.

See 老君 LAOU KEUN. 道德經釋義 *Taou Tĭh king shĭh e.* "The Classic of Reason and Virtue Explained." .. Edited by Mow Mŭh-yuen, &c. 1809. 8°.

—— See 呂嵒 LEU YEN. 金玉經 *Kin yŭh king.* "The Golden Jade Classic." ... Edited by Mow Mŭh-yuen, &c. 1809. 8°.

—— 常清靜經 *Chang tsing tsing king.* "The Classic of Perpetual Purity and Peace." A Taouist Work." Edited by Mow Mŭh-yuen. 1809. 8°.

Another copy.

第一卷

牧童 Mŭh tung.

戒牛圖牧童歌 *Keae new too mŭh tung kŏ.*
"An Admonition to Herd-boys. A Song," the
words of which are made to form the outlines
of the Buffalo and the Boy.

Canton, [1800 ?]. A sheet.

牧類思羅 Mŭh-luy-sze-lo [*i.e.*

愼思指南 *Shin sze che nan.* "A Guide to
Serious Thought." Edited by Mŭh-luy-sze-lo.
6 keuen. 1844. 8°.

穆 Mŭh.

獨孤穆傳 *Tŭh koo Mŭh chuen.* "The Story
of the Orphan Mŭh." *See* 說 Shwŏ. 說淵
Shwŏ yuen. "A Collection of Tales," &c. Vol.
5. 8°.

穆春 Mŭh Tae.

See 伊把漢 E Pa-han. 盛京通志 *Shing
king tung che.* "A Topography of the ..
Province of Moukden." Compiled by ... Mŭh
Tae, &c. 1684. 8°.

目蓮 Mŭh-leen.

挑經救母目蓮全本 *Tseaou king kew moo
Mŭh-leen tseuen pun.* "The Story of Mŭh-leen."
A Drama. 2 keuen. [1850 ?]. 8°.

睦仁蒨 Mŭh Jin-tseen.

睦仁蒨傳 *Mŭh Jin-tseen chuen.* "The Story
of Mŭh Jin-tseen." *See* 說 Shwŏ. 說淵
Shwŏ yuen. "A Collection of Tales," &c. Vol. 7.
8°.

MUIRHEAD (William), *Rev.*

See 靈 Ling. 救靈先路 *Kew ling seen loo.*
"The Road to Salvation." [By W. M.], &c.
1857. 8°.

—— *See* 慕維廉 Moo-wei-leen.

—— *See* 天 Teen. 天人異同 *Teen jin e tung.*
"The Analogy between Religion and Philosophy." Translated by Rev. W. M., &c.
1857. 8°.

門 Mun.

進小門走窄路解論 *Tsin seaou mun tsow
chae loo keae lun.* "A Discourse on the Direction
to Enter in at the Straight Gate and to Walk in
the Narrow Way" [by the Rev. William Milne,
D.D.]. [1850 ?]. 8°.

Another copy.

夢 Mung.

夢遊錄 *Mung yew lŭh.* "Stories of Dreams."
See 說 Shwŏ. 說淵 *Shwŏ yuen.* "A Collection of Tales," &c. Vol. 1. 8°.

夢梅 Mung Mei.

正德遊江南全傳 *Ching Tĭh yew Keang nan
tseuen chuen.* "The Journies of the Emperor
Ching-Tĭh in Keang-nan." With Illustrations.
An Historical Novel. Edited by Mung Mei.
1842. 8°.

This work has been translated into English under the
supervision of Dr. Legge.

—— 梁太師江南訪主 *Leang tae sze Keang nan
fang choo.* "The Search of the Imperial Guardian Leang for the Emperor in Keang-nan."
By Mung Mei. 4 keuen. 1849. 8°.

蒙齋 Mung chae.

蒙齋筆談 *Mung chae peĭh tan.* "Jottings from
the Study of a Dullard." *See* 說 Shwŏ. 說畧
Shwŏ leŏ. "Historical and other Tracts," &c. 8°.

蒙正 Mung-ching.

蒙正全本秀毬記 *Mung ching tseuen pun
Sew kew ke.* "The Story of Mung-ching, or the
Silken Ball." A Drama. 5 keuen. [1850 ?]. 8°.

南卓 Nan Chŏ.

羯鼓錄 *Kĕĕ koo lŭh.* "A Treatise on Beating
the Drum." *See* 王文誥 Wang Wăn-kaou.
唐代叢書 *Tang tae tsung shoo.* "A Collection of Reprints of Works written during the
Tang Dynasty," &c. Series 4. 1806. 8°.

南軒 Nan Heen [*i.e.* 張宣公 Chang Seuen kung?].

南軒先生文集 *Nan Heen Seen sŭng wăn tseĭh.*
"A Collection of the Works of Nan Heen Seen
săng." Edited by Chang Shun. 44 keuen.
[1750 ?]. 8°.

南雄 Nan heung.

南雄珠璣巷來歷故事 *Nan heung choo ke
heang lae leĭh koo sze.* "The Story of Choo-ke
Lane in Nan-heung." [1850 ?]. 8°.

南柯 Nan-ko.

南柯夢 *Nan ko mung.* "A Dream of Nan-ko."
See 曲 Keŭh. 六十種曲 *Lŭh shĭh chung
keŭh.* "Sixty Plays," &c. Taou 2. 8°.

南懷仁 NAN HWAE-JIN. *pseud. i.e.* [Ferdinand Verbiest].
See 郭居靜 KŎ KEU-TSING. 天主聖教日課 *Teen choo shing keaou jĭh ko.* "Daily Christian Religious Exercises." Edited . . by . . Nan Hwae-jin, &c. 8°.

—— 坤輿外記 *Kwăn yu wae ke.* "Records of Natural Curiosities." *See* 說 SHWŎ. 說鈴 *Shwŏ ling.* "Miscellaneous Records," &c. 8°.

—— 教要序論 *Keaou yaou seu lun.* "A General Outline of the Doctrines of the Church of Rome, including Expositions of the Ten Commandments, the Lord's Prayer, and the Apostle's Creed." 1850. 8°.

鄴侯 NËË HOW.
鄴侯外傳 *Nëë how wae chuen.* "The Story of the Earl of Nëĕ." *See* 說 SHWŎ. 說淵 *Shwŏ yuen.* "A Collection of Tales," &c. Vol. 4. 8°.

聶伯多 NËË PĬH-TO.
See 艾儒略 GAE JOO-LEŎ. 天主降生言行紀像 *Teen choo keang săng yen hing ke seang.* "An Illustrated Life of Christ." . . . Edited by . . . Nëĕ Pĭh-to, &c. 8°.

聶崇義 NËË TSUNG-E.
See 陳伯廣 CHIN PĬH-KWANG. 三禮圖 *San le too.* "Illustrations of the Vessels, . . . &c., referred to in the Three Rituals." With a Collection of Comments compiled by Nëĕ Tsung-e, &c. 8°.

聶隱娘 NËË YIN-NEANG.
聶隱娘傳 *Nëë Yin-neang chuen.* "The Story of Nëĕ Yin-neang," *See* 說 SHWŎ. 說淵 *Shwŏ yuen.* "A Collection of Tales," &c. Vol. 7. 8°.

女 NEU.
女才子傳 *Neu tsae tsze chuen.* "Tales of Talented Women." By 'The Dissipated Man of Yen-shwuy.' 10 keuen. [1800?]. 8°.

—— 新賭仔賣女 *Sin too tsze mae neu.* "The Story of a Gambler who Sold his Wife." 2 keuen. [1850?]. 8°.

牛嶠 NEW KEAOU.
靈怪錄 *Ling kwae lŭh.* "Strange Ghost Stories." *See* 王文誥 WANG WĂN-KAOU. 唐代叢書 *Tang tae tsung shoo.* "A Collection of Reprints of Works written during the Tang Dynasty," &c. Series 6. 1806. 8°.

牛鈕 NEW NEW.
See 易經 YĬH KING. 日講易經解義 *Jĭh keang Yih king keae e.* "The Book of Changes, with a Paraphrase." . . Compiled by . . . New New, &c. 1688. 8°.

牛僧孺 NEW TSĂNG-JOO.
幽怪錄 *Yew kwae lŭh.* "A Short Record of Wonders and Monstrosities." By New Tsăng-joo, of the Tang Dynasty. A Reprint. [1741?]. 8°.

NINGPO.
[A Collection of Permits granted to Foreign Vessels trading with Ningpo, issued by the Magistrate of the District of Fung-hwa, during the Years 1831, 1836–1840.] 1840. 8°.

寧波 NING-PO.
寧波會館規條 *Ning-po hwuy kwan kwei teaou.* "Rules of the Ningpo Club," at Peking. 1795. 8°.

—— 體仁局覈實錄 *Te jin keu hĭh shĭh lŭh.* "Report of the Ningpo Practical Benevolent Institution" for the Year 1835. 1836. 8°.

NOËL (FRANÇOIS JOSEPH MICHEL) and CHAPSAL (CHARLES PIERRE).
法國話規 Grammaire Française, copiée presque entièrement sur celle de Noël et Chapsal, avec la traduction chinoise par un Missionaire Lazariste de Pekin. *Pekin,* 1864. 8°.

訥親 NŬH TSIN.
See CHINA. BOARD OF OFFICE. 欽定吏部則例 *Kin ting Le Poo tsĭh le.* "Regulations of the Board of Office." Compiled by . . . Nŭh Tsin, &c. 1741. 8°.

煖堂 NWAN TANG.
食煖堂飯四句 *Shĭh Nwan tang fan sze keu.* "Rhymes for a Marriage Feast." [*Canton,* 1850?]. 8°.
Another copy.

巴 西 侯 PA-SE HOW.

巴 西 侯 傳 *Pa-se How chuen.* "The Story of a Pa-se Noble." *See* 說 SHWŏ. 說 淵 *Shwŏ yuen.* "A Collection of Tales," &c. Vol. 9. 8°.

八 識 PĂ SHĬH.

八 識 略 說 *Pă shĭh leŏ shwŏ.* "A Short Treatise on the Eight Vijñânas," or Perceptions. A Buddhist Work by 'The Old Man of Mount Sŏ-han.' 1792. 8°.

班 固 PAN KOO.

白 虎 通 *Pĭh hoo tung.* The Report of a "Convocation held in the Pĭh-hoo Kwan." *See* 沈 津 CHIN TSIN. 百 家 類 纂 *Pĭh kea luy tswan.* "The Works of a Hundred Authors," &c. Keuen 36. 8°.

—— 前 漢 書 *Tseen Han shoo.* "The History of the Former Han Dynasty." With a Commentary by Yen Sze-koo. 120 keuen. *See* 毛 晉 MAOU TSIN. 十 七 史 *Shĭh tseĭh she.* "The Seventeen Histories," &c. 1656. 8°.

—— See 斌 倚 平 PIN E-PING. 文 選 集 腋 *Wăn seuen tseĭh yĭh.* "Selected Literary Expressions" .... from the Works of .... Pan Koo, &c. 1813. 8°.

—— 兩 都 賦 *Leang Too foo.* "Odes on the Two Capitals." *See* 蕭 統 SEAOU TUNG. 文 選 *Wăn seuen.* "Elegant Extracts from Polite Literature," &c. Keuen 1. 1772. 8°.

—— 漢 武 故 事 *Han Woo koo sze.* "History of Events in the Reign of the Emperor Woo, of the Han Dynasty." *See* 說 SHWŏ. 說 纂 *Shwŏ tswan.* "Miscellaneous Records," &c. Vol. 1. 8°.

—— 漢 武 帝 內 傳 *Han Woo te nuy chuen.* "An Account (of the Visit of Se Wang Moo) to the Emperor Woo te, of the Han Dynasty." [1800?]. 8°.

—— 白 虎 通 *Pĭh hoo tung.* The Report of a "Convocation of Literary Men held in a Chamber of the Palace called the Pĭh-hoo kwan," for the purpose of definitely expressing their views regarding various points in the Classics. Compiled by Pan Koo. Edited by Wang Sze-han. 2 keuen. 1668. 8°.

班 固 PAN KOO. *(Continued.)*
Another edition. Edited by Wang Taou. A Reprint. 4 keuen. [1700?]. 8°.

Another edition. Edited by Chaou E-lun. 4 keuen. [1700?]. 8°.

—— 前 漢 書 *Tseen Han shoo.* "The History of the Former Han Dynasty." Edited by Chin Jin-seĭh. 100 keuen. 1632. 8°.
Imperfect copy, containing only keuen 1–20.

Another edition. With a Commentary by Yen Sze-koo. [120?] keuen. 1642. 8°.
Imperfect, containing only keuen 6–15.

攀 桂 PAN KWEI.

攀 桂 集 *Pan kwei tseĭh.* "The Graduates' Collection of Essays." [1800?]. 8°.
Imperfect.

般 剌 密 帝 PAN-LĂ-MEĬH-TE [*i.e.* Paramiti].

楞 嚴 經 *Lăng yen king.* "The Certain and Firm Sûtra." Translated into Chinese by Pan-lă-meĭh-te, with Interpretorial Notes by Me-kea-`shĭh-kea. 10 keuen. *Canton*, 1800. 8°.

—— 楞 嚴 經 集 註 *Lăng yen king tseĭh choo.* "The Certain and Firm Sûtra." Translated into Chinese by Pan-lă-meĭh-te. With Interpretorial Notes by Me-kea-shĭh-kea, and "with a Collection of Comments" compiled by Chuen-shing. 10 keuen. 1738. 8°.

—— 楞 嚴 正 脈 *Lăng yen ching mĭh.* "The Correct Pulse of the Certain and Firm Sûtra." By Keaou-kwang-chin-keen. Edited by Meaou-fung-fŭh-tang. With the original Chinese Text into which it was translated by Pan-lă-meĭh-te. A Reprint. 10 keuen. 1633. 8°.

龐 廸 我 PANG TEĬH-WO [*i.e.*　　　　], and 陽 瑪 諾 YANG-MA-Nŏ [*i.e.* Emmanuel Diaz].

天 主 耶 穌 受 難 始 末 *Teen choo Yay-soo show nan che wei.* "The Sufferings of Christ." *See* 部 居 靜 Kŏ KEU-TSING. 天 主 聖 教 日 課 *Teen choo shing keaou jĭh ko.* "Daily Christian Religious Exercises," &c. Keuen 3. 8°.

21

龐 元 英 PANG YUEN-YING.

談 藪 *Tan sow.* "Conversational Jottings." *See* 說 SHWǑ. 說 畧 *Shwŏ leŏ.* "Historical and other Tracts," &c.   8º.

彭 曉 PĂNG HEAOU.

See 涵 蟾 子 HAN CHEN-TSZE. 金 丹 正 理 大 要 道 書 全 集 *Kin tan ching le ta yaou taou shoo tseuen tseïh.* "A Complete Collection of Important Taouist Works on the True Principle of the Elixir of Immortality." . . With Commentaries by Păng Heaou, &c. 1538. 8º.

彭 時 PĂNG SHE.

See 李 賢 LE HEEN. 一 統 志 *Yĭh tung che.* "A Geography of the Empire." Compiled by . . Păng She, &c.   8º.

彭 好 古 PĂNG HAOU-KOO.

道 言 內 外 秘 訣 全 書 *Taou yen nuy wae pe keuĕ tseuen shoo.* "A Complete Collection of Taouist Works." Compiled by Păng Haou-koo. In Two Parts. Part I. 3 keuen. Part II. 3 keuen.   [1777?]. 8º.

彭 希 涑 PĂNG HE-SĬH.

二 十 二 史 感 應 錄 *Urh shĭh urh she kan ying lüh.* "Instances of Retributive Rewards and Punishments drawn from the Twenty-two Histories." 2 keuen. *See* 葉 志 詵 YĔ CHE-SIN. 海 山 仙 館 叢 書 *Hae shan seen Kwan tsung shoo.* "The Hae-shan-seen Kwan Collection of Reprints," &c. Vol. 20.   1848. 8º.

—— 二 十 二 史 感 應 錄 *Urh shĭh urh she kan ying lüh.* "Instances of Retributive Rewards and Punishments drawn from the Twenty-two Histories." 2 keuen.   1826. 8º.

彭 人 傑 PĂNG JIN-KĔĔ.

東 莞 縣 志 *Tung kwan heen che.* "A Topography of Tung-kwan Heen," in the Province of Canton. A New and Revised Edition. Compiled by Păng Jin-kĕĕ, Fan Wăn-gan, Hwang She-poo, and others. 46 keuen. 1797. 8º.

彭 際 清 PANG TSE-TSING.

淨 土 三 經 *Tsing too san king.* "The Three Sûtras of the Pure Regions of Bliss," viz.: the *Fŭh shwŏ woo leang show king,* translated into Chinese by Tsăng Kae; the *Fŭh shwŏ O-me-to king,* translated by Kew-mo-lo-shĭh, *i.e.* Kumâragîva; and the *Fŭh shwŏ kwan woo leang show Fŭh king,* translated by Keang-leang-yay-shay, *i.e.* Kalayaças. Edited by Păng Tse-tsing. 4 Vol.   1797. Oblong.

彭 芸 楣 PĂNG YUN-MEI.

宋 四 六 話 *Sung sze lŭh hwa.* "Criticisms on some Portions of the Literature of the Sung Dynasty." 12 keuen. *See* 葉 志 詵 YĔ CHE-SIN. 海 山 仙 館 叢 書 *Hae shan seen Kwan tsung shoo.* "The Hae-shan-seen Kwan Collection of Reprints," &c. Vol. 77-80. 1848. 8º.

包 PAOU.

See 四 書 SZE SHOO. 論 語 註 疏 大 全 合 纂 *Lun yu choo soo ta tseuen hŏ tswan.* "The Confucian Analects." With Commentaries by Paou, &c.   1636. 8º.

包 爾 庚 PAOU URH-KANG.

稿 *Kaou.* "Essays." *See* 長 城 CHANG CHING. 名 家 制 義 *Ming kea che e.* "Essays" on Texts from the Four Books, &c. Tsĭh 95.   1699. 8º.

鮑 桂 星 PAOU KWEI-SING.

鮑 覺 生 時 文 *Paou Keŏ-săng she wăn.* "Occasional Essays."   8º.

鮑 相 璈 PAOU SEANG-GAOU.

驗 方 新 編 *Yen fang sin peen.* "A New Series of Approved Medical Prescriptions." 8 keuen.   1856. 8º.

寶 應 PAOU-YING.

寶 應 錄 *Paou-ying lüh.* "A Record of the Reign of the Emperor Paou-ying." *See* 說 SHWǑ. 說 淵 *Shwŏ yuen.* "A Collection of Tales," &c. Vol. 9.   8º.

PARAMITI.

See 般 刺 密 帝 PAN-LĂ-MEÏH-TE.

PAUTHIER (Guillaume).

See LAOU KEUN. 道 德 經 *Le Tao-Tc-king.* . . . Traduit en Français . . . by G. P. 1838. 8º.

蹴 呢 PE-CHIN [*i.e.* Dr. Pearson].

See 哆 哷 哎 CHAY-LAN-LIN. 嘆 咭 唎 國 新 種 痘 奇 書 *Ying keĭh le kĭcŏ sin chung tow ke shoo.* "A Pamphlet on the English System of Vaccination." ... Edited by Pe-chin, &c.
      1805. 8°.

蚍 蜉 PE FOO.

蚍 蜉 傳 *Pe-foo chuen.* "A Story of Ants." *See* 說 SHWŎ. 說 淵 *Shwŏ yuen.* "A Collection of Tales," &c. Vol. 4.   8°.

琵 琶 PE PA.

琵 琶 記 *Pe pa ke.* "The Story of a Lute." *See* 曲 KEŬH. 六 十 種 曲 *Lŭh shĭh chung keŭh.* "Sixty Plays," &c. Taou 1.   8°.

PEARSON (   ), *M.D.*

See 蹴 呢 PE-CHIN.

編 PEEN.

指 迷 編 *Che me peen.* "A Tract against the Stupefying" Vice of Opium Smoking. By Robert Cobbold, who styles himself Wang-heŭh choo-jin.   *Shanghae,* 1857. 8°.

辯 機 PEEN-KE.

See 玄 奘 HEUEN-TSANG. 大 唐 西 域 記 *Ta Tang se yĭh ke.* "An Account of the Western Frontiers of the Empire." ... Edited by Peen-ke, &c.   &c. 8°.

邊 祚 游 PEEN TSOO-YEW.

See 王 通 WANG TUNG. 中 說 *Chung shwŏ.* "Central Discourses." ... Edited by Peen Tsoo-yew, &c.   8°.

裴 駰 PEI YIN.

史 記 *She ke.* "The Historical Record." With a Commentary by Pei Yin, &c. [*Also*] 三 國 志 *San kwŏ che.* "The History of the Three Kingdoms." With a Commentary by Pei Yin, &c. *See* 毛 晉 MAOU TSIN. 十 七 史 *Shĭh tseĭh she.* "The Seventeen Histories," &c. 1656. 8°.

—— See 司 馬 遷 SZE-MA TSEEN. 史 記 *She ke.* "The Historical Record." With a Commentary by Pei Yin, &c.   1640. 8°.

甓 PEĬH.

運 甓 記 *Yun peĭh ke.* "Removing the Bricks." *See* 曲 KEŬH. 六 十 種 曲 *Lŭh shĭh chung keŭh.* "Sixty Plays," &c. Taou 3.   8°.

畢 沅 PEĬH YUEN.

山 海 經 *Shan hae king.* "The Hill and River Classic." Edited by Peĭh Yuen. With Kŏ Pŏ's Commentary. 18 keuen.   1783. 8°.

畢 方 濟 PEĬH FANG-TSE. *pseud.* [*i.e.* Francis Sambiasi].

靈 言 蠡 勺 *Ling yen le chŏ.* "A Work on the Soul." Transcribed by Seu Kwang-ke. 2 keuen ?   [1750 ?]. 8°.

Imperfect, containing only the first keuen.

辟 PEĬH.

復 辟 錄 *Fŭh Peĭh lŭh.* "An Account of the Re-appearance of the Emperor" King-tae, after an Illness. *See* 說 SHWŎ. 說 纂 *Shwŏ tswan.* "Miscellaneous Records," &c. Vol. 9.   8°.

碧 湖 PEĬH HOO.

碧 湖 雜 記 *Peĭh Hoo tsă ke.* "Miscellaneous Records of Peĭh Hoo." *See* 說 SHWŎ. 說 畧 *Shwŏ leŏ.* "Historical and other Tracts," &c. 8°.

碧 容 PEĬH YUNG.

碧 容 祭 監 *Peĭh yung tse keen.* "Peĭh yung Sacrificing in Prison." A Drama. 2 keuen.
      [1840 ?]. 8°.

璧 星 泉 PEĬH SING-TSEUEN.

See 徐 繼 畬 SEU KE-YU. 瀛 環 志 畧 *Ying hwan che leŏ.* "A Geographical Treatise on all within the Circuit of the Seas." Edited by Peĭh Sing-tseuen, &c.   1848. 8°.

PERIODICAL PUBLICATIONS.

[A Complete Official Directory of the Empire for the Year   ?] 4 Vol. [*Peking,* 1740 ?]. 8°.

First volume is wanting. Without either title-page or head title.

PERIODICAL PUBLICATIONS. (*Continued.*)

察世俗每月統記傳 *Chă she sŭh mei yŭĕ tung ke chuen.* "The Examiner. A Monthly Periodical." Edited by Po-gae-chay [*i.e.* Rev. William Milne]. 1815–1822. 8º.

Imperfect, containing only the numbers from the seventh month of 1815 to the ninth month of 1821, and the first three months of 1822.

Another copy.

Imperfect, containing only the number for the eighth month of 1815, and part of the vol. for the year 1821.

Another copy.

Imperfect. Only the numbers for the seventh to twelfth months of 1815; the fourth, sixth to ninth, eleventh, and twelfth months of 1820; and a supplementary vol.

—— 遐邇貫珍 *Hea urh kwan chin.* "A Serial of Foreign and Domestic News." [Edited by W. H. Medhurst, afterwards by C. B. Hillier, and then by James Legge.]
Hongkong, 1853–1855. 8º.

Very imperfect, containing only in Vol. I. No. 1–5, in Vol. II. No. 1–4, and in Vol. III. No. 1–12.

Another copy.

Imperfect, containing only in Vol. I. No. 2–5, and in Vol. III. No. 7.

—— 各國消息 *Kĭh kwŏ seaou seĭh.* "The News of the World." A Monthly Periodical.
Canton, 1838. 8º.

Imperfect, containing only the numbers for the ninth and tenth months of 1838.

—— 六合叢談 *Lŭh hŏ tsung tan.* "The Universal Miscellany." A Serial edited by Alexander Wylie. No. 1–13. *Shanghae,* 1857. 8º.

—— 大清袖珍搢紳全書 *Ta Tsing sew chin tsin shin tseuen shoo.* "A Complete Official Directory of the Empire" for the Year 1775. Pocket Edition. 4 Vol. [*Peking*], 1775. 8º.

—— 大清仕籍全編 *Ta Tsing sze tseĭh tseuen peen.* "A Complete Official Directory of the Empire" for the Year 1735. [4 Vol.?]
Peking, 1735. 8º.

Imperfect, containing only the first volume.

PERIODICAL PUBLICATIONS. (*Continued.*)

大清搢紳全書 *Ta Tsing tsin shin tseuen shoo.* "A Complete Official Directory of the Empire" for the Year 1835. 4 Vol.
[*Peking?*], 1835. 8º.

Imperfect.

—— 特選撮要每月紀傳 *Tĭh seuen tsŏ yaou mei yŭĕ ke chuen.* "A Monthly Magazine of Useful Information." Edited by Shang-tĭh-chay.
1823. 8º.

Imperfect, containing only the numbers for the sixth and eighth months of 1823.

—— 爵秩新本 *Tseŏ chĭh sin pun.* "A New List of the Officials of the Empire." [1750?]. 8º.

Imperfect.

—— 爵秩全覽 *Tseŏ chĭh tseuen lan.* "A Complete List of the Officials of the Empire" for the Year 1841. 1841. 8º.

—— 東西洋考每月統記傳 *Tung se yang kaou mei yŭĕ tung ke chuen.* "A Monthly Periodical of Foreign and Domestic News." Edited by Gae-han-chay, *i.e.* Rev. C. F. A. Guetzlaff.
1833–37. 8º.

Imperfect, containing only the numbers for the sixth and ninth months of 1833, the first six months of 1835, and the first four and the sixth months of 1837.

—— 英吉利每月雜記傳的通報 *Ying-keĭh-le mei yŭĕ tsă ke chuen teĭh tung paou.* "An English Monthly Magazine." Written in Chinese by Low-lang, Ma-keu-na, and Se-te-pin-yĭh. *London,* [1750?]. A sheet.

Only the Prospectus.

PIERCY (GEORGE).

See JOSEPH, *Poor.* 貧人約瑟 *Pin jin Yŏ-sih.* "An Account of the Conversion and Death of Poor Joseph." Translated into Chinese by G. Piercy, &c. 12º.

白蛇 PĬH SHAY.

白蛇記 *Pĭh shay ke.* "The Story of the White Serpent." *See* 說 SHWŎ. 說淵 *Shwŏ yuen.* "A Collection of Tales," &c. Vol. 9. 8º.

白兔 PĬH TOO.

白兔記 *Pĭh too ke.* "The White Hare." *See* 曲 KEŬH. 六十種曲 *Lŭh shĭh chung keŭh.* "Sixty Plays," &c. Taou 6.   8º.

白猨 PĬH YUEN.

白猨傳 *Pĭh yuen chuen.* "The Story of the White Monkey." By an anonymous Writer of the Tang Dynasty. A Reprint. [1741?]. 8º.

白行簡 PĬH HING-KEEN.

李娃傳 *Le Wa chuen.* "The Story of Le Wa." *See* 王文誥 WANG WĂN-KAOU. 唐代叢書 *Tang tae tsung shoo.* "A Collection of Reprints of Works written during the Tang Dynasty," &c. Series 5.   1806. 8º.

—— 李娃傳 *Le Wa chuen.* "The Story of Le Wa." By Pĭh Hing-keen, of the Tang Dynasty. A Reprint.   [1741?]. 8º.

—— 三夢記 *San mung ke.* "Three Dreams."   [1741?]. 8º.

白居易 PĬH KEU-E.

御製擬白居易新樂府 *Yu che e Pĭh Keu-e sin yŏ foo.* "An Imperial Edition of Pĭh Keu-e's Songs." 2 Vol.   [1800?]. 8º.

白羅衫 PĬH LO SHAN.

白羅衫全本 *Pĭh lo shan tseuen pun.* "The Story of the White Silk Jacket." In Verse. 4 keuen.   [1850?]. 8º.

百家 PĬH KEA.

百家姓法 *Pĭh kea sing fă.* "Information about the Family Names" of China.   [1800?]. 8º.

百慶 PĬH KING.

See CHINA. BOARD OF WAR. 欽定中樞政考 *Kin ting chung choo ching kaou.* "An Examination into the Fundamental System" of Governing the Army. Compiled by . . Pĭh King, &c.   1785. 8º.

柏應理 PĬH YING-LE.

See 利類思 LE LUY-SZE. 超性學要 *Chaou sing heŏ yaou.* "An Epitome of the Theology" of Thomas Aquinas. . . . Edited by Pĭh Ying-le, &c.   8º.

北宋 PĬH SUNG.

北宋志傳 *Pĭh Sung che chuen.* "The History of the Northern Sung Dynasty." A Historical Novel. Edited by 'The Woodman of the Yen-shĭh Mountain.' 10 keuen. [1800?]. 8º.

The first two keuen are wanting.

—— 北宋三遂平妖全傳 *Pĭh Sung san suy ping yaou tseuen chuen.* "The History of the Three Tranquilizing Fairies of the Northern Sung Dynasty." 10 keuen. [1800?]. 8º.

The first two keuen are wanting.

北斗 PĬH TOW.

北斗經 *Pĭh tow king.* "The Sûtra of the Deity Pĭh tow." A Reprint.   *Canton,* 1816. 8º.

—— 北斗九皇眞經 *Pĭh tow kew Hwang chin king.* "The True Sûtra of the Nine Emperors of the North Star."   *Foo-chow,* 1819. 8º.

斌倚平 PIN E-PING.

文選集腋 *Wăn seuen tseĭh yĭh.* "Selected Literary Expressions," arranged according to Subjects, from the Works of Pan Koo, Chang Hăng, Chin Yŏ, and others. Compiled by Pin E-ping and Fei Taou-pei, and edited by Wang Joo-shang. 6 keuen.   1813. 8º.

兵 PING.

八排走兵火毋女矢散 *Pă pae tsow ping ho moo neu shĭh san.* "A Story of the Separation of Mother and Daughter in the Confusion of Battle." A Dramatic Tale. 2 keuen. [*Canton?*], 1852. 8º.

平遠縣 PING-YUEN HEEN.

平遠縣志 *Ping-yuen heen che.* "A Topography of Ping-yuen Heen," in the Province of Kwang-tung. ? keuen.   [1780?]. 8º.

Imperfect, containing only the fourth keuen.

博明 PŎ MING.

See CHINA. 欽定中樞政考 *Kin ting chung choo ching kaou.* "An Examination into the Fundamental System" of Governing the Army. Compiled by . . Pŏ Ming, &c.   1785. 8º.

博愛者 Pŏ-GAE-CHAY. *pseud.* [*i.e.* Rev. William Milne, D.D.]

See BIBLE. 新增聖書節解 *Sin tsăng Shing shoo tsëĕ keae.* With a Commentary by Pŏ-gae-chay, &c. 1825. 8°.

—— See BIBLE. *Appendix.* 古今聖史紀集 *Koo kin shing she ke tseth.* "Extracts from Bible History." By Pŏ-gae-chay, &c. 8°.

—— See LORD'S PRAYER. 祈禱眞法註解 *Ke taou chin fă choo keae.* "The True Model of Prayer ... Commented on and Explained" by Pŏ-gae-chay, &c. 8°.

—— See PERIODICAL PUBLICATIONS. 察世俗每月統記傳 *Chă she sŭh mei yuĕ tung ke chuen:* "The Examiner." .. Edited by Pŏ-gae-chay, &c. 1815–1821. 8°.

—— 鄉訓五十二則 *Heang heun woo shĭh urh tsĕh.* "Fifty-two Village Sermons." 1820. 8°.
Containing only the first keuen.

Another edition. 1820. 8°.
Containing only the first keuen.

Another edition. *Ningpo*, 1845. 8°.
Containing only the first keuen.

—— 救世者言行眞史紀 *Kew she chay yen hing chin she ke.* "The Life of Christ."
[*Canton,* 1814 ?]. 8°.

—— 靈魂篇大全 *Ling hwăn peen ta tseuen.* "An Essay on the Soul." 2 keuen.
Malacca, 1825. 8°.

—— 三寶仁會論 *San paou jin hwuy lun.* "A Discourse about the Three Precious Benevolent Societies," viz.: the Missionary, the Tract, and the Bible Societies. [1835 ?]. 8°.

—— 生意公平聚益法 *Săng e kung ping tseu yĭh fă.* "A Tract on the Advantage of Honesty in Trade." [1847 ?]. 8°.

—— 上帝聖教公會門 *Shang-Te shing keaou kung hwuy mun.* "The Door of Admission to the Christian Church." 8°.

—— 聖書節註十二訓 *Shing shoo tsĕĕ choo shĭh urh heun.* "Twelve Sermons on as many Texts of Scripture." [1855 ?]. 8°.

博愛者 Pŏ-GAE-CHAY. *pseud.* [*i.e.* Rev. William Milne, D.D.] (*Continued.*)

受災學義論說 *Show chae heŏ e lun shwŏ.* "The Duty of Men in Times of Public Calamity." [*Malacca*], 1819. 8°.

—— 新纂靈魂篇大全 *Sin tswan ling hwăn peen ta tseuen.* "An Essay on the Soul." 2 Vol. *Malacca,* 1825. 8°.

—— 賭博明論畧講 *Too pŏ ming lun leŏ keang.* "A Tract on Gambling." [1845 ?]. 8°.

Another edition. [1850 ?]. 8°.

—— 進小門走窄路解論 *Tsin scaou mun tsow chae loo keae lun.* "A Discourse on the Direction to Enter in at the Straight Gate and to Walk in the Narrow Way." [1855 ?]. 8°.

—— 崇眞實棄假謊略說 *Tsung chin shĭh ke kea hwang leŏ shwŏ.* "A Tract on the Importance of Reverencing Truth and Abstaining from Lying." [1845 ?]. 8°.

A paper reprinted from the *Chă she sŭh,* or "The Examiner."

POINTS (JOHN TEVIS).
See EPHEMERIDES. 中外通書 *Chung wae tung shoo.* "A Chinese and Foreign Almanac," for the Year 1858. Compiled by J. T. P., &c. 1858. 8°.

普照 POO-CHAOU.
修心訣 *Sew sin keuĕ.* "Precepts for Regulating the Heart." A Buddhist Tract.
Canton, 1793. 8°.

普明 POO MING.
牧牛圖 *Mŭh new too.* "Tending the Cow. With Illustrations." A Buddhist Allegorical Work. Edited by Choo Hung. 1609. 8°.

Another copy.

普陀 POO TO.
南海勝境普陀山誌 *Nan hae shing chang Poo to shan che.* "A Descriptive Account of the Island of Poo-to," a renowned seat of Buddhism, lying a few miles east of the island of Chusan. [1700 ?]. 8°.
There are seven other copies of this work.

浦泰 Poo Tae.

See 四書 Sze shoo. 四書闡註 Sze shoo chen choo. "The Four Books clearly explained.".. Edited by Poo Tae, &c. 7 keuen. 1815. 8°.

蒲留仙 Poo Lew-seen.

聊齋志異 Leaou chae che e. "Curious Stories from a Careless Man's Study." 16 keuen.
Hăng-chow, 1765. 8°.

Another edition. Edited by Wang E-shang. 16 keuen. 1767. 8°.

本草 Pun tsaou.

大觀本草 Ta kwan Pun tsaou. "An Enlarged Survey of Medical Botany." ? keuen.
[1700?]. 8°.

Imperfect, containing only the second keuen.

蓬蒿子 Pung Haou-tsze.

順治皇過江全傳 Shun-che Hwang kwŏ keang tseuen chuen. "A Complete Account of the Journey of the Emperor Shun-che across the Yellow River." A Reprint. 4 keuen.
1849. 8°.

—— 新世鴻勳 Sin she hung heun. "The Great Loyalty displayed at the Foundation of the New Era," i.e. the Establishment of the Tsing Dynasty. 4 keuen. [1700?]. 8°.

潘相 Pwan Seang.

琉球入學見聞 Lew kew jŭh heŏ keen wăn. "An Account of the Lew kew Islands." By Pwan Seang, the Superintendent of the National Collegiate Institute for Loo-chooans. 4 keuen.
1764. 8°.

潘長吉 Pwan Chang-keïh.

宋稗類鈔 Sung pae luy chaou. "Miscellanies of the History of the Sung Dynasty." Compiled by Pwan Chang-keïh. Edited by Heung Ta-săng. 8 keuen. 1699. 8°.

潘正業 Pwan Ching-nĕĕ.

參証銀論 Tsan ching yin lun. "A Work on Testing Silver Coin." 1830. 8°.

—— 捷法算書 Tsĕĕ fă swan shoo. "A Ready Reckoner." 1830. 8°.

潘安仁 Pwan Gan-jin.

西征賦 Se ching foo. "An Ode on the Conquest of the West," and other Pieces. See 蕭統 Seaou Tung. 文選 Wăn seuen. "Elegant Extracts from Polite Literature," &c. Keuen 10.
1772. 8°.

潘海虞 Pwan Hae-yu.

與圖備攷 Yu too pe kaou. "A Treatise on Geography." An Enlarged and Revised Edition. Edited by Le Yun-seang. 18 keuen. 1650. 8°.

潘肇豐 Pwan Shaou-fung.

六書會原 Lŭh shoo hwuy yuen. "The Origin of the Six Kinds of Characters." Edited by Yĕ Choo-yen. 10 keuen. 1801. 8°.
Imperfect, only keuen 1, 2. Much torn.

潘肇基 Pwan Shaou-ke.

See 關帝 Kwan te, The God of War. 忠義經文 Chung e king wăn. "Canonical Works on Patriotism and Uprightness." ... Edited by Pwan Shaou-ke, &c. 1839. 8°.

潘世恩 Pwan She-găn.

策學新纂 Tsĭh heŏ sin tswan. "The Student's Manual. A New Edition." Compiled by Pwan She-găn. 8 keuen. 1816. 12°.
Imperfect, keuen 2 and 3 being wanting.

—— 策學大全 Tsĭh heŏ ta tseuen. "A Complete Student's Manual." Compiled by Pwan She-găn. 7 keuen. 1819. 12°.

潘仕成 Pwan Sze-ching.

顏氏家藏尺牘 Yen she kea tsang chĭh tŭh. "A Collection of Notes and Short Literary Pieces collected in the Yen Family." Edited by Pwan Sze-ching. 4 keuen. With an Appendix entitled Yen she kea tsang chĭh tŭh sing she kaou. See 葉志詵 Yĕ Che-sin. 海山仙館叢書 Hae shan seen Kwan tsung shoo. "The Hae-shan-seen Kwan Collection of Reprints," &c. Vol. 93–97.
1848. 8°.

潘子聲 Pwan Tsze-shing.

養蒙斜度 Yang mung chin too. "The Student's Guide" to the 'Four Books.' Compiled by Pwan Tsze-shing. 2 keuen. [1840?]. 8°.
First keuen wanting.

Another edition. Edited by Sun Tsang-peïh and Chin Shoo-che. 2 keuen. [1840?]. 8°.
Imperfect, wanting the first keuen.

潘 文 來 Pwan Wăn-lae.

See 易 經 Yĭh king. 周 易 廣 義 *Chow Yĭh kwang e.* "The Book of Changes." .. Compiled by Pwan Wăn-lae, &c.　　1672.　8°.

潘 友 碩 Pwan Yew-chĭh.

See 易 經 Yĭh king. 周 易 廣 義 *Chow Yĭh kwang e.* "The Book of Changes." .. Compiled by Pwan Yew-chĭh," &c.　1672.　8°.

QUARTERMAN (J. W.), *Rev.*

See Euclid. 幾 何 原 本 *Ke ho yuen pun.* Euclid's "Elements of Geometry." .. Edited by Rev. J. W. Q., &c.　　1852.　8°.

REID (　　　　), *Colonel.*

See Macgowan (D. J.), *M.D.* 航 海 金 針 *Hang hae kin chin.* "The Navigator's Golden Needle." A Work based on the Chapter on Typhoons of the China Seas in Col. Reid's Work, &c.
1853.　8°.

RICCI (Matteo).

See Euclid. 幾 何 原 本 *Ke ho yuen pun.* Euclid's "Elements of Geometry." Translated by M. R., &c.　　　　1852.　8°.

ROBERTS (Issachar Jacox).

See 問 答 Wăn tă. 問 答 俗 話 *Wăn tă sŭh hwa.* "A Catechism." .. [By I. J. R.], &c. 8°.

RUSSIA. Alexander II., *Emperor.*

See Great Britain and Ireland. Victoria, *Queen.* 奏 准 天 律 新 議 通 商 條 欵 *Tsow chun Teen tsin sin e tung shang teaou kwăn.* "The New Commercial Treaties of Tientsin," contracted between .. Russia and China, &c.
1860.　8°.

薩 迦 阿 Să Ying-ah.

See China. Board of Ceremonies. 欽 定 禮 部 則 例 *Kin ting Le Poo tsĭh le.* "Regulations of the Board of Ceremonies." Compiled by .. Să Ying-ah, &c.　　1820.　8°.

三 朝 San chaou.

三 朝 野 史 *San chaou yay she.* "Legends of the Three Dynasties." *See* 說 Shwŏ. 說 畧 *Shwŏ lŏ.* "Historical and other Tracts," &c.　　8°.

三 界 San keae.

三 界 萬 靈 聖 燈 *San keae wan ling shing tăng.* "The Ten Thousand Spiritual and Sacred Lamps of the Heaven, the Earth, and the Waters." A Taouist Ritual.　　[1800 ?].　8°.

三 敎 San keaou.

三 敎 源 流 聖 帝 佛 師 搜 神 記 *San keaou yuen lew Shing te Fŭh Sze sow shin ke.* "A History of the Founders of the Three Sects, *i.e.* Confucianism, Buddhism, and Taouism, and of other Saints and Sages."　1819.　8°.

This vol. contains only the portraits of the saints and sages referred to in the work.

三 山 San shan.

三 山 文 小 題 *San shan wăn seaou te.* "Essays from the 'Three Mountains.'" First Series.
[1800 ?].　8°.

Imperfect.

三 泰 San tae.

See China. 督 捕 則 例 *Too poo tsĭh le.* "Regulations concerning the Capture" of Deserters. Compiled by ... San Tae, &c.　1743.　8°.

—— See Tsing Dynasty. 大 清 律 例 *Ta Tsing leŭh le.* "The Fundamental Laws and Subordinate Statutes of the Tsing Dynasty." Compiled by ... San Tae, &c.　　1768.　8°.

三 元 San yuen.

三 元 記 *San yuen ke.* "The Story of the Three Original Ones." *See* 曲 Keŭh. 六 十 種 曲 *Lŭh shĭh chung keŭh.* "Sixty Plays," &c. Taou 4.
8°.

桑 欽 Sang Kin.

水 經 *Shwuy king.* "The Water Classic." A Description of the Watercourses of the Empire. By Sang Kin, of the Han Dynasty. Edited by Heu Heŭh-hwuy. 2 keuen.　[1750 ?].　8°.

Another edition. With a Commentary by Le Taouyuen.　　　　1750.　8°.

Wanting the title-page and the third, fourth, and fifth keuen.

Another edition. With a Commentary by Le Taouyuen. Edited by Ke Yun and others. 40 keuen.
1774.　8°.

The title-page is wanting.

桑 欽 SANG KIN. (*Continued.*)
Another edition. Commented on and Explained by
Chaou Yĭh-tsing. 40 keuen.   1786. 8°.

桑 世 昌 SĂNG SHE-CHANG.
回 文 類 聚 *Hwuy wăn luy tseu.* "A Collection
of Literary Puzzles." In Two Parts. Compiled by Săng She-chang and Choo Seang-heen.
Part I. 4 keuen. Part II. 10 keuen.
                              [1750 ?]. 8°.

西 成 SE CHING.
See CHINA. 乾 隆 KEEN LUNG. *Emperor.* 欽
定 八 旗 則 例 *Kin ting pă ke tsĭh le.* "Regulations for the Bannermen." .. Compiled by ..
Se Ching, &c.   1742. 8°.

西 樓 SE LOW.
西 樓 記 *Se low ke.* "The Story of the Western
Pavilion." *See* 曲 KEŬH. 六 十 種 曲 *Lŭh
shĭh chung keŭh.* "Sixty Plays," &c. Taou 4. 8°.

西 廂 SE SEANG.
西 廂 記 *Se seang ke.* "The Story of the Western
Chamber." *See* 曲 KEŬH. 六 十 種 曲 *Lŭh
shĭh chung keŭh.* "Sixty Plays," &c. Taou 2. 8°.

西 清 SE TSING.
西 清 古 鑑 *Se tsing koo keen.* "Antiquities
[from the Palace ?] of Western Purity." Compiled by an Imperial Commission consisting of
Leang She-ching, Tseang Poo, Wang Yew-tung,
and others. 40 keuen. (錢 錄 *Tseen lŭh.* "A
Record of Coins," compiled by a Commission
consisting of Leang She-ching, Tseang Poo,
Wang Yew-tung, and others. 16 keuen.)
                    Peking, 1749–50. Folio.

西 地 品 損 SE-TE-PIN-YĬH.
See PERIODICAL PUBLICATIONS. 英 吉 利 每 月
雜 記 傳 的 通 報 *Ying-keĭh-le mei yuĕ tsă ke
chuen teĭh tung paou.* "An English Monthly
Magazine." Written in Chinese by .. Se-te-
pin-yĭh, &c.   [1750 ?]. A sheet.

相 杜 SEANG-CHOO.
讚 本 *Tsan pun.* "A Book of Praise." Compiled by the Mendicant Priest Seang-choo.
                              1815. 8°.

相 松 SEANG-SUNG.
天 中 北 斗 古 佛 消 災 延 壽 妙 經 *Teen
chung Pĭh tow koo Fŭh seaou tsae yen show meaou
king.* "The Sûtra of Longevity and Freedom
from Calamities of the Ancient Buddha of the
Polar Star." Edited by the Priest Seang-sung.
                        Canton, 1835. 8°.

蕭 SEAOU.
See 太 平 天 國 TAE PING TEEN KWŏ. 頒 行
詔 書 *Fun hing chaou shoo.* "Proclamations"
of .. Seaou, &c.   1852. 8°.

蕭 綺 SEAOU KE.
拾 遺 記 *Shĭh e ke.* "Lost Pages of History."
... Edited by Seaou Ke, &c. *See* 汪 士 漢
WANG SZE-HAN. 祕 書 廿 八 種 *Pe shoo neen
pă chung.* "A Collection of Twenty-eight Reprints," &c.   1808. 8°.

蕭 統 SEAOU TUNG.
文 選 *Wăn seuen.* "Elegant Extracts from Polite
Literature." Compiled by Prince Seaou Tung,
of the Leang Dynasty. With a Commentary
by Le Shen. Edited by Yĕ Shoo-fan. 60 keuen.
                              1772. 8°.
Another copy.
      Imperfect, containing only keuen 56–60.

蕭 智 漢 SEAOU CHE-HAN.
歷 代 名 賢 列 女 氏 姓 譜 *Leĭh tae ming heen
lĕĕ neu she sing poo.* "A Biographical Dictionary
of the Celebrated Men and Women of all Ages."
157 keuen.   1792. 8°.

蕭 熿 藜 SEAOU HWANG-LE.
語 賦 駢 字 類 珠 *She foo peen tsze luy choo.*
"A Classified Lexicon of Elegant Poetical Expressions." 8 keuen.   [1790 ?]. 8°.
      Imperfect, wanting the first four keuen.

蕭 定 世 SEAOU TING-SHE.
日 用 儀 節 要 宗 *Jĭh yung e tsĕĕ yaou tsung.*
" A Manual of the Ceremonies and Observances
of Daily Life."   [1800 ?]. 8°.

蕭 子 顯 SEAOU TSZE-HEEN.
南 齊 書 *Nan Tse shoo.* "The History of the
Southern Tse Dynasty." 59 keuen. *See* 毛 晉
MAOU TSIN. 十 七 史 *Shĭh tseĭh she.* "The
Seventeen Histories," &c.   1656. 8°.

22

蕭 奕 璋 SEAOU YĬH-CHANG.

天 下 水 陸 路 程 新 編 *Teen hea shwuy lŭh loo ching sin peen.* "A Travelling Guide to the Empire." 2 keuen.   [1750?].   8°.

蕭 應 植 SEAOU YING-CHE.

關 聖 帝 君 靈 籤 *Kwan shing te keun ling tsan.* "A Liturgy in Honour of Kwan te," the God of War.   1789.   8°.

蕭 應 棋 SEAOU YING-KWEI.

See 楊 逢 春 YANG FUNG-CHUN, and SEAOU YING-KWEI. 詳 註 分 韻 試 帖 青 雲 集 *Tseang choo fun yun she tĕĕ tsing yun tseĭh.* "The Tsing-yun Collection of Poetical Essays." .. Compiled by Yang Fung-chun and Seaou Ying-kwei, &c.   1856.   8°.

—— and 顧 德 馨 KOO TĬH-HING. 律 賦 蕋 珠 新 編 *Leŭh foo juy choo sin peen.* "Elegant Odes. New Series." Compiled by Seaou Ying-kwei and Koo Tĭh-hing. Edited by Koo Kea-shwuy.   1815.   8°.

—— and 鄭 伯 壎 CHING PĬH-HEUEN.

律 賦 錦 標 初 集 箋 註 *Leŭh foo kin peaou choo tseĭh tseen choo.* "Elegant Odes. First Series. With Notes." Compiled by Seaou Ying-kwei and Ching Pĭh-heuen.   1816.   8°.
          Imperfect.

嘯 雲 閣 主 人 SEAOU-YUN KŎ CHOO JIN.

See 孟 子 MĂNG TSZE. 孟 子 大 題 萃 *Măng tsze ta te tsuy.* "A Collection of Essays on Texts from the Works of Măng tsze." .... Edited by 'The Master of the Seaou-yun Pavilion,' &c.   1821.   24°.

小 金 SEAOU KIN.

小 金 傳 *Seaou kin chuen.* "The Story of Seaou-kin." See 說 SHWŎ. 說 淵 *Shwŏ yuen.* "A Collection of Tales," &c.   Vol. 10.   8°.

小 子 SEAOU TSZE.

小 子 初 讀 易 識 之 書 課 *Seaou tsze choo tŭh e shĭh che shoo ko.* "Easy Reading Exercises for Children." [By W. H. Medhurst?].
          [Batavia, 1824?].   8°.

謝 遷 SEAY TSEEN.

稿 *Kaou.* "Essays." See 長 城 CHANG CHING. 名 家 制 義 *Ming kea che e.* "Essays" on Texts from the Four Books, &c.   Tsĭh 20.   1699.   8°.

謝 榛 SEAY TSIN.

四 溟 詩 話 *Sze ming she hwa.* "Criticisms on Poetry from Sze ming." 12 keuen. See 葉 志 詵 YĔ CHE-SIN. 海 山 仙 館 叢 書 *Hae shan seen Kwan tsung shoo.* "The Hae-shan-seen Kwan Collection of Reprints," &c.   Vol. 76.   1848.   8°.

謝 溶 SEAY YUNG.

闈 墨 文 龢 珠 囊 *Wei mĭh wăn kow ehoo nany.* "A Valuable Collection of Examination Essays."   1822.   8°.

謝 逢 泰 SEAY FUNG-TAE.

See 甘 馭 麟 KAN YU-LIN. 四 書 類 典 賦 *Sze shoo luy teen foo.* "Odes on Subjects from the Four Books." .... Edited by Seay Fung-tae, &c.   1777.   8°.

謝 啟 昆 SEAY KE-HWĂN.

See 吉 慶 KEĬH KING. 廣 西 通 志 *Kwang-se tung che.* "A Topography of the Province of Kwang-se." Compiled by ... Seay Ke-hwăn, &c.   1800.   8°.

謝 家 蘭 SEAY KEA-LAN.

See 崔 鴻 TSUY HUNG. 十 六 國 春 秋 *Shĭh lŭh kwŏ chun tsew.* "The Annals of the Sixteen Dynasties." .. Edited by Seay Kea-lan, &c.   8°.

謝 金 鑾 SEAY KIN-LWAN.

續 修 臺 灣 縣 志 *Sŭh sew Tae wan heen che.* "A Revised Topography of Tae-wan Heen," in the Island of Formosa. Compiled by Seay Kin-lwan, Ching Keen-tsae, and others.   8 keuen.   1807.   8°.

—— 二 勿 齋 文 集 *Urh wŭh ehae wăn tseĭh.* "A Collection of Literary Papers from the Double Standard Study." 6 keuen.   1836.   8°.
          The title-page is wanting.

謝 梅 林 SEAY MEI-LIN.

See 鄒 景 揚 TSOW KING-YANG. 醉 世 錦 囊 全 書 *Chow she kin nang tseuen shoo.* "A Treasury of Information on Social Etiquette." Edited by Seay Mei-lin, &c.   1771.   8°.

謝 寶 堂 SEAY PAOU-TANG.

See 曹 之 升 TSAOU CHE-SHING. 註 釋 典 制 文 琳 *Choo shĭh teen che wăn lin.* "A Collection of Choice Essays." ... With Notes by Seay Paou-tang, &c. 1799–1808. 8°.

謝 秀 嵐 SEAY SEW-LAN.

雅 俗 通 十 五 音 *Ya sŭh tung shĭh woo yin.* "A Pronouncing Dictionary of the Fuhkeen Dialect, arranged according to the Fifteen Sounds." By Seay Sew-lan. 8 keuen.
1818. 8°.

Another edition. 1820. 8°.

謝 宸 荃 SEAY SHIN-TSEUEN.

安 溪 縣 志 *Gan ke heen che.* "A Topography of Gan-ke Heen," in the Province of Fŭh-keen. Compiled by Seay Shin-tseuen, the Magistrate of the District, and others. 12 keuen. 1673. 8°.

謝 庭 薰 SEAY TING-HEUN.

婁 縣 志 *Low heen che.* "A Topography of Low Heen," in the Prefecture of Sung-keang. Compiled by Seay Ting-heun. Edited by Yang Show-nan, Lŭh Seĭh-heung, and others. 30 keuen. 1786. 8°.

謝 崇 俊 SEAY TSUNG-TSEUN, and 蔣 善 功 TSEANG SHEN-KUNG.

翁 源 縣 新 志 *Ung yuen heen sin che.* "A Topography of Ung-yuen Heen," in the Province of Kwantung. Compiled by Seay Tsung-tseun and Tseang Shen-kung and others. 12 keuen.
1820. 8°.

謝 凝 道 SEAY YING-TAOU.

See 屈 成 霖 KEŬH CHING-LIN. 習 是 編 *Seĭh she peen.* "On Practising what is Right." ... Edited by Seay Ying-taou, &c. 1824. 8°.

薛 昭 SĔĔ CHAOU.

薛 昭 傳 *Sĕĕ Chaou chuen.* "The Story of Sĕĕ Chaou." *See* 說 SHWŏ. 說 淵 *Shwŏ yuen.* "A Collection of Tales," &c. Vol. 8. 8°.

薛 調 SĔĔ CHOW.

劉 無 雙 傳 *Lew Woo-shwang chuen.* "The Story of Lew Woo-shwang." By Sĕĕ Chow, of the Tang Dynasty. A Reprint. [1741?]. 8°.

薛 熙 SĔĔ HE.

練 閱 火 器 陣 記 *Leen yuĕ ho ke chin ke.* "An Account of a Review of Troops." *See* 張 山 來 CHANG SHAN-LAE, and 張 潮 也 CHANG TSIN-YAY. 昭 代 叢 書 *Chaou tae tsung shoo.* "A Collection of Reprints of Works by Authors under the present Dynasty," &c. Keuen 37.
1703. 8°.

薛 瑄 SĔĔ SEUEN.

稿 *Kaou.* "Essays." *See* 長 城 CHANG CHING. 名 家 制 義 *Ming kea che e.* "Essays" on Texts from the Four Books, &c. Tsĭh 9.
1699. 8°.

薛 收 SĔĔ SHOW.

See 王 通 WANG TUNG. 元 經 *Yuen king.* "The Early History" of China. . . With a Commentary by Sĕĕ Show, &c. 8°.

薛 瑩 SĔĔ YUNG.

龍 女 傳 *Lung neu chuen.* "Tales of Dragon Women." *See* 王 文 誥 WANG WĂN-KAOU. 唐 代 叢 書 *Tang tae tsung shoo.* "A Collection of Reprints of Works written during the Tang Dynasty," &c. Series 5. 1806. 8°.

—— 龍 女 傳 *Lung neu chuen.* "Tales of Dragon Women." By Sĕĕ Yung, of the Tang Dynasty. A Reprint. [1741?]. 8°.

薛 正 希 SĔĔ CHING-HE.

See 易 經 YĬH KING. 易 義 析 解 *Yĭh e seĭh keae.* "The Meaning of the Book of Changes, accurately explained" by Sĕĕ Ching-he.
1712. 8°.

薛 居 正 SĔĔ KEU-CHING.

舊 五 代 史 *Kew Woo tae che.* "The History of the Five Dynasties." 150 keuen. *See* 毛 晉 MAOU TSIN. 十 七 史 *Shĭh tseĭh she.* "The Seventeen Histories," &c. 1656. 8°.

薛 生 白 SĔĔ SĂNG-PĬH.

See 李 念 莪 LE NEEN-GO. 內 經 知 要 *Nuy king che yaou.* "A Selection of Passages from the Soo wăn and Ling choo." . . . . . . Edited by Sĕĕ Săng-pĭh, &c. 1764. 8°.

—— See 吳 金 壽 WOO KIN-SHOW. 三 家 醫 案 合 刻 *San kea E gan hŏ kĭh.* "The Medical Practice of the Three Physicians," . . . Sĕĕ Săng-pĭh, &c. 1831. 8°.

薛尚功 Sēĕ Shang-kung.

歷代鐘鼎彝器欵識法帖 *Leĭh tae chung ting e ke kwan shĭh fă tëĕ.* "Fac-similes of Inscriptions on Bells, Tripods, Vases, &c., of Successive Ages, transcribed and explained." By Sēĕ Shang-kung, of the Sung Dynasty. Edited by Yuen Yuen. 20 keuen. 1797. 8º.

薛道光 Sēĕ Taou-kwang.

See 張伯端 Chang Pĭh-twan. 悟眞篇三註 *Woo chin peen san choo.* "On Understanding the Truth." . . . With Commentaries by Sēĕ Taou-kwang, &c. 1809. 8º.

薛應旂 Sēĕ Ying-ke.

稿 *Kaou.* "Essays." *See* 長城 Chang Ching. 名家制義 *Ming kea che e.* "Essays" on Texts from the Four Books, &c. Tsĭh 38. 1699. 8º.

—— 宋元通鑑 *Sung Yuen tung keen.* "A History of the Sung and Yuen Dynasties." Compiled by Sēĕ Ying-ke. Edited by Chin Jin-seĭh. 157 keuen. 1626. 8º.

—— 四書人物備考 *Sze shoo jin wŭh pe kaou.* "An Examination of the Men and Things mentioned in the Four Books." By Sēĕ Ying-ke. With Notes by Choo Fow, and Additions by Choo Shin-keae. Edited by Chin Ming-king. 48 keuen. [1800?]. 8º.

仙 Seen.

八仙出身傳 *Pă seen chŭh shin chuen.* "The Story of the Appearance of the Eight Genii." With Illustrations. [1750?]. 8º.

Imperfect. First twenty pages are wanting.

仙王 Seen Wang.

恭祀仙王打醮科儀 *Kung sze Leen Wang ta tseaou ko e.* "A Devotional Ritual for Sacrificial Services to the Gods." A Taouist Work. [1800?]. 8º.

席世 Seĭh She.

南宋書 *Nan Sung shoo.* "The History of the Southern Sung Dynasty." 68 keuen. *See* 毛晉 Maou Tsin. 十七史 *Shĭh tseĭh she.* "The Seventeen Histories," &c. 1656. 8º.

徐栻 Seu Chĭh.

See 陳善 Chin Shen. 萬曆杭州府志 *Wan leĭh hang chow foo che.* "A Topography of Hang-chow Foo." . . Edited by Seu Chĭh, &c. 1579. 8º.

徐籀 Seu Chow.

See 四書 Sze shoo. 四書直解 *Sze shoo chĭh keae.* "The Four Books clearly explained." . . . . . Edited by Seu Chow, &c. 1766. 8º.

徐巖 Seu E.

物怪錄 *Wŭh kwae lŭh.* "Strange Stories." *See* 王文誥 Wang Wăn-kaou. 唐代叢書 *Tang tae tsung shoo.* "A Collection of Reprints of Works written during the Tang Dynasty," &c. Series 6. 1806. 8º.

徐鳳 Seu Fung.

鍼灸大全 *Chin kew ta tseuen.* "A Complete System of Acupuncture." 6 keuen. [1750?]. 8º.

徐幹 Seu Han.

中論 *Chung lun.* "Central Discourses" on Government, Morals, &c. By Seu Han, of the Han Dynasty. Edited by Tsae Tsoo-pĭ. 2 keuen. [1800?]. 8º.

徐灝 Seu Haou.

通介堂經說 *Tung keae tang king shwŏ.* "Notes on the Classics." 12 keuen. 1854. 8º.

徐鉉 Seu Heuen.

See 許慎 Heu Shin. 說文 *Shwŏ wăn.* "A Dictionary." . . Edited by Seu Heuen, &c. 1627. 8º.

—— 稽神錄 *Ke shin lŭh.* "Ghost Stories." *See* 王文誥 Wang Wăn-kaou. 唐代叢書 *Tang tae tsung shoo.* "A Collection of Reprints of Works written during the Tang Dynasty," &c. Series 6. 1806. 8º.

徐炫 Seu Heuen.

玄怪記 *Heuen kwae ke.* "Ghost Stories." By Seu Heuen, of the Tang Dynasty. A Reprint. [1741?]. 8º.

徐祺 Seu Ke.

See 周子安 Chow Tsze-gan. 五知齋琴譜 *Woo che chae Kin poo.* "The Music Book for the Kin." . . Edited by Seu Ke, &c. 1746. 8º.

徐堅 SEU KEEN.

初學記 *Choo heŏ ke*. "A Book for Beginners." An Encyclopædia. 30 keuen. [1700?]. 8°.

徐釚 SEU KEW.

詞話 *Tsze hwa*. "A Critique on Rhymes." *See* 張山來 CHANG SHAN-LAE, and 張潮也 CHANG TSIN-YAY. 昭代叢書 *Chaou tae tsung shoo*. "A Collection of Reprints of Works by Authors under the present Dynasty," &c. Keuen 32. 1703. 8°.

—— 詞苑叢談 *Tsze yuen tsung tan*. "Discourses on a Garden of Rhymes." 12 keuen. *See* 葉志詵 YĚ CHE-SIN. 海山仙館叢書 *Hae shan seen Kwan tsung shoo*. "The Hae-shan-seen Kwan Collection of Reprints," &c. Vol. 81–84. 1848. 8°.

徐本 SEU PUN.

See CHINA. 督捕則例 *Tŭh poo tsĭh le*. "Regulations concerning the Capture" of Deserters. Compiled by .. Seu Pun, &c. 1743. 8°.

—— See TSING DYNASTY. 大清律例 *Ta Tsing leŭh le*. "The Fundamental Laws and Subordinate Statutes of the Tsing Dynasty." Compiled by .. Seu Pun, &c. 1768. 8°.

徐湯 SEU TANG.

See 陳崑泉 CHIN KWAN-TSEUEN. 氏族大全綱目 *She tsŭh ta tseuen kang mŭh*. "An Epitomised Biographical Dictionary." Edited by Seu Tang, &c. 1573. 8°.

徐衢 SEU TAOU.

佛祖傳燈 *Fŭh tsoo chuen tăng*. "A Lamp applied to the Lives of Buddhist Saints." By Seu Taou. Edited by Le Le. 16 keuen. [1700?]. 8°.

Imperfect, containing only keuen 9–16.

—— 神仙鑑 *Shin seen keen*. "Biographical Notices of Taouist Saints." By Seu Taou and Le Le. Edited by Hwang Chang-lun. First Series. 22 keuen. [1700?]. 8°.

Another copy.

Imperfect, containing only the first eight keuen.

The Third Series. Edited by Chin Chung-yĭh. 22 keuen. [1700?]. 8°.

Imperfect, first sixteen keuen being wanting.

徐積 SEU TSEĬH.

節孝集 *Tsĕĕ heaou tseĭh*. "A Collection of Chaste and Filial Poetry." *See* 吳孟舉 WOO MĂNG-KEU, and 吳自牧 WOO TSZE-MŬH. 宋詩鈔二集 *Sung she chaou urh tseĭh*. "Poetry of the Sung Dynasty," &c. 8°.

徐端 SEU TWAN.

經畬堂課孫草稿 *King fan Tang ko sun tsaou kaou*. "Model Essays from the King-fan Hall." 1727. 8°.

徐渭 SEU WEI.

青藤書屋集 *Tsing tăng shoo ŭh tseĭh*. "A Collection of Literary Pieces from the Green Tăng Library." 30 keuen. *See* 葉志詵 YĚ CHE-SIN. 海山仙館叢書 *Hae shan seen Kwan tsung shoo*. "The Hae-shan-seen Kwan Collection of Reprints," &c. Vol. 59–64. 1848. 8°.

徐忭 SEU WOO.

—— 一統志表 *Yĭh tung che peaou*. "A Tabulated Topographical History of the Empire, chronologically arranged to accompany the 'Yĭh tung che.'" 1794. 8°.

徐朝俊 SEU CHAOU-TSEUN.

高厚蒙求 *Kaou how mung kew*. "Important Lessons" in Astronomical Science. 1807–29. 8°.

Another copy.

Imperfect, containing only one Essay.

徐貞明 SEU CHING-MING.

潞水客談 *Loo shwuy kĭh tan*. "Conversations on the Irrigation of the Empire, between Seu Ching-ming and a Guest." *See* 伍崇曜 WOO TSUNG-YAOU. 粵雅堂叢書 *Yuĕ ya Tang tsung shoo*. "The Yuĕ-ya Tang Collection of Reprints," &c. Series 2. 1853. 8°.

徐以清 SEU E-TSING.

鑑古瑣譚 *Keen koo so tan*. "A Mirror applied to the Sayings of the Ancients." *See* 閔景賢 MIN KING-HEEN. 快書 *Kwae shoo*. "A Book of Amusement," &c. Keuen 9. 1626. 8°.

徐 方 廣 Seu Fang-kwang.

稿 *Kaou*. "Essays." *See* 長 城 Chang Ching. 名 家 制 義 *Ming kea che e*. "Essays" on Texts from the Four Books, &c.　Tsïh 99. 　　　　　　　　　　　　　　　　1699.　8°.

徐 孚 遠 Seu Foo-yuen.

See 司 馬 遷 Sze-ma Tseen. 史 記 *She ke*. "The Historical Record."　With a Commentary by Seu Foo-yuen, &c.　　　1806.　8°.

徐 羖 峰 Seu Go-fung.

See 尹 方 橋 Yin Fang-keaou. 德 潤 書 院 課 藝 *Tïh jun shoo yuen ko e*. "Literary Exercises from the Tïh-jun School." . . . Edited by Seu Go-fung, &c.　　　　1821.　8°.

徐 霞 客 Seu Hea-kïh.

霞 客 遊 記 *Hea-kïh yew ke*. "The Travels of Seu Hea-kïh."　Edited by Seu Keae-leïh.　10 keuen.　　　　　　　　　　　1808.　8°.

徐 興 華 Seu Hing-hwa.

See 周 祥 鈺 Chow Tseang-yüh. 九 宮 大 成 南 北 詞 宮 譜 *Kew kung ta ching nan pïh tsze kung poo*. "A Collection of Southern and Northern Rhymes, with their appropriate Airs." . . . Arranged by Seu Hing-hwa, &c.　　8°.

徐 懷 祖 Seu Hwae-tsoo.

臺 灣 隨 筆 *Tae wan suy peïh*. "Jottings about Formosa."　*See* 張 山 來 Chang Shan-lae, and 張 遴 也 Chang Tsin-yay. 昭 代 叢 書 *Chaou tae tsung shoo*. "A Collection of Reprints of Works by Authors under the present Dynasty," &c.　Keuen 25.　　1703.　8°.

徐 汝 廉 Seu Joo-leen.

枕 餘 *Chin yu*. "Musings on a Pillow."　*See* 閔 景 賢 Min King-heen. 快 書 *Kwae shoo*. "A Book of Amusement," &c.　Keuen 14. 　　　　　　　　　　　　　　　　1626.　8°.

徐 繼 畬 Seu Ke-yu.

俄 羅 斯 國 志 略 *Go-lo-sze kwŏ che leŏ*. "A Short History of Russia."・*See* 何 秋 濤 Ho Tsew-taou. 北 徼 彙 編 *Pïh keaou wei peen*. "Treatises on the Northern Frontier." . . Keuen 3.　　　　　　　　　　　1865.　8°.

徐 繼 畬 Seu Ke-yu. (*Continued.*)

瀛 環 志 畧 *Ying hwan che leŏ*. "A Geographical Treatise on all within the Circuit of the Seas."　By Seu Ke-yu.　Edited by Peïh Sing-tseuen and Lew Yŭh-po.　10 keuen. 　　　　　　　　　　　　　　　　1848.　8°.

徐 介 立 Seu Keae-leïh.

See 徐 霞 客 Seu Hea-kïh. 霞 客 遊 記 *Hea-kïh yew ke*. "The Travels of Seu Hea-kïh." Edited by Seu Keae-leïh, &c.　1808.　8°.

徐 卷 石 Seu Keuen-shïh.

頂 門 針 *Ting mun chin*. "Ting mun Needles." *See* 閔 景 賢 Min King-heen. 快 書 *Kwae shoo*. "A Book of Amusement," &c.　Keuen 19. 　　　　　　　　　　　　　　　　1626.　8°.

徐 乾 學 Seu Keen-heŏ.

See 康 熙 Kang-he. *Emperor*. 御 選 古 文 淵 鑒 *Yu seuen koo wăn yuen keen*. "A Deep Mirror of Ancient Literature."　Edited by . . . Seu Keen-heŏ, &c.　　　1685.　8°.

徐 九 一 Seu Kew-yïh.

See 詩 經 She king. 詩 經 大 全 *She king ta tseuen*. "The Complete Book of Odes." . . Edited by Seu Kew-yïh, &c.　　　8°.

—— *See* 孔 丘 Kung Kew. 書 經 大 全 *Shoo king ta tseuen*. "A Complete Copy of the Book of Historical Documents." . . Edited by Seu Kew-yïh, &c.　　　　　　　8°.

徐 敬 軒 Seu King-heen.

初 學 玉 玲 瓏 *Choo heŏ yüh ling lung*. "Literary Gems for Beginners."　Model Essays.　Compiled by Seu King-heen.　　　1823.　8°.

徐 光 啟 Seu Kwang-ke.

See 利 瑪 竇 Le Ma-tow. 幾 何 原 本 *Ke ho yuen pun*. "The Elements of the Science of Quantity." . . Commenced by Matteo Ricci, with the assistance of Seu Kwang-ke, &c. 　　　　　　　　　　　　　　　　1857.　8°.

—— *See* 畢 方 濟 Peïh Fang-tse. *pseud*. [*i.e.* Francis Sambiasi]. 靈 言 蠡 勺 *Ling yen le chŏ*. "A Work on the Soul."　Transcribed by Seu Kwang-ke, &c.　　　　　　　8°.

徐 光 啟 SEU KWANG-KE. (*Continued.*)

測 量 異 同 *Tsih leang e tung.* "A Treatise on the Analogy between the System of Angular Measurement in the ancient native work 'Kew chang' and the European Method." [Also] 句 股 義 *Keu koo e.* "A Treatise on the Development of the Theory of the Right-angled Triangle, giving an Arithmetical Illustration of its Geometrical Properties." *See* 葉 志 詵 YĔ CHE-SIN. 海 山 仙 館 叢 書 *Hae shan seen Kwan tsung shoo.* "The Hae-shan-seen Kwan Collection of Reprints," &c. Vol. 107.

1848. 8°.

—— 農 政 全 書 *Nung ching tseuen shoo.* "The Thesaurus of Agriculture." [Originally published in 1640.] A Reprint. 60 keuen.

1843. 8°.

徐 光 燦 SEU KWANG-TSAN.

峰 抱 樓 琴 譜 *Fung paou low kin poo.* "The Music Book of the Fung-paou Pavilion." Compiled by Seu Kwang-tsan. Edited by Chin Heŏ-shen.

1826. 8°.

徐 立 綱 SEU LEĬH-KANG.

See 孔 丘 KUNG KEW. 春 秋 讀 本 *Chun tsew tŭh pun.* "The Original Text of the Spring and Autumn Annals." Edited by Seu Leĭh-kang, &c.

8°.

———— 倘 書 讀 本 *Shang shoo tŭh pun.* "The Book of Historical Documents." .. Edited by Seu Leĭh-kang, &c.

8°.

—— See 詩 經 SHE KING. 毛 詩 讀 本 *Maou She tŭh pun.* "Maou Chang's Edition of the Book of Odes." ... Edited by Seu Leĭh-kang, &c. 8°.

徐 白 舫 SEU PĬH-FANG.

桂 宮 梯 *Kwei kung te.* "A Ladder to the Laurus Cassia Palace." A Work published in Illustration of Wăn chang Te keun's Work on the Respect which should be shown to Books and all printed or written Matter. A Reprint. 6 keuen.

1842. 8°.

Another edition. With an Appendix. 6 keuen.

1842. 12°.

徐 試 可 SEU SHĬH-KO.

地 理 琢 玉 斧 *Te le chŏ yŭh foo.* "A Gem-cutting Hatchet applied to the Laws of the Earth." [1750 ?]. 8°.

Imperfect.

徐 實 夫 SEU SHĬH-FOO.

毛 詩 名 物 圖 說 *Maou she ming wŭh too shwŏ.* "Natural Objects mentioned in the Book of Odes illustrated and explained." 9 keuen.

1771. 8°.

徐 士 芬 SEU SZE-FUN.

興 寧 縣 重 建 學 宮 記 *Hing ning heen chung keen heŏ kung ke.* "An Account of the Restoration of the College at Hing-ning Heen," in the Province of Kwang-tung.

[*Hing-ning* ?], 1831. 8°.

徐 辛 菴 SEU SIN-GAN.

直 省 墨 準 *Chĭh săng mĭh chun.* "Select Examination Essays by Authors of the Different Provinces." Edited by Seu Sin-gan. 1832. 8°.

徐 心 魯 SEU SIN-LOO.

萬 寶 全 書 *Wan paou tseuen shoo.* "An Encyclopædia." 22 keuen. [1700 ?]. 8°.

徐 星 伯 SEU SING-PĬH.

西 域 水 道 記 *Se yĭh shwuy taou ke.* "An Account of the Water Ways of the Countries on the Western Frontier of the Empire." Compiled by Seu Sing-pĭh. With Maps. 5 keuen.

1823. 8°.

徐 士 業 SEU SZE-NĔĔ.

See 王 晉 升 WANG TSIN-SHING. 百 家 姓 考 略 *Pĭh kea sing kaou leŏ.* "A Short Account of the Family Names of China." Edited by Seu Sze-nĕĕ, &c.

8°.

徐 天 章 SEU TEEN-CHANG.

See 吳 叉 可 WOO YEW-KO. 溫 疫 方 論 *Wăn yĭh fang lun.* "A Treatise on Prescriptions for the Pestilence." Edited by ... Seu Teen-chang, &c.

8°.

徐 在 漢 SEU TSAE-HAN.

See 易 經 YĬH KING. 易 原 *Yĭh yuen.* "The Origin of the Book of Changes." ... Edited by Seu Tsae-han, &c.

8°.

徐 在 漢 SEU TSAE-HAN. (*Continued.*)

易 或 *Yih hwŏ.* "Doubts on the Book of Changes" Elucidated. Edited by Chaou Chin-fang. With Copious Notes by Hoo Yun-fung, Lew Shĭh-lan, Chang Yen-ling, Ching King-ching, and others. 10 keuen. 1774. 8°.

徐 祖 鎏 SEU TSOO-LEW.

近 科 房 考 清 卓 集 *Kin ko fang kaou tsing chŏ tseih.* "A Collection of Choice Examination Essays." Compiled by Seu Tsoo-lew. Three Series. 1803. 1806. 1810. 8°.

徐 文 長 SEU WĂN-CHANG.

洪 武 全 傳 *Hung woo tseuen chuen.* "A Complete Narrative of the Reign of the Emperor Hung-woo" [1368–97]. 10 keuen. 1800. 8°.

徐 文 初 SEU WĂN-CHOO.

See 禮 記 LE KE. 全 文 禮 記 疏 意 體 註 *Tseuen wăn Le kc soo e te choo.* "The Complete Text of the Book of Rites." .. Compiled by .. Seu Wăn-choo, &c. 1632. 8°.

徐 幼 魯 SEU YEW-LOO.

See 袁 坤 儀 YUEN KWAN-E. 羣 書 備 考 *Keun shoo pe kaou.* "A Literary and Scientific Encyclopædia." .. Edited by Seu Yew-loo, &c. 1642. 8°.

徐 永 勳 SEU YUNG-HEUN.

See 儲 欣 CHOO HIN. 唐 宋 八 大 家 類 選 *Tang Sung pă ta kea luy seuen.* "Selections from the Works of Eight Scholars who Flourished under the Tang and Sung Dynasties." .. Edited by Seu Yung-heun, &c. 1766. 8°.

—— See 司 馬 遷 SZE-MA TSEEN. 史 記 選 *She ke seuen.* "Selections from The Historical Record." ... Edited by .. Seu Yung-heun, &c. 1766. 8°.

—— See 左 丘 明 TSO KEW-MING. 左 傳 選 *Tso chuen seuen.* "Selections from Tso Kew-ming's Narrative." .. Edited by Seu Yung-heun, &c. 8°.

宣 律 師 SEUEN-LEŬH-SZE.

四 分 戒 本 *Sze fun keae pun.* "The Rules of the Four Divisions" for the Mendicant Buddhist Priests. Compiled by Seuen-leŭh-sze, of the Tang Dynasty. A Reprint. *Canton,* [1790 ?]. 8°.

荀 勗 SEUN HEŬH.

穆 天 子 傳 *Mŭh Teen tsze chuen.* "A Narrative of the Adventures of the Emperor Mŭh, of the Chow Dynasty, in his Journey to the West, on a Visit to Se wang moo." Compiled by Seun Heŭh, of the Tsin Dynasty. With Notes by Kŏ Pŏ, of the same epoch. A Reprint. 6 keuen. [1750 ?]. 8°.

荀 況 SEUN HWANG.

荀 子 *Seun tsze.* "The Writings of Seun Hwang." See 沈 津 CHIN TSIN. 百 家 類 纂 *Pĭh kea luy tswan.* "The Works of a Hundred Authors," &c. Keuen 4. 8°.

—— See 黃 海 岸 HWANG HAE-GAN. 周 秦 十 一 子 *Chow Tsin shĭh yĭh tsze.* "The Works of the Eleven Philosophers of the Chow and Tsin Dynasties," &c. 8°.

—— See 黃 丕 烈 HWANG PEI-LĔĔ. 十 子 全 書 *Shĭh tsze tseuen shoo.* "The Complete Works of the Ten Philosophers," &c. 1804. 8°.

—— See 禮 記 LE KE. 欽 定 禮 記 義 疏 *Kin ting Le ke e soo.* "The Meaning of the Book of Rites. With Explanations" by Seun Hwang, &c. 8°.

—— 荀 子 *Seun tsze.* "The Writings of the Philosopher Seun Hwang." With Notes by Yang King, of the Tang Dynasty. 20 keuen. 809. 8°.

荀 爽 SEUN SHWANG.

周 易 注 *Chow Yĭh choo.* "Notes on the Chow Changes." See 孫 堂 SUN TANG. 漢 魏 二 十 一 家 易 注 *Han Wei urh shĭh yĭh kea Yĭh choo.* "Commentaries on the Book of Changes," &c. 1799. 8°.

荀 悅 SEUN YUĔ.

申 鑒 *Shin keen.* "An Explanatory Mirror." An Essay on Government and General Subjects. By Seun Yuĕ, of the Han Dynasty. With Notes by Woo Taou. 5 keuen. 1518. 8°.

SEVERINI (ANTELMO).

Dialoghi Cinesi. Parte Seconda. Trascrizione e doppia versione Italiana Letterale e libera. *Firenze,* 1866. 8°.

紗 SHA.

浣紗記 *Hwan sha ke.* "Washing Gauze." *See*
曲 KEŬH. 六十種曲 *Lŭh shĭh chung keŭh.*
"Sixty Plays," &c.　Taou 1.　　　　8º.

山 SHAN.

二十四山秘訣 *Urh shĭh sze shan pe keuĕ.*
"The Secret Arts of the Twenty-four Mountains." A Work on Divination. [1800 ?]. 8º.

山莊 SHAN CHWANG.

山莊夜怪錄 *Shan chwang yay kwae lŭh.* "The
Strange Nightly Appearances at a Mountain
Farm." *See* 說 SHWŎ. 說淵 *Shwŏ yuen.*
"A Collection of Tales," &c.　Vol. 10.　　8º.

上海 SHANG HAE.

上海輔元堂施醫局徵信錄 *Shang hae
Foo-yuen Tang she e keu ching sin lŭh.* "The
Report of the Shanghae Foo-yuen Tang Medical
Society," for the Year 1851.
　　　　　　　　　　Shanghae, 1851.　8º.

—— 上海縣志 *Shang hae heën che.* "A Topography of Shang-hae Heën." Published by
order of the Emperor Kea-king.　20 keuen.
　　　　　　　　　　　　[1800 ?].　8º.

An imperfect copy, containing only keuen 7–9, 11–13,
15–20.

—— 上海土音字寫法 *Shang hae too yin tsze
seay fă.* "Rules for Writing the Shanghae
Dialect."　　　[*Shanghae,* 1859 ?].　12º.

—— 上海同仁堂徵信錄 *Shang hae Tung jin
Tang ching sin lŭh.* "The Report of the Shang-
hae Benevolent Society" for the Year 1849.
　　　　　　　　　　Shanghae, 1849.　8º.

Another copy.

—— 上海育嬰堂徵信錄 *Shang-hae yŭh ying
Tang ching sin lŭh.* "The Report of the Shang-
hae Foundling Hospital" for the Year 1849.
　　　　　　　　　　Shanghae, 1849.　8º.

上帝 SHANG TE.

上帝垂愛世人 *Shang te chuy gae she jin.*
"The Condescending Love of God towards
Men."　　　　　　　　　[1850 ?].　8º.

—— 上帝總論 *Shang te tsung lun.* "A Discourse
on the Attributes of God." *Hongkong,* 1858. 8º.

上陽子 SHANG YANG-TSZE.

See 涵蟾子 HAN CHEN-TSZE. 金丹正理大
要道書全集 *Kin tan ching le ta yaou taou
shoo tseuen tseih.* "A Complete Collection of
Important Taouist Works on the True Principles
of the Elixir of Immortality." .. With Commentaries by Shang Yang-tsze, &c.　1538. 8º.

佝德 SHANG TĬH. *pseud.* [*i.e.* Walter Henry Medhurst, D.D., the Elder].

晉度施食之論 *Poo too she shĭh che lun.* "A
Controversial Tract on the Buddhist Rite of
Feeding the Hungry Souls of the Dead."
　　　　　　　　Singapore, [1840 ?].　8º.

Another copy.

—— 上帝生日之論 *Shang te săng jĭh che lun.*
"A Discourse on the Birthday of the Deity
Shang te."　　　　*Singapore,* [1850 ?].　8º.

—— 東西史記和合 *Tung se she ke ho hŏ.* "A
Parallel History of the East and West."
　　　　　　　　　　　　1829.　8º.

佝德者 SHANG-TĬH-CHAY. *pseud.* [*i.e.* Walter Henry
Medhurst, D.D., the Elder].

See PERIODICAL PUBLICATIONS. 特選撮要每
月紀傳 *Tĭh seuen tsŏ yaou mei yuĕ ke chuen.*
"A Monthly Magazine of Useful Information."
Edited by Shang-tĭh-chay.　　1823.　8º.

—— 眞理通道 *Chin le tung taou.* "The Principles
of Truth."　　　　[*Shanghae*], 1845.　8º.
Imperfect, wanting the first twenty-five chapters.

—— 中華諸兄慶賀新禧文 *Chung hwa choo
heung king ho sin he wăn.* "An Address on the
Temptations of the New Year Season to his
Chinese Brethren." By Shang-tĭh-chay.
　　　　　　　　Singapore, [1835 ?].　8º.

—— 咬嚠吧總論 *Keaou-lew-pa tsung lun.* "A
Description of Java." With Maps and Plates.
　　　　　　　　　[*Batavia,* 1824 ?].　8º.

商輅 SHANG LOO.

稿 *Kaou.* "Essays." *See* 長城 CHANG CHING.
名家制義 *Ming kea che e.* "Essays" on
Texts from the Four Books, &c.　Tsĭh 10.
　　　　　　　　　　　　1699.　8º.

23

商子 SHANG TSZE.

商子 *Shang tsze.* "The Writings of Shang tsze." *See* 黃海岸 HWANG HAE-GAN. 周秦十一子 *Chow Tsin shǐh yǐh tsze.* "The Works of the Eleven Philosophers of the Chow and Tsin Dynasties," &c.   8°.

賞心 SHANG-SIN.

征四寇傳 *Ching sze kow chuen.* "The Four Banditti Subdued." A Sequel to the *Shwuy hoo chuen.* By the Hermit Shang-sin. Edited by Kin Shing-tan. 10 keuen.   1792. 8°.
Imperfect, wanting keuen 7 and 8.

少室 SHAOU CHǏH.

少室仙姝傳 *Shaou chǐh seen choo chuen.* "The Story of the Fairy of Shaou chǐh." *See* 說 SHWǑ. 說淵 *Shwǒ yuen.* "A Collection of Tales," &c. Vol. 3.   8°.

少林 SHAOU-LIN.

少林寺志 *Shaou-lin sze che.* "An Account of the Shaou-lin Monastery" in Honan.
[1800 ?]. 8°.

邵基 SHAOU KE.

靜遠軒傳稿彙編 *Tsing yuen heen foo kaou wei peen.* "A Collection of Essays on Texts from the Four Books, from the Still and Distant Study." Edited by Sun Hung.   1721. 8°.

邵愷 SHAOU TAN.

靜遠軒傳稿彙編 *Tsing yuen heen foo kaou wei peen.* "A Collection of Essays on Texts from the Four Books, from the Still and Distant Study." Edited by Sun Hung.   1782. 8°.

邵鐸 SHAOU TǑ.

靜遠軒傳稿彙編 *Tsing yuen heen foo kaou wei peen.* "A Collection of Essays on Texts from the Four Books, from the Still and Distant Study." Edited by Sun Hung.   1791. 8°.

邵雍 SHAOU YUNG.

皇極經世書 *Hwang keǐh king she shoo.* *See* 胡廣 HOO KWANG. 性理大全 *Sing le ta tseuen.* "A Complete Work on Mental Philosophy," &c. Keuen 7 to 13.   1414. 8°.

邵希曾 SHAOU HE-TSĂNG.

See 王文誥 WANG WĂN-KAOU. 唐代叢書 *Tang tae tsung shoo.* "A Collection of Reprints of Works written during the Tang Dynasty." Edited by Shaou He-tsăng, &c.   1806. 8°.

邵向榮 SHAOU HEANG-YUNG.

See 王夢弼 WANG MUNG-PĬH. 鎮海縣志 *Chin hae heen che.* "A Topography of Chin-hae Heen.".. Edited by Shaou Heang-yung, &c. 8°.

邵九皐 SHAOU KEW-KAOU.

See 葉九升 YĔ KEW-SHING. 地理山法全書 *Te le shan fǎ tseuen shoo.* . "The Laws of Mountains." . . . The Eighth Keuen is Edited with Notes by Shaou Kew-kaou, &c. 8°.

邵經邦 SHAOU KING-PANG.

弘簡錄 *Hung keen lǔh.* "The Great History" of Events from the Beginning of the Tang Dynasty to the End of the Kin Dynasty. Edited by Sun Yuen-ping. 254 keuen.
1686. 8°.
Another edition.   1686. 8°.
Imperfect, containing only keuen 1 to 39.

邵光鈐 SHAOU KWANG-KEEN.

See 顏希源 YEN HE-YUEN. 儀徵縣續志 *E-ching heen sǔh che.* "A Supplementary Topography of E-ching Heen." Compiled by . . . Shaou Kwang-keen, &c.   1723. 8°.

邵孟遴 SHAOU MĂNG-LIN.

See 王符 WANG FOO. 潛夫論 *Tseen foo lun.* "The Discourses of an Unknown Scholar." . . . Edited by Shaou Măng-lin, &c.   8°.

邵晉涵 SHAOU TSIN-HAN.

爾雅正義 *Urh ya ching e.* "The True Meaning of the Urh ya." *See* 嚴杰 YEN LĔĔ. 皇清經解 *Hwang Tsing king keae.* "The Classics Explained," &c. Keuen 504–523. 1829. 8°.

邵子湘 SHAOU TSZE-SEANG.

古今韻略 *Koo kin yun leǒ.* "A Work on the Ancient and Modern Sounds." Arranged under the 106 Finals. Edited by Sung Mǔh-chung. 5 keuen.   1696. 8°.

邵遠平 SHAOU YUEN-PING.

元史類編 *Yuen she luy peen.* "The History of the Yuen Dynasty." *See* 毛晉 MAOU TSIN. 十七史 *Shih tseih she.* "The Seventeen Histories," &c.　　　　1656. 8°.

—— 元史類編 *Yuen she luy peen.* "The History of the Yuen Dynasty." A Sequel to the *Hung keen lüh.* 42 keuen.　　　1706. 8°.

Another copy.

　　Imperfect, wanting keuen 23 to 42.

世 SHE.

醒世恒言 *Sing she hăng yen.* "A Consistent Narrative to Arouse the World." ·40 keuen ?
　　　　　　　　　[1750 ?]. 8°.
The Title-page, Preface, and first three pages are wanting.

史 SHE.

古史輯要 *Koo she tseih yaou.* "An Epitome of Ancient History." 6 keuen. *See* 葉志詵 YĔ CHE-SIN. 海山仙館叢書 *Hae shan seen Kwan tsung shoo.* "The Hae-shan-seen Kwan Collection of Reprints," &c. Vol. 12–14.
　　　　　　　　　1848. 8°.

—— 新史奇觀 *Sin she ke kwan.* "Wondrous Tales of Modern History."　　　[1800 ?]. 8°.
　　Imperfect, containing only Chapters 17–22.

史記 SHE KE.

史記奇鈔 *She ke ke chaou.* "Extraordinary Events narrated in the Historical Record."
　　　　　　　　　[1700 ?]. 8°.
　　Imperfect, containing only the sixth keuen.

史貽謨 SHE E-MOW.

See 馬端臨 MA-TWAN-LIN. 文獻通考 *Wăn heen tung kaou.* "A General Examination of Records and Scholars." Edited by She E-mow, &c.　　　　　1748. 8°.

史鳴臯 SHE MING-KAOU.

象山縣志 *Seang shan heen che.* "A Topography of Seang-shan Heen," in the Province of Chĕ-keang. Compiled by She Ming-kaou, Fan Tsing-hung, and others. 12 keuen.
　　　　　　　　　1756. 8°.

　　Imperfect, keuen 7–12 wanting.

史夢蛟 SHE MUNG-KEAOU.

See 全祖望 TSEUEN TSOO-WANG. 鮚埼亭集 *Keĭh ke ting tseĭh.* "The Keĭh-ke Pavilion Collection." .. Edited by She Mung-keaou, &c.
　　　　　　　　　1804. 8°.

詩 SHE.

Poetical Examination Essays for the Year 1822.
　　　　　　　　　1822. 8°.
　　　　A Fragment.

詩經 SHE KING.

毛詩 *Maou She.* "Maou Chang's Edition of the Book of Odes." *See* 毛鳳苞 MAOU FUNG-PAOU. 十三經注疏 *Shih san king choo soo.* "The Thirteen Classics, with Commentaries and Expositions," &c.　　1813. 8°.

—— 詩經 *She king.* "The Book of Odes." With Notes. 4 keuen ?　　　[1800 ?]. 8°.
　　Imperfect, containing only part of keuen 1.

——— With the Commentary of Choo He. The Tseu-kin Tang Edition. A Reprint. 8 keuen.
　　　　　　　　　[1750 ?]. 8°.

—— 詩經正文 *She king ching wăn.* "The Correct Text of the Book of Odes." With Notes. 4 keuen.　　　　[1700 ?]. 8°.

—— 詩經便蒙正文 *She king peen mung ching wăn.* "The Correct Text of the Book of Odes for the Use of Students." 5 ? keuen.
　　　　　　　　　[1750 ?]. 8°.

　　Imperfect, containing only part of the first keuen.

—— 詩經大全 *She king ta tseuen.* "The Complete Book of Odes." With Extracts from the Commentaries of Choo He and others. Edited by Seu Kew-yĭh. With an Addenda entitled 詩經考異 *She king kaou e,* or "An Examination of the Various Readings of the Book of Odes," by Wang Ying-lin. 20 keuen.
　　　　　　　　　[1750 ?]. 8°.

—— 毛詩讀本 *Maou she tŭh pun.* "Maou Chang's Edition of the Book of Odes." With an Interlinear Exposition. Edited by Seu Leĭh-kang 4 keuen.　　　[1800 ?]. 8°

—— 毛詩讀本 *Maou She tŭh pun.* "Maou Chang's Edition of the Book of Odes." 5 keuen.
　　　　　　　　　1806. 8°.

詩 經 SHE KING. (*Continued.*)

詩 經 讀 本 *She king tŭh pun.* "The Book of Odes." With an Interlinear Exposition. Edited by Chang she. 4 keuen.　　　1785. 8°.

Another edition. 4 keuen.　　　　　　1816. 8°.

Another edition. 5 keuen.　　　　　　1820. 8°.

Another edition. 4 keuen.　　　[1820 ?]. 8°.

Another copy.

Another copy.

—— 監 本 詩 經 *Keen pun she king.* "The Original Text of the Book of Odes." With Choo He's Commentary. Edited by Le she. The Keaetsze Yuen Edition. 8 keuen.
　　　　　　　　　　　　　Nanking, 1818. 8°.

—— 魁 本 詩 經 *Kwei pun She king.* "The Great Original Book of Odes." Edited with Notes by Yĕ Heang-kaou. 5 keuen.　　[1700 ?]. 8°.

—— 詩 經 增 訂 旁 訓 *She king tsăng ting pang heun.* "The Book of Odes. With an Enlarged Interlinear Commentary." 4 keuen.
　　　　　　　　　　　　　　[1800 ?]. 8°.
Imperfect, containing only keuen 4.

—— 毛 詩 注 疏 *Maou she choo soo.* "Maou Chang's Version of the Book of Odes. With a Commentary" by Ching Kang-ching, "and with Expositions" collected by Kung Ying-tă. Edited by Yuen Yuen. 20 keuen.　　　1815. 8°.

—— 詩 經 楬 要 *She king kĕĕ yaou.* "The Book of Odes. With an Abridgment" of the Commentaries of Choo He and others. Edited by Heu Paou-shen. 4 keuen.　　[1800 ?]. 12°.

Another copy.
Imperfect, containing only the first keuen.

—— 詩 經 體 註 *She king te choo.* "The Book of Odes, with a Body of Comments," including the Commentary of Choo He. Edited by Kaou Chaou-ying. The Tseu-kin Tang Edition. 8 keuen.　　　　　　　　1711. 8°.

詩 經 SHE KING. (*Continued.*)

欽 定 詩 經 傳 說 彙 纂 *Kin ting she king chuen shwŏ wei tswan.* "The Book of Odes. With a Compilation and Digest of the Comments and Remarks thereon" by Choo He, Tsae Chin, Kung Gan-kwŏ, and others. Compiled by an Imperial Commission consisting of Wang Hung-seu, Kwei Seu, and others. 21 keuen.　　　　　　　　　　1727. 8°.

Another copy.
Imperfect, containing only keuen 9, 10.

—— 詩 經 說 約 集 解 *She king shwŏ yŏ tseĭh keae.* "The Book of Odes, with a Compendium of Annotations," and with the Commentary of Choo He. Edited by Fan Kea-heen and Wan Show-yĭh. The Peen-che Tang Edition. 8 keuen.　　　　　　　1688. 8°.

—— 旁 訓 詩 經 體 註 衍 義 *Pang heun She king te choo yen e.* "The Book of Odes, with a Body of Comments and with Copious Interpretations." Containing the Commentary of Choo He. Edited by Koo Tseay-gan. An Enlarged Edition. 8 keuen.　　　　　　　1687. 8°.

—— 詩 經 體 註 衍 義 合 參 *She king te choo yen e hŏ tsan.* "The Book of Odes, with a Body of Comments and with Copious Interpretations." Containing the Commentary of Choo He. Edited by Koo Tseay-gan. An enlarged edition. 8 keuen.　　　　　　　　1689. 8°.

Another edition of the above.

Another edition. 8 keuen.　　　　1689. 8°.

—— 詩 經 衍 義 體 註 大 全 合 參 *She king yen e te choo ta tscuen hŏ tsan.* "The Book of Odes, with Copious Interpretations and with a Body of Comments." Containing the Commentary of Choo He. An enlarged Edition. 8 keuen.
　　　　　　　　　　　　　[1689 ?]. 8°.

Imperfect, keuen 1, 2, being wanting. Another edition of the above.

詩 經 SHE KING. (Continued.)

御 案 詩 經 備 旨 *Yu gan She king pe che.* "The Book of Odes. With a Paraphrase and Notes." Compiled by Tsow Shing-mĭh. Edited by Yew Ko-ting. 8 keuen. [1800?]. 8°.

Imperfect, the first four keuen wanting.

—— 詩 序 廣 義 *She seu kwang e.* "The Book of Odes and its Preface fully explained" by Keang Ping-chang. Edited by Chow Yun. 24 keuen. 1815. 8°.

—— 詩 所 *She so.* "The Correct Meaning and Order of the Book of Odes." By Le Kwang-te. 8 keuen. 1718. 8°.

尸 佼 SHE KEAOU.

尸 子 集 本 *She tsze tseĭh pun.* "The Works of She Keaou." Edited by Sung Sing-yen. 2 keuen. 1806. 8°.

施 耐 菴 SHE NAE-GAN.

水 滸 傳 *Shwuy hoo chuen.* "The Story of the River's Banks." By She Nae-gan. Edited by Kin Shing-tan. 75 keuen. 1734. 8°.

Another copy.

施 山 公 SHE SHAN-KUNG.

心 畧 *Sin leŏ.* "A Short Treatise on Military Tactics." *See* 水 SHWUY. 水 陸 戰 守 攻 畧 方 術 秘 書 七 種 *Shwuy lŭh chen show kung leŏ fang shŭh pe shoo tseĭh chung.* "A Military System for both Land and Sea," &c. 8°.

—— 心 畧 *Sin leŏ.* "A Short Treatise on Military Tactics." [1750?]. 8°.

Title-page wanting.

施 惟 誠 SHE WEI-CHING.

See 劉 熙 LEW HE. 釋 名 *Shĭh ming.* "Phrases Explained." . . Edited by She Wei-ching, &c. 8°.

施 維 翰 SHE WEI-HAN.

See 趙 士 麟 CHAOU SZE-LIN. 浙 江 通 志 *Chĕ-keang tung che.* "A Topography of the Province of Chĕ-keang." Compiled by . . . She Wei-han, &c. 1684. 8°.

施 永 圖 SHE YUNG-TOO.

武 備 地 利 *Woo pe te le.* "A System of Fortification" for the Maritime Provinces of China. 3 keuen. [1800?]. 8°.

Imperfect, containing only keuen 2, 3.

是 亦 軒 SHE YĬH HEEN.

是 亦 軒 詩 稿 *She yĭh Heen she kaou.* "Poetry from the She-yĭh Study." 6 keuen. [1800?]. 8°.

聶 銑 敏 SHĔ SEEN-MIN.

寄 嶽 雲 齋 試 體 詩 *Ke yŏ yun chae she te she.* "A Collection of Poetical Essays from the Ke-yŏ-yun Study." Enlarged and revised by Choo Chaou-fung. With Notes by Chang Heŏ-soo. 3 keuen. 1804. 8°.

扇 SHEN.

盤 龍 寶 扇 *Pwan lung paou shen.* "The Story of the Coiled-Dragon Precious Fan." A Dramatic Tale. [1855?]. 8°.

—— 新 選 玉 葵 寶 扇 全 本 *Sin seuen yŭh kwei paou shen tseuen pun.* "The Precious Malva-leaved Fan." A Dramatic Tale. 3 keuen. [1840?]. 8°.

禪 塔 海 SHEN TĂ-HAE.

刑 部 則 例 *Hing poo tsĭh le.* "The Regulations of the Board of Punishments." Compiled by Shen Tă-hae, &c. *See* TSING DYNASTY. 大 清 律 箋 釋 *Ta Tsing leŭh tseen shĭh.* "The Laws of the Tsing Dynasty," &c. 1725. 8°.

善 德 SHEN TĬH. *pseud.* [*i.e.* Carl F. A. Guetzlaff].

上 帝 萬 物 之 大 主 *Shang te wan wŭh che ta choo.* "God, the Lord of the Universe." 2 keuen. *Singapore*, [1835?]. 8°.

Another edition. 2 keuen. [*Singapore*, 1838?]. 8°.

善 德 者 SHEN-TĬH-CHAY. *pseud.* [*i.e.* Carl F. A. Guetzlaff].

關 繫 重 大 略 說 *Kwan he chung ta leŏ shwŏ.* "A Tract on the Great Concerns of Life." *Singapore*, 1837. 8°.

—— 但 耶 利 言 行 全 傳 *Tan yay le yen hing tseuen chuen.* "The Life of the Prophet Daniel." *Singapore*, 1837. 8°.

石橋 SHǏH KEAOU.

石橋五百尊羅漢像 *Shǐh keaou woo pǐh tsun Lo han seang.* "Likeness of the Five Hundred Venerable Disciples of Buddha of the Stone Bridge." 10 Vol. [1700?]. Oblong.

石龐 SHǏH LUNG.

觀物篇 *Kwan wǔh peen.* "A View of Things in General." *See* 張山來 CHANG SHAN-LAE, and 張進也 CHANG TSIN-YAY. 昭代叢書 *Chaou tae tsung shoo.* "A Collection of Reprints of Works by Authors under the Present Dynasty," &c. Keuen 21. 1703. 8°.

石申 SHǏH SHIN.

See 甘公 KAN KUNG, and SHǏH SHIN. 星經 *Sing king.* "A Work on Astronomy." By Kan Kung and Shǐh Shin, &c. 8°.

石成金 SHǏH CHING-KIN.

家寶 *Kea paou.* "Household Jewels." A Compendium of Useful Knowledge. Compiled by Shǐh Ching-kin. 4 Parts. 1739. 12°.

Another copy.

Another edition. 1739. 8°.

Another edition. [1750?]. 12°.

—— 傳家寶 *Chuen kea paou.* "Traditional Household Jewels." Compiled by Shǐh Ching-kin. 8 keuen. 1707. 8°.
    Imperfect, the first keuen wanting.

Another copy.
    Imperfect, the first keuen wanting.

石和陽 SHǏH HO-YANG.

See 黃帝 HWANG TE. 陰符經 *Yin foo king.* "The Sûtra of Secret Charms." With a Commentary by Shǐh Ho-yang, &c. 1793. 8°.

—— *See* 老君 LAOU KEUN. 黃庭經註 *Hwang ting king choo.* "A Work on the Government of the Inner Man." With a Commentary by Shǐh Ho-yang, &c. 1793. 8°.

石國球 SHǏH KWǒ-KEW.

See 陳鍈 CHIN YING. 海澄縣志 *Hae ching heen che.* "A Topography of Hae-ching Heen." .. Compiled by .. Shǐh Kwǒ-kew, &c. 1762. 8°.

石臨初 SHǏH LIN-CHOO.

See 吳又可 WOO YEW-KO. 溫疫方論 *Wǎn yǐh fang lun.* "A Treatise on Prescriptions for the Pestilence." Edited by Shǐh Lin-choo, &c. 8°.

石天俊 SHǏH TEEN-TSEUN.

浙江鄉試硃卷 *Chě keang heang she choo keuen.* "Essays written by Shǐh Teen-tseun at the Chě-keang District Examination" for the Year 1792. 1792. 8°.

石韞玉 SHǏH WAN-YǓH.

崑新兩縣志 *Kwǎn Sin leang heen che.* "A Topography of Kwǎn-shan Heen and Sin-yang Heen," in the Prefecture of Soo-chow. 41 keuen. 1826. 8°.
An odd vol., containing only the first three keuen.

石有恒 SHǏH YEW-HǍNG.

稿 *Kaou.* "Essays." *See* 長城 CHANG CHING. 名家制義 *Ming kea che e.* "Essays" on Texts from the Four Books, &c. Tsǐh 79. 1699. 8°.

石永齡 SHǏH YUNG-LING.

See 陸璣 LǓH KE. 毛詩草木鳥獸蟲魚疏 *Maou she tsaou mǔh neaou show chung yu soo.* "The Botany and Zoology of the Book of Odes." ... Edited by Shǐh Yung-ling, &c. 8°.

實叉難陀 SHǏH-CHA-NAN-TO [*i.e.* Ṣikshánanda].

大方廣佛華嚴經 *Ta fang kwang Fǔh hwa yen king.* "The Avatamsaka Sûtra." Translated into Chinese by Shǐh-cha-nan-to, a Buddhist Priest. 80 keuen. 1411. 8°.

Another copy.

Another edition. 80? keuen. [1750?]. Oblong.
    Imperfect, containing only the thirty-third keuen.

室 SHǏH.

暗室燈 *Gan shǐh tǎng.* "A Lamp in a Dark Room." A Moral Work, compiled from the Writings of Taouist Authors by Shin-shan keu-sze, or the Retired Scholar of Mount Shin. 3 keuen. [1800?]. 8°.
    Imperfect. Wanting the first keuen.

—— 暗室燈註解 *Gan shǐh tǎng choo keae.* "A Lamp in a Dark Room. With a Commentary and Explanations." A Reprint. 2 keuen. 1835. 8°.

申 培 SHIN PEI.

古 魯 詩 *Koo Loo she.* "The Ancient Loo Odes."
See 汪 士 漢 WANG SZE-HAN. 祕 書 廿 八 種
Pe shoo neen pă chung. "A Collection of Twenty-
eight Reprints," &c.　　　　　1808. 8°.

—— 詩 說 *She shwŏ.* "Remarks on the Book of
Odes." Edited by Wei Yu-kwang. [1790?]. 8°.

申 涵 光 SHIN HAN-KWANG.

荊 園 小 語 *King yuen seaou yu.* "Scraps from
the Thorn-bush Garden." [Also] 荊 園 進 語
King yuen tsin yu. "Introductory Scraps from
the Thorn-bush Garden." *See* 張 山 來 CHANG
SHAN-LAE, and 張 進 也 CHANG TSIN-YAY.
昭 代 叢 書 *Chaou tae tsung shoo.* "A Collection of Reprints of Works written by Authors
under the Present Dynasty," &c. Keuen 15, 16.
1703. 8°.

申 劦 山 SHIN HWŬH-SHAN.

See 周 天 樞 CHOW TA-CHOO. 應 試 五 桃 精 選
Ying she woo pae tsing seuen. "A Collection of
Model Poetical Essays." .. Edited by .. Shin
Hwŭh-shan, &c.　　　　　8°.

申 時 行 SHIN SHE-HING.

See 孔 丘 KUNG KEW. 古 本 官 板 書 經 大 全
Koo pun kwan pan shoo king ta tseuen. "The
Original Official Text of the Book of Historical
Documents." .. Compiled by Shin She-hing, &c.
8°.

申 贊 皇 SHIN TSAN-HWANG.

See 周 大 樞 CHOW TA-CHOO. 應 試 排 律 精
選 鯨 鏗 集 *Ying she pae leŭh tsing seuen king
kăng tseĭh.* "The King-kăng Collection of Successful Poetical Examination Essays." .. With
Notes by Shin Tsan-hwang, &c.　　1758. 8°.

神 SHIN.

眞 神 總 論 *Chin shin tsung lun.* "On the True
God." [By Jehu Lewis Shuck.]
[*Shanghae?*], 1849. 8°.

神 詩 SHIN SHE.

續 纂 省 身 神 詩 *Sŭh tswan săng shin shin she.*
"A Supplementary Collection of Protestant
Hymns."　　　　　[1855?]. 8°.

神 天 SHIN TEEN.

神 天 道 碎 集 傳 *Shin teen taou suy tseĭh chuen.*
"Short Dissertations on the Heavenly Doctrine."
[By Dr. R. Morrison.] [*Malacca*, 1818?]. 8°.

深 山 居 士 SHIN-SHAN KEU-SZE.

See 室 SHĬH. 暗 室 燈 註 解 *Gan shĭh tăng
choo keae.* "The Lamp in a Dark Room." ..
By Shin-shan keu-sze, &c.　　　1835. 8°.

聖 SHING.

聖 跡 全 圖 *Shing tseĭh tseuen too.* "Footsteps
of the Sage" [*i.e.* Confucius]. Completely
Illustrated. 2 keuen.　　　　　4°.

聖 會 SHING HWUY.

聖 會 之 史 *Shing Hwuy che she.* "The History
of the Church" of Christ. [By C. F. A. Guetzlaff.] 4 keuen.　　　　　[1840?]. 8°.
Title-page wanting.

—— 聖 會 準 繩 *Shing hwuy chun shing.* "The
Faith and Practice of a Christian Church"
supported by Texts from Scripture. [By Dr.
James Legge.]　　　*Hongkong*, 1856. 8°.

聖 錄 SHING LŬH.

聖 錄 名 人 問 答 *Shing lŭh ming jin wăn tă.*
"A Catechism on the Celebrated Characters of
the Bible," being a Translation of Ince's Catechism?　　　　　1822. 8°.

聖 廟 SHING MEAOU.

聖 廟 志 輯 要 *Shing Meaou che tseĭh yaou.* "An
Epitomised Topography of the Sacred Temple"
of Confucius in Shantung.　　[1750?]. 8°.
Imperfect, containing only four illustrations belonging to
the above-named Work.

盛 超 然 SHING CHAOU-JEN.

[A Volume of Essays on Texts from the Classics
by Shing Chaou-jen and others. No general
Title.]　　　　　[1790?]. 12°.

盛 梅 溪 SHING MEI-KE.

See 馬 少 雲 MA SHAOU-YUN, and SHING MEI-
KE. 衛 藏 圖 識 *Wei tsang too shĭh.* "An
Itinerary of Tibet." .. Compiled by Ma Shaou-
yun and Shing Mei-ke, &c.　　　1792. 8°.

盛百二 SHING PĬH-URH.
> 佾書釋天 *Shang shoo shih teen.* "The References to the Heavens in the Book of Historical Documents, Explained." 6 keuen. *See* 嚴杰 YEN LĔĚ. 皇清經解 *Hwang Tsing king keae.* "The Classics Explained," &c. Keuen 485–490.   1829. 8°.

乘齋氏 SHING-CHAE-SHE.
> *See* 松雲 SUNG YUN. 英雲夢傳 *Ying yun mung chuen.* "The Dreams of Ying and Yun." . . . Edited by Shing-chae-she, &c.   8°.

舒弘諤 SHOO HUNG-GŎ.
> *See* 易經 YĬH KING. 易經講意去疑 *Yih king keang e keu e.* "The Book of Changes explained, and the Doubtful Passages cleared up." By Shoo Hung-gŏ, &c.   1631. 8°.

樹德堂 SHOO TĬH-TANG.
> 經文彙鈔 *King wăn wei chaou.* "A Collection of Taouist Classical Literature." Compiled by Shoo Tĭh-tang. 6 keuen.   1803. 8°.
> There are two other imperfect copies of this work.

書 SHOO.
> 贈書記 *Tsang shoo ke.* "The Story of the Gift Books." *See* 曲 KEŬH. 六十種曲 *Lŭh shih chung keŭh.* "Sixty Plays," &c. Taou 6.   8°.

—— 書畫同珍 *Shoo hwa tung chin.* "Chefs-d'œuvre of Caligraphy and Drawing."   [1800 ?]. 8°.

書札 SHOO CHĂ.
> 新選珠江書札 *Sin seuen choo keang shoo chă.* "A New and Elegant Letter-writer."   Canton, 1832. 8°.

書經 SHOO KING.
> 書經文茂 *Shoo king wăn mow.* "Elegant Essays on Texts from the Book of Historical Documents."   [1790 ?]. 12°.

SHUCK (JEHU LEWIS).
> *See* 神 SHIN. 眞神總論 *Chin shin tsung lun.* "On the True God." [By J. L. S.], &c.   1849. 8°.

蜀才 SHUH TSAE.
> 周易注 *Chow Yih choo.* "Notes on the Chow Changes." *See* 孫堂 SUN TANG. 漢魏二十一家易注 *Han Wei urh shih yih kea Yih choo.* "Commentaries on the Book of Changes," &c.   1799. 8°.

順治 SHUN-CHE. *Emperor.*
> 御製人臣儆心錄 *Yu che jin chin king sin lüh.* "An Imperial Admonition to Men and Officials." Proclaimed by the Emperor Shunche, in the year 1655. A Reprint. 1837. 8°.

Another copy.

純陽眞人 SHUN YANG CHIN JIN.
> *See* 呂嵒 LEU YEN.

雙 SHWANG.
> *See* FŬH KEEN. 雙 SHWANG. *General.* A Proclamation, &c.   1841. 8°.

雙鳳 SHWANG FUNG.
> 雙鳳奇緣傳 *Shwang Fung ke lüh chuen.* "The Wonderful Story of the Two Phœnices." A Historical Romance, founded upon events which occurred during the Han Dynasty. By the 'Master of Seŭh tseaou.' 80 Chapters.   1809. 12°.
> Imperfect, wanting the last sixteen chapters.

雙清 SHWANG TSING.
> 晉麈 *Tsin choo.* "The Tsin Deer." *See* 閔景賢 MIN KING-HEEN. 快書 *Kwae shoo.* "A Book of Amusement." Keuen 3. 1626. 8°.

說 SHWŎ.
> 說郛 *Shwŏ foo.* "Odds and Ends" from Works in all Branches of Literature. [1750 ?]. 8°.
> Imperfect, containing only Series 31 and 37.

—— 說畧 *Shwŏ leŏ.* "Historical and other Tracts."   [1700 ?]. 8°.

—— 說鈴 *Shwŏ ling.* "Miscellaneous Records." By various Authors. [34 keuen ?]. [1800 ?]. 8°.
> Imperfect, containing only keuen 27–34.

—— 說選 *Shwŏ seuen.* "A Collection of Records." 10 Vol.   [1700 ?]. 8°.

說 SHWŎ. (Continued.)

說纂 Shwŏ tswan. "Miscellaneous Records." 10 Vol. [1700?]. 8°.

—— 說淵 Shwŏ yuen. "A Collection of Tales." 10 Vol. [1700?]. 8°.

說唱 SHWŎ CHANG.

說唱花園會 Shwŏ chang hwa yuen hwuy. "Choice Plays." 20 keuen. [1800?]. 8°.

水 SHWUY.

水滸記 Shwuy hoo ke. "The Story of the River's Banks." See 曲 KEŬH. 六十種曲 Lŭh shĭh chung keŭh. "Sixty Plays," &c. Taou 5. 8°.

—— 水陸戰守攻略方術秘書七種 Shwuy lŭh chen show kung leŏ fang shŭh pe shoo tseĭh chung. "A Military System for both Land and Sea, divided into Seven Sections" [viz.: 1. Ping fă sin yaou; 2. Pĭh chen ke leŏ; by Lew Pĭh-wăn. 3. Sin leŏ, by She Shan-kung. 4. Kin tang shĭh urh chow, by Le Pwan. 5. Teen hea yuen hae hing shĭh lŭh, by Chin Tsze-chae. 6. Han wae hing keuen che chang. 7. E fang pe yaou]. [1800?]. 8°.

水中龍 SHWUY-CHUNG-LUNG.

星平會海 Sing ping hwuy hae. "The Junction of the Stars and the Sea." A Book of Fate. Edited by Choo Hwuy-lung and Wang Ke. 10 keuen. [1750?]. 8°.

Another copy.
Imperfect, containing only parts of keuen 4 and 5.

—— 千里馬集註 Tseen le ma tseĭh choo. "The Thousand-Le Horse Collection" of Divinatory Lore. With a Commentary compiled by Shwuy-chung-lung. 1815. 8°.

ṢIKSHÁNANDA.
See 實叉難陀 SHĬH-CHA-NAN-TO.

心 SIN.

求心錄 Kew sin lŭh. "Seeking a Heart." See 說 SHWŎ. 說淵 Shwŏ yuen. "A Collection of Tales," &c. Vol. 9. 8°.

心 SIN. (Continued.)

正心格言 Ching sin kĭh yen. "Excellent Words to Correct the Heart." A Collection of Buddhist and Taouist Opuscules. 1846. 8°.

—— 快心編全傳 Kwae sin peen tseuen chuen. "A Merry Tale." By 'The Clever Man of Teen-hwa.' In Three Parts. [1750?]. 8°.

—— 明心寶鑑 Ming sin paou keen. "The Precious Mirror for Enlightening the Heart." 2 keuen. [1750?]. 8°.

Another edition. 2 keuen. 1793. 8°.

Another edition. 2 keuen. 1855. 8°.

—— 新增養心神詩 Sin tsăng yang sin shin she. "Hymns. A New and Enlarged Edition." According to a manuscript note on Title-page, this collection of Hymns was compiled by Dr. Milne. [1821?]. 8°.

—— 養心神詩 Yang sin shin she. "Hymns for Improving the Heart." [By Dr. R. Morrison.] [1818?]. 8°.

—— 養心神詩 Yang sin shin she. "Hymns for Improving the Heart." [By Dr. James Legge.] Malacca, 1842. 8°.

—— 一見咲開心 Yĭh keen seaou kae sin. "A Glance at this Book will make you Laugh and Rejoice." 8°.

星 SING.

星眞寶懺 Sing chin paou tsan. "The True and Precious Ritual of the Stars." 1842. 8°.

—— 星平要訣百中經 Sing ping yaou keuĕ pĭh chung king. "The Laws of Astrology. Together with the Classic of a Hundred Hits." 1811. 8°.

Another edition. 1848. 8°.

性理 SING LE.

性理畧論 Sing le leŏ lun. "Discourses on Human Nature." [By F. S. Turner?]. 3 keuen. Hongkong, 1869. 8°.

24

SMITH (JOHN PYE).

See 天 TEEN. 天人異同 *Teen jin e tung.* "The Analogy between Religion and Philosophy." Translated .. from J. P. S.'s Introduction to Butler's Analogy of Religion, &c. 1857. 8°.

梭 So

投梭記 *Tow so ke.* "The Story of Throwing the Shuttle." See 曲 KEŬH. 六十種曲 *Lŭh shĭh chung keŭh.* "Sixty Plays," &c. Taou 4. 8°.

索額圖 Sŏ GĬH-TOO.

See CHINA. 督捕則例 *Tŭh poo tsĭh le.* "Regulations for the Capture" of Deserters. Compiled by .. Sŏ Gĭh-too, &c. 1676. 8°.

朔憨山老人 SŎ-HAN SHAN LAOU JIN.

See 八識 PĂ SHĬH. 八識略說 *Pă shĭh leŏ shwŏ.* "A Short Treatise on the Eight Vidjñânas." .. by 'The Old Man of Mount Sŏ-han.' 1792. 8°.

蘇轍 Soo CHĔ.

稿 *Kaou.* "Essays." See 長城 CHANG CHING. 名家制義 *Ming kea che e.* "Essays" on Texts from the Four Books, &c. Tsĭh 2. 1699. 8°.

—— 蘇文 *Soo wăn.* "Selections from the Writings of Soo Chĕ. See 儲欣 CHOO HIN. 唐宋八大家類選 *Tang Sung pă ta kea luy seuen.* "Selections from the Works of Eight Scholars who Flourished under the Tang and Sung Dynasties," &c. 1766. 8°.

———— See 茅坤 MAOU KWĂN. 唐宋八大家文鈔 *Tang Sung pă ta kea wăn chaou.* "The Works of Eight Scholars who Flourished under the Tang and Sung Dynasties," &c. 1631. 8°.

—— 道德經 *Taou tĭh king.* "The Classic of Reason and Virtue." With a Commentary by Soo Chĕ. See 焦竑 TSEAOU HUNG. 老莊翼合刻 *Laou Chwang yĭh hŏ kĭh.* "The Works of Laou keun and Chwang Chow," &c. 1588. 8°.

蘇鶚 Soo Gŏ.

杜陽雜編 *Too yang tsă peen.* "Miscellanies from Too yang." See 王文誥 WANG WĂN-KAOU. 唐代叢書 *Tang tae tsung shoo.* "A Collection of Reprints of Works written during the Tang Dynasty," &c. Series 1. 1806. 8°.

蘇籀 Soo LEW.

雙溪集 *Shwang ke tseĭh.* "The Shwang Ke Collection" of the Works of Soo Lew. 15 keuen. See 伍崇曜 WOO TSUNG-YAOU. 粵雅堂叢書 *Yŭĕ ya Tang tsung shoo.* "The Yŭĕ-ya Tang Collection of Reprints," &c. Series 8. 1853. 8°.

蘇洵 Soo SEUN.

蘇文 *Soo wăn.* "The Writings of Soo Seun." 10 keuen. See 茅坤 MAOU KWĂN. 唐宋八大家文鈔 *Tang Sung pă ta kea wăn chaou.* "The Works of Eight Scholars who Flourished under the Tang and Sung Dynasties," &c. 1631. 8°.

—— See 四書 SZE SHOO. 蘇老泉批評孟子眞本 *Soo Laou-tseuen pe ping Măng tsze chin pun.* "Soo Seun's Edition of the Works of Mencius," &c. 1803. 8°.

—— See 易經 YĬH KING. 易經兒說 *Yĭh king urh shwŏ.* "The Book of Changes." ... Compiled by Soo Seun, &c. 1687. 8°.

蘇軾 Soo SHĬH.

戒殺論 *Keae shă lun.* "A Discourse against Destroying Life." See 沈培木 CHIN PEI-MŬH. 慈心寶鑑 *Tsze sin paou keen.* "The Precious Mirror of a Merciful Heart," &c. 1771. 8°.

—— 蘇文 *Soo wăn.* "The Writings of Soo Shĭh." 28 keuen. See 茅坤 MAOU KWĂN. 唐宋八大家文鈔 *Tang Sung pă ta kea wăn chaou.* "The Works of Eight Scholars who Flourished under the Tang and Sung Dynasties," &c. 1631. 8°.

—— 雜纂 *Tsă tswan.* "Miscellaneous Aphorisms." Keuen 3. See 說 SHWŎ. 說纂 *Shwŏ tswan.* "Miscellaneous Records," &c. Vol. 8. 8°.

—— 蘇詩補註 *Soo she poo choo.* "The Poems of Soo Shĭh. With a Supplementary Commentary" by Ung Fang-kang. 8 keuen. See 伍崇曜 WOO TSUNG-YAOU. 粵雅堂叢書 *Yŭĕ ya Tang tsung shoo.* "The Yŭĕ-ya Tang Collection of Reprints," &c. Series 6. 1853. 8°.

第一卷

蘇軾 Soo Shĭh. (*Continued.*)

東坡遺意 *Tung-po e e.* "Posthumous Reflections of Soo Shĭh, known as the Poet Soo Tung-po." 1780? 8°.

蘇特 Soo Tĭh.

衣冠盛事 *E kwan shing sze.* "About Dresses and Caps." *See* 說 Shwŏ. 說郛 *Shwŏ foo.* "Odds and Ends," &c. 8°.

蘇煒 Soo Wei.

See 林大謬 Lin Ta-gŏ. 蠒齋詩賦稿 *Kĕen chae she foo kaou.* "Poems from the Silkworm's Cocoon Study." With Notes by Soo Wei, &c. 1820. 8°.

蘇誠額 Soo Ching-gĭh.

See China. Board of Ceremonies. 欽定禮部則例 *Kin ting Le Poo tsĭh le.* "Regulations of the Board of Ceremonies." Compiled by . . . Soo Ching-gĭh, &c. 1820. 8°.

蘇天爵 Soo Teen-tseŏ.

元朝名臣事略 *Yuen chaou ming chin sze leŏ.* "Biographical Notices of Forty-six Famous Ministers under the Yuen Dynasty." 15 keuen. 1774. 8°.

蘇文昌 Soo Wăn-chang.

閑情十二憮 *Heen tsing shĭh urh foo.* "The Twelve Objects of Affection of Gentle Natures." *See* 閔景賢 Min King-heen. 快書 *Kwae shoo.* "A Book of Amusements," &c. Keuen 21. 1626. 8°.

蘇堯松 Soo Yaou-sung.

See 易經 Yĭh king. 易經兒說 *Yĭh king urh shwŏ.* "The Book of Changes." . . Edited by Soo Yaou-sung, &c. 1687. 8°.

STAUNTON (Sir George), *Bart.*

See 嘶噹喃 Sze-tang-tung.

STRONACH (Alexander).

See Jesus Christ. 總論耶穌之榮 *Tsung lun Yay-soo che yung.* "A Discourse on the Glory of Jesus Christ." [By A. S.], &c. 1868. 8°.

STRONACH (John).

See 終 Tung. 善終誌傳 *Shen tung che chuen.* "Stories of Happy Deaths." [By J. S.], &c. 8°.

STRONACH (John). (*Continued.*)

See 耶穌敎 Yay-soo keaou. 耶穌敎或問 *Yay-soo keaou hwŏ wăn.* "A Catechism on the Christian Religion." [By J. S.], &c. 1858. 8°.

孫 Sun.

See 丁 Ting, and Sun. 廣東全塲闈墨 *Kwang-tung tseuen chang wei mĭh.* . . . "Kwang-tung Examination Essays" . . Compiled by . . Ting and Sun, &c. 1831. 8°.

孫璋 Sun Chang.

性理眞詮 *Sing le chin tseuen.* "Truthful Disquisitions on Mental Philosophy." Edited by Sung Keun-yung and others. 4 keuen. 1753. 8°.

—— 性理眞詮提綱 *Sing le chin tseuen te kang.* "An Epitome of Sun Chang's Truthful Disquisitions on Mental Philosophy." Edited by Sung Keun-yung and others. 3 keuen. 1753. 8°.

孫詔 Sun Chaou.

See 曹秉仁 Tsaou Ping-jin. 寧波府志 *Ning po foo che.* "A Topography of Ning-po." . . . Edited by Sun Chaou, &c. 1729. 8°.

孫甫 Sun Foo.

唐史論斷 *Tang she lun twan.* "An Examination of the History of the Tang Dynasty." 3 keuen. *See* 伍崇曜 Woo Tsung-yaou. 粵雅堂叢書 *Yuĕ ya Tang tsung shoo.* "The Yuĕ-ya Tang Collection of Reprints," &c. Series 3. 1853. 8°.

孫洪 Sun Hung.

See 邵恊 Shaou Tan. 靜遠軒傅稿彙編 *Tsing yuen heen foo kaou wei peen.* "A Collection of Essays." . . . Edited by Sun Hung, &c. 1782. 8°.

孫焜 Sun Hwăn.

See 陳世熙 Chin She-he. 霏屑軒尺牘類選 *Fei sĕĕ heen chĭh tŭh luy seuen.* "A Model Letter Writer." . . . Edited by Sun Hwăn, etc. 1802. 8°.

孫棨 SUN KE.
北里誌 *Pĭh le chc.* "Records of the Northern Village." *See* 說 SHWŏ. 說纂 *Shwŏ tswan.* "Miscellaneous Records," &c. Vol. 7. 8°.

———— *See* 王文誥 WANG WĂN-KAOU. 唐代叢書 *Tang tae tsung shoo.* "A Collection of Reprints of Works written during the Tang Dynasty," &c. Series 3. 1806. 8°.

孫鑛 SUN KWANG.
稿 *Kaou.* "Essays." *See* 長城 CHANG CHING. 名家制義 *Ming kea che e.* "Essays" on Texts from the Four Books, &c. Tsĭh 57. 1699. 8°.

—— *See* 左丘明 TSO KEW-MING. 春秋左傳解要 *Chun Tsew Tso chuen keae yaou.* "The Essential Portions of Tso Kew-ming's Narrative . . . explained" by Sun Kwang, &c. 1817. 8°.

孫理 SUN LE.
國朝律賦新機 *Kwŏ chaou leŭh foo sin kc.* "Odes by Authors of the Present Dynasty. In a New Form." Compiled by Sun Le. With Notes by Hoo Kin-chĭh and Hoo Yŭh-shoo. Two Series. [1750 ?]. 8°.
Much torn.

—— 國朝七排詩鈔 *Kwŏ chaou tseĭh pae she chaou.* "A Selection of Odes by Authors of the Present Dynasty in Verses of Seven Characters each." Compiled by Sun Le. Edited by Hoo Yŭh-shoo, Hoo Kin-chĭh, &c. 8 keuen. 1807. 8°.

孫樓 SUN LOW.
稿 *Kaou.* "Essays." *See* 長城 CHANG CHING. 名家制義 *Ming kea che e.* "Essays" on Texts from the Four Books, &c. Tsĭh 45. 1699. 8°.

孫堂 SUN TANG.
漢魏二十一家易注 *Han Wei urh shĭh yĭh kea Yĭh choo.* "Commentaries on the Book of Changes by Twenty-one Writers during the Han and Wei Dynasties." Edited by Sun Tang. 1799. 8°.

孫覿 SUN TEĬH.
鴻慶集 *Hung king tseĭh.* "The Hung king Collection." *See* 吳孟舉 WOO MĂNG-KEU, and 吳自牧 WOO TSZE-MŬH. 宋詩鈔二集 *Sung she chaou urh tseĭh.* "Poetry of the Sung Dynasty," &c. 8°.

孫頠 SUN WEI.
幻異志 *Hwan e che.* "Tales of Witchcraft." *See* 王文誥 WANG WĂN-KAOU. 唐代叢書 *Tang tae tsung shoo.* "A Collection of Reprints of Works written during the Tang Dynasty," &c. Series 6. 1806. 8°.

—— 幻異志 *Hwan e che.* "Tales of Witchcraft." By Sun Wei, of the Tang Dynasty. A Reprint. [1741 ?]. 8°.

—— 神女傳 *Shin neu chuen.* "Tales of Fairies." By Sun Wei, of the Tang Dynasty. A Reprint. [1741 ?]. 8°.

孫武 SUN WOO.
孫子 *Sun tsze.* "The Writings of Sun Woo." *See* 黃海岸 HWANG HAE-GAN. 周秦十一子 *Chow Tsin shĭh yĭh tsze.* "The Works of the Eleven Philosophers of the Chow and Tsin Dynasties," &c. 8°.

孫致彌 SUN CHE-ME.
杕左堂集 *Te tso Tang tseĭh.* "The Te-tso Tang Collection" of Literary Pieces. Edited by Woo Keu and others. 4 keuen. 8°.

孫志祖 SUN CHE-TSOO.
讀書脞錄 *Tŭh shoo tsŏ lŭh.* "Short Remarks on Studying the Classics." 4 keuen. *See* 嚴杰 YEN LĔĔ. 皇清經解 *Hwang Tsing king keae.* "The Classics Explained," &c. Keuen 491–494. 1829. 8°.

孫汝忠 SUN JOO-CHUNG.
金丹眞傳 *Kin tan chin chuen.* "A Trustworthy Treatise on the Philosopher's Stone." With a Commentary by Chang Tsung-lĕĕ, and a Paraphrase by Le Kan. A Taouist Work. *Kwang-ling,* 1615. 8°.

孫 謙 益 SUN KEEN-YĬH.

See 周 興 嗣 CHOW HING-SZE. 千 字 文 釋 義 *Tsĕen tsze wăn shĭh e.* "The Thousand-Character Classic Explained" by Sun Keen-yĭh, &c. 8°.

孫 念 劬 SUN NEEN-KEU.

全 人 矩 矱 *Tseuen jin keu hwŏ.* "The Whole Duty of Man." A Taouist Work. 6 keuen.
1800. 8°.

Another edition. 6 keuen. 1800. 8°.

Another edition. 6 keuen. 1800. 8°.

孫 伯 觀 SUN PĬH-KWAN.

讀 書 通 *Tŭh shoo tung.* "A Treatise on Study." See 閔 景 賢 MIN KING-HEEN. 快 書 *Kwae shoo.* "A Book of Amusement." Keuen 31.
1626. 8°.

孫 上 登 SUN SHANG-TĂNG.

初 學 行 文 語 類 *Choo heŏ hing wăn yu luy.* "Notes on Behaviour and Literature for Beginners." Compiled by Sun Shang-tăng. Edited by Le Tsze-ting. 4 keuen. 1800. 8°.

Imperfect, containing only keuen 1.

孫 慎 行 SUN SHIN-HING.

稿 *Kaou.* "Essays." See 長 城 CHANG CHING. 名 家 制 義 *Ming kea che e.* "Essays" on Texts from the Four Books, &c. Tsĭh 73.
1699. 8°.

孫 星 衍 SUN SING-YEN.

See 尸 佼 SHE KEAOU. 尸 子 集 本 *She tsze tseĭh pun.* "The Works of She Keaou." Edited by Sun Sing-yen, &c. 1806. 8°.

—— 蔡 邕 TSAE YUNG. 琴 操 *Kin tsaou.* "Exercises for the Kin." Edited by Sun Sing-yen, &c. 1806. 8°.

—— 孫 氏 周 易 集 解 *Sun she Chow Yĭh tseĭh keae.* "The Chow Changes." ... Compiled by Sun Sing-yen. See 伍 崇 曜 WOO TSUNG-YAOU. 粤 雅 堂 叢 書 *Yuĕ ya Tang tsung shoo.* "The Yuĕ-ya Tang Collection of Reprints," &c. Series 16.
1853. 8°.

孫 星 衍 SUN SING-YEN. (*Continued.*)

尚 書 今 古 文 注 疏 *Shang shoo kin koo wăn choo soo.* "The Modern and Ancient Text of the Book of Historical Documents Commented on and Discussed." 39 keuen. [Also] 問 字 堂 集 *Wăn tsze Tang tseĭh.* "The Literary Collection of Wăn-tsze Tang." See 嚴 杰 YEN LĔĔ. 皇 清 經 解 *Hwang Tsing king keae.* "The Classics Explained," &c. Keuen 735–774.
1829. 8°.

—— 魏 石 經 考 *Wei shĭh king kaou.* "An Examination of the Stone-engraved Classics of the Wei Dynasty."
1806. 8°.

孫 士 毅 SUN SZE-E.

See 紀 昀 KE YUN. 欽 定 歷 代 職 官 表 *Kin ting leĭh tae chĭh kwan peaou.* "A Series of Tables exhibiting the Changes which have taken place in the Names and Duties of the Officers in the Several Departments of Government." ... Compiled by .. Sun Sze-e, &c. 1783. 8°.

—— 欽 定 勝 朝 殉 節 諸 臣 錄 *Kin ting shing chaou seun tsĕĕ choo chin lŭh.* "Biographical Notices of Officials ... who lost their Lives in the Service of their Country." Compiled by ... Sun Sze-e, &c. 1797. 8°.

孫 思 邈 SUN SZE-MŎ.

銀 海 精 微 *Yen hae tsing wei.* "The Essential Delicacy of the Silver Seas." A Treatise on Eye Complaints. By Sun Sze-mŏ, of the Tang Dynasty. Edited by Chow Leang-tsĕĕ, of the Tsing Dynasty. 2 keuen. [1750?]. 8°.

孫 在 豐 SUN TSAE-FUNG.

See 易 經 YĬH KING. 日 講 易 經 解 義 *Jĭh keang Yĭh king keae e.* "The Book of Changes, with a Paraphrase." .. Compiled by ... Sun Tsae-fung, &c. 1688. 8°.

孫 蒼 璧 SUN TSANG-PEĬH.

See 潘 子 聲 PWAN TSZE-SHING. 養 蒙 針 度 *Yang mung chin too.* "The Student's Guide." .... Edited by Sun Tsang-peĭh, &c. 8°.

孫泲鳴 Sun Tseen-ming.

See 物 Wŭh. 詠物詩選註釋 Yung wŭh she seuen choo shĭh. "A Collection of Songs .. with Explanatory Notes" by .. Sun Tseen-ming, &c. 8°.

孫清標 Sun Tsing-peaou.

天后聖母聖蹟圖誌全集 Teen how shing moo shing tseĭh too che tseuen tseĭh. "The Sacred Footprints of the Queen of Heaven. With Illustrations." Compiled by Sun Tsing-peaou. A Reprint. 2 keuen. Soochow, 1832. 8°.

孫端人 Sun Twan-jin.

昭明選詩初學讀本 Chaou ming seuen she choo heŏ tŭh pun. "A Selection of Brilliant Poems for the Instruction of Students." Compiled by Sun Twan-jin. Edited by Moo Yĭh-săng. 4 keuen. [1820 ?]. 8°.

孫月峰 Sun Yuĕ-fung.

See 孔丘 Kung Kew. 春秋左傳杜林合註 Chun Tsew Tso chuen Too Lin hŏ choo. "The Spring and Autumn Annals." .. Edited by Sun Yuĕ-fung, &c. 8°.

孫遠平 Sun Yuen-ping.

See 邵經邦 Shaou King-pang. 弘簡錄 Hung keen lŭh. "The Great History." ... Edited by Sun Yuen-ping, &c. 1686. 8°.

宋裏 Sung Chung.

周易注 Chow Yĭh choo. "Notes on the Chow Changes." See 孫堂 Sun Tang. 漢魏二十一家易注 Han Wei urh shĭh yĭh kea Yĭh choo. "Commentaries on the Book of Changes," &c. 1799. 8°.

宋濂 Sung Leen.

龍門子 Lung-mun-tsze. "The Writings of Sung Leen." See 沈津 Chin Tsin. 百家類纂 Pĭh kea luy tswan. "The Works of a Hundred Authors," &c. Keuen 11. 8°.

—— 元史 Yuen she. "The History of the Yuen Dynasty." Compiled by Sung Leen and others. 210 keuen. Supplement, 24 keuen. 1824. 8°.

宋慈 Sung Tsze.

洗冤錄集證 Se yuen lŭh tseĭh ching. "Records of the Washing-away of Injuries. With a Collection of Cases in Illustration." A Coroner's Guide. Edited by Wang Yew-hwae, with Additions by Le Kwan-lan. 5 keuen. 1796. 8°.

宋玉 Sung Yŭh.

九辯 Kew peen. "The Nine Changes." See 蕭統 Seaou Tung. 文選 Wăn seuen. "Elegant Extracts from Polite Literature," &c. Keuen 33. 1772. 8°.

宋筠 Sung Yun.

See 呂耀曾 Leu Yaou-tsăng. 盛京通志 Shing king tung che. "A Topography of the Metropolitan Province of Shing king." Compiled by .. Sung Yun, &c. 1736. 8°.

宋兆襘 Sung Chaou-yŏ.

See 蔡清 Tsae Tsing. 易經蒙引 Yĭh king mung yin. "A Guide to the Book of Changes." ..... Edited by Sung Chaou-yŏ, &c. 8°.

宋徵輿 Sung Ching-yu.

See 李雯 Le Wăn. 皇明詩選 Hwang Ming she seuen. "Selections from the Poetry of the Ming Dynasty." Compiled by ... Sung Ching-yu, etc. 8°.

宋若昭 Sung Jŏ-chaou.

牛應貞傳 New Ying-ching chuen. "The Story of New Ying-ching." By Sung Jŏ-chaou, of the Tang Dynasty. A Reprint. [1741 ?]. 8°.

宋如林 Sung Joo-lin.

松江府志 Sung keang foo che. "A Topography of Sung keang Foo," in the Province of Keang soo. Compiled by Sung Joo-lin, Mŏ Tsin, and others. 84 keuen. 1817. 8°.

Imperfect.

宋其沅 Sung Ke-yuen.

See CHINA. BOARD OF CEREMONIES. 欽定禮部則例 Kin ting Le Poo tseĭh le. "Regulations of the Board of Ceremonies." Compiled by ... Sung Ke-yuen, &c. 1820. 8°.

宋君榮 SUNG KEUN-YUNG.
See 孫璋 SUN CHANG. 性理眞詮 *Sing le chin tseuen.* "Truthful Disquisitions on Mental Philosophy." . . . . Edited by Sung Keun-yung, &c.　　　1753. 8º.

—————— 性理眞詮提綱 *Sing le chin tseuen te kang.* "An Epitome of Sun Chang's Truthful Disquisitions on Mental Philosophy." Edited by Sung Keun-yung, &c.　　　1753. 8º.

宋景昌 SUNG KING-CHANG.
See 李兆洛 LE CHAOU-LŎ. 歷代地理志韻編今釋 *Leĭh tae te le che yun peen kin shĭh.* "A Gazetteer." . . Edited by Sung King-chang, &c.　　　1837. 8º.

宋光亨 SUNG KWANG-HĂNG.
See 陳鍾麟 CHIN CHUNG-LIN. 聽雨軒讀本 *Ting yu heen tŭh pun.* "The Listening-to-the-rain Study Reader." . . . Edited by Sung Kwang-hăng, &c.　　　1822. 8º.

宋廣業 SUNG KWANG-NĔĔ.
羅浮山志會編 *Lo fow shan che hwuy peen.* "An Illustrated Topography of the Lo-fow Hills," in the Province of Kwang tung. Compiled by Sung Kwang-nĕĕ. 22 keuen.
　　　1716. 8º.
Another copy.
　Imperfect, containing only Preface and keuen 1.

宋敏求 SUNG MIN-KEW.
長安志 *Chang-gan che.* "A Topography of Chang-gan," the ancient Capital of China, and the modern Se-gan Foo, in the Province of Shen-se. 20 keuen.　　　1784. 8º.

宋牧仲 SUNG MŬH-CHUNG.
See 邵子湘 SHAOU TSZE-SEANG. 古今韻略 *Koo kin yun leŏ.* "A Work on the Ancient and Modern Sounds." . . . Edited by Sung Mŭh-chung, &c.　　　1696. 8º.

宋翔鳳 SUNG SEANG-FUNG.
四書釋地辨證 *Sze shoo shĭh te peen ching.* "The Topography of the Four Books discussed and verified." *See* 嚴杰 YEN LĔĔ. 皇清經解 *Hwang Tsing king keae.* "The Classics Explained," &c. Keuen 1329, 1330. 1829. 8º.

宋思仁 SUNG SZE-JIN.
廣輿吟草附編 *Kwan yu yin tsaou foo peen.* "A Supplement to the Sketch of General Geography."　　　1792. 8º.

宋道勳 SUNG TAOU-HEUN.
See CHINA. BOARD OF WORKS. 欽定工部軍器則例 *Kin ting kung Poo keun ke tsĭh le.* "Regulations issued by the Board of Works for the Supply of Military Stores." Compiled by . . Sung Taou-heun, &c.　　　1812. 8º.

松年 SUNG NEEN.
See CHINA. BOARD OF REVENUE. 戶部則例 *Hoo Poo tsĭh le.* "Regulations of the Board of Revenue." Compiled by . . Sung Neen, &c.
　　　1838. 8º.

松雲 SUNG YUN.
英雲夢傳 *Ying Yun mung chuen.* "The Dreams of Ying and Yun." A Novel. Edited by Shing-chae-she. 8 keuen. [1800?]. 8º.

Another edition.　　　[1810?]. 8º.

松筠 SUNG YUN.
綏服紀略 *Suy fŭh ke leŏ.* "A Short Account of the Pacification and Submission" of Russia. *See* 何秋濤 HO TSEW-TAOU. 北徼彙編 *Pĭh keaou wei peen.* "Treatises on the Countries beyond the Northern Frontier," &c. Keuen 1.
　　　1865. 8º.

—— 伊犂總統事畧 *E le tsung tung sze leŏ.* "A Short Account of Affairs in E le," or Chinese Turkistan. Compiled by Sung Yun, Ke Yun-sze, and others. 12 keuen.　　　1809. 8º.

嵩厓 SUNG YAE.
嵩厓尊生書 *Sung Yae tsun săng shoo.* "The Work of the Honourable Scholar Sung Yae." On Medicine. 15 keuen.　　　1714. 8º.

隨園 SUY YUEN.
隨園詩話 *Suy yuen she hwa.* "Critiques on Poetry from the Suy Garden." By the Retired Scholar of Tsang shan. With a Supplement. 15 keuen. Supplement, 3 keuen. [1790?]. 8º.
　Imperfect, wanting keuen 1, 2, 4-6.

算 法 SWAN FĂ.

校 正 算 法 *Keaou ching swan fă.* "A Carefully Prepared Work on Arithmetic." [1800?]. 8º.
    Very imperfect.

四 喜 SZE HE.

四 喜 記 *Sze he ke.* "The Four Delights." *See* 曲 KEŬH. 六 十 種 曲 *Lŭh shĭh chung keŭh.* "Sixty Plays," &c. Taou 3.   8º.

四 季 SZE KE.

四 季 蓮 花 全 本 *Sze ke leen hwa tseuen pun.* "The Story of the Perpetual Lily." In verse. 4 keuen.   [1850?]. 8º.

四 書 SZE SHOO.

監 本 四 書 *Keen pun sze shoo.* "A Revised Edition of the Four Books." Edited by Yen Mow-yew.   1740. 8º.

Another copy.
    Imperfect, wanting the first part of the *Lun yu.*

—— 四 書 正 文 *Sze shoo ching wăn.* "The Le-joo Tang Edition of the Four Books." Edited by Chin Kŏ-hwan and Yen Mow-yew. 1816. 8º.

Another copy.

Another edition. Edited by Chin Kŏ-hwan.
                     [1818?]. 8º.
Another edition. Edited by Chin Kŏ-hwan and Yen Mow-yew.   1820. 8º.

—————— "The Fŭh-wăn Tang Edition of the Four Books." Edited by Chin Kŏ-hwan.
                     [1820?]. 8º.
Imperfect, containing only the last part of the *Lun yu,* and the *Măng tsze.*

—————— "The Tsuy-king Low Edition of the Four Books." Edited by Yen Mow-yew. [1820?]. 8º.
Imperfect, wanting the *Ta heŏ* and the *Chung yung.*

—————— "The Wăn-yuen Tang Edition of the Four Books." Edited by Chin Kŏ-hwan and Yen Mow-yew.   *Canton,* [1820?]. 8º.
Imperfect, containing only the *Ta heŏ, Chung yung,* and the second part of the *Măng tsze.*

四 書 SZE SHOO. (*Continued.*)

四 書 鹽 本 *Sze shoo keen pun.* "The Original Text of the Four Books." With Choo He's Commentary. Part I. Keuen 1–10. Part II. Keuen 1–7.   1814. 8º.

—— 四 子 書 *Sze tsze shoo.* "The Books of the Four Philosophers." With Choo He's Commentary.   1827. 8º.

—— 四 書 闡 註 *Sze shoo chen choo.* "The Four Books Clearly Explained." With Choo He's Commentary. Edited by Poo Tae. 7 keuen.
                     1815. 8º.

—— 四 書 直 解 *Sze shoo chĭh keae.* "The Four Books, Clearly Explained" by Chang Keuching, a Minister of State. 26 keuen.
                     1572. 8º.

Another edition. Edited by Ching Chung, Choo Fung-e, and Seu Chow.   1766. 8º.

—— 學 源 堂 銅 板 四 書 發 註 *Heŏ yuen Tang tung pan Sze shoo fă choo.* "The Heŏ-yuen Tang Edition of the Four Books, with Notes and the Commentary" of Choo He. Compiled by Choo Ke-săng. Edited by Teĭh Le-chow. With Manuscript Notes.   1723. 8º.

—— 四 書 合 講 *Sze shoo hŏ keang.* "The Four Books Harmoniously Explained" according to the Commentary of Choo He, with a Paraphrase. Compiled by Ung Fŭh. Edited by Chen Wăn-hwan.   [1730?]. 8º.
Imperfect, containing only the *Lun yu,* and keuen 1–3 of the *Măng tsze.*

—— 四 書 便 抄 *Sze shoo peen chaou.* "A Handy Copy of the Four Books," with Choo He's Commentary. With Manuscript Notes. 1794. 8º.
Imperfect, containing only the *Ta heŏ* and the *Chung yung.*

—— 四 書 離 句 集 註 *Sze shoo le keu tseĭh choo.* "The Four Books, commented on, Sentence by Sentence," by Choo He, Ching Haou, and others. Edited by Yang Leĭh-seen. 12 keuen. 1818. 8º.
    There are two other copies of this work.

Another edition.   [1820?]. 8º.
Imperfect, containing only the *Ta heŏ* and the *Chung yung.*

四 書 Sze shoo. (*Continued.*)

四 書 集 註 *Sze shoo tseĭh choo.* "The Four Books. With a Collection of Comments." Compiled by Choo He. The Hwuy-wăn Tang Edition. 7 keuen.   [1815 ?]. 8°.

—— 四 書 集 註 衷 義 *Sze shoo tseĭh choo chung e.* "The Four Books, with a Collection of Comments, and a Just Explanation of their Meaning."   [1750 ?]. 8°.

Imperfect, containing only parts of the thirteenth, fourteenth, and fifteenth keuen.

—— 四 書 補 註 附 考 備 旨 *Sze shoo poo choo foo kaou pe che.* "The Four Books, with a Complete Digest of Supplements to the Commentary, and Additional Suggestions." A New Edition, with Additions by Kew Tsang-choo. Compiled by Tăng Lin. Edited by Too Ting-ke. 8 keuen.   1829. 8°.

Another edition.   1831. 8°.
          Imperfect.

—— 四 書 遵 註 合 講 *Sze shoo tsun choo hŏ keang.* "The Four Books according to the Commentary of Choo He, with a Paraphrase." Compiled by Ung Fŭh. The Cho-ya Study Edition.
          [1730 ?]. 8°.

Imperfect, containing only the *Lun yu,* and keuen 4–7 of the *Măng tsze.*

Another edition.   1805. 8°.
          There are two other copies of this work.

—— 四 書 朱 子 異 同 條 辨 *Sze shoo Choo tsze e tung teaou peen.* "The Four Books. With the Similar and Dissimilar Views contained in the Commentaries of Choo He," Kung Ying-tă, Ching Haou, Hoo Gan-ting, &c., discussed. Edited by Le Pei-lin and Le Ching. 1705. 8°.

Imperfect, wanting the second part of the *Ta heŏ.*

—— 論 語 *Lun yu.* "The Confucian Analects." With Choo He's Commentary. With Copious Manuscript Notes. 10 keuen. [1790 ?]. 8°.

Another copy.

四 書 Sze shoo. (*Continued.*)

論 語 集 註 *Lun yu tseĭh choo.* "The Confucian Analects. With the Commentary" of Choo He. 10 keuen.   [1790 ?]. 8°.

Another edition.   [1800 ?]. 8°.
          Imperfect, containing only keuen 6–10.

Another edition. 10 keuen.   [1800 ?]. 8°.
          Imperfect, containing only keuen 9, 10.

—— 論 語 註 疏 大 全 合 纂 *Lun yu choo soo ta tseuen hŏ tswan.* "The Confucian Analects. With a Collection of Commentaries by Choo He and others, and a Paraphrase." Compiled by Chang Poo. Edited by Hing Ping. 20 keuen.
          1636. 8°.

Another copy.
          Imperfect, wanting the third and fourth keuen.

—— 論 語 集 註 本 義 匯 參 *Lun yu tseĭh choo pun e hwuy tsan.* "The Proper Meaning of the Confucian Analects," as Determined by Choo He, "Compared with and Illustrated by the Writings of other Commentators." 20 keuen.
          [1700 ?]. 8°.

Imperfect, wanting keuen 1, 4, 5, 13, 14, 19, 20.

—— 孟 子 *Măng tsze.* "The Teachings of Mencius." With the Commentary of Choo He. 7 keuen.
          [1800 ?]. 8°.

—— 孟 子 集 註 *Măng tsze tseĭh choo.* "The Teachings of Mencius. With a Collection of Comments" by Choo He. 7 keuen.   8°.
          Title-page wanting.

Another edition. 7 keuen.   [1800 ?]. 8°.

Another edition. 7 keuen.   [1800 ?]. 8°.
          Imperfect, containing only keuen 2, 4, 6, 7.

—— 蘇 老 泉 批 評 孟 子 眞 本 *Soo Laou-tseuen pe ping Măng tsze chin pun.* "Soo Seun's Edition of the Works of Mencius." Edited by Le Lung-yun.   1803. 8°.

—— 大 學 *Ta heŏ.* "The Great Learning."
          [1800 ?]. 8°.

25

四書 SZE SHOO. *(Continued.)*

四書串珠類聯合編 *Sze shoo chuen choo luy leen hŏ peen.* "A String of Pearls from the Four Books," arranged according to Subjects.
[1790?]. 12°.
Imperfect.

—— 四書人物聚考 *Sze shoo jin wŭh tseu kaou.* "The Men and Things of the Four Books collectively Examined." An Enlarged Edition. ? keuen. [1775?]. 8°.
Imperfect, containing only keuen 4–7, 11, 21, 22.

—— 四書考輯要 *Sze shoo kaou tseĭh yaou.* "A Collection of Important Researches on the Four Books." By Chin Hung-mow. 20 keuen.
1771. 8°.
Imperfect, wanting the last three keuen.

—— 四書典林 *Sze shoo teen lin.* "A Dictionary of Classical Expressions employed in the Four Books," Illustrated and Explained by Quotations from the Works of Choo He, Ching Haou, Tsae Chin, and others. Compiled by Keang Yung. 30 keuen. 1795. 8°.

Another copy.
Imperfect, wanting keuen 1, 12–14.

—— 四書典腋 *Sze shoo teen yĭh.* "A Pocket Dictionary to the Four Books." 18 keuen.
1818. 8°.

Another edition. 18 keuen. 1822. 8°.

Another edition. 20 keuen. 1831. 8°.

司昭 SZE CHAOU.
斗母經闡微 *Tow Moo king chen wei.* "The Sutra of the Deity Tow Moo. With a Commentary." 1811. 8°.

司空圖 SZE-KUNG TOO.
詩品詩一百首 *She pin she yĭh pĭh show.* "One Hundred Pieces of Poetry." Edited by Yuen Yuen. 1816. 8°.

—— 二十四詩品 *Urh shĭh sze she pin.* "A Collection of Twenty-four Pieces of Poetry." By Sze Kung-too, of the Tang Dynasty.
[1741?]. 8°.

司馬 SZE-MA.
大晉司馬氏全套 *Ta Tsin Sze-ma she tseuen taou.* "The Story of the Family of Sze-ma, of the Tsin Dynasty." A Drama. [1850?]. 8°.

司馬光 SZE-MA KWANG.
法言 *Fă yen.* "Discourses on Law." With a Commentary by Sze-ma Kwang, &c. *See* 黃丕烈 HWANG PEI-LĚĔ. 十子全書 *Shĭh Tsze tseuen shoo.* "The Complete Works of the Ten Philosophers," &c. 1804. 8°.

—— 稽古錄 *Ke koo lŭh.* "The History" of the Period from the Reign of Fŭh-he down to the Year A.D. 1067. A Reprint. 20 keuen.
[1800?]. 8°.

—— 司馬溫公文集 *Sze-ma wăn kung wăn tseĭh.* "A Collection of the Writings of Sze-ma Kwang." Edited by Woo Yuen-leang and others. 82 keuen. 1708. 8°.

—— 資治通鑑 *Tsze che tung keen.* "A History of China," embracing a Period from the commencement of the Fourth Century B.C. down to the end of the "Five Dynasties" that succeeded the Tang. By Sze-ma Kwang. With a Commentary by Hoo San-sing, who also wrote the *Tsze che tung keen shĭh wăn peen woo,* an exegetical work on the above, and which is appended to this Work. 294 keuen. 1067. 8°.

司馬遷 SZE-MA TSEEN.
See 禮記 LE KE. 欽定禮記義疏 *Kin ting Le ke e soo.* "The Meaning of the Book of Rites. With Explanations" by . . Sze-ma Tseen, &c. 8°.

—— 史記 *She ke.* "The Historical Record." With a Commentary by Pei Yin. 130 keuen. *See* 毛晉 MAOU TSIN. 十七史 *Shĭh tseĭh she.* "The Seventeen Histories," &c. 1656. 8°.

—— 史記 *She ke.* "The Historical Record." With a Commentary by Pei Yin. Edited by Maou Tsin. 130 keuen. 1640. 8°.
Imperfect, containing only keuen 1 to 39.

Another edition. With a Commentary by Seu Fooyuen and Chin Tsze-lung. 130 keuen. 1806. 8°.

司馬遷 Sze-ma Tseen.

史記論文 *She ke lun wăn.* "The Historical Record. With Discussions on the Text." Edited by Woo Keen-sze. 130 keuen. 1686. 8°.

——— 史記選 *She ke seuen.* "Selections from the Historical Record." Compiled by Choo Hin. Edited by Seu Yung-heun. 6 keuen. 1766. 8°.

司馬長卿 Sze-ma Chang-king.

子虛賦 *Tsze-heu Foo.* "An Ode on Tsze-heu." [Also] 上林賦 *Shang lin Foo.* "An Ode on Going to the Forest." *See* 蕭統 Seaou Tung. 文選 *Wăn seuen.* "Elegant Extracts from Polite Literature," &c. Keuen 7, 8. 1772. 8°.

師曠 Sze Kwang.

禽經 *Kin king.* "A Book on Birds." With a Commentary by Chang Hwa, of the Tsin Dynasty. A Reprint. [1750?]. 8°.

獅 Sze.

獅吼記 *Sze how ke.* "The Story of the Lion's Roar." *See* 曲 Keüh. 六十種曲 *Lŭh shĭh chung keüh.* "Sixty Plays," &c. Taou 5. 8°.

——— 碧玉獅 *Peĭh yŭh sze.* "The Azure-jade Lion." A Drama. By 'The Retired Scholar of Tsew-tăng.' 20 keuen. 1820. 8°.

事 Sze.

雜事秘辛 *Tsă sze pe sin.* "Miscellaneous Records." By an Anonymous Writer under the Han Dynasty. A Reprint. [1800?]. 8°.

嘶嘡嗹 Sze-tang-tung [*i.e.* Sir George Staunton].

See 哆唎哎 Chay-lan-lin. 暎咭唎國新種痘奇書 *Ying-keĭh-le kwŏ sin chung tow ke shoo.* "A Pamphlet on the English System of Vaccination." .. Translated into Chinese by Sze-tang-tung, &c. 1805. 8°.

大悲 Ta pei.

大悲懺 *Ta pei tsan.* "The Ritual of the Great Compassionate" Kwan-she-yin.

[1800?]. Oblong.

Much torn.

大嵒隱 Ta-gan-yin.

初參要訣 *Choo tsan yaou keuĕ.* "The Primary Important Rules" of Buddhism.

Canton, 1742. 8°.

大廣智 Ta-kwang-che.

佛說救拔燄口饑鬼陀羅尼經 *Fŭh shwŏ Kew pă yen kow go kwei To lo ne king.* "The To-lo-ne Sûtra, delivered by Buddha for Saving the Fiery-mouthed Hungry Ghosts."

Canton, 1737. 8°.

Another copy.

——— 瑜伽集要施食儀 *Yu kea tseĭh yaou she shĭh e.* "The Yoga Rites of Furnishing Nourishment" to Hungry Ghosts. Translated into Chinese by Ta-kwang-che. Edited by Choo Hung. A Reprint. *Canton*, 1737. 8°.

大英國 Ta Ying kwŏ.

大英國畧論 *Ta Ying kwŏ leŏ lun.* "A Short Account of England." [1840?]. 8°.

達淨 Tă-tsing.

蓮宗輯要 *Leen tsung tseĭh yaou.* "A Collection of Passages from Various Works of the Lotus School" of Buddhism. Edited by Tă-tsing. 2 keuen. *Canton*, 1801. 8°.

塔勒炳阿 Tă-lĭh-ping-ah.

See China. 嘉慶 Kea-king. *Emperor.* 欽定軍器則例 *Kin ting keun ke tsĭh le.* "Military Store Regulations." .. Compiled by .. Tă-lĭh-ping-ah, &c. 1801. 8°.

妲己 Tă-ke.

哪吒收妲己 *Na chă show Tă-ke.* "The Murder of Tă-ke," an Empress famous for her Cruelty and Profligacy. Edited by Tsing-kwan Choo jin, *i.e.* 'The Master of the Peaceful Gallery.' In verse. *Canton*, [1840?]. 8°.

太君 Tae keun.

太君辭朝 *Tae keun tsze chaou.* "Tae keun obtains Leave from Court." A Dramatic Tale. [1800?]. 8°.

太 平 天 國 Tae ping Teen kwŏ.

  頒 行 詔 書 *Fun hing chaou shoo.* "Proclamations" of Yang and Seaou, the Eastern and Western Kings of the Tae-ping Dynasty.
                        Nanking, 1852. 8º.

Another edition.   *Nanking,* 1852. 8º.

—— 三 字 經 *San tsze king.* "The Trimetrical Classic" of the Tae-ping Dynasty.
                        Nanking, 1853. 8º.

Another edition.   *Nanking,* 1853. 8º.

—— 太 平 詔 書 *Tae ping chaou shoo.* "Tae-ping Manifestoes."   *Nanking,* 1852. 8º.
    There are two other copies of this work.

—— 太 平 軍 目 *Tae ping keun mŭh.* "An Index giving the Disposition and Grades of the Tae-ping Army." Published by Command of the Tae-ping Teen Wang.   *Nanking,* 1852. 8º.

—— 太 平 救 世 歌 *Tae ping kew she ko.* "Hymns for Saving the World." Published by Command of the Tae-ping Teen Wang.
                        Nanking, 1853. 8º.

Another copy.

—— 太 平 禮 制 *Tae ping le che.* "Tae-ping Ceremonial Regulations." With Manuscript Notes.
                        Nanking, 1852. 8º.

Another edition.   *Nanking,* 1852. 8º.

—— 太 平 條 規 *Tae ping teaou kwei.* "Tae-ping Army Regulations." Published by Command of the Tae-ping Teen Wang. *Nanking,* 1852. 8º.

Another copy.

—— 天 父 下 凡 詔 書 *Teen Foo hea fan chaou shoo.* "The Declarations of the Heavenly Father's Will, made on the Occasions of his Visits to Earth."   *Nanking,* 1852. 8º.

Another copy.

太 平 天 國 Tae ping Teen kwŏ. (*Continued.*)

  天 父 上 帝 言 題 皇 詔 *Teen Foo Shang Te yen te Hwang chaou.* "The Words of the Heavenly Father. Published by Command" of the Tae-ping Teen Wang. *Nanking,* 1853. 8º.

—— 天 命 詔 旨 書 *Teen ming chaou che shoo.* "The Book of Celestial Decrees and Declarations of the Imperial Will."   *Nanking,* 1852. 8º.

Another edition.   *Nanking,* 1852. 8º.

—— 天 條 書 *Teen teaou shoo.* "The Book of Heavenly Precepts." Published by Order of the Tae-ping Teen Wang. *Nanking,* 1852. 8º.

Another copy.

—— 幼 學 詩 *Yew heŏ she.* "An Ode for Youth." Published by Order of the Tae-ping Teen Wang.
                        Nanking, 1852. 8º.

Another edition.   *Nanking,* 1852. 8º.

太 宗 Tae tsung.

  晉 書 *Tsin shoo.* "The History of the Tsin Dynasty." 130 keuen. *See* 毛 晉 Maou Tsin. 十 七 史 *Shĭh tseĭh she.* "The Seventeen Histories," &c.   1656. 8º.

太 子 Tae tsze.

  太 子 下 魚 舟 痴 人 乞 食 *Tae tsze hea yu chow. Che jin keĭh shĭh.* "The Prince embarks on Board a Fishing Boat; or, The Story of the Half-witted Beggar." In verse. 1856. 8º.

太 上 隱 者 Tae shang yin chay.

  仙 吏 傳 *Seen le chuen.* "Fairy Tales." By Tae-shang-yin-chay, of the Tang Dynasty. A Reprint.   [1741?]. 8º.

戴 震 Tae chin.

  緒 言 *Seu yen.* "Unravelled Expressions." 3 keuen. *See* 伍 崇 曜 Woo Tsung-yaou. 粵 雅 堂 叢 書 *Yuĕ ya Tang tsung shoo.* "The Yuĕ-ya Tang Collection of Reprints," &c. Series 4.   1853. 8º.

戴 震 TAE CHIN. (*Continued.*)

毛鄭詩考正 *Maou Ching She kaou ching.*
"An Examination of the Book of Odes of Maou
and Ching." 4 keuen. [Also] 詩經補注
She king poo che. "Additional Comments on
the Book of Odes." 2 keuen. [Also] 考工
記圖 *Kaou kung ke too.* "An Examination
of Handy Work." With Plates. 2 keuen.
[Also] 東原集 *Tung yuen tseih.* "A Col-
lection of the Writings of Tae Chin." 2 keuen.
See 嚴杰 YEN LËĔ. 皇清經解 *Hwang
Tsing king keae.* "The Classics Explained," &c.
Keuen 557–566.   1829. 8°.

戴 任 TAE JIN.

See 馮應京 FUNG YING-KING. 月令廣義
Yuĕ ling kwang e. "The Seasons Fully Explained." .. With additional explanatory Matter by Tae Jin.   1602. 8°.

戴 明 TAE MING.

See 萬年茂 WAN NEEN-MOW, and 戴第元
TAE TE-YUEN. 策學纂要 *Tseih heŏ tswan
yaou.* "The Student's Manual." ... Edited by
Tae Ming, &c.   1766. 8°.

戴 氏 TAE SHE.

See 玄覺 HEUEN KEŎ.

戴 德 TAE TIH.

大戴禮記 *Ta Tae le ke.* "The Ritual of the
Senior Tae." Edited by Chin Tae, of the Ming
Dynasty. 13 keuen.   1175. 8°.

Another copy.

戴 侗 TAE TUNG.

六書故 *Lŭh shoo koo.* "The Origin of the Six
Kinds of Characters." An Ancient Dictionary.
By Tae Tung. Edited by Le Ting-yuen. 33
keuen.   1784. 8°.

Another copy.

戴 凱之 TAE KAE-CHE.

竹譜 *Chŭh poo.* "A Botanical Work on the
Different Kinds of Bamboo." By Tae Kae-che,
of the Tsin Dynasty. A Reprint. [1750?]. 8°.

戴 第元 TAE TE-YUEN.

See 萬年茂 WAN NEEN-MOW, and TAE TE-
YUEN. 策學纂要 *Tseih heŏ tswan yaou.* "The
Student's Manual." .. Compiled by Wan Neen-
mow and Tae Te-yuen, &c.   1766. 8°.

台 州府 TAE CHOW FOO.

台州府志 *Tae chow Foo che.* "A Topography
of Tae-chow Foo," in the Province of Chĕ-
keang. 18 keuen.   [1800 ?]. 8°.

        Imperfect, wanting keuen 1 and 9.

檀 萃 TAN TSUY.

See EPHEMERIDES. 欽定協紀辨方書日月
表合鈔 *Kin ting hĕĕ ke peen fang shoo jih yuĕ
peaou hŏ chaou.* "An Astrological Almanac."
.. Edited by Tan Tsuy, &c.   1787. 8°.

憺 漪子 TAN E-TSZE.

天下水陸路程 *Teen hea shwuy lŭh loo ching.*
"An Itinerary of China."   [1820 ?]. 12°.

澹 圃主人 TAN POO CHOO JIN.

See 唐 TANG. 大唐全傳 *Ta Tang tseuen
chuen.* "A Complete History of the Great Tang
Dynasty." By Tan poo Choo jin, &c. 1783. 8°.

譚 峭 TAN SEAOU.

化書 *Hwa shoo.* "The Book of Transformation."
See 沈津 CHIN TSIN. 百家類纂 *Pih kea
luy tswan.* "The Works of a Hundred Authors,"
&c. Keuen 18.   8°.

譚 瑩 TAN YUNG.

樂志堂詩集 *Lŏ che Tang she tseih.* "The
Lŏ-che Hall Collection of Poetry." 12 keuen.
                                         1860. 8°.

—— 樂志堂文集 *Lŏ che Tang wăn tseih.* "The
Lŏ-che Hall Collection of Literary Pieces." 18
keuen.   1859. 8°.

譚 友夏 TAN YEW-HEA.

詩法入門 *She fă jŭh mun.* "An Introduction
to the Laws of Poetry." Edited by Tan Yew-
hea. 4 keuen.   [1800 ?]. 12°.

        Imperfect, wanting the third keuen.

談 起 行 Tan Ke-hing.
See 李 文 耀 Le Wăn-yaou. 上 海 縣 志 *Shang hae heen che.* "A Topography of Shang-hae Heen." Compiled ... by .. Tan Ke-hing, &c.   1750. 8°.

唐 Tang.
欽 定 全 唐 文 *Kin ting tseuen Tang wăn.* "The Literature of the Tang Dynasty." 1000 keuen.   [1700 ?]. 8°.
Imperfect, wanting keuen 1, 2, 4–8, 92, 97–100, 105–110, 321, 322, 597–600, 621–624, 627, 628, 631, 632, 681–686, 689–692, 695–700, 707, 708,711–720, 925, 926.

—— 說 唐 全 傳 *Shwŏ Tang tseuen chuen.* "A Complete History of the Tang Dynasty." 14 keuen.   [1750 ?]. 8°.
Imperfect, containing only the first keuen.

—— 說 唐 演 傳 *Shwŏ Tang yen chuen.* "A History of the Tang Dynasty." By Yuen hoo yu, or the Fisherman of Lake Yuen. 14 keuen.   [1750 ?]. 8°.
Another edition of the above.

—— 大 唐 全 傳 *Ta Tang tseuen chuen.* "A Complete History of the Great Tang Dynasty." By Tan poo Choo jin, or the Master of the Tranquil Orchard. 8 keuen.   1783. 8°.

唐 暄 Tang Heuen.
唐 暄 手 記 *Tang Heuen show ke.* "The Story of Tang Heuen's Hand." See 說 Shwŏ. 說 淵 *Shwŏ yuen.* "A Collection of Tales," &c. Vol. 5.   8°.

唐 庚 Tang Kăng.
眉 山 詩 鈔 *Mei shan she chaou.* "A Collection of Poetry from Mei shan." See 吳 孟 舉 Woo Măng-keu, and 吳 自 牧 Woo Tsze-muh. 宋 詩 鈔 二 集 *Sung she chaou urh tseĭh.* "Poetry of the Sung Dynasty," &c.   8°.

唐 龍 Tang Lung.
稿 *Kaou.* "Essays." See 長 城 Chang Ching. 名 家 制 義 *Ming kea che e.* "Essays" on Texts from the Four Books, &c. Tsĭh 29.   1699. 8°.

唐 彪 Tang Peaou.
身 易 *Shin yĭh.* "The Changes of the Body." See 張 山 來 Chang Shan-lae, and 張 遳 也 Chang Tsin-yay. 昭 代 叢 書 *Chaou tae tsung shoo.* "A Collection of Reprints of Works by Authors under the Present Dynasty," &c. Keuen 29.   1703. 8°.

唐 晟 Tang Shing.
范 縣 志 *Fan heen che.* "A Topography of Fan Heen." Compiled by Tang Shing. Edited by Le Yew-tsun and Tang Chin-seu. 4 keuen.   1813. 8°.

唐 寅 Tang Yin.
稿 *Kaou.* "Essays." See 長 城 Chang Ching. 名 家 制 義 *Ming kea che e.* "Essays" on Texts from the Four Books, &c. Tsĭh 24.   1699. 8°.

唐 振 緒 Tang Chin-seu.
See 唐 晟 Tang Shing. 范 縣 志 *Fan heen che.* "A Topography of Fan Heen." ... Edited by ... Tang Chin-seu, &c.   1813. 8°.

唐 順 之 Tang Shun-che.
稿 *Kaou.* "Essays." See 長 城 Chang Ching. 名 家 制 義 *Ming kea che e.* "Essays" on Texts from the Four Books, &c. Tsĭh 36.   1699. 8°.

唐 德 亮 Tang Tĭh-leang.
稿 *Kaou.* "Essays." See 長 城 Chang Ching. 名 家 制 義 *Ming kea che e.* "Essays" on Texts from the Four Books, &c. Tsĭh 108.   1699. 8°.

唐 惟 懋 Tang Wei-mow.
發 蒙 小 品 二 集 *Fă mung seaou pin urh tseĭh.* "A Collection of Model Essays for Beginners." Second Series. Compiled by Tang Wei-mow. With Notes by Woo Fung-e. Edited by Chin Hoo and Tang Wei-tĭh.   1743. 8°.

唐 惟 惪 Tang Wei-tĭh.
See 唐 惟 懋 Tang Wei-mow. 發 蒙 小 品 二 集 *Fă mung seaou pin urh tseĭh.* "A Collection of Model Essays." .... Edited by Tang Wei-tĭh, &c.   1743. 8°.

湯 斌 TANG PIN.

乾 清 門 奏 對 記 *Keen tsing mun tsow tuy ke.*
"Account of an Audience granted to Tang Pin
at the Keen-tsing Gate of the Palace." *See*
張 山 來 CHANG SHAN-LAE, and 張 進 也
CHANG TSIN-YAY. 昭 代 叢 書 *Chaou tae tsung
shoo.* "A Collection of Reprints of Works by
Authors under the Present Dynasty," &c.
Keuen 9. 1703. 8°.

—— See 易 經 YĬH KING. 周 易 口 義 *Chow Yĭh
kow e.* "The Chow Changes." . . . Edited by
Tang Pin, &c. 1687. 8°.

湯 朝 鏞 TANG CHAOU-YUNG.

See 董 仲 舒 TUNG CHUNG-SHOO. 春 秋 繁 露
Chun tsew fan loo. "Dew Drops from the Spring
and Autumn Annals." . . . . Edited by Tang
Chaou-yung, &c. 8°.

湯 顯 祖 TANG HEEN-TSOO.

稿 *Kaou.* "Essays." *See* 長 城 CHANG CHING.
名 家 制 義 *Ming kea che e.* "Essays" on Texts
from the Four Books, &c. Tsĭh 64. 1699. 8°.

—— 牡 丹 亭 *Mow tan ting.* "The Peony Pavilion."
See 曲 KEŬH. 六 十 種 曲 *Lŭh shĭh chung
keŭh.* "Sixty Plays," &c. 8°.

—— 牡 丹 亭 *Mow tan ting.* "The Peony Pavilion."
A Drama. A Reprint. 8 keuen.
Nanking, [1840 ?]. 12°.
Another copy.

湯 卿 謀 TANG KING-MOW.

湘 中 草 *Seang chung tsaou.* "Plants of Lake
Seang." 2 keuen. *See* 尤 侗 YEW TUNG.
西 堂 全 集 *Se Tang tseuen tseĭh.* "A Complete Collection of Literary Pieces from the
Western Hall," &c. 1665–1685. 8°.

湯 賓 尹 TANG PIN-YIN.

See 左 丘 明 TSO KEW-MING. 春 秋 左 傳 解 要
Chun Tsew Tso chuen keae yaou. "The Essential
Portions of Tso Kew-ming's Narrative. . . Ex-
plained " by Tang Pin-yin, &c. 1817. 8°.

湯 小 眉 TANG SEAOU-MEI.

See 繆 蓮 仙 MEW LEEN-SEEN. 文 章 游 戲
Wăn chang yew he. "Rambles in Polite Literature." . . . . Edited by Tang Seaou-mei, &c.
1824. 8°.

湯 泰 時 TANG TAE-SHE.

See 易 經 YĬH KING. 古 易 彙 編 *Koo Yĭh wei
peen.* "The Ancient Text of the Book of
Changes." . . . . Edited by Tang Tae-she, &c.
1612. 8°.

棠 氏 TANG SHE.

留 珍 集 *Lew chin tseĭh.* " A Collection of
Keepsakes," being Excerpta illustrative of the
Domestic Virtues. Compiled by Tang she. 6
keuen. 1870. 8°.

鄧 林 TĂNG LIN.

See 四 書 SZE SHOO. 四 書 補 註 附 考 備 旨
Sze shoo poo choo foo kaou pe che. "The Four
Books." . . . Compiled by Tăng Lin, &c.
1829. 8°.

鄧 析 TĂNG SEĬH.

鄧 子 *Tăng tsze.* "The Writings of Tăng Seĭh."
See 沈 津 CHIN TSIN. 百 家 類 纂 *Pĭh kea
luy tswan.* "The Works of a Hundred Authors,"
&c. Keuen 24. 8°.

鄧 淳 TĂNG SHUN.

嶺 南 叢 述 *Ling nan tsung shŭh.* "An Account
of the Provinces of Kwang-tung and Kwang-se."
By Tăng Shun. Edited by Hwang Pei-fang.
60 keuen. 1830. 8°.

鄧 以 讚 TĂNG E-TSAN.

稿 *Kaou.* "Essays." *See* 長 城 CHANG CHING.
名 家 制 義 *Ming kea che e.* "Essays " on
Texts from the Four Books," &c. Tsĭh 55.
1699. 8°.

鄧 百 拙 TĂNG PĬH-CHUĔ.

黃 眉 故 事 *Hwang mei koo sze.* "An Ancient
Encyclopædia." 9 keuen. 1614. 8°.

鄧 道 淳 TĂNG TAOU-SHUN.

See 黃 帝 HWANG TE. 陰 符 經 *Yin foo king.*
"The Sûtra of Secret Charms." . . With a
Commentary by Tăng Taou-shun, &c. 8°.

陶 埴 TAOU CHĬH.

還 金 術 *Hwan kin shŭh.* "The Art of Changing
Gold." *See* 彭 好 古 PĂNG HAOU-KOO. 道
言 內 外 秘 訣 全 書 *Taou yen nuy wae pe
keuĕ tseuen shoo.* " A Complete Collection of
Taouist Works," &c. 8°.

陶澍 Taou Choo.

See 陶士升 Taou Sze-shing. 奘江古文存 *Yu-keang koo wăn tsun.* "The Writings of Taou Sze-shing." Edited by Taou Choo, &c.
1816. 8°.

—— 奘江詩存 *Yu-keang she tsun.* "The Poetry of Taou Sze-shing." Edited by Taou Choo, &c. 1816. 8°.

—— 印心石屋詩鈔 *Yin sin shĭh ŭh she chaou.* "A Collection of Poetry from the House at Yin-sin shĭh." By Taou Choo. In Two Parts. Part I. 4 keuen. Part II. 3 keuen. 1816. 8°.

陶穀 Taou Kŭh.

清異錄 *Tsing e lŭh.* "Curious Records." By Taou Kŭh, of the Sung Dynasty. A Reprint. 2 keuen. [1800]. 8°.

陶潛 Taou Tseen.

孝傳 *Heaou chuen.* "Stories of Filial Piety." By Taou Tseen, of the Tsin Dynasty. Edited by Chung Tsung-paou. [1750 ?]. 8°.

Another edition.

—— 羣輔錄 *Keun foo lŭh.* "A Record of Renowned Individuals." By Taou Tseen, of the Tsin Dynasty. A Reprint. [1750 ?]. 8°.

—— 搜神後記 *Sow shin how ke.* "A Sequel to the *Sow shin ke.*" By Taou Tseen, of the Tsin Dynasty. A Reprint. [1741 ?]. 8°.

Another edition. Edited by Lew Kĕĕ. 2 keuen. [1800 ?]. 8°.

陶澤 Taou Tsĭh.

稿 *Kaou.* "Essays." See 長城 Chang Ching. 名家制義 *Ming kea che e.* "Essays" on Texts from the Four Books, &c. Tsĭh 48. 1699. 8°.

陶濬 Taou Tsin.

See 陶士升 Taou Sze-shing. 奘江詩存 *Yu-keang she tsun.* "The Poetry of Taou Sze-shing." Edited by ... Taou Tsin, &c. 1816. 8°.

陶貞懷 Taou Ching-gae.

天雨花 *Teen yü hwa.* "The Rain and Flowers of Heaven." A Novel, chiefly in Verse. 1804. 8°.

陶朱公 Taou Choo-kung.

致富全書 *Che foo tseuen shoo.* "A Complete Guide to the Attainment of Wealth." Edited by Chin Ke-joo. 4 keuen. 1784. 8°.

陶中洋 Taou Chung-yang.

堪輿理氣青天白日 *Kan yu le ke tsing teen pĭh jĭh.* "The Principles of the Fung shwuy Art made plain." Edited by Lew Chŭě-heen and others. 3 keuen. 1761. 8°.

陶宏景 Taou Hung-king.

古今刀劍錄 *Koo kin taou keen lŭh.* "An Account of Ancient and Modern Swords." By Taou Hung-king, of the Leang Dynasty. A Reprint. [1800 ?]. 8°.

陶壼村 Taou Hwang-tsun.

文選編珠 *Wăn seuen peen choo.* "A Selection of Literary Gems." Poetical Expressions from the Writings of well-known Authors. Compiled, with Notes, by Taou Hwang-tsun. Edited by Ho Shŭh-chuen. 4 keuen. 1802. 8°.

陶士升 Taou Sze-shing.

奘江古文存 *Yu-keang koo wăn tsun.* "The Writings of Taou Sze-shing." Edited by Taou Choo and Taou Tsin. 4 keuen. 1816. 8°.

—— 奘江詩存 *Yu-keang she tsun.* "The Poetry of Taou Sze-shing." Edited by Taou Choo and Taou Tsin. 3 keuen. 1816. 8°.

陶定求 Taou Ting-kew.

悼亡草 *Taou wang tsaou.* "Verses on the Death of a Friend." 1835. 8°.

陶望齡 Taou Wang-ling.

稿 *Kaou.* "Essays." See 長城 Chang Ching. 名家制義 *Ming kea che e.* "Essays" on Texts from the Four Books, &c. Tsĭh 68. 1699. 8°.

道 Taou.

常言道 *Chang yen taou.* "A Book on Common Philosophy." By "The Taouist of Lŏ-pih." 1809. 8°.

—— 誨謨訓道 *Hwuy moo seun taou.* "Instructions in the Reasons of our Calling." [By C. F. A. Guetzlaff.] [*Singapore*, 1838?]. 8°.

Another copy.

道誠 Taou-ching.

See 王軷 Wang Pŏ. 成道記 *Ching taou ke.* "The Perfect Way." ... With Notes by the Monk Taou-ching, &c. 8°.

道宣 Taou-seuen.

See 鳩摩羅什 Kew-mo-lo-shïh. 妙法蓮華經 *Meaou fă leen hwa king.* "The Lotus of the Excellent Law." .... Edited by .. Taou-seuen, &c. 1764. 8°.

道世 Taou-she.

法苑珠林 *Fă yuen choo lin.* "The Forest of the Pearls of the Garden of the Law." See 王文誥 Wang Wăn-kaou. 唐代叢書 *Tang tae tsung shoo.* "A Collection of Reprints of Works written during the Tang Dynasty," &c. Series 2. 1806. 8°.

—— 法苑珠林 *Fă yuen choo lin.* "The Forest of the Pearls of the Garden of the Law." A Comprehensive View of the Buddhist System. A Reprint. 100 keuen. [1700?]. 8°.
Very imperfect, containing only keuen 61–90.

Another edition. 100 keuen. 1827. 8°.

檮杌 Taou wŭh.

檮杌閒評 *Taou wŭh hëen ping.* "The Work of a Stupid Fellow in his Intervals of Leisure." A Novel. 50 keuen. [1800?]. 8°.

地球 Te kew.

西遊地球聞見畧傳 *Se yew te kew wăn keen leŏ chuen.* "A Short Account of a Tour round the World." [By Dr. R. Morrison.] With a Map. [1819?]. 8°.

地理 Te le.

地理便童畧傳 *Te le peen tung leŏ chuen.* "A Short Catechism on Geography." [By W. H. Medhurst.] Reprinted from the *Chă she sŭh,* or "Examiner." [*Malacca*, 1819?]. 8°.

—— 地理問答 *Te le wăn tă.* "A Catechism on Geography." [By Ira Miller Condit.] With Maps. [*Canton*?], 1865. 8°.

地圖 Te too.

地圖綜要 *Te too tsung yaou.* "An Epitomized Geography." With Maps. 2 keuen. [1750?]. 8°.
An odd Volume, containing only the geography of eight of the provinces of China.

地婆訶羅 Te-po-ho-lo [*i.e.* Divâkara].

陀羅尼經 *To lo ne king.* "The To-lo-ne Sûtra." Translated into Chinese by the Priest Te-po-ho-lo. With a Commentary by Heen-wăn. *Canton*, 1812. 8°.

調爕 Teaou sëĕ.

調爕類編 *Teaou sëĕ luy peen.* "On the Harmony in Nature." 4 keuen. See 葉志詵 Yĕ Che-sin. 海山仙館叢書 *Hae shan seen Kwan tsung shoo.* "The Hae-shan-seen Kwan Collection of Reprints," &c. Vol. 46. 1848. 8°.

鐵 Tĕĕ.

See 劉 Lew. 山東考卷 *Shan-tung kaou keuen.* "Shantung Examination Essays." .. Edited by Tĕĕ, &c. *Tse-nan Foo,* 1803. 8°.

鐵花 Tĕĕ hwa.

鐵花仙史 *Tĕĕ hwa seen she.* "The Sprite of the Iron Flower." By the Mountaineer of Yun fung. 26 keuen. [1750?]. 8°.

鐵樵 Tĕĕ Tseaou.

See 老尹 Laou keun. 感應篇註 *Kan ying peen choo.* "The Book of Rewards and Punishments." With a Commentary by Tĕĕ Tseaou, &c. 1805. 8°.

26

帖 TËĔ.

帖式彙選 *Tëë shĭh wei seuen.* "A Select Compilation of Model Notes, Visiting Cards," &c.
[1800 ?]. 8°.

Much torn.

天 TEEN.

天人異同 *Teen jin e tung.* "The Analogy between Religion and Philosophy." Translated by William Muirhead from J. Pye Smith's Introduction to Butler's Analogy of Religion.
Hongkong, 1857. 8°.

—— 天地人論 *Teen te jin lun.* "Discourses on Heaven, Earth, and Man." [By W. H. Medhurst.] *Hongkong,* 1869. 8°.

—— 通天曉 *Tung teen heaou.* "A Book of General Information." 5 keuen. 1856. 8°.

天下 TEEN HEA.

天下路程途 *Teen hea loo ching too.* "The Roads of the Empire." *Peking,* [1750 ?]. 12°.

天后 TEEN HOW.

天后娘娘現聖靈籤註解 *Teen how neang neang heen shing ling tseen choo keae.* "The Holy and Inspired Sacrificial Lots of the Queen of Heaven Commented on and Explained."
[1830 ?]. 8°.

天然 TEEN-JEN.

同住訓略 *Tung choo heun leŏ.* "Short Instructions for the Government of Brotherhoods."
[1830 ?]. 8°.

天鏡 TEEN KING.

天鏡衡人 *Teen king hăng jin.* "Heaven's Mirror measures Men." Being Extracts from Thomas à Kempis's "Christian's Pattern." [By Rev. John Chalmers ?] *Hongkong,* 1866. 8°.

天文 TEEN WĂN.

天文畧論 *Teen wăn leŏ lun.* "A Digest of Astronomy." [By B. Hobson.]
Canton, 1849. 8°.

天主敎 TEEN CHOO KEÀOU.

天主敎要 *Teen choo keaou yaou.* "The Essentials of the Roman Catholic Religion."
[1790 ?]. 8°.

天隱子 TEEN-YIN-TSZE.

天隱子 *Teen-yin-tsze.* "The Writings of Teen-yin-tsze." *See* 沈津 CHIN TSIN. 百家類纂 *Pĭh kea luy tswan.* "The Works of a Hundred Authors," &c. Keuen 18. 8°.

天花才子 TEEN HWA TSAE TSZE.

See 心 SIN. 快心編全傳 *Kwae sin peen tseuen chuen.* "A Merry Tale." By the Clever Man of Teen-hwa, &c. 8°.

典 TEEN.

典故 *Teen koo.* "The Origin of the [Moral] Canons." 4 ? keuen. [1790 ?]. 8°.
Imperfect, containing only keuen 2–4.

—— 典林瑯環 *Teen lin lang hwan.* "Gems from the Groves of Classical Literature." A Book of Classical Reference. 18 keuen ? [1750 ?]. 8°.
Imperfect, containing only keuen 7–18.

巷隱 TEEN-YIN.

續金瓶梅 *Sŭh kin Ping Mei.* "A Sequel to the *Kin Ping Mei.*" 12 keuen. [1700 ?]. 8°.

翟灝 TEĬH HAOU.

四書考異 *Sze shoo kaou e.* "An Examination of the Various Readings of the Four Books." 36 keuen. *See* 嚴杰 YEN LËĔ. 皇清經解 *Hwang Tsing king keae.* "The Classics Explained," &c. Keuen 449–484. 1829. 8°.

翟元 TEĬH YUEN.

周易義 *Chow Yĭh e.* "The Meaning of the Chow Changes," &c. *See* 孫堂 SUN TANG. 漢魏二十一家易注 *Han Wei urh shĭh yĭh kea Yĭh choo.* "Commentaries on the Book of Changes," &c. 1799. 8°.

翟蠡洲 TEĬH LE-CHOW.

See 四書 SZE SHOO. 四書發註 *Sze shoo fă choo.* . . . "The Four Books." . . . . Edited by Teĭh Le-chow, &c. 1723. 8°.

狄之武 TEĬH CHE-WOO.

See 周大樞 CHOW TA-CHOO. 應試排律精選鯨鏗集 *Ying she pae leŭh tsing seuen king kăng tseĭh.* "The King-kăng Collection of Successful Poetical Examination Essays." . . With Notes by Teĭh Che-woo, &c. 1758. 8°.

TEN COMMANDMENTS.

上帝所設之十條誡 *Shang te so shĕ che shĭh teaou keae.* "The Ten Commandments." Tract No. 37. [By the Preachers of the Chinese Union.] 8°.

—— 十條聖誡 *Shĭh teaou shing keae.* "The Ten Commandments." With a Commentary [by Ho Tsin-shen?]. [*Hongkong*, 1867?]. 8°.

THIRZA.

金屋型儀 *Kin ŭh hing e.* "The Model of the Golden House." Thirza ; or, the Attractive Power of the Cross, by E. F. Ball, translated into Chinese. [1835?]. 8°.

THOM (ROBERT).

See 羅伯聃 LŎ-PĬH TAN.

THOMAS À KEMPIS.

See HAEMMERLEIN (THOMAS), *à Kempis.*

德 TĬH.

德壽集 *Tĭh show tseĭh.* "Poems on Virtue and Longevity." 4 keuen. 1822. 8°.
Imperfect, wanting keuen 1 and 2.

德成 TĬH CHING.

See CHINA. BOARD OF WAR. 欽定中樞政考 *Kin ting chung choo ching kaou.* "An Examination into the Fundamental System of Governing" the Army. Compiled by .. Tĭh Ching, &c. 1764. 8°.

德齡 TĬH LING.

See 杜佑 TOO YEW. 通典 *Tung teen.* "A Complete Treatise on the Political Constitution of China." Edited by ... Tĭh Ling, &c. 1747. 8°.

德沛 TĬH PEI.

易圖解 *Yĭh too keae.* "The Diagrams of the Book of Changes Explained." 1736. 8°.

德清 TĬH-TSING.

See 法藏 FĂ-TSANG. 大乘起信論直解 *Ta shing ke sin lun chĭh keae.* "A Treatise for Promulgating the Doctrine of the Mahâyâna." .. With a Commentary by Tĭh-tsing, &c. 1620. 8°.

德清 TĬH-TSING. (*Continued.*)

See 佛陀多羅 FŬH-TO-TO-LO. 大方廣圓覺經直解 *Ta făng kwang yuen keŏ king chĭh keae.* "The Sûtra of Complete Perception, with a True Exposition" by Tĭh-tsing, &c. 1623. 8°.

—— 求那跋陀羅 KEW-NA-PŎ-TO-LO. 觀楞伽阿跋多羅實經記 *Kwan Lăng-kea a-po-to-lo paou king ke.* "The Lankávatara Máhá-yana Sûtra." With a Commentary by Tĭh-tsing, &c. 1724. 8°.

—— 中庸直指 *Chung yung chĭh che.* "A True Guide to the Chung yung." [1820?]. 8°.

—— 化生儀軌 *Hwa săng e kwei.* "The Law of Transmigration." 8°.

—— 金剛決疑解 *Kin kang keuĕ e keae.* "Doubtful Passages in the Diamond Classic Explained." A Reprint. 1733. 8°.

—— 大學綱目決疑章 *Ta heŏ kang mŭh keuĕ e chang.* "The Doubtful Points in the Opening Chapters of the *Ta heŏ* Decided." [1820?]. 8°.

特通阿 TĬH TUNG-AH.

漳州府志 *Chang chow foo che.* "A Topography of Chang-chow Foo," in the Province of Fukien. Compiled by Tĭh Tung-ah. 46 keuen. 1806. 8°.
Another copy.

丁山 TING-SHAN.

龍舟歌丁山射鴈 *Lung chow ko. Ting shan shay yen.* "The Dragon-boat Song ; or, The Story of Ting-shan, who Shot the Goose." [1850?]. 8°.

丁 TING, and 孫 SUN.

廣東全塲闈墨 *Kwang tung tseuen chang wei mĭh.* "A Complete Collection of Kwang-tung Examination Essays." Edited by the Examiners Ting and Sun. 1831. 8°.

丁南羽 TING NAN-YU.

See 王黼 WANG FOO. 博古圖 *Pŏ koo too.* "An Illustrated Collection of Antiquities." .. Illustrated by Ting Nan-yu, &c. 1588. 8°.

丁 世 明 TING SHE-MING.

See 詹 承 誥 CHEN CHING-KAOU. 佛 門 定 制
Füh mun ting che. " The Established Laws and
Formularies of the Disciples of Buddha." ....
Edited by Ting She-ming.　　　　　8°.

———— 道 門 定 制 *Taou mun ting che.* " The
Established Laws and Formularies of the Disciples of Taouism." ... Edited by Ting She-
ming, &c.　　　　　[1750 ?]. 8°.

丁 陽 彩 TING YANG-TSAE.

See 柳 華 陽 LEW HWA-YANG. 金 仙 証 論
Kin seen ching hun. " The Golden Genii."
Edited by Ting Yang-tsae, &c.　　　　1811. 8°.

朵 思 麻 TO SZE-MA.

兵 錄 *Ping lüh.* " A Treatise on Warlike Implements." By To Sze-ma, a Thibetan ? Illustrated
by Chaou Sze-ching.　　　　[1790 ?]. 8°.

Imperfect, containing only the thirteenth keuen.

托 克 托 TŎ-KĬH-TŎ.

金 史 *Kin she.* " The History of the Kin
Dynasty." Embracing the Period from 1115
to 1234 A.D. By Tŏ-kĭh-tŏ and others. 135
keuen. 12 supplementary keuen.　　　1824. 8°.

——— 遼 史 *Leaou she.* " The History of the Leaou
Dynasty." Embracing the Period from 916 to
1125 A.D. By Tŏ-kĭh-tŏ and others. 115 keuen.
10 supplementary keuen.　　　　　1824. 8°.

挹 穆 齊 圖 TŎ-MŬH-TSE-TOO.

See CHINA. 乾 隆 KEEN-LUNG. *Emperor.* 欽
定 八 旗 則 例 *Kin ting pă ke tsĭh le.* " Regulations for the Bannermen." .. Compiled by ..
Tŏ-mŭh-tse-too, &c.　　　　　1786. 8°.

(唐 廷 樞) T'ONG TING-KÜ.

英 語 集 全 (*Ying ü tsap ts'un*), or The Chinese
and English Instructor. By T'ong Ting-kü.
　　　　　　　　　　　Canton, 1862.

屠 隆 TOO LUNG.

佛 法 金 湯 *Füh fă kin tang.* " The Golden
Essence of the Religion of Buddha." By the
Monk Too Lung. A Reprint. 2 keuen.
　　　　　　　　　　　Ningpo, 1831. 8°.
Imperfect, the last few pages wanting.

——— 標 紬 對 類 大 全 *Peaou seang tuy luy ta tseuen.*
" A Complete Thesaurus of Elegant Expressions
and Phrases, arranged according to Subjects."
Edited by Woo Meen-heŏ. 20 keuen.
　　　　　　　　　　　[1750 ?]. 8°.

——— 婆 羅 舘 清 語 *So lo kwan tsing yu.* " The
Pure Teachings of the Sâla School." 1780. 8°.

屠 羲 英 TOO HE-YING.

童 子 禮 *Tung tsze le.* " Politeness for Boys."
See 張 文 嘉 CHANG WĂN-KEA. 齊 家 寶 要
Tse kea paou yaou. " Valuable Hints for Domestic
Rule." Keuen 1.　　　　　　　8°.

屠 德 修 TOO TĬH-SEW.

See 朱 竹 垞 CHOO CHŬH-TSĬH. 朱 竹 垞 先
生 詩 鈔 *Choo Chŭh-tsĭh seen săng she chaou.*
" The Poems of Dr. Choo E-tsun, otherwise
Chŭh-tsĭh." Compiled by .. Too Tĭh-sew, &c.
　　　　　　　　　　　　　　12°.

——— See 陸 伯 焜 LŬH PĬH-HWĂN, and Too TĬH-
SEW. 愚 山 詩 鈔 *Yu shan she chaou.* " Poetry
from Yu-shan." Compiled by Lŭh Pĭh-hwăn
and Too Tĭh-sew, &c.　　　　　　12°.

——— See 王 阮 亭 WANG YUEN-TING. 詩 鈔 *She
chaou.* " Poems." Edited by .. Too Tĭh-sew, &c.
　　　　　　　　　　　　　　12°.

土 地 福 神 TOO TE FŬH SHIN.

土 地 福 神 靈 籤 *Too te fŭh Shin ling tseen.*
" The Inspired Sacrificial Lots of the God of
the Earth and Land."　　　*Canton,* 1851. 8°.

杜 琳 TOO LIN.

淮 關 統 志 *Hwae kwan tung che.* " A Topography of the Hwae Custom-house District," in
the Prefecture of Hwae gan, in the Province of
Kiang-su. Recast by E Ling-ah in 1778, and
further Supplemented and Re-edited by Le Joo-
mei. 14 keuen.　　　　　　　1806. 8°.

杜本 Too Pun.

谷音 *Kŭh yin.* "Voices from the Valleys." A Collection of Poetry. Compiled by Too Pun. *See* 伍崇曜 Woo Tsung-yaou. 粵雅堂叢書 *Yŭĕ ya Tang tsung shoo.* "The Yŭĕ-ya Tang Collection of Reprints," &c. Series 2. 　　　1853. 8°.

杜佑 Too Yew.

通典 *Tung teen.* "A Complete Treatise on the Political Constitution of China." By Too Yew. Edited by an Imperial Commission, consisting of Prince Hung Chow, Tĭh Ling, Wang Hwuy-fun, and others. 200 keuen. *Peking,* 1747. 8°.

Another edition. 200 keuen. [1750 ?]. 8°.
　　Imperfect, wanting keuen 142–166.

Another edition. 200 keuen. [1790 ?]. 8°.
　　Imperfect, wanting keuen 1–7.

杜預 Too Yu.

See 孔丘 Kung Kew. 春秋經傳集解 *Chun Tsew king chuen tseĭh keae.* "The Spring and Autumn Annals." . . . Compiled by Too Yu, &c. 　　8°.

—— 春秋左傳杜林合註 *Chun Tsew Tso chuen Too Lin hŏ choo.* "The Spring and Autumn Annals. . . With the Commentaries of Too Yu," &c. 　　8°.

—— 欽定春秋傳說彙纂 *Kin ting Chun Tsew chuen shwŏ wei tswan.* "The Spring and Autumn Annals. . . . with . . . . Comments and Remarks" thereon by . . . Too Yu, &c. 　　1721. 8°.

—— 左傳杜解補正 *Tso chuen Too keae poo ching.* "The *Tso chuen.* . . . with Too Yu's Commentary," &c. *See* 嚴杰 Yen Lĕĕ. 皇清經解 *Hwang Tsing king keae.* "The Classics Explained," &c. Keuen 1–3. 　1829. 8°.

杜春生 Too Chun-sǎng.

越中金石記 *Yŭĕ chung kin shĭh ke.* "A Record of Ancient Inscriptions in the Principality of Yŭĕ," the Modern Fŭh-keen. 10 keuen. 　　1823. 8°.

杜詒穀 Too E-kŭh.

See 杜紫綸 Too Tsze-lun, and Too E-kŭh. 中晚唐詩叩彈集 *Chung wan Tang she kow tan tseĭh.* "A Collection of the Poetry of the Tang Dynasty," &c. 　1704. 8°.

杜光庭 Too Kwang-ting.

錄異記 *Lŭh e ke.* "Strange Stories." By Too Kwang-ting, of the Tang Dynasty. A Reprint. 　　[1741 ?]. 8°.

杜定基 Too Ting-ke.

See 四書 Sze shoo. 四書補註附考備旨 *Sze shoo poo choo foo kaou pe che.* "The Four Books." . . . . Edited by Too Ting-ke, &c. 　　1829. 8°.

杜子春 Too Tsze-chun.

杜子春傳 *Too Tsze-chun chuen.* "The Story of Too Tsze-chun." *See* 說 Shwŏ. 說淵 *Shwŏ yuen.* "A Collection of Tales," &c. Vol. 2. 　　8°.

杜紫綸 Too Tsze-lun, and 杜詒穀 Too E-kŭh.

中晚唐詩叩彈集 *Chung wan Tang she kow tan tseĭh.* "A Collection of the Poetry of the Tang Dynasty, elucidated by the Help of Contemporary and later Authorities." Compiled by Too Tsze-lun and Too E-kŭh. 15 keuen. 　　1704. 8°.

圖 Too.

眞八美圖 *Chin pǎ mei too.* "The Eight Admirable Plans." A Drama. 10 keuen. 　　[1800 ?]. 8°.

　Imperfect, containing only keuen 6–10.

圖理琛 Too Le-yin.

異域錄 *E yu lŭh.* "An Account of Various Foreign Countries." *See* 何秋濤 Ho Tsew-taou. 北徼彙編 *Pĭh keaou wei peen.* "Treatises on the Countries beyond the Northern Frontier," &c. Keuen 5, 6. 　1865. 8°.

斗㚼 Tow moo.

戒殺延生經 *Keae shǎ yen sǎng king.* "A Sûtra on the Preservation of Life." By Tow-moo, the Mother of the Imperial Stars, a Buddhist Divinity. 12 keuen. [1800 ?]. 8°.

竇玉 Tow Yŭh.
　竇玉傳 *Tow Yŭh chuen.* "The Story of Tow Yŭh." *See* 說 Shwŏ. 說淵 *Shwŏ yuen.* "A Collection of Tales," &c.　Vol. 8.　　8°.

竇漢卿 Tow Han-king.
　瘡瘍經驗全書 *Chwang yang king yen tseuen shoo.* "A Complete Work on the Treatment of Cutaneous Complaints."　By Tow Han-king. A New and Enlarged Edition.　Edited by Chin Yew-kung, &c.　With Plates.　13 keuen.
　　　　　　　　　　　　　1750.　8°.

TRACEY (Ira).
　See 仁愛者 Jin-gae-chay.

蔡 Tsae.
　蔡狀元起造洛陽橋全本 *Tsae Chwang-yuen ke tsaou Lo-yang keaou tseuen pun.* "The Story of the Building of the Bridge at Loyang by the Chwang-yuen Tsae."　In Verse.　3 keuen.　　　　　　　　　1849.　8°.

蔡沈 Tsae Chin.
　See 孔丘 Kung Kew. 芥子園重訂監本書經 *Keae tsze yuen chung ting keen pun Shoo king.* "The Book of Historical Documents." With Tsae Chin's Commentary, &c.
　　　　　　　　　　　Nanking, 1790.　8°.

　――――― 欽定書經傳說彙纂 *Kin ting Shoo king chuen shwŏ wei tswan.* "The Book of Historical Documents, . . . with Comments and Remarks thereon" by Tsae Chin, &c. 1730. 8°.

　――――― 奎壁書經 *Kwei peĭh Shoo king.* "The Kwei-peĭh Edition of the Book of Historical Documents."　With the Commentary of Tsae Chin, &c.　　　　　8°.

　――――― 袖珍書經 *Sew chin Shoo king.* . . . "The Book of Historical Documents."　With Tsae Chin's Commentary, &c.　　1750.　8°.

　――――― 書經楷要 *Shoo king kĕĕ yaou.* "The Book of Historical Documents. With an Abridgment " of the Commentaries of Tsae Chin, &c.　　　　　　8°.

蔡沈 Tsae Chin.　(*Continued.*)
　See 孔丘 Kung Kew.　書經大全 *Shoo king ta tseuen.* "A Complete Copy of the Book of Historical Documents."　With Comments by Tsae Chin, &c.　　　　　8°.

　――― *See* 詩經 She king. 欽定詩經傳說彙纂 *Kin ting she king chuen shwŏ wei tswan.* "The Book of Odes.　With a Compilation and Digest of Comments and Remarks thereon" by Tsae Chin, &c.　　1727.　8°.

　――― *See* 四書 Sze shoo. 四書典林 *Sze shoo teen lin.* "A Dictionary of Classical Expressions Employed in the Four Books."　Illustrated and Explained by .. Tsae Chin, &c.　1795.　8°.

蔡清 Tsae Tsing.
　四書蒙引 *Sze shoo mung yin.* "A Guide to the Study of the Four Books."　Edited by Woo He-chow and Lin He-yuen.　15 keuen.
　　　　　　　　　　　[1800?].　8°.
　　Imperfect, the first eight keuen wanting.

　――― 易經蒙引 *Yĭh king mung yin.* "A Guide to the Book of Changes."　Edited by Sung Chaou-yŏ.　12 keuen.　　　[1800?].　8°.

蔡羽 Tsae Yu.
　遼陽海神傳 *Leaou yang hae shin chuen.* "The Story of the Leaou-yang God of the Sea."　*See* 說 Shwŏ. 說淵 *Shwŏ yucn.* "A Collection of Tales," &c.　Vol. 3.　　8°.

蔡源 Tsae Yuen.
　小題文津 *Seaou te wăn tsin.* "A Collection of Essays " on Texts from the Four Books.　Two Series.　Compiled by Tsae Yuen. [1820?]. 8°.
　　　　　　　　　Imperfect.

蔡邕 Tsae Yung.
　琴操 *Kin tsaou.* "Exercises for the Kin."　Edited by Sun Sing-yen.　2 keuen.　　1806.　8°.

　――― 獨斷 *Tŭh twan.* "The Book of Decisions " on Matters of Court Etiquette, &c.　By Tsae Yung, of the Han Dynasty.　Edited by Yen Ping-hăng.　A Reprint.　　　[1750?].　8°.

Another edition.　　　　　　[1800?].　8°.

蔡 方 炳 TSAE FANG-PING.

See 陸 應 陽 LŬH YING-YANG. 廣 輿 記 *Kwang yu ke.* "A Geography of the Empire." ... An Enlarged and Revised Edition by Tsae Fang-ping, &c.　　　　　1802. 8°.

—— See TSING DYNASTY. 大 清 律 箋 釋 *Ta Tsing leŭh tseen shĭh.* "The Laws of the Tsing Dynasty." ... Edited by Tsae Fang-ping, &c.　　　　　1725. 8°.

蔡 錫 疇 TSAE SEĬH-CHOW.

See 陳 星 齋 CHIN SING-CHAE. 文 稿 *Wăn kaou.* "Essays." With Notes by Tsae Seĭh-chow, &c.　　　　　1803. 8°.

蔡 少 魚 TSAE SHAOU-YU.

新 選 試 賦 衡 能 *Sin seuen she foo hăng nang.* "A New Collection of Examination Odes." Compiled by Tsae Shaou-yu. 8 keuen.

Fŭh-keen, 1796. 8°.

Imperfect, keuen 2, 4, 8 wanting.

蔡 世 遠 TSAE SHE-YUEN.

古 文 雅 正 *Koo wăn ya ching.* "Elegant and Correct Extracts from Ancient Literature." Compiled by Tsae She-yuen. Edited by Le Leĭh-how and Chang Ke-chang. 14 keuen.

Nanking, 1777. 8°.

蔡 祖 挍 TSAE TSOO-PĂ.

See 徐 幹 SEU HAN. 中 論 *Chung lun.* "Central Discourses." ... Edited by Tsae Tsoo-pă, &c.　　　　　8°.

蔡 應 彪 TSAE YING-PEAOU.

See 郝 碩 HŎ CHĬH. 卽 墨 縣 志 *Tseĭh-mĭh heen che.* "A Topography of Tseĭh-mĭh Heen." ... Compiled ... by Tsae Ying-peaou, &c.　　　　　1763. 8°.

蔡 應 襄 TSAE YING-SEANG.

See 甘 芳 谷 KAN FANG-KŬH. 詩 韻 含 英 題 解 辨 同 合 訂 *She yun han ying te keae peen tung hŏ ting.* "A Copious Tonic Dictionary of Poetical Expressions." ... Edited by Tsae Ying-seang, &c.　　　　　1775. 8°.

蔡 宇 泰 TSAE YU-TAE.

See 陳 星 齋 CHIN SING-CHAE. 文 稿 *Wăn kaou.* "Essays." With Notes by Tsae Yu-tae, &c.　　　　　1803. 8°.

蔡 元 放 TSAE YUEN-FANG.

東 周 列 國 全 志 *Tung chow leĭh kwŏ tseuen che.* "A History embracing the Period from the Eastern Chow Dynasty to the Commencement of the Tsin Dynasty," 800–300 B.C. With Illustrations. Edited by Tsae Yuen-fang. 23 keuen.　　　　　1752. 8°.

Another edition. 23 keuen.　　　　　1843. 8°.

蔡 元 定 TSAE YUEN-TING.

律 呂 新 書 *Leŭh leu sin shoo.* "A New Treatise on Keyed Tones." See 胡 廣 HOO KWANG. 性 理 大 全 *Sing le ta tseuen.* "A Complete Work on Mental Philosophy," &c. Keuen 22, 23.　　　　　1414. 8°.

綵 毫 TSAE HAOU.

綵 毫 記 *Tsae haou ke.* "The Story of the Coloured Pencil." See 曲 KEŬH. 六 十 種 曲 *Lŭh shĭh chung keŭh.* "Sixty Plays," &c. Taou 3.　　　　　8°.

才 郎 TSAE LANG.

五 諫 才 郎 *Woo keen tsae lang.* "The Five Reproving Geniuses."　　　　　[1800 ?]. 8°.

臧 庸 TSANG YUNG.

拜 經 日 記 *Pae king jĭh ke.* "Daily Jottings on the Classics." [Also] 拜 經 文 集 *Pae king wăn tseĭh.* "Essays on the Classics." See 嚴 杰 YEN LËĔ. 皇 清 經 解 *Hwang Tsing king keae.* "The Classics Explained," &c. Keuen 1170–1178.　　　　　1829. 8°.

臧 括 齋 TSANG KWŎ-CHAE.

See 王 容 周 WANG KĬH-CHOW. 文 法 狐 白 *Wăn fă hoo pĭh.* "The Laws of Literary Composition." .... Edited by Tsang Kwŏ-chae, &c.　　　　　1792. 8°.

臧 才 琳 TSANG TSAE-LIN.

經 義 雜 記 *King e tsă ke.* "Memoranda on the Meaning of the Classics." 10 keuen. See 嚴 杰 YEN LËĔ. 皇 清 經 解 *Hwang Tsing king keae.* "The Classics Explained," &c. Keuen 195–204.　　　　　1829. 8°.

臟 腑 TSANG FOO.

臟 腑 明 堂 圖 *Tsang foo ming tang too.* " An Anatomical Plate of the Human Viscera."
[1800 ?].　A sheet.
Another copy.

曾 鞏 TSĂNG KUNG.

曾 文 *Tsăng wăn.* " The Writings of Tsăng Kung." 10 keuen. *See* 茅 坤 MAOU KWĂN. 唐 宋 八 大 家 文 鈔 *Tang Sung pă ta kea wăn chaou.* " The Works of Eight Scholars . . . under the Tang and Sung Dynasties," &c.
1631.　8°.

曾 慥 TSĂNG TSAOU.

樂 府 雅 詞 *Yŏ foo ya tsze.* " Elegant Rhymes." 8 keuen. *See* 伍 崇 曜 WOO TSUNG-YAOU. 粤 雅 堂 叢 書 *Yuĕ ya Tang tsung shoo.* " The Yuĕ-ya Tang Collection of Reprints," &c. Series 20.　　　　　　　　　1853.　8°.

曾 鳳 儀 TSĂNG FUNG-E.

See 鳩 摩 羅 什 KEW-MO-LO-SHĬH. 金 剛 般 若 波 羅 蜜 經 宗 通 *Kin kang Pan-jŏ Po-lo-meĭh king tsung tung.* " The ' Diamond Classic ' thoroughly elucidated " by Tsăng Fung-e, &c.
1810.　8°.

曾 香 田 TSĂNG HEANG-TEEN.

醫 宗 備 要 *E tsung pe yaou.* " A Brief Epitome of Medical Practice." 3 keuen.　1814.　8°.

—— 婦 科 指 歸 *Foo ko che kwei.* " A System of Medicine for Females." 4 keuen. [1800 ?].　8°.

—— 痘 疹 會 通 *Tow chin hwuy tung.* " An Exhaustive Treatise on Smallpox." 5 keuen.
1786.　8°.

曾 耀 巖 TSĂNG YAOU-YEN.

同 館 律 賦 鴻 裁 *Tung kwan leŭh foo hung tsae.* " A Collection of ' Foo ' Poems by Authors of the same School."　Collected by Tsăng Yaou-yen. 6 keuen.　　　　　　　　1807.　8°.

僧 鎧 TSĂNG KAE.

佛 說 無 量 壽 經 *Fŭh shwŏ woo leang show king.* " The Sûtra of the Immeasurable."　Translated into Chinese by Tsăng Kae. *See* 彭 際 清 PĂNG TSE-TSING. 淨 土 三 經 *Tsing too san king.* " The Sûtras of the Pure Regions of Bliss," &c.　　　　　1797.　Oblong.

僧 肇 TSĂNG SHAOU.

See 鳩 摩 羅 什 KEW-MO-LO-SHĬH. 維 摩 詰 所 說 經 註 *Wei-mo-keĭh so shwŏ king choo.* " The Sûtra delivered by Wei-mo-keĭh." . . . With a Commentary by Tsăng Shaou, &c.　8°.

曾 珵 TSAOU CHING.

See CHINA. BOARD OF WAR. 欽 定 中 樞 政 考 *Kin ting chung choo ching kaou.* " An Examination into the Fundamental System of Governing " the Army.　Compiled by . . Tsaou Ching, &c.　　　　　　1779.　8°.

曾 勳 TSAOU HEUN.

稿 *Kaou.* " Essays." *See* 長 城 CHANG CHING. 名 家 制 義 *Ming kea che e.* " Essays " on Texts from the Four Books, &c.　Tsĭh 87.
1699.　8°.

曾 鄴 TSAOU NĔĔ.

梅 妃 傳 *Mei Fei chuen.* " The Story of the Imperial Concubine Mei."　By Tsaou Nĕĕ, of the Tang Dynasty.　A Reprint. [1741 ?].　8°.

曹 之 升 TSAOU CHE-SHING.

註 釋 典 制 文 琳 *Choo shĭh teen che wăn lin.* " A Collection of Choice Essays " on Texts from the Four Books.　In Five Series.　Edited by Tsaou Che-shing.　With Notes by Chow Ying-keaou, Seay Paou-tang, Heu Show-mun, and Chang Chun-po.　　　1799–1808.　8°.

—— 典 制 文 琳 註 釋 *Teen che wăn lin choo shĭh.* " A Collection of Choice Essays " on Texts from the Four Books.　In Five Series.　Edited by Tsaou Che-shing.　With Notes by Heu Show-mun, Chow Ying-keaou, Chang Chun-po, and others.　　　　　　　　1804.　8°.
Imperfect, containing only Series 2 and 3.

—— 曹 寅 谷 制 藝 *Tsaou yin-kŭh che e.* " Essays " on Texts from the Four Books.　1792.　8°.

Another copy.

—— 曹 寅 谷 續 刻 稿 *Tsaou yin yŭh sŭh kĭh kaou.* " A Supplementary Volume of Essays."
[1795 ?].　8°.

曹鑑平 TSAOU KEEN-PING.

See 龔在升 KUNG TSAE-SHING. 三才彙編 *San tsae wei peen*. "An Encyclopædia." . . . . . . The Third Keuen of which is Edited by Tsaou Keen-ping, &c.　　　　　　　　　　　　　　8°.

曹秉仁 TSAOU PING-JIN.

宁波府志 *Ning po foo che*. "A Topography of Ning-po Foo," in the Province of Chĕ-keang. Edited by Sun Chaou and others.　36 keuen.

　　　　　　　　　　　Ningpo, 1729.　8°.
　　Imperfect, wanting kenen 3–6, 10–12.

Another edition.　36 keuen.　　*Ningpo*, 1730.　8°.

Another edition.　36 keuen.　　[1735 ?].　8°.
　　Imperfect, containing only keuen 17.

曹雪芹 TSAOU SEUĔ-KIN.

紅樓夢 *Hung low mung*. "The Dream of the Red Chamber." Edited by Ching Wei.
　　　　　　　　　　　　　　1811.　8°.

Another edition.　　　　　[1820 ?].　8°.
　　Imperfect, containing only Chapters 46–51.

曹子建 TSAOU TSZE-KEEN.

七啓 *Tseĭh ke*. "The Seven Declarations." *See* 蕭統 SEAOU TUNG. 文選 *Wăn seuen*. "Elegant Extracts from Polite Literature," &c. Keuen 34.　　　　　　　　　1772.　8°.

草 TSAOU.

試草 *She tsaou*. "Examination Odes." Written during the Years 1782, 1784–1787.　1787.　8°.

草廬 TSAOU LEU.

草廬經略 *Tsaou leu king leŏ*. "A Resumé of the Classic of the Straw Hut" on Military Operations. 12 keuen. *See* 伍崇曜 WOO TSUNG-YAOU. 粤雅堂叢書 *Yuĕ ya Tang tsung shoo*. "The Yuĕ-ya Tang Collection of Reprints," &c.　Series 7.　1853.　8°.

齊鯤 TSE KWĂN, and 費錫章 FEI SEĬH-CHANG.

續琉球國志畧 *Sŭh Lew kew kwŏ che leŏ*. "A Supplementary Account of the Lew chew Islands." By Tse Kwăn and Fei Seĭh-chang. 5 keuen.　　　　　　　　　　1774.　8°.

齊召南 TSE CHAOU-NAN.

歷代帝王年表 *Leĭh tae Te Wang neen peaou*. "A Tabulated Manual of the Reigns of the Emperors of China." Continued from the Beginning of the Ming to the Beginning of the Tsing Dynasty by Yuen Fŭh.　3 keuen. *See* 伍崇曜 WOO TSUNG-YAOU. 粤雅堂叢書 *Yuĕ ya Tang tsung shoo*. "The Yuĕ-ya Tang Collection of Reprints," &c.　Series 12.
　　　　　　　　　　　　1853.　8°.

—— 注疏考證 *Choo soo kaou ching*. "Commentaries Examined and Verified."　6 keuen. *See* 嚴杰 YEN LĔĔ. 皇清經解 *Hwang Tsing king keae*. "The Classics Explained," &c. Keuen 310–315.　　　　　1829.　8°.

—— 水道提綱 *Shway taou te kang*. "An Epitomized Description of the Watercourses throughout the Empire," including those of Thibet, Corea, and Eastern and Western Tartary.　28 keuen.
　　　　　　　　　　　　1776.　8°.

齊推女 TSE TUY-NEU.

齊推女傳 *Tse Tuy-neu chuen*. "The Story of Tse Tuy-neu." *See* 說 SHWŏ. 說淵 *Shwŏ yuen*. "A Collection of Tales," &c. Vol. 6.　8°.

齊東野人 TSE-TUNG YAY-JIN.

See 煬帝 YANG-TE. 隋煬帝艷史 *Suy Yang-te yen she*. "A History of the Reign of Yang-te and of his Amusements." By Tse-tung yay-jin, &c.　　　　　　　　　　　　8°.

濟能 TSE-NĂNG.

角虎集 *Keŏ hoo tseĭh*. "The Horned Tiger Collection" of the Lives of Buddhist Saints. 2 keucn.　　　　　　　[1750 ?].　8°.

蔣伊 TSEANG E.

See 嚴允肇 YEN YUN-SHAOU. 姚布政傳 *Yaou Poo ching chuen*. "A Biography of the Provincial Treasurer Yaou" Seang-heuen. To which is added a short Biographical Notice of the same Officer by Tseang E.　　1820.　8°.

27

蔣防 TSEANG FANG.

霍小玉傳 *Hŏ Seaou-yŭh chuen.* "The Story of Hŏ Seaou-yŭh." [Also] 幻戲志 *Hwan he che.* "Tales of Conjurors." See 王文誥 WANG WĂN-KAOU. 唐代叢書 *Tang tae tsung shoo.* "A Collection of Reprints of Works written during the Tang Dynasty," &c. Series 5, 6.   1806. 8º.

—— 霍小玉傳 *Hŏ Seaou-yŭh chuen.* "The Story of Hŏ Seaou-yŭh." By Tseang Fang, of the Tang Dynasty. A Reprint.   [1741?]. 8º.

—— 幻戲志 *Hwan he che.* "Tales of Conjurors." By Tseang Fang, of the Tang Dynasty. A Reprint.   [1741?]. 8º.

蔣溥 TSEANG POO.

錢錄 *Tseen lŭh.* "A Record of Coins." Compiled by .. Tseang Poo, &c. See 西清 SE TSING. 西清古鑑 *Se tsing koo keen.* "Antiquities [from the Palace?] of Western Purity," &c.   Folio.

—— 御覽經史講義 *Yu lan king she keang e.* "The Meaning of the Classics and of the Histories Explained. Edited under Imperial Supervision" by Tseang Poo, Lew Tung-heun, Wang Yew-tun, and others. 31 keuen.   1758. 8º.

蔣震青 TSEANG CHIN-TSING.

See 易經 YĬH KING. 易經講意去疑 *Yĭh king keang e keu e.* "The Book of Changes." Edited by Tseang Chin-tsing, &c.   1631. 8º.

蔣學鏞 TSEANG HEŎ-YUNG.

樗莊存稿 *Choo gan tsun kaou.* "Literary Pieces from the Choo Hut." 5 keuen. 1813. 8º.

Another collection. 2 keuen.   1813. 8º.

蔣邢茅 TSEANG HING-MAOU.

See 范題名 FAN TE-MING. 五經題解集要 *Woo king te keae tseĭh yaou.* "A Collection of Essays explanatory of Texts from the Five Classics." By .... Tseang Hing-maou, &c.   12º.

蔣若椰 TSEANG JŬ-YAY.

石桃丙舍草 *Shĭh taou ping shay tsaou.* "Scraps from the Shĭh-taou-ping Cottage." See 閔景賢 MIN KING-HEEN. 快書 *Kwae shoo.* "A Book of Amusement," &c. Keuen 28. 1626. 8º.

蔣景祁 TSEANG KING-KE.

See 孔丘 KUNG KEW. 春秋指掌 *Chun Tsew che chang.* "A Guide to the Spring and Autumn Annals.".. Compiled by .. Tseang King-ke, &c.   1688. 8º.

蔣平階 TSEANG PING-KEAE.

地理辨正 *Te le peen ching.* "The Principles of Geomancy Discussed and Rectified." 5? keuen.   [1800?]. 8º.

Imperfect, containing only keuen 4, 5.

蔣善功 TSEANG SHEN-KUNG.

See 謝崇俊 SEAY TSUNG-TSEUN, and TSEANG SHEN-KUNG. 翁源縣新志 *Ung yuen heen sin che.* "A Topography of Ung-yuen Heen." ... Compiled by Seay Tsung-tseuen and Tseang Shen-kung, &c.   1820. 8º.

蔣廷錫 TSEANG TING-SEĬH.

See 張庭玉 CHANG TING-YŬH. 分類字錦 *Fun luy tsze kin.* "A Classified Lexicon of Elegant Expressions." Compiled by ... Tseang Ting-seĭh, &c.   1722. 8º.

—— See 弘晝 HUNG CHOW. 大清一統志 *Ta Tsing yĭh tung che.* "A Geography of the Empire." Compiled by Tseang Ting-seĭh, &c.   1744. 8º.

—— See 孔丘 KUNG KEW. 欽定春秋傳說彙纂 *Kin ting Chun Tsew chuen shwŏ wei tswan.* "The Spring and Autumn Annals." Compiled by .... Tseang Ting-seĭh, &c. 1721. 8º.

———— 欽定書經傳說彙纂 *Kin ting Shoo king chuen shwŏ wei tswan.* "The Book of Historical Documents." ... Compiled by .. Tseang Ting-seĭh, &c.   1730. 8º.

—— 尚書地理今釋 *Shang shoo te le kin shĭh.* "A Modern Explanation of the Localities mentioned in the Four Books." See 嚴杰 YEN LĔĔ. 皇清經解 *Hwang Tsing king keae.* "The Classics Explained," &c. Keuen 207.   1829. 8º.

TSE   [211]   TSE

蔣子正 TSEANG TSZE-CHING.

山房隨筆 *Shan fang suy peĭh.* "Literary Scraps from the Mountain Dwelling." *See* 説 SHWŎ. 説畧 *Shwŏ leŏ.* "Historical and other Tracts," &c.   8°.

蔣賜棨 TSEANG TSZE-KE.

See 楊錫紱 YANG SEĬH-FŬH. 漕運則例纂 *Tsau yun tsĭh le tswan.* "Laws and Regulations for the Conveyance of Grain." . . . Compiled by . . . . Tseang Tsze-ke, &c.   1767. 8°.

蔣子文 TSEANG TSZE-WĂN.

蔣子文傳 *Tseang Tsze-wăn chuen.* "The Story of Tseang Tsze-wăn." *See* 説 SHWŎ. 説淵 *Shwŏ yuen.* "A Collection of Tales," &c. Vol. 7.   8°.

蔣潁叔 TSEANG YING-SHŬH.

蔣氏日錄 *Tseang she jĭh lŭh.* "Tseang's Jottings." *See* 説 SHWŎ. 説郛 *Shwŏ foo.* "Odds and Ends," &c.   8°.

蔣雲鵬 TSEANG YUN-PĂNG.

See 王阮亭 WANG YUEN-TING. 詩鈔 *She chaou.* "Poems." Edited by Tseang Yunpăng, &c.   12°.

焦勗 TSEAOU HEŬH.

火攻挈要 *Hŏ kung kĕĕ yaou.* "An Epitomized Work on Artillery." 3 keuen. *See* 葉志詵 YĚ CHE-SIN. 海山仙館叢書 *Hae shan seen Kwan tsung shoo.* "The Hae-shan-seen Kwan Collection of Reprints," &c. Vol. 35.   1848. 8°.

焦竑 TSEAOU HUNG.

See 莊周 CHWANG CHOW. 莊子註釋評林 *Chwang tsze choo shĭh ping lin.* "The Nan hwa Classic. . . Commented on and Explained by Tseaou Hung," &c.   8°.

—— 焦氏筆乘 *Tseaou she peĭh shing.* "Tseaou Hung's Literary Fragments." 14 keuen. [Also] 國史經籍志 *Kwŏ she king tseĭh che.* "A Catalogue of Historical, Classical, and Literary Works." 5 keuen. *See* 伍崇曜 WOO TSUNG-YAOU. 粵雅堂叢書 *Yuĕ ya Tang tsung shoo.* "The Yuĕ-ya Tang Collection of Reprints," &c. Series 1, 5.   1853. 8°.

蔣竑 TSEAOU HUNG. (*Continued.*)

老莊翼合刻 *Laou Chwang yĭh hŏ kĭh.* "The Works of Laou keun and Chwang Chow," viz.: The *Taou tĭh king* and the *Nan hwa king.* With Commentaries. Compiled by Tseaou Hung. Edited by Wang Yuen-ching. 11 keuen.   1588. 8°.

焦帕 TSEAOU PA.

焦帕記 *Tseaou pa ke.* "The Story of the Black Handkerchief." *See* 曲 KEŬH. 六十種曲 *Lŭh shĭh chung keŭh.* "Sixty Plays," &c. Taou 5. 8°.

焦循 TSEAOU SEUN.

易章句 *Yĭh chang keu.* "The Book of Changes explained Sentence by Sentence." 11 keuen. [Also] 易通釋 *Yĭh tung shĭh.* "The Book of Changes thoroughly Explained." 20 keuen. [Also] 易圖畧 *Yĭh too leŏ.* "A Short Work on the Diagrams of the Book of Changes." 8 keuen. [Also] 孟子正義 *Măng tsze ching e.* "The True Meaning of the Works of Mencius." 6 keuen. [Also] 周易補疏 *Chow Yĭh poo soo.* "Supplementary Explanations of the Chow Changes." 2 keuen. [Also] 尚書補疏 *Shang shoo poo soo.* "Supplementary Explanations of the Book of Historical Documents." 2 keuen. [Also] 毛詩補疏 *Maou she poo soo.* "Supplementary Explanations of the Book of Odes." 5 keuen. [Also] 禮記補疏 *Le ke poo soo.* "Supplementary Explanations of the Book of Rites." 3 keuen. [Also] 春秋左傳補疏 *Chun Tsew Tso chuen poo soo.* "Supplementary Explanations of the Spring and Autumn Annals, and of Tso Kew-ming's Narrative." 5 keuen. [Also] 論語補疏 *Lun yu poo soo.* "Supplementary Explanations of the Confucian Analects." 2 keuen. *See* 嚴杰 YEN LĔE. 皇清經解 *Hwang Tsing king keae.* "The Classics Explained," &c. Keuen 1077–1165.   1829. 8°.

焦延壽 TSEAOU YEN-SHOW.

焦氏易林 *Tseaou she Yĭh lin.* "A Forest of Changes." Founded on Fŭh He's Diagrams. By Tseaou Yen-show, of the Han Dynasty. Edited by Lŭh E. 16 keuen.   1808. 8°.

Another edition. 4 keuen.   [1810?]. 8°.

Another edition. 4 keuen.   [1820?]. 8°.

Imperfect, keuen 1 wanting.

樵 程 瀚 Tseaou Ching-han.

滕王閣 *Tăng wang kŏ.* "The Tăng-wang Gallery." A Drama. 4 keuen. 1795. 8º.

崔 公 Tseaou Kung.

入藥鏡 *Jŭh yŏ king.* "An Introductory Mirror of Medicine." *See* 彭好古 Păng Haou-koo. 道言內外秘訣全書 *Taou yen nuy wae pe keuĕ tseuen shoo.* "A Complete Collection of Taouist Works," &c. 8º.

峭 闌 氏 Tseaou Lan-she.

四書題管見 *Sze shoo te kwan keen.* "My Opinion on Themes from the Four Books." 2 keuen. 1809. 8º.

節 俠 Tsĕĕ hĕĕ.

節俠記 *Tsĕĕ hĕĕ ke.* "A Story of Dignified and Generous Conduct." *See* 曲 Keŭh. 六十種曲 *Lŭh shĭh chung keŭh.* "Sixty Plays," &c. Taou 6. 8º.

節 儉 Tsĕĕ leen.

尚節儉以惜財用 *Shang tsĕĕ leen e seĭh tsae yung.* "On the Value of Economy, that you may have Money Available for Expenses." [1722 ?]. 8º.

箋 Tseen.

錦箋記 *Kin tseen ke.* "The Story of the Embroidered Notepaper." *See* 曲 Keŭh. 六十種曲 *Lŭh shĭh chung keŭh.* "Sixty Plays," &c. Taou 5. 8º.

錢 洙 Tseen Choo.

See 劉良璧 Lew Leang-peĭh. 臺灣府志 *Tae wan foo che.* "A Topography of Tae-wan Foo." . . . Compiled . . . by . . . . Tseen Choo, &c. 1741. 8º.

錢 枋 Tseen Fang.

See 沈景倩 Chin King-tsing. 野獲編 *Yay hwŏ peen.* "Fugitive Pieces." . . . Edited by Tseen Fang, &c. 1827. 8º.

錢 福 Tseen Fŭh.

稿 *Kaou.* "Essays." *See* 長城 Chang Ching. 名家制義 *Ming kea che e.* "Essays" on Texts from the Four Books, &c. Tsĭh 21. 1699. 8º.

錢 嶸 Tseen Hăng.

See 文昌帝君 Wăn chang te keun. 大洞經註疏 *Ta tung king choo soo.* "The Great Profound Sûtra. With a Commentary" by Tseen Hăng, &c. 1712. 8º.

錢 禧 Tseen He.

稿 *Kaou.* "Essays." *See* 長城 Chang Ching. 名家制義 *Ming kea che e.* "Essays" on Texts from the Four Books, &c. Tsĭh 100. 1699. 8º.

錢 楷 Tseen Keae.

See 吉慶 Keĭh King. 廣西通志 *Kwang se tung che.* "A Topography of the Province of Kwang-se." Compiled by . . . Tseen Keae, &c. 1800. 8º.

錢 林 Tseen Lin.

玉山草堂續集 *Yŭh shan tsaou tang sŭh tseĭh.* "A Supplementary Collection of Poetry from the Yŭh-shan tsaou Tang." 6 keuen. *See* 伍崇曜 Woo Tsung-yaou. 粤雅堂叢書 *Yuĕ ya Tang tsung shoo.* "The Yuĕ-ya Tang Collection of Reprints," &c. Series 6. 1853. 8º.

錢 氏 Tseen she.

錢氏私誌 *Tseen she sze che.* "The Private Records of Tseen she." *See* 說 Shwŏ. 說畧 *Shwŏ leŏ.* "Historical and other Tracts," &c. 8º.

錢 塘 Tseen Tang.

瓶亭述古錄 *Kae ting shŭh koo lŭh.* "An Ancient Record from the Kae Pavilion." 2 keuen. *See* 嚴杰 Yen Lĕĕ. 皇清經解 *Hwang Tsing king keae.* "The Classics Explained," &c. Keuen 717, 718. 1829. 8º.

錢 濤 Tseen Taou.

百花彈詞 *Pĭh hwa tan tsze.* "Rhymes on Flowers." *See* 張山來 Chang Shan-lae, and 張進也 Chang Tsin-yay. 昭代叢書 *Chaou tae tsung shoo.* "A Collection of Reprints of Works by Authors under the Present Dynasty," &c. Keuen 46. 1703. 8º.

錢 彩 Tseen Tsae.

說岳全傳 *Shwŏ Yŏ tseuen chuen.* "The Complete Narrative of Yŏ Fei," a General who served under the Sung Dynasty. 1801. 8º.

錢曾 TSEEN TSĂNG.

述古堂藏書目 *Shŭh koo tang tsang shoo mŭh.* "A Catalogue of the Shŭh-koo Tang Library." Compiled by Tseen Tsăng. 2 keuen. *See* 伍 崇曜 WOO TSUNG-YAOU. 粤雅堂叢書 *Yuĕ ya Tang tsung shoo.* "The Yuĕ-ya Tang Collection of Reprints," &c. Series 9. 1853. 8°.

——— 讀書敏求記 *Tŭh shoo min kew ke.* "An Earnest Introduction to Study." 4 keuen. *See* 葉志詵 YĔ CHE-SIN. 海山仙館叢書 *Hae shan seen kwan tsung shoo.* "The Hae-shan-seen Kwan Collection of Reprints," &c. Vol. 3, 4. 1848. 8°.

錢易 TSEEN YĬH.

南部新書 *Nan poo sin shoo.* "New Records of the Southern Boards." 10 keuen. *See* 伍 崇曜 WOO TSUNG-YAOU. 粤雅堂叢書 *Yuĕ ya Tang tsung shoo.* "The Yuĕ-ya Tang Collection of Reprints," &c. Series 1. 1853. 8°.

錢希祥 TSEEN HE-TSEANG.

See 孔丘 KUNG KEW. 學源堂書經體註 *Heŏ yuen tang Shoo king te choo.* " . . . The . . . Book of Historical Documents." . . Edited by . . Tseen He-tseang, &c. 1725. 8°.

——— 書經瑯環體註 *Shoo king lang hwan te choo.* "The Book of Historical Documents." . . Compiled by Tseen He-tseang, &c. 1789. 8°.

錢謙益 TSEEN KEEN-YĬH.

絳雲樓書目 *Keang yun low shoo mŭh.* "A Catalogue of the Books in the 'Red Cloud' Pavilion." With Notes by Chin King-yun. 4 keuen. *See* 伍 崇曜 WOO TSUNG-YAOU. 粤 雅堂叢書 *Yuĕ ya Tang tsung shoo.* "The Yuĕ-ya Tang Collection of Reprints," &c. Series 9. 1853. 8°.

錢樹掌 TSEEN SHOO-CHANG.

See 雷琳 LUY LIN. 經餘必讀續編 *King yu peĭh tŭh sŭh peen.* "A Supplementary Collection of Elegant Extracts from Ancient Works." . . Compiled by . . Tseen Shoo-chang, &c. 1807. 8°.

錢樹立 TSEEN SHOO-LEĬH.

See 雷琳 LUY LIN. 經餘必讀 *King yu peĭh tŭh.* "Elegant Extracts from Ancient Works exclusive of the Classics." Compiled by . . . . Tseen Shoo-leĭh, &c. 1805. 8°.

——— 經餘必讀續編 *King yu peĭh tŭh sŭh peen.* "A Supplementary Collection of Elegant Extracts from Ancient Works." . . Compiled by . . . Tseen Shoo-leĭh, &c. 1807. 8°.

——— 經餘必讀 *King yu peĭh tŭh.* "Elegant Extracts from Ancient Works exclusive of the Classics." Compiled by . . . . Tseen Shoo-tang, &c. 1805. 8°.

錢澍田 TSEEN SHOO-TEEN.

敬修堂藥說 *King sew tang yŏ shwŏ.* "A Treatise on Medicine from the King-sew Tang." 1804. 8°.

錢士鰲 TSEEN SZE-GAOU.

稿 *Kaou.* "Essays." *See* 長城 CHANG CHING. 名家制義 *Ming kea che e.* "Essays" on Texts from the Four Books, &c. Tsĭh 67. 1699. 8°.

錢大昭 TSEEN TA-CHAOU.

後漢書補表 *How Han shoo poo peaou.* "A Tabulated Genealogy, Supplementary to the History of the Later Han Dynasty." 8 keuen. *See* 伍崇曜 WOO TSUNG-YAOU. 粤雅堂 叢書 *Yuĕ ya Tang tsung shoo.* "The Yuĕ-ya Tang Collection of Reprints," &c. Series 10. 1853. 8°.

錢大昕 TSEEN TA-HIN.

聲類 *Shing luy.* "A Lexicon of Expressions, Arranged according to Subjects." 4 keuen. [Also] 宋遼金元四史朔閏考 *Sung, Leaou, Kin, Yuen sze she sŏ jun kaou.* "An Investigation of the Changes in the Calendar introduced during the Sung, Leaou, Kin, and Yuen Dynasties." 2 keuen. [Also] 疑年錄 *E neen lŭh.* "A Record of Doubtful Dates." With a Supplement by Woo Sew. 8 keuen. *See* 伍崇曜 WOO TSUNG-YAOU. 粤雅堂 叢書 *Yuĕ ya Tang tsung shoo.* "The Yuĕ-ya Tang Collection of Reprints," &c. Series 4, 14. 1853. 8°.

錢 大 昕 TSEEN TA-HIN. (*Continued.*)

See 姚 松 陰 YAOU SUNG-YIN. 初 學 檢 韻 *Tsoo heŏ keen yun.* "A Rhyming Dictionary for Beginners." Edited by Tseen Ta-hin, &c.
1802. 8°.

—— 十 駕 齋 養 新 錄 *Shĭh kea chae yang sin lŭh.* "New and Instructive Treatises [on the Classics] from the Shĭh-kea Study." With a Supplement. 4 keuen. [Also] 潛 研 堂 文 集 *Tseen neen Tang wăn tseĭh.* "The Tseen-neen Tang Collection of Literary Compositions. 6 keuen. *See* 嚴 杰 YEN LĔĔ. 皇 清 經 解 *Hwang Tsing king keae.* "The Classics Explained," &c. Keuen 439–448.
1829. 8°.

—— 潛 研 堂 詩 集 *Tseen neen Tang she tseĭh.* "The Tseen-neen Tang Collection of Poetical Pieces." 10 keuen.
1830. 8°.
Imperfect, containing only keuen 1–4.

—— 潛 研 堂 文 集 *Tseen neen tang wăn tseĭh.* "The Tseen-neen Tang Collection of Literary Compositions." By Tseen Ta-hin. With Portrait. 50 keuen.
1806. 8°.

—— 鄞 縣 志 *Yin heen che.* "A Topography of Yin Heen," in the Province of Che keang. Compiled by Tseen Ta-hin. Edited by Yin Heen-tsăng, Chin Chung-yin, &c. 30 keuen.
1788. 8°.
Another copy.
Imperfect, wanting keuen 8 to 30.
Another copy.

錢 在 培 TSEEN TSAE-PEI.

See 孔 丘 KUNG KEW. 尙 書 離 句 *Shang shoo le keu.* "The Book of Historical Documents, Explained " .. by Tseen Tsae-pei, &c. 8°.

錢 青 選 TSEEN TSING-SEUEN.

See 范 題 名 FAN TE-MING. 袖 珍 五 經 題 旨 *Sew chin woo king te che.* "Essays on Texts from the Five Classics." ... By ... Tseen Tsing-seuen, &c.
1820. 24°.

———— 五 經 題 解 集 要 *Woo king te keae tseĭh yaou.* "A Collection of Essays Explanatory of Texts from the Five Classics." By .. Tseen Tsing-seuen, &c. 12°.

錢 東 垣 TSEEN TUNG-TAN.

鄭 志 *Ching che.* "Ching Kang-ching's Records." .. Edited by Tseen Tung-tan, &c. [Also] 崇 文 總 目 *Tsung wăn tsung mŭh.* "A Catalogue of Celebrated Works." .. With Bibliographical Notes by Tseen Tung-tan, &c. *See* 伍 崇 曜 WOO TSUNG-YAOU. 粵 雅 堂 叢 書 *Yuĕ ya Tang tsung shoo.* "The Yuĕ-ya Tang Collection of Reprints," &c. Series 12, 15. 1853. 8°.

錢 沃 臣 TSEEN WŬH-CHIN.

樂 妙 山 居 集 *Lŏ-meaou shan keu tseĭh.* "A Collection of Poetry from the Dwelling on the Lŏ-meaou Hill." 1805. 8°.

錢 元 龍 TSEEN YUEN-LUNG.

See 程 允 升 CHING YUN-SHING. 幼 學 須 知 句 解 *Yew heŏ seu che keu keac.* "General Knowledge Necessary for Beginners." ... Edited by Tseen Yuen-lung, &c. 1863. 8°.

錢 玉 震 TSEEN YŬH-CHIN.

See 吳 因 之 WOO YIN-CHE. 易 說 *Yĭh shwŏ.* "Discourses on the Book of Changes." Edited by Tseen Yŭh-chin, &c. [1700 ?]. 8°.

箭 TSEEN.

—— 箭 緣 傳 *Yĭh tseen yuen chuen.* "The Fate of an Arrow." A Drama. By the Owner of the Hwan-sew Pavilion. 4 keuen.
1818. 8°.

集 TSEĬH.

便 元 集 *Peen yuen tseĭh.* "The Convenient and Original Collection" of Taouist Tracts. 2 keuen.
[1820 ?]. 8°.
Imperfect. First keuen wanting.

戢 山 TSEĬH SHAN.

戢 山 課 藝 *Tseĭh shan ko e.* "Scholastic Essays from Tseĭh Shan." [1790 ?]. 8°.
Imperfect.
Another Series. [1800 ?]. 8°.
Imperfect.

七 巧 Tseïh keaou.

七 巧 圖 合 璧 *Tseïh keaou too hŏ peïh.* "Drawings of Puzzles." By 'The Guest under the Mulberry Tree.'   [1810 ?]. 8°.

Another edition.   [1815 ?]. 8°.

There are seven other imperfect copies of this edition.

—— 七 巧 圖 解 *Tseïh keaou too keae.* "A Key to the Puzzles" of 'The Guest under the Mulberry Tree.'   1815. 8°.

There are seven other copies of this work.

七 十 一 Tseïh shïh-yïh.

鄂 羅 斯 傳 *Gŏ-lo-sze chuen.* "An Account of Russia." *See* 何 秋 濤 Ho Tsew-taou. 北 徼 彙 編 *Pĭh keaou wei peen.* "Treatises on the Countries beyond the Northern Frontier," &c. Keuen 1.   1865. 8°.

—— 西 域 聞 見 錄 *Se yĭh wăn keen lŭh.* "Things Heard and Seen on the Western Frontiers." A Record principally of Eastern Turkestan, Mohammedan Tartary, and the various Chinese Dependencies on the West. By Tseïh-shĭh-yĭh, a Manchu Officer. 8 keuen.   1777. 8°.

戚 Tseïh, and 林 碧 山 Lin Peïh-shan.

八 音 合 訂 *Pă yin hŏ ting.* "A Dictionary of the Füh-keen Dialect, arranged under the Eight Tones," on an Alphabetical System, by the Japanese General Tseïh and Lin Peïh-shan. Edited by Tsin Gan.   1841. 8°.

戚 藩 Tseïh Fan.

稿 *Kaou.* "Essays." *See* 長 城 Chang Ching. 名 家 制 義 *Ming kea che e.* "Essays" on Texts from the Four Books, &c. Tsïh 105.   1699. 8°.

戚 光 Tseïh Kwang.

See 陸 游 Lŭh Yew. 南 唐 書 *Nan Tang shoo.* "A History of the Southern Tang Dynasty." With a Supplementary Keuen by Tseïh Kwang, &c.   1813. 8°.

戚 學 標 Tseïh Heŏ-peaou.

鶴 泉 集 杜 *Hŏ-tseuen tseïh too.* "The Crane-spring Collection of Poetical Pieces." 2 keuen.   [1800 ?]. 8°.

Imperfect, the first keuen wanting.

—— 景 文 堂 稿 *King wăn tang kaou.* "Essays from the King-wăn Tang" on Texts from the Four Books.   1791. 8°.

—— 四 書 偶 談 *Sze shoo gow tan.* "Occasional Conversations on the Four Books." In Two Parts.   1789. 8°.

—— 四 書 偶 談 續 編 *Sze shoo gow tan sŭh peen.* "A Supplementary Volume of Occasional Conversations on the Four Books." In Three Parts.   [1750 ?]. 8°.

Title-page and few first pages wanting.

戚 繼 光 Tseïh Ke-kwang.

紀 效 新 書 *Ke heaou sin shoo.* "A New Work on the Stratagems of War." By General Tseïh Ke-kwang. Edited by Chang Hae-păng. 18 keuen.   1804. 8°.

Another edition.   [1820 ?]. 8°.

Imperfect, containing only keuen 8–11, 17, 18.

跡 刪 鷥 Tseïh Shan-tsew.

See 莊 周 Chwang Chow. 南 華 內 篇 別 解 *Nan hwa nuy peen pëĕ keae.* "The First Part of the Nan-hwa Classic explained" by Tseïh Shan-tsew, &c.   1721. 8°.

—— *See* 鳩 摩 羅 什 Kew-mo-lo-shïh. 金 剛 直 說 *Kin kang chĭh shwŏ.* "The Diamond Classic .. clearly explained" by Tseïh Shan-tsew, &c. 8°.

全 祖 望 Tseuen Tsoo-wang.

See 王 應 麟 Wang Ying-lin. 困 學 紀 聞 *Kwăn heŏ ke wăn.* "Criticisms on Literature and Science." With Notes by Tseuen Tsoo-wang, &c.   1742. 8°.

全祖望 TSEUEN TSOO-WANG. (*Continued.*)

漢書地理志稽疑 *Han shoo te le che ke e.*
"An Examination of the Doubtful Points in the
Geography of the Han Dynasty." 6 keuen.
See 伍崇曜 WOO TSUNG-YAOU. 粤雅堂
叢書 *Yuĕ ya Tang tsung shoo.* "The Yuĕ-ya
Tang Collection of Reprints," &c. Series 17.
1853. 8°.

—— 經史問答 *King she wăn tă.* "A Catechism
on the Classics and on History." 7 keuen. *See*
嚴杰 YEN LÉĔ. 皇淸經解 *Hwang Tsing
king keae.* "The Classics Explained," &c. Keuen
302–308. 1829. 8°.

—— 鮚埼亭集 *Keĭh ke ting tseĭh.* "The Keĭh-ke
Pavilion Collection of Poetical and Literary
Pieces." Edited by She Mung-keaou. 38
keuen. 1804. 8°.

Another copy.
Imperfect, the first seven keuen wanting.

—— 鮚埼亭集外編 *Keĭh ke ting tseĭh wae peen.*
"An Additional Collection of Literary Pieces
from the Keĭh-ke Pavilion." 50 keuen.
Na-te chow, 1811. 8°.

—— 經史問答 *King she wăn tă.* "A Catechism
on the Classics and on History." Edited by
Yu Yaou-she. 10 keuen. [1800?]. 8°.

Another copy.

—— 句餘土音 *Kow yu too yin.* "A Collection
of Local Poetry." Compiled by Tseuen Tsoo-
wang. A Reprint. 3 keuen. 1814. 8°.

—— 年華錄 *Neen hwa lŭh.* "A Record of the
Years" of Life. 4 keuen. 1816. 8°.

—— 甬上族望表 *Yung shang tsŭh wang peen.*
"The Genealogy of Certain Clans." 2 keuen.
1814. 8°.

秋坪 TSEW PING.
秋坪新語 *Tsew ping sin yu.* "New Stories
from Tsew-ping." Compiled by the Dissipated
Man of Tsew-ping. 12 keuen. 1797. 8°.

秋澄居士 TSEW-TĂNG KEU SZE.
See 獅 SZE. 碧玉獅 *Peĭh yuh sze.* "The
Azure-jade Lion." By 'The Retired Scholar
of Tsew-tăng,' &c. 1820. 8°.

策 TSĬH.
新策茗頴 *Sin tsĭh teaou ying.* "New Schemes
ably Set Forth." A Work on the Waters of
Chĕ-keang. [1800?]. 8°.

—— 策液 *Tsĭh yĭh.* "An Encyclopædia. A Pocket
Edition." 12 keuen. [1700?]. 8°.

Another copy.

策學 TSĬH HEŎ.
策學新纂 *Tsĭh heŏ sin tswan.* "The Students'
Manual." A New Edition. 10 keuen.
[1820?]. 12°.
Imperfect, containing only the last three keuen.

晉安 TSIN GAN.
See 戚 TSEĬH, and 林碧山 LIN PEĬH-SHAN.
八音合訂 *Pă yin hŏ ting.* "A Dictionary
of the Fŭh-keen Dialect, arranged under the
Eight Tones." ... Edited by Tsin Gan, &c.
1841. 8°.

親 TSIN.
尋親記 *Sin tsin ke.* "The Search for Relatives."
See 曲 KEŬH. 六十種曲 *Lŭh shĭh chung
keŭh.* "Sixty Plays," &c. Taou 1. 8°.

秦觀 TSIN KWAN.
淮海集 *Hwae hae tseĭh.* "The Hwae-hae Collection." *See* 吳孟舉 WOO MĂNG-KEU, and
吳自牧 WOO TSZE-MŬH. 宋詩鈔二集
Sung she chaou urh tseĭh. "Poetry of the Sung
Dynasty," &c. 8°.

秦瓊 TSIN LEANG.
秦瓊表功 *Tsin Leang peaou kung.* "Tsin
Leang declares his Meritorious Deeds." A
Drama. [1800?]. 8°.

秦醇 TSIN SHUN.
趙后遺事 *Chaou How e sze.* "A Posthumous
Record of the Empress Chaou (Fei-yen)." By
Tsin Shun, of the Sung Dynasty. A Reprint.
[1741?]. 8°.

秦瀚吉 TSIN CHAN-KEÏH.

遏淫十箴 *Gŏ yin shĭh chin.* "Ten Prohibitions against Lewdness." *See* 黃正元 HWANG CHING-YUEN. 性天眞境 *Sing teen chin king.* "The True Limits of Human and Divine Nature," &c. 1805. 8°.

秦蕙田 TSIN HWUY-TEEN.

觀象授時 *Kwan seang show she.* "A Glance at the Diagrams [of the Book of Changes], as Indicative of Seasons." 14 keuen. *See* 嚴杰 YEN LĔĔ. 皇清經解 *Hwang Tsing king keae.* "The Classics Explained," &c. Keuen 288-301. 1829. 8°.

秦繼宗 TSIN KE-TSUNG.

See 禮記 LE KE. 全文禮記疏意體註 *Tseuen wăn Le ke soo e te choo.* "The Complete Text of the Book of Rites." .. Compiled by Tsin Ke-tsung, &c. 1632. 8°.

秦耀曾 TSIN YAOU-TSĂNG.

普陀山志 *Poo to shan che.* "A Topography of the Island of Poo-to." Compiled by Tsin Yaou-tsăng. Edited by Wang Ting-heun. A New Edition. 20 keuen. 1832. 8°.

Another copy.

Imperfect, wanting keuen 8-15.

津 TSIN.

小題文津 *Seaou te wăn tsin.* "A Ford to the Composition of Literary Essays." A Collection of Model Essays on Texts from the Four Books. [1820?]. 8°.

青衫 TSING SHAN.

青衫記 *Tsing shan ke.* "The Story of the Blue Jacket." *See* 曲 KEÜH. 六十種曲 *Lŭh shĭh chung keŭh.* "Sixty Plays," &c. Taou 4. 8°.

靜觀主人 TSING-KWAN CHOO JIN.

See 妲己 TĂ-KE. 哪吒收妲己 *Na chă show Tă-ke.* "The Murder of Tă-ke." .. Edited by Tsing-kwan Choo jin, &c. 8°.

TSING DYNASTY.

大清會典 *Ta Tsing hwuy teen.* "A Comprehensive Description of the System of Government under the Tsing Dynasty." Compiled by order of the Emperor Yung-ching, by Prince Yun Lŭh, Yin Tae, Chang Ting-yŭh, and others. 250 keuen. 1732. 8°.

Imperfect, containing only books 1, 2, 8, 9, 15-18, 23-27, 36, 37, 38, 39, 42-46, 49, 50, 51, 52, 63, 64, 68, 69, 74-80, 84-92, 96-99, 115-122, 134, 140, 143, 144, 150-154, 159, 160, 164, 165, 168, 169, 172, 173, 174, 179, 180, 181, 182, 187-196, 205-214, and parts of books 246, 247 in MS.

—— 欽定大清會典 *Kin ting ta tsing hwuy teen.* "A Comprehensive Description of the System of Government under the Tsing Dynasty." 100 ? keuen. [1771 ?]. 8°.

Imperfect, containing only keuen 3-38, 78-89.

—— 欽定大清會典事例 *Kin ting Ta Tsing hwuy teen sze le.* "A Historical Summary of the Events which have taken place under the respective Government Offices, since the Commencement of the Ta Tsing Dynasty." 920 keuen. 1818. 8°.

—— 欽定大清會典圖 *Kin ting ta Tsing hwuy teen too.* "Plates accompanying the *Ta Tsing hwuy teen.*" 132 keuen. [1818?]. 8°.

Imperfect, containing only keuen 79-106, 110-132.

—— 欽定大清會典則例 *Kin ting Ta Tsing hwuy teen tseĭh le.* "A Detail of the Modifications which have taken place in the various Departments of State under the Ta Tsing Dynasty." Published by the Order of the Emperor Keen-lung. 180 keuen. 1748. 4°.

Very imperfect, containing only books 1-30, 55-65, 108-138, 140-142, 149-152, 165-170.

—— 大清會典文武相見儀制 *Ta Tsing hwuy teen wăn woo seang keen e che.* "Ceremonies to be Observed by Civil and Military Officers when Meeting, as Laid Down in the *Ta Tsing hwuy teen.*" 2 keuen. [1800?]. 8°.

Without title-page.

28

TSING DYNASTY.　*(Continued.)*

大清律例 *Ta Tsing leŭh le.* "The Fundamental Laws and Subordinate Statutes of the Tsing Dynasty." Compiled by Prince Hung Chow, Seu Pun, San Tae, and others. 47 keuen.
Keang-ning, 1768. 8°.

Another edition.　[47 keuen ?　　1770 ?].　8°.
Imperfect, containing only keuen 1, 2; 8–33.

Another edition.　49 keuen.　　　1814.　8°.
Imperfect, containing only keuen 28–34, 42–45, 48, 49.

Another edition.　39 keuen.　　　1825.　8°.
Wanting keuen 24, 25, 27–29.

—— 大清律纂修條例 *Ta Tsing leŭh tswan sew teaou le.* "The Fundamental Laws and Subordinate Statutes of the Tsing Dynasty Codified."
1830.　8°.

—— 大清律例重訂統纂集成 *Ta Tsing leŭh le chung ting tung tswan tseŭh ching.* "The Fundamental Laws and Subordinate Statutes of the Tsing Dynasty. A Revised and Complete Edition." Compiled by Order of the Emperor Taou-kwang. With a Commentary by Chin Che-ke. Revised and Enlarged by Choo Keun.
1830.　8°.

Another copy.

—— 大清律例新增統纂集成 *Ta Tsing leŭh le sin tsăng tung tswan tseŭh ching.* "The Fundamental Laws and Subordinate Statutes of the Tsing Dynasty. A New and Enlarged Edition." With a Commentary by Chin Che-ke. Edited by Yaou Yu-heang. [42 keuen.] [1830 ?]. 8°.
Imperfect, containing only keuen 9–22, 27, 28.

—— 大清律例增修統纂集成 *Ta Tsing leŭh le tsăng sew tung tswan tseŭh ching.* "The Fundamental Laws and Subordinate Statutes of the Tsing Dynasty. An Enlarged and Improved Edition." Compiled by Order of the Emperor Taou-kwang. With a Commentary by Chin Che-ke. Edited by Yaou Yu-heang. 42 keuen.
1837.　8°.

TSING DYNASTY.　*(Continued.)*

大清律箋釋 *Ta Tsing leŭh tseen shĭh.* "The Laws of the Ta Tsing Dynasty Elucidated and Explained." Compiled by Le Yen. Edited by Tsae Fang-ping. To which is appended the *Hing Poo tsĭh le*, or "The Regulations of the Board of Punishments." Compiled by Hwang Ke, Shen Ta-hae, Fung Soo, and others. 33 keuen.
1725.　8°.

—— 大清通禮 *Ta Tsing tung le.* "A Complete Code of the Ceremonies of the Ta Tsing Dynasty." Compiled by an Imperial Commission consisting of Lae Paou, Chin She-kwan, Wang Gan-kwŏ, and others.　50 keuen.
1756.　8°.
Very imperfect, containing only keuen 1–11, 39–49.

Another edition.　　　　1795.　8°.

Another edition.　54 keuen.　　1824.　8°.

Another copy.
Very imperfect.

精忠 TSING CHUNG.

精忠記 *Tsing chung ke.* "A Story of Sincere Loyalty." *See* 曲 KEŬH. 六十種曲 *Lŭh shĭh chung keŭh.* "Sixty Plays," &c. Taou 1. 8°.

左史 TSO SHE.

See 向日貞 HEANG JĬH-CHING. 註釋向太史全稿 *Choo shĭh Heang tae she tseuen kaou.* "A Complete Collection of the Essays of Heang Jĭh-ching, the Historian." . . Annotated by Tso She, &c.　　　　1771. 8°.

左輝春 TSO HWUY-CHUN.

史學提要補 *She heŏ te yaou poo.* "A Supplement to Hwang Ke-shen's Epitome of History." In Verse. By Tso Hwuy-chin. With Notes by Ho Yung. *See* 陸清獻 LŬH TSING-HEEN. 小四書 *Seaou Sze shoo.* "The Lesser Four Books," &c.　Keuen 6.　　1845. 8°.

左丘明 TSO KEW-MING.

國語 *Kwŏ yu.* "The Narratives of the States." *See* 沈津 CHIN TSIN. 百家類纂 *Pĭh kea luy tswan.* "The Works of a Hundred Authors," Keuen 2.　　　　　8°.

左 丘 明 Tso Kew-ming. *(Continued.)*

See 陳 明 卿 Chin Ming-king, and 鍾 伯 敬 Chung Pih-king. 國 語 國 策 詳 注 *Kwŏ yu kwŏ tsĭh tseang choo.* "The Narratives of the States," by Tso Kew-ming, &c. Part I.
1724. 8°.

—— See 康 熙 Kang-he. *Emperor.* 御 選 古 文 淵 鑒 *Yu seuen koo wăn yuen keen.* "A Deep Mirror of Ancient Literature." .. With the Narrative of Tso Kew-ming, &c. Keuen 1–4.
1685. 8°.

—— See 高 其 名 Kaou Ke-ming, and 鄭 師 成 Ching Sze-ching. 四 書 左 國 輯 要 *Sze shoo Tso kwŏ tseĭh yaou.* "Extracts from Tso Kew-ming's Narrative," &c. 1789. 8°.

—— See 孔 丘 Kung Kew. 春 秋 大 全 *Chun Tsew ta tseuen.* "A Complete Copy of the Spring and Autumn Annals." With Commentaries by by Tso Kew-ming, &c. 1625. 8°.

———— 春 秋 指 掌 *Chun Tsew che chang.* "A Guide to the Spring and Autumn Annals." ... Containing Extracts from the Commentaries of Tso Kew-ming, &c. 1688. 8°.

———— 春 秋 經 傳 集 解 *Chun Tsew king chuen tseĭh keae.* "The Spring and Autumn Annals, and Tso Kew-ming's Narrative," &c. 8°.

———— 春 秋 左 傳 杜 林 合 註 *Chun Tsew Tso chuen Too Lin hŏ choo.* "The Spring and Autumn Annals, and Tso Kew-ming's Narrative," &c. 8°.

———— 春 秋 三 傳 楬 要 *Chun Tsew san chuen kĕĕ yaou.* "The Spring and Autumn Annals, with Extracts from the Three Narratives" of Tso Kew-ming, &c. 12°.

———— 春 秋 三 傳 通 經 合 纂 *Chun Tsew san chuen tung king hŏ tswan.* "The Spring and Autumn Annals. With the Three Narratives" of Tso Kew-ming, &c. 8°.

———— 欽 定 春 秋 傳 說 彙 纂 *Kin ting Chun Tsew chuen shwŏ wei tswan.* "The Spring and Autumn Annals. With Comments and Remarks" thereon by Tso Kew-ming, &c.
1721. 8°.

左 丘 明 Tso Kew-ming. *(Continued.)*

See 劉 豫 菴 Lew Yu-gan. 詳 訂 古 文 評 註 *Tseang ting koo wăn ping choo.* "Extracts from Ancient Literature." ... With Extracts from the Narrative of Tso Kew-ming, &c. Keuen 1, 2. 1823. 8°.

—— See 林 西 仲 Lin Se-chung. 古 文 析 義 合 編 *Koo wăn seĭh e hŏ peen.* "Ancient Compositions, with Notes on their Meaning." ... With Extracts from the *Tso chuen* and *Kwŏ yu,* by Tso Kew-ming, &c. Keuen 1–3. 1716. 8°.

—— 春 秋 分 國 左 傳 *Chun Tsew fun kwŏ Tso chuen.* "Extracts from the *Tso chuen* Relating to some of the Kingdoms of the Chun Tsew Period." Compiled by Ling Seuen-wang, and Edited by Loo Wăn-tsze. 10 keuen. 1761. 8°.

—— 春 秋 左 傳 解 要 *Chun Tsew Tso chuen keae yaou.* "The Essential Portions of Tso Kew-ming's Narrative on the Spring and Autumn Annals Explained," by Sun Kwang, Maou Kwăn, Tang Pin-yin, and others. An enlarged Edition. Edited by Han Tan. 8 keuen. 1817. 8°.

—— 國 語 選 *Kwŏ yu seuen.* "Selections from the Narratives of the States" by Tso Kew-ming, &c. 1766. 8°.

——- 左 傳 選 *Tso chuen seuen.* "Selections from Tso Kew-ming's Narrative." Compiled by Choo Hin. Edited by Seu Yung-heun and others. 14 keuen. [1766?]. 8°.

Imperfect, containing only keuen 7–14.

-—— 讀 左 補 義 *Tŭh Tso poo e.* "Aids to Reading Tso Kew-ming's Commentary" on the Spring and Autumn Annals. With the Text of the same. By Keang Ping-chang. 50 keuen.
1772. 8°.

Imperfect, keuen 1–13 wanting.

鄒 浩 Tsow Haou.

道 鄉 集 *Taou heang tseĭh.* "The Taou-heang Collection." *See* 吳 孟 舉 Woo Măng-keu, and 吳 自 牧 Woo Tsze-mŭh. 宋 詩 鈔 二 集 *Sung she chaou urh tseĭh.* "Poetry of the Sung Dynasty," &c. 8°.

鄒璟 Tsow King.

乍浦備志 *Cha poo pe che.* "A Topography of Cha-poo," a Seaport in the Province of Chĕ-keang. Compiled by Tsow-king. 36 keuen.
1828. 8°.

鄒金生 Tsow Kin-săng.

See 周祥鈺 Chow Tseang-yŭh. 九宮大成 南北詞宮譜 *Kew kung ta ching nan pĭh tsze kung poo.* "A Collection of Southern and Northern Rhymes, with their Appropriate Airs." Compiled by . . . Tsow Kin-săng, &c. 8°.

鄒景揚 Tsow King-yang.

酬世錦囊全書 *Chow she kin nang tseuen shoo.* "A Treasury of Information on Social Etiquette." Edited by Seay Mei-lin and Tsow Ko-ting. 8 keuen. 1771. 8°.

鄒可庭 Tsow Ko-ting.

See 鄒景揚 Tsow King-yang. 酬世錦囊全書 *Chow she kin nang tseuen shoo.* "A Treasury of Information on Social Etiquette." Edited by . . . Tsow Ko-ting, &c. 1771. 8°.

鄒升恒 Tsow Shing-hang.

See 華希閔 Hwa He-min. 廣事類賦 *Kwang sze luy foo.* "An Encyclopædia." . . Edited by Tsow Shing-hăng, &c. 1788. 8°.

鄒聖脈 Tsow Shing-mĭh.

See 程允升 Ching Yun-shing. 幼學故事 瓊林 *Yew heŏ koo sze keung lin.* "An Encyclopædia for Beginners." Edited by Tsow Shing-mĭh, &c. 1833. 8°.

——— See 詩經 She king. 御案詩經備旨 *Yu gan She king pe che.* "The Book of Odes." . . Compiled by Tsow Shing-mĭh, &c. 8°.

鄒廷忠 Tsow Ting-chung.

吐玉新聯 *Too yŭh sin leen.* "A String of [Poetic] Pearls." 2 keuen.
Fŭh shan, [1850?]. 8°.

宗主 Tsung choo.

宗主詩章 *Tsung choo she chang.* "Hymns to the God of our Fathers." [By W. H. Medhurst.] [*Shanghae*], 1855. 8°.

This is a revised edition of the *Yang sin shin she*, by the same author.

宗懍 Tsung Lin.

歲時記 *Suy she ke.* "A Record of the Seasons of the Year." By Tsung Lin, of the Tsin Dynasty. A Reprint. [1750?]. 8°.

宗密 Tsung-meĭh.

See 佛陀多羅 Fŭh-to-to-lo. 大方廣圓 覺經署疏 *Ta fang kwang yuen keaou king leŏ soo.* "The Sûtra of Complete Perception." . . . With a Commentary by Tsung-meĭh, &c.
1573. 8°.

——— 佛說盂蘭盆經疏 *Fŭh shwŏ Yu lan pun king soo.* "The Sûtra of the Yu-lan pun Festival, delivered by Buddha." Edited, with a Commentary, by Tsung-meĭh. 2 keuen.
1765. 8°.

宗室文吉 Tsung-chĭh-wăn-keĭh.

See CHINA. 嘉慶 Kea-king. *Emperor.* 欽定 軍器則例 *Kin ting keun ke tsĭh le.* "Military Store Regulations." . . Compiled by . . Tsung-chĭh-wăn-keĭh, &c. 1801. 8°.

崔鴻 Tsuy Hung.

十六國春秋 *Shĭh lŭh kwŏ chun tsew.* "The Annals of the Sixteen Dynasties" [which existed independently of the central Imperial Government during the Tsin and Sung Dynasties]. Edited by Seay Kea-lan and others.
[1810?]. 8°.

Another edition. Edited by Seu Jin-yŭh and others.
[1810?]. 8°.

崔豹 Tsuy Paou.

古今注 *Koo kin choo.* "An Examination of Historical Antiquities." By Tsuy Paou. 3 keuen. [1750?]. 8°.

崔弼 Tsuy Peĭh.

波羅外紀 *Po lo wae ke.* "A Further Account of the Island of Polo." 8 keuen. 1804. 8°.

Another copy.

崔 致 遠 Tsuy Che-yuen.

桂 苑 筆 耕 集 *Kwei yuen peĭh kăng tseĭh.* "The Kwei-yuen Collection of Pencil Ploughings," *i.e.* Forms of Addresses, Memorials, &c. 20 keuen. *See* 葉 志 詵 Ye Che-sin. 海 山 仙 館 叢 書 *Hae shan seen Kwan tsung shoo.* "The Hae-shan-seen Kwan Collection of Reprints," &c. Vol. 51-54.   1848. 8º.

崔 希 範 Tsuy He-fan.

入 藥 鏡 *Jŭh yŏ king.* "An Introductory Mirror of Medicine." *See* 彭 好 古 Păng Haou-koo. 道 言 內 外 秘 訣 全 書 *Taou yen nuy wae pe keuĕ tseuen shoo.* "A Complete Collection of Taouist Works," &c. Part I. Keuen 3. 8º.

崔 蓮 生 Tsuy Leen-săng.

See 易 經 Yĭh king. 易 經 來 註 *Yĭh king Lae choo.* "The Book of Changes." .... Edited by Tsuy Leen-săng, &c.   1688. 8º.

崔 令 欽 Tsuy Ling-kin.

敎 坊 記 *Keaou fang ke.* "Records of the Department of Instruction in the Palace." *See* 王 文 誥 Wang Wăn-kaou. 唐 代 叢 書 *Tang tae tsung shoo.* "A Collection of Reprints of Works written during the Tang Dynasty," &c. Series 3.   1806. 8º.

崔 應 榴 Tsuy Ying-lew.

吾 亦 廬 稿 *Woo yĭh leu kaou.* "Papers from the Woo-yĭh Cottage." *See* 嚴 杰 Yen Lĕĕ. 皇 清 經 解 *Hwang Tsing king keae.* "The Classics Explained," &c. Keuen 1323–1326.   1829. 8º.

子 夏 Tsze Hea.

易 傳 *Yĭh chuen.* "A Commentary on the Book of Changes." *See* 孫 堂 Sun Tang. 漢 魏 二 十 一 家 易 注 *Han Wei urh shĭh yĭh kea Yĭh choo.* "Commentaries on the Book of Changes," &c.   1799. 8º.

字 Tsze.

三 字 經 *San tsze king.* "The Three-character Classic."   [1780 ?]. 8º.

Another edition.   [1810 ?]. 8º.

Another edition.   [1820 ?]. 8º.

Another copy.

子 Tsze. *(Continued.)*

三 字 經 *San tsze king.* "A Three-character Classic." Containing an Outline of the Christian Religion.   *Hongkong*, 1843. 8º.

—— 增 補 便 覽 日 用 雜 字 *Tsăng poo peen lan jĭh yung tsă tsze.* "A Thesaurus of Common Expressions in Daily Use. An Enlarged Edition."   1866. 8º.

紫 釵 Tsze chae.

紫 釵 記 *Tsze chae ke.* "The Story of the Black Hair Pin." *See* 曲 Keŭh. 六 十 種 曲 *Lŭh shĭh chung keŭh.* "Sixty Plays," &c. Taou 2. 8º.

紫 栢 Tsze Pĭh.

心 經 論 *Sin king lun.* "A Discourse on the Heart Classic."   [1800 ?]. 8º.

紫 簫 Tsze Seaou.

紫 簫 記 *Tsze seaou ke.* "The Story of the Black Pan Pipes." *See* 曲 Keŭh. 六 十 種 曲 *Lŭh shĭh chung keŭh.* "Sixty Plays," &c. Taou 2. 8º.

慈 悲 Tsze fei.

慈 悲 金 剛 寶 懺 法 *Tsze pei kin kang paou tsan fă.* "The Diamond Ritual of the Compassionate" Kwan-she-yin? 3 keuen.   [1790 ?]. Oblong.

慈 恩 Tsze găn.

慈 恩 玉 歷 *Tsze găn yŭh leĭh.* "The Precious Doctrine of Successive Existences of Compassionate Grace." A Buddhist Work.   [1750 ?]. 8º.

慈 雲 Tsze-yun.

慈 雲 走 國 全 傳 *Tsze-yun tsow kwŏ tseuen chuen.* "A Complete Narrative of the Wanderings of Prince Tsze-yun." A Historical Romance referring to Events supposed to have taken place during the Sung Dynasty. With Illustrations. 8 keuen.   1815. 8º.

慈 山 居 士 Tsze shan keu sze.

See 永 字 溪 Yung yu ke. 永 字 溪 莊 識 畧 *Yung yu ke chwang shĭh leŏ.* "A Short Account of Yung-yu-ke Farm House." By Tsze shan keu sze, &c.   1765. 8º.

自 誠 氏 Tsze-ching-she.

  長 生 詮 *Chang săng tseuen.* "On Obtaining Longevity." *See* 列 仙 Lëě seen. 列 仙 傳 *Lëě seen chuen.* "Biographies of Eminent Taouist Saints," &c.   8°.

牘 Tŭh.

  試 牘 *She tŭh.* "Examination Essays."
                           [1800 ?].   8°.
           Imperfect.

終 Tung.

  善 終 誌 傳 *Shen tung che chuen.* "Stories of Happy Deaths." [By J. Stronach.]
                  Hongkong, 1863.   8°.

東 郭 Tung kŏ.

  東 郭 記 *Tung kŏ ke.* "The Story of the Eastern Suburb." *See* 曲 Keŭh. 六 十 種 曲 *Lŭh shĭh chung keŭh.* "Sixty Plays," &c. Taou 1.   8°.

東 園 Tung yuen.

  東 園 雜 字 *Tung yuen tsă tsze.* "The Miscellany of the Eastern Garden."   1838.   8°.

東 方 朔 Tung Fang-sŏ.

  十 洲 記 *Shĭh chow ke.* "An Account of the Ten Islands." By Tung Fang-sŏ, of the Han Dynasty. A Reprint.   [1800 ?].   8°.

—— 神 異 經 *Shin e king.* "The Book of Supernatural Wonders."   [1800 ?].   8°.

同 人 公 Tung Jin-kung.

  種 福 堂 精 選 瓦 方 *Chung fŭh Tang tsing seuen leang fang.* "The Skilfully Selected Collection of Medical Prescriptions from the Chung-fŭh Hall." Edited by Tung Jin-kung. Keuen ?
                           [1790 ?].   8°.
      Imperfect, containing only keuen 3 and 4.

董 燧 Tung Hwang.

  資 生 集 *Tsze săng tseĭh.* "A Collection of Prescriptions for the Preservation of Life."
                           [1750 ?].   8°.

董 遇 Tung Yu.

  周 易 章 句 *Chow Yĭh chang keu.* "Notes on the Chow Changes." *See* 孫 堂 Sun Tang. 漢 魏 二 十 一 家 易 注 *Han Wei urh shĭh yĭh kea Yĭh choo.* "Commentàries on the Book of Changes," &c.   1799.   8°.

董 仲 舒 Tung Chung-shoo.

  春 秋 繁 露 *Chun tsew fan loo.* "Dewdrops from the Spring and Autumn Annals." *See* 沈 津 Chin Tsin. 百 家 類 纂 *Pĭh kea luy tswan.* "The Works of a Hundred Authors," &c. Keuen 5.   8°.

—— 春 秋 繁 露 *Chun tsew fan loo.* "Dewdrops from the Spring and Autumn Annals." A Series of Critical Discourses. Edited by Tang Chaou-yung. 17 keuen.   [1800 ?].   8°.

董 慶 翁 Tung Fei-ung.

  See 高 鼓 峰 Kaou Koo-fung. 己 任 編 *E jin peen.* "A Treatise which has proved itself to be Trustworthy." ... Keuen 6 to 8 by Tung Fei-ung, &c.   1830.   8°.

董 公 振 Tung Kung-chin.

  See 沈 辛 田 Chin Sin-teen. 名 法 指 掌 *Ming fă che chang.* "A Digest of Ordinances." Compiled by ... Tung Kung-chin, &c.   8°.

董 斯 張 Tung Sze-chang.

  廣 博 物 志 *Kwang pŏ wŭh che.* "An Encyclopædia." Edited by Yang Hŏ. 50 keuen.
                           1615.   4°.
Another edition.   50 keuen.   1761.   8°.
Another copy.

董 天 工 Tung Teen-kung.

  武 夷 山 志 *Woo e shan che.* "A Topography of the Bohea Hills," in the Province of Fŭh-keen. With Illustrations. Compiled by Tung Teen-kung. 24 keuen.   1753.   8°.

童 子 Tung tsze.

  童 子 範 圍 *Tung tsze fan wei.* "Precepts [for the Conduct and Guidance] of Boys."
                           [1840 ?].   8°.
Another copy.

童 立 成 Tung Leĭh-ching.

  See 馮 登 府 Fung Tăng-foo. 象 山 縣 志 *Seang shan heen che.* "A Topography of Seang-shan Heen." .. Compiled by Tung Leĭh-ching, &c.   1834.   8°.

佟寳 TUNG PAOU.

See 伊把漢 E PA-HAN. 盛京通志 *Shing king tung che.* "A Topography of the ... Province of Moukden." Compiled by ... Tung Paou, &c.   1684. 8°.

TURNER (F. S. ?).

See 性理 *Sing le.* 性理畧論 *Sing le leŏ lun.* "Discourses on Human Nature." [By F. S. Turner].   1869. 8°.

端木賜 TWAN MŬH-SZE.

詩傳 *She chuen.* "A Commentary on the Book of Odes." By Twan Mŭh-sze, of the Wei Dynasty. Edited by Chung Ying. 1790. 8°.

段長基 TWAN CHANG-KE.

歷代疆域表 *Leĭh tae keang yĭh peaou.* "A Tabulated Statement of the Boundaries of the Empire during the Successive Dynasties." 3 keuen.   1817. 8°.

—— 歷代二十四史統紀全表 *Leĭh tae urh shĭh sze she tung ke tseuen peaou.* "A Complete Tabulated System of the Chronology of the twenty-four Histories." Edited by Twan Tsin-shoo. 13 keuen.   1817. 8°.

—— 歷代沿革表 *Leĭh tae yuen kĭh peaou.* "A Tabular Statement of the Successive Topographical Changes in the Divisions of the Empire." 3 keuen.   1817. 8°.

段成式 TWAN CHING-SHĬH.

劍俠傳 *Keen hëë chuen.* "Tales of Celebrated Swordsmen." See 王文誥 WANG WĂN-KAOU. 唐代叢書 *Tang tae tsung shoo.* "A Collection of Reprints of Works written during the Tang Dynasty," &c. Series 4.   1806. 8°.

—— 劍俠傳 *Keen hëë chuen.* "Tales of Celebrated Swordsmen." By Twan Ching-shĭh, of the Tang Dynasty. A Reprint.   [1741 ?]. 8°.

—— 諾皐記 *Nŏ kaou ke.* "Tales." A Reprint.   [1741?]. 8°.

—— 西陽雜俎 *Se yang tsă tsoo.* "Miscellanies from Se-yang." A Reprint. 2 keuen.   [1741?]. 8°.

段安節 TWAN GAN-TSËĔ.

樂府雜錄 *Lŏ foo tsă lŭh.* "Records of the Music Office." See 王文誥 WANG WĂN-KAOU. 唐代叢書 *Tang tae tsung shoo.* "A Collection of Reprints of Works written during the Tang Dynasty," &c. Series 4.   1806. 8°.

段公路 TWAN KUNG-LOO.

北戸錄 *Pĭh hoo lŭh.* "Records of the North." See 王文誥 WANG WĂN-KAOU. 唐代叢書 *Tang tae tsung shoo.* "A Collection of Reprints of Works written during the Tang Dynasty," &c. Series 3.   1806. 8°.

段揩書 TWAN TSIN-SHOO.

See 段長基 TWAN CHANG-KE. 歷代二十四史統紀全表 *Leĭh tae urh shĭh sze she tung ke tseuen peaou.* "A Complete Tabulated System of the Chronology of the Twenty-four Histories." ... Edited by Twan Tsin-shoo, &c. 1817. 8°.

段玉裁 TWAN YŬH-TSAE.

古文尙書撰異 *Koo wăn Shang-shoo seuen e.* "The Various Readings of the Ancient Text of the Book of Historical Documents Collected." 33 keuen. [Also] 毛詩故訓傳 *Maou She koo heun chuen.* "Maou's Commentary on the Book of Odes." 30 keuen. [Also] 詩經小學 *She king seaou heo.* "Rudimentary Learning applied to the Book of Odes." 4 keuen. [Also] 周禮漢讀考 *Chow le Han tŭh kaou.* "An Examination of the Han Text of the Chow Ritual." 6 keuen. [Also] 儀禮漢讀考 *E le Han tŭh kaou.* "An Examination of the Han Text of the Decorum Ritual." [Also] 說文解字注 *Shwŏ wăn keae tsze choo.* "A Commentary on the Explanation of Characters in the Shwŏ wăn." 15 keuen. [Also] 六書音均表 *Luh shoo yin keun peaou.* "The Sounds of the *Lŭh shoo* Adjusted and Tabulated." 11 keuen. [Also] 經韻樓集 *King yun low tseĭh.* "The King-yun Low Collection of writings on the Classics." 10 keuen. See 嚴杰 YEN LĔĔ. 皇清經解 *Hwang Tsing king keae.* "The Classics Explained," &c. Keuen 567–666.   1829. 8°.

翁 復 UNG FŬH.

See 四 書 SZE SHOO. 四 書 合 講 *Sze shoo hŏ keang.* "The Four Books.".. Compiled by Ung Fŭh. 8°.

——— 四 書 遵 註 合 講 *Sze shoo tsun choo hŏ keang.* "The Four Books.". . . Compiled by Ung Fŭh, &c.   8°.

翁 正 春 UNG CHING-CHUN.

See 莊 周 CHWANG CHOW. 莊 子 註 釋 評 林 *Chwang tsze choo shĭh ping lin.* "The Nan hwa Classic, . . . with a Collection of Criticisms" by Ung Ching-chun, &c.   8°.

翁 仲 仁 UNG CHUNG-JIN.

痘 疹 玉 髓 金 鏡 錄 *Tow chin yŭh suy kin king lŭh.* "A Searching Treatise on Small Pox." An Enlarged and Improved Edition. By Ung Chung-jin. Edited by Kew Teen-yĭh. 4 keuen. With Illustrations.   1768. 8°.

翁 方 綱 UNG FANG-KANG.

經 義 考 補 正 *King e kaou poo ching.* "Choo E-tsun's Work on the Meaning of the Classics, Enlarged and Corrected." By Ung Fang-kang. 12 keuen. [Also] 小 石 帆 亭 五 言 詩 續 鈔 *Seaou shĭh fan ting woo yen she sŭh chaou.* "The Seaou-shĭh-fan Pavilion Supplementary Collection of Five-Syllable Poetry." Compiled by Ung Fan-kang. 8 keuen. [Also] 蘇 詩 補 註 *Soo she poo choo.* "The Poems of Soo Tung-po, with a Commentary" by Ung Fang-kang. [Also] 石 洲 詩 話 *Shĭh chow she hwa.* "Criticisms on Poetry from the Rocky Island." 8 keuen. [Also] 米 海 岳 年 譜 *Me hae yŏ neen poo.* "A Chronological Record of the Life of Me Hae-yŏ." [Also] 元 遺 山 先 生 年 譜 *Yuen wei shan Seen-săng neen poo.* "A Chronological Record of the Life of Yuen Wei-shan Seen-săng." 3 keuen. [Also] 通 志 堂 經 解 目 錄 *Tung-che tang king keae mŭh lŭh.* "A Catalogue of the Tung-che Tang Collection of Commentaries on the Classics." [Also] 蘇 米 齋 蘭 亭 考 *Soo me chae lan ting kaou.* "An Examination of the Inscriptions in the Lan Pavilion of the Soo-me Study." 8 keuen. *See* 伍 崇 曜 WOO TSUNG-YAOU. 粵 雅 堂 叢 書 *Yuĕ ya Tang tsung shoo.* "The Yuĕ-ya Tang Collection of Reprints," &c. Series 6, 14, 15.   1853. 8°.

翁 克 夫 UNG KĬH-FOO.

See 翁 復 UNG FŬH.

翁 葆 光 UNG PAOU-KWANG.

See 涵 蟾 子 HAN CHEN-TSZE. 金 丹 正 眞 大 要 道 書 全 集 *Kin tan ching le ta yaou taou shoo tseuen tseĭh.* "A complete Collection of Important Taouist Works on the True Principle of the Elixir of Immortality." . . . With Commentaries by Ung Paou-kwang, &c.   1538. 8°.

UNITED STATES OF AMERICA. BUCHANAN (JAMES). *President.*

See GREAT BRITAIN AND IRELAND. VICTORIA. *Queen.* 奏 准 天 津 新 議 通 商 條 欵 *Tsow chun Teen tsin e tung shang teaou kwăn,* "The New Commercial Treaties of Tientsin," contracted between . . The United States of America and China, &c.   1860. 8°.

爾 雅 URH YA.

爾 雅 音 圖 *Urh ya yin too.* "The Literary Expositor, with the Sounds of the Characters, and with Plates." With a Commentary by Kŏ Pŏ. 3 keuen.   1801. 4°.

爾 哈 善 URH-HŎ-SHEN.

蘇 州 府 志 *Soo chow Foo che.* "A Topography of Soochow Foo." Compiled by Urh-hŏ-shen, Chaou Seĭh-le, and Foo Chun. 80 keuen.   1748. 8°.

VERBIEST (FERDINAND).

See 南 懷 仁 NAN-HWAE-JIN.

——— 康 熙 十 年 二 月 十 五 日 丁 酉 夜 望 月 食 圖 *Kang-he shĭh neen urh yuĕ shĭh woo jĭh ting yew yay wang yuĕ shĭh too.* "Observations of the Eclipse of the Moon, on the 15th of the 2nd month of the tenth year of the reign of Kang-ke, *i.e.* 1671, taken at the Meridian of Peking." With Drawings of the Eclipse as Visible in the various Provinces of the Empire. By F. V. In Chinese and Manchoo, with a Latin Title-page.   1671. 8°.

There are two other imperfect copies of this work.

瓦 岡 WA KANG.

瓦 岡 寨 演 義 傳 *Wa kang chae yen e chuen.* "The Story of the Wa kang Fortress." With Portraits. 5 keuen.   1861. 8°.

WADE (THOMAS FRANCIS), C.B.

See 逑 KEW. 好 逑 傳 *Haou kew chuen.* "The Fortunate Union." . . . Edited by T. F. W., &c.   1863. 8°.

萬 國 WAN KWŎ.

萬 國 史 傳 *Wan kwŏ she chuen.* "The History of the World." [By C. F. A. Guetzlaff.] 41 keuen.   [1840 ?]. 8°.

Another copy.

—— 萬 國 地 理 全 集 *Wan kwŏ te le tseuen tseĭh.* "A Complete Geography of the World." [By C. F. A. Guetzlaff.] 38 keuen. [1838 ?]. 8°.

萬 寶 WAN PAOU.

萬 寶 全 書 *Wan paou tseuen shoo.* "An Encyclopædia." [20 keuen]. [1700 ?]. 8°.

Imperfect, containing only part of the first keuen, and the second and third keuen.

Another edition.

Imperfect, containing only keuen 11–18.

Another edition.

Imperfect, containing only keuen 4, 5, 6.

萬 樹 WAN SHOO.

詞 律 *Tsze leŭh.* "A Collection of Ancient and Modern Rhymes," from the Tang Dynasty downwards. Each Type of Rhyme is Referred to its Appropriate Air, according to the Length of the Lines, the Mechanical Structure, the Tones and other Characteristics. With Critical Notes. Compiled by Wan Shoo. Edited by Woo Ta-sze-ma. 20 keuen.   1687. 8°.

Another copy.

萬 之 裔 WAN CHE-HĂNG, and 吳 寶 彝 WOO PAOU-E.

漢 關 侯 事 蹟 彙 編 *Han Kwan how sze tseĭh wei peen.* "A Memoir of Kwan Yu of the Han Dynasty." Edited by Ching Hwan and others. 12 keuen.   [1750 ?]. 8°.

萬 承 紀 WAN CHING-KE.

See 贵 中 孚 KWEI CHUNG-FOO and WAN CHING-KE. 丹 徒 縣 志 *Tan too heen che.* "A Topography of Tan-too Heen," &c.   1805. 8°.

萬 國 欽 WAN KWŎ-KIN.

See 呂 不 韋 LEU PŬH-WEI. 呂 氏 春 秋 *Leu she chun tsew.* "The Spring and Autumn Annals of Leu Pŭh-wei." . . . Edited by Wan Kwŏ-kin, &c.   1581. 8°.

萬 年 茂 WAN NEEN-MOW, and 戴 第 元 TAE TE-YUEN.

策 學 纂 要 *Tsĭh heŏ tswan yaou.* "The Student's Manual." Compiled by Wan Neen-mow, and Tae Te-yuen. Edited by Tae Ming and Hwang keuen. 16 keuen.   1766. 8°.

Another edition. 16 keuen.   1767. 8°.

Another edition. 16 keuen.   1786. 8°.

Imperfect, wanting keuen 12–16.

Another edition. 16 keuen.   [1790 ?]. 8°.

Imperfect, containing only keuen 10–12.

萬 授 一 WAN SHOW-YĔH.

See 詩 經 SHE KING. 詩 經 說 約 集 解 *She king shwŏ yŏ tseĭh keae.* "The Book of Odes." . . . Edited by . . Wan Show-yĭh, &c. 1688. 8°.

—— See 易 經 YĬH KING. 辨 志 堂 新 輯 易 經 集 解 *Peen-che Tang sin tseĭh yĭh king tseĭh keae.* "The Peen-che Tang Edition of the Book of Changes." . . . Compiled by Wan Show-yĭh, &c.   1686. 8°.

萬 斯 大 WAN SZE-TA.

學 禮 質 疑 *Heŏ Le chĭh e.* "A Help to the Doubtful Points in Studying the Rituals." 2 keuen. [Also] 學 春 秋 隨 筆 *Heŏ Chun tsew suy peĭh.* "A Help to the Study of the Spring and Autumn Annals." 10 keuen. See 嚴 杰 YEN LĔĔ. 皇 清 經 解 *Hwang Tsing king keae.* "The Classics Explained," &c. Keuen 48–59.   1829. 8°.

29

萬 斯 同 WAN SZE-TUNG.

漢魏石經考 *Han Wei shĭh king kaou.* "An Examination of the Stone Classics of the Han and Wei Dynasties." [Also] 唐宋石經考 *Tang Sung shĭh king kaou.* "An Examination of the Stone Classics of the Tang and Sung Dynasties." *See* 張 山 來 CHANG SHAN-LAE, and 張 廷 也 CHANG TSIN-YAY. 昭 代 叢 書 *Chaou tae tsung shoo.* "A Collection of Reprints of Works by Authors under the present Dynasty," &c. Keuen 1, 2. 1703. 8º.

萬 廷 莘 WAN TING-SIN.

See 桓 寬 HWAN KWAN. 鹽 鐵 論 *Yen-tĕĕ lun.* "Discourses on Salt and Iron." ... Edited by Wan Ting-sin, &c. 1553. 8º.

萬 維 藜 WAN WEI-HAN.

律 例 圖 說 *Leŭh le too shwŏ.* "The Fundamental Laws and Subordinate Statutes of the Empire Illustrated and Commented on." By Wan Wei-han. 10 keuen. 1761. 8º.

—— 幕 學 舉 要 *Mŏ heŏ keu yaou.* "An Abstract of the Knowledge necessary for the Discharge of the Duties of an Official Clerk." 1770. 8º.

萬 玉 卿 WAN YŬH-KING.

紅 樓 夢 傳 奇 *Hung low mung chuen ke.* "The Dream of the Red Chamber" Dramatized by Wan Yŭh-king. Edited by Le Tan. 1800. 8º.

Imperfect.

文 WĂN.

佩 文 詩 韻 *Pei wăn she yun.* "A Poetical Dictionary Arranged according to the Sounds and Tones of the Characters." 5 keuen. [1800?]. 8º.

Title-page wanting.

—— 佩 文 韻 府 *Pei wăn yun foo.* "A Lexicon Arranged according to the Usual System of One Hundred and Six Finals Distributed among the Five Tones." [Compiled under the Special Superintendence of the Emperor Kang he.] 106 keuen. [1711]. 8º.

Imperfect.

文 WĂN. *(Continued.)*

先 正 小 題 文 錄 *Seen ching seaou te wăn lŭh,* "A Collection of Corrected Essays" on Texts from the Four Books. [1700?]. 8vo.

Imperfect.

文 震 孟 WĂN CHIN-MĂNG.

See 歸 有 光 KWEI YEW-KWANG. 諸 子 彙 函 *Choo tsze wei han.* "Extracts from the Writings of all the Philosophers." ... Edited by Wăn Chin-măng, &c. 1625. 8º.

文 徵 明 WĂN CHING-MING.

End. 嘉 靖 二 十 五 年 秋 八 月 阮 望 [An Illustrated Roll containing a Number of Instructions on Domestic Duties.] *Chang Chow,* 1546.

文 昌 帝 君 WĂN-CHANG TE KEUN.

孝 經 *Heaou king.* "The Classic on Filial Piety." By Wăn chang te keun, the God of Literature. A Reprint. *Canton,* [1750?]. 8º.

Another edition. Edited by Kew Seun. 1811. 8º.

Another edition. To which are Appended the *Pun yuen king,* the *Kew kĕĕ king,* and the *Yen sze king,* all of which are attributed to the same author. *Canton,* 1833. 8º.

—— 化 書 *Hwa shoo.* "The Book of Transformations." A Reprint. 3 keuen. 1820. 8º.

—— 戒 淫 文 *Keae yin wăn.* "A Warning against Lewdness." [1820?]. 8º.

—— 救 劫 勸 善 文 *Kew kĕĕ keuen shen wăn.* "Admonitory Tracts for the Salvation of the Age." 1830. 8º.

—— 寶 訓 *Paou heun.* "The Precious Teachings" of Wăn chang te keun, contained in the *Yin chĭh wăn.* With Illustrative Stories by Hwang Ching-yuen, and Comments by Yen Ching. 2 keuen. 1820. 8º.

—— 惜 字 文 *Seĭh tsze wăn.* "A Tract on the Respect due to Paper on which anything is Written or Printed." [1820?]. 8º.

文昌帝君 WǍN-CHANG TE KEUN. (Continued.)

天洞經註疏 Ta tung king choo soo. "The Great Profound Sûtra. With a Commentary by Tseen Hǎng, and Explanations" by Wei Tsoo-yuen. A Taouist Work. 3 keuen.

1712. 8°.

—— 大洞經詮註 Ta tung king tseuen choo. "The Great Profound Sûtra. With a Complete Commentary," by Ma Teen-keun. [1819?]. 8°.

Another edition.   1819. 8°.

—— 陰隲文 Yin chǐh wǎn. "A Treatise on Secret Rewards and Retributions." [1820?]. 8°.

—— 陰隲文註釋 Yin chǐh wǎn choo shǐh. "A Treatise on Secret Rewards and Retributions." With a Commentary by Chang Ting-neen.

Keang-ning, 1836. 8°.

There are three other copies of this work.

—— 陰隲文勸戒編 Yin chǐh wǎn keuen keae peen. "A Treatise on Secret Rewards and Retributions. A Tract of Advice and Warning." With a Commentary by Hung Tǐh-yuen. Edited by Kung Ke-kwang. A Reprint. 4 keuen.   1819. 8°.

—— 陰隲文廣義節錄 Yin chǐh wǎn kwang e tsǐh lǔh. "The Full Meaning of Wǎn-chang te keun's Treatise on Secret Rewards and Retributions." By Chow Mung-yen. 3 keuen.

Soo choo, 1828. 8°.

—— 陰隲文詩牋 Yin chǐh wǎn she tscen. "A Treatise on Secret Rewards and Retributions." With Poetical Essays thereon by Ching Tseaou-tseaou.   1812. 8°.

—— 陰隲文圖說 Yin chǐh wǎn too shwǒ. "A Treatise on Secret Rewards and Retributions. With Illustrations and a Commentary." Compiled by Hwang Ching-yuen. Edited by Yang Hin. Illustrated by Koo Kin.   1801. 8°.

Another edition. Edited by Hwang Ching-kang. Illustrated by Chow Chaou-peǐh. [1800?]. 8°.

Wanting the first vol.

文武帝君 WǍN Woo Te keun.

文武帝君勸善文 Wǎn Woo Te keun keuen shen wǎn. "Instructive Pamphlets by the Gods of Literature and War."   1800. 8°.

Imperfect.

問答 WǍN TǍ.

緊要問答 Kin yaou wǎn tǎ. "A Catechism on Important Doctrines of Christianity." [By C. F. A. Guetzlaff.]   [1840?]. 8°.

—— 問答俗話 Wǎn tǎ sǔh hwa. "A Catechism in the Macao Dialect," on Religion and Geography. With a Map. By J. G. Roberts. 3 keuen.   [Macao, 1840?]. 8°.

Imperfect, containing only keuen 1.

溫岐山 WǍN KE-SHAN.

分韻撮要 Fun yun tsǒ yaou. "A Phonetic Dictionary." Edited by Chǐh Twan-shǐh. 2 keuen.   8°.

溫岐石 WǍN KE-SHǏH.

See 虞學圃 YU HEǑ-POO and WǍN KE-SHǏH.

江湖尺牘分韻撮要合集 Keang hoo chǐh tǔh fun yun tsǒ yaou hǒ tseǐh. "A Letter-writer for Travellers," &c.   1772. 8°.

WANG (STEFANUS).

See 王德望 WANG TǏH-WANG.

王 WANG.

十七史蒙求 Shǐh tseǐh she mung kew. "The Student's Guide to the Seventeen Histories." Edited by Ching Tsung-teen. ? keuen.

[1750?]. 8°.

An odd vol., containing only keuen 9–16.

王煦 WANG CHAOU.

說文五翼 Shwǒ wǎn woo yǐh. "Five Wings to the Shwǒ wǎn Lexicon." 8 keuen. 1808. 8°.

王質 WANG CHǏH.

雪山集 Seuě shan tseǐh. "A Collection of Literary Pieces from the Snowy Mountain." By Wang Chǐh, of the Sung Dynasty. A New Edition. 16 keuen?   1779. 8°.

Imperfect, containing only keuen 1–9, 14–16.

王儞 WANG CHING.

東都事畧 *Tung too sze leŏ.* "A Short History of the Eastern Capital," in Honan, during part of the Sung Dynasty. *See* 毛晉 MAOU TSIN. 十七史 *Shih tseĭh She.* "The Seventeen Histories," &c. 1656. 8°.

王晫 WANG CHŎ.

文苑異稱 *Wăn yuen e ching.* "Pseudonymes from the Garden of Literature." *See* 張山來 CHANG SHAN-LAE, and 張進也 CHANG TSIN-YAY. 昭代叢書 *Chaou tae tsung shoo.* "A Collection of Reprints of Works by Authors under the present Dynasty," &c. Keuen 42. 1703. 8°.

—— 今世說 *Kin she shwŏ.* "Records of Modern Times." 8 kenen. *See* 伍崇曜 WOO TSUNG-YAOU. 粵雅堂叢書 *Yuĕ ya Tang tsung shoo.* "The Yuĕ-ya Tang Collection of Reprints," &c. Series 7. 1853. 8°.

王洙 WANG CHOO.

東陽夜怪錄 *Tung yang yĕ kwae lŭh.* "An Account of Nocturnal Appearances at Tung yang." *See* 王文誥 WANG WĂN-KAOU. 唐代叢書 *Tang tae tsung shoo.* "A Collection of Reprints of Works Written during the Tang Dynasty," &c. Series 6. 1806. 8°.

王充 WANG CHUNG.

論衡 *Lun hăng.* "Discussions by Means of Comparisons." *See* 沈律 CHIN TSIN. 百家類纂 *Pĭh keă luy tswan.* "The Works of a Hundred Authors," &c. Keuen 33, 34, 35. 8°.

—— 論衡 *Lun hăng.* "Discussions by Means of Comparisons" on Philosophical and Scientific Subjects. Edited by Lew Kwang-tow. 30 keuen. [1700?]. 8°.

Another edition. Edited by Koo Joo-lĕen. 30 keuen. [1720?]. 8°.

王符 WANG FOO.

潛夫論 *Tseen foo lun.* "The Discourses of an Unknown Scholar." By Wang Foo, of the Han Dynasty. Edited by Hwang Kea-hwuy. 10 keuen. [1700?]. 8°.

Another edition. Edited by Shaou Măng-lin. A Reprint. 10 keuen. [1750?]. 8°.

王黼 WANG FOO.

博古圖 *Pŏ koo too.* "An Illustrated Collection of Antiquities." Compiled by Wang Foo and others. Edited by Lew Ke-jen. Illustrated by Ting Nan-yu and Woo Laou-kan. 30 keuen. 1588. 8°.

Another copy.

Another copy.

Imperfect, wanting the first four keuen.

Another edition. Edited by Hwang Heaou-fung. To which is Appended a Work on the same Subject, in 12 keuen, Entitled 考古圖 *Kaou koo too.* "An Illustrated Examination into Antiquities." 30 keuen. 1752. 8°.

王皓 WANG HAOU.

See 朱棟 CHOO TUNG. 千巷志 *Kan-heang che.* "A Topography of the Village of Kan-heang." ... Edited by Wang Haou, etc. 1801. 8°.

王煦 WANG HEU.

See 孔鮒 KUNG FOO. 小爾雅疏 *Seaou Urh ya soo.* "The Lesser Literary Expositor." ... Edited by Wang Heu, &c. 1800. 8°.

王河 WANG HO.

See 呂耀曾 LEU YAOU-TSĂNG. 盛京通志 *Shing king tung che.* "A Topography of the Metropolitan Province of Shing-king." Compiled by .. Wang Ho, &c. 1736. 8°.

王暅 WANG KAOU.

六經圖定本 *Lŭh king too ting pun.* "Illustrations to Accompany the Six Classics." Compiled by Wang Kaou. 1740. 8°.

王圻 WANG KE.

續文獻通考 *Sŭh wăn heen tung kaou.* "A Continuation of the *Wăn heen tung kaou.*" By Wang Ke. Revised and Edited by an Imperial Commission consisting of Yung Seuen, King Kwei, Choo Kwei, and others. 250 keuen. 1784. 8°.

Another copy.

王嘉 WANG KEA.

拾遺記 *Shĭh e ke.* "Lost Pages of History." By Wang Kea, of the fourth century. Edited by Seaou Ke. 10 keuen. *See* 汪士漢 WANG SZE-HAN. 祕書廿八種 *Pe shoo neen på chung.* "A Collection of Twenty-eight Reprints," &c. 1808. 8º.

—— 拾遺記 *Shĭh e ke.* "Lost Pages of History." By Wang Kea, of the Tsin Dynasty. Edited by Hoo Fung-tsaou. 10 keuen. A Reprint. [1750?]. 8º.

王毅 WANG KŬH.

讀史管見 *Tŭh she kwan keen.* "My Views on Reading History." *See* 張山來 CHANG SHAN-LAE, and 張進也 CHANG TSIN-YAY. 昭代叢書 *Chaou tae tsung shoo.* "A Collection of Reprints of Works by Authors under the present Dynasty," &c. Keuen 8. 1703. 8º.

王令 WANG LING.

廣陵集 *Kwang ling tseĭh.* "The Kwang-ling Collection." *See* 吳孟舉 WOO MĂNG-KEN, and 吳自牧 WOO TSZE-MŬH. 朱詩鈔二集 *Sung she chaou urh tseĭh.* "Poetry of the Sung Dynasty." 8º.

王楠 WANG NAN.

See 林奮 LIN FUN. 閼遊縣志 *Seen yew heen che.* "A Topography of Seen-yew Heen." ... Compiled by ... Wang Nan, &c. 1771. 8º.

王弼 WANG PEĬH.

周易疏 *Chŏw Yĭh soo.* "The Chow Changes." .. With a Commentary by Wang Peĭh. *See* 毛鳳苞 MAOU-FUNG-PAOU. 十三經注疏 *Shĭh san king choo soo.* "The Thirteen Classics," &c. 1813. 8º.

—— 周易略例 *Chow Yĭh leŏ le.* "Short Generalizations on the Chow Changes." By Wang Peĭh, of the Tsin Dynasty. A Reprint. [1800?]. 8º.

王勃 WANG PŎ.

成道記 *Ching taou ke.* "The Perfect Way." With Notes by the Monk Taou-ching. [1790?]. 8º.

王相 WANG SEANG.

應酬帖式 *Ying chow tëĕ shĭh.* "Models of Visiting Cards and Notes." [1750?]. 8º.

王燮 WANG SËĔ.

香雪齋詩鈔 *Heang seuĕ chae she chaou.* "Poems from the Study of Fragrant Snow." 1838. 8º.

王澍 WANG SHOO.

竹雲題跋 *Chŭh yun te pŏ.* "Chŭh-yun's Researches in Ancient Inscriptions." 4 keuen. *See* 葉志詵 YE CHE-SIN. 海山仙館叢書 *Hae shan seen Kwan tsung shoo.* "The Hae shan seen Kwan Collection of Reprints," &c. Vol. 85–86. 1848. 8º.

王蘇 WANG SOO.

See 毛履謙 MAOU LE-KEEN, and 吳涵一 WOO HAN-YĬH. 十家詩詳註 *Shĭh kea she tseang choo.* "The Poetical Works of Ten Authors," viz.: .. Wang Soo, &c. 1813. 8º.

王肅 WANG SŬH.

周易注 *Chow yĭh choo.* "Notes on the Chow Changes." *See* 孫堂 SUNG TANG. 漢魏二十一家易注 *Han Wei urh shĭh yĭh kea yĭh choo.* "Commentaries on the Book of Changes," etc. 1799. 8º.

—— 孔子家語 *Kung tsze keae yu.* "The Family Sayings of Confucius." Edited with a Commentary by Wang Sŭh. 10 keuen. 1507. 8º.

—— 孔子家語原註 *Kung tsze kea yu yuen choo.* "The Family Sayings of Confucius. Edited with a Commentary" by Wang Sŭh. 10 keuen. 1782. 8º.

Another edition. 4 keuen. 1805. 8º.

王嵩 WANG SUNG.

說緯 *Shwŏ wei.* "Essays on the Woof of Literature." *See* 嚴杰 YEN LĔĔ. 皇清經解 *Hwang Tsing king keae.* "The Classics Explained," &c. Keuen 1370. 1829. 8º.

王道 WANG TAOU.

See 涵蠜子 HAN CHEN-TSZE. 金丹正理大要道書全集 *Kin tan ching le ta yaou taou shoo tseuen tseih.* "A Complete Collection of Important Taouist Works on the True Principles of the Elixir of Immortality." . . . With Commentaries by Wang Taou, &c.　　1538. 8°.

—— See 班固 PAN KOO. 白虎通 *Pih hoo tung.* "The Report of a Convocation . . . held in the Pïh-hoo kwan. . . Edited by Wang Taou," &c. 8°.

王度 WANG TOO.

古鏡記 *Koo king ke.* "The Story of an Ancient Mirror." By Wang Too of the Suy Dynasty. A Reprint.　　　　[1741?]. 8°.

王粲 WANG TSAN.

英雄記鈔 *Ying heung ke chaou.* "Memoirs of Heroes." By Wang Tsan, of the Wei Dynasty. A Reprint.　　[1750?]. 8°.

王存 WANG TSUN.

元豐九域志 *Yuen Fung kew yih che.* "A Geography of the Nine Frontiers," during the reign of Yuen-fung. 10 keuen. [1750?]. 8°.

Imperfect, wanting the title-page and first keuen.

王通 WANG TUNG.

中說 *Chung shwŏ.* "Central Discourses." With a Commentary by Yuen Yĭh. 10 keuen. *See* 黃丕烈 HWANG PEI-LIĔ. 十子全書 *Shíh tsze tseuen shoo.* "The Complete Works of the Ten Philosophers," &c.　　1804. 8°.

—— 中說 *Chung shwŏ.* "Central Discourses" on Legislation, &c., being Conversations between Wang Tung and his Disciples. Edited by Chang Yĭh. A Reprint. 2 keuen. [1750?]. 8°.

Another edition. Edited by Peen Tsoo-yew. A Reprint. 2 keuen.　　　　[1800?]. 8°.

Another edition. With Notes by Yuen Yĭh. A Reprint. 10 keuen.　　　1825. 8°.

王通 WANG TUNG.

元經 *Yuen king.* "The Early History" of China from the Beginning of the Tsin Dynasty to the Beginning of the Tang Dynasty. With a Commentary by Sëĕ Show, and with Notes by Yuen Yĭh. 10 keuen.　　[1750?]. 8°.

Another edition. 10 keuen.　　[1800?]. 8°.

王爺 WANG YAY.

恭請王爺并打醮科 *Kung tsing Wang yay ping ta tseaou ko.* "A Sacrificial Ritual to be Used when Preferring Humble Requests to the Gods."　　　　[1800?]. 8°.

王錟 WANG YEN.

See 張英 CHANG YING. 淵鑑類函 *Yuen keen luy han.* "An Encyclopædia." . . . Compiled by . . . Wang Yen, &c. [1754?]. 8°.

—— See 康熙 KANG HE. *Emperor.* 御製文第三集 *Yu che wăn te san tseih.* "A Third Collection of the Works of the Emperor Kanghe." Edited by . . . Wang Yen, &c. 1714. 8°.

—— See 孔丘 KUNG KEW. 欽定春秋傳說彙纂 *Kin ting Chun Tsew chuen shwŏ wei tswan.* "The Spring and Autumn Annals." . . . Compiled by . . Wang Yen, &c.　　1721. 8°.

—— 雙溪集 *Shwang ke tseih.* "The Double-Stream Collection of Poetry." *See* 吳孟舉 WOO MĂNG-KEU, and 吳自牧 WOO TSZE-MŬH. 宋詩鈔二集 *Sung she chaou urh tseih.* "Poetry of the Sung Dynasty," &c. 8°.

王廙 WANG YĬH.

周易注 *Chow Yih choo.* "Notes on the Chow Changes." *See* 孫堂 SUN TANG. 漢魏二十一家易注 *Han Wei urh shïh yih kea Yih choo.* "Commentaries on the Book of Changes," &c.　　　　1799. 8°.

王原 WANG YUEN.

See 吳繩如 WOO SHING-JOO. 松江桿海石塘錄 *Sung keang han hae shïh tang lŭh.* "An Account of the Stone Sea-Dykes in . . . Sung keang." . . . Edited by Wang Yuen, &c.　　　　1723. 8°.

王惲 WANG YUN.

幽怪錄 *Yew kwae lüh.* "Strange and Wonderful Stories." *See* 王文誥 WANG WĂN-KAOU. 唐代叢書 *Tang tae tsung shoo.* "A Collection of Reprints of Works Written during the Tang Dynasty," &c. Series 6. 1806. 8°.

—— 幽怪錄 *Yew kwae lüh.* "Strange and Wonderful Stories." By Wang Yun, of the Tang Dynasty. A Reprint.   [1741 ?]. 8°.

王朝佐 WANG CHAOU-TSO.

安州誌 *Gan chow che.* "A Topography of Gan-chow," in the Province of Chili. Compiled by Wang Chaou-tso, Le Hung-chǐh, and Fang Seun-hwŏ. 10 keuen.   1680. 8°.

王愼齋 WANG CHIN-CHAE.

西江祝嘏 *Se keang chŭh kea.* "Supplications for Blessings at Se-keang." A Drama in Four Acts.   1751. 8°.

王初陽 WANG CHOO-YANG.

歷代帝王紀要 *Leĭh tae Te Wang ke yaou.* "A Chronological List of Emperors and Kings" of China, down to the end of the Ming Dynasty. With Short Historical Notes. Edited by Chang Han-chen and Wang King-mun. 2 keuen.   1737. 8°.

王畫三 WANG CHOW-SAN.

See 莊周 CHWANG CHOW. 南華內篇別解 *Nan hwa nuy peen pëë keae.* "The First Part of the Nan-hwa Classic." . . . Edited by Wang Chów-san, &c.   1721. 8°.

王瑞鼎 WANG CHUY-TING.

征塗記 *Ching too ke.* "An Account of the Subjugation of the Empire." *See* 王子音 WANG TSZE-YIN. 今古地理述 *Kin koo te le shŭh.* "Modern and Ancient Geography," &c. Keuen 18.   1807. 8°.

王貽上 WANG E-SHANG.

See 蒲留仙 POO LEW-SEEN. 聊齊志異 *Leaou chae che e.* "Curious Stories from a Careless Man's Study." Edited by Wang E-shang, &c.   1767. 8°.

王棐臣 WANG FEI-CHIN.

寶善編 *Paou shen peen.* "A Series of Valuable and Virtuous [Taouist] Works." Compiled by Wang Fei-chin. 2 keuen.   1795. 8°.

Another edition. 2 keuen.   *Canton,* 1820. 8°.

王鳳喈 WANG FUNG-KEAE.

續廣事類賦 *Sŭh kwang sze luy foo.* "A Supplement to the *Kwang sze luy foo,* an Encyclopædia in Verse." . . Compiled by Wang Fung-keae. A Reprint. 30 keuen. 1801. 8°.

Imperfect, containing only keuen 1, 2, 10, 18, 23–30.

王鳳生 WANG FUNG-SĂNG.

浙西水利備考 *Chĕ se shwuy le pe kaou.* "An Examination of the Districts Watered by the Rivers of Chĕ-se," part of the Province of Chĕ-keang.   1824. 8°.

—— 湖州府水道圖 *Hoo chow foo shwuy taou too.* "Maps of the Water-courses in the Prefecture of Hoo-chow," in Chĕ-keang. [1804 ?]. 8°.

王安國 WANG GAN-KWŎ.

See TSING DYNASTY. 大清通禮 *Ta Tsing tung le.* "A Complete Code of the Ceremonies of the Tsing Dynasty." Compiled by . . . Wang Gan-kwŏ, &c.   1824. 8°.

王安石 WANG GAN-SHĬH.

王文 *Wang wăn.* "The Writings of Wang Gan-shĭh." 16 keuen. *See* 茅坤 MAOU KWĂN. 唐宋八大家文鈔 *Tang Sung pă ta kea wăn chaou.* "The Works of Eight Scholars . . . under the Tang and Sung Dynasties," &c.   1631. 8°.

—— 周官新義 *Chow kwan sin e.* "A New Interpretation of 'the Officers of the Chow.'" 16 keuen. *See* 伍崇曜 WOO TSUNG-YAOU. 粵雅堂叢書 *Yuĕ ya Tang tsung shoo.* "The Yuĕ-ya Tang Collection of Reprints," &c. Series 16.   1853. 8°.

王安節 WANG GAN-TSĔĔ.

See 李笠翁 LE LEĬH-UNG. 芥子園畫傳 *Keae tsze Yuen hwa chuen.* "The Keae-tsze Yuen Drawing Book." Illustrated . . by Wang Gan-tsĕĕ, &c.   1679–1800. 8°.

王安節 WANG GAN-TSĔĔ. (*Continued.*)

See 王澤弘 WANG TSĬH-HUNG? 翎毛花卉譜 *Ling maou hwa hwuy poo.* "Directions in the Art of Drawing." . . Illustrated by . . Wang Gan-tsĕĕ, &c. 1821. 8°.

王涵眾 WANG HAN-CHUNG.

See 黃正元 HWANG CHING-YUEN. 性天眞境 *Sing teen chin king.* "The True Limit of Human and Divine Nature." . . . Edited by . . . Wang Han-chung, &c. 1737. 8°.

王賢嚯 WANG HEEN-KEAE.

竹書紀年 *Chŭh shoo ke neen.* "The Bamboo Record." With a Commentary by Chin Yŏ, of the Leang Dynasty. Edited by Wang Heen-keae. This work, which is said to have been found in the Grave of Seang king of Wei, in the year 279 A.D., contains the History of China from about 2400 B.C. to 300 B.C. 2 keuen. [1750?]. 8°.

王項齡 WANG HEŬH-LING.

See 孔丘 KUNG KEW. 欽定書經傳說彙纂 *Kin ting Shoo king chuen shwŏ wei tswan.* "The Book of Historical Documents." . . . Compiled by . . . Wang Heŭh-ling, &c. 1730. 8°.

王鶴年 WANG HŎ-NEEN.

See 何士祁 HO SZE-KE. 川沙撫民廳志 *Chuen sha foo min ting che.* "A Topography of the Borough of Chuen-sha." Edited by Wang Hŏ-neen, &c. 1837. 8°.

王鴻春 WANG HUNG-CHUN.

補蕙叢訓 *Poo tseaou tsung heun.* "A Compilation of Moral Instructions" gathered from Classical Writers. Edited by Wang Hung-chun. 8 keuen. 1838. 8°.

王鴻緒 WANG HUNG-SEU.

明史藁 *Ming she kaou.* "The History of the Ming Dynasty." *See* 毛晉 MAOU TSIN. 十七史 *Shĭh tseĭh she.* "The Seventeen Histories," &c. 1656. 8°.

—— See 詩經 SHE KING. 欽定詩經傳說彙纂 *Kin ting she king chuen shwŏ wei tswan.* "The Book of Odes." . . . Compiled by . . Wang Hung-seu, etc. 1727. 8°.

王弘撰 WANG HUNG-CHUEN.

See 易經 YĬH KING. 周易圖說述 *Chow Yĭh too shwŏ shŭh.* "Dissertations and Commentaries on the Diagrams of the Book of Changes." Compiled by Wang Hung-chuen, &c. 1687. 4°.

王會汾 WANG HWUY-FUN.

See 張廷玉 CHANG TING-YŬH. 御撰資治通鑑明紀綱目 *Yu chuen tsze che tung keen ming ke kang mŭh.* "A Condensed History of the Ming Dynasty." Compiled . . . by Wang Hwuy-fun, &c. 1746. 8°.

—— See 杜佑 TOO YEW. 通典 *Tung teen.* "A Complete Treatise on the Political Constitution of China." Edited by . . . Wang Hwuy-fun, &c. 1747. 8°.

王日休 WANG JĬH-HEW.

龍舒淨土文 *Lung shoo Tsing too wăn.* "A Buddhist Hortatory Treatise on the Pure Regions of Bliss." 11 keuen. 1658. 8°.

Another edition. 10 keuen. Canton, 1822. 8°.

—— 大阿彌陀經 *Ta O-me-to king.* "The Great Amita Sûtra." Edited by Wang Yĭh-hew. A Reprint. 2 keuen. Canton, 1792. 8°.

王仁圃 WANG JIN-POO.

十三經策案 *Shĭh san king tsĭh gan.* "Critical Disquisitions on the Thirteen Classics." Compiled by Wang Jin-poo. Edited by Yu Tseanglin. 22 keuen. 1808. 8°.

Another copy.

王仁裕 WANG JIN-YU.

開元天寶遺事 *Kae-yuen Teen-paou wei sze.* "Posthumous Records of the Emperor Kae-yuen." *See* 王文誥 WANG WĂN-KAOU. 唐代叢書 *Tang tae tsung shoo.* "A Collection of Reprints of Works written during the Tang Dynasty," &c. Series 1. 1806. 8°.

王若虛 WANG JŎ-HEU.

嫭南詩話 *Hoo nan she hwa.* "Criticisms on Poetry from Hoo-nan." 3 keuen. [1741?]. 8°.

王 肯 堂 WANG KĂNG-TANG.

證 治 準 繩 *Ching che chun shing.* "A Manual of Medicine." Edited by Ching Yung-pei.
1791. 8°.

This work is divided into Six Parts, each Part having a Title-Page, Index, &c.

—— 類 方 證 治 準 繩 *Luy fang ching che chun shing.* "Medical Prescriptions." 8 keuen.
1602. 8°.

—— 女 科 證 治 準 繩 *Neu ko ching che chun shing.* "A Treatise on the Cure of Diseases Peculiar to Females." Edited by Min Ching-chaou. 5 keuen.
1607. 8°.

—— 傷 寒 證 治 準 繩 *Shang han ching che chun shing.* "The Medical Treatment of Diseases arising from Cold." 8 keuen. 1604. 8°.

Imperfect, wanting keuen 2, 3.

—— 雜 症 證 治 準 繩 *Tsă ching ching che chun shing.* "The Medical Treatment of Various Complaints." 8 keuen. 1602. 8°.

—— 幼 科 證 治 準 繩 *Yew ko ching che chun shing.* "The Medical Treatment of the Young." 9 keuen. [1604 ?]. 8°.

Imperfect, wanting the first keuen.

王 芑 孫 WANG KE-SUN.

See 毛 履 謙 MAOU LE-KEEN, and 吳 涵 — WOO-HAN-YĬH. 十 家 詩 詳 註 *Shǐh kea she tseang choo.* "The Poetical Works of Ten Authors," viz. . . Wang Ke-sun, &c. 1813. 8°.

王 起 宗 WANG KE-TSUNG.

See 張 燮 CHANG SĚĚ. 東 西 洋 考 *Tung se yang kaou.* "A Complete Account of . . . Countries in the Southern and Eastern Seas." . . . Edited by Wang Ke-tsung, &c. 1618. 8°.

王 家 相 WANG KEA-SEANG.

See 衛 廷 璞 WEI TING-PŎ. 建 平 縣 志 *Keen-ping heen che.* "A Topography of Keen-ping Heen." . . . Edited by Wang Kea-seang, &c.
1731. 8°.

王 客 周 WANG KĬH-CHOW.

文 法 狐 白 *Wăn fă hoo pĭh.* "The Laws of Literary Composition" Illustrated by Examples. Compiled by Wang Kĭh-chow. Edited by Tsang Kwŏ-chae and Woo Kĭh-yen. First Series.
1792. 8°.

王 欽 若 WANG KIN-JŎ.

崇 文 總 目 *Tsung wăn tsung mǔh.* "A Catalogue of Celebrated Works." With Bibliographical Notes by Tseen Tung-yuen. 6 keuen.
See 伍 崔 曜 WOO TSUNG-YAOU. 粵 雅 堂 叢 書 *Yuě ya Tang tsung shoo.* "The Yuě-ya Tang Collection of Reprints," &c. Series 15.
1853. 8°.

王 廣 心 WANG KWANG-SIN.

王 尤 合 刻 注 釋 *Wang Yew hŏ kĭh choo shĭh.* "The Essays of Wang Kwang-sin, and Yew Tung. With Notes and Comments." 1810. 8°.

王 鬼 谷 WANG KWEI-KŬH.

四 字 金 *Sze tsze kin.* "The Precious Truths of the Four Characters." On Fortune-telling. 2 keuen. [1850 ?]. 8°.

王 國 安 WANG KWŎ-GAN.

See 趙 士 麟 CHAOU SZE-LIN. 浙 江 通 志 *Chě keang tung che.* "A Topography of the Province of Chě-keang." Compiled by . . . Wang Kwŏ-gan, &c. 1684. 8°.

王 笠 草 WANG MEĬH-TSAOU.

See 李 笠 翁 LE LEĬH-UNG. 芥 子 園 畫 傳 *Keae tsze Yuen hwa chuen.* "The Keae-tsze Yuen Drawing Book." Illustrated . . . by Wang Meĭh-tsaou, &c. 1679–1818. 8°.

—— See 王 澤 弘 WANG TSĬH-HUNG. 翎 毛 花 卉 譜 *Ling maou hwa hwuy poo.* "Directions in the Art of Drawing." . . Illustrated by Drawings taken from Ancient Models, by Wang Meĭh-tsaou. 1821. 8°.

30

王 鳴 盛 WANG MING-SHING.

尚 書 後 案 *Shang shoo how gan.* "Later Decisions on the Book of Historical Documents." 31 keuen. [Also] 周 禮 軍 賦 說 *Chow le keun foo shwŏ.* "On the Military Taxes of the Chow Ritual." 4 keuen. *See* 嚴 杰 YEN LĔĔ. 皇 清 經 解 *Hwang Tsing king keae.* "The Classics Explained," &c. Keuen 404–438. 1829. 8º.

—— 十 七 史 商 榷 *Shĭh tseĭh She shang kĕŏ.* "The Seventeen Histories Examined and Displayed." 100 keuen. 1787. 8º.

王 懋 竑 WANG MOW-HWANG.

朱 子 年 譜 *Choo tsze neen poo.* "A Chronological Record of the Events in the Life of Choo He." 10 keuen. *See* 伍 崇 曜 WOO TSUNG-YAOU. 粵 雅 堂 叢 書 *Yuĕ-ya Tang tsung shoo.* "The Yuĕ-ya Tang Collection of Reprints," &c. Series 13. 1853. 8º.

—— 白 田 草 堂 存 稿 *Pĭh teen tsaou Tang tsun kaou.* "The Preserved Documents from the Pĭh-teen-tsaou Tang." *See* 嚴 杰 YEN LĔĔ. 皇 清 經 解 *Hwang Tsing king keae.* "The Classics Explained," &c. Keuen 243. 1829. 8º.

王 夢 弼 WANG MUNG-PĬH.

鎮 海 縣 志 *Chin hae heen che.* "A Topography of Chin-hae Heen, in the Province of Chĕ-keang." Edited by Shaou Heang-yung. 8 keuen. 1752. 8º.

There are three other imperfect copies of this work.

王 南 珍 WANG NAN-CHIN.

二 十 一 史 精 義 *Urh shĭh yĭh she tsing e.* "The Essence of the Twenty-one Histories." 21 keuen. 1763. 8º.

王 業 恫 WANG NĔĔ-SEUN, and 王 資 治 WANG TSZE-CHE.

越 絕 書 *Yuĕ tseuĕ shoo.* "Incidents in the History of the Secession of Yuĕ." Edited by Wang Nĕĕ-seun and Wang Tsze-che. 15 keuen. 1552. 8º.

王 念 孫 WANG NEEN-SUN.

廣 雅 疏 證 *Kwang ya soo ching.* "The *Kwang-ya* Commented on and Verified." 10 keuen. [Also] 讀 書 雜 志 *Tŭh shoo tsă che.* "Various Records on the Study of the Classics." 2 keuen. *See* 嚴 杰 YEN LĔĔ. 皇 清 經 解 *Hwang Tsing king keae.* "The Classics Explained," &c. Keuen 667–678. 1829. 8º.

王 保 定 WANG PAOU-TING.

摭 言 *Chĭh yen.* "A Collection of Jottings." *See* 王 文 誥 WANG WĂN-KAOU. 唐 代 叢 書 *Tang tae tsung shoo.* "A Collection of Reprints of Works written during the Tang Dynasty," &c. Series 2. 1806. 8º.

王 伯 雪 WANG PĬH-SEUĔ.

See 呂 元 臣 LEU YUEN-CHIN. 初 學 問 津 集 *Choo hĕŏ wăn tsin tseĭh.* "A Collection of Model Essays for Beginners." . . . Edited by Wang Pĭh-seuĕ, &c. 8º.

王 平 仲 WANG PING-CHUNG.

See 周 禮 CHOW LE. 周 禮 註 疏 *Chow le choo soo.* "The Chow Ritual." . . Compiled by Wang Ping-chung, &c. 1792. 8º.

王 象 晉 WANG SEANG-TSIN.

羣 芳 譜 *Keun fang poo.* "A Herbarium." Edited by Maou Fung-paou, and others. 4 Parts. 1621. 8º.

王 錫 爵 WANG SEĬH-TSEŎ.

稿 *Kaou.* "Essays." *See* 長 城 CHANG CHING. 名 家 制 義 *Ming kea che e.* "Essays" on Texts from the Four Books," &c. Tsĭh 51. 1699. 8º.

王 修 玉 WANG SEW-YŬH.

歷 朝 賦 楷 *Lĕĭh chaou foo keae.* "Pattern Odes by Authors of Successive Dynasties." Compiled by Wang Sew-yŭh. Edited by Koo Tseay-gan. 8 keuen. [1750?]. 8º.

王 世 貞 WANG SHE-CHING.

See 張 竹 坡 CHANG CHŬH-PO. 金 瓶 梅 *Kin Ping Mei.* "The Story of Kin, Ping and Mei." . . Attributed to Wang She-ching, &c. 1695. 8º.

王聖俞 WANG SHING-YU.

秋濤 *Tsew taou.* "Autumn Waves." *See* 閔景賢 MIN KING-HEEN. 快書 *Kwae shoo.* "A Book of Amusement," &c. Keuen 1.
1628. 8°.

王守仁 WANG SHOW-JIN.

稿 *Kaou.* "Essays." *See* 長城 CHANG CHING. 名家制義 *Ming kea che e.* "Essays" on Texts from the Four Books, &c. Tsïh 26.
1699. 8°.

—— 王陽明先生文集 *Wang Yang-ming Seen săng wăn tseïh.* "The Literary Productions of Wang Show-jin." 16 keuen. 1685. 8°.

王叔和 WANG SHŬH-HO.

圖註脈訣大全 *Too choo mïh keuĕ ta tseuen.* "A Complete Work on the Pulse. By Wang Shŭh-ho. With a Commentary and Plates" by Chang She-heen. Edited by Chin Wei-yuen. 2 keuen. 1693. 8°.

—— 圖註難經脈訣 *Too choo Nan king mïh keue.* "The Nan-king," a Solution of Eighty-one Doubtful Medical Questions. "And a Work on the Pulse." By Wang Shŭh-ho. With Commentary and Plates by Chang She-heen. Edited by Chin Wei-yuen. 4 keuen. 1800. 8°.

Second keuen of the Nan-king wanting.

王遜齋 WANG SUN-CHAE.

註釋發蒙針度初集 *Choo shïh fă mung chin too choo tseïh.* "A Collection of Model Essays for Beginners. With Notes and Explanations." Compiled by Wang Sun-chae. Edited by Choo Wei-yin and others. First Series. 1791. 8°.

王司直 WANG SZE-CHÏH.

See 李笠翁 LE LEIH-UNG. 芥子園畫傳 *Keae-tsze Yuen hwa chuen.* "The Keae-tsze Yuen Drawing Book." Illustrated . . . by Wang Sze-chïh, &c. 1679–1800. 8°.

—— See 王澤弘 WANG TSÏH-HUNG? 翎毛花卉譜 *Ling maou hwa hwuy poo.* "Directions in the Art of Drawing." . . Illustrated by . . Wang Sze-chïh, &c. 1821. 8°.

王士禛 WANG SZE-CHIN.

See 張英 CHANG YING. 淵鑑類函 *Yuen keen luy han.* "An Encyclopædia." . . . Compiled by . . . Wang Sze-chin, &c. 8°.

王士正 WANG SZE-CHING.

五代詩話 *Woo tae she hwa.* "Criticisms on the Poetry of the Five Dynasties" (immediately succeeding the Tang). Enlarged by Ching Fang-kwăn. 10 keuen. *See* 伍崇曜 WOO TSUNG-YAOU. 粵雅堂叢書 *Yuĕ ya Tang tsung shoo.* "The Yuĕ-ya Tang Collection of Reprints," &c. Series 3. 1853. 8°.

王士驌 WANG SZE-SEW.

稿 *Kaou.* "Essays." *See* 長城 CHANG CHING. 名家制義 *Ming kea che e.* "Essays" on Texts from the Four Books, &c. Tsïh 80.
1699. 8°.

王仕雲 WANG SZE-YUN.

格言俚錄 *Kïh yen kin lŭh.* "A Record of Wise Sayings." *See* 張山來 CHANG SHAN-LAE, and 張進也 CHANG TSIN-YAY. 昭代叢書 *Chaou tae tsung shoo.* "A Collection of Reprints of Works by Authors under the present Dynasty," &c. Keuen 17. 1703. 8°.

王大方 WANG TA-FANG.

一片石 *Yïh peen shïh.* "The Stone Tablet." A Drama. [1800 ?]. 8°.

王殿金 WANG TEEN-KIN.

See 黃徵乂 HWANG CHING-E. 瑞安縣志 *Suy gan heen che.* "A Topography of Suy-gan Heen." . . . Compiled by . . Wang Teen-kin, &c. 1808. 8°.

王惕甫 WANG TEÏH-FOO.

See 楊慧樓 YANG HWUY-LOW, and 王惕甫 WANG TEÏH-FOO. 國朝七栟雲襄二集 *Kwŏ chaou tseïh pae Yun seang urh tseïh.* "The Yung-seang Collection of Verses of Seven Syllables, by Authors of the Ta Tsing Dynasty," &c. 1807. 8°.

王德望 WANG TÏH-WANG.

[A Notice announcing the Death of Pope Innocent the 13th ?] Written by Wang Tïh-wang, Christened Stefanus. [1724 ?]. A sheet.

王 德 望 WANG TĬH-WANG, and 蔡 本 爲 TSAE PUN-TŬH.

[A Notice announcing the Death of Pope Innocent the 13th?] Written by Wang Tĭh-wang, Christened Stefanus, and Tsae Pun-tŭh, Christened Benedictus.　[1724 ?].　A sheet.

王 鼎 勳 WANG TING-HEUN.

See 秦 耀 曾 TSIN YAOU-TSĂNG. 普 陀 山 志 Poo to shan che. "A Topography of the Island of Poo-to." . . . Edited by Wang Ting-heun, &c.
　　　　1832.　8°.

王 澤 弘 WANG TSĬH-HUNG?

翎 毛 花 卉 譜 Ling maou hwa hwuy poo. "Directions in the Art of Drawing Feathers, Hair, and Flowers." Illustrated by Drawings taken from Ancient Models by Wang Meĭh-tsaou, Wang Gan-tsĕĕ, and Wang Sze-chĭh.
　　　　Nanking, 1821.　8°.

This Vol. forms part of the Third Part of the Keae-tsze Yuen hwa chuen.

王 澤 泩 WANG TSĬH-SĂNG.

試 帖 百 篇 冣 豁 解 She tĕĕ pĭh peen tsuy hwŏ keae. "A Hundred Pieces of Examination Poetry, clearly Explained" by Wang Tsĭh-săng.
　　　　[1750 ?].　8°.

王 晉 升 WANG TSIN-SHING.

百 家 姓 考 略 Pĭh kea sing kaou leŏ. "A Short Account of the Family Names of China." Edited by Seu Sze-nĕĕ.　[1800 ?].　8°.

There are six other copies of this work.

王 作 霖 WANG TSO-LIN.

See 陳 鍈 CHIN YING. 海 澄 縣 志 Hae ching heen che. "A Topography of Hae-ching Heen." . . . Compiled by . . Wang Tso-lin, &c.
　　　　1762.　8°.

王 奐 安 WANG TSUN-GAN.

二 三 塲 逢 元 Urh san chang fung yuen. "Select Essays from the Second and Third Examinations" of the Year 1752? Compiled by Wang Tsun-gan.　1752.　8°.

王 宗 瑞 WANG TSUNG-SHWUY.

禮 記 Le ke. Essays on Texts from "the Book of Rites," by Wang Tsung-shwuy, and others.
　　　　[1800 ?].　12°.
　　　　Imperfect.

王 資 治 WANG TSZE-CHE.

See 王 業 恂 WANG NĔĔ-SEUN and WANG TSZE-CHE. 越 絕 書 Yuĕ tseuĕ shoo. "Incidents in the History of the Secession of Yuĕ," &c.
　　　　1552.　8°.

王 子 音 WANG TSZE-YIN.

今 古 地 理 述 Kin koo te le shŭh. "Modern and Ancient Geography." Compiled by Wang Tsze-yin. With Notes by Fei Tae-shing, Yen Pĭh-chow, and others. The last Keuen terminates with a Tract entitled Ching too ke, by Wang Chuy-ting. 18 keuen.　1807.　8°.

王 文 治 WANG WĂN-CHE.

See 葉 堂 YĔ TANG. 邯 鄲 記 全 譜 Han tan ke tseuen poo. "Songs from the Play entitled Han tan ke." Edited by Wang Wăn-che, &c.
　　　　1792.　8°.

———— 牡 丹 亭 全 譜 Mow tan ting tseuen poo. "Songs from the Play entitled Mow tang ting." . . . Edited by Wang Wăn-che, &c. 1792.　8°.

———— 納 書 楹 補 遺 曲 譜 Nă shoo ying poo e keŭh poo. "A Supplementary Collection of Songs." . . . Edited by Wang Wăn-che, etc.
　　　　1794.　8°.

———— 納 書 楹 續 集 曲 譜 Nă shoo ying sŭh tseĭh keŭh poo. "A Book of Songs." . . . Edited by Wang Wăn-che, etc.　1792.　8°.

———— 納 書 楹 外 集 曲 譜 Nă shoo ying wae tseĭh keŭh poo. "An Additional Collection of Songs." . . . Edited by Wang Wăn-che, etc.
　　　　1792.　8°.

———— 南 柯 記 全 譜 Nan ko ke tseuen poo, "Songs from the Play entitled Nan ko ke." . . . Edited by Wang Wăn-che, &c.　1792.　8°.

第一卷

王文誥 WANG WĂN-KAOU.

唐代叢書 *Tang tae tsung shoo.* "A Collection of Reprints of Works written during the Tang Dynasty." Compiled by Wang Wăn-kaou. Edited by Shaou He-tsăng. 6 Series. 1806. 8°.

Another copy.

王文祿 WANG WĂN-LŬH.

See 周祥鈺 CHOW TSEANG-YŬH. 九宮大成 南北詞宮譜 *Kew kung ta ching nan pĭh tsze kung poo.* "A Collection of Southern and Northern Rhymes with their appropriate Airs." ... Arranged by .. Wang Wăn-lŭh, &c. 8°.

王聞脩 WANG WĂN-SEW.

四六法海 *Sze lŭh fă hae.* "A Collection of Literary Pieces Composed in Sentences of Four and Six Characters." Compiled by Wang Wăn-sew. 12 keuen. 1758. 8°.

Imperfect, containing only keuen 1, 2, 9, 11, 12.

王維德 WANG WEI-TĬH.

卜筮正宗 *Pŭh she ching tsung.* "A Work on Divination." [1750?]. 8°.

Imperfect, containing only keuen 13, 14.

—— 銅人腧穴鍼灸圖經 *Tung jin shoo heuĕ chin kew too king.* "A Work on Acupuncture Exemplified by Drawings of Two Brass Anatomical Figures, made to Illustrate the System." By Wang Wei-tĭh. With Plates. A Reprint. 3 keuen. [1750?]. 8°.

王叉槐 WANG YEW-HWAE.

See 宋慈 SUNG TSZE. 洗冤錄集證 *Se yuen lŭh tseĭh ching.* "Records of the Washing away of Injuries." ... Edited by Wang Yew-hwae, etc. 1796. 8°.

王翼雲 WANG YĬH-YUN.

See 王阮亭 WANG YUEN-TING. 唐詩合解 箋註 *Tang she hŏ keae tseen choo.* "A Selection of Poems." ... With a Commentary by Wang Yĭh-yun, etc. 1732. 8°.

王翼雲 WANG YĬH-YUN. *(Continued.)*

唐詩直解 *Tang she chĭh keae.* "A Selection of Poems by the most Celebrated Authors of the Tang Dynasty, clearly Explained." Compiled by Wang Yĭh-yun. With a Commentary by Woo Ting-wei. A Revised Edition. 1790. 8°.

王引之 WANG YIN-CHE.

經義述聞 *King e shŭh wăn.* "Explanations of the Meaning of the Classics." [Also] 經傳 釋詞 *King chuen shĭh tsze.* "Particles made use of in the Classics Explained." See 嚴杰 YEN LĔĔ. 皇清經解 *Hwang Tsing king keae.* "The Classics Explained," etc. Keuen 1180-1217. 1829. 8°.

—— 經傳釋詞 *King chuen shĭh tsze.* "Particles made use of in the Classics Explained." 10 keuen. 1819. 8°.

王應麟 WANG YING-LIN.

詩經考異 *She king kaou e.* "An Examination of the Various Readings of the Book of Odes." See 詩經 SHE KING. 詩經大全 *She king ta tseuen.* "The Complete Book of Odes," &c. 8°.

—— 深寧先生文鈔 *Chin ning Seen săng wăn chaou.* "The Literary Papers of the Doctor of Chin-ning," *i.e.* Wang Ying-lin. Edited by Yĕ Heung and others. 8 keuen. 1829. 8°.

Another copy.

—— 困學紀聞 *Kwan heŏ ke wăn.* "Criticisms on Literature and Science." By Wang Ying-lin. With Notes by Yen Jŏ-keu, Ho Ke-chen. With MS. notes. 20 keuen. 1603. 8°.

Wanting keuen 3-5.

Another edition. With notes by Yen Jŏ-ken, Ho Ke-chen, and Tseuen Tsoo-wang. 20 keuen. 1742. 8°.

—— 小學紺珠 *Seaou heŏ kan choo.* "A Treasury of Knowledge for the Young." 10 keuen. 1301. 12°.

王 元 長 WANG YUEN-CHANG.

永明九年（十一年）策秀才文 *Yung ming kew (shǐh yǐh) neen tsǐh Sew tsae wǎn.* "Papers for the Sew-tsae Examination in the Ninth and Eleventh Years of the Emperor Yung-ming." *See* 蕭統 SEAOU TUNG. 文選 *Wǎn seuen.* "Elegant Extracts from Polite Literature," &c. Keuen 36. 1772. 8°.

王 元 貞 WANG YUEN-CHING.

See 焦竑 TSEAOU HUNG. 老莊翼合刻 *Laou Chwang yǐh hǒ kǐh.* "The Works of Laou keun, and Chwang Chow." . . . Edited by Wang Yuen-ching, &c. 1588. 8°.

王 元 澤 WANG YUEN-TSǏH.

道德經 *Taou tǐh king.* "The Classic of Reason and Virtue." With a Commentary by Wang Yuen-tsǐh, &c. *See* 焦竑 TSEAOU HUNG. 老莊翼合刻 *Laou Chwang yǐh hǒ kǐh.* "The Works of Laou keun and Chwang Chow," &c. 1588. 8°.

王 元 馭 WANG YUEN-YU.

諸史品節 *Choo She pin tsëë.* "Extracts from the Pages of History." Compiled by Wang Yuen-yu. Edited by Chin Tsze-yuen, &c. 40 keuen. 1593. 8°.

王 阮 亭 WANG YUEN-TING.

池北偶談 *Che pǐh gow tan.* "Conversational Scraps from the North Side of the Pond." 26 keuen. 1761. 8°.

Title-page and first page of Preface mutilated.

—— 唐詩合解箋注 *Tang she hǒ keae tscen choo.* "A Selection of Poems by the most Celebrated Authors of the Tang Dynasty." Compiled by Wang Yuen-ting. With a Commentary by Wang Yǐh-yun. Part 1, 12 keuen. Part 2, 4 keuen. *Nanking*, 1732. 8°.

Another copy.

Imperfect, wanting keuen 5.

Another edition. 16 keuen. 1805. 8°.

—— 詩鈔 *She chaou.* "Poems." Edited by Tseang Yun-pǎng and Too Tǐh-sew. 8 keuen. [1800 ?]. 12°.

汪 柱 WANG CHOO.

詩扇記傳奇 *She shen ke chuen ke.* "The Tale of the Poetical Fan." A Drama in Thirty-two Acts. 2 keuen. 1778. 12°.

汪 中 WANG CHUNG.

述學 *Shǔh heǒ.* "Teachings on the Classics." 2 keuen. [Also] 經義知新錄 *King e che sin lǚh.* "A New Intelligible Treatise on the Meaning of the Classics." [Also] 大戴禮正誤 *Ta Tae le ching woo.* "The Errors of the Elder Tae's Book of Rites Corrected." *See* 嚴杰 YEN LËĚ. 皇清經解 *Hwang Tsing king keae.* "The Classics Explained," &c. Keuen 799–802. 1829. 8°.

—— 醫方集解 *E fang tseǐh keae.* "A Collection of Medical Prescriptions, with Elucidations." 2 keuen ? 1682. 8°.

汪 昂 WANG GAN.

醫方湯頭歌括 *E fang tang tow ko kwǒ.* "Medical Prescriptions and Recipes in Verse." 1694. 8°.

—— 經絡歌訣 *King lǒ ko keuě.* "On the Veins and Arteries of the Human Body. In Verse." 1694. 8°.

—— 素問靈樞類纂 *Soo wǎn Ling choo luy tswan.* "A Rearrangement of the *Soo wan* and the *Ling choo.*" Compiled by Wang Gang. Edited by Wang Hwan, Wang Twan, and others. 3 keuen. 1824. 8°.

—— 增補詳註本草備要 *Tsǎng poo tseang choo Pun tsaou pe yaou.* "A Brief Epitome of the *Pun tsaou.* With Notes and Comments." A New and Enlarged Edition. 4 keuen. 1694. 8°.

Imperfect, fourth keuen wanting.

—— 增訂圖註本草備要 *Tsǎng ting too choo Pun tsaou pe yaou.* "A Brief Epitome of the *Pun tsaou.* With Illustrations and Comments." With Appendix. 4 keuen. 1694. 8°.

汪灝 WANG HAOU.
韻府拾遺 *Yun foo shĭh e.* "A Supplement to the *Pei wăn yun foo.*" Compiled by an Imperial Commission, consisting of Wang Haou and others. 106 keuen. 1720. 8°.

汪桓 WANG HWAN.
See 汪昂 WANG GANG. 素問靈樞類纂 *Soo wăn Ling choo luy tswan.* "A Rearrangement of the *Soo wăn* and *Ling choo.*" . . . Edited by Wang Hwan, &c. 1824. 8°.

汪圻 WANG KE.
See 郝碩 HŎ CHĬH. 即墨縣志 *Tseĭh-mĭh heen che.* "A Topography of Tseĭh-mĭh Heen." . . . Compiled . . . by Wang Ke, &c. 1763. 8°.

汪淇 WANG KE.
See 水中龍 SHWUY CHUNG-LUNG. 星平會海 *Sing ping hwuy hae.* "The Junction of the Stars and the Sea." . . Edited by . . Wang ke, &c. 8°.

汪汲 WANG KEĬH.
事物原會 *Sze wŭh yuen hwuy.* "The Origin of all Things." An Encyclopædia. Compiled by Wang Keĭh. 40 keuen. 1797. 8°.

汪鈞 WANG KEUN.
官樣文章 *Kwan yang wăn chang.* "Official Documents." 1826. 8°.

汪森 WANG SĂN.
See 朱彝尊 CHOO E-TSUN. 詞綜 *Tsze tsung.* "A Collection of Rhymes." . . . Edited with Additions by Wang Săn, &c. 1678. 8°.

汪端 WANG TWAN.
See 汪昂 WANG GANG. 素問靈樞類纂 *Soo wăn Ling choo luy tswan.* "A Rearrangement of the *Soo wăn* and *Ling choo.*" . . . Edited by Wang Twan, &c. 1824. 8°.

汪佑 WANG YEW.
五子近思錄 *Woo tsze kin sze lŭh.* "Records of the Approximating Thoughts" on Mental Philosophy "of the Five Philosophers," Chow Leen-ke, Chang Tsze-how, Ching Haou, Ching E, and Choo He. Compiled by Wang Yew. 14 keuen. 1693. 8°.

汪兆柯 WANG CHAOU-KO.
東安縣志 *Tung gan heen che.* "A Topography of Tung-gan Heen." 3 keuen ? [1800 ?]. 8°.
Imperfect, containing only keuen 2, 3.

汪之顯 WANG CHE-HEEN.
啓蒙天機斷易大全 *Ke mung teen ke twan yĭh ta tseuen.* "A Complete Work on the Transmutations of Fate. For Beginners." A Work on Divination. 3 keuen. 1825. 8°.

汪如洋 WANG JOO-YANG.
See 毛履謙 MAOU LE-KEEN, and 吳涵一 WOO HAN-YĬH. 十家詩詳註 *Shĭh kea she tseang choo.* "The Poetical Works of Ten Authors," viz. Wang Joo-yang, &c. 1813. 8°.

汪建封 WANG KEEN-FUNG.
See 李之洣 LE CHE-TUNG and WANG KEEN-FUNG. 叩鉢齋纂 *Kow pŏ chae tswan.* "A Collection of Literary Pieces from the Kow-pŏ Study," &c. 8°.

汪靈川 WANG LING-CHUEN.
四書題鏡 *Sze shoo te king.* "A Mirror of Themes from the Four Books." 16 keuen. 1765. 8°.

Another edition. 1775. 8°.

Another edition. 1820. 8°.
Imperfect.

汪嘯尹 WANG SEAOU-YIN.
See 周興嗣 CHOW HING-SZE. 千字文釋義 *Tseen tsze wăn shĭh e.* "The Thousand Character Classic." . . Edited by Wang Seaou-yin. 8°.

汪瑟庵 WANG SĬH-GAN.
See 劉燦 LEW TSAN. 嚴氏詩緝補義 *Yen she she tseĭh poo e.* "A Supplement to Yen Tsan's Commentary on the Book of Odes." . . Edited by Wang Sĭh-gan, &c. 1811. 8°.

汪士漢 WANG SZE-HAN.
See 班固 PAN KOO. 白虎通 *Pĭh hoo tung.* "The Report of a Convocation . . . in . . . the Pĭh-hoo kwan." . . . Edited by Wang Sze-han, &c. 1668. 8°.

汪士漢 WANG SZE-HAN. *(Continued.)*

See 應劭 YING SHAOU. 風俗通 *Fung sŭh tung.* "Popular Traditions." . . . Edited by Wang Sze-han, &c.   8º.

—— 祕書廿八種 *Pe shoo neen pă chung.* "A Collection of Twenty-eight Reprints." Compiled by Wang Sze-han.   1808.   8º.

汪廷珍 WANG TING-CHIN.

浙江試牘立誠編 *Chĕ keang she tŭh lĕih ching peen.* "Chĕ-keang Examination Essays." Edited by Wang Ting-chin.   1814.   8º.

—— 江西試牘立誠編 *Keang se she tŭh lĕih ching peen.* "Keang-se Examination Essays." Edited by Wang Ting-chin.   1807–1810.   8º.

—— 增訂成均課士錄初集 *Tsăng ting ching keun ko sze lŭh choo tsĕih.* "An Enlarged Collection of Essays on Texts from the Four Books by Ripe Scholars." First Series. Compiled by Wang Ting-chin.   1804.   8º.

Imperfect.

汪廷楷 WANG TING-KEAE.

See 松筠 SUNG YUN. 伊犂總統事畧 *E le tsung tung sze lcŏ.* "A Short Account of Affairs in E-le." . . . Compiled by . . Wang Ting-keae, &c.   1809.   8º.

汪鑒霞 WANG TSAN-HEA.

See 褚健鄉 CHOO KEEN-KING. 新科墨卷英華 *Sin kŏ mĭh keuen ying hwa.* "Elegant Essays Selected from Recent Examination Papers." . . Edited by Wang Tsan-hea, &c.   1821.   8º.

汪作賓 WANG TSO-PIN.

See 李之泌 LE CHE-TUNG, and 汪建封 WANG KEEN-FUNG. 叩鉢齋纂 *Kow pŏ chae tswan.* "A Collection of Literary Pieces from the Kow-pŏ Study." . . . With Notes by Wang Tso-pin, &c.   8º.

汪右衡 WANG YEW-HĂNG.

朱熹 CHOO HE. 朱字家禮 *Choo tsze kea le.* "Domestic Ceremonies as taught by Choo He." Edited by Wang Yew-hăng, &c.   8º.

汪右衡 WANG YEW-HĂNG. *(Continued.)*

See 孔丘 KUNG KEW. 書經補註備旨 *Shoo king poo choo pe che.* "The Book of Historical Documents." . . Compiled by Wang Yew-hăng, &c.   1822.   8º.

汪由敦 WANG YEW-TUN.

See 乾隆 KEEN-LUNG. *Emperor.* 御製盛京賦 *Yu che Shing king foo.* "A Poetical Eulogium on the City of Moukden." . . . This Edition . . . was brought out under the Superintendence of Wang Yew-tun, &c.   1748.   4º.

—— 錢錄 *Tseen lŭh.* "A Record of Coins." Compiled by . . . Wang Yew-tun, &c. *See* 西清 SE TSING. 西清古鑑 *Se tsing koo keen.* "Antiquities [from the Palace?] of Western Purity," &c.   Folio.

—— See 蔣溥 TSEANG POO. 御覽經史講義 *Yu lan king she keang e.* "The Meaning of the Classics and of the Histories Explained." Edited . . . by Wang Yew-tun, &c.   1758.   8º.

—— See 允祿 YUN LŬH. 欽定同文韻統 *Kin ting tung wăn yun tung.* "A Sanskrit, Thibetan, and Manchoo Syllabary." Compiled by . . . Wang Yew-tun, &c.   1750.   8º.

闈 WEI.

棘闈勸戒錄 *Keĭh wei keuen keae lŭh.* "Admonitory Records for Competitors for Literary Honours." By the Retired Scholar of Chun-ke. A New Edition. A Taouist Work.   1809.   8º.

—— 闈墨 *Wei mĭh.* "Examination Essays."   8º.

A number of fragmentary Volumes, containing Essays from different Provinces.

韋述 WEI SHŬH.

兩京新記 *Leang king sin ke.* "A New Record of the Two Metropolitan Cities." Only One out of the Five Books of this Work is now extant, and that imperfect, being part of the Record respecting Chang-gan, the Western Metropolis. *See* 伍崇曜 WOO TSUNG-YAOU. 粵雅堂叢書 *Yuĕ-ya Tang tsung shoo.* "The Yuĕ-ya Tang Collection of Reprints," &c. Series 2.   1853.   8º.

韋 廉 臣 Wei-leen-chin [*i.e.* Alexander Williamson].

植 物 學 *Chĭh wŭh heŏ.* "A Work on Botany." Completed by Gae Yŏ-sĭh, *i.e.* Rev. J. Edkins. With the Chinese Text Revised by Le Shen-lan, the Author of the Preface. With Illustrations. 8 keuen.   1858. 8°.

Another copy.

偉 烈 亞 力 Wei-lĕĕ Ah-leĭh, *i.e.* [Alexander Wylie.]

See 利 瑪 竇 Le Ma-tow. 幾 何 原 本 *Ke ho yuen pun.* "The Elements of the Science of Quantity.". . . . Completed by Wei-lĕĕ Ah-leĭh, &c.   1857. 8°.

—— See 羅 密 士 Lo-meĭh-sze. 代 微 積 拾 級 *Tae wei tseĭh shĭh keĭh.* "Analytical Geometry.". . . . Translated into Chinese by Wei-lĕĕ Ah-leĭh, &c.   1855. 8°.

衛 宏 Wei Hung.

漢 官 舊 儀 *Han kwan kew e.* "The Ancient Ceremonies of the Officials of the Han Dynasty." By Wei Hung, of the Han Dynasty. Edited by Ke Yun and others. 2 keuen.   1774. 8°.

衛 廷 璞 Wei Ting-pŏ.

建 平 縣 志 *Keen-ping heen che.* "A Topography of Keen-ping Heen," in the Province of Ngan-hwuy. Compiled by Wei Ting-pŏ. Edited by Wang Kea-seang and Ho Ying. 22 keuen.   1731. 8°.

魏 徵 Wei Ching.

隋 書 *Suy shoo.* "A History of the Suy Dynasty." 85 keuen. *See* 毛 晉 Maou Tsin. 十 七 史 *Shĭh tseĭh She.* "The Seventeen Histories," &c.   1656. 8°.

—— 隋 書 *Suy shoo.* "A History of the Suy Dynasty." 85 keuen.   8°.

Imperfect, containing only keuen 32–85.

魏 校 Wei keaou.

六 書 精 蘊 *Lŭh shoo tsing wăn.* "The Essence of the Six Classes of Characters." A Dictionary arranged according to Subjects.   1540. 8°.

魏 鑑 Wei Keen.

象 吉 大 通 書 *Seang keĭh ta tung shoo.* "A Code of Rules for the Discrimination of Lucky and Unlucky Days" by means of the usual Conventional System of Cycles and Symbols. A New and Enlarged Edition. 29 keuen.
     1721. 8°.

—— 象 吉 備 要 通 書 *Seang keĭh pe yaou tung shoo.* "A Code of Rules for the Discrimination of Lucky and Unlucky Days" by means of the usual Conventional System of Cycles and Symbols. A New and Enlarged Edition. 29 keuen.
     [1804?]. 8°.

Imperfect, containing only keuen 1–9, 15–29.

魏 收 Wei Show.

魏 書 *Wei shoo.* "A History of the Wei Dynasty." 114 keuen. *See* 毛 晉 Maou Tsin. 十 七 史 *Shĭh tseĭh She.* "The Seventeen Histories."   1656. 8°.

—— 魏 書 *Wei shoo.* "A History of the Wei Dynasty." 114 keuen.   1636. 8°.

魏 泰 Wei Tae.

臨 漢 隱 居 詩 話 *Lin han yin keu she hwa.* "Criticisms on Poetry."   [1741?]. 8°.

魏 靜 Wei Tsing.

See 玄 覺 Heuen-keŏ. 永 嘉 集 *Yung kea tseĭh.* "The Yung-kea Collection.". . Edited by Wei Tsing, &c.   1801. 8°.

魏 源 Wei Yuen.

盟 聘 記 *Ming ping ke.* "An Account of the Alliances" formed with Russia during the Reigns of Kang-he and Keen-lung. *See* 何 秋 濤 Ho Tsew-taou. 北 徼 彙 編 *Pĭh keaou wei peen.* "Treatises on the Countries beyond the Northern Frontier.". . Keuen 3, &c.
     1865. 8°.

—— 海 國 圖 志 *Hae kwŏ too che.* "A History of Foreign Countries." Compiled by Wei Yuen, from Materials Collected by Commissioner Lin and himself. 60 keuen.   1849. 8°.

31

魏伯陽 WEI PĬH-YANG.

參同契 *Tsan tung këĕ.* A Work on Alchemy. *See* 彭好古 PĂNG HAOU-KOO. 道言內外秘訣全書 *Taou yen nuy wae pe keuĕ tseuen shoo.* "A Complete Collection of Taouist Works," &c.   8°.

—— 參同契 *Tsan tung këĕ.* A Work on Alchemy founded on the Principles of the *Yĭh King.* By Wei Pĭh-yang of the Han Dynasty. A Reprint.   [1750?]. 8°.

魏廷珍 WEI TING-CHIN.

See 李光地 LE KWANG-TE. 性理精義 *Sing le tsing e.* "The Essence of Works on Mental Philosophy." Compiled by ... Wei Ting-chin, &c.   1715. 8°.

—— *See* 易經 YĬH KING. 御纂周易折中 *Yu tswan Chow Yĭh chĕ chung.* "Decisions on the Chow Changes." ... Compiled by Wei Ting-chin, &c.   1715. 8°.

—— *See* 尹繼善 YIN KE-SHEN. 江南通志 *Keang nan tung che.* "A Topography of the Province of Keang-nan." Compiled by ... Wei Ting-chin, &c.   1737. 8°.

魏晉錫 WEI TSIN-SEĬH.

欽定學政全書 *Kin ting heŏ ching tseuen shoo.* "A Complete Collection of Educational Statutes." Compiled by Imperial Order by a Commission consisting of Wei Tsin-seĭh, Lŭh Tsang-lin, Le Hĭh, and others. 80 keuen.   1781. 8°.

魏祖元 WEI TSOO-YUEN.

See 文昌帝君 WĂN CHANG TE KEUN. 大洞經註疏 *Ta tung king choo soo.* "The Great Profound Sûtra. With ... Explanations" by Wei Tsoo-yuen, &c.   1712. 8°.

魏宇光 WEI YU-KWANG.

See 申培 SHIN PEI. 詩說 *She shwŏ.* "Remarks on the Book of Odes." Edited by Wei Yu-kwang, &c.   8°.

魏漁汀 WEI YU-TING.

刑部平反節要 *Hing Poo ping fan tsĕĕ yaou.* "Abridged Decisions of the Board of Punishments on Cases of Appeal." Compiled by Wei Yu-ting. 8 keuen.   1785. 8°.

Imperfect, containing only the first three keuen.

尉遲樞 WEI CHE-CHOO.

南楚新聞 *Nan Tsoo sin wăn.* "Scraps from Nan Tsoo." *See* 王文誥 WANG WĂN-KAOU. 唐代叢書 *Tang tae tsung shoo.* "A Collection of Reprints of Works Written during the Tang Dynasty," &c. Series 2. 1806. 8°.

遺民 WEI MIN.

鐵冠圖 *Tĕĕ kwan too.* "The Stratagem of the Iron Cap." 4 keuen.   [1750?]. 12°.

爲仁者 WEI-JIN-CHAY. *pseud.*

See BIBLE. OLD TESTAMENT. *Genesis.* 創世傳註釋 *Chwang she chuen choo shĭh.* "The Book of Genesis with a Commentary" by Wei-jin-chay, &c.   1851. 8°.

WELLS.

化學初階 *Hwa heŏ choo keae.* Wells's "Principles of Chemistry"—Inorganic Part. Translated into Chinese by J. G. Kerr. 2 keuen.   *Canton,* 1871. 8°.

WHEATON (HENRY).

Wheaton's International Law, Translated into Chinese by W. A. P. Martin, D.D., Assisted by a Commission appointed by Prince Kung.   *Peking,* 1864. 8°.

This work has also the Chinese title of 萬國公法 *Wan kwŏ kung fä.* "The International Law of Ten Thousand Countries."

WILLIAMSON (ALEXANDER).

See 韋廉臣 *Wei-leen-chin.*

WINNES (PHILIP).

See JESUS CHRIST. 耶穌受苦壽源 *Yay-soo show koo tsin yuen.* "A Search into the Causes of the Sufferings of Jesus Christ." [By P. Winnes,] &c.   1868. 8°.

WOO [243] WOO

吳 Woo.

See 陳 CHIN, and 吳 Woo. 山西闈墨 *Shan se wei mǐh.* "Shan-se Examination Essays." Edited by ... Chin and Woo, &c. 1821. 8⁰.

—— See 龔 KUNG and Woo. 山右闈墨 *Shan yew wei mǐh.* "Shan se Examination Essays." Compiled by ... Kung and Woo, &c. 1822. 8⁰.

吳 澄 Woo CHING.

道德眞經註 *Taou tǐh chin king choo.* "The True Classic of Reason and Virtue.... With a Commentary" by Woo Ching, &c. *See* 伍 崇曜 Woo TSUNG-YAOU. 粵雅堂叢書 *Yuě ya Tang tsung shoo.* "The Yuě-ya Tang Collection of Reprints," &c. Series 12. 1853. 8⁰.

吳 涵 Woo HAN.

See 朱熹 CHOO HE. 朱子全書 *Choo tsze tseuen shoo.* "The Complete Works of Choo He." Compiled .. by Woo Han, &c. 1713. 8⁰.

吳 岐 Woo KE.

See 林奎 LIN FUN. 僊遊縣志 *Seen yew heen che.* "A Topography of Seen-yew Heen." Compiled by ... Woo Ke, &c. 1771. 8⁰.

吳 謙 Woo KEEN.

金鑑外科 *Kin keen wae ko.* "The Golden Mirror of Medicine for the Cure of External Complaints." Published by Imperial Order. 16 keuen. 1742. 8⁰.

—— 御纂醫宗金鑑 *Yu tswan e tsung kin keen.* "The Golden Mirror of Medicine." A Collection of Medical Works, consisting of the *Shang han lun* and *Kin kwei yaou leŏ,* by Chang Ke, Prescriptions of Celebrated Physicians, and Rules regarding the Pulse and various Classes of Complaints. Compiled by Imperial Order by Woo Keen, Lew Yu-tŏ, and other Officers of the Medical Hall, under the Supervision of Prince Hung Chow. 90 keuen. 1740. 8⁰.

Another copy.

Imperfect, containing only keuen 3, 4.

吳 鉅 Woo KEU.

See 孫致彌 SUN CHE-ME. 杕左堂集 *Te tso tang tseih.* "The Te-tso Tang Collection of Literary Pieces." Edited by Woo Keu, &c. 8⁰.

吳 均 Woo KEUN.

續齊諧記 *Sŭh Tse heae ke.* "A Supplementary Collection of Marvellous Tales." By Woo Keun. Edited by Chang Shang-chung. A Reprint. [1750 ?]. 8⁰.

吳 京 Woo KING.

See 凌迪知 LING TEĬH-CHE. 萬姓統譜 *Wan sing tung poo.* "A General Biographical Dictionary." ... Edited by Woo King, &c. 1579. 8⁰.

吳 琯 Woo KWAN.

汲冢周書 *Keih mung Chow shoo.* "A History of the Chow Dynasty for Beginners." Edited by Woo Kwan. With Notes by Kung Chaou. 10 keuen. [Also] 三墳 *San fun.* "The History of the Three First Mythical Emperors." Edited by Woo Kwan. *See* 汪士漢 WANG SZE-HAN. 祕書廿八種 *Pe shoo nёen pa chung.* "A Collection of Twenty-eight Reprints," &c. 1808. 8⁰.

吳 寬 Woo KWAN.

稿 *Kaou.* "Essays." *See* 長城 CHANG CHING. 名家制義 *Ming kea che e.* "Essays" on Texts from the Four Books, &c. Tsĭh 18. 1699. 8⁰.

吳 林 Woo LIN.

吳蕈譜 *Woo sin poo.* "On Mushrooms." *See* 張山來 CHANG SHAN-LAE, and 張進也 CHANG TSIN-YAY. 昭代叢書 *Chaou tae tsung shoo.* "A Collection of Reprints of Works by Authors under the present Dynasty," &c. Keuen 48. 1703. 8⁰.

吳 摛 Woo LUN.

See 吳錫麒 Woo SEĬH-KE. 有正味齋試帖詳註 *Yew ching wei chae she tёě tseang choo.* "A Collection of Elegant Odes," with a Commentary by Woo Lun, &c. 1803. 8⁰.

吳 默 Woo Mǐh.

稿 *Kaou.* "Essays." *See* 長 城 Chang Ching. 名 家 制 義 *Ming kea che e.* "Essays" on Texts from the Four Books, &c. Tsǐh 71.

1699. 8°.

吳 奕 Woo Peen.

See 張 燮 Chang Sĕĕ. 東 西 洋 考 *Tung se yang kaou.* "A Complete Account of . . . Countries in the Southern and Eastern Seas." . . Edited . . . Woo Peen, &c. 1618. 8°.

吳 襄 Woo Seang.

See 朱 軾 Choo Shǐh. 駁 呂 留 良 四 書 講 義 *Pŏ Leu Lew-leang sze shoo keang e.* "A Refutation of Leu Lew-leang's Commentary." . . by . . Woo Seang, &c. 1731. 8°.

吳 修 Woo Sew.

疑 年 錄 *E neen lŭh.* "A Record of Doubtful Biographical Dates." With Four Supplementary Keuen by Woo Sew. *See* 伍 崇 曜 Woo Tsung-yaou. 粵 雅 堂 叢 書 *Yŭĕ ya Tang tsung shoo.* "The Yŭĕ-ya Tang Collection of Reprints," &c. Series 14. 1853. 8°.

吳 淑 Woo Shŭh.

事 類 賦 *Sze luy foo.* "A Classified Literary Encyclopædia in Irregular Verse." Edited by Hwa Lin-tseang. 30 keuen. 1780. 8°.

Another edition. 30 keuen. 1810. 8°.

吳 道 Woo Taou.

See 荀 悦 Seun Yŭĕ. 申 鑒 *Shin keen.* "An Explanatory Mirror." . . . With Notes by Woo Taou, &c. 1518. 8°.

吳 珽 Woo Ting.

See China. 乾 隆 Keen lung. *Emperor.* 欽 定 八 旗 則 例 *Kin ting pǎ ke tsǐh le.* "Regulations for the Bannermen." . . Compiled by . . Woo Ting, &c. 1742. 8°.

吳 鼐 Woo Tsze.

See 韓 非 Han Fei. 韓 非 子 *Han Fei tsze.* "The Writings of Han Fei." . . Edited by Woo Tsze, &c. 1845. 8°.

吳 鼐 Woo Tsze. *(Continued.)*

晏 子 春 秋 *Gan Tsze chun tsew.* "A Biography of Gan Ying," a reputed Disciple of Mǐh tsze, the Opponent of Mencius. Edited by Woo Tsze. 8 keuen. 1804. 8°.

吳 渭 Woo Wei.

月 泉 吟 社 *Yŭĕ tseuen yin shay.* "Sacrificial Hymns to the Moon's Springs." Compiled by Woo Wei. *See* 伍 崇 曜 Woo Tsung-yaou. 粵 雅 堂 叢 書 *Yŭĕ ya Tang tsung shoo.* "The Yŭĕ-ya Tang Collection of Reprints," &c. Series 2. 1853. 8°.

吳 鏞 Woo Yung.

同 安 縣 志 *Tung gan heen che.* "A Topography of Tung-gan Heen, in the Province of Fŭh-keen." Compiled by Woo Yung, Lo Tseen-yin, Hwang Mei, and others. 30 keuen.

1767. 8°.

Very imperfect, containing only keuen 1–7.

吳 兆 騫 Woo Chaou-keen.

秋 笳 集 *Tsew kea tseih.* "The Autumn-Flageolet Collection" of Poetry. 8 keuen. *See* 伍 崇 曜 Woo Tsung-yaou. 粵 雅 堂 叢 書 *Yŭĕ ya Tang tsung shoo.* "The Yŭĕ-ya Tang Collection of Reprints," &c. Series 8.

1853. 8°.

吳 闡 思 Woo Chen-sze.

匡 廬 紀 游 *Kwang leu ke yew.* "Wanderings in Kwang and Leu." *See* 說 Shwŏ. 說 鈴 *Shwŏ ling.* "Miscellaneous Records," &c. Keuen 33. 8°.

吳 擇 賢 Woo Chǐh-heen.

See 周 興 嗣 Chow Hing-tsze. 千 字 文 篆 書 *Tseen tsze wǎn chuen shoo.* "The Thousand Character Classic in the Seal Character." Edited by Woo Chǐh-heen.

1803. 8°.

吳 震 方 Woo Chin-fang.

嶺 南 雜 記 *Ling nan tsa che.* "Records from Ling-nan." *See* 說 Shwŏ. 說 鈴 *Shwŏ ling.* "Miscellaneous Records," &c. 8°.

WOO [245] WOO

吳 振 乾 Woo Chin-keen.
See 儲 欣 Choo Hin. 唐宋八大家類選
Tang Sung pă ta kea luy seuen. "Selections from the Works of Eight Scholars .. under the Tang and Sung Dynasties." . . Edited by Woo Chin-keen, &c. 1766. 8°.

吳 振 鑣 Woo Chin-peaou.
See 張 鳳 翼 Chang Fung-yĭh. 瑞芝閣天崇名文枕中秘 *Shwuy che kŏ teen tsung ming wăn chin chung pe.* "The Shwuy-che Kŏ Collection of Celebrated Essays." . . . . Edited by . . . Woo Chin-peaou, &c. 1790. 8°.

吳 陳 埃 Woo Chin-yen.
五經今文古文考 *Woo king kin wăn koo wăn kaou.* "The Ancient and Modern Texts of the Five Classics Examined." [Also] 放生會約 *Fang săng hwuy yŏ.* "An Agreement to spare Life." See 張 山 來 Chang Shan-lae, and 張 進 也 Chang Tsin-yay. 昭代叢書 *Chaou tae tsung shoo.* "A Collection of Reprints of Works by Authors under the present Dynasty," &c. Keuen 3, 41. 1703. 8°.

吳 承 恩 Woo Ching-găn.
See 顧 鼎 臣 Koo Ting-chin. 狀元圖考 *Chwang yuen too kaou.* "Biographical Notices of Chwang yuen" . . . with Poetry . . . Edited by Woo Ching-găn, &c. 1643. 8°.

吳 傳 鍇 Woo Chuen-keae.
See 密 如 椿 Meĭh Joo-chun. 帖體詩存註釋 *Tĕĕ te she tsun choo shĭh.* "Poems." With a Commentary and Notes by Woo Chuen-keae, &c. 1817. 8°.

吳 中 珩 Woo Chung-hăng.
山海經 *Shan hae king.* "The Hill and River Classic." With Kŏ Pŏ's Commentary. Edited by Woo Chung-hăng. 18 keuen. [1667 ?]. 8°.
Imperfect, wanting keuen 1–4.

—— 山 海 經 註 解 *Shan hae king choo keae.* "The Hill and River Classic." With Kŏ Pŏ's Commentary. Edited by Woo Chung-hăng. With Illustrations. 18 keuen. 1667. 8°.
Another edition of the above.

吳 宜 燮 Woo E-sĕĕ.
See 黃 惠 Hwang Hwuy, and 李 疇 Le Chow. 龍溪縣志 *Lung ke heen che.* "A Topography of Lung-ke Heen." . . Edited by Woo E-sĕĕ, &c. 1762. 8°.

吳 鳳 儀 Woo Fung-e.
See 唐 惟 懋 Tang Wei-mow. 發蒙小品二集 *Fă mung seaou pin urh tsĕĭh.* "A Collection of Model Essays." . . . With Notes by Woo Fung-e, &c. 1743. 8°.

吳 韓 起 Woo Han-ke.
See 孔 丘 Kung Kew. 春秋詳解 *Chun tsew tseang keae.* "The Spring and Autumn Annals Explained." . . . Edited by Woo Han-ke, &c. 1103. 12°.

—— 書 經 詳 解 *Shoo king tseang keae.* "The Book of Historical Documents Explained." . . . Edited by Woo Han-ke, &c. 1209. 8°.

吳 涵 一 Woo Han-yĭh.
See 毛 履 謙 Maou Le-keen, and Woo Han-yĭh, 十家詩詳註 *Shĭh kea she tseang choo.* "The Poetical Works of Ten Authors." . . Edited with Explanatory Notes by Maou Le-keen and Woo Han-yĭh, &c. 1813. 8°.

吳 孝 銘 Woo Heaou-ming.
浙江鄉試同年齒錄 *Chĕ keang heang she tung neen che lŭh.* "A List of the Successful Candidates at the Chĕ-keang District Examinations" for the year 1821. Compiled by Woo Heaou-ming, one of the two Principal Examiners. 1821. 8°.

—— 浙 江 鄉 試 恩 科 同 榜 齒 錄 *Chĕ keang heang she gan ko tung pang che lŭh.* "A List of the Successful Candidates at the Chĕ-keang District Examinations" of the year 1821. Compiled by Woo Heaou-ming, one of the two Principal Examiners. 1821. 8°.
Another copy.

吳 興 凌 Woo Hing-ling.
史 記 短 長 說 *She ke twan chang shwŏ.* "Remarks on the Shortcomings and the Excellencies of the Historical Records." 2 keuen. *See* 葉 志 詵 Yĕ Che-sin. 海 山 仙 館 叢 書 *Hae shan seen Kwan tsung shoo.* "The Hae-shan-seen Kwan Collection of Reprints," &c. Vol. 15. 1848. 8°.

吳 興 潘 Woo Hing-pwan.
增 補 三 十 科 五 經 長 篇 *Tsăng poo san shih ko woo king chang peen.* "Superior Essays on Texts from the Five Classics, selected from the Papers of Thirty Examinations," by Woo Hing-pwan. 1818. 12°.
Imperfect, containing only Essays on Texts from the *Yih king* and the *She king.*

吳 鶴 樵 Woo Hŏ-tseaou.
See 林 瀚 Lin Han. 隋 唐 演 義 *Suy tang yen e.* "A History of the Suy and Tang Dynasties." ... Edited by Woo Hŏ-tseaou, &c. 1801. 8°.

吳 任 臣 Woo Jin-chin.
山 海 經 *Shan hae king.* "The Hill and River Classic." With Kŏ Pŏ's Commentary. Edited by Woo Jin-chin. 18 keuen. 1667. 8°.

—— 山 海 經 廣 注 *Shan hae king kwang choo.* "The Hill and River Classic. Copiously Annotated," by the Editor Woo Jin-chin and Kŏ Pŏ. 18 keuen. 1696. 8°.
Another edition of the above.

吳 繼 綬 Woo Ke-show.
See 程 大 位 Ching Ta-wei. 算 法 統 宗 全 書 *Swan fă tung tsung tseuen shoo.* "A Complete Work on the Rules of Arithmetic." ... Edited by Woo Ke-show. 1593. 8°.

———— 算 法 統 宗 *Swan fă tung tsung.* "The Rules of Arithmetic." .. Edited by Woo Ke-show. 1832. 8°.

吳 見 思 Woo Keen-sze.
See 司 馬 遷 Sze-ma Teen. 史 記 論 文 *She ke lun wăn.* "The Historical Record." ... Edited by Woo Keen-sze, &c. 1686. 8°.

吳 金 壽 Woo Kin-show.
See 吳 葉 桂 Woo Yĕ-kwei. 醫 效 秘 傳 *E heaou pe chuen.* "An Efficacious System of Medicine." ... Corrected by Woo Kin-show. 1831. 8°.

—— 三 家 醫 案 合 刻 *San keae E gan hŏ kih.* "The Medical Practice of the Three Physicians," Yĕ Teen-sze, Sĕĕ Săng-pǐh, and Mew E-ting. Compiled by Woo Kin-show. 1831. 8°.
The volume containing the practice of Sĕĕ Săng-pǐh is wanting.

吳 敬 恆 Woo King-hăng.
See 吳 錫 麒 Woo Seĭh-ke. 有 正 味 齋 試 帖 詳 註 *Yew ching wei chae she tĕĕ tseang choo.* "A Collection of Elegant Odes." With Commentaries by Woo King-hăng, &c. 1803. 8°.

吳 穀 人 Woo Kŭh-gin.
安 定 書 院 課 藝 *Gan ting shoo yuen ko e.* "Examination Essays from the Gan-ting College." Edited by Woo Kŭh-jin, Chang Han-chae, and Fung Loo-ting. 1803. 8°.

吳 光 義 Woo Kwang-e.
See 馮 琦 Fung Ke. 經 濟 類 編 *King tse luy peen.* "Aids to Classical Literature." ... Edited by ... Woo Kwang-e, &c. 1604. 8°.

吳 老 于 Woo Laou-kan.
See 王 黼 Wang Foo. 博 古 圖 *Pŏ koo too.* "An Illustrated Collection of Antiquities." .. Illustrated by Woo Laou-kan, &c. 1588. 8°.

吳 立 性 Woo Leĭh-sing.
See 顧 鼎 臣 Koo Ting-chin. 狀 元 圖 考 *Chwang yuen too kaou.* "Biographical Notices of Chwang yuen" ... with Poetry .. Compiled by Woo Leĭh-sing, &c. 1643. 8°.

吳 留 村 Woo Lew-tsun.
古 文 觀 止 *Koo wăn kwan che.* "A Survey of Ancient Literature. The Pŏ-koo Tang edition." Compiled by Woo Lew-tsun. Edited by Woo Shing-keuen and Woo Ta-chĭh. 12 keuen. [1750?]. 8°.
Imperfect, first 4 keuen wanting.
Another copy.
Imperfect, containing keuen 11, 12.
Another edition. 12 keuen. 1821. 8°.

吳 孟 舉 Woo Măng-keu, and 吳 自 牧 Woo Tsze-mŭh.

宋 詩 鈔 二 集 *Sung she chaou urh tseĭh.*
"Poetry of the Sung Dynasty. Second Collection." Compiled by Woo Măng-keu and Woo Tsze-mŭh. [1800 ?]. 8º.

This Work contains Twenty-three Collections of Poems by as many Authors.

吳 勉 學 Woo Meen-heŏ.

See 屠 隆 Too Lung. 綿 絹 對 類 大 全 *Peaou seang tuy luy ta tseuen.* "A Complete Thesaurus of Elegant Expressions and Phrases." . . . Edited by Woo Meen-heŏ, &c. 8º.

吳 梅 村 Woo Mei-tsun.

吳 詩 集 覽 *Woo she tseĭh lan.* "A Collective View of Woo Mei-tsun's Poetry." Compiled by Kin Yung-fan. 20 keuen. 1781. 8º.

吳 懋 政 Woo Mow-ching.

八 銘 塾 鈔 *Pă ming shŭh chaou.* "A Copy of Essays from the Pă-ming College," on Texts from the Four Books. Compiled by Woo Mow-ching. With Explanatory Notes by Le Wăn-shan. 2 Series. 1782, 1783. 8º.

Another copy. 2 Series. 1783. 8º.
Imperfect.

Another edition. 1832. 8º.

—— 八 銘 塾 課 *Pă ming shŭh ko.* "Examination Essays from the Pă-ming College" on Texts from the Four Books. Compiled by Woo Mow-ching. 1818. 8º.

—— 天 崇 讀 本 百 篇 *Teen tsung tŭh peen pĭh peen.* "A Collection of a Hundred Essays of Celestial Eminence" [on Texts from the Four Books, Compiled by Woo Mow-ching]. [1790 ?]. 8º.

吳 實 彝 Woo Paou-e.

See 萬 之 薲 Wan Che-hăng and Woo Paou-e. 漢 關 侯 事 蹟 彙 編 *Han Kwan how sze tseĭh wei peen.* "A Memoir of Kwan Yu," &c. 8º.

吳 實 謨 Woo Paou-moo.

經 義 圖 說 *King e too shwŏ.* "The Meaning of the Classics Illustrated and Explained." Edited by Chin Fung-kăng. 8 keuen. 1819. 8º.

吳 實 卿 Woo Paou-king.

[Poetical Essays]. By Woo Paou-king and others. [1815 ?]. 8º.
A Fragment.

吳 錫 疇 Woo Seĭh-chow.

See 馮 登 府 Fung Tăng-foo. 象 山 縣 志 *Seang shan heen che.* "A Topography of Seang-shan Heen." . . Compiled by . . Woo Seĭh-chow, &c. 1834. 8º.

吳 錫 麒 Woo Seĭh-ke.

See 毛 履 謙 Maou Le-keen, and 吳 涵 一 Woo Han-yĭh. 十 家 詩 詳 註 *Shĭh kea she tseang choo.* "The Poetical Works of Ten Authors," viz. Woo Seĭh-ke, &c. 1813. 8º.

—— 有 正 味 齋 帖 試 詳 註 *Yew Ching wei chae she tëĕ tseang choo.* "A Collection of Elegant Odes." By Woo Seĭh-ke. With Commentaries by Woo Lun and Woo King-hăng. 4 keuen. 1803. 8º.

Another copy.

Another edition. 4 keuen. 1805. 8º.

吳 紹 泰 Woo Shaou-tae.

See 關 朗 Kwan Lang. 關 氏 易 傳 *Kwan she Yĭh chuen.* "Kwan Lang's Commentary on the Book of Changes." . . . Edited by Woo Shaou-tae, &c. 8º.

吳 世 杰 Woo She-lĕĕ.

See 嚴 允 肇 Yen Yun-shaou. 姚 布 政 傳 *Yaou Poo ching chuen.* "A Biography of the Provincial Treasurer Yaou" Seang-heuen . . . With a Supplementary Notice by Woo She-lĕĕ, &c. 1820. 8º.

吳 世 錫 Woo She-seĭh.

See 吳 台 位 Woo Tae-wei. 百 繪 詩 箋 *Pĭh hwuy she tseen.* "A Hundred Pieces of Descriptive Poetry." With Notes by Woo She-seĭh, &c. 1797. 8º.

吳世德 Woo She-tǐh.

> See 吳台位 Woo Tae-wei. 百繪詩箋 *Pǐh hwuy she tseen.* "A Hundred Pieces of Descriptive Poetry." . . With Notes by . . Woo She-tǐh, &c. 1797. 8°.

吳乘權 Woo Shing-keuen.

> See 吳留村 Woo Lew-tsun. 古文觀止 *Koo wǎn kwan che.* "A Survey of Ancient Literature." . . . Edited by Woo Shing-keuen, &c. 8°.

—— 綱鑑易知錄 *Kang keen e che lǔh.* "The Mirror of History made Easy." By Woo Shing-keuen, Chow Che-hing, and Chow Che-tsan. 107 keuen. 1711. 8°.

Another edition. 92 keuen. 1711. 8°.

Another edition. 107 keuen. 1711. 8°.

吳繩如 Woo Shing-joo.

> 松江捍海石塘錄 *Sung keang han hae shǐh tang lǔh.* "An Account of the Stone Sea-Dykes in the Prefecture of Sung Keang." Compiled by Woo Shing-joo. Edited by Wang Yuen. 1723. 8°.

吳舒鳬 Woo Shoo-foo.

> 徐園秋花譜 *Seu yuen tsew hwa poo.* "The Autumn Flowers in Seu's Garden." *See* 張山來 Chang Shan-lae, and 張進也 Chang Tsin-yay. 昭代叢書 *Chaou tae tsung shoo.* "A Collection of Reprints of Works by Authors under the present Dynasty," &c. Keuen 47. 1703. 8°.

吳守一 Woo Show-yǐh.

> 春秋日食質疑 *Chun Tsew jǐh shǐh chǐh e.* "Doubtful Points with Reference to the Eclipses of the Sun mentioned in the Spring and Autumn Annals, settled." *See* 張山來 Chang Shan-lae, and 張進也 Chang Tsin-yay. 昭代叢書 *Chaou tae tsung shoo.* "A Collection of Reprints of Works by Authors under the present Dynasty," &c. Keuen 5. 1703. 8°.

吳大職 Woo Ta-chǐh.

> See 吳留村 Woo Lew-tsun. 古文觀止 *Koo wǎn kwan che.* "A Survey of Ancient Literature." . . Edited by . . . Woo Ta-chǐh, &c. 8°.

吳台位 Woo Tae-wei.

> 百繪詩箋 *Pǐh hwuy she tseěn.* "A Hundred Pieces of Descriptive Poetry." With Notes by Woo She-seǐh and Woo She-tǐh. 1797. 8°.

吳廷華 Woo Ting-hwa.

> See 張鳳翼 Chang Fung-yǐh. 瑞芝閣天崇名文枕中秘 *Shwuy che kǒ Teen tsung ming wǎn chin chung pe.* "The Shwuy-che Kǒ Collection of Celebrated Essays." . . . . Edited by Woo Ting-hwa, &c. 1790. 8°.

—— See 儀禮 E le. 儀禮章句 *E le chang keu.* "The Decorum Ritual Explained Sentence by Sentence," by Woo Ting-hwa, &c. 1757. 8°.

—— 儀禮章句 *E le chang keu.* "The Decorum Ritual Explained Sentence by Sentence." *See* 嚴杰 Yen Lěě. 皇清經解 *Hwang Tsing king keae.* "The Classics Explained," &c. Keuen 271–287. 1829. 8°.

吳遵程 Woo Tsun-ching.

> 本草從新 *Pun tsaou tsung sin.* "A Newly Arranged Materia Medica." Edited by Woo Yew-yu and Woo Yew-too. 6 keuen. 1757. 8°.

Another copy.

> Fifth keuen wanting.

Another edition. 6 keuen. 1817. 8°.

吳自牧 Woo Tsze-mǔh.

> See 吳孟舉 Woo Mǎng-keu, and Woo Tsze-mǔh. 宋詩鈔二集 *Sung she chaou urh tseǐh.* "Poetry of the Sung Dynasty." Compiled by . . . Woo Tsze-mǔh, &c. 8°.

吳紫陽 Woo Tsze-yang.

> 紫陽書院課選 *Tsze yang shoo yuen ko seuen.* "Select Literary Essays and Poems by the Scholars of the Tsze Yang College." Edited by Woo Tsze-yang. 4 vols. 1805–1807. 8°.
>
> In four vols. called respectively *Fung, Hwa, Yuě,* and *Seuě.*

WOO [249] WOO

吳偉業 WOO WEI-NĔĔ.
See 寇 KOW. 綏寇紀畧 Suy kow ke leŏ. "Short Records of the Suppression of Banditti." By Woo Wei-nĕĕ, &c. 8º.

吳葉桂 WOO YĔ-KWEI.
醫效祕傳 E heaou pe chuen. "An Efficacious System of Medicine." Corrected by Woo Kin-show. Edited by Chang Yew-tseaou. 3 keuen. 1831. 8º.

吳又可 WOO YEW-KO.
溫疫方論 Wăn yĭh fang lun. "A Treatise on Prescriptions for the Pestilence." Edited by Shĭh Lin-choo, Seu Teen-chang, and others. 2 keuen. [1800?]. 8º.

吳有杜 WOO YEW-TOO.
See 吳遵程 WOO TSUN-CHING. 本草從新 Pun tsaou tsung sin. "A Newly Arranged Materia Medica." Edited by .. Woo Yew-too, &c. 1757. 8º.

吳有榆 WOO YEW-YU.
See 吳遵程 WOO TSUN CHING. 本草從新 Pun tsaou tsung sin. "A Newly Arranged Materia Medica." Edited by Woo Yew-yu, &c. 1757. 8º.

吳因之 WOO YIN-CHE.
易說 Yĭh shwŏ. "Discourses on the Book of Changes." Edited by Tseen Yŭh-chin. 6 keuen. [1700?]. 8º.

吳應箕 WOO YING-KE.
樓山堂集 Low shan tang tseĭh. "A Collection of Literary Pieces from Low-shan Tang." 27 keuen. See 伍崇曜 WOO TSUNG-YAOU. 粵雅堂叢書 Yuĕ ya Tang tsung shoo. "The Yuĕ-ya Tang Collection of Reprints," &c. Series 13. 1853. 8º.

吳踴龍 WOO YU-LUNG.
探芹捷訣 Tsae kin tsĕĕ keuĕ. "A Collection of Prize Essays." Selected and Commented on by Woo Yu-lung. An Enlarged Edition. 4 keuen. 1818. 8º.

吳元亮 WOO YUEN-LEANG.
See 馬光 SZE-MA KWANG. 司馬溫公文集 Sze ma wăn kung wăn tseĭh. "A Collection of the Writings of Sze-ma Kwang." Edited by Woo Yuen-leang, &c. 1708. 8º.

吳毓昌 WOO YŬH-CHANG.
See 李時珍 LE SHE-CHIN. 本草綱目 Pun tsaou kang mŭh. "The Materia Medica." ... Edited by Woo Yŭh-chang, &c. 1655. 8º.

吳大司馬 WOO TA-SZE-MA.
See 萬樹 WAN SHOO. 詞律 Tsze leŭh. "A Collection of ... Rhymes." ... Edited by Woo Ta-sze-ma, &c. 1687. 8º.

無能子 WOO-NĂNG-TSZE.
無能子 Woo-năng-tsze. "The Writings of Woo-năng-tsze." See 沈津 CHIN TSIN. 百家類纂 Pĭh kea luy tswan. "The Works of a Hundred Authors," &c. Keuen 19. 8º.

五虎 WOO HOO.
五虎平西前傳 Woo Hoo ping se tseen chuen. "The History of the Pacification of the West by the Five Tigers." With Portraits. 14 keuen. 1805. 8º.

五經 WOO-KING.
五經擬題類典 Woo king e te luy teen. "A Classified Encyclopædia on the Five Classics." 75 keuen. [1790?]. 24º.
Imperfect, keuen 41 to 58 being wanting.

——— 五經句解 Woo king keu keae. "The Five Classics Explained Sentence by Sentence." Edited by Chang-she. 1817. 8º.

——— 五經文集 Woo king wăn tseĭh. "A Classified Collection of Notes on the Five Classics." 75 keuen. [1750?]. 12º.
Imperfect, keuen 45–60 being wanting.

五鼠 WOO-SHOO.
五鼠鬧東京 Woo shoo naou tung king. "The Quarrels of the Five Rats at the Eastern Capital." 2 keuen. [1850?]. 8º.

32

五郎 Woo-tseïh.

五郎救弟 *Woo-tseïh kew te.* "(Yang) Woo-tseïh Rescues his Brother." A Drama.

[1800?]. 8º.

伍希周 Woo He-chow.

See 蔡清 Tsae Tsing. 四書蒙引 *Sze shoo mung yin.* "A Guide to the Study of the Four Books." . . . Edited by Woo He-chow, &c. 8º.

伍奎府 Woo Kwei-foo.

初學破承開講入門全集 *Choo heŏ po ching kae keang jŭh mun tseuen tseïh.* "An Introduction to the Art of Analysing and Explaining Sentences. For Beginners." An Enlarged Edition. [1810?]. 8º.

伍崇曜 Woo Tsung-yaou.

粵雅堂叢書 *Yuĕ ya Tang tsung shoo.* "The Yuĕ-ya Tang Collection of Reprints." Edited by Woo Tsung-yaou. 20 series. 1853. 8º.

吾衍 Woo Yen.

楚史檮杌 *Tsoo she taon wŭh.* "A Collection of Memoranda Regarding the State of Tsoo." [Also] 晉史乘 *Tsin she shing.* "A Short Historical Record of the State of Tsin." See 汪士漢 Wang Sze-han. 祕書廿八種 *Pe shoo neen pă chung.* "A Collection of Twenty-eight Reprints," &c. 1808. 8º.

武億 Woo E.

經讀考異 *King tŭh kaou e.* "An Examination of the Various Readings of the Classics." 8 keuen. See 嚴杰 Yen Lĕĕ. 皇清經解 *Hwang Tsing king keae.* "The Classics Explained," &c. Keuen 727–734. 1829. 8º.

武帝 Woo te. *Emperor.*

覺世經 *Keaou she king.* "A Tract to arouse the World." See 關帝 Kwan te. 忠義經文 *Chung e king wăn.* "Canonical Works on Patriotism and Uprightness," &c. 1839. 8º.

—— 慈悲懺 *Tsze pe tsan.* "The Ritual of Mercy and Repentance." Compiled by the Emperor Woo-te. A Reprint. 10 keuen. [1750?]. 8º.

武夷山 Woo-e shan.

武夷山志 *Woo-e shan che.* "A Topography of the Bohea Hills." [24 keuen?] [1750?]. 8º.

An odd vol., containing only parts of keuen 9, 10.

武克繩 Woo Kĭh-yen.

See 王客周 Wang Kĭh-chow. 文法狐白 *Wăn fă hoo pĭh.* "The Laws of Literary Composition." . . . Edited by . . . Woo Kĭh-yen, &c. 1792. 8º.

武光賜 Woo Kwang-tsze.

See 韓非 Han Fei. 韓非子纂 *Han Fei tsze tswan.* "The Writings of Han Fei." . . With Notes by Woo Kwang-tsze. 8º.

—— See 管仲 Kwan Chung. 管子纂 *Kwan tsze tswan.* "The Work of Kwan Chung." . . With Explanations by Woo Kwang-tsze, &c. 8º.

婆源齊 Woo Yuen-tse.

南澳志 *Nan gaou che.* "A Topography of the Island of Nan-gaou." 12 keuen. 1783. 8º.

物 Wŭh.

詠物詩選註釋 *Yung wŭh she seuen choo shĭh.* "A Collection of Songs on Things, with Explanatory Notes," by Yĭh Kae-tsin, and Sun Tseen-ming. 8 keuen. [1800?]. 8º.

Imperfect, wanting keuen 1 and 4.

WYLIE (Alexander).

See Herschel (Sir John Frederick William), Bart. 談天 *Tan teen.* "Herschel's 'Outlines of Astronomy.'" Translated into Chinese by A. Wylie, &c. 1859. 8º.

—— See Periodical Publications. 六合叢談 *Lŭh hŏ tsung tan.* "The Universal Miscellany." . . . Edited by Alexander Wylie, &c. 1857. 8º.

楊 Yang.

See 太平天國 Tae-ping Teen Kwŏ. 頒行詔書 *Fun hing chaou shoo.* "Proclamations" of Yang, &c. 1852. 8º.

第一卷

楊億 YANG E.

西崑酬唱集 *Se kwǎn chow chang tseǐh.*
"The Se-kwǎn Collection of Songs." Compiled by Yang E. 2 keuen. *See* 伍崇曜 WOO TSUNG-YAOU. 粵雅堂叢書 *Yuě ya Tang tsung shoo.* "The Yuě-ya Tang Collection of Reprints," &c. Series 20. 1853. 8°.

揚雄 YANG HEUNG.

法言 *Fǎ yen.* "Discourses on Law." With Commentaries by Le Kwei and Sze-ma Kwang. 10 keuen. *See* 黃丕烈 HWANG PEI-LĔĔ. 十子全書 *Shǐh Tsze tseuen shoo.* "The Complete Works of the Ten Philosophers," &c. 1804. 8°.

—— 法言 *Fǎ yen.* "Discourses on Law." By Yang Heung. Giving a brief Development of his Philosophical Views. Edited by Chang Pang. [1750?]. 8°.

Another edition. 10 keuen. [1815?]. 8°.

Another edition. 13 keuen. 1818. 8°.

—— 方言 *Fang yen.* "Foreign Words." A Work on Dialects. Compiled by Yang Heung. With Notes by Kǒ Pǒ. Edited by Chaou Ping-yu. 13 keuen. [1800?]. 8°.

Another edition. 13 keuen. [1800?]. 8°.

—— 太玄經 *Tae heuen king.* "The Great Deep Classic." A Work professedly in Elucidation of the *Yǐh king.* With Notes by Chin Jin-seǐh. [1750?]. 8°.

楊炘 YANG HIN.

See 文昌帝君 WǍN-CHANG TE KEUN. 陰騭文圖說 *Yin chǐh wǎn too shwǒ.* "A Treatise on Secret Rewards and Retributions." . . Edited by Yang Hin, &c. 1801. 8°.

楊鶴 YANG HǑ.

See 董斯張 TUNG SZE-CHANG. 廣博物志 *Kwǎng pǒ wǔh che.* "An Encyclopædia." . . . Edited by Yang Ho, &c. 1615. 4°.

揚甲 YANG KEǍ.

六經圖 *Lǔh king too.* "Illustrations to Accompany the Six Classics." Edited by Maou Pang-han, Chin Sǎn and others. 1614. 4°.

楊倞 YANG KING.

荀子 *Seun tsze.* "The Writings of Seun Hwang." With a Commentary by Yang King, &c. *See* 黃丕烈 HWANG PEI-LĔĔ. 十子全書 *Shǐh Tsze tseuen shoo.* "The Complete Works of the Ten Philosophers," &c. 1804. 8°.

—— See 荀況 SEUN HWANG. 荀子 *Seun tsze.* "The Writings of the Philosopher Seun Hwang." With Notes by Yang King, &c. 809. 8°.

楊廉 YANG LEEN.

嘉善縣志 *Kea-shen heen che.* "A Topography of Kea-shen Heen." Compiled by Yang Leen. Edited by Maou Fan and Yŭh Kwang. 12 keuen. 1677. 8°.

楊波 YANG PO.

斬楊波 *Chan Yang Po.* "Yang Po is beheaded." A Dramatic Tale. [1800?]. 8°.

楊氏 YANG SHE.

See 孔丘 KUNG KEW. 古本官板書經大全 *Koo pun kwan pan Shoo king ta tseuen.* "The Original Official Text of the Book of Historical Documents." . . Compiled by . . Yang She, &c. 8°.

楊慎 YANG SHIN.

稿 *Kaou.* "Essays." *See* 長城 CHANG CHING. 名家制義 *Ming kea che e.* "Essays" on Texts from the Four Books, &c. Tsǐh 31. 1699. 8°.

—— See 屈原 KEŬH YUEN. 離騷經 *Le saou king.* "The Classic of the Exiled Mourner." . . With Notes by Yang Shin. 8°.

楊榮 YANG YUNG.

See 胡廣 HOO KWANG. 性理大全 *Sing le ta tseuen.* "A Complete Work on Mental Philosophy." . . . Compiled by . . . Yang Yung, &c. 1597. 8°.

楊 昌 光 YANG CHANG-KWANG.

　醉 芸 窗 詩 註 釋 *Tsuy yun chwang she choo shǐh.* "Odes from the 'Window of Intoxicating Herbs.'" With Notes by Yang Yen-leang. 4 keuen. 1820. 8°.

　　Imperfect, the second keuen wanting.

楊 正 筍 YANG CHING-SEUN.

　See 馮 鴻 模 FUNG HUNG-MOO. 慈 谿 縣 志 *Tsze ke heen che.* "A Topography of Tsze-ke Heen." . . Edited by Yang Ching-seun, &c. 1738. 8°.

楊 以 任 YANG E-JIN.

　稿 *Kaou.* "Essays." *See* 長 城 CHANG CHING. 名 家 制 義 *Ming kea che e.* "Essays" on Texts from the Four Books," &c. Tsǐh 92. 1699. 8°.

楊 方 達 YANG FANG-TĂ.

　See 易 經 *Yih king.* 周 易 輯 說 存 正 *Chow Yih tseǐh shwǒ tsun ching.* "The 'Chow Changes.' With a Compilation of Notes in which is Preserved the Correct Meaning." Compiled by Yang Fang-tă, &c. 1750. 8°.

楊 逢 春 YANG FUNG-CHUN, and 蕭 應 櫆 SEAOU YING-KWEI.

　詳 註 分 韻 試 帖 青 雲 集 *Tseang choo fun yun she tĕĕ tsing yun tseǐh.* "The Tsing-yun Collection of Poetical Essays on Themes Phonetically arranged." Compiled by Yang Fung-chun, and Seaou Ying-kwei. With Explanatory Notes by Chin Pin-hwa, Chin Pin-kin and others. 4 keuen. 1856. 8°.

楊 衒 之 YANG HEUEN-CHE.

　洛 陽 伽 藍 記 *Lǒ yang kea lan ke.* "A Description of the Buddhist Monasteries at Lǒ-yang," in the Province of Honan. By Yang Heuen-che, of the latter Wei Dynasty. A Reprint. 5 keuen. [1750 ?]. 8°.

楊 慧 樓 YANG HWUY-LOW, and 王 愓 甫 WANG TEǏH-FOO.

　國 朝 七 栟 雲 襄 二 集 *Kwǒ chaou tsǐh pae yun seang urh tseǐh.* "The Yun-seang Collection of Verses in Seven Syllables, by Authors of the Tsing Dynasty. Second series." Compiled by Yang Hwuy-low and Wang Teǐh-foo. Edited by Choo Chow. 1807. 8°.

楊 起 元 YANG KE-YUEN.

　稿 *Kaou.* "Essays." *See* 長 城 CHANG CHING. 名 家 制 義 *Ming kea che e.* "Essays" on Texts from the Four Books, &c. Tsǐh 60. 1699. 8°.

—— 諸 經 品 節 *Choo king pin tsĕĕ.* "The Taouist Classics." Arranged and Annotated by Yang Ke-yuen. 10 keuen. 1594. 8°.

楊 巨 源 YANG KEU-YUEN.

　紅 線 傳 *Hung-seen chuen.* "The Story of Hung-seen." By Yang Keu-yuen, of the Tang Dynasty. A Reprint. [1741 ?]. 8°.

楊 救 貧 YANG KEW-PIN.

　疑 龍 經 *E lung king.* "The Classic of the Doubtful Dragon," in which the Principles of Selecting Sites by means of the Indications of Nine Stars are Investigated, and Ten Questions on the Subject Answered. 1837. 8°.

—— 撼 龍 經 *Han lung king.* "The Classic for moving the Dragon." A Work on the Selection of Sites by means of the Indications of Nine Stars. 1837. 8°.

楊 金 城 YANG KIN-CHING.

　四 書 人 物 左 國 舉 玉 類 纂 *Sze shoo jin wǔh Tso kwǒ keun yǔh luy tswan.* "The Men and Things of the Four Books, as Explained in the *Tso chuen* and *Kwǒ tsǐh.*" 8 keuen. 1818. 8°.

楊 景 曾 YANG KING-TSĂNG.

　See 李 兆 洛 LE CHAOU-LǑ. 江 陰 縣 志 *Keang yin heen che.* "A Topography of Keang-yin Heen." . . . Compiled by . . . Yang King-tsăng, &c. 1840. 8°.

楊 光 烈 YANG KWANG-LĔĔ.

　See 于 寶 KAN PAOU. 搜 神 記 *Sow shin ke.* "Marvellous Tales." . . . Edited by Yang Kwang-lĕĕ, &c. 8°.

楊 立 先 YANG LEǏH-SEEN.

　See 四 書 SZE SHOO. 四 書 離 句 集 註 *Sze Shoo le keu tseǐh choo.* "The Four Books." . . . Edited by Yang Leǐh-seen. 1818. 8°.

YAN   [253]   YAN

楊 明 智 Yang Ming che.

通書 *Tung shoo.* "Astrological Almanacs,"
for the Years 1844, 1847, 1865.
                              1844, 1847, 1865. 8°.

楊 伯 嵒 Yang Pïh-gan.

九經補韻 *Kew king poo yun.* "A Supplementary Work on the Rhyming Sounds of
the Nine Classics." With an Appendix. By
Yang Pïh-gan. 2 keuen. *See* 伍崇曜 Woo
Tsung-yaou. 粵雅堂叢書 *Yuě-ya Tung
tsung shoo.* "The Yuě-ya Tang Collection of
Reprints," &c.   Series 17. 1853. 8°.

楊 炳 南 Yang Ping-nan.

海錄 *Hae lŭh.* "A General Record of Foreign
Nations." By Yang Ping-nan. *See* 葉志詵
Yě Che-sin. 海山仙館叢書 *Hae shan
seen kwan tsung shoo.* "The Hae-shan-seen
Kwan Collection of Reprints," &c. Vol. 113.
                                    1848. 8°.

楊 錫 紱 Yang Seïh-fŭh.

漕運則例纂 *Tsaou yun tsïh le tswan.* "Laws
and Regulations for the Conveyance of Grain"
to the Capital. Compiled by a Commission,
consisting of Yang Seïh-fuh, Yaou Ching-lëě,
Tseang Tsze-ke, and others. 20 keuen.
                                    1767. 8°.

楊 聲 和 Yang Shing-ho.

See 范題名 Fan Te-ming. 五經題解
集要 *Woo king te keae tseïh yaou.* "A Collection of Essays explanatory of Texts from
the Five Classics." By .... Yang Shing-ho, &c.
                                          12°.

楊 壽 楠 Yang Show-nan.

See 謝庭薰 Seay Ting-heun. 婁縣志 *Low
heen che.* "A Topography of Low Heen." ...
Edited by Yang Show-nan, &c. 1786. 8°.

楊 士 勛 Yang Sze-heun.

See 孔丘 Kung Kew. 春秋穀梁傳註疏
Chun tsew kŭh-leang chuen choo soo. "The
Spring and Autumn Annals." ... With Ex-
planations by Yang Sze-heun, &c.   8°.

楊 大 鸞 Yang Ta-haou.

A Collection of Essays by Yang Ta-haou and
others. 2 keuen.   [1750 ?]. 12°.
Imperfect, containing only the last keuen. No head title.

楊 大 鶴 Yang Ta-hŏ.

See 陸游 Lŭh Yew. 劍南詩鈔 *Keen nan
she chaou.* "The Keen-nan Collection of
Poetry." ... Edited by Yang Ta-hŏ, &c.
                                    1685. 8°.

楊 廷 樞 Yang Ting-choo.

稿 *Kaou.* "Essays." *See* 長城 Chang Ching.
名家制義 *Ming kea che e.* "Essays" on
Texts from the Four Books, &c. Tsïh 90.
                                    1699. 8°.

楊 廷 筠 Yang Ting-yun.

天釋明辨 *Teen shĭh ming peen.* "The
Doctrines of the Christian and the Buddhist
Religions Clearly Distinguished."
                        [*Peking* ? 1700 ?]. 8°.

楊 爾 曾 Yang Urh-tsăng.

圖繪宗彝 *Too hwuy tsung e.* "A Treatise
on the Art of Drawing." 6 keuen.
                              [1750 ?]. 8°.

楊 萬 里 Yang Wan-le.

稿 *Kaou.* "Essays." *See* 長城 Chang Ching.
名家制義 *Ming kea che e.* "Essays" on
Texts from the Four Books, &c. Tsïh 3.
                                    1699. 8°.

楊 延 亮 Yang Yen-leang.

See 楊昌光 Yang Chang-kwang. 醉芸窗
詩註釋 *Tsuy yun chwang she choo shĭh.*
"Odes." .. With Notes by Yang Yen-leang,
&c.   1820. 8°.

楊 應 象 Yang Ying-seang.

See 丘濬 Kew Seun. 幼學故事尋源
Yew heŏ koo sze tsin yuen. "A Search into
Antiquities." . . With a Collection of Com-
ments Compiled by Yang Ying-seang, &c. 8°.

楊 元 凱 Yang Yuen-kae.

平閩記 *Ping min ke.* "The History of the
Pacification of the Province of Fŭh-keen,"
during the Reign of the Emperor Kang-he.
13 keuen.   1683. 8°.

陽直樵雲山人 YANG CHǏH TSEAOU YUN SHAN JIN. See 鬼 KWEI. 平鬼傳 *Ping kwei chuen.* "The Story of the Pacification of the Demons." . . By the Man of the Yang-chǐh-tseaou-yun Mountain, &c. 1720. 8°.

陽湖惲 YANG HOO-WĂN. 大雲山房文稿 *Ta yun shan fang wăn kaou.* "Literary Pieces from the House on Mount Ta-yun." In Two Series. Series I. 4 keuen. Series II. 4 keuen. 1815–16. 8°.

陽斬賢 YANG KIN-HEEN. 鍼灸大成 *Chin kew ta ching.* "A Complete System of Acupuncture." Edited by Le Yuĕ-kwei. 10 keuen. 1798. 8°.

陽瑪諾 YANG-MA-NǑ. *pseud.* [*i.e.* Emmanuel Diaz.] See BIBLE. *Appendix.* 天主降生聖經直解 *Teen choo keang săng shing king chǐh keae.* "The Gospel of Christ clearly Explained," by Yang-ma-nǒ. 1790. 8°.

—— See 艾儒略 GAE JOO-LEǑ. 三山論學紀 *San shan lun heŏ ke.* "A Dialogue . . . on God as the Creator and Governor of the Universe." . . . Edited by . . . Yang Ma-nŏ. 8°.

—— 天主降生言行紀像 *Teen choo keang săng yen hing ke seang.* "An Illustrated Life of Christ." . . . Edited by . . . Yang-ma-nŏ, etc. 8°.

—— See 郭居靜 KŎ KEU-TSING. 天主聖教日課 *Tsen choo Shing keaou jǐh ko.* "Daily Christian Religious Exercises." Compiled by Yang Ma-nŏ, &c. 8°.

—— 輕世金書 *King she kin shoo.* A Translation of the "Imitation of Christ" by Thomas à Kempis. Written by Yang Ma-nŏ, in A.D. 1640. Published with the Approval of Jŏ-a-king-kung, a Roman Catholic Bishop. 4 keuen. 1815. 8°.

—— 天堂直路 *Teen tang chǐh loo.* "The Straight Road to Heaven." A Guide for the Disciple in his Daily Conduct and Conversation. 1762. 8°.

陽盛公 YANG SHING-KUNG. 玉華子 *Yŭh hwa tsze.* "The Writings of Yang Shing-kung." See 沈津 CHIN TSIN. 百家類纂 *Pĭh kea huy tswan.* "The Works of a Hundred Authors," &c. Keuen 19. 8°.

揚廷 YANG TING. 崇川賦鈔 *Tsung chuen foo chaou.* "Odes from *Tsung chuen.*" Edited by Yang Ting. 1819. 8°.

揚子雲 YANG TSZE-YUN. 甘泉賦 *Kan tseuen foo.* "An Ode on Sweet Springs of Water." [Also] 羽獵賦 *Yu lëe foo.* "An Ode on Hunting." *See* 蕭統 SEAOU TUNG. 文選 *Wăn seuen.* "Elegant Extracts," &c. Keuen 7, 8. 1772. 8°.

煬帝 YANG-TE. 煬帝迷樓記 *Yang te me low ke.* "An Account of the Emperor Yang-te's Labyrinth." [Also] 煬帝海山記 *Yang te hae shan ke.* "An Account of the Emperor Yang-te's Islands." [Also] 煬帝開河記 *Yang te kae ho ke.* "An Account of the Canal made by the Emperor Yang-te." *See* 說 SHWŎ. 說纂 *Shwŏ tswan.* "Miscellaneous Records," &c. Vol. 2. 8°.

—— 隋煬帝艷史 *Suy Yang-te yen she.* "A History of the Reign of Yang-te and of his Amusements." By Tse-tung Yay-jin. 8 keuen. [1700?]. 8°.

姚宏 YAOU HUNG. See 劉向 LEW HEANG. 戰國策 *Chen kwŏ tsĭh.* "The Story of the Contending States." . . . Edited by Yaou Hung. 1803. 8°.

姚寬 YAOU KWAN. 姚氏殘語 *Yaou she tsan yu.* "The Sayings of Yaou Kwan." *See* 說 SHWŎ. 說郛 *Shwŏ foo.* "Odds and Ends," &c. 8°.

姚鼐 YAOU NAE. See 呂燕昭 LEU YEN-CHAOU. 新修江寧府志 *Sin seu keang ning foo che.* "The Topography of Keang-ning Foo." Compiled by . . . Yaou Nae, &c. 1811. 8°.

姚 信 YAOU SIN.

周易注 *Chow Yĭh choo.* "Notes on the Chow Changes." *See* 孫堂 SUN TANG. 漢魏二十一家易注 *Han Wei urh shĭh yĭh kea yĭh choo.* "Commentaries on the Book of Changes," &c.   1799. 8º.

姚 瑩 YAOU YUNG.

記英俄二夷搆兵 *Ke Ying Go urh e kow ping.* "Engagements between the English and Russian Armies" in Central Asia. *See* 何秋濤 HO TSEW-TAOU. 北徼彙編 *Pĭh keaou wei peen.* "Treatises on the Countries beyond the Northern Frontier." ... Keuen 3, &c.   1865. 8º.

姚 成 烈 YAOU CHING-LĔĔ.

See 楊錫紱 YANG SEĬH-FŬH. 漕運則例纂 *Tsaou yun tsĭh le tswan.* "Laws and Regulations for the Conveyance of Grain." ... Compiled by ... Yaou Ching-lĕĕ, &c.   1767. 8º.

姚 姬 傳 YAOU KE-CHUEN.

See 魯賓 LOO PIN. 魯賓之文鈔 *Loo pin che wăn chaou.* "Literary Essays by Loo Pin." Edited by Yaou Ke-chuen, &c.   1800. 8º.

—— See 魯習 LOO SEĬH. 魯習之文鈔 *Loo Seĭh che wăn chaou.* "Literary Essays by Loo Seĭh." Edited by Yaou Ke-chuen, &c.   1800. 8º.

—— See 魯絜非 LOO KĔĔ-FEI. 魯山木先生文集 *Loo Shan-mŭh Seen săng wăn tseĭh.* "A Collection of the Writings" of Loo Kĕĕ-fei. Edited by Yaou Ke-chuen, &c. 1831. 8º.

———— 魯山木先生外集 *Loo-shan-mŭh seen săng wae tseĭh.* "An Additional Collection of the Writings" of Loo Kĕĕ-fei. Edited by Yaou Ke-chuen, &c.   1798. 8º.

姚 培 謙 YAOU PEI-KEEN.

類腋 *Luy yĭh.* "A Thesaurus of Phrases." A Pocket Edition. Compiled by Yaou Pei-keen, with the help in the Second and Third Parts of Chang King-yun. With a Supplement by Chang Han-shun. 4 parts. 55 keuen.
    1742–1765. 8º.

Another copy.   1742–1765. 8º.
    Imperfect.

Another edition. 58 keuen.   1742–65. 12º.

    Imperfect, containing only keuen 1–4 in Part 1, 3–8 in Part 2, 1–4, 8–15 in Part 3; 7, 8, 11, 12, 15, 16 in Part 4, and the 3 supplementary keuen.

—— and 張景星 CHANG KING-SING.

通鑑攬要 *Tung keen lan yaou.* "An Epitome of Choo He's Condensation of the General Mirror of History." Compiled by Yaou Pei-keen and Chang King-sing. A Reprint. In Four Parts.   1760. 12º.

—— 通鑑綱目攬要 *Tung keen kang mŭh lan yaou.* "An Epitome of Choo He's Condensation of the General Mirror of History." Compiled by Yaou Pei-keen and Chang King-sing. In Two Parts.   1818. 8º.
    Another edition of the above.

姚 松 陰 YAOU SUNG-YIN.

初學檢韻 *Tsoo heŏ keen yun.* "A Rhyming Dictionary for Beginners." Edited by Tseen Ta-hin.   1802. 8º.

姚 思 廉 YAOU SZE-LEEN.

梁書 *Leang shoo.* "The History of the Leang Dynasty." 56 keuen. [Also] 陳書 *Chin shoo.* "The History of the Chin Dynasty." 36 keuen. *See* 毛晉 MAOU TSIN. 十七史 *Shĭh tseĭh she.* "The Seventeen Histories," &c.   1656. 8º.

姚 廷 傑 YAOU TING-KĔĔ.

戒淫錄 *Keae yin lŭh.* "A Warning against Lust." *See* 張山來 CHANG SHAN-HAE, and 張進也 CHANG TSIN-YAY. 昭代叢書 *Chaou tae tsung shoo.* "A Collection of Reprints of Works by Authors under the present Dynasty," &c. Keuen 19.   1703. 8º.

姚 文 然 YAOU WĂN-JEN.

See 方鯤 FANG KWĂN. 易鹽 *Yĭh tang.* "The Permutations of the Diagrams of the Book of Changes." .... Edited by Yaou Wăn-jen, &c.   1718. 8º.

姚 文 燮 Yaou Wăn-sĕĕ.

See 方 鯤 Fang Kwăn. 易 盪 *Yĭh tang.* "The Permutations of the Diagrams of the Book of Changes." . . . Edited by Yaou Wăn-sĕĕ, &c. 1718. 8°.

—— See 方 以 智 Fang E-che. 通 雅 *Tung ya.* "A Perspicuous and Learned" Encyclopædia. Edited by Yaou Wăn-sĕĕ, &c. 1666. 8°.

姚 文 田 Yaou Wăn-teen.

說 文 聲 系 *Shwŏ wăn shing he.* "The Tones of the *Shwŏ wăn* Arranged iu Order." 14 keuen. See 伍 崇 曜 Woo Tsung-yaou. 粵 雅 堂 叢 書 *Yuĕ ya Tang tsung shoo.* "The Yuĕ ya Tang Collection of Reprints," &c. Series 11. 1853. 8°.

—— 江 蘇 試 牘 *Keang soo she tŭh.* "Keang-soo Examination Essays." Compiled by Yaou Wăn-teen. 1820. 8°.

姚 雨 瓣 Yaou Yu-heang.

See Tsing Dynasty. 大 清 律 例 新 增 統 纂 集 成 *Ta Tsing leŭh le sin tsang tung tswan tsĕh ching.* "The Fundamental Laws and Subordinate Statutes of the Tsing Dynasty." . . . Edited by Yaou Yu-heang, &c. 8°.

———— 大 清 律 例 增 修 統 纂 集 成 *Ta Tsing leŭh le tsăng sew tung tswan tsĕh ching.* "The Fundamental Laws and Subordinate Statutes of the Tsing Dynasty." . . . . Edited by Yaou Yu-heang, &c. 1837. 8°.

耶 穌 教 Yay-soo Keaou.

耶 穌 教 或 問 *Yay-soo keaou hwŏ wăn.* "A Catechism on the Christian Religion." [By J. Stronach.] *Hongkong,* 1858. 8°.

—— 耶 穌 教 畧 *Yay-soo keaou leŏ.* "An Outline of the Christian Religion." [By W. H. Medhurst.] *Hongkong,* 1855. 8°.

—— 問 答 淺 註 耶 穌 教 法 *Wăn tă tseen choo Yay-soo keaou fă.* "A Catechism Explanatory of the Doctrines of the Christian Religion." [By R. Morrison.] [*Canton,* 1812.] 8°.

There are two other copies of this work.

耶 穌 信 徒 Yay-soo sin too.

耶 穌 信 徒 受 苦 總 論 *Yay-soo sin too show koo tsung lun.* "A History of the Early Christian Martyrs." [By T. Hamberg.] 1855. 8°.

野 鶴 老 人 Yay-hŏ Laou jin.

See 李 坦 Le Tan. 增 刪 卜 易 *Tsăng shan poo Yih.* "A Work on Divination." By the Old Man of Ya-hŏ, &c. 1714. 8°.

野 客 Yay kĭh.

野 客 問 難 記 *Yay kĭh wăn nan ke.* "A Rustic's Inquiries on Difficult Subjects." [By W. H. Medhurst.] *Hongkong,* 1870. 8°.

This is a revised edition of the *Tsing ming saou moo che lun,* by the same author.

夜 Yay.

夜 探 觀 兵 *Yay tan kwan ping.* "A Midnight Inspection of Soldiers." A Dramatic Tale. [1800 ?]. 8°.

夜 譚 Yay tan.

夜 譚 隨 錄 *Yay tan suy lŭh.* "Evening Entertainments." A Collection of Tales. 12 keuen. 1791. 8°.

葉 承 Yĕ Ching.

See 李 文 耀 Le Wăn-yaou. 上 海 縣 志 *Shang hae heen che.* "A Topography of Shang-hae Heen." Compiled . . . by . . . Yĕ Ching, &c. 1750. 8°.

葉 熊 Yĕ Heung.

See 王 應 麟 Wang Ying-lin. 沈 寧 先 生 文 鈔 *Chin ning Seen săng wăn chaou.* "The Literary Papers of the Doctor of Chin-ning." . . . Edited by Yĕ Heung, &c. 1829. 8°.

葉 修 Yĕ Sew.

稿 *Kaou.* "Essays." *See* 長 城 Chang Ching. 名 家 制 義 *Ming kea che e.* "Essays" on Texts from the Four Books, &c. Tsĭh 65. 1699. 8°.

葉 氏 Yĕ she.

絳 囊 撮 要 *Keang nang tsŏ yaou.* "Choice Prescriptions from the Red Bag." A Medical Work. Edited by Yĕ she. 5 keuen. 1853. 8°.

葉 盛 YĚ SHING.

茶 竹 堂 書 目 *Lǔh chǔh Tang shoo mǔh*. "A Catalogue of Books in the Lǔh-chǔh Tang." 6 keuen. [Also] 茶 竹 堂 碑 目 *Lǔh chǔh Tang pe mǔh*. "A Catalogue of Memorial Tablets in the Lǔh-chǔh Tang." 6 keuen. *See* 伍 崇 曜 WOO TSUNG-YAOU. 粵 雅 堂 叢 書 *Yuě ya Tang tsung shoo*. "The Yuě ya Tang Collection of Reprints," &c. Series 15.
1853. 8°.

葉 堂 YĚ TANG.

邯 鄲 記 全 譜 *Han tan ke tseuen poo*. "Songs from the Play entitled *Han tan ke*," adapted to Music. Compiled by Yě Tang. Edited by Wang Wǎn-che. 2 keuen. 1792. 8°.

—— 牡 丹 亭 全 譜 *Mow tan ting tseuen poo*. "Songs from the Play entitled *Mow tan ting*," adapted to Music. Compiled by Yě Tang. Edited by Wang Wǎn-che. 2 keuen. 1792. 8°.

—— 納 書 楹 續 集 曲 譜 *Nǎ shoo ying sǔh tseǐh keǔh poo*. "A Book of Songs adapted to Music, Published by the Nǎ-shoo-ying Printing Press. A Supplementary Collection." Compiled by Yě Tang. Edited by Wang Wǎn-che. 4 keuen. 1792. 8°.

—— 納 書 楹 補 遺 曲 譜 *Nǎ shoo ying poo e keǔh poo*. "A Supplementary Collection of Songs Published by the Nǎ-shoo-ying Printing Press," adapted to Music. Compiled by Yě Tang. Edited by Wang Wǎn-che. 4 keuen. 1794. 8°.

—— 納 書 楹 外 集 曲 譜 *Nǎ shoo ying wae tseǐh keǔh poo*. "An Additional Collection of Songs Published by the Nǎ-shoo-ying Printing Press," adapted to Music. Compiled by Yě Tang. Edited by Wang Wǎn-che. 2 keuen. 1792. 8°.

—— 南 柯 記 全 譜 *Nan ko ke tseuen poo*. "Songs from the Play entitled *Nan ko ke*," adapted to Music. Compiled by Yě Tang. Edited by Wang Wǎn-che. 2 keuen. 1792. 8°.

葉 燕 YĚ YEN.

葉 次 巷 時 文 稿 *Yě tsze gan she wǎn kaou*. "Occasional Essays" on Texts from the Four Books. By Yě Yen. 1808. 8°.
Imperfect.

葉 志 詵 YĚ CHE-SIN.

海 山 仙 館 叢 書 *Hae shan seen Kwan tsung shoo*. "The Hae-shan-seen Kwan Collection of Reprints." Edited by Yě Che-sin. 120 vols.
1848. 8°.

葉 桂 嚴 YĚ CHOO-YEN.

See 潘 肇 豐 PWAN SHAOU-FUNG. 六 書 會 原 *Lǔh shoo hwuy yuen*. "The Origin of the Six Kinds of Characters." Edited by Yě Choo-yen, &c. 1801. 8°.

葉 方 藹 YĚ FANG-GAE.

See 庫 勒 納 KOO LĬH-NǍ. 日 講 書 經 解 義 *Jǔh keang Shoo king keae e*. "Daily Lectures on the Meaning of the *Shoo king*." Compiled by ... Yě Fang-gae, &c. 1680. 8°.

葉 方 恒 YĚ FANG-HǍNG.

山 東 全 河 備 考 *Shan tung tseuen ho pe kaou*. "The River-system of the Province of Shan-tung Examined." 4 keuen. 1680. 8°.

葉 向 高 YĚ HEANG-KAOU.

See 詩 經 SHE KING. 魁 本 詩 經 *Kwei pun She king*. "The Great Original Book of Odes." Edited with Notes by Yě Heang-kaou, &c. 8°.

葉 九 升 YĚ KEW-SHING.

地 理 平 陽 全 書 *Te le ping yang tseuen shoo*. "A Complete Work on Geomancy." 15 keuen.
1721. 8°.
The last ten keuen are wanting.

—— 地 理 山 法 全 書 *Te le shan fǎ tseuen shoo*. "The Laws of Mountains." A Work on Geomancy. By Yě Kew-shing. The 1st keuen is Edited with Notes by Hwang Keae, 2nd by Kǒ Ting-yen, 3rd by Chin He, 4th by Chang Chung-tan, 5th by Chang Tsǎng-che, 6th by Le Mow, 7th by Chǒ Chang-ling, 8th by Shaou Kew-kaou, 9th by Chǒ Fan, 10th by Lǔh Ming-kaou, 11th by Hoo Seuen, 12th by Chow Yun-chin, 13th by Yě Chow, 14th by Woo Shang, sew, 15th by Yě Sew, 16th by Chang Tsǎng-che, 17th by Chin Tsze-fung, 18th by Woo Shaou-sew, 19th by Lin Che-man. 19 keuen.
[1790 ?]. 8°.
33

葉 隆 禮 YĔ LUNG-LE.

契 丹 國 志 *Kĕĕ tan kŭŏ che.* "The History of the Kĕĕ-tan or Leaou Dynasty." 27 keuen. *See* 毛 晉 MAOU TSIN. 十 七 史 *Shĭh tsĕĭh she.* "The Seventeen Histories," &c.

1656. 8°.

—— 遼 志 *Leaou che.* "The History of the Leaou Dynasty." *See* 說 SHWŎ. 說 選 *Shwŏ seuen.* "A Collection of Records," &c. 8°.

葉 納 清 YĔ-NĂ TSING [*i.e.* Ferdinand Genaehr].

眞 道 衡 平 *Chin taou hăng ping.* "True Doctrines Compared and Adjusted." By Yĕ-nă Tsing. [*Hongkong*]. 1863. 8°.

葉 培 恕 YĔ PEI-SHOO.

See 周 禮 CHOW-LE. 周 禮 註 疏 *Chow le choo soo.* "The Chow Ritual." . . . Edited by Yĕ Pei-shoo, &c. 1639. 8°.

葉 樹 藩 YĔ SHOO-FAN.

See 蕭 統 SEAOU TUNG. 文 選 *Wăn seuen.* "Elegant Extracts from Polite Literature." Edited by Yĕ Shoo-fan, &c. 1772. 8°.

葉 大 慶 YĔ TA-KING.

考 古 質 疑 *Kaou koo chĭh e.* "An Examination of the Old Explanations of Literary Doubts." 6 keuen. *See* 葉 志 詵 YĔ CHE-SIN. 海 山 仙 館 叢 書 *Hae shan seen Kwan tsung shoo.* "The Hae-shan-seen Kwan Collection of Reprints," &c. Vol. 39. 1848. 8°.

葉 天 士 YĔ TEEN-SZE.

See 吳 金 壽 WOO KIN-SHOW. 三 家 醫 案 合 刻 *San kea E gan hŏ kĭh.* "The Medical Practice of the Three Physicians," Yĕ Teen-sze, &c. 1831. 8°.

葉 子 奇 YĔ TSZE-KE.

草 木 子 *Tsaou mŭh tsze.* "Herbs, Trees, and Scholars." *See* 閔 景 賢 MIN KING-HEEN. 快 書 *Kwae shoo.* "A Book of Amusement," &c. Keuen 35. 1626. 8°.

葉 文 康 YĔ WĂN-KANG.

禮 經 會 元 *Le king hwuy yuen.* "On the Ritual Classics." By Yĕ Wăn-kang. Edited by Lŭh Kea-shoo. 4 keuen. 1189. 8°.

葉 奕 苞 YĔ YĬH-PAOU.

賓 告 *Pin kaou.* "An Examination of Guests." [*Also*] 醉 鄉 約 法 *Tsuy heang yŏ fă.* "Rules of Agreement in Drunken Company." *See* 張 山 來 CHANG SHAN-LAE, and 張 進 也 CHANG TSIN-YAY. 昭 代 叢 書 *Chaou tae tsung shoo.* "A Collection of Reprints of Works by Authors under the present Dynasty," &c. Keuen 33, 36. 1703. 8°.

顏 正 YEN CHING.

See 趙 松 一 CHAOU SUNG-YĬH. 丹 桂 籍 *Tan kwei tsĕĭh.* "The Tan-kwei Collection" of Taouist Works. With Notes by Yen Ching, &c. 1818. 8°.

—— *See* 文 昌 帝 君 WĂN-CHANG TE KEUN. 寶 訓 *Paou heun.* "The Precious Teachings" of Wăn-chang te keun. . . With . . . Comments by Yen Ching, &c. 1820. 8°.

顏 璹 YEN SHOW.

See 鄭 一 崧 CHING YĬH-SUNG. 永 春 州 志 *Yung chun chow che.* "A Topography of Yung-chun Chow." Compiled by . . Yen Show, &c. 1787. 8°.

顏 之 推 YEN CHE-TUY.

還 冤 記 *Hwan yuen ke.* "Instances of Retributive Justice." By Yen Che-tuy, of the Pĭh Tse Dynasty. A Reprint. 8°.

—— 顏 氏 家 訓 *Yen she kea heun.* "Domestic Instructions." 2 keuen. [1800 ?]. 8°.

顏 希 源 YEN HE-YUEN.

儀 徵 縣 續 志 *E-ching heen sŭh che.* "A Supplementary Topography of E-ching Heen." Compiled by Yen He-yuen, Shaou Kwang-keen, and others. 10 keuen. 1723. 8°.

—— 百 美 新 詠 圖 傳 *Pĭh mei sin yung too chuen.* "A New Collection of Sonnets to the Hundred Beauties. With Illustrated Biographies." Compiled by Yen He-yuen. Edited by Yuen Mei. To which is Appended the *Woo Shwang poo,* by Kin Koo-leang. *Canton*, 1790. 8°.

Another edition. *Canton*, 1790. 8°.

Another copy.

顏光敏 YEN KWANG-MIN.

稿 *Kaou.* "Essays." *See* 長城 CHANG CHING. 名家制義 *Ming kea che e.* "Essays" on Texts from the Four Books, &c. Tsĭh 116.
1699. 8°.

顏茂猷 YEN MOW-YEW.

See 四書 SZE-SHOO. 監本四書 *Keen pun sze shoo.* "A Revised Edition of the Four Books." Edited by Yen Mow-yew, &c.
1740. 8°.

―――― 四書正文 *Sze shoo ching wăn.* "The Le-joo Tang edition of the Four Books." Edited by Yen Mow-yew, &c.　1816. 8°.

顏伯燾 YEN PĬH-CHOW.

See 王子音 WANG TSZE-YIN. 今古地理述 *Kin koo te le shŭh.* "Modern and Ancient Geography." ... With Notes by ... Yen Pĭh-chow, &c.　1807. 8°.

顏師古 YEN SZE-KOO.

前漢書 *Tseen Han Shoo.* "The History of the former Han Dynasty." .. With a Commentary by Yen Sze-koo, &c. *See* 毛晉 MAOU TSIN. 十七史 *Shĭh tseĭh she.* "The Seventeen Histories," &c.　1656. 8°.

―――― *See* 班固 PAN KOO. 前漢書 *Tseen Han shoo.* "A History of the Former Han Dynasty." .. With a Commentary by Yen Sze-koo, &c.　1642. 8°.

嚴杰 YEN LĔĔ.

皇清經解 *Hwang Tsing king keae.* "The Classics Explained by Authors of the Tsing Dynasty." Compiled by Yen Lĕĕ, under the Direction and partly at the Expense of Yuen Yuen. 1400 keuen.　1829. 8°.

嚴榮 YEN YUNG.

武義縣志 *Woo e heen che.* "A Topography of Woo-e Heen." Compiled by Yen Yung, Chang Ying-how, Choo Kwei, and others. 12 keuen.　1804. 8°.

嚴徵道 YEN CHING-TAOU.

See 瞿汝稷 KEU JOO-TSEĬH. 指月錄 *Che yuĕ lŭh.* [A Thesaurus of Buddhist Biography.] .. Revised by Yen Ching-taou, &c. 8°.

嚴秉衡 YEN PING-HĂNG.

See 蔡邕 TSAE YUNG. 獨斷 *Tŭh twan.* "The Book of Decisions." ... Edited by Yen Ping-hăng, &c.　8°.

嚴思萇 YEN SZE-GAN.

文獻通考詳節 *Wăn heen tung kaou tseang tsĕĕ.* "Explanatory Chapters on Ma Twan-lin's *Wăn heen tung kaou.*" 24 keuen.　1764. 8°.

Another copy.

The title-page and the last two keuen are wanting.

嚴作哲 YEN TSŎ-CHĔ.

汲冢周書 *Keĭh mung Chow Shoo.* "A History of the Chow Dynasty for Beginners." Edited by Yen Tsŏ-chĕ. With Notes by Kung Chaou, of the Tsin Dynasty. A Reprint. 10 keuen.
[1800?]. 8°.

嚴允肇 YEN YUN-SHAOU.

姚布政傳 *Yaou Poo ching chuen.* "A Biography of the Provincial Treasurer Yaou" Seang-heuen. By Yen Yun-shaou. To which is added a Short Biographical Notice of the same Officer by Tseang E. With a Supplementary Notice by Woo She-lĕĕ.　1820. 8°.

閻選 YEN SEUEN.

再生記 *Tsae săng ke.* "Accounts of Restorations to Life." By Yen Seuen, of the Tang Dynasty. A Reprint.　[1741?]. 8°.

閻王 YEN WANG.

半日閻王全傳 *Pwan jĭh Yen wang tseuen chuen.* "The Story of Prince Yen."
[1850?]. 8°.

閻若璩 YEN JŎ-KEU.

See 王應麟 WANG YING-LIN. 困學紀聞 *Kwăn heŏ ke wăn.* "Criticisms on Literature and Science." With Notes by Yen Jŏ-keu, etc.
1742. 8°.

―――― 四書釋地 *Sze shoo shĭh te.* "The Topography of the Four Books." 4 keuen. [Also] 孟子生卒年月考 *Măng tsze săng tsŭh neen yuĕ kaou.* "An Examination of the Dates of the Birth and Death of Mencius." [Also] 潛邱劄記 *Tseen kew chă ke.* "Tseen-kew's Notes." 2 keuen. *See* 嚴杰 YEN LĔĔ. 皇清經解 *Hwang Tsing king keae.* "The Classics Explained," &c. Keuen 20-26.　1829. 8°.

閻 若 璩 YEN JŎ-KEU. *(Continued.)*
    四 書 釋 地 *Sze Shoo shĭh te.* "The Topography of the Four Books." To which are added Three Supplements, and a Short Treatise on the Dates of the Birth and Death of Mencius. 1698. 8º.

—— 四 書 釋 地 補 註 *Sze shoo shĭh te poo choo.* "The Topography of the Four Books," together with the Three Supplements. "With Additional Notes" by Fan Ting-mei. An Enlarged Edition. 1816. 8º.

閻 其 淵 YEN KE-YUEN.
    四 書 典 制 類 聯 音 註 *Sze shoo teen che luy leen yin choo.* "Essays on the Canonical Passages of the Four Books, arranged according to Subjects, with Notes." Compiled by Yen Ke-yuen. Edited by Fang Chun-che. 33 keuen. 1799. 8º.
        Imperfect, keuen 25, 30–33 wanting.

Another edition. 33 keuen. 1800. 8º.
        Imperfect, containing only keuen 31–33.

烟 水 散 人 YEN-SHWUY SAN JIN.
    See 女 NEU. 女 才 子 傳 *Neu tsae tsze chuen.* "Tales of Talented Women." By The Dissipated Man of Yen-shwuy, &c. 8º.

幽 閨 YEW KWEI.
    幽 閨 記 *Yew kwei ke.* "A Story of the Harem." *See* 曲 KEŬH. 六 十 種 曲 *Lŭh shĭh chung keŭh.* "Sixty Plays," &c. Taou 2. 8º.

幼 YEW.
    幼 學 雜 子 *Yew heŏ tsă tsze.* "An Illustrated Dictionary for Children." [1800 ?]. 8º.

尤 袤 YEW MOW.
    遂 初 堂 書 目 *Suy choo Tang shoo mŭh.* "A Catalogue of the Books of the Suy-choo Tang." *See* 葉 志 詵 YĔ CHE-SIN. 海 山 仙 館 叢 書 *Hae shan seen Kwan tsung shoo.* "The Hae-shan-seen Kwan Collection of Reprints," &c. Vol. 1. 1848. 8º.

尤 侗 YEW TUNG.
    See 王 廣 心 WANG KWANG-SIN. 王 尤 合 刻 注 釋 *Wang Yew ho kĭh choo shĭh.* "The Essays of Wang Kwang-sin and Yew Tung," &c. 1810. 8º.

尤 侗 YEW TUNG. *(Continued.)*
    西 堂 全 集 *Se Tang tseuen tseĭh.* "A Complete Collection of Literary Pieces from the Western Hall." Compiled by Yew Tung. 1665–1685. 8º.
        Imperfect.

猷 可 庭 YEW KO-TING.
    See 詩 經 SHE KING. 御 案 詩 經 備 旨 *Yu gan She king pe che.* "The Book of Odes." .. Edited by Yew Ko-ting, &c. 8º.

猶 龍 子 YEW LUNG-TSZE.
    古 今 列 女 傳 演 義 *Koo kin lĕĕ neu chuen yen e.* "Lives of Eminent Women of Ancient and Modern Times." 6 keuen. [1800 ?]. 8º.

優 婆 塞 支 謙 YEW-PO-SĬH-CHE-KEEN.
    See 李 嘉 果 LE KEA-KWO. 八 師 經 *Pă sze king.* "The Sutra of the Eight Teachers." .. Translated into Chinese by Yew-po-sĭh-che-keen, &c. 1797. 8º.

一 鼇 靈 峻 YĬH-TSEW-LING-TSEUN.
    經 懺 直 音 *King tsan chĭh yin.* "The Correct Sounds of Characters used in the Buddhist Sûtras and Liturgical Works." Compiled by the Priest Yĭh-tsew-ling-tseun. Edited by the Priest Chuen-tan-yuĕ-too. *Canton,* 1745. 8º.

一 元 宗 本 YĬH YUEN TSUNG PUN.
    歸 元 直 指 *Kwei yuen chĭh che.* "Directions for Returning to the First Cause." *Canton,* 1762. 8º

益 泰 YĬH TAE.
    [A Book of Patterns]. [1800 ?]. 8º.

易 經 YĬH KING.
    周 易 疏 *Chow Yĭh soo.* "The Chow Changes Explained." By Kung Ying-tă. With a Commentary by Wang Peĭh. 9 keuen. *See* 毛 鳳 苞 MAOU FUNG-PAOU. 十 三 經 注 疏 *Shĭh san king choo soo.* "The Thirteen Classics," &c. 1813. 8º.

—— 孫 氏 周 易 集 解 *Sun she Chow Yĭh tseĭh keae.* "The Chow Changes, with a Collection of Comments." Compiled by Sun Sing-yen. 10 keuen. *See* 伍 崇 曜 WOO TSUNG-YAOU. 粵 雅 堂 叢 書 *Yuĕ ya tang tsung shoo.* "The Yue-ya Tang Collection of Reprints," &c. Series 16. 1853. 8º.

YĬH   [261]   YĬH

易 經 YĬH KING. (*Continued.*)

易 經 *Yĭh king.* "The Book of Changes." *See* 嚴 杰 YEN LĔĔ. 皇 清 經 解 *Hwang Tsing king keae.* "The Classics Explained," &c. Keuen 5–7.   1829. 8°.

—— 周 易 讀 本 *Chow Yĭh tŭh pun.* "The Chow Changes." 4 keuen.   1806. 8°.

—— 監 本 周 易 *Keen pun Chow Yĭh.* "The Original Text of the Chow Changes." Edited by Choo Seĭh-ying and others. 4 keuen.   1670. 8°.

—— 周 易 正 解 *Chow Yĭh ching keae.* "The Chow Changes Correctly Explained" by Hŏ King. 20 keuen.   [1800?]. 8°.

—— 周 易 楬 要 *Chow Yĭh kĕĕ yaou.* "The Book of Changes, with an Abridgement" of the Commentaries of Choo He and others. Edited by Heu Paou-shen. 3 keuen.   1789. 12°.

Another copy.

     Imperfect, the first keuen wanting.

—— 周 易 口 義 *Chow Yĭh kow e.* "The Chow Changes. With an Oral Explanation of the Meaning," by Hoo Gan-ting. Edited by Tang Pin and Le Chin-yu. 12 keuen.   1687. 8°.

—— 周 易 廣 義 *Chow Yĭh kwang e.* "The Book of Changes, with a full Explanation." With the Commentary of Choo He. Compiled by Pwan Yew-chĭh, Pwan Wăn-lae, and others. Edited by Lew Shĭh-che. 6 keuen. 1672. 8°.

—— 周 易 述 義 *Chow Yĭh shŭh e.* "The Meaning of the Chow Changes." An Imperial Work. ? keuen.   [1700?]. 8°.

     Odd vol. containing only keuen 5–7.

—— 周 易 義 傳 合 訂 *Chow Yĭh e chuen hŏ ting.* "The Book of Changes. With the Explanations of Choo He and the Commentary of Ching Haou." With the Sounds of Doubtful Characters supplied by Chang Taou-seu. 14 keuen ?.   [1800?]. 8°.

     Imperfect, containing only keuen 3, 4, 7, 8, 11, 12.

易 經 YĬH KING. (*Continued.*)

周 易 圖 說 述 *Chow Yĭh too shwŏ shŭh.* "Dissertations and Commentaries on the Diagrams of the Book of Changes." Compiled by Wang Hung-chuen. Edited by Ma Joo-lung. 4 keuen.   1687. 4°.

—— 周 易 輯 說 存 正 *Chow Yĭh tseĭh shwŏ tsun ching.* "The Chow Changes. With a Compilation of Notes in which is Preserved the Correct Meaning." Compiled by Yang Fang-tä. 12 keuen.   1750. 8°.

—— 御 纂 周 易 折 中 *Yu tswan Chow Yĭh chĕ chung.* "Decisions on the Book of Changes." With the Notes and Comments of Choo He, Ching Haou, Kung Gan-kwŏ, and others. Compiled by an Imperial Commission consisting of Le Kwang-te, Wei Ting-chin, Ho Kwŏ-tsung, and others. 22 keuen.   1715. 8°.

—— 易 經 *Yĭh king.* "The Book of Changes." With the original Meaning as Explained by Choo He. 4 keuen.   12°.

     Imperfect, containing only keuen 1.

—— 監 本 易 經 *Keen pun Yĭh king.* "The Original Text of the Book of Changes." With the Commentary of Choo He. The *Keae tsze yuen* edition. 4 keuen.   1790. 8°.

—— 易 經 正 文 *Yĭh king ching wăn.* "The Correct Text of the Book of Changes." [1800?]. 8°.

—— 易 經 讀 本 *Yĭh king tŭh pun.* "The Book of Changes." 3 keuen.   *Canton*, 1775. 8°.

—— 易 經 備 旨 眞 本 *Yĭh king pẹ che chin pun.* "A Correct Copy of the Book of Changes, with a Digest of its Meaning." Compiled by Hwang Kew-shĭh and Leang Kwei-chang. Edited by Kew Tsang-choo. An Enlarged and Revised Edition. 6 keuen.   1707. 8°.

—— 古 易 彙 編 *Koo Yĭh wei peen.* "The Ancient Text of the Book of Changes." With a Collection of Comments Compiled by Le Pun-koo, Edited by Tang Tae-she. To which is added an Addenda of Five Books on the Art of Divination. 17 keuen.   1612. 8°.

易 經 YĬH KING. (Continued.)

日 講 易 經 解 義 Jĭh keang Yĭh king keae e. "The Book of Changes, with a Paraphrase for Daily Reading." Compiled by Order of the Emperor Kang-he, by a Commission Consisting of New New, Sun Tsae-fung, Chang Ying, and others. 18 keuen. 1688. 8°.

Another copy.
The last ten keuen wanting.

—— 易 經 講 意 去 疑 Yĭh king keang e keu e. "The Book of Changes Explained, and the Doubtful Passages cleared up." By Shoo Hung-gŏ. Edited by Tseang Chin-tsing. 11 keuen. 1631. 8°.

—— 易 義 析 解 Yĭh e seĭh keae. "The Meaning of the Book of Changes accurately Explained." By Sëĕ Ching-he. 1712. 8°.

—— 易 經 大 全 會 解 Yĭh king ta tseuen hwuy keae. "The Book of Changes, with Explanatory Comments," by Choo He, Choo Fung-lin, and others. Compiled by Lae Muh-chin. The Tsung-taou Tang edition. 4 keuen. 1681. 8°.
There are two other copies of this work.

—— 易 經 來 註 Yĭh king Lae choo. "The Book of Changes, with a Commentary by Lae Keu-tang." Edited by Tsuy Leen-säng. 16 keuen. 1688. 8°.
Another edition of the above.

—— 易 經 來 註 圖 解 Yĭh king Lae choo too keae. "The Book of Changes, with a Commentary by Lae Keu-tang, and with Illustrations." Edited by Kaou Seuĕ-keun and Ling How-tsze. 15 keuen and appendix. 1598. 8°.

—— 詳 訂 易 經 集 註 Tseang ting Yĭh king tseĭh choo. "The Book of Changes, with a Collection of Comments" of Choo He and others. The Wei-tĭh Tang edition. 4 keuen.
[1800 ?]. 8°.

易 經 YĬH KING. (Continued.)

辨 志 堂 新 輯 易 經 集 解 Peen che Tang sin tseĭh Yĭh king tseĭh keae. "The Peen-che Tang Edition of the Book of Changes." With a Commentary by Choo He, and a Collection of Notes. Compiled by Wan Show-yĭh. 4 keuen. 1686. 8°.

—— 易 傳 Yĭh chuen. "The Book of Changes. With a Commentary" by Le Ting-tsoo. A Reprint. 17 keuen. 1756. 8°.

—— 傳 家 易 說 Chuen kea Yĭh shwŏ. "The Book of Changes, with a Commentary. For Domestic Use." Compiled by Kŏ Yung. Edited by Ke Yun and others. 11 keuen. 1775. 8°.

—— 復 齋 易 說 Fuh chae Yĭh shwŏ. "A Commentary on the Book of Changes." By Chaou Tsze-kin. 6 keuen. 1676. 8°.

—— 易 經 兒 說 Yĭh king urh shwŏ. "The Book of Changes, with a Family Commentary." Compiled by Soo Seun. Edited by Soo Yaou-sung and others. 4 keuen. 1687. 8°.

易 開 縉 YĬH KAE-TSIN.
See 物 WŬH. 詠 物 詩 選 註 釋 Yung wŭh she seuen choo shĭh. "A Collection of Songs." . . With Explanatory Notes by Yĭh Kae-tsin, &c. 8°.

尹 泰 YIN TAE.
See TSING DYNASTY. 大 清 會 典 Ta Tsing hwuy teen. "A Comprehensive Description of the Government under the Tsing Dynasty." Compiled by . . . . Yin Tae, &c. 1732. 8°.

尹 文 YIN WĂN.
大 道 Ta taou. "The Great Taou." See 沈 津 CHIN TSIN. 百 家 類 纂 Pĭh kea luy tswan. "The Works of a Hundred Authors," &c. Keuen 24. 8°.

尹 眞 人 YIN CHIN-JIN.
性 命 圭 旨 Sing ming kwei che. [A Taouist Work on the Government of the Inner Man]. By Yin Chin-jin. 1669. 4°.

Another edition. 1669. 8°.

Another copy.

YIN [263] YU

尹方橋 YIN FANG-KEAOU.

德潤書院課藝 *Tĭh jun shoo yuen ko e.*
"Literary Exercises from the Tĭh-jun College."
Compiled by Yin Fang-keaou. Edited by Seu
Go-fung, Hwang Choo-ping and Hwang Yu-tseuen. 1821. 8°.

尹繼善 YIN KE-SHEN.

See 周鼎臣 CHOW TING-CHIN. 增訂敬
信錄 *Tsăng ting king sin lŭh.* "Works on
Reverence and Faith." . . Edited by Yin Ke-shen, &c. 1769. 8°.

—— 直隸通州志 *Chĭh le Tung chow che.* "A
Topography of Tung Chow" in the Province of
Keangsoo. Compiled by Yin Ke-shen, Chwang
Yew-kung, Le Yin-pei, and others. 22 keuen.
1755. 8°.

—— 江南通志 *Keang nan tung che.* "A Topography of the Province of Keang nan." Compiled by Yin Ke-shen, Wei Ting-chin, Kaou
Ke-chŏ, and others. 200 keuen. 1737. 8°.

Another copy.

Imperfect, containing only keuen 1–73, 107–110, 130–137,
142–151.

印憲曾 YIN HEEN-TSĂNG.

See 錢大昕 TSEEN TA-HIN. 鄞縣志 *Yin
heen che.* "A Topography of Yin Heen." . .
Edited by Yin Heen-tsăng, &c. 1788. 8°.

印光任 YIN KWANG-JIN, and 張汝霖 CHANG
JOO-LIN.

澳門記 *Gaou-mun ke.* "A History of Macao."
By Yin Kwang-jin and Chang Joo-lin. With
Illustrations. 2 keuen. 1800. 8°.

英吉利國 YING KEĬH LE KWŎ.

英吉利國人品國事畧說 *Ying keĭh le
kwŏ jin pin kwŏ sze leŏ shwŏ.* "A Short Account
of the English." [1840?]. 8°.

鸚鵡 YING KO.

鸚鵡行孝 *Ying ko hing heaou.* "The Dutiful
Conduct of a Parrot." Illustrated.
[*Canton*, 1800?]. A sheet.

蠱卲 YING SHAOU.

風俗通 *Fung sŭh tung.* "Popular Traditions."
See 沈津 CHIN TSIN. 百家類纂 *Pĭh kea
luy tswan.* "The Works of a Hundred
Authors," &c. Keuen 36. 8°.

—— 風俗通 *Fung sŭh tung.* "Popular Traditions."
By Ying Shaou, of the Han Dynasty. Edited
by Wang Sze-han. 4 keuen. [1750?]. 8°.

Another edition. 10 keuen. 1790. 8°.

岳正 YŏCHING.

稿 *Kaou.* "Essays." See 長城 CHANG CHING.
名家制義 *Ming kea che e.* "Essays" on
Texts from the Four Books, &c. Tsĭh 12.
1699. 8°.

岳珂 YŏKO.

九經三傳沿革例 *Kew king san chuen yuen
kĭh le.* "The Nine Classics and the Three
'Narratives' critically Compared." See 伍崇
曜 WOO TSUNG-YAOU. 粵雅堂叢書 *Yuĕ
ya Tang tsung shoo.* "The Yuĕ-ya Tang Collection of Reprints," &c. Series 17. 1853. . 8°.

約瑟 Yŏ-SĬH.

約瑟紀畧 *Yŏ-sĭh ke leŏ.* "The History of
Joseph." [By James Legge].
Hongkong, 1870. 8°.

樂府 YŏFOO.

樂府紅珊 *Yŏ Foo hung san.* "Operatic
Gems." By the "Literary Man of Tsin hwae."
A Reprint. 1800. 12°.

庾子山 YU TSZE-SHAN.

庾開府全集箋注 *Yu kae foo tseuen tseĭh
tseen choo.* "The Poetical and other Works
of Yu Tsze-shan. With Notes" by E Loo-yŭh.
16 keuen. [1790?]. 8°.

于謙 YU KEEN.

稿 *Kaou.* "Essays." See 長城 CHANG CHING.
名家制義 *Ming kea che e.* "Essays" on Texts
from the Four Books, &c. Tsĭh 8. 1699. 8°.

于鄴 YU NĔĔ.

揚州夢記 *Yang-chow mung ke.* "A Dream
of Yang-chow." By Yu Nĕĕ, of the Tang
Dynasty. A Reprint. [1741?]. 8°.

于 遾 Yu Teïh.
聞 奇 錄 *Wăn ke lŭh.* "Strange Reports." *See* 王 文 誥 Wang Wăn-kaou. 唐 代 叢 書 *Tang tae tsung shoo.* "A Collection of Reprints of Works written during the Tang Dynasty," &c. Series 6. 1806. 8°.

于 仔 Yu Tsze.
玉 堂 才 調 集 *Yŭh tang tsae teaou tseïh.* "The Odes of the Jade Hall." Compiled by Yu Tsze, Yu Sing-tsan, and others.
[1750?]. 8°.

于 義 方 Yu E-fang.
黑 心 符 *Hĭh sin fŭh.* "A Charm against a Black [bad] Heart." By Yu E-fang, of the Tang Dynasty. A Reprint. [1741?]. 8°.

于 星 燦 Yu Sing-tsan.
See 于 仔 Yu Tsze. 玉 堂 才 調 集 *Yŭh tang tsae teaou tseïh.* "The Odes of the Jade Hall." ... Compiled by ... Yu Sing-tsan, &c. 8°.

宇 文 Yu Wăn.
大 金 國 志 *Ta kin kwŏ che.* "The History of the Kin Dynasty." 40 keuen. *See* 毛 晉 Maou Tsin. 十 七 史 *Shĭh tseïh she.* "The Seventeen Histories," &c. 1656. 8°.

—— 金 志 *Kin che.* "The History of the Kin Dynasty." *See* 說 Shwŏ. 說 選 *Shwŏ seuen* "A Collection of Records," &c. 8°.

余 照 Yu Chaou.
詩 韻 珠 璣 *She yun choo ke.* "A Treasury of Rhymes." 5 keuen. 1800. 8°.

余 苗 Yu Saou.
See 張 賣 勝 Chang Kwei-shing. 遣 愁 集 *Keen tsew tseïh.* "Anti-Melancholia." ... Edited by Yu Saou, &c. 8°.

余 象 Yu Seang.
詩 學 圓 機 活 法 大 成 *She heŏ yuen ke hwŏ fă ta ching.* "The Complete Laws of Versification for Students of Poetry." 18 keuen.
1828. 8°.

Another edition. 18 keuen. 1856. 8°.

余 常 吉 Yu Chang-keïh.
郎 川 答 問 *Lang chuen tă wăn.* "Conversations with Lang-chuen." *See* 閔 景 賢 Min King-heen. 快 書 *Kwae shoo.* "A Book of Amusement," &c. Keuen 18. 1626. 8°.

余 步 雲 Yu Poo-yun.
訓 兵 要 言 *Heun ping yaou yen.* "Important Instructions for Soldiers" as to their General Conduct. [1800?]. 8°.

Another copy.

—— 行 軍 要 語 *Hing keun yaou yu.* "Important Discourses on Military Tactics." 2 keuen.
1834. 8°.

余 象 斗 Yu Seang-tow.
華 光 天 王 南 遊 志 傳 *Hwa kwang Teen Wang nan yew che chuen.* "An Account of a Journey to the South made by the Deity Hwa kwang." Edited by Le She. 4 keuen.
[1750?]. 8°.

—— 北 遊 記 玄 帝 出 身 傳 *Pĭh yew ke Heuen Te chŭh shin chuen.* "A Record of the Wanderings of Heuen Te in the North." 4 keuen. [1750?]. 8°.

余 文 儀 Yu Wăn-e.
See 覺 羅 四 明 *Keŏ-lo-sze-ming.* 續 脩 臺 灣 府 志 *Suh sew Tae wan foo che.* "A Revised Topography of Tae-wan Foo." ... Compiled by ... Yu Wăn-e, &c. 8°.

余 仰 止 Yu Yang-che.
See 羅 貫 中 Lo Kwan-chung. 三 國 志 *San kwŏ che.* "The History of the Three Kingdoms." .. Edited by Yu Yang-che, &c.
1592. 8°.

餘 姚 史 Yu Yaou-she.
See 全 祖 望 Tseuen Tsoo-wang. 經 史 問 答 *King she wăn tă.* "A Catechism on the Classics and on History." Edited by Yu Yaou-she, &c. 8°.

俞 長 仁 Yu Chang-jin.
歷 朝 咏 物 詩 選 *Leĭh chaou yung wŭh she seuen.* "Select Pieces of Descriptive Poetry by Authors of Successive Dynasties." Arranged according to the Subjects. Compiled by Yu Chang-jin. 8 keuen. 1724. 8°.

俞之琰 Yu Che-yen.

稿 *Kaou.* "Essays." See 長城 Chang Ching. 名家制義 *Ming kea che e.* "Essays" on Texts from the Four Books," &c. Tseĭh 110.
1699. 8º.

俞瞻白 Yu Chen-pĭh.

五嶽卻遊 *Woo yŏ go yew.* "Restful Wanderings on the Five Yŏ." See 閔景賢 Min King-heen. 快書 *Kwae shoo.* "A Book of Amusement," &c. Keuen 47. 1626. 8º.

俞正燮 Yu Ching-sĕë.

俄羅斯事輯 *Go-lo-sze sze tseĭh.* "A Treatise on Russian Affairs," and Two other Short Essays. See 何秋濤 Ho Tsew-taou. 北徼彙編 *Pĭh keaou wei peen.* "Treatises on the Countries beyond the Northern Frontier," &c. Keuen 1. 1865. 8º.

俞鳳芝 Yu Fung-che.

See 密如椿 Meĭh Joo-chun. 燕山制義 *Yen shan che e.* "Essays." . . Edited with Notes by Yu Fung-che, &c. 1813. 8º.

俞僧蜜 Yu Tsăng-meĭh.

客齋使令 *Kĭh chae she ling.* "Orders sent from the Guest's Study." See 閔景賢 Min King-heen. 快書 *Kwae shoo.* "A Book of Amusement," &c. Keuen 40. 1626. 8º.

喻梅 Yu Mei.

See 鳩摩羅什 Kew-mo-lo-shĭh. 金剛經直解 *Kin kang king chĭh keae.* "The Diamond Classic Clearly Explained." . . . Edited by Yu Mei, &c. 1813. 8º.

喻本亨 Yu Pun-hăng.

See 喻本元 Yu Pun-yuen and Yu Pun-hăng. 療馬集 *Leaou ma tseĭh.* "A Work on the Veterinary Art," &c. 8º.

喻本元 Yu Pun-yuen, and 喻本亨 Yu Pun-hăng.

療馬集 *Leaou ma tseĭh.* "A Work on the Veterinary Art." 4 keuen. [1800?]. 8º.

—— 馬經 *Ma king.* "A Work on the Veterinary Art." 1660? 8º.

This work is divided into two parts. Entitled *Leaou ma tseĭh* and *Leaou new tseĭh*, the former treating of Horses, with an Appendix on Camels, and the latter treating of Cattle.

喻元本 Yu Pun-yuen, and 喻本亨 Yu Pun-hnăg. (*Continued.*)

牛經大全 *New king ta tseuen.* "A Work on the Medical Treatment of Cattle." With Illustrations. 2 keuen. 8º.

喻祥麟 Yu Tseang-lin.

See 王仁圖 Wang Jin-poo. 十三經策案 *Shih san king tsĭh gan.* "Critical Disquisitions on the Thirteen Classics." . . Edited by Yu Tseang-lin, &c. 1808. 8º.

裕 Yu. *Governor of Keang-soo.*

[A Proclamation forbidding the Natives to hold any Communication with the "Barbarian Rebels."] 1841. A sheet.

魚 Yu.

魚服記 *Yu fŭh ke.* "The Story of a Transformation into the Likeness of a Fish." See 說 Shwŏ. 說淵 *Shwŏ yuen.* "A Collection of Tales," &c. 8º.

漁洋山人 Yu-yang Shan Jin.

See 錄 Lŭh. 精華錄 *Tsing hwa lŭh.* "Elegant Poetical Pieces." By the Man of Mount Yu Yang, &c. 1704. 8º.

虞翻 Yu Fan.

周易注 *Chow Yĭh choo.* "Notes on the Chow Changes." See 孫堂 Sun Tang. 漢魏二十一家易注 *Han Wei urh shĭh yĭh kea Yĭh choo.* "Commentaries on the Book of Changes," &c. 1799. 8º.

虞荔 Yu Le.

鼎錄 *Ting lŭh.* "An Historical Record of the Manufacture of Metal Vases." By Yu Le, of the Leang Dynasty. A Reprint. [1700?]. 8º.

虞學圃 Yu Heŏ-poo, and 温岐石 Wăn Ke-shĭh.

江湖尺牘分韻撮要合集 *Keang hoo chĭh tŭh fun yun tsŏ yaou ho tseĭh.* "A Letter-Writer for Travellers, and a Phonetic Dictionary." 4 keuen. *Canton,* 1772. 8º.

Another edition. 4 keuen. *Fŭh-shan,* 1833. 8º.

Another edition. 4 keuen. 1803. 8º.

34

虞 德 升 Yu Tĭh-shing.

諧 聲 品 字 箋 *Heae shing pin tsze tseen.* "A Phonetic Dictionary." Compiled by Yu Tĭh-shing.   1687. 8°.

虞 淵 沈 Yu Yuen-chin.

綏 寇 紀 畧 補 遺 *Suy kow ke leŏ poo e.* "Supplementary Records of the Suppression of Banditti." 2 keuen.   1804. 8°.

粵. Yuĕ.

丙 辰 粵 事 公 牘 要 畧 *Ping shin Yuĕ sze kung tŭh yaou leŏ.* "The Official Correspondence, &c., anent the Rupture at Canton in the Year 1856."   *Hongkong,* 1856. 8°.

粵 西 Yuĕ se.

粵 西 闈 墨 *Yuĕ se wei mĭh.* "Kwang-se Examination Essays."   [1780 ?]. 8°.
A Fragment.

悅 容 編 Yuĕ Yung-peen.

鴛 鴦 譜 *Yuen ying poo.* "A Treatise on Yuens and Yiugs." *See* 閔 景 賢 Min King-heen. 快 書 *Kwae shoo.* "A Book of Amusement," &c. Keuen 22.   1626. 8°

元 稹 Yuen Chin.

會 眞 記 *Hwuy chin ke.* "The True Story of a Re-union." By Yuen Chin, of the Tang Dynasty. A Reprint.   [1741 ?]. 8°.

元 海 Yuen-hae.

See 鳩 摩 羅 什 Kew-mo-lo-shĭh. 金 剛 般 若 波 羅 密 經 如 義 *Kin kang Pan-jŏ po-lo-mĕh king joo e.* "The Diamond Classic Explained." Edited by Yuen-hae. 1787. 8°.

元 應 Yuen Ying.

一 切 經 音 義 *Yĭh tsĕĕ king yin e.* "An Explanation of all the Foreign Technical Terms found in the Buddhist Works translated from the Sanscrit, with an Examination of the Correct Sounds." By Yuen Ying. 25 keuen. *See* 葉 志 詵 Yĕ Che-sin. 海 山 仙 館 叢 書 *Hae shan seen kwan tsung shoo.* "The Hae-shan-seen Kwan Collection of Reprints," &c. Vol. 6-11.   1848. 8°.

阮 福 Yuen Fŭh.

歷 代 帝 王 年 表 *Leĭh tae Te Wang neen peaou.* "A Tabulated Manual of the Reigns of the Emperors of China." Continued from the Beginning of the Ming to the Beginning of the Tsing Dynasty. By Yuen Fŭh, &c. *See* 伍 崇 曜 Woo Tsung-yaou. 粵 雅 堂 叢 書 *Yuĕ ya Tang tsung shoo.* "The Yuĕ-ya Tang Collection of Reprints," &c. Series 12.   1853. 8°.

—— 孝 經 義 疏 *Heaou king e soo.* "The Meaning of the Classic on Filial Piety Elucidated." *See* 嚴 杰 Yen Lĕĕ. 皇 清 經 解 *Hwang Tsing king keae.* "The Classics Explained," &c. Keuen 1360.   1829. 8°.

阮 咸 Yuen Han.

See 朱 湜 Choo Chĭh. 三 墳 *San fun.* "The Works of the Three Emperors." . . . With Notes by Yuen Han, &c.   8°.

阮 逸 Yuen Yĭh.

中 說 *Chung shwŏ.* "Central Discourses." With a Commentary by Yuen Yĭh, &c. *See* 黃 丕 烈 Hwang Pei-lĕĕ. 十 子 全 書 *Shĭh Tsze tseuen shoo.* "The Complete Works of the Ten Philosophers," &c.   1804. 8°.

—— *See* 王 通 Wang Tung. 中 說 *Chung shwŏ.* Central Discourses." . . With Notes by Yuen Yĭh, &c.   1825. 8°.

—— 元 經 *Yuen king.* "The Early History" of China . . . With Notes by Yuen Yĭh, &c. 8°.

阮 元 Yuen Yuen.

See Catalogues. 天 一 閣 書 目 *Teen yĭh kŏ shoo mŭh.* "A Catalogue of the Library Collected in the Teen-yĭh Pavilion." . . Edited by Yuen Yuen, &c.   1808. 8°.

—— *See* 嘉 慶 Kea-king. *Emperor.* 大 行 皇 帝 遺 詔 *Ta hing Hwang te e chaou.* "The last Testament of the Emperor Kea-king." Prepared by Yuen Yuen, &c.   1820. 8°.

—— *See* 李 明 徹 Le Ming-chĕ. 圜 天 圖 說 *Yuen teen too shwŏ.* "A Treatise on Astronomy." . . Edited by Yuen Yuen, &c. 1819. 8°.

阮元 YUEN YUEN. (Continued.)

See 李明徹 LE MING-CHĔ. 圜天圖說 續編 *Yuen teen too shwŏ sŭh peen*. "A Supplement to the *Yuen teen too shwŏ*." . . . . Edited by Yuen Yuen, &c.   1821. 8°.

—— See 薛尚功 SEĔ SHANG-KUNG. 歷代鐘鼎彝器欵識法帖 *Leĭh tae chung ting e ke kwan shĭh fă tëĕ*. "Facsimiles of Inscriptions on Bells, Tripods, Vases, &c." . . Edited by Yuen Yuen, &c.   1797. 8°.

—— See 詩經 SHE KING. 毛詩注疏 *Maou she choo soo*. "Maou Chang's Version of the Book of Odes." . . . Edited by Yuen Yuen, &c.   1815. 8°.

—— See 司空圖 SZE-KUNG TOO. 詩品詩一百首 *She pin she yĭh pĭh show*. "One Hundred Pieces of Poetry." . . . Edited by Yuen Yuen.   1816. 8°.

—— 詩書古訓 *She Shoo koo heun*. "Ancient Teachings drawn from the Books of Odes and of Historical Documents." 6 keuen. [Also] 石渠隨筆 *Shĭh keu suy peĭh*. "Notes on Drawings of Rocks and Water-courses." 8 keuen. [Also] 儀禮石經勘校記 *E le shĭh king keaou kan ke*. "The Texts of the Decorum Ritual and the Stone Classics Critically Examined." 4 keuen. [Also] 擘經室詩錄 *Yen king shĭh she lŭh*. "Poetical Records from the Yen-king Dwelling." 5 keuen. See 伍崇曜 WOO TSUNG-YAOU. 粤雅堂叢書 *Yuĕ ya Tang tsung shoo*. "The Yuĕ-ya Tang Collection of Reprints," &c. Series 11, 15, 18, 20.   1853. 8°.

—— 曾子註釋 *Tsăng tsze choo shĭh*. "The Works of Tsang Tsan Commented on and Explained." 4 keuen. [Also] 周易校勘記 *Chow Yĭh keaou kan ke*. "The various Texts of the Chow Changes Critically Examined." 11 keuen. [Also] 尙書校勘記 *Shang shoo keaou kan ke*. "The various Texts of the Book of Historical Documents Critically Examined." 22 keuen. [Also] 毛詩校勘記 *Maou she keaou kan ke*. "The various Texts of the Book

阮元 YUEN YUEN. (Continued.)

of Odes Critically Examined." 10 keuen. [Also] 周禮校勘記 *Chow le keaou kan ke*. "The various Texts of the Chow Ritual Critically Examined." 14 keuen. [Also] 儀禮校勘記 *E le keaou kan ke*. "The various Texts of the Decorum Ritual Critically Examined." 18 keuen. [Also] 禮記校勘記 *Le ke keaou kan ke*. "The various Texts of the Book of Rites Critically Examined." 67 keuen. [Also] 春秋左氏傳校勘記 *Chun tsew Tso she chuen keaou kan ke*. "The various Texts of Tso Kew-ming's Commentary on the Spring and Autumn Annals Critically Examined." 42 keuen. [Also] 春秋公羊傳校勘記 *Chun tsew Kung-yang chuen keaou kan ke*. "The various Texts of Kung-yang Kaou's Commentary on the Spring and Autumn Annals Critically Examined." 12 keuen. [Also] 春秋穀梁傳校勘記 *Chun tsew Kŭh-leang chuen keaou kan ke*. "The various Texts of Kŭh-leang Chih's Commentary on the Spring and Autumn Annals Critically Examined." 13 keuen. [Also] 論語校勘記 *Lun yu keaou kan ke*. "The various Texts of the Confucian Analects Critically Examined." 11 keuen. [Also] 孝經校勘記 *Heaou king keaou kan ke*. "The various Texts of the Classic of Filial Piety Critically Examined." 4 keuen. [Also] 爾雅校勘記 *Urh ya keaou kan ke*. "The various Texts of the Literary Expositor Critically Examined." 8 keuen. [Also] 孟子校勘記 *Măng tsze keaou kan ke*. "The various Texts of the Works of Mencius Critically Examined." 16 keuen. [Also] 車制圖解 *Chay che too keae*. "The Manufacture of Carriages Illustrated and Explained." 2 keuen. [Also] 鐘鼎彝器欵識 *Chung ting e ke kwan shĭh*. "A Record of Bells, Tripods, and Vases." 2 keuen. [Also] 疇人傳 *Chow jin chuen*. "Biographical Memoirs of Mathematicians." 9 keuen. [Also] 擘經室集 *Yen king chĭh tseĭh*. "A Collection of Writings from the Yen-king Dwelling." 7 keuen. See 嚴杰 YEN LEĔ. 皇清經解 *Hwang Tsing king keae*. "The Classics Explained." Keuen 802–1074.   1829. 8°.

阮元 YUEN YUEN. (*Continued.*)

[Poetical Essays]. By Yuen Yuen and others.

1830. 8º.

A fragment.

—— 疇人傳 *Chow jin chuen.* "Biographical Memoirs of Mathematicians," from the Commencement of History down to the End of the Eighteenth Century. The last Three Keuen contain Notices of European Mathematicians, beginning with Meton and Aristarchus. Compiled by Yuen Yuen. 46 keuen. 1799. 8º.

—— 經籍籑詁 *King tseĭh chuen koo.* "A Classical Dictionary." [Arranged according to the Sounds and Tones.] Compiled by Yuen Yuen. 106 keuen. 1812. 8º.

—— 詁經精舍文集 *Koo king tsing shay wăn tseĭh.* "A Collection of Essays Explanatory of Classical Subjects." Compiled by Yuen Yuen. 12 keuen. 1801. 8º.

Imperfect, containing only keuen 1–4.

—— 廣東通志 *Kwang tung tung che.* "A Topography of the Province of Kwang-tung." Compiled by Yuen Yuen, Le Hung-pin, Kang Shaou-yung, and others. 334 keuen. 1822. 8º.

袁枚 YUEN MEI.

See 顏希源 YEN HE-YUEN. 百美新詠圖傳 *Pĭh mei sin yung too chuen.* "A New Collection of Sonnets to the Hundred Beauties." ... Edited by Yuen Mei, &c. 1790. 8º.

—— 小倉山房詩集 *Seaou tsang shan fang she tseĭh.* "Poetry from the House on Mount Seaou-tsang." 31 keuen and Appendix.

[1800 ?]. 8º.

The last six keuen and Appendix wanting.

—— 小倉山房外集 *Seaou tsang shan fang wae tseĭh.* "An Additional Collection of Literary Pieces from the House on Mount Seaou-tsang." 7 keuen. 1803. 8º.

袁燮 YUEN SĔĔ.

絜齋毛詩經筵講義 *Kĕĕ chae maou she king yen keang e.* "The Meaning of Maou Chang's Edition of the Book of Odes Explained." By Yuen Sĕĕ. 4 keuen.

Peking, 1775. 8º.

Another copy.

袁中郎 YUEN CHUNG-LANG.

德山暑譚 *Tĭh shan shoo tan.* "Summer Discussions on the Mountain of Virtue." *See* 閔景賢 MIN KING-HEEN. 快書 *Kwae shoo.* "A Book of Amusement," &c. Keuen 20.

1626. 8º.

袁福徵 YUEN FŬH-CHING.

稿 *Kaou.* "Essays." *See* 長城 CHANG CHING. 名家制義 *Ming kea che e.* "Essays" on Texts from the Four Books, &c. Tsĭh 44.

1699. 8º.

袁若思 YUEN JŎ-SZE.

See 袁坤儀 YUEN KWAN-E. 羣書備考 *Keun shoo pe kaou.* "A Literary and Scientific Encyclopædia." .. With Notes by Yuen Jŏ-sze, &c. 1642. 8º.

袁坤儀 YUEN KWAN-E.

羣書備考 *Keun shoo pe kao.* "A Literary and Scientific Encyclopædia." Compiled by Yuen Kwan-e. With Notes by Yuen Jŏ-sze. Edited by Seu Yew-loo. 4 keuen. 1642. 8º.

袁一州 YUEN YĬH-CHOW.

官語詳編 *Kwan yu tseang peen.* "A Vocabulary of Expressions in the Mandarin Dialect." 1729. 8º.

Another copy.

袁一鳴 YUEN YĬH-MING.

浙江鄉試硃卷 *Chĕ keang heang she choo keuen.* "Essays Written by Yuen Yĭh-ming at the Chĕ-keang District Examination" for the Year 1789. 1789. 8º.

袁永綸 YUEN YUNG-LUN.

靖海氛記 *Tsing hae fun ke.* "An Account of the Suppression of Piracy," in the Canton Waters. 2 keuen. *Canton,* 1830. 8º.

Another edition. With Illustrations. 2 keuen.

Canton, 1830. 8º.

遠 YUEN.

See 張 CHANG. 張遠兩友相論 *Chang Yuen leang yew seang lun.* "A Discussion between the Two Friends Chang and Yuen," &c. 8º.

轅門 Yuen-mun.

轅門斬子 *Yuen mun chan tsze.* "The Execution of a Boy at the Yamun Gate." A Drama. 2 keuen. [1800?]. 8°.

Another edition. [*Canton*, 1820?]. 8°.

園 Yuen.

灌園記 *Kwan yuen ke.* "The Story of Watering the Garden." See 曲 Keŭh. 六十種曲 *Lŭh shĭh chung keŭh.* "Sixty Plays," &c. Taou 5. 8°.

鴛湖漁 Yuen-hoo-yu.

See 唐 Tang. 說唐演傳 *Shwŏ Tang yen chuen.* "A History of the Tang Dynasty." By the Fisherman of Lake Yuen, &c. 8°.

郁廣 Yŭh Kwang.

See 楊廉 Yang Leen. 嘉善縣志 *Kea-shen heen che.* "A Topography of Kea-shen Heen." .... Edited by Yŭh Kwang, &c. 1677. 8°.

郁永河 Yŭh Yung-ho.

探硫日記 *Tsae lew jĭh ke.* "A Journal of a Tour in Formosa in Search of Sulphur." 3 keuen. See 伍崇曜 Woo Tsung-yaou. 粤雅堂叢書 *Yuĕ ya Tang tsung shoo.* "The Yuĕ-ya Tang Collection of Reprints," &c. Series 15. 1853. 8°.

玉 Yŭh.

種玉記 *Chung yŭh ke.* "The Story of the Planted Jewel." See 曲 Keŭh. 六十種曲 *Lŭh shĭh chung keŭh.* "Sixty Plays," &c. Taou 5. 8°.

玉蟬 Yŭh-chen.

玉蟬附荐全本 *Yŭh chen foo tseen tseuen pun.* "Yŭh-chen gets a Soul out of Purgatory." A Tale in verse. 4 keuen. [1850?]. 8°.

玉匣 Yŭh heă.

玉匣記廣集 *Yŭh heă ke kwang tseĭh.* "An Enlarged Edition of the Record of the Jewelled Casket." [A Work on Divination, by Heu Tsing-yang.] 2 keuen? [1700?]. 8°.
Imperfect, containing only part of last keuen.

玉合 Yŭh hŏ.

玉合記 *Yŭh hŏ ke.* "The Precious Union." See 曲 Keŭh. 六十種曲 *Lŭh shĭh chung ke keŭh.* "Sixty Plays," &c. Taou 3. 8°.

玉壺 Yŭh hoo.

玉壺記 *Yŭh hoo ke.* "The Story of the Jade Tea-pot." See 說 Shwŏ. 說淵 *Shwŏ yuen.* "A Collection of Tales," &c. 8°.

玉環 Yŭh hwan.

玉環記 *Yŭh hwăn ke.* "The Jade Ring." See 曲 Keŭh. 六十種曲 *Lŭh shĭh chung keŭh.* "Sixty Plays," &c. Taou 6. 8°.

玉皇 Yŭh Hwang.

心印經 *Sin yin king.* "The Sûtra of the Heart's Seal." [Also] 胎息經 *Tae seĭh king.* "The Sûtra of the Womb's Breath." See 彭好古 Păng-haou-koo. 道言內外秘訣全書 *Taou yen muy wac pe keuĕ tseuen shoo.* "A Complete Collection of Taouist Works," &c. First Part. Keuen 1. 8°.

—— 高上玉皇本行集經 *Kaou shang yŭh hwang pun hing tseĭh king.* "The Sûtra of Yŭh-hwang-shang-te." *Canton*, 1818. 8°.

玉玦 Yŭh keuĕ.

玉玦記 *Yŭh keuĕ ke.* "The Jade Waist Buckle." See 曲 Keŭh. 六十種曲 *Lŭh shĭh chung keŭh.* "Sixty Plays," &c. Taou 5. 8°.

玉簪 Yŭh tsan.

玉簪記 *Yŭh tsan ke.* "The Jade Hair-pin." See 曲 Keŭh. 六十種曲 *Lŭh shĭh chung keŭh.* "Sixty Plays," &c. Taou 2. 8°.

—— 玉簪記 *Yŭh tsan ke.* "The Jade Hair-pin." In Verse. Also Entitled *Chin koo chuy chuen.* "Mrs. Chin Pursues the Boat." 4 keuen. [1840?]. 8°.

玉華子 Yŭh Hwa-tsze.

玉華子 *Yŭh Hwa-tsze.* "The Writings of Yŭh Hwa-tsze." See 沈津 Chin Tsin. 百家類纂 *Pĭh kea luy tswan.* "The Works of a Hundred Authors," &c. Keuen 19. 8°.

玉　鏡　臺　Yŭh king tae.

　　玉　鏡　臺　記　*Yŭh king tae ke.* "The Jade-Mirror Gallery." *See* 曲 Keŭh. 六 十 種 曲 *Lŭh shĭh chung keŭh.* "Sixty Plays," &c. Taou 3. 8°.

玉　堂　春　Yŭh Tang-chun.

　　審　玉　堂　春　*Shin Yŭh Tang-chun.* "Yŭh Tang-chun is Examined." A Dramatic Tale.
[1800?]. 8°.

育　吾　山　人　Yŭh-woo shan jin.

　　See 命 Ming. 三　命　通　會 *San ming tung hwuy.* "A Complete Work on the Three Fates." By the 'Man of the Yŭh-woo Mountain,' &c.　　　　　8°.

允　禮　Yun Le.

　　See 允　祿 Yun Lŭh. 子　史　精　華 *Tsze she tsing hwa.* "Choice Quotations from the Works of Philosophers and Historians." Compiled by . . . Yun Le, &c.　　1727. 8°.

允　祿　Yun Lŭh.

　　See China. 康　熙 Kang-he. *Emperor.* 上　諭 *Shang yu.* "Imperial Edicts." . . . Compiled by Yun Lŭh, &c.　　1730. 8°.

—— See Tsing Dynasty. 大　清　會　典 *Ta Tsing hwuy teen.* "A Comprehensive Description of the System of Government under the Tsing Dynasty." Compiled by Yun Lŭh, &c. 1732. 8°.

—— 欽　定　同　文　韻　統 *Kin ting tung wăn yun tung.* "A Sanskrit, Thibetan and Manchoo Syllabary." Compiled by Imperial Commission, consisting of Prince Yun Lŭh, Foo Hăng, Wang Yew-tun, and others. 6 keuen.　　　1750. 8°.

—— 子　史　精　華 *Tsze she tsing hwa.* "Choice Quotations from the Works of Philosophers and Historians." Compiled by an Imperial Commission consisting of Princes Yun Lŭh, Yun Le, and Chang Ting-yŭh, and others. 160 keuen.
1727. 8°.

雲　南　Yun-nan.

　　雲　南　闈　墨 *Yun nan wei mĭh.* "Yun-nan Examination Essays." [1815?]. 8°.
　　　　A fragment.

雲　棲　Yun Tse.

　　竹　窗　合　筆 *Chŭh chwang hŏ pĭh.* "Harmonious Pencillings from the Bamboo Window." *See* 閔　景　賢 Min King-heen. 快　書 *Kwae shoo.* "A Book of Amusement," &c. Keuen 12.
1626. 8°.

雍　正　Yung-ching. *Emperor.*

　　See China. 康　熙 Kang-he. *Emperor.* 上　諭 *Shang yu.* "Imperial Edicts," Issued during . . . the First Seven Years of the Emperor Yung-ching, &c.　　　1730. 8°.

—— See 康　熙 Kang-he. *Emperor.* 聖　諭　廣　訓 *Shing yu kwang heun.* "The Maxims of the Emperor Kang-he, Amplified" by his Successor Yung-ching, &c.　　　1815. 8°.

—— 御　製　圓　明　園　四　十　景　詩 *Yu che Yuen-ming-yuen sze shĭh king she.* "Forty Elegant Poems on Yuen-ming-yuen." With Plates. 2 keuen.　　　　　　　　8°.

雍　陶　Yung Taou.

　　英　雄　傳 *Ying heung chuen.* "Tales of Heroes." By Yung Taou, of the Tang Dynasty. A Reprint.　　　　　[1741?]. 8°.

永　和　Yung ho.

　　An Inscription Commemorating the Repairing of the "Epidendrum Portico," in the Ninth Year of the Reign of Yung ho. 1840. 8°.

永　樂　Yung-lŏ. *Emperor.*

　　See 知　旭 Che-heŭh. 慈　悲　水　懺 *Tsze pe shwuy tsan.* "The Ritual of the Purifying Water of the Merciful Tathâgata.". . With a Preface by the Emperor Yung-lŏ, &c. 1415. 8°.

—— See 蝎　試 Kĕĕ-ching. 千　手　千　眼　大　悲　心　咒　懺　法 *Tseen show tseen yen ta pei sin chow tsan fă.* "The Confessional Services of the Great Compassionate Kwan-yin." . . . With a Preface by the Emperor Yung-lŏ, &c.
1801. Oblong.

永　瑆　Yung Seuen.

　　See Catalogues. 欽　定　四　庫　全　書　總　目 *Kin ting sze koo tseuen shoo tsung mŭh.* "A . . Catalogue of the Imperial Library.". . Drawn up by . . . Prince Yung Seuen, &c. 1790. 8°.

永 璇 YUNG SEUEN. *(Continued.)*

    See 王圻 WANG KE. 續文獻通考 *Sŭh wăn heen tung kaou.* "A Continuation of the ' Wăn heen tung kaou.' " ... Revised and Edited ... by Yung Seuen, &c.   1784. 8º.

永 瑆 YUNG SING.

    See CATALOGUES. 欽定四庫全書總目 *Kin ting sze koo tseuen shoo tsung mŭh.* "A .. Catalogue of the Imperial Library." ... Drawn up by ... Prince Yung Sing, &c.   1790. 8º.

永 瑢 YUNG YUNG.

    See CATALOGUES. 欽定四庫全書總目 *Kin ting szè koo tseuen shoo tsung mŭh.* "A Catalogue of the Imperial Library." .. Drawn up by ... Prince Yung Yung, &c.   1790. 8º.

永 明 壽 YUNG-MING-SHOW.

    萬善同歸 *Wan shen tung kwei.* "A Treatise on the Unity of Origin of every Excellence." By the Buddhist Monk Yung-ming-show. 6 keuen.   1733. 8º.

永 宇 溪 YUNG YU KE.

    永宇溪莊識畧 *Yung yu ke chwang shĭh leŏ.* "A Short Account of Yung-yu-ke Farm House." By Tsze shan keu sze, or the Retired Scholar of Mount Tsze. 6 keuen.   1765. 8º.

容 保 YUNG PAOU.

    See 高晉 KAOU TSIN. 南巡盛典 *Nan seun shing teen.* "An Account of Four Royal Progresses ... in the South." ... Compiled by ... Yung Paou, &c.   1771. 8º.

INDEX OF TITLES.

35

INDEX.

36

INDEX.

牧牛圖 *Muh new too.* See 普明 Poo Ming.

穆天子傳 *Muh Teen tsze chuen.* See 荀勗 Seun Heuh.

夢遊錄 *Mung yew luh.* See 任蕃 Jin Fan.

夢遊錄 *Mung yew luh.* See 夢 Mung.

蒙齋筆談 *Mung chae peih tan.* See 蒙齋 Mung Chae.

蒙正全本秀毬記 *Mung ching tseuen pun, sew kew ke.* See 蒙正 Mung Ching.

蒙韃備錄 *Mung Tä pe luh.* See 孟珙 Mäng Hung.

滿漢禮記 *Mwan han Le ke.* See 禮記 Le Ke.

納書楹補遺曲譜 *Nä shoo ying poo e keuh poo.* See 葉堂 Yě Tang.

納書楹續集曲譜 *Nä shoo ying suh tseih keuh poo.* See 葉堂 Yě Tang.

納書楹外集曲譜 *Nä shoo ying wae tseih keuh poo.* See 葉堂 Yě Tang.

哪咤收妲己 *Na chä show Tä-ke.* See 妲己 Tä-ke.

南齋集 *Nan chae tseih.* See 馬曰璐 Ma Yuě-loo.

南中志 *Nan chung che.* See 常璩 Chang Keu.

南方草木狀 *Nan fang tsaou muh chwang.* See 稽含 Ke Han.

南澳志 *Nan gaou che.* See 婺源齊 Woo Yuen-tse.

南海勝境普陀山誌 *Nan hae shing chang Poo to shan che.* See 普陀 Poo To.

南軒先生文集 *Nan Heen Sëen säng wän tseih.* See 南軒 Nan Heen.

南雄珠璣巷來歷故事 *Nan heung choo ke heang lae leih koo sze.* See 南雄 Nan-heung.

南華眞經 *Nan hwa chin king.* See 莊周 Chwang Chow.

南華眞經副墨 *Nan hwa chin king foo mih.* See 莊周 Chwang Chow.

南華經 *Nan hwa king.* See 莊周 Chwang Chow.

南華內篇別解 *Nan hwa nuy peen pëe keae.* See 莊周 Chwang Chow.

南柯記 *Nan ko ke.* See 李公佐 Le Kung-tso.

南柯記全譜 *Nan ko ke tseuen poo.* See 葉堂 Yě Tang.

南柯夢 *Nan ko mung.* See 南柯 Nan Ko.

南雷文定 *Nan luy wän ting.* See 黃梨洲 Hwang Le-chow.

南雷文約 *Nan-luy wän yǒ.* See 黃梨洲 Hwang Le-chow.

南部新書 *Nan poo sin shoo.* See 錢易 Tseen Yĭh.

南巡盛典 *Nan seun shing teen.* See 高晉 Kaou Tsin.

南史 *Nan she.* See 李延壽 Le Yen-show.

南宋書 *Nan Sung shoo.* See 席世 Seĭh She.

南唐書 *Nan Tang shoo.* See 陸游 Lŭh Yew.

南唐書 *Nan Tang shoo.* See 馬令 Ma Ling.

南齊書 *Nan Tse shoo.* See 蕭子顯 Seaou Tsze-heen.

南楚新聞 *Nan Tsoo sin wän.* See 尉遲樞 Wei Che-choo.

能深念基督之恩者其罪可得贖矣 *Näng shin neen Ke-tŭh che gän chay ke tsuy ko tĭh shŭh e.* See Chinese Union.

鄰侯外傳 *Nëë how wae chuen.* See 鄰侯 Nëë how.

業報差別經 *Nëë paou cha pëë king.* See 瞿曇法智 Keu-tan-fä-che.

聶隱娘傳 *Nëë Yin-neang chuen.* See 聶隱娘 Nëë Yin-neang.

年中每日早晚祈禱敘式 *Neen chung mei jĭh tsaou wan ke taou seu shĭh.* See Liturgies. England, Church of.

年華錄 *Neen hwa lŭh.* See 全祖望 Tseuen Tsoo-wang.

廿一史約編 *Neen yĭh she yǒ peen.* See 鄭芷畦 Ching Che-hwuy.

女科 *Neu ko.* See 傅山 Foo Shan.

女科證治準繩 *Neu ko ching che chun shing.* See 王肯堂 Wang Käng-tang.

女仙外史 *Neu seen wae she.* See 呂叟 Leu Sow.

女才子傳 *Neu tsae tsze chuen.* See 女 Neu.

牛經大全 *New king ta tseuen.* See 喻本元 Yu Pun-yuen, and 喻本亨 Yu Pun-häng.

牛應貞傳 *New Ying-ching chuen.* See 宋若昭 Sung Jǒ-chaou.

寧古塔志 *Ning koo tä che.* See 力捄乾 Fang Kung-keen.

寧波府誌 *Ning po foo che.* See 曹秉仁 Tsaou Ping-jin.

寧波會館規條 *Ning po hwuy kwan kwei teaou.* See 寧波 Ning-po.

諾皋記 *Nǒ kaou ke.* See 段成式 Twan Ching-shĭh.

農政全書 *Nung ching tseuen shoo.* See 徐光啓 Seu Kwang-ke.

內河則例 *Nuy ho tsĭh le.* See Kwang-tung, Province of.

內家筆法 *Nuy kea keuen fä.* See 黃百家 Hwang Pĭh-kea.

41

42

四書類典賦 *Sze shoo luy teen foo.* See 甘馭麟 Kan Yu-lin.
四書蒙引 *Sze shoo mung yin.* See 四書 Sze shoo.
四書便抄 *Sze shoo peen chaou.* See 四書 Sze shoo.
四書補註附考備旨 *Sze shoo poo choo foo kaou pe che.* See 四書 Sze shoo.
四書詩題 *Sze shoo she te.* See 周目藻 Chow Mŭh-tsaou.
四書釋地 *Sze shoo shĭh te.* See 閻若璩 Yen Jŏ-keu.
四書釋地辨證 *Sze shoo shĭh te peen ching.* See 宋翔鳳 Sung Seang-fung.
四書釋地補註 *Sze shoo shĭh te poo choo.* See 閻若璩 Yen Jŏ-keu.
四書姓氏題文 *Sze shoo sing she te wăn.* See 褚邦慶 Choo Pang-king.
四書題鏡 *Sze shoo te king.* See 汪靈川 Wang Ling-chuen.
四書題管見 *Sze shoo te kwan keen.* See 峭闌氏 Tseaou Lan-she.
四書典制類聯音註 *Sze shoo teen che luy leen yin choo.* See 閻其淵 Yen Ke-yuen.
四書典制辨正 *Sze shoo teen che peen ching.* See 毛奇齡 Maou Ke-ling.
四書典林 *Sze shoo teen lin.* See 四書 Sze shoo.
四書典林榖 *Sze shoo teen lin kŏ.* See 江永 Keang Yung.
四書典腋 *Sze shoo teen yĭh.* See 四書 Sze shoo.
四書集註 *Sze shoo tseĭh choo.* See 四書 Sze shoo.
四書集註衷義 *Sze shoo tseĭh choo chung e.* See 四書 Sze shoo.
四書左國輯要 *Sze Shoo Tso kwŏ tseĭh yaou.* See 高其名 Kaou Ke-ming, and 鄭師成 Ching Sze-ching.
四書遵註合講 *Sze shoo tsung choo hŏ keang.* See 四書 Sze shoo.
四書逸箋 *Sze shoo yĭh tseen.* See 程大中 Ching Ta-chung.
四書賸言 *Sze shoo ying yen.* See 毛奇齡 Maou Ke-ling.
四子書 *Sze tsze shoo.* See 四書 Sze shoo.
四字金 *Sze tsze kin.* See 王鬼谷 Wang Kwei-kŭh.
思舊錄 *Sze kew lŭh.* See 靳治荊 Kin Che-king.
司馬温公文集 *Sze-ma wăn kung wăn tseĭh.* See 司馬光 Sze-ma Kwang.
大方廣佛華嚴經 *Ta fang kwang Fŭh hwa yen king.* See 實叉難陀 Shĭh-cha-nan-to.
大方廣圓覺經 *Ta fang kwang yuen keaou king.* See 佛陀多羅 Fŭh-to-to-lo.
大方廣圓覺經直解 *Ta fang kwang yuen keaou king chĭh keae.* See 佛陀多羅 Fŭh-to-to-lo.
大方廣圓覺經畧疏 *Ta fang kwang yuen keaou king leŏ soo.* See 佛陀多羅 Fŭh-to-to-lo.
大學 *Ta heŏ.* See 四書 Sze shoo.
大學綱目決疑章 *Ta heŏ kang mŭh keuĕ e chang.* See 德清 Tĭh-tsing.
大學古本說 *Ta heŏ koo pun shwŏ.* See 李光地 Le Kwang-te.
大行皇帝遺詔 *Ta hing Hwang te e chaou.* See 嘉慶 Kea-king. *Emperor.*
大金國志 *Ta Kin kwŏ che.* See 宇文 Yu Wăn.
大觀本草 *Ta kwan Pun tsaou.* See 本草 Pun tsaou.
大六壬大全 *Ta lŭh jin ta tseuen.* See 六壬 Lŭh jin.
大明中興永曆二十五年大統曆 *Ta Ming chung hing Yung-leĭh urh shĭh woo neen ta tung leĭh.* See Ephemerides.
大明會典 *Ta ming hwuy teen.* See Ming Dynasty.
大阿彌陀經 *Ta O-me-to king.* See 王日休 Wang Jĭh-hew.
大悲懺 *Ta pei tsan.* See 大悲 Ta pei.
大悲懺法 *Ta pei tsan fă.* See 沈希聲 Chin He-shing.
大乘起信論直解 *Ta shing ke sin lun chĭh keae.* See 法藏 Fă-tsang.
大戴禮正誤 *Ta Tae le ching woo.* See 汪中 Wang Chung.
大戴禮記 *Ta Tae le ke.* See 戴德 Tae Tĭh.
大戴禮記補註 *Ta Tae Le ke poo soo.* See 孔廣森 Kung Kwang-săn.
大唐西域記 *Ta Tang se yĭh ke.* See 玄奘 Heuen-tsang.
大唐新語 *Ta Tang sin yu.* See 劉肅 Lew Sŭh.
大唐全書 *Ta Tang tseuen shoo.* See 唐 Tang.
大道 *Ta taou.* See 尹文 Yin Wăn.
大全通書 *Ta tseuen tung shoo.* See Ephemerides.
大晉司馬氏全套 *Ta Tsin Sze-ma she tseuen taou.* See 司馬 Sze-ma.
大清咸豐二年時憲書 *Ta tsing Heen-fung urh neen she heen shoo.* See Ephemerides.
大清會典 *Ta Tsing hwuy teen.* See Tsing Dynasty.

45

讀 雅 筆 記 *Tŭh ya peĭh ke.* See 李 鐵 垣 LE TĔĔ-YUEN.

督 捕 則 例 *Tŭh poo tsĭh le.* See CHINA.

督 捕 則 例 附 纂 *Tŭh poo tsĭh le foo tswan.* See CHINA.

童 子 範 圍 *Tung tsze fan wei.* See 童 子 TUNG TSZE.

童 子 禮 *Tung tsze le.* See 屠 羲 英 TOO HE-YING.

東 城 雜 記 *Tung ching tsă ke.* See 厲 鶚 LE GŎ.

東 周 列 國 全 志 *Tung Chow leĭh kwŏ tseuen che.* See 蔡 元 放 TSAE YUEN-FANG.

東 潘 林 氏 闔 族 邉 *Tung fan Lin she hŏ tsŭh tsun.* See 林 LIN.

東 安 縣 志 *Tung gan heen che.* See 汪 兆 柯 WANG CHAOU-KO.

東 軒 詩 鈔 *Tung heen she chaou.* See 胡 湟 HOO TANG.

東 郭 記 *Tung kŏ ke.* See 東 郭 TUNG KŎ.

東 莞 縣 志 *Tung kwan heen che.* See 彭 人 傑 PĂNG JIN-KĔĔ.

東 坡 遺 意 *Tung-po e e.* See 蘇 軾 SOO SHĬH.

東 西 漢 全 傳 *Tung se Han tseuen chuen.* See 鍾 伯 敬 CHUNG PĬH-KING.

東 西 史 記 和 合 *Tung se she ke ho hŏ.* See 佫 德 SHANG tĬh.

東 西 晉 演 義 *Tung se Tsin yen e.* See 陳 蟄 齋 CHIN HŎ-CHAE.

東 西 洋 考 *Tung se yang kaou.* See 張 燮 CHANG SĔĔ.

東 西 洋 考 每 月 統 記 傳 *Tung se yang kaou mei yuĕ tung ke chuen.* See PERIODICAL PUBLICATIONS.

東 都 事 畧 *Tung too sze leŏ.* See 王 偁 WANG CHING.

東 晉 疆 域 志 *Tung Tsin keang yĭh che.* See 洪 亮 吉 HUNG LEANG-KEĬH.

東 陽 夜 怪 錄 *Tung yang yay kwae lŭh.* See 王 洙 WANG CHOO.

東 隅 錄 *Tung yu lŭh.* See 張 犀 CHANG LIN.

東 圖 雜 字 *Tung yuen tsă tsze.* See 東 圖 TUNG YUEN.

東 原 集 *Tung yuen tsĕh.* See 戴 震 TAE CHIN.

同 住 訓 畧 *Tung choo heun leŏ.* See 天 然 TEEN-JEN.

同 安 縣 志 *Tung gan heen che.* See 吳 鏞 WOO YUNG.

同 館 律 賦 鴻 裁 *Tung kwan leŭh foo hung tsae.* See 曾 耀 嚴 TSĂNG YAOU-YEN.

同 館 試 律 *Tung kwan shĭh leŭh.* See 洪 瑩 HUNG YING, and 法 式 善 FĂ SHĬH-SHEN.

同 文 算 指 *Tung wăn swan che.* See 李 之 藻 LE CHE-TSAOU.

峒 谿 纎 志 志 餘 *Tung ke sëen che che yu.* See 陸 次 雲 LŬH TSZE-YUN.

洞 冥 記 *Tung ming ke.* See 郭 憲 KŎ HEEN.

洞 天 清 祿 *Tung teen tsing lŭh.* See 趙 希 鵠 CHAOU HE-KŬH.

銅 人 腧 穴 針 灸 圖 經 *Tung jin shoo heŭ chin kew too king.* See 王 惟 德 WANG WEI-TĬH.

通 志 *Tung che.* See 鄭 樵 CHING TSEAOU.

通 志 堂 經 解 目 錄 *Tung-che tang king keae mŭh lŭh.* See 翁 方 綱 UNG FANG-KANG.

通 介 堂 經 說 *Tung-keae tang King shwŏ.* See 徐 鱟 SEU HAOU.

通 鑑 綱 目 *Tung keen kang mŭh.* See 朱 熹 CHOO HE.

通 鑑 綱 目 擥 要 *Tung keen kang mŭh lan yaou.* See 姚 培 謙 YAOU PEI-KEEN, and 張 景 星 CHANG KING-SING.

通 鑑 擥 要 *Tung keen lan yaou.* See 姚 培 謙 YAOU PEI-KEEN, and 張 景 星 CHANG KING-SING.

通 書 *Tung shoo.* See 周 敦 頤 CHOW TUN-E.

通 書 *Tung shoo.* See 羅 傳 炳 LO CHUEN-PING.

通 書 *Tung shoo.* See 楊 明 智 YANG MING-CHE.

通 典 *Tung teen.* See 杜 佑 TOO YEW.

通 天 曉 *Tung teen heaou.* See 天 TEEN.

通 雅 *Tung ya.* See 方 以 智 FANG E-CHE.

翁 源 縣 新 志 *Ung yuen heen sin che.* See 謝 崇 俊 SEAY TSUNG-TSEUN, and 蔣 善 功 TSEANG SHEN-KUNG.

二 知 軒 詩 鈔 *Urh che Heen she chaou.* See 方 濬 頤 FANG SEUN-E.

二 論 啟 幼 引 端 *Urh lun ke yew yin twan.* See 劉 忠 LEW CHUNG.

二 論 題 備 *Urh lun te pe.* See 章 香 艇 CHANG HEANG-TING.

二 三 塲 逢 元 *Urh san chang fung yuen.* See 王 奠 安 WANG TSUN-GAN.

二 十 四 山 秘 訣 *Urh shĭh sze shan pe keuĕ.* See 山 SHAN.

二 十 四 詩 品 *Urh shĭh sze she pin.* See 司 空 圖 SZE-KUNG TOO.

二 十 二 史 感 應 錄 *Urh shĭh urh she kan ying lŭh.* See 彭 希 涑 PĂNG HE-sĬh.

二 十 一 史 精 義 *Urh shĭh yĭh she tsing e.* See 王 南 珍 WANG NAN-CHIN.

46

47

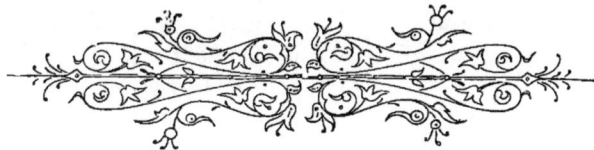

TITLES OF WORKS RECENTLY ADDED TO THE COLLECTION.

製 火 藥 法 *Che ho yŏ fă.* 3 keuen.

浙 江 鄉 試 硃 卷 *Chĕ-keang heang she choo keuen.*

陳 忠 愍 公 殉 難 詩 文 錄 *Chin chung min kung seun nan she wăn lŭh.* 4 keuen.

鎮 撫 事 宜 *Chin foo sze e.* 5 keuen.

正 教 眞 詮 *Ching keaou chin tseuen.* 2 keuen.

正 韻 通 *Ching yun tung.* 30 keuen.

硃 批 諭 旨 *Choo pe yu che.* 6 Vols.

殊 域 周 咨 錄 *Choo yĭh chow tsze lŭh.* 20 keuen.

籌 海 初 集 *Chow hae choo tseĭh.* 12 keuen.

周 官 祿 田 考 *Chow kwan lŭh teen kaou.* 3 keuen.

周 禮 精 華 *Chow le tsing hwa.* 6 keuen.

中 外 新 報 *Chung wae sin paou.* (Keuen 2, Nos. 2, 3, 19; keuen 3, Nos. 2, 12; keuen 4, No. 1).

中 原 音 韻 *Chung yuen yin yun.* 2 keuen.

狀 元 幼 學 詩 *Chwang yuen yew hŏ she.*

埶 文 備 覽 *E wăn pei lan.* 120 keuen.

依 樣 葫 蘆 *E yang hoo loo.* 4 keuen.

法 寶 勘 同 總 錄 *Fă paou kan tung tsung lŭh.* 10 keuen.

反 唐 女 媧 鏡 全 集 *Fan Tang neu kwo king tseuen tseĭh.* 4 keuen.

翻 譯 名 義 集 選 *Fan yĭh ming e tseĭh seuen.*

方 田 通 法 補 例 *Fang teen tung fă poo le.* 6 keuen.

防 海 新 論 *Fang hae sin lun.* 18 keuen.

佛 說 解 冤 劫 神 咒 *Fŭh shŭŏ keae yuen kĕĕ shin chow.*

奉 使 朝 鮮 驛 程 日 記 *Fung she Chaou seen yĭh ching jĭh ke.*

恩 科 浙 江 鄉 試 硃 卷 *Găn ko Chĕ-keang heang she choo keuen.*

海 瑞 大 紅 袍 全 傳 *Hae shwuy ta hung paou tseuen chuen.* 10 keuen.

海 島 逸 志 *Hae taou yĭh che.* 6 keuen.

橫 財 玉 尺 圖 *Hăng tsae yŭh chĭh too.*

孝 經 *Heaou king.* (Man. and Chin.)

禊 帖 類 聯 *Hĕĕ tĕĕ luy leen.*

行 述 *Hing shŭh.*

行 水 金 鑑 *Hing shwuy kin keen.* 135 keuen.

護 法 論 *Hoo fă lun.*

弧 角 設 如 *Hoo kĕŏ she joo.* 3 keuen.

弧 三 角 舉 隅 *Hoo san kĕŏ keu yu.*

紅 藕 山 莊 尺 牘 *Hung gow shan chwang chĭh tŭh.* 12 keuen.

紅 樓 復 夢 *Hung low fŭh mung.* 100 Chapters.

化 學 指 南 *Hwa hĕŏ che nan.* 5 keuen.

化 學 分 原 *Hwa hĕŏ fun yuen.* 8 keuen.

化 學 鑑 原 *Hwa hĕŏ keen yuen.* 6 keuen.

皇 朝 中 外 壹 統 輿 圖 *Hwang chaou chung wae yĭh tung yu too.* 21 keuen.

皇 朝 藩 部 要 略 *Hwang chaou fan poo yaou lĕŏ.* 22 keuen.

皇 明 直 文 淵 閣 諸 臣 表 *Hwang ming chĭh wăn yuen kŏ choo chin peaou.*

惠 州 府 志 *Hwuy chow foo che.* 20 keuen.

會 元 千 字 文 *Hwuy yuen tseen tsze wăn.*

開 煤 要 法 *Kae mei yaou fă.* 12 keuen.

高 弧 細 草 *Kaou hoo se tsaou.*

器 象 顯 眞 *Ke seang heen chin.* 4 keuen.

奇 緣 鴈 翎 媒 新 選 *Ke yuen yen ling mei sin seuen.* 4 keuen.

嘉 定 府 志 *Kea ting foo che.* 48 keuen.

皆 山 樓 吟 稿 *Keae shan low kin kaou.* 4 keuen.

江 蘇 海 運 全 案 *Keang soo hae yun tseuen gan.* 12 keuen.

交 食 細 草 *Keaou shĭh se tsaou.* 3 keuen.

校 正 日 用 雜 字 書 *Keaou ching jĭh yung tsă tsze shoo.*

教 會 新 報 *Keaou hwuy sin paou.*

48

敎稼書 *Keaou kca shoo.* 2 keuen.

敎乘法數 *Kcaou shing fä soo.* 12 keuen.

敎外別傳 *Keaou wae pĕĕ chuen.* 16 keuen.

乾坤法竅 *Keen kwăn fä keaou.*

吉金志存 *Keïh kin che tsun.* 4 keuen.

勸世戻言 *Kenen she leang yen.* 2 vols.

羣仙祝禱 *Keun seen chüh taou.*

九皇新經註 *Kew Hwang sin king choo.* 3 keuen.

九皇延生錫福寶懺 *Kew Hwang yen săng seïh fŭh paou tsan.* 9 keuen.

九品蓮臺經咒 *Kew pin leen tae king chow.*

九十二法 *Kew shĭh urh fä.*

舊金山唐人新聞紙 *Kew kin shan Tang jin sin wăn che.*

今古奇觀 *Kin koo ke kwan.* 40 keuen.

金華罟漏中星表 *Kin hwa kwei low chung sing peaou.* 2 keuen.

金石索 *Kin shĭn sö.* 12 keuen.

欽定重修兩浙鹽法志 *Kin ting chung sew leang Chĕ yen fä che.*

欽定回疆則例 *Kin ting Hwuy keang tsĭh le.*

欽定滿洲源流 *King ting Mwan chow yuen lew.* 20 keuen.

欽定新疆識畧 *Kin ting sin keang chĭh leŏ.* 12 keuen.

欽定萬年書 *Kin ting wan neen shoo.*

京報 *King paou.*

敬勝堂試藝 *King shing tang she e.*

經義叢鈔 *King e tsung chaou.* 30 keuen.

經韻集字析解 *King yun tseïh tsze che keae.*

各省外海戰般總畧 *Kŏ sing wae hae chen chuen tsung leŏ.* 3 keuen.

古今算法記 *Koo kin swan fä ke.* 6 keuen.

古玉圖譜 *Koo yǔh too poo.* 100 keuen.

穀梁廢疾申何 *Kŭh-leang fei che shin ho.* 2 keuen.

功過格輯要 *Kung kwo kïh tseïh yaou.* 16 keuen.

孔子集語 *Kung tsze tseïh yu.* 17 keuen.

公羊何氏解詁箋 *Kung yang Ho she keae koo tseen.*

公羊何氏釋例 *Kung yang Ho she shĭh le.* 10 keuen.

官話彙解 *Kwan hwa wei keae.* 3 keuen.

官話約翰福音書 *Kwan hwa Yŏ-han fŭh yin shoo.*

廣州府屬歷案鬱宮題名錄 *Kwang chow foo shŭh leïh gan hung kung te ming lǔh.*

廣東歷科拔貢題名錄 *Kwang-tung leïh ko pä kung te ming lǔh.*

廣興古今鈔 *Kwang yu koo kin chaou.* 2 keuen.

廣韻 *Kwang yun.* 5 keuen.

癸花記全本 *Kwei hwa ke tseuen pun.* 4 keuen.

國朝重訂庚辰集 *Kwŏ chaou chung ting kăng shin tseïh.* 5 keuen.

國朝館閣律賦集腋 *Kwŏ chaou kwan kŏ leŭh foo tseïh yïh.* 4 Parts.

國朝諡法考 *Kwŏ chaou she fä kaou.*

楞嚴經會解 *Lăng yen king hwuy keae.* 10 keuen.

吏治輯要 *Le che tseïh yaou.*

律曆淵源 *Leŭh leïh jun yuen.* 110 keuen.

劉後主志 *Lew how choo che.*

劉先主志 *Lew seen choo che.*

羅浮山志 *Lo fow shan che.*

論上帝造萬物之全能 *Lun Shang te tsaou wan wŭh che tseuen năng.*

論語述何 *Lun yu shǔh ho.* 2 keuen.

孟子大題萃 *Măng tsze ta te tsuy.*

墨子批選 *Mĭh-tsze pe seuen.* 4 keuen.

巴志 *Pa che.*

八旗通志 *Pä ke tung che.* 250 keuen.

八家四六 *Pä kea sze lǔh.*

八線類編 *Pä seen luy peen.* 3 keuen.

八線對數類編 *Pä seen tuy shoo luy peen.* 2 keuen.

般若波羅蜜多心經 *Pan-jo Po-lo-meïh-to sin king.*

保免攔除 *Paou mèen lan choo.*

寶山縣志 *Paou shan heen che.* 10 keuen.

評註淵海子平大全 *Ping choo jun hae tsze ping ta tseuen.* 4 keuen.

普法戰紀 *Poo Fä chen ke.* 8 vols.

蓬島樵歌 *Pung taou tseaou ko.*

三合劍全傳 *San hŏ keen tseuen chuen.* 6 keuen.

三元消愆寶懺 *San Yuen seaou keen paou tsan.*

西陲要畧 *Se chuy yaou leŏ.* 4 keuen.

西番碧玉帶全本 *Se fan peïh yǔh tae tseuen pun.* 2 keuen.

西江志 *Se keang che.* 206 keuen.

西國樂法啟蒙 *Se kwŏ lŏ fä keïh mung.* 2 keuen.

西域聞見錄 *Se yïh wăn keen lǔh.* 8 keuen.

西藥畧釋 *Se yŏ leŏ shïh.*

小學註解 *Seaou heŏ choo keae.* 6 keuen.

嘯古堂文集 *Seaou koo tang wăn tseïh.* 8 keuen.

嘯堂集古錄考異 *Seaou tang tseïh koo lǔh kaou e.*

袖珍日課 *Sew chin jïh ko.* 3 keuen.

繡 虎 軒 尺 牘 *Sew hoo heen chĭh tŭh.* 4 Parts.

修 習 瑜 伽 集 要 施 食 壇 儀 應 門 *Sew seĭh yu kea tseĭh yaou she shĭh tan e ying nun.* 2 keuen.

山 法 全 書 *Shan fă tseuen shoo.* 2 keuen.

上 海 徽 寧 思 恭 堂 徵 信 錄 *Shang-hae hwuy ning sze kung tang ching sin lŭh.*

上 海 大 關 則 例 *Shang hae ta kwan tsĭh le.*

上 海 同 仁 堂 義 學 條 規 *Shang-tae Tung jin Tang e heŏ teaou kwei.*

上 帝 造 創 天 地 來 歷 論 *Shang te tsaou chwang teen te lae leĭh lun.*

上 帝 曰 吾 終 日 伸 手 招 頑 逆 辨 駁 之 民 也 *Shang te yuĕ Wo chung jĭh shin show chaou wan ne peen pŏ che min yay.*

商 賈 便 覽 *Shang koo peen lan.* 8 keuen.

尚 書 後 案 *Shang shoo how gan.* 30 keuen and Appendix.

尚 書 釋 天 *Shang shoo shĭh teen.* 6 keuen.

赦 罪 之 道 *Shay tsuy che taou.*

使 喀 爾 喀 紀 程 艸 *She kĭh-urh-kĭh ke ching tsaou.*

示 我 周 行 *She wo chow hing.* 6 keuen.

石 龍 宮 五 朝 賽 願 祈 安 保 境 植 福 意 悃 *Shĭh lung kung woo chaou sae yuen ke găn paou king chĭh fŭh e kwan.*

石 點 頭 *Shĭh teen tow.* 14 keuen.

神 峰 闢 謬 命 理 正 宗 *Shin fung peĭh meaou ming le ching tsung.* 4 keuen.

神 道 總 論 *Shin taou tsung lun.* 3 keuen.

聖 差 言 行 *Shing cha yen hing.*

聖 賢 讚 像 圖 *Shing heen tsan seang too.*

聲 律 啟 蒙 撮 要 *Shing leuh keĭh mung tso yaou.* 2 keuen.

順 天 鄉 試 硃 卷 *Shun teen heang she choo keuen.*

雙 釘 記 *Shwang ting ke.*

說 唱 繡 香 囊 全 傳 *Shwŏ chang sew Heang nang tseuen chuen.*

說 唐 後 傳 *Shwŏ Tang how chuen.* 11 keuen.

水 師 操 練 *Shwuy sze tsaou leen.* 20 keuen.

新 刻 玉 簫 琴 記 全 本 *Sin kĭh yŭh seaou kim ke tseuen pun.* 8 keuen.

新 碧 桃 錦 帕 全 本 *Sin peĭh taou kim pĭh tseuen pun.*

新 選 玉 癸 寶 扇 全 本 *Sin seuen yŭh kwei paou shen tseuen pun.*

新 增 五 方 元 音 全 書 *Sin tsăng woo fang yuen yin tseuen shoo.* 2 keuen.

新 測 中 星 圖 表 *Sin tsĭh chung sing too peaou.*

新 測 恒 星 圖 表 *Sin tsĭh hăng sing too peaou.*

新 測 更 漏 中 星 表 *Sin tsĭh kang low chung sing peaou.* 3 keuen.

新 鴈 翎 扇 墜 全 本 *Sin yen ling shan chuy tscuen pun.*

醒 世 姻 緣 傳 *Sing she yin yuen chuen.*

蘇 松 浮 糧 核 議 *Soo sung fow leang hĭh e.*

淞 江 府 志 *Sung keang foo che.* 84 keuen.

送 彩 科 儀 *Sung tsae ko e.*

頌 揚 真 神 歌 *Sung yang chin shin ko.*

算 法 指 掌 *Swan fă che chang.* 4 keuen.

算 學 啟 蒙 *Swan heŏ ke mung.* 3 keuen.

大 成 通 志 *Ta ching tung che.* 18 keuen.

大 婚 禮 *Ta hwăn le.*

大 明 全 傳 繡 球 緣 *Ta ming tseuen chuen sew kew yuen.* 4 keuen.

大 清 咸 豐 七 年 時 憲 書 *Ta tsing Heen-fung tseĭh neen she heen shoo.*

大 清 會 典 *Ta tsing hwuy teen.* 100 keuen.

大 清 道 光 二 十 二 年 時 憲 書 *Ta tsing Taou-kwang urh shĭh urh neen she heen shoo.*

大 清 道 光 二 十 三 年 癸 卯 便 民 通 書 *Ta tsing Taou-kwang urh shĭh san neen kwei maou peen min tung shoo.*

大 清 道 光 二 十 三 年 時 憲 書 *Ta tsing Taou-kwang urh shĭh san neen she heen shoo.*

大 清 道 光 二 十 四 年 甲 辰 便 民 通 書 *Ta tsing Taou-kwang urh shĭh sze neen keă shin peen min tung shoo.*

大 清 道 光 二 十 四 年 時 憲 書 *Ta tsing Taou-kwang urh shĭh sze neen she heen shoo.*

大 清 道 光 二 十 五 年 時 憲 書 *Ta tsing Taou-kwang urh shĭh woo neen she heen shoo.*

大 清 道 光 二 十 六 年 便 民 通 書 *Ta tsing Taou-kwang urh shĭh lŭh neen peen min tung shoo.*

大 清 搢 紳 *Ta tsing tsin shin.* 16 vols.

大 易 象 數 鉤 深 圖 *Ta yĭh seang soo kow shin too.*

達 生 編 *Tă săng peen.* 2 keuen.

太 上 感 應 篇 詩 *Tae shang kan ying peen she.*

太 上 洞 玄 靈 寶 無 量 度 人 上 品 妙 經 *Tae shang tung heuen ling paou woo leang too jin shang pin meaou king.*

代 數 術 *Tae soo shŭh.* 25 keuen.

臺 灣 奏 摺 上 諭 *Tae wan tsow chĕ shang yu.*

胎 產 秘 書 *Tae chan pe shoo.*

唐 兩 京 城 坊 考 *Tang leang king ching fang kaou.* 5 keuen.

道光二十四年日用便覽 *Taou-kwang urh shǐh sze neen jǐh yung peen lan.*

題名錄 *Te ming lǔh.*

地球說畧 *Te kew shwǒ leǒ.*

地藏菩薩本願經 *Te tsang Poo-să pun yuen king* (Man. and Chin.). 2 keuen.

地元眞訣 *Te yuen chin keuě.*

天方性理 *Teen fang sing le.* 5 keuen.

天方典禮 *Teen fang teen le.* 21 keuen.

天下路程 *Teen hea loo ching.*

天花藏合刻七才子書 *Teen hwa tsang hǒ kǐh tseǐh tsae tsze shoo.*

滇南礦厰與程圖畧 *Teen nan hwang chang yu ching too leǒ.*

剔奬元音新編 *Teǐh pe yuen yin sin peen.*

渡江書剛部 *Too keang shoo kang poo.*

透膽寒 *Tow tan han.* 4 keuen.

讚美詩 *Tsan mei she.*

籤書簿 *Tsan shoo po.*

倉田通法 *Tsang teen tung fǎ.* 5 keuen.

倉田通法續編 *Tsang teen tung fǎ sǔh peen.* 3 keuen.

詳註文範初編 *Tseang choo wǎn fan choo peen.*

蕉軒摭錄 *Tseaou heen chǐh lǔh.* 12 keuen.

千字文釋句 *Tseen tsze wǎn shǐh keu.*

七修類稿 *Tseǐh sew luy kaou.*

策海 *Tsih hae.* 10 keuen.

測海集 *Tsih hae tseǐh.* 6 keuen.

靖逆記 *Tsing neǐh ke.* 6 keuen.

左傳杜林合註 *Tso chuen Too Lin hǒ choo.* 50 keuen.

左氏春秋考証 *Tso she Chun tsew kaou ching.* 2 keuen.

作印集字 *Tso yin tseǐh tsze.*

Ts'u 'ǒh Di-lǐ reng-teh. Nying-po T'u wǒ.

字部緝解 *Tsze poo tseǐh keae.*

讀史方輿紀要 *Tǔh she fang yu ke yaou.* 9 keuen.

東華錄 *Tung hwa lǔh.* 32 keuen.

東萊博議 *Tung lae po e.* 4 keuen.

東西兩晉全志 *Tung se leang Tsin tseuen che.* 12 keuen.

同門錄 *Tung mun lǔh.*

銅符鐵帒 *Tung foo tëě keuen.* 3 keuen.

通鑑直解 *Tung keen chǐh keae.* 44 keuen.

萬國公報 *Wan kwǒ kung paou.*

文昌化書 *Wǎn chang hwa shoo.* 6 keuen.

文殊志 *Wǎn choo che.* (Man.)

文房肆考 *Wǎn fang sze kaou.* 8 keuen.

僞忠王親筆口供 *Wei chung wang tsin peǐh kow hung.*

彙刻書目合編 *Wei kǐh shoo mǔh hǒ peen.* 10 Parts.

五車韻府 *Woo chay yun foo.* 10 keuen.

五車韻端 *Woo chay yun twan.* 160 keuen.

五方元音 *Woo fang yuen yin.* 2 keuen.

五虎平南後傳 *Woo hoo ping nan how chuen.* 6 keuen.

五代地理考 *Woo tae te le kaou.* 4 keuen.

Imperfect, containing only keuen 3, 4.

無上玉皇心印妙經 *Woo shang yǔh hwang sin yin meaou king.* 8 keuen.

武備秘書 *Woo pei pe shoo.*

勿效此世之俗乃以心改化成新 *Wǔh heaou tsze she che sǔh keǐh e sin kae hwa ching sin.*

挨星秘竅 *Yae sing pe keaou.*

楊椒山先生家訓 *Yang Shǔh shan seen săng keǎ heun.*

養心詩調叙 *Yang sin she teaou seu.*

耶穌聖敎禱告文 *Yay-soo Shing keaou taou kaou wǎn.*

柚堂筆談 *Yew tang peǐh tan.* 4 keuen.

柚堂文存 *Yew tang wǎng tsun.* 4 keuen.

幼童習字法 *Yew tung seǐh tsze fǎ.*

奕妙 *Yǐh meaou.*

域外叢書 *Yih wae tsung shoo.*

咽喉脈證通論 *Yin how mǐh ching tung lun.*

約色弗言行錄 *Yǒ-sih-fǔh yen hing lǔh.*

御製盛京賦 *Yu che Shing-king foo.*

御定萬年書 *Yu ting wan neen shoo.*

粤海關外洋船牌 *Yuě hae kwan wae yang chuen pae.*

月令粹編 *Yuě ling suy peen.* 24 keuen.

閱史約書 *Yuě she yǒ shoo.*

元龍通考 *Yuen lung tung kaou.* 3 keuen.

鉛字拼法集全 *Yuen tsze peen fǎ tseǐh tseuen.*

玉蟬附荂全本 *Yǔh pe foo tsun tseuen pun.*

玉臺新詠箋註 *Yǔh tae sin yung tseen choo.* 10 keuen.

玉堂字彙 *Yǔh tang tsze wei.*

韻府羣音 *Yun foo tsuy yin.*

運規約指 *Yun kwei yǒ che.* 3 keuen.

MANUSCRIPTS.

AMOY.

[Chart of Amoy and the surrounding Coast.
1800 ?].

ANECDOTES.

[A Collection of Anecdotes and Historical Facts.
1750 ?]. 8°.

BAYER (Gottlieb Siegfried).

Specimen Lexici Sinensis auctore G. S. B.
[1740 ?]. fol.

BIBLE. Miscellaneous Parts.

[A narrative of the Gospel History, followed by
that portion of the New Testament from the first
chapter of the Acts of the Apostles to the end of
the first chapter of the Epistle to the Hebrews.]
Canton, 1737–38. fol.

BIRDS.

[Twenty-eight coloured Drawings of Birds, Flowers,
etc. 1700 ?]. 4°.

BLAXLAND (George).

Sketch of part of the east Coast of China and
western Part of Formosa. By G. B. 1827.

BRANCATUS (Franciscus).

字音辯異 *Tsze yin peen e.* "A Chinese and
Latin Dictionary, phonetically arranged." With
a Supplement. 1671. 4°.

BUDDHA.

[A number of Vignettes representing Manifestations of Buddha. Without title. 1750 ?]. 8°.

—— [A number of Vignettes representing Manifestations of Buddha, etc. Without title.]
[1750 ?]. 8°.

CANTON.

[A Canton Custom House clearance issued by the
Hoppo Yen to the Foreign Ship "Pe-chen."]
1828. A sheet.

—— [Draft Map of the Embouchure of the Canton
River. 1820 ?].

—— [A Map of Part of the City of Canton, showing
the extent of the Fire which occurred in the
foreign Settlements and surrounding Parts in
the year 1822. 1822 ?].

—— [A Muster Roll of the Chinese Army assigned for
the Defence of the City of Canton in 1841.] 8°.

CANTON. Custom House.

粵海關外洋船牌 *Yuĕ hae kwan wae yang
chuen pae.* A Custom Clearance for the ship
[Juliet, Capt. Wilson] from the Port of Canton.
[Printed.] 1836.

張方平 Chang Fang-ping.

See 蘇軾 Soo Shĭh. 代張方平諫用兵書
Tae Chang Fang-ping keen yung ping shoo. . . . .
"On Chang Fang-ping's advice on War," etc. 8°.

張得中 Chang Tĭh-chung.

[A Collection of Odes, beginning with one entitled
四明形勝賦 *Sze ming hing shing foo,* by
Chang Tĭh-chung. 1840 ?]. 8°.

張玉衡 Chang Yŭh-hăng.

See Chin-hae Heen. [Instructions . . . issued
by the Admiral Chang Yŭh-hăng] 1838. 8°.

常州府 Chang-chow Foo.

[A Map of the coast Fortifications on the Banks of
the Grand Canal in the Prefecture of Chang-
chow in the Province of Keang-soo. 1810 ?].

49

330   MANUSCRIPTS.

常 州 營 CHANG-CHOW YING.
  [A Map of the Chang-chow Camp, in the Province
   of Keang-soo.   1820 ?].

趙 翼 CHAOU YĬH.
  皇 朝 武 功 紀 盛 *Hwang chaou woo kung ke
  shing.* "A Narrative of the Contests of the
  present Dynasty with the neighbouring Insub-
  ordinate States." 4 keuen.   1837. 8°.

杯 林 營 CHAY-LIN YING.
  [A Map of the Chay-lin Camp in the Province of
   Keang-soo.   1840 ?].

CHĔ KEANG.
  浙 海 關 日 徵 環 簿 *Chĕ hae kwan jih ching
  hwan pŏ.* "A daily Return of the Receipts at
  the Custom House at Cha-poo in the Province of
  Chĕ keang.   [1835 ?]. 8°.

—— [A Map of a Portion of the Province of Chĕ-
   kéang.   1840 ?].

—— [A Military Map of Ning-po Foo, Tsze-ke Heen
   and Fung-hwa Heen in the Province of Chĕ-
   keang, with an account of their respective
   Garrisons.   1800 ?].

—— [A Number of official Documents connected with
   the Military Establishments of the Province of
   Chĕ-keang, bearing dates from 1763–1835.] 4°.

—— [A Volume containing the Draft and fair Copy of
   a Legal Statement, and a few pages from the
   Chĕ keang Examination "Red book."
                                    1841 ?]. 8°.

陳 兆 崙 CHIN CHAOU-LUN.
  [A Collection of Essays on Texts from the Four
   Books, two of which are written by Chin Chaou-
   lun. 12 folios.   1770 ?]. 8°.

陳 弘 謀 CHIN HUNG-MOW.
  See 呂 坤 叔 LEU KWĂN-SHŬH. 呂 子 節 錄 補
  遺 *Leu tsze tsëĕ. lŭh poo e.* "A Supplement to
  the Ethics." . . . Edited by Chin Hung-mow,
  etc.   8°.

陳 鴻 聲 CHIN HUNG-SHING.
  王 氏 宗 譜 *Wang she tsung poo.* "The Genealogy
  of the Wang Family" during 34 generations.
  With coloured Portraits of some of the more

陳 鴻 聲 CHIN HUNG-SHING. (*Continued.*)
  celebrated members. Edited by Chin Hung-
  shing. 3 keuen.   1781. 8°.

陳 慶 槐 CHIN KING-HWAE.
  惜 樹 山 房 詩 *Tseay shoo shan fang she.* "Poems
  from the House on Mount Tseay-shoo." 96
  folios. 8 keuen.   1803. 8°.

—— 惜 樹 山 房 詩 草 *Tseay shoo shan fang she
  tsaou.* "A rough copy of Poems from the House
  on Mount Tseay-shoo."   1788–1806. 8°.

鎮 海 縣 CHIN-HAE HEEN.
  鎮 海 靖 字 船 戶 姓 名 梁 頭 清 冊 *Chin-
  hae tsing tsze chuen hoo sing ming leang tow tsing
  tsĭh.* A list of the registered Shipping of the
  Port of Chin-hae for the 19th year of the Emperor
  Taou-kwang.   1839. 4°.

—— [A Collection of various Chinese Documents,
   among which are a number of Essays, and
   several public Documents issued by the native
   and the English Authorities at Chin-hae, in the
   year 1841.]   4°.

—— [Instructions for the troops garrisoning Chin-hae
   Heen, issued by the Admiral Chang Yŭh-hăng.]
                                    1838. 8°.

—— [A Map of the District of Chin-hae.   1840 ?].

—— [A Map of the District of Chin-hae.   1840 ?].

—— 鎮 海 營 水 陸 圖 冊 *Chin-hae ying shwuy lŭh
  too tsĭh.* Instructions for the Troops garrisoning
  Chin-hae Heen (issued by the Admiral Woo kin-
  peaou).   1841. 8°.

CHINA.
  [An Atlas containing seven European Maps of
   Parts of China and of Tartary.   1800 ?].

—— [An Atlas, containing 32 Maps of the different
   Provinces of China, and of the outlying Colonial
   Dialects.   1820 ?].

—— [An Atlas, containing 33 Maps of the different
   Provinces of China, and of the outlying Colonial
   Districts.   1820 ?].

—— [A Chart of the Coast from Breaker Point to
   Amoy. With Manuscript notes.   1820 ?].
           Much torn.

CHINA. (*Continued.*)

[Chart of the Coast from Namoa Island to Füh-chow Foo. 1850 ?].

—— [Chart of the Coast from Namoa Island to Füh-chow Foo. 1850 ?].

—— [Maps of China and Japan, collected and translated from native Atlases by H. J. von Klaproth. 1820 ?]. folio.

—— [Skeleton Maps of the Provinces of China, and of Manchuria, with a Plan of the Imperial city at Peking.] [1800 ?]. 8°.

—— 雍正 YUNG CHING. *Emperor.*

[An Edict issued by the Emperor Yung ching in the 7th year of his reign against Gambling.] 1729.

CHINESE DIALOGUES.

Decem personarum convivium Dialogus Sinicus sic dictus. [1750 ?].

CHINESE LETTER.

[A Chinese Letter and Envelopes. 7 folios. 1840 ?]. 8°.

CHINESE PLANTS.

[A number of Coloured Drawings of Chinese Plants. 1840 ?]. 4°.

CHOO-CHOW FOO.

[A Map of the Prefecture of Choo-chow, in the Province of Chĕ-keang. 1840 ?].

—— [A paper showing the Strength of the Garrisons in the Centre and Left Camps in the Prefecture of Choo-chow. 1840 ?].

周詩 CHOW SHE.

周詩天機釋解婚姻圖 *Chow she teen ke shĭh keae hwăn yin too.* "The System of Marriage ordained by heaven, according to the poetry of the Chow dynasty, explained." [1800 ?]. 8°.

周禮 CHOW LE.

Extracts from the Chow Ritual. 108 folios. [1800 ?]. 8°.

周興嗣 CHOW HING-SZE.

千字文 *Tseen tsze wăn.* "The Thousand Character Classic." [1790 ?]. 8°.

周思憲 CHOW SZE-TĬH.

上清靈寶濟度大成金書 *Shang tsing Ling paou tse too ta ching kin shoo.* "The complete golden Book of the celestial Magnate Ling paou." Edited by Chow Sze-tĭh. 54 folios. ? keuen. [1830 ?]. 8°.

Very imperfect, containing only keuen 23.

酬柬 CHOW KEEN.

Music to the Song called Chow keen. [1750 ?]. 8°.

川沙營 CHUEN-SHA YING.

[A Map of the Chuen-sha Camp, in the Province of Keang-soo. 1840 ?].

CHUSAN.

[A Map of the Island of Chusan. 1820 ?].

—— [A Map of the Island of Chusan. 1840 ?].

莊綸渭 CHWANG LUN-WEI.

晚翠樓時藝 *Wan tsuy low she e.* "Occasional Essays from the Wan-tsuy Pavilion." 129 folios. 1832. 8°.

CUN-FU'-TSU'.

See 孔丘 KUNG KEW.

CUSTOMS REGULATIONS.

[A Collection of Customs Regulations on Salt and other Commodities, together with a number of Judicial Cases, etc. 1650 ?]. 8°.

DIAZ (ANTONIO).

諧聲品字箋 *Keae shing ping tsze tseen.* "A phonetic Chinese and Spanish Dictionary." 359 folios. *Füh-ning Chow,* 1704. 8°.

DICTIONARIES.

[A Chinese and English Vocabulary, in which the Chinese Words are transcribed in Roman Letters. 1780 ?]. fol.

—— A Chinese Dictionary with explanations in Portuguese, Latin and French. [1750 ?]. fol.

—— "Dictionarium Chinense, hoc est, lingua Belgica juxta alphabeti ordinem et Latiné et Mandarinicé quoque explicati Chinensium characteres." [1650 ?]. fol.

—— "Dictionarium Sinico-Latinum et Latino-Sinicum." 2 Vols. [1700 ?]. 4°

—— 漢 字 西 譯 *Han tsze se yih.* "Basilii a Glemona Dictionarium Sinico-Latinum juxta clavium ordinem auctum et emendatum ab H. J. von Klaproth." 1813–1834. 4°.

—— "Basilii a Glemona Dictionarium Sinico-Latinum." 1788, fol.

—— "Lexicon Sinicum cum adjuncta pronunciatione et versione Lusitanica, nitide exaratum, et in auctione Densoiana comparatum ab Olao Gerhardo Tychsen." 1795. 8°.

—— "Speculum Linguæ Tartariæ." (A complete Alphabetical Manchoo Dictionary.) 4 Vols. [1750 ?]. 4°.

—— "Vocabularium Sinico-Gallicum." [1750 ?]. obl.

ESSAYS.
[A Collection of Essays on Texts from the Four Books. 29 folios. 1800 ?]. 8°.

FISHES.
[A number of Sepia Drawings of Fishes. 1840 ?]. 4°.

FLOWERS.
[Twenty-four Coloured Botanical Drawings of Flowers and Fruits. 1750 ?]. 4°.

FORMOSA.
[A coloured Map of the western Coast of the Island of Formosa. 1840 ?].

—— [Map of the Chinese Portion of Formosa. Without title.] [1800 ?]. 8°.

宰 寧 縣 Fow-ning Heen.
[A Map of Fow-ning Heen in the Province of Keang-soo. 1840 ?].

FOUQUET (Jean François).
Catalogue des Livres Chinois apportés de la Chine par Le Pere Fouquet, Jusuite, en année 1722. 25 folios. 1722. 8°.

佛 Füh.
論 佛 妄 自 稱 尊 不 肯 敬 認 神 天 上 帝 之 大 逆 *Lun Füh wang tsze ching tsun, puh kang king jin shin teen Shang te che ta neth.* "Tract on the Assumption of Buddha in calling himself 'Honourable,' and the great Disobedience of being unwilling to acknowledge the true God." 7 folios. [1800 ?]. 8°.

Füh-keen and Chĕ-keang.
[A Military Map of the Country on the Borders of the Provinces of Füh-keen, and Chĕ-keang lying between the Districts of Poo-ching on the South and Keang-shan on the North. 1840 ?].

福 山 營 Füh-shan Ying.
[A Map of the Camp of Füh-shan in the Province of Keang-soo. 1840 ?].

Fung-hwa Heen.
[Correspondence between the officials of Fung-hwa Heen on the Subject of the distribution of Charity during the year 1840. 1840]. 8°.

安 懷 宮 Gan hwae kung.
安 懷 宮 五 朝 祠 安 金 章 *Gan hwae kung woo chaou ke gan kin chang.* "The golden volume of Prayers for prosperity, from the Gan-hwae kung." 1846. 8°.

安 鑱 Gan lŭh.
安 鑱 科 儀 *Gan lŭh ko e.* "The Ritual of the peaceful charm." A Taouist work. 1847. 8°.

安 宅 Gan tsĭh.
安 宅 聯 五 方 符 誥 在 內 *Gan tsĭh leen woo fang foo kaou tsae nuy.* "Parallel aphorisms of the Peaceful dwelling, together with an examination into universal charms." [1800 ?]. 8°.

海 齡 Hae Ling.
[A Memorial addressed to the Emperor by Hae Ling the Tartar at Chin-keang Foo, returning Thanks for having been reinstated in Office. Dated 16th May, 1842.]

海 門 廳 Hae-mun Ting.
查 造 海 門 閫 境 各 港 分 界 全 圖 *Cha tsaou Hae-mun kae chang kih heang fun keae tseuen too.* "A complete Map of Hae-mun Ting" [in the Province of Keang soo. 1840 ?].

—— [A Map of Hae-mun Ting, in the Province of Keang-soo. 1840 ?].

海 寧 州 Hae-ning Chow.
[A Map of the Coast Defences in the sub-Prefecture of Hae-ning, in the Province of Chĕ-keang. 1840 ?].

—— [Map of the Coast Defences in the sub-Prefecture of Hae-ning. 1830 ?].

HANG-CHOW FOO.

[A Map of the City of Hang-chow Foo. 1800?].

This map forms a continuation of Add. 16361. F.

—— [A Plan showing the River Defences in the Neighbourhood of Hang-chow Foo. 1820?].

下 南 廳 HEA-NAN TING.

[A Map of the Military Posts and Coast Lines in Hea-nan Ting, in the Province of Honan. 1840?].

遐 域 HEA YĬH.

遐 域 瑣 談 *Hea yĭh so tan.* "Conversational Discourses on the distant Frontier Countries (*i.e.* Turkestan)." By a man calling himself *Chun yuen she* or the Gentleman of the Chun garden. 5 keuen. [1840?]. 8°

HONGKONG.

[A pencil Sketch of the Island of Hongkong and the adjacent Coast. 1842?].

皇 明 HWANG MING.

皇 明 經 濟 錄 *Hwang ming king tse lŭh.* "Records of the political Institutions of the Ming Dynasty." [1700?]. 8°.

回 疆 HWUY KEANG.

滿 漢 回 疆 傳 *Mwan Han hwuy keang chuen.* "A History of the Mahommedan Countries" [*i.e.* Djungaria and Eastern Turkestan, conquered by the Emperor Keen-lung]. In Manchoo and Chinese. 666 folios. [1790?]. 8°.

HYDE (THOMAS), *D.D.*

"Adversaria Chinensia a scripto et ore nativi Chinensis excerpta." 1788? 8°.

人 命 JIN MING.

"Trials for Capital Offences." 119 folios. [1830?]. 8°.

如 皋 縣 JOO-KAOU HEEN.

[A Map of the Coast-line of Joo-kaou Heen, in the Province of Keang-soo. 1820?].

JULIEN (STANISLAS AIGNAN).

See PREMARE (JOSEPH HENRI DE), *Jesuit.* Notitia Linguæ Sinicæ. [Transcribed by S. A. J. etc.] 8°.

高 上 神 KAOU SHANG SHIN.

高 上 神 密 玉 樞 寶 經 *Kaou shang shin meĭh yŭh choo paou king.* "The precious Sutra of the secret jade pivot of the exalted Gods." [1800?]. 8°.

KE YING.

[A Letter from Ke Ying, the Imperial Commissioner, to Sir Henry Pottinger expressing his regret at the Death of Mr. Morrison. 1843].

—— [A letter from Ke Ying to Sir Henry Pottinger acknowledging the receipt of seven Maps, etc. Dated November. 1843].

—— A Letter from Ke Ying to Sir Henry Pottinger acknowledging the receipt of the latter's Portrait. 1844?].

—— [A Letter from Ke Ying to Sir Henry Pottinger enclosing a Portrait of the former's Wife. 1844?].

嘉 興 KEA HING.

浙 江 嘉 興 城 守 營 *Chě-keang Kea-hing ching show ying.* "Regulations for the Garrison at Kea-hing in Chě-keang." 1842. 8°.

江 西 KEANG SE.

江 西 省 全 圖 *Keang se săng tseuen too.* "A Complete Atlas of the Province of Keang-se," [containing a general map of the Province, followed by maps of the 13 Prefectures into which it is divided. 1790?].

KEANG SOO.

[A fragment containing a Map of the Grand Canal between Hwae-ngan and Tae-chow in the Province of Keang-soo. 1840?].

—— [A Map of the Sea Coast in the neighbourhood of the Mouth of the Lew Ho in the Province of Keang-soo. 1840?].

—— 風 俗 條 約 *Fung sŭh teaou yŏ.* "Rules for the Regulation of Customs and Usages for the People of Keang-soo, issued by the Governor of the Province in the year 1759. [1820?]. 8°.

江 陰 縣 KEANG-YIN HEEN.

[A Map of Keang-yin Heen, in the Province of Keang-soo. 1820?].

MANUSCRIPTS.

敎 匪 KEAOU FEI.

平 定 敎 匪 紀 事 *Ping ting keaou fei ke sze.*
"An Account of the Suppression of the White
Lily secret Society." [1800 ?]. 8°.

簡 KEEN.

簡 鍊 揣 摩 *Keen leen chuy mo.* "Critically selected [Essays." 44 folios. 1840 ?]. 8°.

屈 原 KEŬH YUEN.

離 騷 *Le saou.* "The Exiled Mourner." [An
ode] by Keŭh Yuen. [Together with pieces of
a similar description by Sung Yŭh, and others.]
67 folios. [1840 ?]. 8°.

鳩 摩 羅 什 KEW-MO-LO-SHĬH [*i.e.* Kumâragîva].

See 金 剛 KIN KANG. 金 剛 般 若 波 羅 蜜 經
Kin kang pan jŏ po lo meĭh king. "The Diamond
Classic" [. . . translated into Chinese by Kew-
mo-lo-shĭh, etc. 8°.

金 華 府 KIN HWA FOO.

[A Military Map of the Prefecture of Kin-hwa in
the Province of Chĕ-keang. 1840 ?].

金 華 縣 KIN-HWA HEEN.

[A Map of Kin-hwa Heen, in the Province of Chĕ
keang. 1840 ?].

金 剛 KIN KANG.

金 剛 般 若 波 羅 蜜 經 *Kin kang pan jŏ po lo
meĭh king.* "The Diamond Classic," translated
into Chinese by Kew-mo-lo-shĭh. Illustrated by
hand. [1750 ?]. 8°.

金 古 爰 KIN KOO-LEANG.

無 雙 譜 *Woo shwang poo.* [Illustrated] "Biographical Notices of Peerless Worthies."
Nanking, [1750 ?]. 8°.

金 籙 KIN LŬH.

金 籙 正 醮 朝 眞 膳 奏 *Kin lŭh ching tseaou
chaou chin tang tsow.* "The correct morning
Ritual of the 'Golden Talisman.'"
[1800 ?]. 8°.

—— 金 籙 中 普 賑 濟 科 儀 *Kin lŭh chung poo
chin tse ko e.* "The ritual of universal beneficence
of the 'Golden Talisman.'" [1800 ?]. 8°.

—— 金 籙 中 普 科 儀 *Kin lŭh chung poo ko e.* "A
general Ritual of the 'Golden Talisman.'"
[1800 ?]. 8°.

金 籙 KIN LŬH. (*Continued.*)

—— 金 籙 拜 表 文 科 儀 *Kin lŭh pae peaou wăn ko e.*
"The Ritual to be employed when worshipping
and offering up Peaou wăn [a kind of prayer
read before an idol and then burnt], of the
'Golden Talisman.'" [1810 ?]. 8°.

—— 金 籙 宿 啓 道 塲 科 儀 *Kin lŭh sŭh ke taou
chang ko e.* "The Ritual for the cultivation of
virtue of the 'Golden Talisman.'" [1800 ?]. 8°.

—— 金 籙 道 塲 陞 壇 科 儀 *Kin lŭh taou chang
shing tan ko e.* "The Ritual for ascending the
altar of the arena for cultivating virtue of the
'Golden Talisman.'" [1810 ?]. 8°.

—— 金 籙 早 朝 關 奏 科 儀 *Kin lŭh tsaou chaou
kwan tsow ko e.* "The morning Ritual of the
'Golden Talisman.'" [1800 ?]. 8°.

—— 金 籙 晚 朝 科 儀 *Kin lŭh wan chaou ko e.*
"The evening Ritual of the 'Golden Talisman.'"
1822. 8°.

—— 金 籙 五 朝 啓 白 聖 班 *Kin lŭh woo chaou ke
pĭh shing pan.* "The Sacred Formularies for universal use of the 'Golden Talisman.'" 1848. 8°.

—— 金 籙 午 朝 科 儀 *Kin lŭh woo chaou ko e.*
"The Midday Ritual of the 'Golden Talisman.'"
1824. 8°.

—— 金 籙 禳 熒 火 部 科 儀 *Kin lŭh yang yung ho
poo ko e.* "The ritual for dispelling conflagra-
tions of the 'Golden Talisman.'" [1800 ?]. 8°.

—— 金 籙 玉 壇 發 奏 科 儀 *Kin lŭh yŭh tan fă
tsow ko e.* "The ritual of the jewelled altar of
the 'Golden Talisman.'" 1841. 8°.

金 山 縣 KIN-SHAN HEEN.

[A Map of Kin-shan Heen, and of the Sea Embankment along the Coast. 1820 ?].

金 山 營 KIN-SHAN YING.

[A Map of the Kin-shan Camp, in the Province of
Keang-soo. 1840 ?].

荆 州 KING-CHOW.

駐 防 荆 州 滿 營 事 宜 *Choo fang King-chow
mwan ying sze e.* "Regulations for the Manchoo
Garrison at King-chow," [in the Province of Hoo
pĭh]. Issued in the year 1683. [1830 ?]. 8°.

荆 州 KING-CHOW. (*Continued.*)

—— 駐 防 荆 州 滿 營 事 宜 *Choo fang King-chow mwan ying sze e.* "Regulations for the Manchoo garrison at King chow." Issued in the year 1683. [1830?]. 8°.

京 房 KING FANG.

易 傳 *Yih chuen.* "A commentary on the Book of Changes." With notes by Woo Lǔh. 3 keuen. See 屠 隆 Too LUNG. 漢 魏 叢 書 *Han Wei tsung shoo.* "Reprints," etc. 8°.

KLAPROTH (HEINRICH JULIUS VON).

See CHINA. [Maps of China and Japan collected and translated from native Atlases by H. J. von K.] fol.

—— See DICTIONARIES. 漢 字 西 譯 *Han tsze se yih.* "Basilii a Glemona Dictionarium Sinico-Latinum . . . auctum et emendatum ab H. J. v. K." 1834. 8°.

—— "Chinesische Grammatic nach Fourmont." Copied by H. J. v. K. 1830. fol.

古 文 KOO WĂN.

手 抄 古 文 讀 本 *Show chaou koo wăn tŭh pun.* "Extracts from ancient Literature." [With Notes and Comments. 1800?]. 8°.

孔 丘 KUNG KEW.

Lun yu: or Moral Discourses [attributed by the writer to] Cun-fú-tsú [*i.e.* Kung Kew or Confucius]. The original Chinese in European characters with an interlinear Latin Version. Also Proverbs of Tao su: Chinese and Latin. [1700?]. 8°.

瓜 䣂 KWA TËË.

瓜 䣂 絲 長 *Kwa tëë neen chang.* "A Genealogical Table." [1840?]. 8°.

官 KWAN.

陞 官 圖 *Shing kwan too.* A Register of official Promotions throughout the Empire. [1790?]. A roll.

老 君 LAOU KEUN.

See 孔 丘 KUNG KEW. *Lun yu:* . . . . also Proverbs of Tao su [*i.e.* Laou keun, etc. 1700?]. 8°.

老 君 LAOU KEUN. (*Continued.*)

—— 太 上 焚 燈 卷 簾 科 儀 *Tae shang fun tăng keuen leen ko e.* "The Taouist Rituals of burning the lamps and of rolling up the screens." [1800?]. 8°.

—— 太 上 玄 靈 北 斗 延 生 妙 經 *Tae shang heuen ling Pǐh tow yen săng meaou king.* "The Classic of the North Star delivered by Laou keun." [1850?]. obl. 8°. Imperfect.

—— 太 上 靈 寶 發 奏 科 儀 *Tae shang ling paou fă tsow ko e.* "A Ritual in Honour of Laou keun." 1778. 8°.

—— 太 上 靈 寶 朝 天 謝 罪 懺 *Tae shang ling paou chaou teen seay tsuy tsan.* "Laou keun's spiritual and precious morning confessional Tantra." 10 keuen. [1810?]. 8°.

李 筌 LE TSEUEN.

太 白 陰 經 *Tae pǐh yin king.* "An Illustrated treatise on Military Tactics." 10 keuen. [1830?]. 8°. Imperfect, first two keuen wanting.

—— 太 白 陰 經 *Tae pǐh yin king.* An illustrated treatise on Military Tactics. 10 keuen. [1830?]. 8°. Imperfect, containing only keuen 3-6, 9, 10.

李 士 村 LE SZE-TSUN.

宰 相 眞 心 *Tsae seang chin sin.* [Notes on Medicine. 1830?]. 8°.

禮 記 LE KE.

檀 弓 *Tan kung.* [The second Section of the Book of Rites.] 24 folios. 2 keuen. [1830?]. 8°.

擱 藻 LE TSAOU.

擱 藻 揚 芳 *Le tsaou yang fang.* "Elegant compositions of eminent Excellence." [1830?]. 8°.

黎 崱 LE TSǏH.

安 南 志 畧 *Gan nan che lěŏ.* "An Account of Annan," by Le Tsǐh [a native of that country who sought refuge in China after having been party to the surrender of a city to the Chinese troops, during the reign of Kublai Khan. 20 keuen. 1750?]. 8°.

曆 Leĭh.

曆 法 問 答 *Leĭh fă wăn tă.* "A Catechism on Astronomy." [By a Jesuit Missionary?] 663 folios. [1750?]. 8°.
  With Latin notes on the last few pages.

呂 坤 叔 Leu Kwăn-shŭh.

呂 子 節 錄 補 遺 *Leu tsze tsëë lŭh poo e.* "A Supplement to the Ethics of Leu tsze." Edited by Chin Hung-mow. 2 keuen. [1800?]. 8°.
  Imperfect, containing only the first keuen.

律 賦 Leŭh foo.

精 選 律 賦 *Tsing seuen leŭh foo.* "Carefully selected Odes." [1840?]. 8°.

劉 河 營 Lew ho ying.

劉 河 營 輿 圖 *Lew ho ying yu too.* A Map of the Camp of Lew-ho [in the Province of Keang-soo, with an account of the strength and disposition of the Garrison. 1800?].

靈 魂 Ling hwăn.

靈 魂 篇 *Ling hwăn peen.* "A Treatise on the Soul." [By W. Milne. 1824?]. 8°.

羅 Lo.

羅 甸 遺 風 *Lo teen wei fung.* The customs [of the inhabitants] of the Lo Districts [in Kwei chow]. With Illustrations. [1800?]. 8°.

樂 清 Lo-tsing.

[A Map of the District of Lo-tsing, in the Province of Chĕ-keang. 1820?].

LORD'S PRAYER.

[Several scraps in Chinese, containing amongst other things the Lord's Prayer, the Creed, and the Ten Commandments according to the Roman Catholic versions. 1750?]. fol.

龍 游 縣 Lung-yew Heen.

[A Map of the District of Lung-yew, in the Province of Chĕ-keang. 1840?].

雷 霆 Luy ting.

雷 霆 解 關 科 儀 *Luy ting keae kwan ko e.* "A ritual for letting loose and restraining Thunder." 1832. 8°.

MACAO.

[A rough Sketch of Macao. 1840?].

MAIGROT (Charles), *Bishop of Conon.*

[Letters relating to China addressed to Cardinal Gualterio? also a translation of the Will of the Empress of China, and of an Imperial Edict. 57 folios. 1701?]. 4°.

孟 河 營 Măng-ho Ying.

[A Map of the Măng-ho Camp, in the Province of Keang-soo. 1840?].

MANUSCRIPT BOOKS.

[Two Manuscript Books. 1750?].

MAP.

[A Map of a District not specified. 1840?].

MARTINI (Martin).

See Masson (Philip). "Miscellanea quædam Sinica partim a P. Martinio, ... accepta," etc. fol.

MASSON (Philip).

"Miscellanea quædam Sinica partim a P. Martinio, ejusque famulo Sinensi Dominico accepta, partim ex eorundem ore per me [*i.e.* P. M.] excerpta." [1650?]. fol.

MAUGHAN (Philip).

See Ross (Daniel) and Maughan (Philip), *Bombay Marine.* Survey of part of the south Coast of China, etc. 1807.

緬 甸 Meen teen.

緬 甸 譯 語 *Meen teen yĭh yu.* "A Chinese and Burmese Vocabulary." [1800?]. 8°.
  With notes in Russian.

MEMORIALS.

[A Collection of Memorials addressed to the Emperor. 1800?]. 8°.

MILNE (William), *D.D.*

See 靈 魂 Ling hwăn. 靈 魂 篇 *Ling hwăn peen.* "A Treatise on the Soul." [By W. M.], etc. 8°.

MORRISON (John Robert).

[A Map of the Chĕ-keang Coast in the neighbourhood of Seang-shan Heen, drawn by J. R. M. 1840?].

—— [A Map of the Chĕ-keang Coast in the neighbourhood of Hang-chow Foo, drawn by John Robert Morrison. 1840?].

宁 波 NING PO.
[A Map of the country at the mouth of the Ning po river. 1840?].

—— [Map of the Sea Coast in the neighbourhood of the Districts of Ting-hae, and Fung-hwa in the Prefecture of Ning-po. 1840?].

—— [Seven official Documents recording the Virtue of various Widows, issued by the Authorities at Ning-po in the year 1838.] 8°.

NOTE BOOK.
[A Chinese Note Book, containing Memoranda on the various Offices of Government, etc. 1830?]. 8°.

—— [Notes on Natural History. 93 folios. 1840?]. 8°.

ODD LEAVES.
A number of odd leaves from printed books, with a few scraps of manuscript, and also some specimens of Chinese paper. 1750?]. 8°.

ODES.
[A Collection of Odes. 83 folios. 1800?]. 8°.

—— [A Collection of Odes. 14 folios. 1800?]. 8°.

—— [A Collection of Odes, beginning with one entitled 如 玉 如 蘭 *Joo yŭh joo lan.* 30 folios. 1840?]. 8°.

—— [A Collection of Sixty-six Odes. With notes. 65 folios. 1840?]. 8°.

磐 石 衛 PAN-SHĬH WEI.
[A Map of Pan-shĭh Wei in the Province of Chĕ-keang. 1840?].

磐 石 營 PAN-SHĬH YING.
[A Map of the Pan-shĭh Camp in the Province of Chĕ-keang. 1840?].

邦 阿 爲 PANG A-WEI.
摺 *Chĕ.* "A Memorial" addressed by Pang A-wei to the General commanding at ? on the subject of the promotion of officers. 1841. 8°.

PAOU-SHAN HEEN.
[A Plan of the sea Embankment in the District of Paou-shan, in the Province of Keang-soo. 1800?].

PEKING.
首 善 全 圖 *Show shen tseuen too.* A complete Map of the supreme excellence [*i.e.* Peking. 1750?].

—— [A Map of Peking, without title.] [1800?].

PERIODICAL PUBLICATIONS. PEKING.
京 報 *King paou.* "The Peking Gazette" of the 18th of the 12th month of the 20th year of the reign of Taou kwang [*i.e.* 1840]. 8°.

PETITIONS.
[A collection of Petitions and other short Official Documents of the 20th year of the reign of Taou kwang. 9 folios.] 1840. 8°.

北 斗 PĬH TOW.
北 斗 眞 經 *Pĭh tow chin king.* "The true Sutra of the Deity Pĭh tow." 1761. 8°.

—— 北 斗 消 災 散 禍 眞 經 *Pĭh tow seaou tsae san hwŏ chin king.* "The true sutra of the Deity Pĭh-tow for causing calamities to cease, and misfortune to disappear." A Taouist work. [1800?]. 8°.

稟 PIN.
具 副 稟 *Keu foo pin.* "A Collection of Petitions." 1841. 8°.

—— 稟 帖 *Pin tëĕ.* "A Collection of Letters and Petitions." [1840?]. 8°.

兵 PING.
摘 錄 訓 兵 輯 要 *Tsĭh lŭh heun ping tsĕh yaou.* "An epitomised Work on Military Tactics." [1820?]. 8°.

平 陽 營 PING-YANG YING.
平 陽 營 輿 圖 *Ping yang ying yu too.* "A Map of the Camp at Ping-yang," [with a full description, and the muster roll of the Garrison. 1800?].

Another copy.

—— [A Map of the Ping-yang Camp, in the Province of Chĕ keang. 1840?].

普 天 POO TEEN.
普 天 心 修 *Poo teen sin sew.* "Religious Exercises for the Edification of the Hearts of Mankind." 716 folios. 7 keuen. [1750?]. obl.

51

REES (John).
Birdseye view of the Coast of China from Quemoy
Island to Meichow Island and Harbour. By
J. R. 1834.

REES (Thomas).
Chart of the entrance to the River Min in Fu chau
fu. By Captain T. R. (Together with a chart
of the Bay of Hocsieu . . . from a Dutch MS.)
1832.

—— [Chart of the entrance of the River Min in Fu
chau fu. By Captain T. R. (Together with a
chart of the Bay of Hocsieu . . . . from a
Dutch MS. Another copy of the above without
letters.) 1832].

RICE.
[A number of Coloured Drawings illustrating the
cultivation of Rice. 1840 ?]. 4°.

ROSS (Daniel).
Continuation of the coast of China from Breaker
Point to the Lamock Islands. By D. R. 1816.

—— Plan of Namo Harbour on the South Coast of
China. By D. R. 1807.

ROSS (Daniel) and MAUGHAN (Philip). *Bombay
Marine.*
Survey of part of the south coast of China [from
the City of Teen-pĭh to the Boćca Tigris, in the
Province of Kwang-tung]. By D. R. and P. M.
1807.

桑 Sang.
農桑雅化 *Nung sang ya hwa.* [The Customs
of] the Mulberry - growing tribes [in Kwei-
chow]. With illustrations. [1800 ?]. 8°

象山縣 Seang-shan Heen.
[A Map of the Coast of Seang-shan Heen.
1840 ?].

—— [A Map of Seang-shan Heen. 1840 ?].

—— [A Map of Seang-shan Heen in the Province of
Chĕ-keang. 1840 ?].

選 Seuen.
雜選 *Tsă seuen.* "Miscellaneous Selections."
[Poetry.] 1825. 8°.

示 She.
錄呈續出示文冊 *Lŭh ching sŭh chŭh she wăn
tsĭh.* "Memoranda of the Proclamations issued"
[by the Prefect of Soochow. 1830 ?]. 8°.

時 She.
時哉弗矢 *She tsae fŭh shĭh.* "No time should
be lost." A collection of Foo Poems.
[1800 ?]. 8°.

詩 She.
御製全韻詩 *Yu che tseuen yun she.* "An
Historical Poem." By the Emperor [Keen-
lung ?]. [1790 ?]. 8°.

試策 She tsĭh.
試策讀本 *She tsĭh tŭh pun.* "Examination
Studies." [A Collection of Essays.
1840 ?]. 8°.

SILK.
[A Number of Coloured Drawings illustrating the
Manufacture of Silk. 1840 ?]. 4°.

辛棄疾 Sin Ke-tseĭh.
阿計替傳 *A Ke-tsan chuen.* A biography of
A ke-tsan. [1800 ?]. 8°.

—— 竊憤錄 *Tsëĕ fun lŭh.* Private Political Records.
[Embracing the period from 1132 to 1309.
With a supplement. 1800 ?]. 8°.

性涵 Sing-han.
祜緣善慶 *Fŭh yuen shen king.* "Divinely
caused Benedictions" [being a promise of Blessings to be conferred on the subscribers for the
Restoration of the Bell Tower of the Teen-kung-
hung-fă temple. By the Priest Sing-han].
1839. 4°.

踈 Soo.
踈矢餉鞘 *Soo shĭh heang seaou.* "Paper relating to the Distribution of Rations" in Keang-
shan Heen. 1812. 8°.

蘇軾 Soo Shĭh.
代張方平諫用兵書 *Tae Chang Fang-ping
keen yung ping shoo.* "An Essay on Chang
Fang-ping's Advice on War." [1840 ?]. 8°.

松江營 Sung-keang Ying.
[A Map of the Sung-keang Camp. 1840 ?].

松 陽 縣 SUNG-YANG HEEN.

[A Map of the Military Posts in the District of Sung-yang in the Province of Chĕ-keang. 1840?].

朱 玉 SUNG YŬH.

See 屈 原 KEÜH YUEN. 離 騷 Le saou. "The exiled mourner." . . . . Together with pieces by Sung Yŭh, etc. 8°.

遂 安 縣 SUY-GAN HEEN.

遂 安 縣 山 川 之 圖 Suy-gan Heen shan chuen che too. "A Map of the mountains and streams of Suy-gan Heen." [1820?].

SZE-CHUEN.

A Military Map of the Country between Hung-ya Heen and Se-chang Heen in the Province of Sze-chuen. 1840?].

大 悲 TA PEI.

大 悲 懺 儀 合 節 Ta Pei tsan e ho tsĕĕ. "The Ritual addressed to the Great Compassionate [Kwan she yin], with directions as to the Rites to be observed." Transcribed by the Priest Yĕ-lin. 1837. 8°.

大 荊 營 TA-KING YING.

大 荊 營 水 陸 輿 圖 Ta-king ying shwuy lŭh yu too. "A plan of the Ta-king Camp showing the land and water communications." [1820?].

台 州 府 TAE CHOW FOO.

海 洋 全 圖 Hae yang tseuen too. "A Map of the Sea Coast of the Prefecture of Tae chow" [in the Province of Chĕ keang. 1800?].

台 協 營 TAE-HĔĔ YING.

[A Map of the Tae-hĕĕ Camp in the Province of Chĕ-keang. 1840?].

太 湖 TAE HOO.

太 湖 圖 說 Tae hoo too shwŏ. "The Geography of the Tae Lake" [in the Province of Keang-soo]. [1820?]. 8°.

太 湖 營 TAE-HOO YING.

[A Map of the Tae-hoo Ying in Chĕ-keang. 1840?].

—— [A Map of the Tae-hoo Ying. 1840?].

太 平 營 TAE-PING YING.

[A Map of the Tae-ping Ying in Chĕ-keang. 1840?].

TAE TSANG.

[A Map of the fortifications of the Lew river in the sub-Prefecture of Tae tsang. 1800?].

TALES.

[A collection of tales, and a few medical prescriptions. 1790?]. 16°.

道 德 堂 TAOU TĬH TANG.

道 德 堂 秘 傳 正 体 洪 範 陰 陽 二 宅 要 訣 Taou tĭh tang pe chuen ching te Hung fan yin yang urh tsĭh yaou keuĕ. "The Taou tĭh Hall treatise on the important geomantic Secrets of the eternal Rule of Fitness." [1800?]. 8°.

TCHARN-SHARNG.

[A list of the contents of a room, on which, according to the presentation note, is stamped the seal of the prison of Tcharn-sharng where Messrs. Bowen and Flint were imprisoned from Dec. 6, 1759 to Nov. 2, 1762.] 8°.

弔 TEAOU.

弔 奠 登 記 Teaou tsun tăng ke. A Record of the number of Candles offered in Ancestral Worship [at some unnamed temple?]. 1835. 8°.

帖 TĔĔ.

往 來 帖 式 Wang lae tĕĕ shĭh. "Specimens of occasional visiting cards, polite notices, etc." [1790?]. 8°.

天 師 TEEN SZE.

天 師 靈 符 奇 驗 Teen sze ling fu ke yen. "Testimonies to the efficacy of the Spiritual Charms of the Head of the Taouist Sect." [1800?]. 8°.

定 海 TING HAE.

[A Map of the District of Ting-hae, i.e. The Island of Chusan. 1820?].

TING HAE.

[Map of the city of Ting hae, and the surrounding country. 1800?].

屠 隆 TOO LUNG.

漢 魏 叢 書 Han Wei tsung shoo. "Reprints of Works by Authors under the Han and Wei Dynasties." 147 folios. [1800?]. 8°.

彩 TSAE.

送 彩 科 儀 Sung tsae ko e. "The prosperity-bringing ritual." 1769. 8°.

MANUSCRIPTS.

籤 書 Tsan shoo.
　籤書籅 *Tsan shoo po.* "A note book of Expressions used in Taouist rituals."
　　　　　　　　　　　[1800?]. 8°.

曹 春 林 Tsaou Chun-lin.
　苗蠻合志 *Meaou Man hŏ che.* "An Account of the Meaou-tsze, and Man-tsze tribes." 4 keuen. 　　　　　　8°.

蔣 良 騏 Tseang Leang-ke.
　東華錄 *Tung hwa lŭh.* "A Summary of Events" [from the origin of the present Dynasty down to the year 1735.] 32 keuen. 　[1750?]. 8°.

　　Imperfect, containing only keuen 7–16.

焦 延 壽 Tseaou Yen-show.
　焦氏易林 *Tseaou she Yih lin.* "A Forest of Changes." See 屠隆 Too Lung. 漢魏叢書 *Han Wei tsung shoo.* "Reprints," etc. 8°.

錢 塘 Tseen tang.
　[A military map of the District of Tseen tang, in the Province of Chĕ keang. 　1820?].

七 十 一 Tseïh Shĭh-yĭh.
　西域瑣談 *Se yĭh so tan.* "Notes on the Western Frontier." 4 keuen. 　1777. 8°.

青 田 縣 Tsing-teen Heen.
　[List of the strength of the Garrisons in the Districts of Tsing-teen, Tsin-yun, King-ning, Lung-tseuen, and Yun-ho. 　1830?]. 8°.

青 村 營 Tsing-tsun Ying.
　[A Map of the Tsing-tsun Camp in the Province of Keang-soo. 　　　1840?].

靖 江 營 Tsing-keang Ying.
　[A Map of the Tsing-keang Camp in the Province of Keang-soo. 　　　1840?].

字 Tsze.
　雜字 *Tsă tsze.* "Mixed Characters." [A Collection of moral Maxims, Arithmetical Tables, etc.] 　　　　　1822. 8°.

慈 谿 縣 Tsze-ke Heen.
　慈谿縣呈送輿圖 *Tsze-ke Heen ching sung yu too.* "A Map of Tsze-ke Heen." 　[1820?].

自 遠 堂 Tsze-yuen Tang.
　自遠堂琴譜 *Tsze-yuen Tang kin poo.* "A Work on Music from the Tsze-yuen Hall."
　　　　　　　　　　　[1840?]. 8°.

桐 盧 Tung-loo.
　[A Map of the District of Tung-loo, in the Province of Chĕ keang. 　1820?].

VARO (Francisco).
　Vocabulario de la lengua Mandarina con el estilo y vocablos con que se habla sine legancia; compuesto por el P. F. F. V. 　　1695. 8°.

文 Wăn.
　四子文箋註 *Sze tsze wăn tseen choo.* "A Collection of Chinese Phrases composed of four Characters, with the Meanings attached." [Arranged in Alphabetical order.] 　[1790?]. 4°.

溫 州 府 Wăn-chow Foo.
　[A Map of the Coast in the Prefecture of Wăn-chow, in the Province of Chĕ-keang.
　　　　　　　　　　　1840?].

王 苑 先 Wang Yuen-seen.
　舉子詩 *Keu tsze she.* "The Poetry of a Graduate of the second Rank." 　[1820?]. 8°.

僞 Wei.
　集古僞錄 *Tseïh koo wei lŭh.* "A Collection of ancient Superstitions." 　[1750?]. 8°.

五 經 Woo king.
　五經類編節要 *Woo king luy peen tsĕĕ yaou.* "A Compendium of [Chow She-chang's?] Encyclopædia of the Five Classics."
　　　　　　　　　　　[1830?]. 8°.

五 斗 Woo tow.
　祈禳五斗天曹奏錢科儀 *Ke jang woo tow teen tsaou tsow tseen ko e.* "A Form of Prayer for Happiness and immunity from Sorrow."
　　　　　　　　　　　[1800?]. 8°.

吳 陸 Woo Lŭh.
　易傳 *Yih chuen.* "A commentary on the Book of Changes." With notes by Woo Lŭh, etc. See 屠隆 Too Lung. 漢魏叢書 *Han Wei tsung shoo.* "Reprints," etc. 8°.

吳 奇 彩 WOO KE-TSAE.

[Vocabularium Sinico-Anglicum. In this work the English words are represented by Chinese transcriptions. 1800?]. 24°.

吳 金 標 WOO KIN-PEAOU.

See 鎮 海 CHIN HAE. 鎮 海 營 水 陸 圖 冊 *Chin hae ying shwuy lŭh too tsih*. "Instructions" . . . [issued by . . . Woo Kin-peaou], etc. 1841. 8°.

武 義 縣 WOO-E HEEN.

[A Map of Woo-e in the Province of Chĕ-keang. 1840?].

物 WŬH.

詠 物 詩 選 *Yung wŭh she seuen*. "A Collection of Songs on Things." [8 keuen. 1800?]. 8°.

YANG-TSZE KEANG.

[A Chart of the Mouth of the Yang-tsze keang. 1840?].

瑤 天 列 宿 童 子 YAOU TEEN LĔĔ SŬH TUNG TSZE.

瑤 天 列 宿 童 子 法 懺 *Yaou teen lĕĕ sŭh tung tsze fă tsan*. "The Ritual on the Precepts of Yaou-teen-lĕĕ-sŭh-tung-tsze," [a Taouist Deity?] 1810. 8°.

野 林 YĔ-LIN.

See 大 悲 TA PEI. 大 悲 懺 儀 合 節 *Ta Pei tsan e ho tsĕĕ*. "The Ritual addressed to the Great Compassionate." . . . Transcribed by the Priest Yĕ-lin, etc. 1837. 8°.

鹽 城 縣 YEN-CHING HEEN.

[A Map of the District of Yen-ching in the Province of Keang-soo. 1840?].

鹽 城 營 YEN-CHING YING.

[A Map of the Yen-ching Camp in the Province of Keang-soo. 1840?].

嚴 州 府 YEN-CHOW FOO.

[A Map of Yen-chow Foo in the Province of Chĕ-keang. 1840?].

月 YUĔ.

月 中 每 日 念 聖 道 *Yuĕ chung mei jih neen shing taou*. "Studies of the Sacred Doctrine [of Christianity] for every Day in the Month." 2 keuen. [1840?]. 8°.

—— 月 令 *Yuĕ ling*. "A Treatise on the Periods into which the Year is divided." [1830?]. 8°.

元 辰 星 YUEN SHIN SING.

總 讚 元 辰 星 燈 *Tsung tsan yuen shin sing tăng*. "Hymns of Praise in honour of the Sun, Moon and Stars." [1800?]. 8°.

玉 環 廳 YŬH-HWAN TING.

[A Map of Yŭh-hwan Ting. 1840?].

—— [A Map of Yŭh-hwan Ting. 1840?].

雲 和 縣 YUN-HO HEEN.

[A Map of Yun-ho Heen. 1840?].

雲 臺 YUN TAE.

雲 臺 獻 瑞 *Yun tae heen shwuy*. "A Keepsake from the Cloud Gallery." [Beautifully illustrated. 1750?]. fol.

342

INDEX OF TITLES.

總 讚 元 辰 星 燈 *Tsung tsan yuen shin sing tăng.* See 元 辰 星 YUEN SHIN SING.

慈 裕 縣 呈 送 輿 圖 *Tsze-ke Heen ching sung yu too.* See 慈 裕 縣 TSZE-KE HEEN.

字 音 辯 異 *Tsze yin peen e.* See BRANCATUS (FRANCISCUS).

自 遠 堂 琴 譜 *Tsze-yuen Tang kin poo.* See 自 遠 堂 TSZE-YUEN TANG.

東 華 錄 *Tung hwa lŭh.* See 蔣 瓦 騏 TSEANG LEANG-KE.

睆 翠 樓 時 藝 *Wan tsuy low she e.* See 莊 綸 渭 CHWANG LUN-WEI.

王 氏 宗 譜 *Wang she tsung poo.* See 陳 鴻 聲 CHIN HUNG-SHING.

往 來 帖 式 *Wang lae tëĕ shĭh.* See 帖 TĔĔ.

五 經 類 編 節 要 *Woo king luy peen tsëĕ yaou.* See 五 經 WOO KING.

無 雙 譜 *Woo shwang poo.* See 金 古 瓦 KIN KOO-LEANG.

瑤 天 列 宿 童 子 法 懺 *Yaou teen lëĕ sŭh tung tsze fă tsan.* See 瑤 天 列 宿 童 子 YAOU TEEN LËĔ SŬH TUNG TSZE.

易 傳 *Yĭh chuen.* See 京 房 KING FANG.

御 製 全 韻 詩 *Yu che tseuen yun she.* See 詩 SHE.

月 中 每 日 念 聖 道 *Yuĕ chung mei jĭh neen shing taou.* See 月 YUĔ.

月 令 *Yuĕ ling.* See 月 YUĔ.

粵 海 關 外 洋 船 牌 *Yuĕ hae kwan wae yang chuen pae.* See CANTON. CUSTOM HOUSE.

雲 臺 獻 瑞 *Yun tae heen shwuy.* See 雲 臺 YUN TAE.

詠 物 詩 選 *Yung wŭh she seuen.* See 物 WŬH.

NEWLY ACQUIRED MANUSCRIPTS.

呈 報 運 到 茶 葉 件 數 清 冊 *Ching paou yun taou cha yĕ keen shoo tsing tsĭh.*

礙 勸 洗 嘆 咭 唎 策 *E tseaou se Ying-keĭh-le tsĭh.*

佛 祖 歷 代 通 載 *Fŭh tsoo leĭh tae tung tsae.* 10 keuen.

江 南 海 關 則 例 *Keang nan hae kwan tsĭh le.*

各 省 地 名 *Kŏ săng te ming.*

廣 東 探 報 *Kwang tung tan paou.*

釋 迦 方 誌 *Shĭh kea fang che.*

守 邊 輯 要 *Show peen tseĭh yaou.*

騰 黃 勅 命 告 示 賞 格 *Tăng hwang chĭh ming kaou she shang kĭh.*

粗 定 各 口 章 程 *Tsoo ting kŏ kow chang ching.*

諭 示 抄 錄 *Yu she chaou lŭh.*

STEPHEN AUSTIN AND SONS, PRINTERS, HERTFORD.

Supplementary Catalogue of Chinese Books and Manuscripts in the British Museum

大英博物馆藏中文刻本写本目录续编

SUPPLEMENTARY CATALOGUE

OF

CHINESE BOOKS AND MANUSCRIPTS

IN THE

BRITISH MUSEUM

BY

ROBERT KENNAWAY DOUGLAS,

KEEPER OF THE DEPARTMENT OF ORIENTAL PRINTED BOOKS AND MSS. AT THE BRITISH MUSEUM.

PRINTED BY ORDER OF THE TRUSTEES OF THE BRITISH MUSEUM.

LONDON.

1903.

HERTFORD:

STEPHEN AUSTIN AND SONS,
PRINTERS.

PREFACE.

SINCE the appearance of the Catalogue of the Chinese Books in the British Museum, published in 1877, a large number of works have been added to the collection. These are represented in the present Supplementary Catalogue, and consist of much the same description of works as those which appear in the earlier volume. Some few, however, are on subjects which suggest special mention.

As is well known, the art of printing spread from China to Korea, and onward to Japan, in both of which last-named countries the literature was adopted as well as the art. It is, in this connection, interesting to observe the class of works which the scholars in the two empires especially delighted to honour. These mostly consist of classical, literary, and religious (Buddhist) works, and are, as a rule, excellent specimens of typography. Through the gift of Sir Ernest Satow, whose bibliographical labours have extended over many lands, a considerable number of these Chinese books, printed at early dates in Korea and Japan, have been added to the Museum Library.

A valuable collection of letters and papers connected with General Gordon's campaign against the T'aip'ing rebels will be found recorded, many being letters from Le Hung-chang with reference to the conduct of the campaign, and clearly proving the international difficulties with which General Gordon had to contend when in command of the " Ever Victorious Army."

As might be expected from the efforts which for some years have been made by philanthropists to enlighten the Chinese, the Catalogue makes mention of many translations of European works. Most of these are either of a religious tendency or bear on the mechanical inventions of the West. And in connection with these may be mentioned a certain number of works on reforms in the Constitution by native authors, notably a work entitled " China's only Hope " by the great Viceroy Chang Che-t'ung.

A few volumes from the Imperial libraries of Peking have lately been added to the collection, the most important of which is a volume from the huge Encyclopædia compiled by the order of the Emperor Yung-lo (1403–1425) and consisting of 22,877 sections in 11,100 volumes. This volume was saved from the fire which destroyed the Hanlin College, during the siege of the Legations in 1900, and was presented to the Museum by Professor Giles, of Cambridge.

The orthography employed in the present volume is that which was adopted in the earlier Catalogue, with some slight modifications.

ROBERT K. DOUGLAS.

May, 1903.

前　言

1877年出版的《大英博物馆馆藏中文图书目录》问世以来，又有大量著作加入馆藏。本《目录续编》著录了这些图书，对这些著作的描述方式与之前的目录几乎完全相同，但有些问题还需要特别说明。

众所周知，印刷术由中国传入韩国，然后传入日本，随印刷术一同传入韩国和日本的还有中国文献。有鉴于此，观察韩国和日本学者特别乐意捐献哪类作品是一件极为有趣之事。这些文献主要包括古代典籍、文学作品、宗教（佛教）著作，一般都是活版印刷的精品。萨道义爵士（Sir Ernest Satow）拥有很多国家的书籍，通过他的捐赠，韩国和日本早期印刷的大量中文书籍成为大英博物馆的馆藏。

《目录续编》还包含一些有价值的书信和文件，这些藏品与戈登（Gordon）将军镇压太平天国运动有关，大部分是李鸿章关于作战的书信，清晰地反映了戈登将军在指挥"常胜军"时需要克服的国际性困难。

近年来有很多博爱主义者可能致力于启蒙中国人，翻译了大量的欧洲作品，本《目录续编》中也著录了很多此类翻译著作。这些译著大部分具有宗教倾向，或介绍西方的机械发明。与此类图书相关，还应该提及中国本土作者有关政体改革的一些著作，特别是张之洞总督名为《劝学篇》（*China's only Hope*）的作品。

最近，来自北京朝廷图书馆的数册图书也成为大英博物馆的馆藏，其中最重要的一册图书来自永乐皇帝（1403–1425年）下令编纂的《永乐大典》，共22877卷，11100册。1900年清廷和义和团围攻使馆时，翰林院毁于大火，上述一册图书幸免于难，由剑桥大学的翟理斯（Giles）教授赠与大英博物馆。

本册《目录》所使用的拼字法与之前《目录》使用的拼字法保持一致，只进行了一些微调。

罗伯特·K·道格拉斯（Robert K. Douglas）

1903年5月

（管宇译，彭萍校）

SUPPLEMENTARY CATALOGUE

OF

CHINESE BOOKS AND MSS.

ACA—AHT

ACADEMIES, ETC.: *Helsingfors. — Suomalais - Ugrilainen Seura.* Inscriptions de l'Orkhon. Recueilliés par l'expédition finnoise 1890. [With plates.] pp. xliv, 48. *Helsingfors,* 1892. Fol. **15299. d. 3.**

—— *Paris: École spéciale des Langues Orientales vivantes. — Chih louh kouoh kiang yuh tchi.* Histoire géographique des Seize Royaumes. Ouvrage traduit du Chinois . . . et annoté par Abel des Michels. Fasc. 1. *Paris: E. Leroux,* 1891, *etc.* 8°. **11098. b. 1.**

In progress.

—— *Paris: École spéciale des Langues Orientales vivantes.*—COURANT (MAURICE). Bibliographie Coréenne. Tableau littéraire de la Corée, contenant la nomenclature des ouvrages publiés dans ce pays jusqu'en 1890 ainsi que la description et l'analyse détaillées des principaux d'entre ces ouvrages. 3 vols. 1894–96. 8°. **11098. c. 11.**

ÆSOP. "Æsop's Fables." Compiled [by R. Thom, and adapted and arranged by A. J. May] for the use of Chinese studying English, and English studying Chinese. *Hongkong: "China Mail" Office,* 1891, *etc.* 8°. **11100. c. 9.**

In progress.

—— *E shih pe chuen.* "Tales of E Shih pe." [Nine fables of Æsop translated into Chinese by Robt. Thom.] Presented by the Rev. David Thom. Nos. 1–4. [*Canton?*], 1837–39. 8°. **15331. d. 6.**

ÆSOP. 意拾喻言 *E-shih yu yen.* "Æsop's Fables." Translated into Chinese by R. Thom. MS. [1840?] 4°. **15331. d. 18.**

—— 伊娑菩喻言 *E-so-p'oo yu yen.* "Æsop's Fables." Translated into Chinese by "Po wăn keu sze." *Hongkong,* 1890. 12°. **15331. b. 17.**

阿桂 AH KWEI. 欽定滿洲源流考 *K'in ting Man chow yuen lew k'aou.* "An Examination into the Origin of the Manchoos." Compiled, by Imperial Order, by Ah Kwei, Yu Min-chung, Ho Shin, and others. 20 keuen. 1777. 8°. **15297. b. 1.**

—— 八旬萬壽盛典 *Pă seun wan show shing teen.* "A Memorial of the 80th Birthday of the Emperor K'ien-lung." Compiled by Ah-kwei, Ke Hwang, Ho Shin, and others. 120 keuen. 1792. 8°. **15296. e. 4.**

阿字無 AH-TSZE WOO. 海幢阿字無禪師語錄 *Hai chwang Ah-tsze woo shen sze yu lüh.* "The Sayings of the Priest Ah-tsze woo, of the Hai-chwang Monastery" at Canton. Edited by the Priest Lŏ-shwŏ-kin-peen. 2 keuen. [1800?] 8°. **15101. b. 27.**

Imperfect, containing only Keuen 1.

—— 光宣臺集 *Kwang seuen t'ai tseih.* The Kwang-seuen Gallery Collection of Buddhist Writings. By Ah-tsze-woo. Edited by Koo-ching and Koo-yun. 25 keuen. [1810?] 8°. **15101. b. 26.**

1

ALE—BIB

ALENI (Julio). See 四字經 Sze tsze king. 四字經文 Sze tsze king wăn. "The Four-character Classic . . ." [Said to have been written by J. A. ?], etc. 1898. 12°.

15200. aa. 1.

ALLEN (Clement Francis Romilly). See She King. "The Book of Chinese Poetry . . ." Metrically translated by C. F. R. A., etc. 1891. 8°.

11099. c. 4.

ALLEN (Young John). See 林樂知 Lin Yoh-chih.

15296. a. 30.

An anatomical Plate of the human frame. Without title. [1800?] A sheet. 15252. e. 10 (1).

—— [Another copy.] 15252. e. 10 (2).

'ANG-TSE. 'Ang-tse t'u-wa z-ü. "A Primer for learning to read the Romanized Dialect of Hangchow." [By A. Elwin.] pp. 21. London, 1876. 8°. 15229. b. 23.

—— 'Ang-tse t'u-yin Tsan-Me-s. "A Hymn-book in the Romanized Dialect of Hangchow." Shanghai, 1872. 8°. 15118. a. 21.

ANNAM. See France: Napoleon III, Emperor. 和約書 Ho yŏ shoo. "The . . . Text of the Treaty" concluded in 1862 between France and Spain on the one part and Annam on the other part. 1862. 8°. 15241. c. 5.

A Notice announcing Death of Pope Innocent XIII. Without title. [1724?] A sheet. 15303. d. 12.

ARMENGAUD (Jacques Eugène). See 白力蓋 Pih Leih-kai. 器象顯奧 K'e seang heen chin. "Drawings for Engineers and Machinists . . ." Adapted from the work of . . . J. E. Armengaud, etc. 8°. 15259. h. 2.

AUBERT (Charles). See Tin Tun-ling. "Tin Tun-ling . . . La Petite Pantoufle . . . Traduction de . . . C. A., etc. [1875?] 8°.

11100. f. 3.

A volume of Copperplate Engravings (without title), representing scenes in the mountains near Jehol, the originals of which are used to illustrate the Book of Poems on the beauty of those mountains by the Emperor K'ang-he.

15255. e. 19.

A volume of Drawings illustrating the various processes employed in the preparation of Tea. Without title. [1800?] 4°. 15257. d. 33.
No letterpress.

BAKER (Charles), Headmaster of the Yorkshire Institution for the Deaf and Dumb. Graduated Reading; comprising a circle of knowledge in 200 lessons. Translated into Chinese by J. Legge. Hongkong, 1856. 8°. 11099. c. 6.

—— [Another copy.] 11099. c. 42.

—— [Another edition.] Shanghai, 1873. 8°.

15229. a. 34.

BALL (Dyer), M.D. See Periodical Publications. Hongkong. 華番和合通書 Hwa Fan ho hŏ t'ung shoo. "The Anglo-Chinese Almanac . . ." [Edited by Dr. D. B.] 1847. 8°. 15298. a. 38.

—— "The Höng shán, or Macao Dialect: a comparative syllabary of the Höng shán and Cantonese pronunciations. . . ." Reprinted from the China Review, p. 31. Hongkong, 1897. 8°. 11098. a. 32.

BALLADS. A collection of 258 Ballads from Peking. 14 vols. MS. [Peking, 1880?] 8°.

Or. 4447.

BALLER (F. W.). See K'ang He, Emperor. "The Sacred Edict, with a translation . . . notes and vocabulary by F. W. Baller." 1892. 8°. 11098. b. 15.

BARCHET (S. P.). See 酒 Tsew. 戒酒論 K'eae tsew lun. "On Temperance." [By S. P. B.?], etc. 1876. 8°. 15200. c. 48.

BAU, Cō. See Fautrat (   ).

BEAL (Samuel). See Lung shu. Suh-ki-li-lih-kiu . . . or "Friendly Letter," written by Lung shu . . . Translated . . . By S. B., etc. 1892. 8°. 11100. b. 27.

BIBLE. 舊約全書 (新約全書) Kiu yŏ ts'euen shoo (Sin yŏ ts'euen shoo). Both Testaments have English title-pages. Shanghai, 1864. 8°. 15117. a. 34.

—— 舊約全書 (新約全書) Kew yŏ ts'euen shoo (Sin yŏ ts'euen shoo). The Old and New Testaments. Translated by a Committee of Translators. Old Testament, 7 vols. ; New Testament, 2 vols. Hongkong, 1864–66. 8°.

15116. b. 5.

—— 舊約全書 Kew yŏ ts'euen shoo. "The Old Testament," translated into Chinese by E. C. Bridgman and M. S. Culbertson. 39 keuen. Shanghai, 1863. 8°. 15118. d. 1.

2

BIBLE : OLD TESTAMENT. 欽定舊遺詔聖書 *K'inting kew e chaou shing shoo.* "The Old Testament. Edited by command" of the T'aip'ing T'eenwang. 6 keuen. [*Nanking* ?], 1853. 8°. **15117. e. 20.**
This version contains only the Books of Genesis, Exodus, Leviticus, Deuteronomy, and Joshua.

—— *Amoy Dialect.* Kū-iok ê sèng-keng. Printed in Roman characters. Containing only 1 Kings, Job, Psalms, Ezekiel (in duplicate), and Daniel to Malachi. *London*, 1882, etc. 8°. **15116. a. 9.**

—— [Another edition.] Containing only Genesis to Deuteronomy, Joshua, Judges, 1 Samuel to 2 Kings, Job to Proverbs, Isaiah, Jeremiah, and Lamentations. *London*, 1883. 8°. **3070. aa. 42.**

—— *Pentateuch. Mandarin Dialect.* 摩西五經 *Mo se woo king.* "The Five Books of Moses." Translated into the Mandarin Dialect by the Peking Committee. *Shanghai*, 1875. 8°.
15117. d. 22.

—— *Genesis.* [*Mandarin Dialect.*] 創世記 *Ch'wang she ke.* [Translated by Rev. William Ashmore and Miss A. M. Fielde ?] *Foochow Foo*, 1879. 8°. **15117. c. 1.**

—— *Genesis.* 創世記 *Ch'wang she ke.* [Translated into the Mandarin Dialect by Bishop Schereschewsky ?] *Shanghai*, 1883. 12°.
15117. d. 35.

—— *Genesis. Swatow Dialect.* Kū-ieh Tshàng-sì-kì T'shûan-tsu Èk-tso Tîe-chiu Péh-ūe phoi ū tshùan-tsu. *Swatow*, 1888. 8°. **15117. d. 38.**

—— *Chronicles. Amoy Dialect, romanized.* Kū-iok ē sèng-keng. Lek-tāi chì-liók Siōng-koàn (Hā-koàn). *London*, 1884. 8°. **15116. d. 51.**

—— *Psalms. Ningpo Colloquial.* The Book of Psalms. Translated by E. C. Lord, D.D. pp. 204. *Shanghai*, 1877. 8°. **15117. b. 36.**

—— *Minor Prophets. Amoy Dialect.* Daniel to Malachi. 1883. 8°. **15116. c. 35.**

—— *Jonah. Swatow Dialect.* Kū-ieh Iak-ná Tsu. Èk tsò Tîe-chiu péh-ūe phoi ū tshùan-tsu. *Swatow*, 1888. 8°. **15117. d. 37.**

—— *Parts. Ningpo Dialect.* Ts'ōng-shü kyi (C'ih yiæ-gyih kyi). The Books of Genesis and Exodus. A romanized version, by H. V. V. Rankin. *Shanghai*, 1871. 8vo. **15117. d. 27.**

BIBLE : NEW TESTAMENT. *Romanized Ningpo Dialect.* Ah-lah Kyiu-cü, Yi-su Kyi-toh-go, Sing Iah Shü. [Translated by the Ningpo Committee ?] *London*, 1868. 8°. **15117. c. 2.**

—— [Another edition.] *Cing-kōng Fu*, 1870. 4°. **15117. e. 17.**

—— [Another edition.] Revised for the American Bible Union by Rev. E. C. Lord, D.D. *Shanghai*, 1874. 8°. **15117. b. 17.**

—— 欽定前遺詔聖書 *K'in ting ts'een e chaou shing shoo.* "The New Testament. Edited by command" of the T'aip'ing T'eenwang. 8 keuen. 1853. 8°. **15117. e. 19.**
Wanting Keuen 3, containing the Gospel of St. John.

—— *Romanized Mandarin Dialect.* Kuan-hua Sin ioh ts'üen shu. Han-tsï fan Lo-ma-tsï. *London*, 1888. 8°. **15117. d. 42.**

—— *Romanized Amoy Colloquial.* Lán ē kiù-tsū Iā-so Ki-tok ē sin iok. Tsoàn su. 1882. 8°. **15116. d. 52.**

—— Seng io Cuing su. Guing-naing hu ga tu-kiong. Loma ci. pp. 655. *London : British and Foreign Bible Society*, 1896. 8°. **15117. d. 21.**

—— *Mandarin Dialect.* 新約聖書 *Sin yo shing shoo.* "The Sacred Books of the New Testament." An odd volume, containing only the Gospel of St. Luke and the Acts of the Apostles. *Shanghai*, 1879. 8°. **15117. d. 32.**

—— *Literary Style.* 新約全書 *Sin yŏ ts'euen shoo.* 24 keuen. *Shanghai*, 1880. 12°.
15117. d. 18.

—— *Literary Style.* 新約全書 *Sin yŏ ts'euen shoo.* "The New Testament," translated into *Wǎn le*, or Literary Style, by Yang Kih-fei, i.e. Dr. Griffith John. *Hankow*, 1890. 8°.
15116. a. 7.

—— *Mandarin Dialect.* 新約全書 *Sin yŏ ts'euen shoo.* "The New Testament," translated into the *Kwan hwa*, or Mandarin Dialect, by Yang Kih-fei, i.e. Dr. Griffith John. *Hankow*, 1892. 8°. **15116. a. 8.**

—— *Hakka Dialect.* "The New Testament. . . . By some Missionaries of the Basel Evangelical Missionary Society." *Basel*, 1874. 8°.
15117. d. 20.
Containing only the Four Gospels, and from the Epistle to the Galatians to the Revelations.

3

BIB

BIBLE: NEW TESTAMENT. *Gospels. Polyglott: Selections. Begin* Permulaan. Introduction. [Narrative of the Birth of Christ from the Gospels.] *Chinese, Malay,* and *English.* pp. 56. [1850 ?] 8°. 15116. d. 47.

—— *Gospels.* 四史聖經譯註 *Sze she shing king yih choo.* The Four Gospels. With notes. 4 keuen. *Hongkong,* 1852, 1893. 8°. 15117. d. 19.

Imperfect, containing the Gospels of Mark, Luke, and John.

—— *Matthew. Polyglott.* The Gospel of St. Matthew in Formosan, Sinkiang Dialect, with corresponding versions in Dutch and English. Edited and [reprinted] from Gravius's edition of 1661, by W. Campbell. *Formosan, Dutch,* and *English. London : Trübner & Co.,* 1888. 4°. 3068. eee. 19.

—— *Matthew. Amoy Dialect.* 馬太福音傳 *Má-thài hok-im toān. Amoy,* 1872. 8°. 15116. d. 48.

—— *Mark.* 馬可福音 *Ma k'o fuh yin.* "The Gospel of St. Mark." By the Peking Committee. *Peking,* 1873. 8°. 15200. c. 35.

—— *Mark. Canton Dialect.* 馬可福音傳 *Ma k'o fuh yin chuen.* "The Gospel of St. Mark." *Canton,* 1882. 8°. 15117. d. 33.

—— *Luke, Gospel. Romanized Foochow Dialect.* Lō-gă diong Hók-ĭng cŭ. *London,* 1889. 8°. 15117. d. 39.

—— *Luke. Swatow Dialect. Lū-kia kāi Hok-im-tñg.* "The Gospel of St. Luke." 1877. 8°. 15117. a. 23.

—— *John, Gospel. Hangchow Dialect.* An Sen Jah-'an dzun foh-in sö. Translated by G. E. Moule. pp. 86. *London,* 1878. 8°. 15117. b. 35.

—— *John, Gospel. Romanized Foochow Dialect.* Iók-hāng diong Hók-ĭng cŭ. *London,* 1886. 8°. 15117. d. 40.

—— [Another edition.] *London,* 1889. 8°. 15117. d. 41.

—— *John, Gospel.* 約翰真經釋解 *Yohan chin king shih keae.* "The [first seventeen chapters of the] true Gospel of St. John, with explanatory comments." By Hosin [i.e. B. Hobson]. *Hongkong,* 1853. 8°. 15116. a. 12.

BIBLE: NEW TESTAMENT. *John, Gospel. Cantonese Dialect.* 約翰傳福音書 *Yŏhan chuen fuh yin shoo. Canton : American Bible Society,* 1884. 8°. 15118. a. 46.

A manuscript note on the cover states that this Gospel was translated by the Rev. G. Preston.

—— *John, Gospel.* 約翰聖經釋解 *Yŏhan shing king shih keae.* "The Gospel of St. John, with a commentary" by Ho-sin [i.e. B. Hobson] and Moo-teh. pp. iii, 94. *Shanghai,* 1879. 8°. 15200. c. 22.

—— *John, Gospel. Selections.* The 3rd chapter of the Gospel according to Saint John, in T. M. Lucas's embossed stenographic characters, adapted to the Chinese language. *London : London Society for teaching the Blind to read,* 1853. Obl. 8°. 13007. b.

—— *Romans.* 羅馬書註解 *Lo-ma shoo choo keae.* "The Epistle to the Romans. With an explanatory commentary." [Translated into Chinese by W. H. Medhurst.] *Shanghai,* 1857. 8°. 15117. d. 28.

—— *Corinthians, 2nd Epistle.* 哥林多後書註釋 *Ko-lin-to how shoo choo shih.* "The 2nd Epistle to the Corinthians. Translated, with a commentary." By 陶錫祈 *T'aou Seih-k'e,* i.e. S. Dodd. pp. viii, 81. *Shanghai,* 1882. 8°. 15200. c. 21.

—— *Ephesians.* 使徒保羅寄以弗所聖會書註 *She t'oo Pao-lo ke E-fuh-so shing hwuy shoo choo.* "The Epistle of Paul to the Ephesians, with notes" by Lo Urh-te [i.e. E. C. Lord]. *Ningpo,* 1855. 8°. 15200. b. 14.

—— *Colossians.* 哥羅西書註釋 *Ko-to-se shoo choo shih.* "The Epistle to the Colossians. Commented on and explained." [By William Muirhead?] *Shanghai,* 1878. 8°. 15200. c. 38.

—— *James, Epistle. Swatow Dialect.* Sin-ieh Iá-kok tsu-sin. Ek tsò Tiē-chiu Péh-ue. *Swatow,* 1888. 8°. 15117. b. 34.

—— [Another edition.] 1888. 4°. 15117. b. 33.

—— *Peter, Epistles. Romanized Amoy Dialect.* Pí-tek chiān su. [Translated by Rev. J. Stronach?] [*Amoy,* 1867 ?] 8°. 15117. a. 17.

—— *John, Epistles. Romanized Amoy Dialect.* Sù-tō Iok-hān ē sam-su. "The three Epistles of St. John." [Translated by J. van N. Talmage?] *Amoy,* 1870. 8°. 15117. d. 36.

4

BIBLE: New Testament. *John, Epistles.* 約翰一二三書註釋 *Yo-han yih, urh, san, shoo choo shih.* "The three Epistles of St. John. With an explanatory commentary" by S. Dodd. *Shanghai,* 1881. 8°.   **15116. c. 34.**

—— *Parts. Romanized Amoy Dialect.* Ka-liáp-thài. I-hut-só. Hiu-lip-pi. Ko-tō-se. "The Epistles to the Galatians, the Ephesians, the Philippians, and the Colossians." [Translated by Rev. John van N. Talmage?] *Amoy,* 1870. 8°.   **15117. a. 16.**

—— *Parts.* 四史攸編耶穌基利斯督福音之會編 *Sze she yew pien Yaysoo Keleszetuh fuh yin che hwuy peen.* "A Narrative of the History of the Four Gospels, followed by that portion of the New Testament from the 1st chapter of the Acts to the end of the 1st chapter of the Epistle to the Hebrews." A note on the flyleaf describes this volume as "Evangelia quatuor Sinicè MSS.," and states that "this transcript was made at Canton in 1737. and 1738 by order of Mr. Hodgson, junior, who says that it has been collated with care and found very correct. Given by him to Sir Hans Sloane, Bart., in September, 1739." MS. ff. 378. 1737–38. Fol.   **Sl. 3599. 28. c.**

BILLEQUIN (A.). See 畢利幹 *Peih-le-kan.*

BLAIKIE (William). 幼學操身 *Yew heō ts'aou shin.* "Sound Bodies for our Boys and Girls." Translated into Chinese by K'ing P'ei, i.e. Paul King, with the assistance of Tih Joo-tan. With illustrations. pp. 16, 58. *Shanghai,* 1890. 8°.   **15344. e. 17.**

BLODGET (Henry). *See* Butt, afterwards Sherwood (Mary Martha). 亨利實錄 *Hăng-le shih luh.* "Little Henry and his Bearer." Translated into Chinese by H. B., etc. 1867. 8°.   **15200. c. 17.**

—— [Another copy.]   **15118. b. 47.**

—— [Another edition.] *Shanghai,* 1869.   **15200. c. 32.**

BLOXAM (Charles Loudon). See 浦陸山 *P'ooluh shan.*   **15259. g. 5.**

BLOXAM (Charles Loudon). 化學鑑原補編 *Hwa heō keen yuen poo peen.* "An Examination of the Principles of Chemistry. An amended edition." Being an adaptation of the Inorganic portion of Bloxam's "Chemistry, Inorganic and Organic." Translated into Chinese by Foolanya, i.e. J. Fryer. With plates. 6 keuen. With an appendix. [*Shanghai,* 1880?] 8°.   **15259. g. 4.**

BLUNTSCHLI (Johann Caspar). See 步倫 Poo-lun.   **15236. e. 7.**

BOGUSLAWSKY (A. von). See 斯拉弗司 Sze-la-fu-sze.

BONAPARTE (Roland), *Prince.* Documents de l'époque Mongole des xiiie et xive siècles. Inscriptions en six langues de la Porte de Kiu-yong koan, près Pekin ; Lettres, stèles, et monnaies en écriture Ouigoure et 'Phags-pa, dont les originaux ou les estampages existent en France. *Paris,* 1895. Fol.   **15300. c. 1.**

BOONE (William Jones). See 崇敎者 Tsung keaou chay.

BOREL (Henri). De Chineesche filosofie toegelicht voor niet-Sinologen. I, Kh'oeng Foe Tsz' (Confucius). Doon H. B. *Amsterdam : P. N. van Kampen & Zoon* (1896). 8°.   **11098. b. 19.**

BOUCHER (H.), S.J. *See* Kwan Hwa. Koan Hoa Tche-Nan. Boussole du langage mandarin, traduite et annotée par H. Boucher. 1887. 8°.   **11099. f. 9.**

BOURNE (John), *Civil Engineer.* See 蒲而捺 P'oo-urh-nă.

BREWITT-TAYLOR (C. H.). *See* Li Hungchang. Celebration of the 70th Birthday of Li Hungchang . . . Accompanying this English version is the Chinese text of the address presented by Chang Chihtung and others, translated by C. H. B-T., etc. 1892. 8°.   **15305. b. 11.**

BRIALMONT (Alexis Henri). See 伯里牙芒 Pih-le-ya-mang.

BRIDGMAN (Elijah Coleman). See Bible: *Old Testament.* 舊約全書 *Kew yŏ ts'euen shoo.* "The Old Testament," translated into Chinese by E. C. Bridgman, etc. 1863. 8°. **15118. d. 1.**

BROWN (Thomas). See 白勞那 Pih-laou-na.

BROWN (Thomas Marsh). Sketch Map of the Chu-kiang or Pearl River. *London,* [1895?].   **15261. c. 3 (1).**

BUDDHIST HELL. A coloured engraving representing the tortures of the Buddhist Hell. Without title. [1850?]　　15204. a. 1.

BUNYAN (John). See 鄱 陽 約 翰 P'oyang Yohan.　　15118. d. 4.

—— 人 靈 戰 紀 *Jin ling chen ke.* "The Holy War." Translated into Chinese by Moo Weileen, i.e. William Muirhead. pp. 159. *Shanghai,* 1884. 8°.　　15118. d. 27.

—— 續 天 路 歷 程 土 話 *Suh t'een loo leih ch'ing t'oo hwa.* "A sequel to Bunyan's Pilgrim's Progress, in the Canton Dialect." 6 keuen. *Canton,* 1871. 8°.　　15118. c. 37.

—— 天 路 歷 程 *T'een loo leih ch'ing.* "The Pilgrim's Progress." Translated into Chinese by W. C. Burns. A new edition. 5 keuen. *Shanghai,* 1869. 8°.　　15200. c. 13.

—— [Another copy.]　　15118. d. 25.

—— [Another edition.] *Shanghai,* 1872. 8°.　　15118. d. 24.

BURGH (Nicholas Proctor). See 白 爾 格 Pih-urh-kih.

BURNS (William C.). *See* Bunyan (John). 天 路 歷 程 *T'een loo leih ch'ing.* "The Pilgrim's Progress." Translated into Chinese by W. C. B., etc. 1869. 8°.　　15200. c. 13.

—— [Another edition.] 1872. 8°. 15118. d. 24.

BUTT, afterwards SHERWOOD (Mary Martha). 亨 利 實 錄 *Hăng-le shih luh.* "Little Henry and his Bearer." Translated into Chinese by H. Blodget. pp. 55. *Shanghai,* 1867. 8°.　　15200. c. 17.

—— [Another copy.]　　15118. b. 47.

—— [Another edition.] pp. 21. *Shanghai,* 1869. 8°.　　15200. c. 32.

—— *Siao Hyin-li teng gyi-go ti-'ŏ nying bu-zi.* "Little Henry and his Bearer." In the Romanized Ningpo Dialect. [Translated by Mrs. McCartee?] pp. 35. *Shanghai,* 1868. 8°.　　15200. b. 5.

BYRNE (Oliver). See 白 爾 捺 Pih-urh-na.

CALLERY (J　　M　　). The Encyclopædia of the Chinese Language, by J. M. C. 1842. 8°.　　15344. c. 25.

This volume, which consists only of the Preface and a specimen chapter, has on the cover the Chinese title 漢 文 總 書 *Han wăn tsung shoo.*

CAMPBELL (William). *See* Bible—New Testament : *Matthew, Polyglott.* The Gospel of St. Matthew, in Formosan. . . . Edited from Gravius's edition of 1661 by William Campbell, etc. 1888. 4°.　　3068. eee. 19.

—— The Articles of Christian Instruction in Favorlang-Formosan, Dutch, and English, from Vertrecht's Manuscript of 1650. With Psalmanazar's Dialogue between a Japanese and a Formosan, and Happart's Favorlang Vocabulary. Edited by the Rev. W. C. pp. xix, 199. *London : Kegan Paul, Trench, Trübner, & Co.,* 1896. 4°.　　11098. b. 17.

CANTON. A volume of Drawings illustrating the principal Trades at Canton. [1840?] Obl.　　15255. e. 23.

—— 粵 海 關 比 例 *Yuĕ hae kwan pe le.* "Customs Tariff for the Ports of the Province of Canton." [*Canton?*], 1809. 8°. 15239. a. 30.

—— 粵 海 關 稅 務 文 *Yuĕ hae kwan shwuy woo wăn.* "Canton Customs Permits." *Canton,* 1843.　　15239. a. 41.

CAPP (　　). See 哈 邦 Ka-pang.

CARUS (Paul). *See* Laou-Tsze. Lao-Tsze's Tao-Teh - King, Chinese - English. With introduction, transliteration, and notes. By Dr. P. Carus. 1898. 8°.　　11099. c. 40.

CATALOGUES. 彙 刻 書 目 合 編 *Wei kih shoo mŭh hŏ peen.* "A Catalogue of Books contained in the various collections of Reprints." Compiled by Koo Sew. 1799. 8°.　　15350. a. 1.

—— [Another copy.]　　15350. a. 2.

CAVAGNAC (P. de). See 眞 道 Chin taou. 眞 道 自 證 *Chin taou tsze ching.* "The true Religion proved by itself." [By Rev. P. de Cavagnac?], etc. 1898. 8°.　　15200. d. 17.

茶 Ch'a. 茶 總 *Ch'a tsung.* "A Tea Account Book." 1844. Obl.　　15297. d. 18.

查 樞 超 Ch'a Ke-chaou. 詞 學 全 書 *Tsze heŏ ts'euen shoo.* "A Complete Work on the Art of Rhyming," consisting of the *T'een tsze ming keae* by Maou Seen-shoo; the *Koo Kin tsze lun* by Wang Yew-hwa; the *T'een tsze too pao* by Lae E-pin; and the *Tsze yun* by Chung Han? Compiled by Ch'a Ke-chaou. 14 keuen. 1746. 8°.　　15321. d. 14.

CHALMERS (JOHN). See 湛約翰 CHIN YO-HAN.

張 CHANG. A letter addressed by Chang to Colonel Gordon on the subject of reports of disorganization in the Ever Victorious Army. MS. [1863 ?]　　　　　　　　　Or. 2338.

—— 張袁兩友相論 *Chang Yuen leang yew seang lun.* "Discussion [on Christianity] between the two friends Chang and Yuen." [By Dr. W. Milne.] pp. 44. A new edition. *Shanghai,* 1882. 8°.　　　　15200. c. 26.

—— 長遠兩友相論 *Ch'ang Yuen leang yew seang lun.* "Discussion between the two friends Ch'ang and Yuen." [By Dr. William Milne.] A new edition. 11 chapters. *Hankow,* 1883. 8°.　　　　　　15200. c. 5.

張昶 CHANG CH'ANG. See 張熙宇 CHANG HE-YU. 硃批增註七家詩選 *Choo p'e tsǎng choo ts'ih kea she seuen.* "Imperially Endorsed Poems . . ." With notes and commentaries by Chang Ch'ang, etc. 1857. 8°.　15323. e. 14.

張栻 CHANG CH'IH. 二程先生傳道粹言 *Urh Ch'ing seen sǎng chuen taou suy yen.* "A true expression of the doctrines of the two brothers Ch'ing Haou and Ch'ing E." 10 keuen. 1562. Fol.　　　　　15103. d. 22.
Printed in Korea from blocks.

張丞 CHANG CH'ING. See 四書 SZE SHOO. 四書合講 *Sze shoo hŏ keang.* "The Four Books" . . . Edited by Chang Ch'ing, etc. 1865. 8°.　　　　　　　15202. b. 20.

章程 CHANG CH'ING. 通商章程 *T'ung shang chang ch'ing.* [An Index to Characters employed] in the Trade Regulations ? MS. [1840 ?] 8°.　　　　15344. c. 26.

張仲景 CHANG CHUNG-KING. 金匱方歌括 *Kin kwei fang ko kwŏ.* "Prescriptions in Verse from the Golden Casket of Medicine by Chang Chung-king." By Ch'in Neen-tsoo. Edited by Ch'in Wei. 8 keuen. 1836. 8°.　　　　　　　15251. f. 11.

張仲純 CHANG CHUNG-SHUN. 大易象數鉤深圖 *Ta Yih seang soo kow shin t'oo.* "A Study of the Diagrams of the Book of Changes. With Illustrations." 3 keuen. 8°.　15212. c. 8.

爭春園 CHǍNG CH'UN YUEN. 爭春園 *Chǎng ch'un yuen.* "The Garden of Struggling Spring." A novel. With illustrations. 48 chapters. 1821. 12°.　　15331. a. 4.

張飛疇 CHANG FEI-CHOW. See 張路玉 CHANG LOO-YÜH. 張氏醫通 *Chang she e t'ung.* "The Complete Medical Work of Chang Loo-yüh." Edited by . . . Chang Fei-chow, etc. 1709. 8°.　　　　　15253. a. 5.

—— 傷寒兼證析義 *Shang han keen ching seïh e.* "Complete Evidence and Discriminating Explanations of Diseases arising from Cold." By Chang Fei-chow. [1709 ?] 8°. 15253. a. 10.

張海鵬 CHANG HAI-P'ǍNG. See 朱長文 CHOO CH'ANG-WǍN. 吳郡圖經續紀 *Woo keun t'oo king sǔh ke.* "A Supplement to the Illustrated Topography of Soo-chow Foo . . ." Edited by Chang Hai-p'ǎng, etc. 8°.　　15271. e. 9.

張熙宇 CHANG HE-YU. 硃批增註七家詩選 *Choo p'e tsǎng choo ts'ih kea she seuen.* "Imperially Endorsed Poems by seven Authors, viz.: Wang T'ingshao, Na Ts'ingngan, Lew Szewan, Lew Tihjun, Yang Kǎng, Le Sing, and Ch'in Ch'in." With notes and commentaries by Chang Ch'ang. Compiled by Chang Heyu. 7 keuen. 1857. 8°.　　15323. e. 14.

—— 七家詩輯註彙鈔 *Ts'ih kea she tseih choo wei ch'aou.* "A Collection of the Writings of the Seven Poets (Wang T'ing-shaou, Na Ts'ing-ngan, Le Sing, Ch'in Hang, Yang Kǎng, Loo Tih, and Lew Sze-wan). With notes and comments" by Wang Chih-kwei. Edited by Chang He-yu. 1870. 8°.　　15324. a. 12.

張華 CHANG HWA. 禽經 *Kin king.* "A Book on Birds." With a Commentary by Chang hwa. pp. 38. See 程榮 CH'ING YUNG. 漢魏叢書 *Han Wei ts'ung shoo.* "A Collection of Works by Authors of the Han and Wei Dynasties," etc. 1791. 8°.　　15318. a. 1.

—— 博物志 *Po wǔh che.* "Treatises on Diverse Matters." 10 keuen. See 程榮 CH'ING YUNG. 漢魏叢書 *Han Wei ts'ung shoo.* "A Collection of Works by Authors of the Han and Wei Dynasties," etc. 1791. 8°. 15318. a. 1.

張惠言 CHANG HWUY-YEN. See 周易 CHOW YÏH. 周易審義 *Chow yih shin e.* "The Meaning of the Chow Changes Examined . . ." Edited by Chang Hwuy-yen, etc. 1857. 8°.　　15212. d. 14.

7

CHA

張儒珍 CHANG JOO-CHIN. See 高第丕 KAOU TE-P'EI, and 張儒珍 CHANG JOO-CHIN. 文學書官話 *Wăn heŏ shoo kwanhwa.* "A Mandarin Grammar," etc. 1869. 8°. **15344. a. 9.**

張考夫 CHANG K'AOU-FOO. 楊園先生全集 *Yang yuen seen săng ts'euen tseĭh.* "The Complete Writings of the Doctor of the Aspen Garden," i.e. Chang K'aou-foo. Compiled by Yaou Leen. Edited by Hing Kwŏ-wan. 54 keuen. 1869. 8°. **15315. c. 1.**

章圭績 CHANG K'E-TSEĬH. 思綺堂文集 *Sze-k'e T'ang wăn tseĭh.* "Literary Papers from the Sze-k'e Hall." By Chang K'e-tseĭh. With notes. 10 keuen. 1722. 8°. **15319. e. 8.**

常璩 CHANG KEU. 華陽國志 *Hwa yang kwŏ che.* "An Account of the Kingdom of Hwa-yang," consisting of the States of Pa, Hanchung, Shuh, Tat'ung, and Nanchung, in Western and North-Eastern China. See 程榮 CH'ING YUNG. 漢魏叢書 *Han Wei ts'ung shoo.* "A Collection of Works by Authors of the Han and Wei Dynasties," etc. 1791. 8°. **15318. a. 1.**

張居正 CHANG KEU-CHING. 帝鑑圖說 *Te keen t'oo shwŏ.* "Illustrated Imperial Records." 6 parts. [1620?] Fol. **15236. c. 9.**
Printed in Japan with movable type.

—— 通鑑直解 *T'ung keen chĭh keae.* "An Explanatory Commentary on the Mirror of History." Edited by Kaou Chaou-lin. 28 keuen, with supplementary records of the Ming Dynasty in 16 keuen. 1631. 8°. **15288. e. 1.**

張景星 CHANG KING-SING. 宋詩別裁集 *Sung she pёĕ ts'ai tseĭh.* "A Collection of the Poetry of the Sung Dynasty." Compiled by Chang King-sing, Yaou Pei-keen, and Wang Yung-ke. 8 keuen. 1761. 8°. **15324. a. 2.**

—— 元詩別裁集 *Yuen she pёĕ ts'ai tseĭh.* "A Collection of the Poetry of the Yuen Dynasty." Compiled by Chang King-sing, Yaou Pei-keen, and Wang Yung-ke. 8 keuen and appendix. 1764. 8°. **15324. a. 3.**

昌觀 CH'ANG-KWAN. 稱讚淨土經 *Ch'ing tsan Tsing t'oo king.* "Sūtra in praise of the Pure Land." Edited by the Priest Ch'ang-kwan. A Japanese edition. 1380. Obl. 8°. **15103. c. 39.**

長老公 CH'ANG LAOU-KUNG. 福音讚美歌 *Fuh yin tsan mei ko.* "Gospel Hymns." In the Soochow Dialect. With an index in English. By Mrs. Fitch, as stated in a manuscript note on cover. Edited by Ch'ang Laou-kung. pp. i, 72. [*Shanghai?*], 1877. 8°. **15200. c. 30.**

張瓦 CHANG LEANG. 陰符經 *Yin fuh king.* "The Sūtra of Secret Charms." pp. ii, 24, 3. See 程榮 CH'ING YUNG. 漢魏叢書 *Han Wei ts'ung shoo.* "A Collection of Works by Authors of the Han and Wei Dynasties," etc. 1791. 8°. **15318. 1. a.**

張履安 CHANG LE-GAN. See 陳枚 CH'IN MEI. 留青新集 *Lew ts'ing sin tseĭh.* "A New Collection of Entertaining Stories . . ." Edited by Chang Le-gan, etc. 1707. 8°. **15334. d. 13.**

張路玉 CHANG LOO-YŬH. 張氏醫通 *Chang she e t'ung.* "The Complete Medical Work of Chang Loo-yŭh." Edited by Chang Tan-seen and Chang Fei-chow. 16 keuen. 1709. 8°. **15253. a. 5.**

—— 診宗三昧 *Chin tsung san mei.* "On Devoting the Energies to Examining the Centres" of Disease. By Chang Loo-yŭh. [1709?] 8°. **15253. a. 6.**

—— 本經逢原 *Pun king fung yuen.* "The Sources of the *Pun king.*" By Chang Loo-yŭh. 4 keuen. 1695. 8°. **15253. a. 7.**

—— 傷寒緒論 *Shang han seu lun.* "Successive Discourses on Diseases arising from Cold." By Chang Loo-yŭh. Edited by She Yuen-ts'een. 3 keuen. [1850?] 8°. **15252. a. 28.**

—— 傷寒大成 *Shang han ta ch'ing.* "A Complete Work on Diseases arising from Cold." By Chang Loo-yŭh. 2 keuen. 1668. 8°. **15253. a. 8.**

張穆 CHANG MŬH. 蒙古游牧記 *Mung koo yew mŭh ke.* "A History of the Nomad Mongol Tribes." By Chang Mŭh. Edited by Ho Tsew-taou. 16 keuen. 1867. 8°. **15275. a. 16.**

張穆誦 CHANG MŬH-SUNG. See 徐松星 SEU SUNG-SING. 唐兩京城坊考 *T'ang leang king ch'ing fang k'aou.* "An Examination of the Sites of the two Capitals of the T'ang Dynasty." Edited by Chang Mŭh-sung, etc. 1848. 8°. **15296. e. 2.**

8

張 寶 CHANG PAOU. 泛槎圖 *Fan ch'a t'oo.* "Illustrated Journeys in Central China." With four supplements, entitled—(1) *Suh fan ch'a t'oo,* 3 parts; (2) *E ch'a t'oo,* 4 parts; (3) *Le keang fan ch'aou t'oo,* 5 parts; and (4) *Suh fan ch'a t'oo,* 6 parts. *Canton,* 1819. 8°.

15269. e. 10.

張 寶 自 CHANG PAOU-TSZE. 汎槎圖 *Fan ch'a t'oo.* "Pencillings by the Way." With a Supplement. 6 parts. 1819–31. 8°. 15271. c. 12.

張 補 山 CHANG POO-SHAN. See 曹 之 升 TS'AOU CHE-SHING. 四書撼餘說 *Sze shoo chĭh yu shŏ.* "A Collection of Notes on the Four Books . . ." Edited by Chang Poo-shan, etc. 1832. 8°. 15202. b. 18.

張 浦 山 CHANG P'OO-SHAN. 國朝畫徵錄 *Kwŏ ch'aou hwa ching lŭh.* "Biographical Notices of Artists of the present Dynasty." By Chang P'oo-shan. Edited by Tseang Woowang and T'ang Nan-k'e. 3 keuen. 1739. 8°. 15305. b. 1.

章 象 德 CHANG SEANG-TĬH. See 蘅 退 士 SOO T'UY-SZE. 唐詩三百首註疏 *T'ang she san pĭh show choo soo.* "Three Hundred Pieces of Poetry . . ." With notes by Chang Seangtĭh, etc. 1835. 8°. 15321. c. 11.

張 小 浦 CHANG SEAOU-P'OO. 十三經集字摹本 *Shĭh san king tseĭh tsze moo pun.* "The Old Form of the Characters employed in the Thirteen Classics copied from the Original Texts." By Chang Seang-p'oo. Edited by Wang P'ung-shan. 4 keuen. 1849. 8°.

15344. a. 6.

—— [Another edition.] 1850. 8°. 15344. b. 10.

張 銑 CHANG SEEN. See 蕭 統 SEAOU T'UNG. 六臣註文選 *Luh ch'in choo wăn seuen.* "Elegant Extracts . . . with the Commentaries" of . . . Chang Seen, etc. 1607. Fol. 15320. e. 39.

張 西 源 CHANG SE-YUEN. 繡虎軒尺牘全集 *Sen hao heen ch'ĭh tŭh ts'euen tseĭh.* "The Variegated-Tiger Study Letter-writer." Compiled by Chang Se-yuen. 4 parts. 1796. 8°.

15348. a. 7.

張 上 若 CHANG SHANG-JŎ. See 杜 甫 TOO FOO. 杜文註解 *Too wăn choo keae.* "The Writings of Too Foo. . . ." Edited by Chang Shang-jŏ, etc. 1872. 8°. 15324. e. 3.

This is a volume appended to *Too she king ts'euen.*

張 商 英 CHANG SHANG-YING. 護法論 *Hoo fă lun.* "A Treatise on the Dharma." 1797. 8°.

15103. d. 7.

張 山 來 CHANG SHAN-LAI. See 王 丹 麓 WANG TAN-LUH. 檀几叢書 *T'an ke ts'ung shoo.* "The T'an ke Collection of Reprints. . . ." Edited by Chang Shan-lai, etc. 1695. 8°.

15315. b. 2.

—— 昭代叢書 *Chaou tai ts'ung shoo.* "A Collection of Reprints of Works by Authors under the present Dynasty." Compiled by Chang Shan-lai. In two parts. Pt. i, 40 keuen; Part ii, 50 keuen. [1700?] 8°. 15312. e. 6.

This is quite another collection to that contained in a compilation with the same title and placed at 15312. a. 5.

張 心 敬 CHANG SIN-KING. See 宋 鳴 琦 SUNG MING-K'E. 嘉定府志 *Kea ting foo che.* "A Topography of Kea-ting Foo." Compiled by . . . Chang Sin-king, etc. 1803. 8°.

15267. a. 2.

張 士 登 CHANG SZE-TĂNG. 三分夢全傳 *San fun mung ts'euen chuen.* "The Story of a Day-dream." Edited by Ho Fang-e. 16 keuen. 1823. 8°. 15334. d. 7.

張 誕 先 CHANG TAN-SEEN. See 張 路 玉 CHANG LOO-YŬH. 張氏醫通 *Chang she e t'ung.* "The Complete Medical Work of Chang Looyŭh." Edited by Chang Tan-seen, etc. 1709. 8°. 15253. a. 5.

—— 傷寒舌鑑 *Shang han she keen.* "The Tongue Test applied to Diseases arising from Cold." By Chang Tan-seen. [1709?] 8°.

15253. a. 9.

張 德 彝 CHANG TIH-E. 四述奇 *Sze shuh k'e.* "Strange Records from the Four Quarters of the World." By Chang Tih-e, who was sent to Europe after the murder of Margary in Yunnan. 16 keuen. 1883. 8°. 15297. c. 11.

—— [Another copy.] 15297. b. 21.

張 廷 輝 CHANG T'ING-HWUY. 武夷山 *Woo-e shan.* Eleven views in the Woo-e hills. Drawn and painted on silk, with the names of the celebrated sites added. By Chang T'ing-hwuy. [1750?] 4to. Or. 2351. 28. a.

張 廷 玉 CHANG T'ING-YŬH. See 乾 隆 K'EENLUNG, *Emperor.* 御製盛京賦 *Yu che Shing-king foo.* "A Poetical Eulogium on the City of Moukden. . . ." Edited by Chang T'ing-yŭh, etc. 8°. 15321. e. 3.

張度 CHANG TOO. 臨清直隸州志 *Lin ts'ing chih le chow che.* "A Topography of the Independent District of Lin ts'ing." By Chang Too and others. 11 keuen. 1785. 8°.
15269. e. 13.

張贄虞 CHANG TSAN-YU. 記事珠 *Ke sze choo.* "An Encyclopædia" of useful information. Edited by Wang Sun-heen. An enlarged edition. 10 keuen. 1827. 8°. 15024. c. 6.

張集馨 CHANG TSEÏH-HING. 金臺書院課士錄 *Kin t'ai Shoo yuen k'o sze luh.* "Examination Essays on Texts from the Classics by Scholars from the Kin-t'ai College." Compiled by Chang Tseïh-hing. *Peking,* 1873. 8°.
15319. e. 5.

張青父 CHANG TS'ING-FOO. 清河書畫舫 *Ts'ing ho shoo hwa fang.* "Criticisms on Caligraphy and Drawing, with Biographical Notices of men eminent in those Arts." By Chang Ts'ing-foo. 12 vols. 1763. 8°.
15255. e. 21.

張作楠 CHANG TSO-NAN. 揣籥小錄 *Ch'uy yŏ seaou luh.* "Tables of Terrestrial Longitude and Latitude." Edited by Keang Lin-t'ai. [1830 ?] 8°.
15255. c. 9.

—— 方田通法補例 *Fang t'een t'ung fă poo le.* "Additional Rules for Plane Mensuration." Edited by Fan King-fuh. 6 keuen. [1850 ?] 8°.
15255. c. 3.

—— 弧角設如 *Hoo keŏ she joo.* "Problems on Spherical Trigonometry." Edited by Keang Lin-t'ai. 2 keuen. 1832. 8°. 15255. c. 5.

—— 高弧細草 *Kaou hoo se ts'aou.* "On Calculating Arcs." 1821. 8°. 15255. d. 30.

—— 交食細草 *Keaou shih se ts'aou.* "Formulæ for Calculating Eclipses." 3 keuen. [1830 ?] 8°.
15255. c. 10.

—— [Another copy.] 15255. c. 10a.

—— 金華暑漏中星表 *Kin hwa kwei low chung sing peaou.* "Tables of the Meridian Stars according to the several hours." [1830 ?] 8°.
15255. c. 11.

—— [Another copy.] 15255. c. 11a.

—— 量倉通法 *Leang ts'ang t'ung fă.* "Rules for Solid Mensuration." Edited by Fan King-fuh. 5 keuen. [1830 ?] 8°. 15255. c. 1.

—— [Another copy ?] 15255. c. 19.

張作楠 CHANG TSO-NAN. 八線類編 *Pă seen luy peen.* "Tables of the Eight Lines of the Canon." [1830 ?] 8°. 15255. c. 8.

—— 八線對數類編 *Pă seen tuy soo luy peen.* "Logarithmic Tables on the Eight Lines." [1830 ?] 8°. 15255. c. 4.

—— 新測中星圖表 *Sin ts'ih chung sing t'oo peaou.* "Newly Projected Maps and Tables of the Meridian Stars." [1830 ?] 8°. 15255. c. 7.

—— [Another copy.] 15255. d. 31.

—— 新測更漏中星表 *Sin ts'ih kăng low chung sing peaou.* "Tables of Meridian Stars according to the several hours." [1830 ?] 8°.
15255. c. 19.

—— [Another copy.] 15255. c. 12.

—— 倉田通法續編 *Ts'ang t'een t'ung fă săh peen.* "Supplementary Rules for Solid and Plane Mensuration." Edited by Yu Tseun. 3 keuen. [1830 ?] 8°. 15255. c. 2.

張宗瓦 CHANG TSUNG-LEANG. See 王韜 WANG TAOU and CHANG TSUNG-LEANG. 普法戰紀 *P'oo Fă chen ke.* "A History of the Franco-German War. . . ." Compiled by . . . Wang Taou, and Chang Tsung-leang, etc. 1872. 8°.
15298. d. 1.

—— [Another edition.] 1898. 8°. 15297. a. 18.

張文炳 CHANG WĂN-PING. See 呂伯恭 LEU PIH-KUNG. 東萊博議 *Tung-lae pŏ e.* "The Writings of Leu Pih-kung. . . ." Edited by Chang Wăn-ping, etc. 1790. 8°.
15317. c. 11.

張問陶 CHANG WĂN-T'AOU. 船山詩草 *Ch'uen shan she ts'aou.* "The Poems" of Chang Wăn-t'aou. 20 keuen. 1874. 8°. 15324. b. 4.

張維屏 CHANG WEI-P'ING. 龍門縣志 *Lung-mun heen che.* "A Topography of Lung-mun heen" in the Province of Chihli. With maps. Compiled by Chang Wei-p'ing. 16 keuen. 1851. 8°. 15276. a. 1.

張揖 CHANG YIH. 博雅 *Pŏ ya.* "A Glossary of Terms." 10 keuen. See 程榮 CH'ING YUNG. 漢魏叢書 *Han Wei ts'ung shoo.* "A Collection of Works by Authors of the Han and Wei Dynasties," etc. 1791. 8°.
15318. a. 1.

10

張瑛 CHANG YING. See 曾國藩 TSĂNG KWŎ-FAN. 曾文正公文鈔 *Tsăng Wăn-ching Kung wăn ch'aou.* "The Literary Productions of Tsăng Kwŏ-fan. . . ." Edited by Chang Ying, etc. 8°.　　　　15317. d. 10.

———— 曾文正公奏議 *Tsăng wăn ching kung tsow e.* "The Memorials of Tsăng Kwŏ-fan. . . ." Edited by Chang Ying, etc. 1873. 8°.　　　　15241. c. 9.

———— 曾文正公奏議補編 *Tsăng wăn ching kung tsow e poo peen.* "A Supplementary Collection of the Memorials of Tsăng Kwŏ-fan. . . ." Edited by Chang Ying, etc. 1873. 8°.　　　　15317. d. 11.

張瑛如 CHANG YING-JOO. See 唐介軒 T'ANG KEAE-HEEN. 古文翼 *Koo wăn yih.* "Extracts from Ancient Literature. . . ." Edited by Chang Ying-joo, etc. 1873. 8°. 15312. b. 7.

張映璟 CHANG YING-KE. See 延豐 YEN FUNG. 欽定重修兩浙鹽法志 *K'in ting chung sew leang Chĕ yen fă che.* A Record of the Laws on the Salt Monopoly in the Province of Chĕ-keang. An Imperial republication. By Yen fung and others. 1801. 8°.　　15239. e. 1.

張遠 CHANG YUEN. See 杜甫 TOO FOO. 杜詩會稡 *Too she hwuy ts'uy.* "A Collection of the Poems of Too Foo. . . ." Edited with notes by Chang Yuen, etc. 1688. 8°. 15324. e. 7.

張玉書 CHANG YUH-SHOO. 佩文韻府 *Pei wăn yun foo.* "A Lexicon arranged according to the usual system of one hundred and six finals distributed among the five tones." Compiled under the special superintendence of the Emperor K'ang-he by a Commission consisting of Chang Yuh-shoo, Ch'in T'ing-king, Le Kwang-te, and others. 106 keuen. 1711. 8°.　　　　15347. d. & e.

張雲中 CHANG YUN-CHUNG. See 李時珍 LE SHE-CHIN. 本草綱目 *Pun ts'aou kang muh.* "A Materia Medica." Edited by Chang Yun-chung, etc. 1826. 8°.　　　　15252. e. 1.

張蓉鏡 CHANG YUNG-KING. See 王休 WANG KEW. 嘯堂集古錄考異 *Seaou t'ang tseĭh koo luh k'aou e.* "A Catalogue of the Antiquities collected at the Seaou T'ang. . . ." "With an Examination of the Different Readings" of the Inscriptions by Chang Yung-king, etc. 1812. 8°.　　　　15299. b. 8.

張餘圃 CHANG YU-POO. 佩文韻篆 *Pei wăn yun chuen.* "A Dictionary of the Seal Character, arranged according to the finals." By Chang Yu-poo. Edited by Lŭh Urh-p'eĭh. 6 keuen. 1797. 8°.　　　　15344. b. 7.

詹氏 CHAN SHE. See 王槐敬 WANG HWAI-KING. "An illuminated genealogy of the Chan Family. . . ." 1774. A scroll. 15296. e. 5.

湛約翰 CHAN YŎHAN [i.e. John Chalmers]. 正名要論 *Ching ming yaou lun.* "An important discourse on the correct name" of God in Chinese. pp. 30. *Hongkong,* 1876. 8°.　　　　15118. a. 28.

趙貞清 CHAOU CHING-TS'ING. 救嬰錄 *Kew ying luh.* "Admonitory Records against the practice of Infanticide." Compiled by Chaou Ching-ts'ing. 1875. 8°.　　15229. c. 38.

趙恒夫 CHAOU HĂNG-FOO. 寄園寄所寄 *Ke yuen ke so ke.* "The Guests who Lodge in the 'Dwelling Garden.'" A collection of essays. By Chaou Hăng-foo. 12 keuen. 1695. 8°.　　　　15320. a. 21.

趙宏 CHAOU HUNG. See 雷俠兒 LUY-HĔĔ-URH. 地學淺釋 *Te heŏ ts'een shih.* "Elements of Geology. . . ." With plates drawn by Chaou Hung, etc. 1873. 8°.　　　　15259. f. 4.

趙如光 CHAOU JOO-KWANG. See 江戴德 KEANG TAI-TIH. 地理志畧 *Te le che leŏ.* "A short work on Geography. . . ." Edited by Chaou Joo-kwang, etc. 1882. 4°. 15261. e. 9.

趙光 CHAOU KWANG. 桃花源記 *T'aou hwa yuen ke.* "The History of the Peach-blossom Spring." 1848. 8°.　　15297. a. 16.
　　In white characters on black ground.

趙烈文 CHAOU LĔĔ-WĂN. 淮軍平捻記 *Hwai keun p'ing neen ke.* "An Account of the Campaign of the Honan and Ganhwuy Troops against the Neenfei Rebels" in 1865-1868. Compiled by Chaou Lĕĕ-wăn. 12 keuen. 1877. 8°.　　　　15297. b. 18.

趙普 CHAOU P'OO. 煙波釣叟歌 *Yen po teaou sow ko.* "Verses on Military Tactics, with Superstitious Rules for the Guidance of Generals." By Chaou P'oo. Edited with notes by Lo Tung. [1800?] 8°. 15323. d. 9.

CHA

趙 怨 軒 CHAOU SHOO-HEEN. 本草綱目拾遺
Pun ts'aou kang mŭh shǐh e. "Omissions in the
Materia Medica of Le She-chin supplied" by
Chaou Shoo-heen. 10 keuen. 1871. 8°.

15255. a. 6.

朝 廷 CH'AOU T'ING. 朝廷准行正敎錄
Ch'aou t'ing chun hing ching keaou luh. "A
Record of the Sanction given by the Emperor
to the Correct Religion," i.e. Christianity. pp. 6.
1845. 8°. 15118. c. 44.

趙 子 昂 CHAOU TSZE-GANG. 趙子昂詩集
Chaou Tsze-gang she tseih. "Chaou Tsze-gang's
Poetry." Edited by T'an Pih-yuh. 7 keuen.
[1650?] 8°. 15324. a. 6.

Printed in Japan from blocks.

趙 文 晁 CHAOU WĂN-MEEN. See 徐 位 山 SEU
WEI-SHAN. 禹貢會箋 *Yu kung hwung
tseen.* "The Tribute of Yu. . . ." Edited by
Chaou Wăn-meen, etc. 1848. 8°. 15292. c. 3.

趙 曄 CHAOU YĔ. 吳越春秋 *Woo Yuĕ ch'un
ts'ew.* "A History of the States of Woo and
Yuĕ." 6 keuen. See 程 榮 CH'ING YUNG.
漢魏叢書 *Han Wei ts'ung shao.* A collection of works by authors of the Han and Wei
Dynasties, etc. 1791. 8°. 15318. a. 1.

趙 酉 CHAOU YEW. 寶山縣志 *Paou-shan heen
che.* "A Topography of Paou-shan Heen."
Compiled by Chaou Yew. 10 keuen. 1746. 8°.
15269. a. 11.

趙 翼 CHAOU YĬH. 甌北全集 *Gow pih ts'euen
tseĭh.* A complete collection of the writings
of Chaou Yĭh, otherwise Chaou Gow-pih, consisting of: *Urh shih urh she chă ke,* "Notes on
the Twenty-two Histories," 36 keuen; *Kae
yu ts'ung k'aou,* "A Collection of Occasional
Memoranda," 43 keuen; *Yen puh tsă ke,*
"Miscellanies from the Sunny Side of the
Eaves," 7 keuen; *Hwang ch'aou woo kung ke
shing,* "A Record of the Military Exploits of
the Present Dynasty," 4 keuen; *She chaou,*
"Poetry"; *She hwa,* "Criticisms on Poetry,"
10 keuen; and *Gow pih tseĭh,* "A Collection of
the Writings of Chaou Gow-pih," 53 keuen.
1811. 8°. 15315. b. 1.

—— 簷曝雜記 *Yen puh tsă ke.* "Miscellanies
from the Sunny Side of the Eaves" on events
during the present Dynasty. 6 keuen. [1800?]
8°. 15296. a. 29.

Imperfect, containing only keuen 1 to 3.

趙 鉞 CHAOU YUĔ. 國朝諡法考 *Kwŏ ch'aou
she fă k'aou.* "An Examination of the Laws
for granting Honorary Titles to the Dead."
1831. 8°. 15241. b. 2.

趙 元 益 CHAOU YUEN-YIH. See 海 得 蘭 HAI-
TĬH-LAN. 儒門醫學 *Joo mun e heŏ.*
"Medical Science. . . ." Transcribed by
Chaou Yuen-yih, etc. 8°. 15259. d. 25.

—— See 連 提 LEEN-T'E. 行軍測繪 *Hing
keun ts'ĭh hwuy.* "On Military Drawing. . . ."
Revised by Chaou Yuen-yih, etc. 8°.
15259. d. 6.

—— See 阿 發 滿 O-FĂ MWAN. 冶金錄 *Yay
kin luh.* "On Smelting Gold. . . ." Revised
by Chaou Yuen-yih, etc. 8°. 15259. h. 5.

—— See 田 大 里 T'EEN-TA-LE. 光學 *Kwang heŏ.*
"On Light. . . ." Revised by Chaou Yuen-
yih, etc. 8°. 15259. d. 2.

—— See 韋 更 斯 WEI-KĂNG-SZE. 海塘輯要
Hai t'ang tseĭh yaou. "On Building Sea-
dikes. . . ." Transcribed by Chaou Yuen-
yih, etc. 8°. 15259. d. 23.

趙 澐 CHAOU YUN. See 顧 有 孝 KOO YEW-
HEAOU AND CHAOU YUN. 江左三大家
詩鈔 *Keang tso san ta kea she ch'aou.* "The
Writings of the Three Poets," etc. Edited by
Koo Yew-heaou and Chaou Yun, etc. 8°.

15323. e. 9.

CHAPIN (LYMAN DWIGHT). See 江 戴 德 KEANG
TAI-TĬH.

CHAVANNES (ÉDOUARD), *of the Peking Oriental
Society. See* E TSING. Mémoire . . . sur les
Religieux éminents qui allèrent chercher la loi
dans le pays d'Occident. . . . Traduit en
français par É. CHAVANNES. 1894. 8°.

11100. e. 25.

—— See 司 馬 遷 SZEMA TS'EEN. Les Mémoires
de Sema Ts'ien. Traduits . . . par É. C., etc.
1895. 8°. 11098. b. 23.

—— [Another copy.] 11098. b. 16.

—— Les Inscriptions Chinoises de Bodhgayā.
pp. 58. *Paris: Ernest Leroux,* 1896. 8°.

11098. b. 26.

茶 葉 CH'A YĔ. 呈報運到茶葉件數清冊
Ch'ing paou yun taou ch'a yĕ keen soo ts'ing tsĭh.
"A list of the quantities of Teas brought by
the various native Merchants" [to Shanghae?].
MS. [1850?] 8°. 15297. d. 11.

車 萬 育 Ch'ay Wan-yuh. 聲 律 啟 蒙 撮 要
Shing leu k'e mung ts'ŏ yaou. "A Guide for
Beginners to the Laws of Sound." Edited by
Tseang T'ai-she. 2 keuen. 1857. 8°.
15346. a. 13.

CHEAH (Toon Hoon). *See* Maung Gyi (J. A.)
and Cheah (Hoon Toon). The Hokkien
Library Series. Vol. i. The Celestial Mirror,
an English translation by . . . T. H. C. of
Pó Kàm, etc. 1894. 8°. 11100. c. 32.

浙 江 Chĕkeang. 浙 江 嘉 興 城 守 營 *Chĕkeang
Keahing ch'ing show ying.* "The Muster Roll
of the Camp at Keahing in Chĕkeang." MS.
ff. 4. 1841. 8°. Add. 16309. 39. B. e.

浙 江 關 Chĕkeang kwan. 浙 江 關 日 徵 環 簿
Chĕkeang kwan jih ching hwan poo. "A Daily
Register of the Taxes levied at the Chĕkeang
Customs House." MS. ff. 58. 1836. 4°.
Add. 16289. Or. 28. a.

智 覺 Che-keŏ. 宗 鏡 錄 *Tsung king luh.*
"Records of the Mirrors of the Patriarchs."
A thesaurus of Buddhist doctrine. 100 keuen.
1734. 8°. 15103. d. 21.

智 境 Che-king. 禪 林 類 聚 *Shen lin luy tseu.*
"Buddhist Miscellanea." Compiled by the
priest Che-king. 20 keuen. 1361. 8°.
15103. b. 3.
Printed in Japan from blocks.

至 天 隱 Che-t'een-yin. *See* 周 弼 Chow Pih.
箋 註 唐 賢 絕 句 三 體 詩 法 *Ts'een choo
T'ang heen tseue keu san t'e she fa.* "Specimens
of Poems by Authors of the T'ang Dynasty."
. . . With the notes of Che-t'een-yin, etc.
1306. Fol. 15324. e. 6.

CHEVALIER (Frédéric). *See* Jin Jun-ling.
Jin Jun-ling . . . La Petite Pantoufle . . .
Avec six eaux-fortes originales reproduites par
F. C. [1875.] 8°. 11100. f. 3.

沈 Ch'in. 環 字 簿 *Hwan tsze poo.* "A Register
of Silk and Tea Sales," bearing the signature
and seal of the Sub-Prefect Ch'in. MS. 3 vols.
1844. 8°. 15241. b. 6.

CHINA. [A collection of thirty-two coloured maps
of the provinces of China Proper and her
Dependencies. The maps are arranged in the
volume on the European principle, and begin
with a map of Manchuria. MS. 1820?]
Add. 16355. 28. c.

CHINA. [Forty-two maps of the Chinese Empire,
including maps of Kuldja and Tibet.] MS.
[1790?] Fol. Add. 12183. 28. c.

—— [352 maps of the geographical divisions of
China and Japan. These maps, or at least
a large proportion of them, have been taken,
as is stated in a note in the handwriting of
Klaproth, from the Chinese atlas entitled 內 府
輿 地 圖 *Nuy fu yü te t'oo,* and have been
filled in possibly by Klaproth. 84 maps at the
end of the volume are only in outline, as also
are some others in other parts of the collection.
ff. 418. 1830?] 4°. Add. 11705. 28. c.

—— [Maps of the various provinces of the Empire.
1800?] 8°. 15271. a. 20.

—— 咸 豐 Heen-fung, *Emperor.* 大 中 國 與
大 亞 美 利 駕 合 衆 國 和 約 章 程
*Ta Chung kwŏ yu Ta A-mei-le-kea ho tsung kwŏ
hŏ yŏ chang ch'ing.* "The Articles of the Treaty
made between China and the United States of
America." 1858. 8°. 15241. c. 1.

CHINA : *Inspectorate General of Customs.* Catalogue
of the Collection exhibited in the Palais du
Champ de Mars, Universal Exhibition, Paris,
1878. pp. xiii, 122. *Shanghai,* 1878. 4°
11093. e.
No. 5 of the Miscellaneous Series of the "Imperial
Maritime Customs of China."

—— Catalogue spécial de la Collection exposée au
Palais de Mars, Exposition Universelle, Paris,
1878. Publié par ordre du Directeur Général
des Douanes. pp. xiii, 122. *Shanghai,* 1878. 4°.
11093. e.
No. 5 of the General Series of the "Imperial Maritime
Customs of China."

—— China Trade Statistics of the Treaty Ports
for the period 1863–1872. Compiled for the
Austro-Hungarian Universal Exhibition, Vienna,
1873, to illustrate international exchange of
products. Published by order of the Inspector
General of Chinese Maritime Customs. *Shanghai,*
1873. 4°. 11092. e.

—— Chinese Music. By J. A. van Aalst. pp. iv, 84.
Shanghai, 1884. 4to. 11093. e.
No. 6 of the Special Series of the "Imperial Maritime
Customs of China."

—— Corea. Annual Report on the Trade in
Foreign Vessels. No 1, year 1885. pp. 20.
Shanghai, 1886. 4°. 11092. e.

13

CHI

CHINA: *Inspectorate General of Customs.* Customs Gazette. No. 9, etc. *Shanghai*, 1872, etc. 4°. **11093. a. b.**

In progress. Forming part of the Statistical Series of the "Imperial Maritime Customs of China."

—— 咸豐入年原定稅則核與同治五六年進出貨物貿易並抽值成數及征稅來源合開清冊 *Heen-fung pa neen yuen ting shuy tsih ho yu T'ung-che woo luh neen tsin ch'uh hwo wuh maou e ping ch'ow chih ch'ing shu keih ching shwuy lai yuen ho k'ai ts'ing ts'ih.* Returns of Trade at the Treaty Ports for the year 1867 in accordance with the terms of the Treaty of 1858. [*Shanghai*, 1868?] 4°. **15241. e. 2.**

—— 光緒九年通商各關警船鐙浮椿總冊 *Kwang-seu kew neen t'ung shang kŏ kwan king ch'uen tăng fow chwang tsung ts'ih.* List of the Chinese Lighthouses, Light-vessels, Buoys, and Beacons for the year 1876. With map. Chinese text. *Shanghai*, 1876, etc. 4°. **15241. e. 2.**

In progress.

—— 光緒十五年通商各關華洋貿易總冊 *Kwang-seu shih woo neen t'ung shang kŏ kwan hwa yang maou e tsung ts'ih.* "Returns of Trade and Trade Reports for the year 1889." *Shanghai*, 1889, etc. 4°. **15241. e. 2.**

In progress.

—— List of the Chinese Lighthouses, Light-vessels, Buoys, and Beacons for 1880. Eighth ( ) issue. *Shanghai*, 1880, etc. 4°. **11093. e.**

In progress. No. 6 of Miscellaneous Series of the "Imperial Maritime Customs of China."

—— Medical Reports (forwarded by the Surgeons to the Customs at the Treaty Ports in China) for the half-year ended 30th September, 1871 (31st March, 1872, etc.) . . . . published by order of the Inspector General of Customs. *Shanghai*, 1871, etc. 4°. **11093. d.**

In progress.

—— Miscellaneous Series. No. 19. Treaties, Regulations, etc., between Corea and other Powers, 1876–1889. Published by order of the Inspector General of Customs. pp. viii, 386. *Shanghai*, 1891. 4°. **11098. b. 14.**

CHINA: *Inspectorate General of Customs.* Names of Places on the China Coast and the Yangtze River. First issue. pp. 20. *Shanghai*, 1882. 4°. **11093. e.**

No. 10 of the Miscellaneous Series of the "Imperial Maritime Customs of China."

—— Port Catalogues of the Chinese Customs' Collection at the Austro-Hungarian Universal Exhibition, Vienna, 1873, to illustrate the International Exchange of Products. pp. xvi, 518. *Shanghai*, 1873. 4°. **11093. e.**

—— [Another copy.] **11093. e.**

—— Reports on Trade at the Ports in China open by Treaty to Foreign Trade for the year 1866 (1871–72, etc.). Published by order of the Inspector General of Customs. *Shanghai*, 1867, etc. 4°. **11092. a. b.**

In progress.

—— Returns of Trade at the Treaty Ports for . . . 1871, etc. *Shanghai*, 1872, etc. 4°. **11092. c. & d.**

In progress. No. 3 of the Statistical Series of the "Imperial Maritime Customs of China."

—— Silk. [Official Reports on its Culture in China. With coloured illustrations.] pp. v, 163. *Shanghai*, 1881. 4°. **11093. e.**

Part of the Special Series of the Statistical Department of the Inspectorate General.

—— Special Catalogue of the Chinese Collection of Exhibits for the International Fisheries Exhibition, London, 1883 (Supplement). pp. ix, 75, 10. *Shanghai*, 1883. 4°. **11093. e.**

No. 11 of the Miscellaneous Series of the "Imperial Maritime Customs of China."

—— Special Catalogue of the Ningpo Collection of Exhibits for the International Fishery Exhibition, Berlin, 1880. Preceded by a description of the Fisheries of Ningpo and the Chusan Archipelago. pp. vii, 40. *Shanghai*, 1880. 4°. **11093. e.**

No. 9 of the Miscellaneous Series of the "Imperial Maritime Chinese Customs of China."

—— Statistical Series, No. 6. Decennial Reports on the Trade, Navigation, Industries, etc., of the Ports open to Foreign Commerce in China and Corea, and on the condition and development of the Treaty Port Provinces, 1882–92. With maps, etc. pp. vi, 694, 84. Published by order of the Inspector General of Customs. *Shanghai*. **11093. e.**

CHINA: *Inspectorate General of Customs.* Statistics of Trade at the Port[s] of Amoy (Canton, Chefoo, Chinkiang, Hankow, Foochow, Kiu-kiang, Newchwang, Ningpo, Shanghai, Swatow, Takow, Tamsui, Tientsin), for the period 1863–72. To illustrate the international exchange of products. Compiled for the Austro-Hungarian Universal Exhibition, Vienna, 1873, etc. 14 parts. *Shanghai*, 1873. 4°. **11093. e.**

—— 通商各關華洋貿易總冊 *T'ung shang kŏ kwan hwa yang maou e tsung ts'ih.* "Returns of Trade at the Treaty Ports of China for the year 1879." *Shanghai*, 1879, etc. 4°. **15241. e. 2.**

In progress.

—— 通商各關沿海沿江建置鐙塔鐙船鐙杆警船浮椿總冊 *T'ung shang kŏ kwan yen hai yen keang keen che tăng t'ă tăng ch'uen tăng kan king ch'uen fow ch'wang tsung ts'ih.* The Lighthouses, Light-vessels, Beacons, and Buoys at every Customs House Station on the coast and banks of Rivers. [*Shanghai?*], 1881, 1882. 4°. **15241. e. 2.**

CHINA. 嘉慶 KEA-K'ING, *Emperor.* 條例 *T'eaou le.* "Laws and Regulations." [This work contains the laws promulgated by the Emperor Kea-k'ing during his reign, viz. from 1795 to 1820.] 9 vols. 8°. **15237. b.**

—— 乾隆 K'EEN LUNG, *Emperor.* 欽定四庫全書簡明目錄 *K'in ting sze koo ts'euen shoo keen ming muh luh.* An epitome of the Imperial descriptive catalogue of books, divided into four sections. Published by the order of the Emperor K'een Lung. [The work is arranged exactly as is the "K'in ting sze koo ts'euen shoo tsung mŭh t'e yaou," and is an epitome of that work.] 3 vols. 1784. 8°. **15350. a. 3.**

—— 御批歷伐通鑑輯覽 *Yu p'e lĭh tai t'ung keen tseĭh lan.* A chronological history. An Imperial publication. [This history, published by the Emperor K'een-Lung and edited by Foo-hăng, etc., commences about the year 3250 B.C., and goes down to the close of the Ming Dynasty, about 1644.] 116 keuen. 1768. Fol. **15288. c.**

CHINA. 光緒 KWANG-SEU, *Emperor.* 中英新增條讌 *Chung Ying sin tsăng t'eaou e.* "The Chefoo Convention made between Le Hung-chang on the part of China and Sir Thomas Wade on the part of England" in the year 1876. *Shanghai*, 1876. 8°. **15297. b. 16.**

—— 光緒 KWANG-SEU, *Emperor.* 諭旨 *Yu che.* "Imperial Edicts" issued during the Autumn and Winter of the 20th year of the reign of Kwang-seu, i.e. 1894. [*Shanghae?*], 1894. 8°. **15236. c. 11.**

—— SIX BOARDS. 六典條例 *Luh teen t'eaou-le.* "The Rules of Procedure of the Six Boards." A Korean edition. 10 keuen. [1750 ?] Fol. **15236. d. 11.**

沈之奇 CH'IN CHE-K'E. See TS'ING DYNASTY. 大清律例統纂集成 *Ta Ts'ing leŭh le t'ung tswan tseĭh ch'ing.* A complete code of the Laws of the Tsing Dynasty, etc. 1820. 8°. **15236. b. 1.**

沈志祖 CH'IN CHE-TSOO. See 朱熹 CHOO HE. 朱子格言 *Choo tsze kih yen.* "Choo He's Maxims." Compiled by Ch'in Che-tsoo, etc. 1743. 8°. **15312. d. 13.**

陳栻 CH'IN CHIH. 直省郷墨 *Chih săng heang mŭh.* Provincial examination essays. Compiled by Ch'in Chih. 1882. 8°. **15320. a. 3.**
Title and first few pages are wanting.

陳沆 CH'IN CH'IN. See 張熙宇 CHANG HEYU. 硃批增註七家詩選 *Choo p'e tsăng choo ts'ih kea she seuen.* "Imperially Endorsed Poems" by . . . Ch'in Ch'in, etc. 1857. 8°. **15323. c. 14.**

鎮澄 CHIN CH'ING. 清凉山志 *Ts'ingleang shan che.* "A Topography of the Ts'ingleang Mountain," on which the Bōddhisattva Munjusri is said to have resided. Compiled by Chin Ch'ing in 1596. A new edition. With plates. 10 keuen. 1755. 8°. **15111. a. 1.**

陳澄泉 CH'IN CH'ING-TS'EUEN, and 汪之田 WANG CHE-T'EEN. 草書習慎 *Ts'aou shoo seĭh shin.* "Carefully Selected Exercises in the Grass Character." By Ch'in Ch'ing-ts'euen and Wang Che-t'een. 1749. 8°. **15342. b. 8.**

CHINESE. A Chinese and English Vocabulary. MS. [1850 ?] 8°. **15346. b. 28.**

CHI

CHINESE CONVERSATIONS. Translated from native authors [Chinese and English]. *Shanghae*, 1852. 8°. **11098. a. 37.**

CHINESE DOCUMENTS. [A collection of nineteen documents consisting of official papers relating to the defences of the Central Provinces during the war of 1840–42, of legal papers, and of examination essays, with a drawing of a crater.] MS. ff. 19. 1820–43. Fol. **Add. 14420. 28. c.**

CHINESE DRAWINGS. [A collection of highly finished coloured Chinese drawings, consisting of thirty-six drawings illustrating as many trades; one hundred and ten drawings of plants; and twelve of different kinds of boats. These three parts are described as Nos. 1351, 1352, and 1347 in the Lansdowne Catalogue.] MS. ff. 160. [1700?] Fol. **Lansd. 1242. 28. c.**

—— [Drawings of plants, butterflies, moths, and silkworms. Without title or any letterpress. 1800?] Fol. **15257. d. 25.**

—— [11 coloured drawings of flowers, to which are added two drawings of lanterns and one of a pagoda. All excellent specimens of the art.] MS. [1790?] Fol. **Or. 1060. 28. c.**

—— [43 coloured drawings of itinerant hucksters and of street stalls.] MS. [1840?] 4°. **Or. 1055. 28. c.**

—— [100 coloured drawings of Chinese landscapes taken in the littoral provinces of the Empire.] MS. 2 vols. [1790?] Obl. fol. **Lansd. 1243. 28. c.**

—— [72 coloured drawings of Chinese boats of all kinds from the Emperor's yacht to the duck and fishing boats of the people.] MS. [1800?] Obl. fol. **Or. 1059. 28. c.**

—— [39 coloured drawings of the Emperor Kia-k'ing and his Empress; Mandarins and their wives, most of whom are Manchus, as is evidenced by the natural-sized feet of the ladies; and ending with drawings of a Soochow belle, and of a woman slave-dealer leading two little girls for sale.] MS. [1840?] Fol. **Or. 1053. 28. c.**

—— [31 coloured drawings of conjurors' tricks, dancing performances, theatrical scenes, and domestic sketches.] MS. [1810?] Obl. fol. **Or. 1057. 28. c.**

CHINESE DRAWINGS. [37 coloured mythological drawings, representing gods and goddesses with their several attributes.] MS. [1840?] Fol. **Or. 1051. 28. c.**

—— [12 coloured drawings representing the death and funeral of an official. Some of the drawings are misplaced.] MS. [1840?] Obl. fol. **Or. 1058. 28. c.**

—— [28 coloured drawings of Mandarins of the various ranks and their wives.] MS. [1820?] Fol. **Or. 1054. 28. c.**

—— [24 exquisite coloured drawings of mythological figures.] MS. [1800?] Fol. **Eg. 941. 28. c.**

—— [27 coloured drawings of Chinese punishments and tortures.] MS. [1820?] Obl. fol. **Or. 1056. 28. c.**

—— 二 十 四 轉 輪 *Urh shih sze chuen lun.* "Twenty-four Revolutions of the Wheel" [of Fate?], being representations of the punishments inflicted in the other world on sinners. MS. [1820?] Obl. fol. **Or. 1052. 28. c.**

CHINESE ENGRAVINGS. A collection of coloured Chinese engravings representing natural objects such as rocks, plants, birds, etc. 2 vols. [1800?] Obl. **15257. e. 19.**

CHINESE PHONETIC VOCABULARY. A Chinese Phonetic Vocabulary, containing all the most common characters, with their sounds in the Canton dialect. *Hongkong*, 1855. 8°. **15347. a. 4.**

陳 服 旆 CH'IN FUH-CHEN. See 陳 維 崧 CH'IN WEI-SUNG. 陳 檢 討 四 六 *Ch'in Keen-t'aou sze luh.* "The Writings of Ch'in Wei-sung." Edited by Ch'in Fuh-chen, etc. 1770. 8°. **15319. d. 19.**

—— See 陸 拒 石 LUH KEU-SHĬH. 善 卷 堂 四 六 *Shen-keuen T'ang sze luh.* "The Writings of Luh Keu-shĭh." . . . Edited by Ch'in Fŭh-chen, etc. 1875. 8°. **15319. d. 21.**

程 赤 文 CH'ING CH'IH-WĂN. See 閔 齊 伋 MIN TS'E-KEIH. 六 書 通 *Luh shoo t'ung.* "A Dictionary of the Six Forms of Characters." . . . Edited by . . . Ch'ing Ch'ih-wăn, etc. 1824. 8°. **15342. e. 9.**

16

鄭 成 功 CHING CH‘ING-KUNG. See 江東旭 KEANG TUNG-KEU. 臺灣外記 *T‘aiwan wai ke.* "An Extra History of Formosa," being a biography of the Pirate Ching Ch‘ing-kung, etc. 1704. 8°.　　　　15291. a. 12.

鄭 承 衮 CHING CH‘ING-KWĂN. 鄭 氏 易 譜 *Ching she yih p‘oo.* "Ching's Treatise on the Book of Changes." Edited by Ching Wei-shang. 12 keuen. 1753. 8°.　　15212. e. 4.

程 冲 斗 CH‘ING CH‘UNG-TOW. 蹶 張 心 法 *Keuě chang sin fă.* "On Archery." 1842. 4°.　　　　　　　15259. e. 12.

程 頤 CH‘ING E. See 張 栻 CHANG CH‘IH. 二 程 先 生 傳 道 粹 言 *Urh Ch‘ing seen săng chuen taou suy yen.* "A True Expression of the Doctrines of . . . Ch‘ing E," etc. 1562. Fol. **15103. d. 22.**

—— See 紀 昀 KĔ YUN. 二 程 全 書 *Urh Ch‘ing ts‘euen shoo.* "The Writings of Ch‘ing E," etc. 1787. 8°.　　15318. c. 1.

鄭 方 坤 CHING FANG-K‘WĂN. 本 朝 名 家 詩 鈔 小 傳 *Pun ch‘aou ming kea she ch‘aou seaou chuen.* Poems by celebrated Poets of the present Dynasty. With short biographical notices. Compiled by Ching Fang-k‘wăn. Edited by Ma Tseun-leang. 4 keuen. [1741?] 8°.　　　　　　　**15323. b. 30. 4.**

程 顥 CH‘ING HAOU. See 張 栻 CHANG CH‘IH. 二 程 先 生 傳 道 粹 言 *Urh Ch‘ing seen săng chuen taou suy yen.* "A True Expression of the Doctrines of . . . Ch‘ing Haou," etc. 1562. Fol.　　　　　15103. d. 22.

—— See 紀 昀 KĔ YUN. 二 程 全 書 *Urh Ch‘ing ts‘euen shoo.* "The Writings of Ch‘ing Haou," etc. 1787. 8°.　　15318. c. 1.

鄭 曉 CHING HEAOU. 皇 明 直 文 淵 閣 諸 臣 表 *Hwang ming chih wăn yuen kih choo ch‘in peaou.* "A Record of the Officers of the Chih-wăn-yuen-kih during the Ming Dynasty." 1566. 8°.　　　　15296. e. 1.

程 學 啟 CH‘ING HEŎ-K‘E. A fragment of a letter addressed to General Gordon apparently in answer to remonstrances on Ch‘ing's conduct in a recent engagement, and on disputes with Gordon's troops. Ch‘ing declares that he has always worked with Gordon to sweep away the rebels, and asks to be told when Gordon proposes to advance to the attack of Soochow, and promises to act with him. Dated 2nd of the 5th month [of 1863?].　　**Or. 2338.**

程 學 啟 CH‘ING HEŎ-K‘E. A letter addressed to General Gordon explaining an attack made on his steamer by Ch‘ing's men, who mistook it for a rebel steamer. This would appear to be another occasion from that mentioned in Wilson's "Ever Victorious Army," in which Ch‘ing's gunboats fired on a party of Gordon's men. A fragment. MS. [1863?] **Or. 2338.**

—— A letter addressed to General Gordon in reply to a requisition from him for three steamers to assist in the attack on Soochow. The writer thinks that the Governor of the Province ought to pay for these. Dated the 16th of the 5th month [of 1863?]. MS. ff. 2.　**Or. 2338.**

—— A letter addressed presumably to General Gordon protesting against a proposal made by "Mets‘ee sung" to hire three steamers for the use of the Imperial forces, an extravagance which would entail a large expenditure monthly. Dated 29th day, neither month nor year stated, probably during 1864. MS. ff. 3. **Or. 2338.**

—— A letter addressed to General Gordon with regard to arrangements for an advance on Soochow? The writer acknowledges the arrival of a steamer, but contends that the two steamers with General Gordon should take part in the attack. He wishes also to have the "Hyson," as the steamer he has does not carry guns. ff. 2. Without date [1863?].　**Or. 2338.**

—— A letter probably addressed to General Gordon, who is spoken of as *Mohsia,* apparently an attempt to reproduce the French "Monsieur." The purport of the letter is to acknowledge the receipt of two guns and stores from the steamer "Hyson." Dated the 20th, neither month nor year stated, probably 1864. MS. ff. 2. **Or. 2338.**

—— A letter probably addressed to General Gordon on matters connected with the campaign before Soochow, stating among other things that he had bought two 18-pound "opening-flower" guns, and asking for ammunition for them. Dated the 20th, neither month nor year stated, probably 1864. MS. ff. 3.　**Or. 2338.**

—— A letter addressed to General Gordon asking him to direct that his troops should not interfere with the vessels carrying grain, ammunition, etc., to the various camps in the neighbourhood of Soochow? Dated the 24th, neither month nor year stated, probably 1864. MS. ff. 2.　　**Or. 2338.**

CHI

程 學 啟 CH'ING HEŬ-K'E. A letter addressed to Le Ait'ang with reference to the movements preparatory to the capture of Soochow, and reporting a sortee in which the writer had 40 or 50 men wounded. Dated the 2nd day, neither month nor year stated, probably 1864. MS. ff. 2.   **Or. 2338.**

—— A letter addressed to General Gordon [?] announcing the capture of upwards of thirty rebel camps, and stating that he had captured upwards of 800 rebels, killed and wounded more than 10,000, besides countless numbers who were drowned. That in addition he had taken 40 ships of war, more than 1,000 junks, and had burnt upwards of 300 more. The letter is dated the 15th of the 2nd month [1864?]. MS.   **Or. 2338.**

—— A series of letters addressed to Colonel Gordon, viz.: (1) A letter dated between 3 and 5 in the afternoon of the 2nd of a month not stated, in which the writer describes the arrangements he has made for the reception of deserters from the enemy, i.e. the T'aip'ing rebels. (2) A letter dated the 20th of a month not indicated acknowledging the receipt of a letter from Colonel Gordon.   **Or. 2338.**

鄭 康 成 CHING K'ANG-CH'ING. See 儀 禮 E LE. 欽 定 儀 禮 義 疏 *K'in ting E le e soo.* "The Meaning of the Decorum Ritual." With explanations by . . . Ching K'ang-ch'ing, etc. 8°.   **15219. b. 3. & c. 1.**

正 教 CHING KEAOU. 正 教 異 詮 *Ching keaou chin ts'euen.* "A True Exposition of the Mahommedan Religion." By Chin hwuy laou jin, i.e. The True Old Mussulman. 2 keuen. 1782. 8°.   **15200. a. 4.**

鄭 克 CH'ING K'IH. 折 獄 龜 鑑 *Chĕ yŏ kwei keen.* "A Review of the Criminal Law," illustrated by *causes célèbres.* A new edition. 8 keuen. 1835. 8°.   **15241. a. 10.**

鄭 慶 祜 CHING K'ING-HOO. 揚 州 休 園 志 *Yang-chow heu yuen che.* "An Account of the 'Restful Gardens' at Yang-chow." 8 keuen. 1773. 8°.   **15269. e. 1.**

程 孟 梅 CH'ING MĂNG-MEI. See 惲 珍 浦 HWĂN CHIN-P'OO. 國 朝 閨 秀 正 始 續 集 *Kwŏ ch'aou kwei sew ching che suh tseih.* "A Supplement to the *Chingche* Collection of Poems." . . . With an appendix compiled by Ch'ing Măng-mei, etc. 1836. 8°. **15327. e. 5.**

程 氏 CH'ING SHE. 廣 輿 古 今 鈔 *Kwang yu koo kin ch'aou.* "The Ancient and Modern Geography of the Empire." 2 keuen. 1767. 8°.   **15271. c. 6.**

程 叔 才 CH'ING SHUH-TS'AI. See 陳 維 崧 CH'IN WEI-SUNG. 陳 檢 討 四 六 *Ch'in keen-t'aou sze luh.* "The Writings of Ch'in Wei-sung." . . . With notes by Ch'ing Shuh-ts'ai, etc. 1770. 8°.   **15319. d. 19.**

程 大 位 CH'ING TA-WEI. 增 刪 算 法 統 宗 *Tsăng shan swan fă t'ung tsung.* "A Work on Mathematics," the main object of which is to elucidate the principle of the *Kew chang* or nine sections into which mathematics may be divided. Enlarged and critically edited by Mei Kow-ch'ing. With diagrams. 11 keuen. *Shanghai,* 1877. 8°.   **15259. h. 5.**

程 際 盛 CH'ING TSE-SHING. See 徐 陵 孝 SEU LING-HEAOU. 玉 臺 新 詠 箋 註 *Yuh t'ai sin yung tseen choo.* "New Songs from the Beautiful Tower." . . . Edited by Ch'ing Tse-shing, etc. 1774. 8°.   **15323. c. 12.**

鄭 惟 上 CHING WEI-SHANG. See 鄭 承 袤 CHING CH'ING-KWĂN. 鄭 氏 易 譜 *Ching she yih p'oo.* "Ching's Treatise on the Book of Changes." Edited by Ching Wei-shang, etc. 1753. 8°.   **15212. e. 4.**

程 瑤 田 CH'ING YAOU-T'EEN. 通 藝 錄 *T'ung e luh.* "A Collection of Treatises on Ethics, Arts, and Sciences." Compiled by Ch'ing Yaou-t'een. 20 vols. 1804. 8°. **15257. c. 5.**

程 愈 CH'ING YU. See 朱 熹 CHOO HE. 小 學 集 說 *Seaou heŏ tseih shwo.* "The Youth's Instructor." . . . Edited by Ch'ing Yu, etc. Fol.   **15229. d. 1.**

鄭 元 美 CHING YUEN-MEI. 增 補 指 明 算 法 *Tsăng poo che ming swan fă.* "A New Work on Arithmetic." By Ching Yuen-mei. 2 keuen. *Nanking,* 1873. 8°.   **15255. c. 16.**

18

正韻 CHING YUN. 正韻訓蒙增廣 *Ching yun heun mung tsăng kwang.* "Instruction to Youth, in correct rhyme. Enlarged." ff. 19. [1800?] 8°. **15344. a. 10.**

程榮 CH'ING YUNG. 漢魏叢書 *Han Wei ts'ung shoo.* "Reprints of Works by Authors under the Hán and Wei Dynasties." The original compilation, which consisted of 38 reprints, was edited by Ch'ing Yung during the Ming Dynasty. Subsequent editions added works, until the collection took its present form, containing 90 reprints, under the hand of Ch'in Lan-săn. 1791. 8°. **15318. a. 1.**

—— [Another edition.] 1880. 12°. **15313. a. 1.**

程允升 CH'ING YUN-SHING. 幼學須知句解 *Yew heŏ seu che keu keae.* "General Knowledge, necessary to Beginners. With explanations." Edited by Ts'een Yuen-lung. 4 keuen. [1790?] 8°. **15022. e. 19.**

陳沆 CH'IN HANG. See 張熙宇 CHANG HE-YU. 七家詩輯註彙鈔 *Ts'ih kea she tseih choo wei ch'aou.* "A Collection of the Writings of" ... Ch'in Hang, etc. 1870. 8°. **15324. a. 12.**

陳淏子 CH'IN HAOU-TSZE. See 梅膺祚 MEI YING-TSOO. 玉堂字彙 *Yüh t'ang tsze wei.* "The Jade Hall Dictionary." Edited by Ch'in Haou-tsze, etc. 1676. 8°. **15344. d. 6.**

沈數曾 CH'IN HEAOU-TSĂNG. See 江瓘 KEANG KWAN. 名醫類案 *Ming e luy gan.* "The Medical Practice of Celebrated Physicians." ... Edited by Ch'in Heaou-tsăng, etc. 1871. 8°. **15252. b. 30.**

陳希夷 CH'IN HE-E. 適情雅趣 *Shih ts'ing ya ts'eu.* A work on Chess, otherwise entitled 象棋譜 *Seang k'i p'oo,* "A Treatise on Chess." 8 keuen. 1802. 12°. **15257. d. 24.**

—— 韜略元機 *T'ao leŏ yuen ke.* "Primary Strategic Manœuvres." Chess problems. With diagrams. 8 keuen. 1801. 8°. **15257. d. 28.**

沈弘照 CH'IN HUNG-CHAOU. 大清全書 *Ta Ts'ing ts'euen shoo (Daitsing gurun i yauni pitghe).* "A Manchu-Chinese Dictionary" arranged alphabetically. Compiled by Ch'in Hung-chaou. 14 keuen. 1681. 8°. **15354. a. 1.**

—— [Another copy.] **15354. a. 2.**

陳化成 CH'IN HWA-CH'ING. See 黃仁 HWANG JIN. 陳忠愍公殉難詩文錄 *Ch'in chung min kung seun nan she wăn luh.* Records in Verse and Prose of the Deaths of ... Ch'in Hwa-ch'ing, etc. 1843. 8°. **15303. d. 2.**

眞回老人 CHIN HWUY LAOU JIN. See 正教 CHING KEAOU. 正教眞詮 *Ching keaou chin ts'euen.* "A True Exposition of the Mahommedan Religion." By Chin hwuy laou jin, etc. 1782. 8°. **15200. a. 4.**

陳仁錫 CH'IN JIN-SEIH. See 眞德秀 CHIN TIH-SEW. 大學衍義 *Ta heŏ yen e.* "The Doctrines of the *Ta heŏ* ..." Edited by Ch'in Jin-seih, etc. 1837. 8°. **15223. d. 2.**

陳仁子 CH'IN JIN-TSZE. See 蕭統 SEAOU T'UNG. 六臣註文選 *Luh ch'in choo wăn seuen.* "Elegant Extracts ..." Edited by Ch'in Jin-tsze, etc. 1607. Fol. **15320. e. 39.**

沈容齋 CH'IN JUNG-CHAI. 答客芻言 *Tă k'ih ch'oo yen.* "The Simple Words [on Religion] of an Answering Guest." pp. iv, 119. *Hongkong,* 1889. 8°. **15200. d. 54.**

眞界 CHIN-KEAE. See 馬嗚菩薩 MA-MING P'OO-SA. 大乘起信論纂註 *Ta shing k'e sin lun tswan choo.* "The Mahāyāna-shrāddhotpāda Shāstra. With a Commentary" by Chin-keae, etc. 1876. 8°. **15101. b. 29.**

沈催 CH'IN KEŎ. 墨苑緇黃 *Mih yuen tsze hwang.* "Literary Jottings by the Black and Yellow" Priests of Buddha and Taou. Compiled by Ch'in Keŏ. 2 vols. [1820?] 8°. **15317. c. 13.**

陳其泰 CH'IN K'ET'AI. 宮閨百詠 *Kung kwei pih yung.* "A Hundred Odes on Historical Events connected with the Imperial Hareem." Compiled by Ch'in K'et'ai. 4 keuen. 1845. 8°. **15327. e. 4.**

陳君 CH'IN KEUN. See 楊椒山 YANG TSEAOU-SHAN. 楊椒山先生家訓 *Yang Tseaou-shan seen săng kea heun.* "The Family Teachings of Yang Tseaou-shan." Edited by Ch'in Keun, etc. 1856. 8°. **15103. d. 12.**

沈鏡涵 CH'IN KING-HAN. 發蒙小品式集註釋 *Fă mung seaou p'in urh tseih choo shih.* Unpretentious Essays. Second series. With comments. Arranged by Ch'in King-han and T'ang Shing-wăn. [These essays are on Texts from the Four Books, and were selected by T'ang Wei-mow. With comments by Woo Fung-e.] 1743. 8°. **15319. a. 7.**

CHI

陳 慶 借 Ch'in K'ing-keae. 試 行 蠶 桑 說 She hing ts'an sang shwŏ. "A Treatise on the Management of Silkworms and Mulberry Trees." 1847. 8°. 15241. b. 11.

陳 光 臣 Ch'in Kwang-ch'in. 古 今 俗 語 Koo kin suh yü. "Old and New Proverbs." Collected by Chin Kwang-ch'in. 2 keuen. 1874. 8°. 15317. c. 14.
Imperfect, containing only Keuen 2.

陳 米 瑩 Ch'in Kwang-ying. 剖 惑 至 言 P'ow hwo che yen. "A good Treatise on Dissolving Religious Doubts." pp. viii, 80. Hongkong, 1897. 8°. 15200. d. 25.

陳 觀 民 Ch'in Kwan-min. See 秦 霞 峰 Ts'in Hea-fung, and 郭 禮 堂 Kŏ Le-t'ang. 詩 料 詳 註 She leaou tseang choo. "Poetical Expressions . . ." With explanations by Ch'in Kwan-min, etc. 1762. 8°. 15346. a. 20.

陳 朗 Ch'in Lang. 雪 月 梅 傳 Seuĕ Yueh Mei chuen. "The Story of Seuĕ, Yueh, and Mei." A novel. 50 chapters. A reprint. Shanghai, [1870?]. 8°. 15327. e. 10.

陳 蘭 森 Ch'in Lan-săn. See 程 榮 Ch'ing Yung. 漢 魏 叢 書 Han Wei ts'ung shoo. "A Collection of Works by Authors of the Han and Wei Dynasties . . ." Edited by Ch'in Lan-săn, etc. 1791. 8°. 15318. a. 1.

—— [Another edition.] 1880. 12°. 15313. a. 1.

陳 澧 Ch'in Le. 番 禺 陳 氏 東 塾 叢 書 Pwan yu Ch'in she tung shuh ts'ung shoo. "A Collection of Reprints from the 'Eastern Schoolroom.' Compiled by Ch'in Le of Pwan-yu." 31 keuen. 1856. 8°. 15316. e. 17.

眞 亮 Chin-leang. 語 錄 彙 集 Yu luh wei tseih. "A Classified Collection of Buddhist Discourses." Edited by Chin-leang. pp. x, 146. 1853. 8°. 15103. b. 18.

沈 李 龍 Ch'in Le-lung. 食 物 本 草 會 纂 Shih wuh pun ts'aou hwuy tswan. "A Medical Work on Edibles." With illustrations. 12 keuen. 1691. 8°. 15251. e. 4.

—— [Another edition.] 12 keuen. 1783. 8°. 15251. e. 3.

陳 龍 標 Ch'in Lung-peaou. See 周 禮 Chow Le. 周 禮 精 華 Chow le tsing hwa. "The Essence and Flower of the Chow Ritual." Edited by Ch'in Lung-peaou, etc. 1826. 8°. 15220. b. 5.

陳 勱 Ch'in Mai. 玉 堂 楷 則 Yuh t'ang k'eae tsih. "Regular Rules for the Formation of the Written Characters, from the Jade Hall." 60 pp. 1872. 8°. 15229. b. 21.

陳 枚 Ch'in Mei. 留 青 新 集 Lew ts'ing sin tseih. "A New Literary Encyclopædia." Compiled by Ch'in Mei. Edited by Chang Le-gan. 30 keuen. 1707. 8°. 15334. d. 13.

陳 銘 章 Ch'in Ming-chang. See 郭 雨 三 Kŏ Yu-san. 詩 韻 類 錦 She yun luy kin. "A Poetical Dictionary . . ." Edited by Ch'in Ming-chang, etc. 1852. 8°. 15346. a. 22.

諶 母 元 君 Chin moo yuen keun. 銅 符 鐵 券 Tung foo t'ëĕ keuen. "Brass Charms and Iron Tokens." See 彭 好 古 P'ăng Haou-koo. 道 言 內 外 秘 訣 全 書 Taou yen nuy wae pe keuĕ ts'euen shoo. A complete collection of Taouist works, etc. 8°. 15111. b. 3.

沈 念 農 Ch'in Neen-nung. 敷 文 書 院 課 藝 Foo wăn shoo yuen k'o e. "Essays from the Foo-wăn College." Edited by Ch'in Neen-nung. 1870. 8°. 15319. e. 1.

陳 念 祖 Ch'in Neen-tsoo. See 張 仲 景 Chang Chung-king. 金 匱 方 歌 括 Kin kwei fang ko kwŏ. "Prescriptions from the Golden Casket of Medicine . . . put into verse." By Ch'in Neen-tsoo, etc. 1836. 8°. 15251. f. 11.

陳 省 堂 Ch'in Săng-t'ang. 越 南 遊 記 Yueh nan yew ke. "An Account of a Journey in Annam." pp. ii, 20. Singapore, 1888. 4°. 15275. a. 18.

陳 湘 鄉 Ch'in Seang-heang. 紫 琅 玕 院 遺 稿 Tsze lankan yuen e kaou. "Poetical Remains from the Purple-jewelled Hall." pp. 18. [1850?] 8°. 15324. a. 15.

陳 選 Ch'in Seuen. See 朱 熹 Choo He. 小 學 註 解 Seaou hŏ choo keae. "The Youth's Instructor. . . . With a Collection of Comments" compiled by Ch'in Seuen, etc. 1727. 8°. 15229. b. 13.

陳 修 園 Ch'in Sew-yuen. 陳 修 園 公 餘 醫 錄 十 五 種 合 刻 Ch'in Sew-yuen kung yu e luh shih woo chung hŏ k'ih. "Fifteen additional Medical Works by Ch'in Sew-yuen." 1876. 8°. 15253. a. 4.

20

陝 世 筬 CH'IN SHE-CHIN. 敏 求 軒 述 記 *Min k'ew heen shuh ke.* "Tales from the Study of Supplication." Compiled by Ch'in She-chin. 16 keuen. 1848. 8°. **15331. b. 7.**

陳 詩 霠 CH'IN SHE-WĂN. See 樵 南 陽 TS'EAOU NAN-YANG. 紅 樓 復 夢 *Hung low fuh mung.* "A New Dream from the Red Chamber . . ." Edited by Ch'in She-wăn, etc. 1805. 8°. **15333. a. 3.**

陳 樹 基 CH'IN SHOO-KE. 西 湖 拾 遺 *Se hoo shih e.* "A Collection of Records from the Western Lake." Compiled by Ch'in Shoo-ke. With illustrations. 48 keuen. 1811. 8°. **15327. f. 4.**

眞 司 騰 CHIN-SZE-T'ĂNG [i.e. JAMES FINLAY WEIR JOHNSTON]. 化 學 衛 生 論 *Hwa heŏ wei săng lun.* "The Chemistry of Common Life," adapted from the work under that title by J. F. W. Johnston. Translated into Chinese by Foolanya [i.e. John Fryer]. With plates. 2 vols. *Shanghai,* 1881. 8°. **15259. g. 3.**

眞 道 CHIN TAOU. 眞 道 自 證 *Chin taou tsze ching.* "The True (Roman Catholic) Religion proved by itself." [By Rev. P. de Cavagnac ?] pp. 190. *Hongkong,* 1898. 8°. **15200. d. 17.**

眞 諦 CHIN-TE. 金 七 十 論 *Kin ts'ih shih lun.* "The Golden Seventy Discourses." Translated into Chinese by the Indian Chin-te. A Japanese edition. 3 keuen. 1637. Fol. **15103. e. 11.**

眞 德 秀 CHIN TIH-SEW. 心 經 附 註 *Sin king foo choo.* "The Heart Sutra, with a Collection of Comments." Edited by Chin Tih-sew. 4 keuen. 1566. Fol. **15103. e. 15.** Printed in Japan from blocks.

—— 大 學 衍 義 *Ta heŏ yen e.* "The Doctrines of the *Ta heŏ* illustrated by Historical Examples." Edited by Ch'in Jin-seih. 43 keuen. 1837.* 8°. **15223. e. 2.**

—— 大 學 衍 義 補 *Ta heŏ yen e poo.* "The Doctrines of the *Ta heŏ* illustrated by Historical Examples." Enlarged by K'ew Chün. 160 keuen. 1837. 8°. **15223. e. 1.**

沈 德 潛 CH'IN TIH-TS'EEN. 欽 定 國 朝 詩 別 裁 集 *K'in ting kwŏ ch'aou she pëĕ ts'ai tseih.* "A Collection of the Poems of the Present Dynasty." Compiled by Ch'in Tih-ts'een. 32 keuen. [1761 ?] 8°. **15324. a. 5.**

沈 德 潛 CH'IN TIH-TS'EEN, and 周 準 CHOW CHUN. 明 詩 別 裁 集 *Ming she pëĕ ts'ai tseih.* "A Collection of the Poetry of the Ming Dynasty." Compiled by Ch'in Tih-ts'een and Chow Chun. 12 keuen. 1739. 8°. **15324. a. 4.**

—— 唐 詩 別 裁 集 *T'ang she pëĕ ts'ai tseih.* "A Collection of the Poems of the T'ang Dynasty." Compiled by Ch'in Tih-ts'een. A new edition. 20 keuen. 1763. 8°. **15324. a. 1.**

沈 廷 芳 CH'IN T'ING-FANG. See 胡 寶 琳 HOO PAOU-LIN. 武 定 府 志 *Woo-ting foo che.* "A Topography of Woo-ting foo . . ." Edited by . . . Ch'in T'ing-fang, etc. 1759. 8°. **15269. b. 9.**

陳 廷 敬 CH'IN T'ING-KING. See 張 玉 書 CHANG YUH-SHOO. 佩 文 韻 府 *Pei wăn yun foo.* "A Lexicon . . ." Compiled by . . . Chin T'ing-king, etc. 1711. 8°. **15347. d. & e.**

眞 在 體 CHIN TSAI-T'E. See 靈 操 竹 LING TS'AOU-CHUH. 瑜 伽 集 要 施 食 壇 儀 應 門 *Yu-kea tseih yaou she shih tan e ying mun.* "A Manual of the Rites of the Yoga Sect." Edited by Chin Tsai-t'ê, etc. 8°. **15103. d. 13.**

陳 藻 垣 CH'IN TSAOU-YUEN. 周 易 象 義 集 成 *Chow yih seang e tseih ch'ing.* "A Complete Collection of Explanations of the Diagrams of the Chow Changes." Compiled by Ch'in Tsaou-yuen. Edited by Ch'in Yaou-ming. 3 keuen. 1852. 8°. **15225. a. 20.**

眞 濟 CHIN-TSE. 遍 照 發 揮 性 靈 集 *Peen chaou fa hwuy sing ling tseih.* "A Collection of the animated, natural, and spiritual Poems" of the Priest Chin-tse. 10 keuen. [1650 ?] Fol. **15324. b. 6.** Printed in Japan with movable type.

陳 駿 孫 CH'IN TSEUN-SUN. 經 扤 權 *King e ts'uy.* "Essays on Texts from the Classics." Edited by Ch'in Tseun-sun. 1873. 12°. **15319. a. 13.**

沈 清 塵 CH'IN TS'INGCH'IN, and 周 遠 振 CHOW YUENCHIN. 西 方 公 據 *Sefang kungkeu.* "Evidences from the West." A collection of excerpta from Buddhist Works. Compiled by Ch'in Ts'ingch'in and Chow Yuenchin. With illustrations. pp. xviii, 66. *Canton,* 1765. 8°. **15101. c. 38.**

21

CHI

陳 藎 謨 CH'IN TSIN-MOO. 五車韻府 *Woo ch'ay yun foo.* "A Phonetic Dictionary," in which the sounds are divided among 128 finals, the sounds under each final being arranged according to the 36 initials. Edited by Hoo Shaou-ying. 10 keuen. [1800?] 8°.
15346. d. 2.

陳 子 莊 CH'IN TSZE-CHWANG. 庸閒齋筆記 *Yung-heen chai peth ke.* "Notes from the Yung-heen Study." By Ch'in Tsze-chwang. Edited by Yu Yueh. 8 keuen. 1874. 8°.
15331. b. 12.

陳 剌 史 CH'IN TS'ZE-SHE. 廣東通省水道圖 *Kwang tung t'ung shing shwuy taou t'oo.* "A Map of the Water-ways of the Province of Kwang-tung." [1840?] 15276. e. 1.

沈 彤 CH'IN T'UNG. 周官祿田考 *Chow kwan luh t'een k'aou.* "An Examination of the Emoluments of the Officers of the Chow Dynasty." 3 keuen. 1751. 8°. 15219. c. 10.

沈 桐 威 CH'IN T'UNG-WEI. 諧鐸 *Heae tŏ.* "Humorous Tinklings." A collection of tales. Compiled by Ch'in T'ung-wei. 12 keuen. 1808. 8°. 15331. c. 12.

陳 王 賓 CH'IN WANG-PIN. 華其昌 HWA K'E-CH'ANG. 畫禪室隨筆 *Hwa shen shih suy peth.* "Literary Notes . . ." Edited by Ch'in Wang-pin, etc. 1720. 8°. 15320. e. 35.

陳 文 述 CH'IN WĂN-SHUH. See 王大同 WANG TA-T'UNG. 上海縣志 *Shang hai heen che.* "A Topography of Shang-hai Heen." Compiled by Ch'in Wăn-shuh, etc. 1814. 8°. 15269. b. 5.

陳 蔚 CH'IN WEI. See 張仲景 CHANG CHUNG-KING. 金匱方歌括 *Kin kwei fang ko kwŏ.* "Prescriptions from the Golden Casket of Medicine . . ." Edited by Ch'in Wei, etc. 1836. 8°. 15251. f. 11.

沈 味 辛 CH'IN WEI-SIN. See 朱梅叔 CHOO MEI-SHUH. 埋憂集 *Mai yew tseth.* "A Collection of Tales for burying Grief . . ." Edited by Ch'in Wei-sin, etc. *Hangchow,* 1874. 8°. 15331. b. 13.

陳 維 崧 CH'IN WEI-SUNG. 陳檢討四六 *Ch'in keen-t'aou sze luh.* "The Writings of Ch'in Wei-sung, otherwise Ch'in Keen-t'aou." Edited by Ch'in Fuh-chen. With notes by Ch'ing Shuh-tsai. 20 keuen. 1770. 8°. 15319. d. 19.

陳 堯 農 CH'IN YAOU-NUNG. See 陳藻垣 CH'IN TSAOU-YUEN. 周易象義集成 *Chow yih seang e tseth ch'ing.* "A Complete Collection of Explanations of the Diagrams of the Chow Changes . . ." Edited by Ch'in Yaou-nung, etc. 1852. 8°. 15225. a. 20.

箴 言 CHIN YEN. 箴言摘錄 *Chin yen tsih luh.* "Extracts from the Book of Proverbs." With coloured illustrations. By, as is stated in a manuscript note on the cover, Mrs. Williamson. 1882. 4°. 15117. d. 23.

沈 約 CH'IN YŏÆ. 竹書紀年 *Chuh shoo ke neen.* "The Bamboo Record." 2 keuen. See 程榮 CH'ING YUNG. 漢魏叢書 *Han Wei ts'ung shoo.* "A Collection of Works by authors of the Han and Wei Dynasties," etc. 1791. 8°. 15318. a. 1.

—— 績齊諧記 *Suh ts'e heae ke.* "A Supplementary Record of Marvels." pp. 22. See 程榮 CH'ING YUNG. 漢魏叢書 *Han Wei ts'ung shoo.* "A Collection of Works by Authors of the Han and Wei Dynasties," etc. 1791. 8°. 15318. a. 1.

—— 竹書紀年統箋 *Chŭh shoo ke neen t'ung tseen.* "The Record of the Bamboo Books. With Ch'in Yŏ's Commentary and with Notes by Seu Wei-shan." Edited by Ma Kwei-chai and Ts'uy Yuh-ch'in. 12 keuen. 1750. 8°. 15292. c. 4.

潛 約 翰 CHIN YŏÆ-HAN [i.e. REV. JOHN CHALMERS]. See 康熙 K'ANG-HE. 康熙字典撮要 *K'ang-he tsze teen ts'o yaou.* "A Concise Edition of K'ang-he's Dictionary." Compiled by Chin Yŏ-han, etc. 1878. 8°. 15341. d. 2.

陳 與 義 CH'IN YU-E. 簡齋詩集 *Keen-chai she tseth.* "Keen-chai's [i.e. Ch'in Yu-e's] Poems." Edited with notes by Lew Ch'in-ung. 15 keuen. 1545. 8°. 15324. c. 5.
Printed in Korea from wooden blocks.

陳 元 龍 CH'IN YUEN-LUNG. 格致鏡原 *Kih che king yuen.* "An Encyclopædia of Arts and Sciences." Compiled by Ch'in Yuen-lung. 100 keuen. 1735. 8°. 15024. b. 3.
Imperfect, containing only Keuen 1–12, 35–44, 64–72.

—— [Another copy.] 15024. b. 4.
Imperfect, containing only Keuen 37–42.

陳 遇 乾 CH'IN YU-K'EEN. 繡 像 義 妖 傳 *Sew seang e yaou chuen.* "The Story of the Patriotic Fairies." A drama. With illustrations. 28 keuen. 1809. 8°. **15334. f. 6.**

陳 允 錫 CH'IN YUN-SEÏH. 二 十 一 史 緯 *Urh shih yih she wei.* "The Woof of the Twenty-one Histories." Compiled by Ch'in Yun-seïh. Edited by Kung Heen-tsäng. 330 keuen. 1870. 8°. **15292. a–c. 1.**

主 CHOO. 遵 主 聖 範 *Tsun choo shing fan.* "On Obeying the Laws of God." By a Roman Catholic Missionary. 4 keuen. *Hongkong*, 1891. 8°. **15118. a. 29.**

朱 昌 壽 CHOO CH'ANG-SHOW. 漢 儒 易 義 針 度 *Han joo yih e chin too.* "A Guide to the Meaning of the Book of Changes according to the Scholars of the Han Dynasty." By Choo Ch'ang-show. 4 keuen. 1843. 8°. **15225. a. 19.**

朱 長 文 CHOO CH'ANG-WÄN. 吳 郡 圖 經 續 記 *Woo keun t'oo king suh ke.* "A Supplement to the Illustrated Topography of Soo-chow Foo." By Choo Ch'ang-wän. Edited by Chang Hai-päng. 3 keuen. [The latest preface to which a date is affixed is one written in 1134. 1800?] 8°. **15271. c. 9.**

朱 周 望 CHOO CHOW-WANG. See 李 義 山 LE E-SHAN. 樊 南 文 集 詳 註 *Fan-nan wän tseih tseang choo.* "A Collection of Writings from Fan-nan . . ." Edited by Choo Chow-wang, etc. 1765. 8°. **15318. b. 5.**

儲 意 比 CHOO-E-PE [i.e.   ]. 營 城 揭 要 *Ying ch'ing kee yaou.* "A Treatise on Fortification." By the Englishman Choo-e-pe. With plans. Translated into Chinese by Foo-lan-ya. 2 keuen. [1870?] 8°. **15259. g. 9.**

—— [Another copy.] **15259. d. 8.**

朱 彝 尊 CHOO E-TSUN. 經 義 考 *King e k'aou.* "An Examination of the Explanations of the Classics." Compiled by Choo E-tsun. Edited by Choo Kwän. With a preface by the Emperor K'een-lung. 298 keuen. 1777. 8°. **15225. b. 1.**

朱 恩 錫 CHOO GÄN-SEÏH. *See* UNITED STATES OF AMERICA, ADMIRALTY. 兵 船 礮 法 *Ping ch'uen p'aou fä.* "On Naval Gunnery . . ." Transcribed by Choo Gän-seïh, etc. 8°. **15259. d. 12.**

朱 熹 CHOO HE. See 周 濂 溪 CHOW LEEN-K'E. 通 書 *T'ūng Sū* . . . mit Čū-Hi's Commentare, etc. 1880. 8°. **11100. b. 35.**

—— See 周 敦 頤 CHOW TUN-E. 太 極 圖 *Thai-kih-thu* . . . mit Tschu-Hi's Commentare, etc. 1876. 8°. **11100. b. 5.**

—— See 傳 恒 FOO HÄNG. 御 批 歴 代 通 鑑 輯 覽 *Yu p'e leih tai t'ung keen tseih lan.* "An Imperially Revised Survey of Choo He's Mirror of History," etc. 1768. 8°. **15290. e. 3.**

—— See 韓 愈 HAN YU. 朱 文 公 校 昌 黎 先 生 集 *Choo wän kung keaou Ch'ang-le seen säng tseih.* "A Collection of the Writings of Han Yu. Edited by Choo He," etc. 8°. **15315. c. 3.**

—— See 詩 經 SHE KING. 詩 經 *She king.* "The Book of Odes." With a collection of comments compiled by Choo He, etc. 1868. Fol. **15210. c. 17.**

—— See 四 書 SZE SHOO. 四 書 合 講 *Sze shoo hŏ keang.* "The Four Books . . ." With a collection of comments compiled by Choo He, etc. 1865. 8°. **15202. b. 20.**

—— See 四 書 SZE SHOO. 四 書 便 蒙 *Sze shoo peen mung.* "The Four Books for the Use of Children." With Choo He's Commentary, etc. 1878. 8°. **15201. a. 8.**

—— See 四 書 SZE SHOO. 四 書 讀 本 辨 義 *Sze shoo tuh pun peen e.* "The Text of the Four Books, with Choo He's Commentary," etc. 1747. 8°. **15202. e. 14.**

—— See 四 書 SZE SHOO. 四 子 書 *Sze tsze shoo.* "The Books of the Four Philosophers." With Choo He's Commentary. 1827. 8°. **15201. b. 2.**

—— See 四 書 SZE SHOO. 中 庸 章 句 *Chung yung chang keu.* "The Doctrine of the Mean, explained . . ." by Choo He, etc. Fol. **15202. c. 26.**

—— See 四 書 SZE SHOO. 學 庸 *Hcŏ Yung.* "The Great Learning and the Doctrine of the Mean." With . . . comments arranged . . . by Choo He, etc. 1867. Fol. **15202. d. 21.**

—— See 四 書 SZE SHOO. 論 語 *Lun yu.* "The Confucian Analects." With comments collected by Choo He, etc. 1868. Fol. **15202. d. 19.**

CHO

朱 熹 Choo He. See 四 書 Sze shoo. 孟 子 *Mǎng-tsze.* "The Teachings of Mencius." With comments collected by Choo He, etc. 1868. Fol. 15202. d. 20.

—— See 四 書 Sze shoo. 孟 子 集 註 *Mǎng-tsze tseǐh choo.* "The Teachings of Mencius. With a collection of comments" compiled by Choo He, etc. Fol. 15323. d. 27.

—— 四 書 Sze shoo. 大 學 章 句 *Ta heǒ chang keu.* "The Great Learning, explained . . ." by Choo He, etc. Fol. 15202. c. 24.

—— 朱 子 格 言 *Choo tsze kih yen.* "Choo He's Pattern Sayings." Compiled by Ch'in Che-tsoo. Printed in white on a black ground. 1743. 8°. 15312. d. 13.

—— 朱 子 大 全 *Choo tsze ta ts'euen.* "The Complete Works of Choo He." 66 keuen. [1750?] 8°. 15314. c. 2.
Imperfect, containing only Keuen 30–53.

—— 合 璧 小 學 *Hǒ peǐh seaou heǒ.* "The Youth's Instructor in Chinese and Manchu." Edited by Mǎng Paou. 12 keuen. 1850. 8vo. 15229. b. 9.

—— and 呂 祖 謙 Leu Tsoo-k'een. 近 思 錄 *Kin sze luh.* "A Record of nearly agreeing Philosophies." 14 keuen. 1579. Fol. 15315. e. 9.
Printed in Korea from blocks.

—— [Another edition. 14 keuen. 1610?] Fol. 15315. e. 10.
Printed in Korea with movable type.

—— 孟 子 要 略 *Mǎng tsze yaou leǒ.* "An important Epitome of the Doctrines of Mencius." With notes by Tsǎng Kwo-fan. 5 keuen. 1849. 8°. 15101. b. 30.

—— 小 學 註 解 *Seaou heǒ choo keae.* "The Youth's Instructor" by Choo He. "With a collection of comments" compiled by Ch'in Seuen, "and with explanations." 6 keuen. 1727. 8°. 15229. b. 13.

—— 小 學 大 全 *Seaou heǒ ta ts'euen.* "The Complete Youth's Instructor." With notes and comments. Edited by Woo Noh. 10 keuen. [1620?] Fol. 15229. d. 4.
Printed in Japan with movable type.

朱 熹 Choo He. 小 學 集 說 *Seaou heǒ tseǐh shuǒ.* "The Youth's Instructor. With a collection of comments." Edited by Ch'ing Yu. 6 keuen. [1620?] Fol. 15229. d. 2.
Printed in Korea with movable type.

—— [Another edition. 1620?] Fol. 15229. d. 1.
Printed in Japan with movable type.

—— [Another edition. 1625?] Fol. 15229. d. 3.
Printed in Korea from blocks.

—— See 蔡 九 霞 Ts'ai Kew-hea. 正 積 廣 治 平 畧 *Ching suh kwang che p'ing leǒ.* "A Correct Enlarged Epitome of the Imperial System of Government," . . . based . . . on the *Che p'ing leǒ* of Choo He, etc. 12°. 15239. d. 14.

—— 通 鑑 綱 目 *T'ung keen kang muh.* "A Condensation of the Mirror of History." By Choo He and his disciples. Edited by Ch'in Jin-seǐh. Part i, 25 keuen; Part ii, 59 keuen; Part iii, 27 keuen. 1808. 8°. 15288. d. 1.

—— 文 公 先 生 資 治 通 鑑 綱 目 *Wǎn kung seen sǎng tsze che t'ung keen kang muh.* "Choo He's Condensation of the Mirror of History." With copious notes. [59 keuen? 1250?] 8°. 15290. b. 4.
Imperfect, containing only Keuen 54–56.

朱 鶴 齡 Choo Hǒ-ling. See 李 義 山 Le E-shan. 李 義 山 詩 集 *Le E-shan shǐ tseǐh.* "A Collection of the Poetry of Le E-shan." Edited with notes by Choo Hǒ-ling, etc. 1659. 8°. 15323. e. 16.

初 會 Ch'oo hwuy. 初 會 問 答 *Ch'oo hwuy wǎn tǎ.* "A discussion on Religion at first meeting." pp. ii, 66. *Hongkong,* 1889. 8°. 15200. c. 68.

諸 儒 Choo joo. 諸 儒 註 解 古 文 眞 寶 前 集 *Choo joo choo keae koo wǎn chin paou ts'een tseǐh.* "Poetic Gems from Ancient Literature, with explanatory comments. First series." 10 keuen. [1500?] 8°. 15324. a. 7.
Printed in Japan from blocks.

—— 諸 儒 箋 解 古 文 眞 寶 前 集 *Choo joo tseen keae koo wǎn chin paou ts'een tseǐh.* "Gems from ancient literature with explanatory comments." First series. 10 keuen. [1620?] Fol. 15315. e. 2.
Printed in Japan from movable types.

諸 儒 CHOO JOO. 諸 儒 箋 解 古 文 眞 寶 後 集 *Choo joo tseen keae koo wăn chin paou how tseih.* "Gems from ancient literature, with explanatory comments. Second series." 10 keuen. With manuscript notes by Hayashi Rasan. 1624. Fol. 15315. e. 1.
Printed in Japan from blocks.

朱 岡 西 CHOO KANG-SE. See 陶 遜 亭 T'AOU SUN-T'ING. 草 韻 彙 編 *Ts'aou yun wei p'een.* "A Dictionary of the Grass Character . . ." Edited by Choo Kang-se, etc. 1755. 8°. 15344. b. 8.

朱 鏡 蓉 CHOO KING-YUNG. See 朱 駿 聲 CHOO TSEUN-SHING. 說 文 通 訓 定 聲 *Shwŏ wăn t'ung heun ting shing.* "Deep Instructions on the *Shwŏ wăn* . . ." Edited by Choo Tseun-shing, etc. 1850. 15344. c. 4.

諸 葛 亮 CHOOKO LEANG. 心 書 *Sin shoo.* "The Book of the Heart." A work on military matters. pp. iii, 33. See 程 榮 CH'ING YUNG. 漢 魏 叢 書 *Han Wei ts'ung shoo.* "A Collection of Works by Authors of the Han and Wei Dynasties," etc. 1791. 8°. 15318. a. 1.

—— 諸 葛 忠 武 侯 文 集 *Chooko chung woo how wăn tseih.* "The collected writings of Chooko, canonised as 'the patriotic military noble.'" Edited by Lew Ke-chaou. 6 keuen. 1873. 8°. 15317. a. 7.

朱 孔 彰 CHOO K'UNG-CHANG. See 林 君 復 LIN KEUN-FUH. 林 和 靖 集 *Lin Ho-tsing tseih.* "A Collection of the Poetry of Lin Keun-fuh." Edited by Choo K'ung-chang, etc. 1873. 8°. 15323. e. 12.

朱 昆 CHOO K'WĂN. See 朱 彝 尊 CHOO E-TSUN. 經 義 考 *King e k'aou.* "An Examination of the Explanations of the Classics . . ." Edited by Choo K'wăn, etc. 1777. 8°. 15225. b. 1.

朱 梅 谿 CHOO MEI-K'E, and 冷 諫 庵 LĂNG LEEN-GAN. 朱 元 明 詩 約 鈔 三 百 首 *Sung Yuen Ming she yŏ ch'aou san pih show.* "Three Hundred Pieces of Poetry of the Sung, Yuen, and Ming Dynasties." Compiled by Choo Mei-k'e and Lăng Leen-gan. Edited by Lăng Seaou-keu. 1841. 8°. 15323. d. 21.

朱 梅 叔 CHOO MEI-SHUH. 埋 憂 集 *Mai yew tseih.* "A Collection of Tales for Burying Grief." Compiled by Choo Mei-shuh. Edited by Ch'in Wei-sin. 10 keuen. Supplement, 2 keuen. *Hangchow*, 1874. 8°. 15331. b. 13.

諸 名 家 CHOO MING-KEA. 同 音 字 彙 *T'ung yin tsze wei.* "A Dictionary arranged phonetically." By Choo Ming-kea. 1774. 8°. 15342. b. 9.

CH'OO PIH-LOO, *pseud.* See CH'OO YUNG-SHUN. 11099. f. 12.

朱 世 傑 CHOO SHE-KEĔ. 算 學 啓 蒙 *Swan hŏ k'e mung.* "A General Treatise on Arithmetic." Written in A.D. 1299. 3 keuen. [1750?] 8°. 15259. h. 3.
A Japanese edition.

—— [Another edition.] For some centuries the work was lost in China, and was recovered from a Korean envoy. It was reprinted at Yang-chow in 1829. The present edition was edited by Yuen Yuen, who published it with the emendations of Lo Ming-heang. 3 keuen. 1839. 8°. 15255. e. 1.

朱 深 揚 CHOO SHIN-YANG. 律 例 七 言 *Lĕuh le ts'ih yen.* "An Abstract of the Laws of the Empire versified in lines of seven characters." 1808. 16°. 15241. a. 6.

芋 田 CH'OO T'EEN. See 司 馬 遷 SZE-MA TS'EEN. 史 記 菁 華 *She ke tsing hwa.* "An Anthology from the Historical Record . . ." Compiled by Ch'oo T'een, etc. 1824. 8°. 15296. b. 7.

—— See 司 馬 遷 SZE-MA TS'EEN. 史 記 菁 華 錄 *She ke tsing hwa luh.* "An Anthology from the Historical Record." Compiled by Ch'oo T'een, etc. 1824. 8°. 15286. a. 6.

朱 駿 聲 CHOO TSEUN-SHING. 說 文 通 訓 定 聲 *Shwŏ wăn t'ung heun ting shing.* "Deep Instructions on the *Shwŏ wăn* of Heu Shin. With a determination of the Sounds." By Choo Tseun-shing. Edited by Choo King-yung. 18 keuen. With four appendices. 1850. 8°. 15344. c. 4.

朱 宗 元 CHOO TSUNG-YUEN. 答 客 問 *Tă k'ih wăn.* "A Dialogue on Christianity." A reprint. pp. iv, 88. *Hongkong*, 1893. 8°. 15200. d. 41.

朱 蔚 然 CHOO WEI JEN. 南 燕 錄 *Nan yen luh.* "The Records of the Nan Yen Dynasty." Edited by Choo Wei-jen. See 崔 鴻 TS'UY HUNG. 十 六 國 春 秋 *Shih luh kwŏ ch'un ts'ew.* "The Annals of the Sixteen Dynasties," etc. 8°.

初 渭 園 CH'OO WEI-YUEN. 吉 金 所 見 錄 *Keih kin so keen luh.* "The lucky coins I have seen." 16 keuen. 1819. 15300. b. 3.

CHO

朱 玉 堂 CHOO YUH-T'ANG. 國朝律賦攟金錄 *Kwŏ chaou leuh foo keen kin luh.* "A Select Golden Record of Odes by Authors of the Present Dynasty." Compiled by Choo Yuh-t'ang. In two series. Series i, 12 keuen; Series ii, 12 keuen. 1792. 8°. **15323. d. 8.**

CH'OO YUNG-SHUN. Les Instructions familières du Dr. Tchou Pô-lou [*pseud.*, i.e. Ch'oo Yung-shun]. Traité de morale pratique, publié pour la première fois avec deux traductions françaises . . . accompagné de notes . . . et d'un vocabulaire . . . par C. Imbault-Huart. pp. xx, 133. *Péking*, 1881. 8°. **11099. f. 12.**

朝 鮮 CHŌSEN. 朝鮮板類合 *Chōsenban riugō.* "A Chinese and Korean Vocabulary." [1650?] 8°. **15344. e. 20.**

周 馳 CHOW CH'E. 閑邪公家傳 *Heen-seay kung kea chuen.* "An Account of the Family of Le Chung-chang, Duke Heen-seay." By Chow Ch'e. [White characters on black paper. 1800?] Obl. **15303. c. 14.**

周 準 CHOW CHUN. See 沈 德 潛 CH'IN TIH-TSEEN, and CHOW CHUN. 明 詩 別 裁 集 *Ming she pĕĕ ts'ai tseih.* "A Collection of the Poetry of the Ming Dynasty," etc. 1739. 8°. **15324. a. 4.**

周 與 嗣 CHOW HING-SZE. Chinese School-books. Ts'in-tsz-man [by Chow Hing-sze]. Translated by E. J. Eitel. pp. 26. *Hongkong*, 1893. 8°. **11099. c. 32.**

—— 滿 漢 千 字 文 *Man Han ts'een tsze wăn.* "The Thousand-Character Classic in Mantchoo and Chinese." Edited by Ch'in K'e-leang. *Peking*, [1800?]. 8°. **15229. c. 48.**

—— 百 體 千 字 文 *Pih t'e ts'een tsze wăn.* "The Thousand-Character Classic in a hundred forms of character." 1685. 8°. **15223. c. 13.**

—— 千 字 文 *Tsiăn dsú wén*, sive Mille Literæ ideographicæ. Opus Sinicum origine [by Chow Hing-sze] cum interpretatione Kooraiana, in peninsula Koorai impressum in lapide exaratum a Sinensi 郭 成 章 Ko Tsching Dschang, et redditum curante Ph. Fr. de Siebold. (Annexo systemate scripturæ Koorianæ.) *Leiden*, 1833. 4°. **11099. g. 3.**

周 與 嗣 CHOW HING-SZE. Das 千 字 文 *Tsiän dsü wen*, oder Buch von tausend Wörtern, aus dem Schinesischen, mit Berücksichtigung der Koraischen und Japanischen Übersetzung, ins Deutsche. Übertragen von Dr. J. Hoffmann. *Leiden*, 1840. 4°. **11099. g. 1.**

—— 千 字 文 *Ts'een tsze wăn.* "The Thousand-Character Classic." MS. [1840?] A folded sheet. **Or. 970. 39. B. g.**

—— 千 字 文 釋 義 *Ts'een tsze wăn shih e.* "The Thousand-Character Classic with the meaning explained." See 徐 建 勳 SEU KEEN-HEUN. 徐 氏 三 種 *Seu she san chung.* "Seu's reprints of the three works," etc. 1875. 8°. **15202. b. 21.**

—— 千 字 文 釋 句 *Ts'een tsze wăn shih keu.* "The Thousand-Character Classic. With explanations." 1858. 8°. **15229. c. 13.**

周 嘉 猷 CHOW KEA-YEW. See 李 延 壽 LE YEN-SHOW. 南 北 史 捃 華 *Nan pih she keun hwa.* "An Anthology from the Histories of the South and North." Compiled by Chow Kea-yew, etc. 8°. **15291. a. 5.**

周 官 CHOW KWAN. 欽 定 周 官 義 疏 *K'in ting Chow kwan e soo.* "The Meaning of the Offices of Chow. With explanations." Compiled by an Imperial Commission presided over by Prince Yun-luh and Hung-yen. 48 keuen. 1754. 8°. **15219. c. 9.**

周 蘭 九 CHOW LAN-KEW. See 吳 遵 程 WOO TSUN-CH'ING. 成 方 切 用 *Ch'ing fang ts'ĕĕ yung.* "Medical Prescriptions . . ." Edited by Chow Lan-kew, etc. 1761. 8°. **15252. e. 7.**

周 禮 CHOW LE. 周 禮 *Chow le.* "The Chow Ritual." With a collection of comments. Compiled by Keang Chaou-seĭh. 12 keuen. 1731. 8°. **15219. c. 3.**

—— 周 禮 *Chow le.* "The Chow Ritual." With a Commentary by Ching K'ang-ch'ing, and with explanatory notes by Luh Tih-ming. Edited by Le Han-chang and others. 12 keuen. 1868. Fol. **15220. b. 7.**

—— 周 禮 節 訓 *Chow le tseih heun.* "The Chow Ritual. With sectional explanations" by Hwang K'un-poo. 6 keuen. 1783. 8°. **15217. a. 8.**

26

周禮 CHOW LE. 周禮精華 Chow le tsing hwa. "The Essence and Flower of the Chow Ritual." Edited by Ch'in Lung-peaou. 6 keuen. 1826. 8°. 15220. b. 5.

周漾溪 CHOW LEEN-K'E. 通書 [T'ung shoo] T'ŭng-sŭ des Čeŭ-tsï, mit Cŭ-Hï's commentare nach dem Sing-li tsīng i. Chinesisch mit Mandschuischen und Deutschen übersetzung und ammerkungen herausgegeben von Wilhelm Grube. Theil I, Cap. i–viii. Wien: Adolf Holzhausen, 1880. 8°. 11100. b. 35.

周樂之 CHOW LO-CHE. Second book of Chinese and English lessons, for the use of schools. Translated by Chow Loke-chee. Second edition. pp. 30. Hongkong, 1893. Sm. 4°. 11099. a. 15.

CHOW LOKE CHEE. See 周樂之 CHOW LO-CHE.

周弼 CHOW PIH. 箋註唐賢絕句三體詩法 Tseen choo T'ang heen tseue keu san t'e she fa. "Specimens of poems of authors of the T'ang Dynasty in the styles of composition (i.e., Tseue keu, heptameter, and pentameter)." With notes. Compiled by Chow Pih. With the notes of Che-teen-yin. 20 keuen. 1306. Fol. 15324. e. 6.

周參元 CHOW SAN-YUEN. See 楊慎 YANG SHIN. 升菴全集 Shing gan ts'euen tseĭh. "A Complete Collection of the Writings of Yang Shin." Edited by Chow San-yuen, etc. 1795. 8°. 15317. e. 9.

周德清 CHOW TIH-TS'ING. 中原音韻 Chung yuen yin yun. "A Pronouncing Dictionary of the Mandarin Dialect." By Chow Tih-tsing of the Yuen Dynasty. With notes by Wang Wăn-peĭh. Edited by Yĕ E-chin. A new edition. 2 keuen. 8°. 15346. b. 21.

周鼎臣 CHOW TING CH'IN. 敬信錄 King sin luh. Works on reverence and faith. Compiled by Chow Ting-ch'in. Edited by Chin Ying. [A collection of Taouist works.] 1776. 8°. 15111. b. 31.

—— [Another edition. 1800?] 8°. 15111. b. 9. Imperfect, wanting the first 59 pages.

周馘坤 CHOW TSAI-K'WĂN. 敬勝堂試藝 King-shing T'ang she e. "Essays from the King-shing Hall." Shanghai, [1840?] 8°. 15320. e. 24.

周敦頤 CHOW TUN-E. 太極圖 Thai-kih-thu, des Tscheu-tsï (Chow Tun-e) Tafel des Urprinzipes, mit Tschu-Hi's Commentare . . . mit Mandschuischer und Deutscher Übersetzung Einleitung und Anmerkungen herausgegeben von Georg von der Gabelentz. Dresden, 1876. 8°. 11100. b. 5.

周易 CHOW YIH. 周易 Chow Yih. "The Chow Changes." With a commentary. Edited by Le Han-chang and others. 4 keuen. 1868. Fol. 15212. e. 5.

—— 周易審義 Chow yih shin e. "The Meaning of the Chow Changes examined." By Yu Fan. Edited by Chang Hwuy-yen. 4 keuen. 1857. 8°. 15212. d. 14.

仇英實 CH'OW YING-SHIH. See 汪庚 WANG KĂNG. 列女傳 Lëĕ neu chuen. "Biographical notices of celebrated women." Illustrated by Ch'ow Ying-shih, etc. 1778. 8°. 13303. d. 14.

竹莊 CHUH CHWANG. 晚笑堂畫傳 Wan seaou t'ang hwa chuen. "The Evening-laughter Hall collection of illustrated biographies." 3 keuen. 1743. 8°. 15303. c. 16.

—— [Another copy.] 15303. d. 4.

祝穆 CHUH MUH. 新編古今事文類聚 Sin peen koo kin sze wăn luy tseu. "A classified Encyclopædia of General Knowledge. (First published in 1246.) A new edition." 221 keuen. [1610?] 4°. 15019. c. & d. Printed in Japan with movable type.

竹勿山石道人 CHUH WUH SHAN SHIH TAOU JIN [pseud.]. 瑣蛣雜記 So keih tsa ke. "Trifling miscellaneous records." A collection of stories. Compiled by an author calling himself Chuh wuh shan shih taou jin. 20 keuen. Peking, 1795. 8°. 15327. e. 1.

竹隱主人 CHUH-YIN CHOO JIN, pseud. See 試策 SHE TSIH. 試策補要 She tsih poo yaou. "Supplementary Notes . . ." By "Chuh-yin Choo-jin," etc. 1876. 8°. 15319. a. 14.

仲 恒 CHUNG HAN. 詞 韻 *Tsze yun.* "The Sounds of Rhymes." See 查 繼 超 CHA KE-CHAOU. 詞 學 全 書 *Tsze heŏ ts'euen shoo.* "A complete work on the Art of Rhyming," etc. 1746. 8°. **15321. d. 14.**

鍾 嶸 CHUNG HĂNG. 詩 品 *She p'in.* "Poetry classified." 3 keuen. See 程 榮 CH'ING YUNG. 漢 魏 叢 書 *Han Wei ts'ung shoo.* "A collection of Works by Authors of the Han and Wei Dynasties," etc. 1791. 8°. **15318. a. 1.**

冲 虛 伍 眞 人 CHUNG HEU WOO CHIN JIN, *pseud.* 天 仙 正 理 *T'een seen ching le.* "The Orthodox Doctrine of Heavenly Genii." A revised edition. 2 vols. 1819. 8°. **15103. b. 16.**

崇 厚 CH'UNG How. A letter addressed to Colonel Gordon by Ch'ung How on the eve of his departure for England [in 1864?] and asking his advice as to the manufacture of powder and guns in China. With visiting card. MS. [1864?] **Or. 3534.**

鍾 謙 鈞 CHUNG K'EEN-KEUN. 古 經 解 彙 函 *Koo king keae wei han.* "A Collection of the Ancient Classics." Edited by Chung K'een-keun. *Canton*, 1873. 8°. **15225. c.**

仲 均 安 CHUNG KEUN-NGAN [i.e REV. A. G. JONES]. 義 學 新 法 *E heŏ sin fa.* "A new method of learning the meaning" of the less common characters used in the translation of the New Testament. *Shanghai*, 1896. 8°. **15342. a. 6.**

鍾 伯 敬 CHUNG PIH-KING. 繡 像 東 西 漢 演 義 *Sew seang tung se Han yen e.* "An illustrated popular History of the Eastern and Western Han Dynasties." Edited by Chung Pih-king Seen-săng. 8 keuen. [1850?] 8°. **15333. e. 11.**

鍾 惺 CHUNG SING. 夏 商 合 傳 *Hea Shang hŏ chuen.* "The Histories of the Hea and Shang Dynasties." By Chung Sing. Edited by Fung Mung-lung. 10 keuen. 1814. 8°. **15296. b. 8.**

種 德 者 CHUNG TIH CHAY [i.e. REV. DAVID COLLIE]. 新 纂 聖 道 備 全 *Sin tswan shing taou pe ts'euen.* A scripture help. A new publication. By Chung tih-chay. [*Singapore*, 1835?] 8°. **15116. e. 36.**

鍾 文 烝 CHUNG WĂN-CHING. See 穀 梁 赤 KUH-LEANG CHIH. 春 秋 穀 梁 經 傳 補 注 *Ch'un ts'ew Kuh-leang king chuen poo choo.* "Kuh-leang's Commentary on the Spring and Autumn Annals . . ." With additional explanations by Chung Wăn-ching, etc. 1875. 8°. **15212. e. 1.**

忠 王 CHUNG WANG. 僞 忠 王 親 筆 口 供 *Wei Chung Wang ts'in pelh k'ow hung.* "The Confessions of Chung Wang," a leader of the T'aip'ing Rebels. 1864. 8°. **15297. c. 2.**

春 暉 堂 CH'UN-HWUY T'ANG. 春 暉 堂 叢 書 *Ch'un-hwuy T'ang ts'ung shoo.* "The Ch'un-hwuy T'ang Collection of Reprints." 1841. 8°. **15316. e. 15.**

椿 園 氏 CH'UN YUEN SHE, *pseud.* 遐 域 瑣 談 *Hea yuh so tan.* "Notes on Chinese Turkestan." MS. ff. 55. [1800?] 8°. **Add. 16285. 39. B. e.**

—— 新 疆 外 叛 紀 略 *Sin keang wai Fan ke leŏ.* A short topography of the New Borders [i.e. Turkistan]. By Ch'un yuen she. The title-page and first book are wanting in this copy. 2 keuen. [1800?] 8°. **15271. b. 9.**

莊 周 CHWANG CHOW. 莊 子 盧 齋 口 義 *Chwang-tsze keu chai k'ow e.* "The Writings of Chwang Chow, with the verbal interpretations" of Lin He. 10 keuen. 1629. Fol. **15113. c. 6.**
Printed in Japan with movable type.

—— [A facsimile reprint of the above edition.] [1650?] Fol. **15113. c. 7.**
Printed in Japan from blocks.

—— 南 華 眞 經 *Nan hwa chin king.* "The Nan-hwa Classic." With comments by Kŏ Seang and with notes on the sounds of the characters by Luh Tih-ming. 10 keuen. [1300?] 8°. **15212. e. 9.**

COBBOLD (ROBERT HENRY). *See* KO PO-YI.

COLLIE (DAVID). See 四 書 SZE SHOO. The Chinese classical work commonly called the Four Books. Translated, etc., by Rev. David Collie. 1828. 8°. **11100. b. 1.**

CORBETT (HUNTER). See 郭 顯 德 KŎ HEEN-TIH.

CORDIER (HENRI). *See* SCHEGEL (GUSTAVE) and CORDIER (HENRI). 通 報 *T'oung pao* . . . Rédigées par MM. G. S. et H. C., extrait du vol. i, etc. 1890. 8°. **11098. b. 2.**

CORDIER (HENRI). A Catalogue of the Library of the North China Branch of the Royal Asiatic Society (including the Library of Alex. Wylie, Esq.). Systematically classed. By H. C. pp. viii, 86. *Shanghai*, 1872. 8°. 11098. a. 21.

COURANT (MAURICE). *See* ACADEMIES — *Paris: Ecole spéciale des Langues Orientales vivantes.* Bibliographie Coréenne, etc. 1894–96. 8°. 11098. c. 11.

COUREL (H.). *See* MÉLY (F. DE). Les Lapidaires de l'Antiquité et du moyen âge . . . Tom. i. Les Lapidaires Chinois. Introduction, texte, et traduction, avec la collaboration de M. H. C., etc. 1896. 4°. 11098. b. 28.

COUVREUR (SÉRAPHIN). *See* 孔丘 K'UNG K'EW. 書經 *Chou King.* Texte Chinois, avec une double traduction en Français et en Latin . . . Par S. C., etc. 1897. 8°. 11098. b. 31.

—— Choix de Documents, Lettres officielles, Proclamations, Édits, Mémoriaux, Inscriptions, . . . Texte Chinois, avec traduction en Français et en Latin. Par S. C. pp. iv, 560. *Hokien Fu*, 1894. 8°. 11098. a. 19.

—— 官話 Mandarin Language. Guide to conversation in French, English, and Chinese, containing a vocabulary and familiar dialogues. By S. C. pp. x, 222. *Hokien Fu*, 1892. 8°. 11098. a. 20.

CRAWFORD (TARLETON P.). *See* 高第丕 KAOU TE P'EI.

CULBERTSON (MICHAEL SIMPSON). *See* BIBLE: *Old Testament* 舊約全書 *Kew yŏ ts'euen shoo.* "The Old Testament." Translated into Chinese by . . . M. S. Culbertson, etc. 1863. 8°. 15118. d. 1.

—— See 以利亞 E-LE-YA. 以利亞言行傳 *E-le-ya yen hing chuen.* "A Life of Elijah." [By M. S. C.], etc. 1861. 8°. 15200. c. 40.

—— See 福音 FUH YIN. 福音道問答合講 *Fuh yin taou wăn tă ho keang.* "A Catechism on the Doctrine of the Gospel" . . . by M. S. C., etc. 1861. 8°. 15118. a. 35.

—— See 約瑟 Yŏ-SIH. 約瑟言行全傳 *Yŏ-sih yen hing ts'euen chuen.* "A complete life of Joseph." [By M. S. C.?], etc. 1861. 8°. 15200. b. 4.

DABRY DE THIERSANT (PIERRE). Guide des Armées Alliées en Chine ou Dialogues sur les Reconnaissances Militaires en trois langues: Français, Anglais, Chinois, etc. *Paris* [printed], *London*, 1859. 12°. 11100. b. 13.

DANA (JAMES DWIGHT). See 代那 TAI-NA.

DAVIS (SIR JOHN FRANCIS), Bart. *See* SAN-YU-LOW. 三與樓 *San-yu-low*; or the three dedicated rooms . . . Translated by J. F. D. 1815. 8°. 11099. c. 1 (2).

—— Poeseos Sinensis commentarii. On the poetry of the Chinese (from the Royal Asiatic Transactions), to which are added translations and detached pieces. By J. F. D. *Macao*, 1834. 8°. 11099. d. 5.

DEAN (WILLIAM). *See* STOW (BARON). Daily Manna for Christian Pilgrims . . . Translated into Chinese by W. D., etc. 1844. 8°. 15117. b. 39.

DE MORGAN (AUGUSTUS). See 棣麽甘 TE MOKAN.

DES MICHELS (ÉTIENNE ABEL). Chih louh kouoh kiang yuh tchi. Histoire géographique du Seizes Royaumes . . . traduit par A. des M. *See* ACADEMIES, etc.—*Paris: Ecole spéciale des langues orientales vivantes*, etc. 1892. 8°. 11098. b. 1.

—— Chrestomathie Cochinchinoise. Recueil de Textes Annamites, publiés traduits et transcrits en caractères figuratifs. Par A. des M. Premier fascicule. pp. xv, 47, 67. *Maisonneuve & Cie.: Paris*, 1872. 8°. 11099. f. 39.

—— Dialogues en langue Cochinchinoise. Publiés à l'usage des Commerçants et des Voyageurs. Par A. des M. pp. iv, 24. *Maisonneuve & Cie.: Paris*, 1869. 8°. 11099. c.

—— Les Poèmes de l'Annam. Kim vân kiêu tân truyên. Publié et traduit . . . par A. des M. *See* ACADEMIES, etc.—*Paris: Ecole spéciale des Langues orientales vivantes*, etc. 1884. 8°. 11100. f. 4.

—— Manuel de la Langue Chinoise écrite destiné à faciliter la rédaction des pièces dans cette langue. Par A. des M. pp. xvi, 439. *Ernest Leroux: Paris*, 1888. 8°. 11100. f. 6.

DES MICHELS (ÉTIENNE ABEL). Petit Dictionnaire pratique à l'usage des Elèves du cours d'Annamite. Par A. des M. pp. 60. *Maisonneuve et Cie.: Paris*, 1877. 8°. **11099. c. 25.**

DICTIONARIES. Dictionnaire Chinois-Français de la langue Mandarine parlée dans l'ouest de la Chine, avec un Vocabulaire Français-Chinois. Par plusieurs Missionnaires du Sé‑tch'oūan méridional. *Imprimerie de la Société des Missions étrangères, Hongkong*, 1893. 4°. **12910. dd. 24.**

—— Dictionary of the Chinese Language. This is the beginning of an English and Chinese Dictionary. It contains only from A to the beginning of E. The last three folios contain miscellaneous phrases. MS. ff. 63. [1840?] 4°. **Or. 2284. 28. a.**

—— Lexicon Anamitico-Latinum. pp. 63. *Ninh phu*, 1878. 4°. **11100. b. 24.**

—— Notions pour servir à l'étude de la langue Annamite. pp. 381. *Tân Dinh*, 1878. 8°. **11100. b. 26.**

DODD (SAMUEL). See 陶錫祈 T'AOU SEIH-K'E.

—— *See* BIBLE—NEW TESTAMENT: *John, Epistles.* 約翰一二三書註释 *Yo-han yih, urh, san, Shoo choo shih.* "The three epistles of St. John. With an explanatory commentary" by S. D., etc. 1881. 8°. **15116. c. 34.**

DONNER (O.). Wörterverzeichniss zu den Inscriptions de l'Jénisseï. Von O. D. pp. 69. *Helsingfors*, 1892. 8°. **11098. b. 7.**
A paper from the Suomalais-Ugrilaisen Seuran Toimituksia IV.

DOUGLAS (ROBERT KENNAWAY). Chinese Stories. With illustrations. pp. xxxvii, 348. *Blackwood & Sons: Edinburgh & London*, 1893. 8°. **11100. c. 30.**

DOUTHWAITE (A. W.). See 靈魂 LING HWAN. 靈魂之糧 *Ling hwan che leang.* "Food for the Soul." By A. W. D., etc. 1880. 8°. **15200. c. 4.**

DUCAT (CHARLES M.). An Elementary Manual of the Pekinese Dialect, for the use of officers preparing for the preliminary examination. Arranged by Captain C. M. D. pp. 24. *Rangoon*, 1898. 8°. **11098. a. 27.**

EDE (GEORGE). Sam-jū-keng Sin-chōan Pek-oa Chù-kái. [The Three Character Classic. With notes. In the Amoy dialect.] Edited by G. E. pp. iv, 179. *T'aiwan Fu*, 1894. 8°. **15229. c. 45.**

宜興 E HING. 清文補彙 *Ts'ing wăn poo wei.* A Mantchoo and Chinese Dictionary. By E. Hing. [This Dictionary is arranged alphabetically on the model of the Tsing wăn wei shoo, and was intended to supply the deficiencies of that Dictionary. It is divided into eight books.] 2 vols. 1802. 8°. **15354. a. 3.**

—— [Another copy.] **15354. a. 4.**

EITEL (E. J.). See 周興嗣 CHOW HING-SZE. Chinese Schoolbooks. Ts'in-tsz-man. Translated by E. J. E., etc. 1893. 8°. **11099. c. 32.**

—— See 字 TSZE. Chinese Schoolbooks. Sam-tsz-king. Translated by E. J. E., etc. 1892. 8°. **11099. c. 31.**

宜稼堂 E-KEA T'ANG. 宜稼堂叢書 *E-kea T'ang ts'ung shoo.* "The E-kea T'ang Collection of Reprints." 1841. 8°. **15316. c. 2.**

儀禮 E LE. 儀禮 *E le.* "The 'Decorum Ritual.'" With a commentary by Ching K'ang-ch'ing, and with explanatory notes by Luh Tih-ming. 17 keuen. 1868. Fol. **15220. b. 2.**

—— 儀禮 *I-li.* Cérémonial de la Chine antique, avec des extraits des meilleurs Commentaires, traduit pour la première fois par C. de Harlez. pp. xvi, 408. *J. Maisonneuve: Paris*, 1890. 8°. **11099. d. 38.**

—— 欽定儀禮義疏 *K'in ting E le e soo.* "The Meaning of the Decorum Ritual. With explanations" by Kea Kung-yen, Ching K'ang-ch'ing, and others. 48 keuen. [1754?] 8°. **15219. b. 3. & c. 1.**

以利亞 E-LE-YA. 以利亞言行傳 *E-le-ya yen hing chuen.* "A life of Elijah." [By M. S. Culbertson.] pp. iv, 36. *Shanghai*, 1861. 8°. **15200. c. 40.**

ELWIN (A.). *See* 'ANG-TSE. *'Ang-tse t'u-wa z-ü.* "A Primer . . ." [By A. E.], etc. 1876. 8°. **15229. b. 23.**

ENGLISH AND CHINESE. A lexilogus of the English and Chinese languages. Fourth edition. pp. 36. *Hongkong*, 1896. 8°. **11099. c. 33.**

EPHEMERIDES. 欽定選擇詳註便覽吉用憲書大清道光二十五年 *K'in ting seuen tsih tseang choo peen lan k'ih yung heen shoo. Ta Ts'ing Taou-kwang urh shih woo neen.* "An Astrological Almanac for the 25th year of the reign of the Emperor Taou-kwang," i.e. 1845. 1845. 8°. 15298. a. 43.

—— [Another copy.] 15298. a. 44.

—— 欽定萬年書 *K'in ting wan neen shoo.* An almanac for the years from the 4th year of the reign of T'een-k'e [1625] to the year 1895. [1840?] 8°. 15298. a. 20.

—— 連元閣紅字頭新通書 *Leen-yuen-kih hung tsze t'ow sin t'ung shoo.* "The Leen-yuen-kih Astrological Almanac" for the year 1896. With illustrations. 1896. 8°. 15257. d. 33.

—— 道光二十四年日用便覽 *Taou-kwang urh shih sze neen jih yung peen lan.* "An Almanac for the 24th year of the reign of the Emperor Taou-kwang," i.e. 1844. 1844. 8°. 15298. a. 39.

—— 大清咸豐入年歲次戊午選吉擇日便民通書 *Ta Ts'ing Heen-fung pá neen suy ts'ze woo woo seuen keih tsih jih peen min t'ung shoo.* "An Almanac for the 8th year of the reign of the Emperor Heen-fung," i.e. 1858. 1858. 8°. 15298. a. 1.

—— 大清咸豐便民通書 *Ta Ts'ing Heen-fung peen min t'ung shoo.* "Almanacs for (the 7th and 8th years of) the reign of the Emperor Heen-fung," i.e. 1857–58. 8°. 15298. a. 2.

—— 大清咸豐十年時憲書 *Ta Ts'ing Heen-fung shih neen she heen shoo.* "An Almanac for the 10th year of the reign of the Emperor Heen-fung," i.e. 1860. 1860. 8°. 15298. a. 25.

—— 大清咸豐七年歲次丁巳時憲書 *Ta Ts'ing Heen-fung ts'ih neen suy ts'ze ting sze she heen shoo.* "An Almanac for the 7th year of the reign of the Emperor Heen-fung," i.e. 1857. *Peking*, 1857. 8°. 15298. a. 26.

—— 大清道光年時憲書 *Ta Ts'ing Taou-kwang neen she heen shoo.* "Almanacs" for the 22nd, 23rd, 24th, 25th, and 26th years of the reign of the Emperor Taou-kwang. 1842–46. 8°. 15298. a. 23.

—— [Another copy.] 15298. a. 24.

EPHEMERIDES. 大清道光二十六年丙午便民通書 *Ta Ts'ing Taou-kwang urh shih luh neen ping woo peen min t'ung shoo.* "An Almanac for the 26th year of the reign of the Emperor Taou-kwang," i.e. 1846. 1846. 8°. 15298. a. 45.

—— 大清道光二十三年癸卯便民通書 *Ta Ts'ing Taou-kwang urh shih san neen kwei maou peen min t'ung shoo.* "An Almanac for the 23rd year of the reign of the Emperor Taou-kwang," i.e. 1843. 1843. 8°. 15298. a. 21.

—— [Another copy.] 15298. a. 41.

—— 大清道光二十四年甲辰便民通書 *Ta Ts'ing Taou-kwang urh shih sze neen kea shin peen min t'ung shoo.* "An Almanac for the 24th year of the reign of the Emperor Taou-kwang," i.e. 1844. 1844. 8°. 15298. a. 22.

—— [Another copy.] 15298. a. 42.

—— 萬福攸同 *Wan fuh t'eaou t'ung.* "An Astrological Almanac for the year 1858." 1858. 8°. 15257. a. 25.

—— 耶穌降生一千八百八十九年主日瞻禮齋期日表 *Yay-soo keang săng yih ts'een pa-pih pa-shih-kew neen choo jih chen le chai k'e jih peaou.* "An Almanac for the year 1889 of the feasts and fasts." *Hongkong*, 1889. A sheet. 15200. c. 61.

—— 一本萬利 *Yih pun wan le.* "An Astrological Almanac for the year 1858." 1858. 8°. 15257. a. 25.

—— 御定萬年書 *Yu ting wan neen shoo.* "An Imperial Almanac" for the period from the 17th year of the reign of the Emperor Keen-lung (1752) to the (possible) 60th year of the reign of the Emperor Taou-kwang (1880). [1840?] 8°. 15298. a. 40.

ESSAYS. Essays on texts from the *Lun yu* by sixty different scholars. Without title. MS. ff. 133. [1850?] 8°. Or. 2180. 39. B. e.

伊都立 E TOO-LEIH. A circular letter written by E Too-leih, Wang Taou-hwa, Chaou Ch'ang, and others, in Latin, Chinese, and Manchoo, asking for information with regard to the Missions to Europe undertaken by A. Barros, A. Beauvolier in 1706, and by J. Provana and R. de Arxo in 1708. The letter is subscribed by M. Ripa and others, and is dated October 31, 1716. A roll. 15200. e. 2.

E-TSING. *See* LUNG SHU. Suh-ki-li-lih-kiu . . . or "Friendly Letter." Written by Lung shu . . . Translated from the Chinese edition of I-tsing, etc. 1892. 8°. **11100. b. 27.**

—— Mémoire composé à l'époque de la grande dynastie T'ang sur les Religieux éminents qui allèrent chercher la loi dans les pays d'Occident. Traduit en Français par Édouard Chavannes. pp. xxi, 218. *Paris*, 1894. 8°. **11100. e. 25.**
The running title of the book is "Voyages des pélerins bouddhistes."

異端 E TWAN. 異端總論 *E twan tsung lun.* "A discussion on heterodox and orthodox religions." A Christian pamphlet. pp. 100, 2. 1845. 8°. **15113. a. 17.**

倪雲瓏 E YUN-KEU. 桐陰清話 *T'ung yin ts'ing hwa.* "Pure Discourses from the T'ung Grove." By E. Yun-keu. 8 keuen. 1874. 8°. **15319. b. 18.**

FABER (ERNST). See 花之安 HWA CHE-NGAN.

—— *See* JOHN (GRIFFITH) and FABER (E). A collection of nineteen Protestant tracts . . . one by E. F., etc. **15200. e. 1. (1).**

—— 大德國學校論畧 *Ta Tih kwŏ heŏ keaou lun leŏ.* "A short account of the educational system of the German Empire." Edited by J. G. Kerr. *Canton*, 1873. 8°. **15320. c. 13.**
With preface in English.

法顯 FĂ HEEN. 佛國記 *Fuh kwŏ ke.* "An account of Buddhist countries." pp. 82. See 程榮 CH'ING YUNG. 漢魏叢書 *Han Wei ts'ung shoo.* "A collection of works by authors of the Han and Wei Dynasties," etc. 1791. 8°. **15318. a. 1.**

—— 法顯傳 *Fă heen chuen.* "The life of Fă heen." MS. [1850?] 8°. **15305. b. 9.**

—— 佛國記 Record of the Buddhist Kingdoms. (By Fă-heen.) Translated from the Chinese by H. A. Giles. *London* and *Shanghai* [printed 1878?]. 8°. **11099. d. 1.**

梵 FAN. 梵網經 *Fan kang king.* "The Brahma jala sūtra." [Translated into Chinese by Che K'een?] 2 keuen. 1290? 8°. **15103. b. 8.**
Imperfect, containing only Keuen 1. Printed in Japan from blocks.

范宜賓 FAN E-PIN. 乾坤法竅 *K'een k'wan fă keaou.* "The Laws of Heaven and Earth," being extracts from works on Geomancy. Compiled by Fan E-pin. 3 keuen. 1766. 8°. **15257. a. 5.**

方華樸 FANG HWA-PŎ. See 汪體齋 WANG T'E-CHAI. 天下有山堂墨竹蘭石譜 *T'een hea yew shan t'ang mih chuh lan shih poo.* "Sketches . . ." Edited by Fang Hwa-pŏ, etc. 1724. 8°. **15255. e. 22.**

方謙之 FANG K'EEN-CHE. 三車一覽 *San ch'ay yih lan.* "A view of the 'three carriages,'" or the three degrees of saintship. A Korean edition. 10 keuen. [1600?] Fol. **15212. e. 8.**

方觀承 FANG KWAN-CH'ING. 御題棉華圖 *Yu t'e kin hwa t'oo.* "Engravings (on a black ground) illustrating the various processes employed in the manufacture of cotton. With notes by the Emperor K'een-lung." Compiled by Fan Kwan-ch'ing. 1765. 4°. **15255. e. 2.**

方密之 FANG MEIH-CHE. 天經或問天 *T'een king hwo wăn t'een.* "The Classic of the Heavens, or a Catechism on the Universe." A Japanese edition. pp. 104. [1800?] 8°. **15210. c. 18.**

芳西學 FANG SE-HEŎ. 楊文憲公升庵先生全集 *Yang wăn heen kung shing gan Seen-săng ts'euen tseih.* "A complete collection of the works of Yang Shin." [The contents of this work might be more accurately described as "The Record of the Years of Yang Shin."] See 孫澍 SUN SHOO. 古棠書屋叢書 *Koo t'ang shoo wuh ts'ung shoo.* "A collection of Reprints," etc. 1831–49. 8°. **15315. d. 1.**

方佐 FANG TSO. See 王大同 WANG TA-T'UNG. 上海縣志 *Shang-hai heen che.* "A Topography of Shang-hai Heen." Compiled by . . . Fang Tso, etc. 1814. 8°. **15269. b. 5.**

濤介人 FAN KEAE-JIN. See 吳梅村 WOO MEI-TS'UN. 吳詩談藪 *Woo she t'an shoo.* "Notes on the Poetry of Woo Mei-ts'un." By Fan Keae-jin, etc. 8°. **15323. e. 14.**

—— See 吳梅村 WOO MEI-TS'UN. 吳詩集覽 *Woo she tseih lan.* "The Collected Poems of Woo Mei-ts'un. Reviewed" by Fan Keae-jin, etc. 1781. 8°. **15323. e. 13.**

范景福 FAN KING-FUH. See 張作楠 CHANG TSO-NAN. 方田通法補例 *Fang t'een t'ung fǎ poo le.* "Additional rules for plane mensuration." Edited by Fan King-fuh, etc. 8°.
15255. c. 3.

—— See 張作楠 CHANG TSO-NAN. 量倉通法 *Leang ts'ang t'ung fǎ.* "Rules for solid mensuration." Edited by Fan King-fuh, etc. 8°.
15255. c. 1.

范甯 FAN NING. See 穀梁赤 KUH-LEANG CHIH. 春秋穀梁經傳補注 *Ch'un ts'ew Kuh-leang king chuen poo choo.* Kuh-leang's Commentary on the Spring and Autumn Annals. With supplementary notes by Fan Ning, etc. 1875. 8°.
15212. e. 1.

反唐 FAN T'ANG. 反唐女媧鏡全集 *Fan T'ang Neu-kwa king ts'euen tseih.* "The Story of the Neu-kwa Mirror during the time of the Rebellious T'ang Dynasty." In verse. 4 keuen. [1850?] 8°.
15327. d. 19.

樊騰鳳 FAN T'ĂNG-FUNG. 新增五方元音全書 *Sin tsǎng woo fang yuen yin ts'euen shoo.* "The Original Universal Sounds of the Characters." A dictionary in which the sounds are all classified under twelve categories of finals. A new and enlarged edition. Edited by Neen He-yaou. 2 keuen. 1835. 8°.
15346. b. 22.

—— 五方元音 *Woo fang yuen yin.* "Original Sounds from the Five Parts of the Universe." A tonic dictionary in which the characters are arranged under twelve finals. Edited by Neen He-yaou. 2 keuen. 1698. 8°. **15346. b. 24.**

—— [Another edition.] 2 keuen. 1810. 8°.
15346. b. 23.

—— [Another edition.] 2 keuen. [1820?] 8°.
15346. b. 20.
Title and preface wanting; the index is supplied in MS.

潘庭筠 FAN T'ING YUN. See 延豐 YEN FUNG. 欽定重修兩浙鹽法志 *K'in ting chung sew leang Chě yen fǎ che.* A record of the laws on the salt monopoly for the Province of Chě-keang. An Imperial republication. By Yen Fung and others, etc. 1801. 8°. **15239. e. 1.**

范祖禹 FAN TSOO-YU. 唐鑑 *T'ang keen.* "A History of the T'ang Dynasty." With notes on phoneticisms by Leu Tsoo-k'een. A Korean edition. 24 keuen. [1600?] Fol. **15288. e. 4.**

范端昂 FAN TWAN-GAN. 粵中見聞 *Yuě chung keen wǎn.* "Sights and Records of Yuě," i.e. the Provinces of Kwang-tung and Kwang-se. Compiled by Fan Twan-gan. 1801. 8°.
15271. c. 5.
Imperfect.

法藏 FĂ-TS'ANG. 華嚴一乘教分記 *Hwa yen yih shing keaou fun ke.* "A treatise on the distinction of the meaning of the doctrine of one vehicle of the Buddhăvatamsaka Sūtra." By Fă-ts'ang. 3 keuen. 1283. 8°. **15103. c. 40.**
Imperfect. Printed in Japan from blocks.

FAUTRAT ( ). Elementa litteraturœ. Sách Tóm lại các mẹo cho ctu'ợu lám các thú˙ văn bài Cố' Báu (M. F.) dã dọn và Cố' Khánh (M. Ravier) dã xem lại. pp. i, 117, 192. *Ninh phú*, 1880. 8°. **11100. b. 25.**

費仲若 FEI CHUNG-JŎ. 蜀詩 *Shuh she.* "Poetry from Shuh" [Sze-chuen]. Compiled by Fei Chung-jŏ. 15 keuen. See 孫澍 SUN SHOO. 古棠書屋叢書 *Koo t'ang shoo wuh ts'ung shoo.* "A Collection of Reprints," etc. 1831–49. 8°.
15315. d. 1.

飛蛇 FEI SHAY. 飛蛇全傳 *Fei shay ts'euen chuen.* "The complete story of the flying serpent." 4 keuen. 1817. 8°. **15327. f. 2.**

FITCH ( ), MRS. See 長老公 CH'ANG LAOU-KUNG. See 福音讚美歌 *Fuh yin tsan mei ko.* "Gospel Hymns . . ." By Mrs. F., etc. 1877. 8°. **15200. c. 30.**

FLOWERS. [Sixty-six beautifully coloured illustrations of flowers and fruit.] MS. ff. 66. [1840?] Fol. **Add. 11028. 28. c.**

FOH-ING. *Foh-ing dao-li ling kying veng-teh.* "The Westminster Catechism." *Shanghai,* 1870. 4°.
15200. b. 12.

傅恒 FOO HĂNG. See 乾隆 K'EEN-LUNG, *Emperor.* 御製西域同文志 *Yu che se yih t'ung wǎn che.* "A polyglot vocabulary of the languages of the western territories . . ." Edited by Foo Hăng, etc. 1750. 8°. **15344. b. 11.**

—— See 詩經 SHE KING. 御纂詩義折中 *Yu tswan She e che chung.* "Well-weighed decisions on the meaning of the Book of Odes." Compiled by Imperial order by Foo Hăng, etc. 1755. 8°. **15212. e. 2.**

FOO

傳恒 Foo Hăng. See 允祿 Yun-luh. 欽定 同文韻統 K'in ting t'ung wăn yun t'ung. The Primary Sanskrit Characters represented in Chinese . . . by . . . Foo Hăng, etc. 1750. 8°.   **15354. a. 5.**

—— 欽定皇輿西域圖志 K'in ting Hwang yu se yih t'oo che. "An illustrated topography of the Imperial western frontier countries. Compiled by Imperial order" by Foo Hăng, Lai Paou, and others. 48 keuen, with 4 introductory keuen. [Peking?], 1782. 8°.
                                      15271. a. 21.

—— 御批歷代通鑑輯覽 Yu p'e leih tai t'ung keen tseih lan. "A chronological abstract of Chinese history." Compiled by a commission composed of Foo Hăng and others, supervised by the Emperor K'een-lung. 116 keuen. 1767. Fol.   **15288. c.**

—— [Another edition.] 120 keuen. 1768. 8°.
                                       15290. e. 3.

傳蘭雅 Foolanya [i.e. J. Fryer]. See Bloxam (Charles London) 化學鑑原補編 Hwa heŏ keen yuen poo peen. "An examination of the principles of Chemistry . . ." Translated into Chinese by Foolanya, etc. 8°. **15259. g. 4.**

—— See 眞司騰 Chin-sze-tăng. 化學衛生論 Hwa heŏ wei săng lun. "The chemistry of common life . . ." Translated into Chinese by J. Fryer, etc. 1881. 8°.   **15259. g. 3.**

—— See 儲意比 Choo-e-pe. 營城揭要 Ying ch'ing kĕĕ yaou. "A treatise on fortification . . ." Translated into Chinese by Foolanya, etc. 8°.   **15259. g. 9.**

—— [Another copy.]   **15259. d. 8.**

—— See 富路瑪 Foolooma. 測地繪圖 Ts'ih te hwuy t'oo. "An outline of the method of conducting a trigonometrical survey . . ." Translated into Chinese by Foolanya, etc. 8°.
                                       15259. g. 2.

—— [Another copy.]   **15259. d. 21.**

—— See Great Britain and Ireland, Admiralty. 水師操練 Shwuy sze ts'aou leen. "Naval Drill." Translated into Chinese by Foolanya, etc. 8°.   **15259. e. 4.**

傳蘭雅 Foolanya [i.e. J. Fryer]. See 海麻士 Hai-ma-sze. 三角數理 San keŏ shoo le. "A Treatise on Plane and Spherical Trigonometry . . ." Translated into Chinese by Foolanya, etc. 8°.   **15259. f. 11.**

—— See 海得蘭 Hai-tih-lan. 儒門醫學 Joo mun e heŏ. "A medical handbook . . ." Translated into Chinese by Foolanya, etc. 1867. 8°.   **15259. d. 25.**

—— See 哈司韋 Ha-sze-wei. 算式集要 Swan shih tseih yaou. "The mensuration of areas, lines, and surfaces." Translated into Chinese by Foolanya, etc. 8°.   **15259. i. 5.**

—— [Another copy.]   **15259. d. 18.**

—— See 希理哈 He-le-ha. 防海新論 Fang hai sin lun. "On Coast Defences . . ." Translated into Chinese by Foolanya, etc. 8°.
                                       15259. g. 3.

—— See 華里司 Hwa-le-sze. 代數術 Tai shoo shuh. "A Treatise on Algebra . . ." Translated into Chinese by Foolanya, etc. 1873. 8°.   **15259. f. 7.**

—— See 華里司 Hwa-le-sze. 微積溯源 Wei tseih soo yuen. "On the differential and integral Calculus." Translated . . . by Foolanya, etc. 8°.   **15259. f. 10.**

—— See 華特 Hwa-t'ih. 電氣鍍金略法 Teen k'e too kin leŏ fa. "Electro-metallurgy." Translated into Chinese by Foolanya, etc. 8°.
                                       15259. e. 11.

—— See 買密倫 Kea-meïh-lun. 輪船布陣 Lun ch'uen poo chin. "Steamship Manœuvres." Translated into Chinese by Foolanya, etc. 8°.
                                        15259. i. 1.

—— See 金約翰 Kin Yŏhan. 海道圖說 Hai taou t'oo shwŏ. "The China Pilot . . ." Translated into Chinese by J. Fryer, etc. 8°.
                                       15259. d. 9.

—— See 連提 Leen-t'e. 行軍測繪 Hing keun ts'ih hwuy. "A practical course of Military Surveying . . ." Translated into Chinese by Foolanya, etc. 8°. **15259. d. 6.**

—— See 利稼孫 Le-kea-sun, and 華得斯 Hwa-tih-sze. 製火藥法 Che ho yaou fa. "The Manufacture of Gunpowder." Translated into Chinese by Foolanya, etc. 8°. **15259. e. 7.**

傳蘭雅 FOOLANYA [i.e. J. FRYER]. See 倫德 LUN-TIH. 代數難題 *Tai shoo nan t'e.* Lund's "Companion to Wood's Algebra." Translated into Chinese by Foolanya, etc. 8°.
15259. f. 9.

—— See 瑙挨德 NAOU-AI-TIH. 電學 *Teen heŏ.* "A Manual of Electricity . . ." Translated into Chinese by Foolanya, etc. 8°.
11259. f. 1.

—— See 諾格德 NŎ-KIH-TIH. 西藝知新 *Se e che sin.* "On Western Mechanical Science . . ." Translated into Chinese by J. Fryer, etc. 8°.
15259. d. 17.

—— See 阿發滿 O-FA-MAN. 冶金錄 *Yay kin luh.* "The Moulder's and Founder's pocket guide . . ." Translated into Chinese by Foolanya, etc. 8°.
15259. d. 3.

—— 裴路 P'EI-LOO. 輪船布陣 *Lun ch'uen poo chin.* "Steamship Manœuvres . . ." Translated into Chinese by Foolanya, etc. 8°.
15259. c. 18.

—— See 白起德 PIH-K'E-TIH. 運規約指 *Yun kwei yŏ che.* "A Work on Practical Geometry." Translated into Chinese by Foolanya, etc. 8°.
15255. d. 19.

—— See 白力蓋 PIH LEIH-KAI. 器象顯奧 *K'e seang heen chin.* "Drawings for Engineers and Machinists . . ." Translated into Chinese by Foolanya, etc. 8°.
15259. c. 15.

—— See 白爾格 PIH-URH-KIH. 汽機新制 *K'e ke sin che.* "New Rules for the Steam Engine." Translated into Chinese by Foolanya, etc. 8°.
15259. d. 16.

—— See 白爾捺 PIH-URH-NA. 井礦工程 *Tsing hwang kung ch'ing.* "Methods of sinking wells and of boring for sulphur . . ." Translated into Chinese by Foolanya, etc. 8°.
15259. i. 2.

—— See 浦陸山 P'OOLUH SHAN. 化學鑑原續編 *Hwa heŏ keen yuen suh peen.* . . . "An adaptation of the Organic portion of Bloxam's Chemistry, Inorganic and Organic." Translated into Chinese by Foolanya, etc. 8°.
15259. g. 5.

—— See 蒲而捺 P'OO-URH-NA. 汽機 *K'e ke.* "Handbook of the Steam Engine . . ." Translated into Chinese by Foolanya, etc. *Shanghai.* 8°.
15259. d. 4.

傳蘭雅 FOOLANYA [i.e. J. FRYER]. See 蒲而捺 P'OO-URH-NA. 汽機必以 *K'e ke pe e.* "A Catechism of the Steam Engine." Adapted and translated into Chinese by Foolanya, etc. 8°.
15259. f. 8.

—— See 士密德 SZE-MEIH-TIH. 開煤要法 *K'ai mei yaou fǎ.* "A treatise on Coal and Coal-mining . . ." Translated into Chinese by Foolanya, etc. 8°.
15259. h. 1.

—— See 田大里 T'EEN-TA-LE. 聲學 *Shing heŏ.* "On Sound." Translated into Chinese by Foolanya, etc. 8°.
15259. h. 4.

—— [Another copy.]
15259. d. 1.

—— See 田大里 T'EEN-TA-LE. 電學綱目 *Teen heŏ kang muh.* "Notes on Electricity." Translated into Chinese by Foolanya, etc. 8°.
15259. h. 9.

—— See 棣麼甘 TE MOKAN. 數學理 *Shoo heŏ le.* "The Elements of Arithmetic . . ." Translated into Chinese by Foolanya, etc. 8°.
15259. h. 3.

—— *See* WATT (ALEXANDER). 電氣鍍金 *Teen k'e too kin.* "Electro Metallurgy . . ." Translated into Chinese by Foolanya, etc. 1880. 8°.
15259. g. 13.

—— See 韋更斯 WEI-KĂNG-SZE. 海塘輯要 *Hai t'ang tseih yaou.* "On Building Sea-dikes . . ." Translated into Chinese by J. Fryer, etc. 8°.
15259. d. 23.

—— 韋而司 WEI-URH-SZE. 化學鑑原 *Hwa heŏ keen yuen.* "The principles and application of Chemistry." Translated into Chinese by Foolanya, etc. 8°.
15259. f. 10.

—— 照像畧法 *Chaouseang leŏ fǎ.* "The Laws of Photography." The translation by J. Fryer of, according to a manuscript note on the cover, a work by "Fowler." pp. i, 36. *Shanghai,* 1881. 8°.
15257. d. 27.

—— 格致釋器 *Kih che shih k'e.* "Scientific instruments explained." With illustrations. Keuen 1, concerning meteorological instruments. 1880. 8°.
15259. g. 12.

—— 歷覽記畧 *Leih lan ke leŏ.* "Notes of a tour through the English iron country." With illustrations. pp. 38. 1881. 8°. 15259. g. 10.

35

傳蘭雅 FOOLANYA [i.e. J. FRYER]. 西藝知新 *Se e che sin.* "Modern arts and manufactures from the West." Translated into Chinese from the works of various authors by Foolanya. With diagrams. 10 keuen. [*Shanghai*, 1880 ?] 8°. **15259. f. 3.**

—— 地志須知 *Te che seu che.* "The elements of physical geography." pp. 46. 1882. 8°. **15263. b. 5.**

—— 地學須知 *Te heŏ seu che.* "A geological primer." With illustrations. pp. 52. 1883. 8°. **15259. g. 14.**

—— 地理須知 *Te le seu che.* "The elements of geography." With illustrations. pp. 52. 1883. 8°. **15263. b. 3.**

—— [Another copy.] **15263. b. 6.**

—— 譯書事畧 *Yih shoo sze lĕŏ.* "A short account of the translation work done at Keang-nan Arsenal." pp. i, 22. 1880. 8°. **15259. h. 12.**

富路瑪 FOOLOOMA [i.e. Lieut.-Gen. EDWARD C. FROME]. 測地繪圖 *Ts'ih te hwuy t'oo.* "An outline of the method of conducting a trigonometrical survey," by Lieut.-Gen. E. C. Frome. Translated into Chinese by Foolanya, i.e. J. Fryer. With plates. 10 keuen. With a supplement. [*Shanghai*, 1880 ?] 8°. **15259. g. 2.**

—— [Another copy.] **15259. d. 21.**

傅鸞祥 Foo LWAN-TSEANG. 六書分類 *Luh shoo fun luy.* "A Dictionary of the Ancient Forms of Characters" arranged according to the Radicals. Compiled by Foo Lwan-tseang. Edited by Chow Ching-chaou. 12 keuen. 1705. 8°. **15342. e. 10.**

傳澤洪 Foo TSIH-HUNG. 行水金鑑 *Hing shwuy kin keen.* "The Golden Mirror of Running Waters." A hydrography of the Empire. Compiled by Foo Tsih-hung. With maps. 175 keuen. 1725. 8°. **15275. c. 6.**

賦役 Foo YIH. 賦役全書 *Foo yih ts'euen shoo.* "Laws for the Conscription in the Prefectures of Soo-chow, Sung-keang, Ch'ang-chow, Chin-keang, and T'ai-ts'ang." 1865. 8°. **15241. c. 1.**

FORKE (A.). Blüthen Chinesischer Dichtung, mit 21 reproducirten Chinesischen Original-Pinsel zeichnungen. Aus der Zeit der Han- und Sechs-Dynastie. . . . Aus dem Chinesischen metrisch übersetzt von A. F. pp. xvi, 148. *Magdeburg*, 1899. 8°. **11098. a. 23.**

—— [Another copy.] **11098. a. 33.**

FORMOSA. [A map of Taiwan Foo in the island of Formosa. 1840 ?] Fol. **Add. 16356. 28. c.**

FRANCE. NAPOLEON III, *Emperor.* 和約書 *Ho yŏ shoo.* "The (Chinese) Text of the Treaty" concluded in 1862 between France and Spain on the one part and the King of Annam on the other part. 1862. 8°. **15241. c. 5.**

FRANCIS [XAVIER], SAINT, School of, at Shanghai. *See* SHANGHAI, Saint Francis Xavier's School.

FRITSCHE. See 曾紀澤 TSĂNG KĚ-TSIH. 中西合歷 *Chung se ho leih.* "A Chinese and Foreign Comparative Calendar . . ." Compiled by Professor . . . Fritsche, etc. 1877. 8°. **15298. b. 40.**

FRYER (JOHN). See 傅蘭雅 Foo-LAN-YA.

—— *See* PERIODICAL PUBLICATIONS. *Shanghai.* 格致彙編 *Kih che wei peen.* The Chinese Scientific Magazine. . . . Edited by J. F., etc. 1876, etc. 8°. **15298. c. 26.**

—— See 上海 SHANGHAI. 上海格致書院第一次記錄 *Shanghai kih che shoo yuen ti yih ts'ze ke luh.* "The first report of the Polytechnic Institution at Shanghai." By . . . J. F., etc. 1875. 8°. **15229. b. 26.**

—— See 天文 T'EEN WĂN. 天文須知 *T'een wăn seu che.* "Elements of Astronomy." By J. F., etc. 1881. 8°. **15257. a. 28.**

—— See 益智 YIH CHE. 益智書彙 *Yih che shoo wei.* "A list of books for the advancement of knowledge." [By J. F.?], etc. 8°. **15229. b. 27.**

佛 FUH. 佛說解冤去刼神咒 *Fuh shwŏ keae yuen kĕĕ shin chow.* "Sacred prayers delivered by Buddha for relief from distress and violence." *Canton,* [1870 ?] A sheet. **15103. d. 11.** There are six other copies of this sheet.

佛 FUH. 佛說摩利支天陀羅尼經 *Fuh shwŏ Mo-le-che t'een T'o-lo-ne king.* "The Dharani of the Mo-le-che t'een, delivered by Buddha." Edited by the priest Sin-tsung. *Canton,* [1810?] Obl. **15103. d. 19.**

—— 選擇本願念佛集 *Seuen tsih pun yuen neen Fuh tseih.* "A collection of essays on studying Buddha." With a Japanese transcription of the Chinese characters. [1250?] 8°. **15103. b. 7.**
Printed in Japan from blocks.

佛柱 FUH CHOO. See 托津 TŎ TSIN. 欽定回疆則例 *K'in ting hwuy keang tsih le.* "Regulations for the Government of the Muhammedan Dependencies of China." Compiled by Fuh Choo, etc. 1814. 8°. **15271. b. 6.**

福建 FUH-KEEN. 福建通志 *Fuh-keen t'ung che.* "A Topography of the Province of Fuh-keen." [1750?] 8°. **15269. e. 14.**
Imperfect, containing only the volume of maps.

佛頂 FUH TING. 佛頂尊勝陀羅尼 *Fuh ting tsun shing t'o lo ne.* "Sūtra on the honourable and excelling Dhārani of Buddha's head." Printed in Tibetan characters with an interlineal transcription in Japanese. [1840?] 12°. **15103. b. 12.**

佛陀跋陀羅 FUHT'OPŎT'OLO [i.e. BUDDHA-BHADRA]. 大方廣佛華嚴經 *Ta fang kwang fuh hwa yen king.* "The Buddhāvatamsaka-mahāvaipulya-sūtra." Translated into Chinese by Buddhabhadra. 60 keuen. 1167? **15103. a. 5.**
Much damaged and imperfect, containing only Keuen 38. Printed in Japan from blocks.

佛陀多羅 FUHT'OTOLO [i.e. BUDDHATĀTA]. 大方廣圓覺修多羅了義經 *Ta fang kwang yuen keaou sew tolo leaou e king* (*Mahāvaipulya-pûrnabuddha Sūtra-prasannārtha Sūtra*). Translated by Fuht'otolo. 2 keuen. See 劉翰清 LEW HANTS'ING. 大乘法寶十種 *Ta shing fă paou shih chung.* "Ten precious works on the Law of the Mahāyana . . ." 1881. 8°. **15103. b. 13.**

福音 FUH YIN. 福音聖詩 *Fuh yin shing she.* "Gospel Hymns." Stated in a manuscript note on the cover to be by W. Muirhead. pp. 52. *Shanghai,* 1881. 8°. **15200. c. 1.**

福音 FUH YIN. 福音道問答合講 *Fuh yin taou wăn tă ho keang.* "A Catechism on the Doctrine of the Gospel (a paraphrase of the Shorter Catechism), with explanations." [A note on the cover states that the work is by M. S. Culbertson. This is confirmed by the list of Culbertson's works published in "Memorials of Protestant Missionaries to the Chinese."] pp. i, 26. *Shanghai,* 1861. 8°. **15118. a. 35.**

佛芸保 FUH-YUN-PAOU. See 惲珍浦 HWĂN CHINP'OO. 國朝閨秀正始續集 *Kwŏ ch'aou kwei sew ching che suh tseih.* "A Supplement to the Ching che Collection of Poems . . ." Edited by . . . Fuh-yun-paou, etc. 1836. 8°. **15327. e. 5.**

粉粧樓 FUN CHWANG LOW. 粉粧樓全傳 *Fun chwang low ts'euen chuen.* "The Story of the Painted Pavilion." With illustrations. 80 chapters. 1806. 8°. **15327. f. 3.**
Imperfect, containing only Chapters 1–25.

馮浩 FUNG HAOU. See 李義山 LE E-SHAN. 玉谿生詩箋註 *Yuh k'e săng she tseen choo.* "Poems from the 'Jade Valley' . . ." Edited by Fung Haou, etc. 1767. 8°. **15324. d. 4.**

奉化縣 FUNG-HWA HEEN. Reports from the Magistrate of Fung-hwa Heen on the number of graduates who received degrees within his jurisdiction between the years 1772 and 1794. MS. 1795. 8°. **15320. e. 32.**

鳳凰山 FUNG HWANG SHAN. 鳳凰山 *Fung hwang shan.* "The Phœnix Mountain." An historical novel in verse. A supplement to the *Gan pang ts'euen chuen.* 72 keuen. [1850?] 8°. **15334. f. 5.**

鳳岡闚 FUNG KANG-KWAN. 篆書唐詩選 *Chuen shoo T'ang she seuen.* "A selection of T'ang Dynasty poems in the Seal character." Edited by Fung Kang-kwan. A Japanese edition. 1756. 8°. **15323. d. 26.**

馮孟亭 FUNG MĂNG-T'ING. See 李義山 LE E-SHAN. 樊南文集詳註 *Fan-nan wăn tseih tseang choo.* "A collection of writings from Fan-nan . . ." Compiled by Fung Măng-t'ing, etc. 1765. 8°. **15318. b. 5.**

—— See 李義山 LE E-SHAN. 玉谿生詩詳註 *Yuh k'e săng she tseang choo.* "Poems from the Jade Valley . . ." Compiled by Fung Măng-t'ing, etc. 1780. 8°. **15324. e. 1.**

FUN—GAI

馮夢龍 Fung Mung-lung. See 鍾惺 Chung Sing. 夏商合傳 *Hea Shang hŏ chuen.* "The Histories of the Hea and Shang Dynasties . . ." Edited by Fung Mung-lung, etc. 1814. 8°. **15296. b. 8.**

—— 新增智囊補 *Sin tsăng che nang poo.* "A Treasury of Wisdom. A new and enlarged edition." Edited by Fung Mung-lung. 28 keuen. [1688?] 8°. **15026. a. 2.**

—— [Another copy.] **15026. a. 3.**

—— [Another copy.] **15026. a. 4.**

馮星實 Fung Sing-shih. See 蘇軾 Soo Shih. 蘇文忠公詩合註 *Soo Wăn-chung she hŏ choo.* "The Poems of Soo Shih . . ." Edited by Fung Sing-shih, etc. 1870. 8°. **15324. b. 2.**

馮楚瞻 Fung Ts'oo-chen. 馮氏錦囊秘錄 *Fung she kin nang pe luh.* "Fung's Repertoire of Medical Works." Edited by Wang Shin-choo and others. 34 keuen. 1813. 8°. **15253. c. 2.**

—— 痘疹全集 *Tow chin ts'euen tseih.* "A complete collective treatise on Small-pox." By Fung Ts'oo-chen. Edited by Lo Tan-chin. 15 keuen. [1820?] 8°. **15252. b. 28.**

馮冶堂 Fung Yay-t'ang. 國朝畫識 *Kwŏ ch'aou hwa shih.* "Biographical Notices of Artists during the present Dynasty." By Fung Yay-t'ang. Edited by Woo Tsin-che. 17 keuen. 1831. 8°. **15305. b. 7.**

—— 墨香居畫識 *Mih heang keu hwa shih.* "Biographical Notices of Artists." By Fung Yay-t'ang. 10 keuen. [1835?] 8°. **15305. b. 8.**

馮猶龍 Fung Yew-lung. See 羅貫中 Lo Kwan-chung. 繡像平妖全傳 *Sew seang p'ing yaou ts'euen chuen.* "The Pacification of the 'Imps' . . ." Edited by Fung Yew-lung, etc. 8°. **15331. b. 14.**

馮應榴 Fung Ying-lew. See 蘇軾 Soo Shih. 蘇文忠公詩合註 *Soo Wăn-chung Kung she ho choo.* "The Poems of Soo Shih . . . with a collection of commentaries." Edited by Fung Ying-lew, etc. 1795. 8°. **15322. a. 1.**

馮雲鵬 Fung Yun-p'Äng. 金石索 *Kin shih sŏ.* "A Collection of Ancient Inscriptions" on bells, tripods, stones, etc. Compiled by Fung Yun-p'ăng, assisted by Fung Yun-yuen. 1820. 4°. **15299. c. 1.**

馮雲鵷 Fung Yun-yuen. See 馮雲鵬 Fung Yun-p'Äng. 金石素 *Kin shih sŏ.* "A Collection of Ancient Inscriptions . . ." Compiled by . . . Fung Yun-yuen, etc. 1820. 4°. **15299. a. 1.**

分野 Fun yay. 分野奇書 *Fun yay k'e shoo.* "A Work on the Ancient Geography of the Empire." [1840?] 8°. **15271. e. 4.**

GABELENTZ (Georg von der). See 周敦頤 Chow Tun-e. 太極圖 Thai-kĭh-thu . . . mit mandschuischer und Deutscher Übersetzung Einleitung und Anmerkungen herausgegeben von G. von der G., etc. 1876. 8°. **11100. b. 5.**

愛孩提女史 Gai hai t'e nu she [i.e. Mrs. Happer]. 舊約史記問答 *Kew yŏ she ke wăn tă.* "A Catechism on the Old Testament History." By the "Child-loving authoress." pp. iv, 124. 1875. 8°. **15118. e. 2.**

愛漢者 Gai han chay [i.e. Carl F. A. Guetzlaff]. 贖罪之道 *Shuh tsuy che taou.* "The Doctrine of the Redemption." A story. 3 keuen. [*Singapore*, 1836?] 8°. **15118. b. 46.** Imperfect, wanting Keuen 1.

—— 贖罪之道傳 *Shuh tsuy che taou chuen.* "The Story of the Doctrine of Redemption." 2 keuen. 1836. 8°. **15118. d. 13.**

—— 耶穌之寶訓 *Yay-soo che paou heun.* "The precious teachings of Jesus." pp. 68. *Singapore*, 1836. 8°. **15118. d. 14.**

艾儒畧 Gai Joo-leŏ [i.e. Julio Aleni]. 三山論學 *San shan lun heŏ.* "A conversation at San shan" between J. Aleni and a native dignitary on God. A reprint. pp. iv, 44. *Hongkong*, 1896. 8°. **15200. d. 27.**

—— 聖人言行 *Shing jin yen hing.* "The Lives of the Saints." First and second months. 2 vols. *Hongkong*, 1896. 8°. **15200. d. 63.**

—— 聖體要理 *Shing t'e yaou le.* "The essential doctrines of the Mass." A reprint. 2 keuen. *Hongkong*, 1894. 12°. **15200. c. 55.**

—— 萬物真原 *Wan wuh chin yuen.* "The true origin of all things." A reprint. pp. ii, 54. *Hongkong*, 1896. 8°. **15200. b. 23.**

艾約瑟 GAI Yŏ-SIH [i.e. Rev. JOSEPH EDKINS]. 重學 *Chung heŏ.* "On the Science of Weight" Translated into Chinese by Gai Yŏ-sih. Transcribed by Le Shen-lan. 20 keuen. [*Shanghai?*], 1866. 8°.　　　　　　　　　　**15259. e. 1.**

—— 圓錐曲線 *Hwan chuy k'eŭh seen.* "On Conic Sections." Translated into Chinese by J. Edkins and transcribed by Le Shen-lan. 3 keuen. [1876?] 8°.　　　**15259. e. 3.**

GALE (JAMES S.). A Korean-English Dictionary. By J. S. G. pp. vii, 1096, 64. *Kelly & Welsh: Yokohama,* 1897. 8°.　　　**11098. c. 12.**

安古琴 GAN KOO-K'IN. 六書韻徵 *Luh shoo yun ching.* "A Dictionary of Characters in their Ancient Forms, arranged according to their finals." Compiled by Gan Koo-k'in. Edited by Hwa Chan-gǎn. 16 keuen. 1838. 8°.
　　　　　　　　　　15344. e. 9.

GILES (HERBERT ALLEN). *See* FĂ-HEEN. 佛國記 Record of the Buddhistic Kingdoms. Translated by H. A. G. [1878?] 8°. **11099. d. 1.**

—— *See* 字 TSZE. 三字經 *San tzŭ ching.* Translated and annotated by H. A. G., etc. 1900. 8°.　　　　　　**11095. c. 2.**

—— Chinese Poetry in English verse by H. A. G. pp. 212. *Bernard Quaritch: London,* 1898. 8°.
　　　　　　　　　　11098. a. 17.

GODDARD (JOSIAH). 耶穌登山敎衆體註 *Yay-soo tăng shan keaou chung t'e choo.* "Christ's Sermon on the Mount, with notes" by E. C. Lord. pp. 30. *Ningpo,* 1851. 8°. **15200. b. 9.**

GOH. 官話指南 The Guide to the Kuan Hua. A translation of the "Kuan hua chih nan." With an essay on tone and accent in Pekingese, and a glossary of phrases. By L. C. Hopkins. *Kelly & Walsh: Shanghai,* 1889. 8°. **11098. b. 8.**

GONÇALVES (JOACHIMO ALFONSO). Lexicon magnum Latino-Sinicum, ostendens etymologiam, prosodiam, et constructionem vocabulorum. pp. iv, 779. *Macao,* 1841. 4°.
　　　　　　　　　　11098. d. 3.

GOODRICH (CHAUNCEY). A character study in Mandarin colloquial, alphabetically arranged. Prepared by C. G. pp. 526. *University Press, Peking,* 1898. 8°.　　　**15348. c. 6.**
This work has also the following Chinese title: 官話萃珍 *Kwan hwa ts'uy chin.*

GOODRICH (CHAUNCEY). A pocket dictionary [Chinese-English] and Pekingese syllabary. By C. G. pp. vi, 237. *Peking,* 1891. 12°.
　　　　　　　　　　11099. a. 10.

GORDON (CHARLES GEORGE). A letter addressed to Colonel Gordon by a Peking official whose name does not appear, and who explains that he had communicated Gordon's request for an interview with the Prince [Kung], and that he had sent a letter to Gordon's rooms only to find that he had suddenly left. In conclusion he asks Gordon to consult with Le Hungchang on the defences of Tientsin. MS. [1880?]
　　　　　　　　　　Or. 3534.

—— A memorandum accompanying a sum of a thousand taels, made up of twenty shoes of silver, for travelling expenses, forwarded to His Excellency General Ko, i.e. Gordon. MS. [1862?]　　　　　　　**Or. 3534.**

鄂爾泰 Gŏ URH-T'AI. *See* 弘晝 HUNG CHOW. 八旗通志初集 *Pă k'e t'ung che ch'oo tseth.* "A complete statistical account of the Eight Banners." Compiled by ... Gŏ Urh-t'ai, etc. 1739. 8°.　　　　　**15296. c. & d.**

—— *See* 乾隆 K'EEN-LUNG, *Emperor.* 御製盛京賦 *Yu che Shing-king foo.* "A poetical eulogium on the city of Moukden ..." Edited by Gŏ Urh-t'ai, etc. 8°.　**15321. e. 3.**

歐陽直 GOW-YANG CHIH. 歐陽氏遺書 *Gow-yang she e shoo.* "The bequeathed writings of Gow-yang Chih." Edited by Gow-yang Ting. pp. 114. 1840. 8°.　　**15318. b. 6.**

歐陽鼎 GOW-YANG TING. *See* 歐陽直 GOW-YANG CHIH. 歐陽氏遺書 *Gow-yang she e shoo.* "The bequeathed writings of Gow-yang Chih." Edited by Gow-yang Ting, etc. 1840. 8°.
　　　　　　　　　　15318. b. 6.

GRASSERIE (RAOUL DE LA). Des recherches récentes de la linguistique relatives aux langues de l'extrême orient, principalement d'après les travaux de M. Terrien de Lacouperie. pp. 31. *Paris,* 1891. 8°.　　　**11098. c. 4.**

GRAVES (ROSEWELL HOBART). *See* 紀好弼 KE HAOU-PEIH.

GRAY (HENRY). *See* OSGOOD (D. W.). 全體闡微 *Ts'euen t'e shen wei.* Gray's "Anatomy" ... adapted and translated into Chinese, etc. 1881. 8°.　　　**15253. e. 5.**

39

GREAT BRITAIN AND IRELAND: ADMIRALTY. 水師章程 *Shwuy sze chang ch'ing.* "Admiralty Regulations." Translated into Chinese by Lin Lŏ-che, i.e., according to the wrapper, Y. J. Allen. 14 keuen, with a supplement in 6 keuen. [1875?] 8°. **15235. b. 1.**

—— 水師操練 *Shwuy sze ts'aou leen.* "Naval Drill." Translated into Chinese by Foolanya [i.e. John Fryer]. 18 keuen, with a supplementary volume. [1888?] 8°. **15259. e. 5.**

—— [Another copy.] **15259. c. 16.**

GRIFFIN (JOHN JOSEPH). See 格致 KIH CHE. 格致釋器 *Kih che shih k'e.* "An explanation of utensils used in (chemical) researches." A translation of J.J.G.'s "Chemical Handicraft," etc. 8°. **15257. d. 26.**

GRUBE (WILHELM). See 周濂溪 CHOW LEEN-K'E. 通書 T'ūng-šū . . . herausgegeben von W. G., etc. 1880. 8°. **11100. b. 35.**

GUELUY (A.). *See* SCHLEGEL (GUSTAVE). La Loi du parallélisme en style Chinois . . . La traduction de la Preface du *Si-yü ki* par feu Stanislas Julien défendue contre la nouvelle traduction du Père A. G., etc. 1896. 8°. **11098. b. 24.**

GÜTZLAFF (KARL FRIEDRICH AUGUST). See 善德 SHEN-TIH.

—— See 彼得羅 PE-TIH-LO. 彼得羅言行全傳 *Pe-tih-lo yen hing ts'euen chuen.* "The Life of St. Peter." [By K. F. A. G.], etc. 8°. **15118. d. 12.**

—— See 贖 SHUH. 救贖何義 *Kew shuh ho e.* "The Theory of Redemption." [By C. F. A. G.], etc. 8°. **15118. d. 19.**

—— See 大英國 TA YING KWO. 大英國統志 *Ta Ying kwo t'ung che.* "A History of England." [By K. F. A. G.], etc. 1834. 8°. **15291. a. 13.**

GWEN. 閨娜傳 *Kwei-no chuen.* "The Story of Kwei-no," or Little Gwen's story. Translated into Chinese by Miss Porter, as stated in a manuscript note on cover. 13 chapters. [*Shanghai?*], 1882. 8°. **15200. c. 2.**

HAEMMERLEIN (THOMAS) à KEMPIS. 輕世金書 *K'ing she kin shoo.* The Imitation of Christ, by Thomas à Kempis. Translated into Chinese by Yang Ma-nŏ, i.e. E. Diaz. 4 keuen. *Hongkong,* 1890. 8°. **15200. d. 60.**

海麻士 HAI-MA-SZE [i.e. JOHN HYMERS]. 三角數理 *San keŏ shoo le.* "A treatise on Plane and Spherical Trigonometry." Together with a selection of problems and their solutions. By Hai-ma-sze. Translated into Chinese by Foolanya, i.e. J. Fryer. 12 keuen. *Shanghai,* [1885?]. 8°. **15259. f. 11.**

海得蘭 HAI-TIH-LAN [i.e. F. W. HEADLAND]. 儒門醫學 *Joo mun e heŏ.* "A medical handbook." Comprehending such information on medical and sanitary subjects as is desirable for educated persons. By Hai-tih-lan. With a vocabulary of the Chinese names of medicines used in translating the Medical Handbook. Translated into Chinese by Foolanya, i.e. J. Fryer. 3 keuen. 1867. 8°. **15253. f. 1.**

—— [Another copy.] **15259. d. 25.**

漢川曹 HAN CH'UEN-TS'AOU. 圖書府 *T'oo shoo foo.* "A store-house of seals and their readings." [1688?] 8°. **15319. b. 20 (1).**

恒 HĂNG. 粵海關外洋船牌 *Yueh haikwan wai Yang ch'uen pei.* A clearance granted by Hăng Ke, the Hoppo of Canton, to the English ship *Ketulutze* loaded for England. MS. *Canton,* 1856. **Or. 3534.**

HANGCHOW. Hangchow Primer. Translation and Notes. [By G. E. Moule?] pp. 34. *London,* 1876. 8°. **11098. a. 31.**

恆壽之 HĂNG SHOW-CHE. 知古錄 *Che koo luh.* "On understanding the military system of the ancients." Edited by Yuh Kwei-shan. 3 keuen, with a supplement entitled *T'aou k'ien shih hwuy luh.* "A scabbard and spear handle collection of able military records." 1863. 8°. **15259. e. 21.**

恒泰 HĂNG T'AI. See 穆克登頼 MUH-KIH-TĂNG-GIH. 大清通禮 *Ta Ts'ing t'ung le.* The Code of the Rites and Ceremonies of the Ts'ing Dynasty, etc. 1824. 8°. **15239. c. 9.**

衡塘退士 HĂNG T'ANG TUY SZE, *pseud.* 唐詩三百首註疏 *T'ang she san pih show choo soo.* "Three hundred poems of the T'ang Dynasty, with explanatory notes." Compiled by Hăng t'ang Tuy sze, the retired scholar of Hăng t'ang. 6 keuen. 1847. 8°. **15324. a. 9.**

杭 資 能 HĂNG TSZE-NĂNG. See 羅 貫 中 LO KWAN-CHUNG. 三 國 志 *San kŭŏ che.* "The History of the Three Kingdoms." Edited by Hăng Tsze-năng. 1850. 8°.　　15334. e. 9.

漢 話 HAN HWA. 漢 話 初 階 *Han hwa ch'oo keae.* "First Steps to Chinese." 50 sections. [*Shanghai,* 1875 ?] 8°.　　15346. a. 26.

韓 泰 華 HAN T'AI-HWA. See 大 秦 景 敎 TA TS'IN KING KEAOU. 大 秦 景 敎 流 行 中 國 碑 *Ta Ts'in king keaou lew hing Chung kwo pei.* "The rubbing of a tablet set up in Segnan Fu . . ." Re-set up in the year 1859 by Han T'ai-hwa, etc.　　15300. b. 9.

韓 菼 HAN T'AN. See 左 丘 明 TSO K'EW-MING. 春 秋 綱 目 左 傳 句 解 *Ch'un ts'ew kang muh Tso chuen keu keae.* "Tso's commentary on the text of the Ch'un ts'ew . . ." Edited by Han T'an, etc. 8°.　　15348. e. 1.

—— 批 點 春 秋 左 傳 綱 目 句 解 *P'e teen Ch'un ts'ew Tso chuen kang muh keu keae.* "The text of, and commentaries on, the Tso chuen, with notes." 6 keuen. [1700 ?] 8°.
15212. b. 24.

韓 道 昭 HAN TAOU-CHAOU. 重 刊 改 倂 五 音 集 韻 *Chung k'an kai ping woo yin tseĭh yun.* A new and revised Chinese Dictionary in which the characters are arranged under 160 finals, under each of which the characters are referred in order to the 36 initial sounds, these being subdivided under the four tones. Compiled by Han Taochaou of the Kin Dynasty. 15 keuen. 1515. Fol.　　15348. d. 1.

韓 雅 各 HAN YAKOH [i.e. JAMES HENDERSON]. 上 海 醫 院 述 署 十 四 冊 *Shanghai eyuen shuh leŏ shih sze shan.* "The fourteenth Report on the Shanghai Hospital," being for the year 1860. ff. 12. *Shanghai,* 1861. 8°. 15253. a. 13.

韓 嬰 HAN YING. 韓 詩 外 傳 *Han she wai chuen.* "Han Ying's illustration of the Book of Odes from external sources." 10 keuen. See 程 榮 CH'ING YUNG. 漢 魏 叢 書 *Han Wei ts'ung shoo.* "A collection of works by authors of the Han and Wei Dynasties," etc. 1791. 8°.
15318. a. 1.

韓 愈 HAN YU. 朱 文 公 梭 昌 黎 先 生 集 *Choo wăn kung keaou Ch'ang-le seen săng tseĭh.* "A collection of the writings of Han Yu. Edited by Choo He." 34 (?) keuen. [1200 ?] 8°.
15315. c. 3.
Imperfect, containing only Keuen 18–34.

—— 韓 詩 增 註 証 訛 *Han she tsăng choo ching go.* "The Poems of Han Yu." With corrective notes by Hwang Tso-teen. Edited by Koo Hëe-keun. 11 keuen. 1827. 8°.
15324. e. 2.

—— 五 百 家 注 音 辯 韓 昌 黎 先 生 全 集 *Woo pih kea choo yin peen Han Ch'ang-le seen-săng ts'euen tseĭh.* "A complete collection of the writings of Han Yu, otherwise Han Ch'ang-le [A.D. 768–824], with the comments and explanations of the sounds by five hundred scholars." Edited by Heu Taou-ke. 4 keuen. 1784. 8°.　　15315. c. 7.

好 古 主 人 HAOU KOO CHOO JIN. See 太 祖 T'AI TSOO. 宋 太 祖 三 下 南 唐 *Sung T'ai Tsoo san hea Nan T'ang.* "The History of the three conquests of the Southern T'ang Dynasty . . ." By "Haou koo choo jin," etc. 1874. 8°.
15331. c. 10.

哈 巴 安 德 HA-PA GAN-TIH [i.e. A. P. HAPPER]. 聖 書 衍 義 *Shing shoo yen e.* "A Dictionary of the Bible." pp. v, 91. *Canton,* 1874. 8°.

哈 巴 禮 理 HA-PA LE-LE [i.e. MISS LILY HAPPER]. 發 蒙 益 慧 錄 *Fă mung yih hwuy luh.* "A Primer for children." With illustrations. 3 vols. 1881. 8°.　　15344. d. 14.

HAPPART (GILBERTUS). See CAMPBELL (WILLIAM). The Articles of Christian Instruction in Favor-lang-Formosan . . . With . . . Happart's Favorlang Vocabulary, etc. 1896. 4°.
11098. b. 17.

HAPPER (ANDREW PATTON). See 馬 太 MA-T'AI. 馬 太 福 音 書 問 答 *Ma-t'ai fuh yin shoo wăn ta.* "A Catechism on the Gospel of St. Matthew." [By A. P. Happer], etc. 1874. 8°.　　15117. d. 25.

—— 舊 約 史 記 條 問 *Kew yŏ she ke t'eaou wăn.* "Questions on Old Testament History." pp. 114. *Shanghai,* 1875. 8°.　　15117. d. 26.

—— See 哈 巴 安 德 HA-PA GAN-TIH.

HAPPER (LILY). See 哈巴禮理 HA-PA LE-LE.

HAPPER (MRS). See 愛孩提女史 GAI HAI T'E NU SHE.

HARE (GEORGE THOMPSON). A Text-book of Documentary Chinese selected and designed for the special use of the Members of the Civil Service of the Straits Settlements and the protected Native States. 3 vols. *Singapore*, 1894. 4°. **11098. d. 1.**

HARLEZ (CHARLES DE). See 儀禮 E LE. 儀禮 *I-li*. Cérémonial de la Chine antique . . . traduit pour la première fois par C. de H., etc. 1890. 8°. **11099. d. 38.**

—— See 孔丘 K'UNG K'EW. Kong-tze Kia-yu . . . Traduits pour la 1re fois par C. de H., etc. 1899. 8°. **11098. a. 22.**

—— *See* YIH-KING. L'Interprétation du Yi-king . . . Par C. de H., etc. 1896. 8°. **11098. b. 21.**

—— —— The Yih-king. A new translation from the original Chinese. By C. de H., etc. 8°. **11098. b. 20.**

—— La Religion et les Cérémonies Impériales de la Chine moderne, d'après le cérémonial et les décrets officiels. Par C. de H. pp. 556. *E. Leroux: Paris*, 1899. 4°. **11098. c. 15.**

—— Vocabulaire Bouddhique Sanscrit-Chinois. 漢梵集要 *Han-Fan Tsih-yao*. Précis de doctrine Bouddhique par C. de H. pp. 66. *E. J. Brill: Leide*, 1897. 8°. **11098. b. 37.**

HARRINGTON ( ). See 曾紀澤 TSĂNG KE-TSIH. 中西合歷 *Ching Se ho leih*. "A Chinese and foreign comparative calendar . . ." Compiled by Professor Harrington, etc. 1877. 8°. **15298. b. 40.**

HARTMANN (FRANZ). See 老君 LAOU KEUN . . . Betrachtungen über das Tao-Teh-King . . . von F. H., etc. 8°. **11099. b. 39.**

HASWELL (CHARLES H.). See 哈司韋 HA-SZE-WEI. **15259. i. 5.**

哈司韋 HA-SZE-WEI [i.e. CHARLES H. HASWELL?]. 算式集要 *Swan shih tseih yaou*. "The mensuration of areas, lines, and surfaces." Translated into Chinese by Foolanya, i.e. John Fryer. With diagrams. 4 keuen. [*Shanghai*, 1880?] 8°. **15259. i. 5.**

HAVRET (HENRI). Variétés Sinologiques, No. 12: La Stèle Chrétienne de Sin-ngan-fou. IIme Partie: Histoire du Monument. Par le P. H. H. *Shanghai*, 1897. 8°. **11095. b. 1.**

HEADLAND (FREDERICK WILLIAM). See 海得蘭 HAI-TIH-LAN.

項懷 HEANG HWAI. 隸法彙纂 *Le fă wei tswan*. "A Dictionary of the 'Official' Characters." By Heang Hwai. 10 keuen. 1780. 8°. **15344. a. 7.**

項名達 HEANG MING-TAH. 勾股六術 *Kow koo luh shuh*. "Six propositions in geometry." With diagrams. pp. ii, 104, 12. 1832. 8°. **15259. h. 11.**

孝 HEAOU. 二十四孝 *Urh shih sze heaou*. "Twenty-four instances of Filial Piety." With illustrations. pp. 48. 1873. 8°. **15331. b. 15.**

HEAOU KING. "The Book of Filial Piety." Being a conversation between K'ung K'ew and Tsăng Tsan. With comments by Ming Hwang, and with notes on the sounds by Luh Tih-ming. Edited by Le Han-chang and others. pp. x, 52. 1868. Fol. **15229. c. 40.**

夏味堂 HEA WEI-T'ANG. 拾雅 *Shih ya*. "Explanation of Terms and Expressions" not found in the *Urh ya*, the *Kwang ya*, *Fang yen*, and *Seaou Urh ya*. By Hea Wei-t'ang. 20 keuen. 1820. 8°. **15346. b. 25.**

閒鷗霞逸 HEEN GOW HEA YIH, *pseud*. 廣策學纂要 *Kwang ts'ih heŏ tswan yaou*. "An epitomised encyclopædia of literary knowledge." By Heen gow hea yih. 32 keuen. 1873. 12°. **15026. a. 6.**

咸鏡道 HEENKING TAOU. A Corean examination ode on the phrase 四方來觀者皆感化其德 *Szefang lai kwanchay kanhwa k'e tih*. "All those coming to gaze from the four quarters were influenced and converted by his virtue." Written from the examination in the Circuit of Heenking. MS. [1890?] A roll. **Or. 4612.**

禧恩 HE GĂN. See 線忻 MEEN HIN. 欽定新疆識畧 *K'in ting sin keang shih lŏ*. "An account of the newly acquired Muhammedan District . . ." Compiled by . . . He Găn, etc. 1820. 8°. **15271. b. 12.**

希 理 哈 HE-LE-HA [i.e.　　　　]. 防 海 新 論 *Fang hai sin lun.* "On Coast Defences" based on the experience of the American War [1864–66]. By He-le-ha. Translated into Chinese by Foolanya, i.e. J. Fryer. With plates. 18 keuen. [1875?] 8°. 15259. g. 3.

—— [Another copy.] 15259. c. 17.

HENDERSON (JAMES). See 韓 雅 各 HAN YAKOH.

學 HEŎ. 學 考 *Heŏ k'aou.* "Critical essays" on the Classics, History, and Literature. MS. [1688?] 8°. 15319. b. 20 (3).

學 宮 HEŎKUNG. 學 宮 圖 考 *Heŏkung t'oo k'aou.* "The Confucian College, illustrated and examined." With notices of the Sage. 4 vols. 1873. 8°. 15301. b. 4.

學 善 居 士 HEŎ SHEN KEU SZE [i.e. WILLIAM MILNE, D.D.]. 揀 巽 勸 世 要 言 *Keen seuen k'euen she yaou yen.* "A selection of important works to admonish the age." *Singapore,* [1830?]. 8°. 15118. a. 40.

—— 勸 世 瓦 言 *K'euen she leang yen.* "Wholesome Words of Exhortation for the Age." By W. M. A collection of Christian Tracts. *Malacca,* [1829?]. 8°. 15116. e. 61.

—— [Another copy.] 15116. e. 60.

—— 求 福 免 禍 要 論 *K'ew fu meen hwo yaou lun.* "An important discourse on seeking happiness and escaping misery." pp. iv, 160. *Singapore,* [1830?]. 8°. 15118. a. 39.

學 院 大 人 HEŎ YUEN TA JIN. 學 院 大 人 考 取 全 省 遺 才 題 名 錄 *Heŏ yuen ta jin k'aou ts'eu ts'euen sǎng e ts'ai t'e ming luh.* "A list of the unsuccessful candidates at the Canton examination" in 1840. 1840. 8°. 15320. e. 27.

HERNISZ (STANISLAS). A Guide to Conversations in the English and Chinese languages. *Boston* [*Mass.*], 1854. Obl. 8°. 11099. b. 31.

—— [Another copy.] 11099. b.

HERSCHEL (SIR JOHN FREDERICK WILLIAM), Bart. 談 天 *T'an t'een.* "Conversations on the Heavens." Herschel's outlines of Astronomy. Translated into Chinese by Wei-lĕĕ-a-lĕĭh [i e. A. Wylie] and Le Shen-lan. 18 keuen. *Shanghai,* 1859. 8°. 15259. f. 12.

HERSCHEL (SIR JOHN FREDERICK WILLIAM), Bart. (*continued*). [Another edition.] 18 keuen. *Shanghai,* 1874. 8°. 15359. f. 5.

—— [Another copy.] 15255. f. 1.

—— 玄 奘 HEUEN-TS'ANG. 大 般 若 波 羅 密 多 經 *Ta pan jo po lo me to king.* "The Mahā-pragnāpāramitā Sūtra." Translated into Chinese by Heuen-ts'ang. 600 keuen. 1157. 8°. 15101. d. 8.

Imperfect, containing only the 284th keuen. Printed in Japan from blocks.

HERVEY-SAINT-DENYS (MARIE JEAN LÉON DE), Marquis. La Tunique de Perles, Un Serviteur Méritant, et Tang le Kiai-youen: trois Nouvelles chinoises traduites pour la première fois, par le Marquis d'Hervey-Saint-Denys. pp. viii, 247. *Paris,* 1889. 12°. 11100. a. 15.

許 球 HEU K'EW. 養 雲 山 館 試 帖 注 釋 *Yang yun shan kwan shih t'ieh choo shih.* "Essays from the Yang yun shan Hall, with notes and comments." 4 keuen. 1868. 8°. 15313. a. 2.

許 九 日 HEU KEW-JIH. See 吳 梅 村 WOO MEI-TS'UN. 吳 詩 集 覽 *Woo she tseĭh lan.* "The collected Poems of Woo Mei-ts'un . . ." Edited by Heu Kew-jih, etc. 1781. 8°. 15323. e. 13.

許 楗 HEU LEEN. 咽 喉 脈 證 通 論 *Yen how mih ching t'ung lun.* "On Diseases of the Throat." Edited by Heu Leen. 1838. 12°. 15252. b. 18.

—— and 熊 莪 HEUNG GO. 刑 部 比 照 加 減 成 案 *Hing Poo pe chaou kea keen ch'ing gan.* "Board of Punishment precedents for adding to and diminishing penalties in analogous cases." Compiled by Heu Leen and Heung Go. 32 keuen. Together with a supplementary collection. Edited by Heu Leen. 32 keuen. 1834, 1845. 12°. 15241. b. 12.

許 勉 燉 HEU MEEN-TUN. 氾 水 縣 志 *Sze shwuy heen che.* "A Topography of Sze shwuy heen" in Honan. With plans and maps. Edited by Heu Meen-tun, the Magistrate of the district, and others. 22 keuen. 1743. 8°. 15276. e. 1.

HEU—HIN

熊羆 HEUNG GO. See 許槤 HEU LEEN and HEUNG GO. 刑部比照加減成案 *Hing Poo pe chaou kea keen ch'ing gan.* "Board of Punishment precedents for adding to and diminishing penalties in analogous cases." Compiled by . . . Heung Go, etc. 1834. 12°. **15241. b. 12.**

纛沐 HEUN-MUH. 涵三鏡 *Han san king.* "Three large-minded mirrors" for the illumination of Taouism. Compiled by Heun-muh. 3 parts. *Canton*, 1876. 8°. **15111. c. 20.**

—— 廣鈔海心珠 *Kwang meaou hai sin choo.* "Heart Pearls from the mysterious sea." A collection of moral discourses compiled by Heun-muh. 4 keuen. 1860. 8°. **15113. a. 24.**

—— 釋迦如來應化事蹟 *Shih kea joo lai ying hwa sze tse.* "The Transformations of Sākya Tathāgata." With illustrations. By Heun-muh (1793). A new edition. Edited by Wang Yu-fung. 4 vols. 1808. 4°. **15113. e. 5.**

許慎 HEU SHIN. See 朱駿聲 CHOO TSEUN-SHING. 說文通訓定聲 *Shwŏ wăn t'ung heun ting shing.* "Deep Instructions on the *Shwŏ wăn* of Heu Shin, etc." 1850. 8°. **15344. c. 4.**

—— 說文解字通釋 *Shwŏ wăn keae tsze t'ung shih.* "The explanations of characters in (Heu Shin's) *Shwŏ wăn* thoroughly expounded" by Seu K'eae-chuen. 40 keuen, with an appendix in 3 keuen. 1839. 4°. **15346. d. 4.**

—— 說文廣義 *Shwŏ wăn kwang e.* "Extended Meanings of Heu Shin's *Shwŏ wan.*" By Wang Foo-che. 3 keuen. *Nanking*, 1865. 8°. **15344. c. 3.**

許水南 HEU SHWUY-NAN. 許水南徵君詩集 *Heu Shwuy-nan ching keun she tseih.* "A Collection of the Poetry of Heu Shwuy-nan." 2 keuen. See 孫澍 SUN SHOO. 古棠書屋叢書 *Koo t'ang shoo wuh ts'ung shoo.* "A Collection of Reprints," etc. 1831–49. 8°. **15315. d. 1.**

許道基 HEU TAOU-KE. See 韓愈 HAN YU. 五百家注音辯韓昌黎先生全集 *Woo pih kea choo yin peen Han Ch'ang-le Sien-săng ts'euen tseih.* "A complete collection of the writings of Han Yu . . ." Edited by Heu Taou-ke, etc. 1784. 8°. **15315. c. 7.**

許雲蟠 HEU YUN-KEAOU. 六觀樓北曲六種 *Luh kwan low pih k'eŭh luh chung.* "Six Plays accompanied with Northern Airs from the Six-view Pavilion." By Heu Yun-keaou. Edited by Yuen Yun-tai and Loo Jun-săng. 6 keuen. 1874. 8°. **15327. d. 29.**

許孫蕘 HEU YU-YANG. 白門新柳記 *Pih mun sin lew ke.* "A collection of new and amusing stories from 'The White Gate.'" Compiled by Heu Yu-yang. 1875. 8°. **15334. d. 14.**

希渭 HE-WEI. 景德傳燈錄 *King-tih chuen tăng luh.* "Biographical notices of the Buddhist teachers who have handed down the light of the Law from the reign of King-tih" (A.D. 1004–8) to that of Yen Yew (1314–21). By the Priest He-wei. A new edition. With Japanese punctuation and manuscript notes. 30 keuen. [1350?] Fol. **15103. b. 1.**
Printed in Japan from blocks.

HILLIER (WALTER CAINE). List of the higher metropolitan and provincial authorities of China. . . . Corrected to December 31st, 1888. pp. 34. *Kelly & Walsh: Shanghai*, 1889. 4°. **11100. f. 12.**

HIMLY (CARL), Philologist. See TA TS'ING YIH T'UNG YU T'U. Nord-Tibet und Lob-Nur-Gebiet in der Darstellung des Ta-Thsing i Thung yü Thu . . . unter Mitwirkung des Herrn K. Himly . . . herausgegeben, etc. 1893. 8°. **Pam. 88.**

省察 HING CH'A. 省察規矩要理 *Hing ch'a kwei keu yaou le.* "Essential points in the practice of self-examination." pp. 25. *Hongkong*, 1890. 12°. **15200. aa. 28.**

興國萬 HING KWO-WAN. See 張考夫 CHANG K'AOU-FOO. 楊園先生全集 *Yang yuen seen săng ts'euen tseih.* "The Complete Writings of the Doctor of the Aspen Garden . . ." Edited by Hing Kwo-wan, etc. 1869. 8°. **15315. c. 1.**

行明 HINGMING. 畫譜一本 *Hwa p'oo yih pun.* "A volume of sketches" by the Buddhist Deacon Hingming. MS. ff. 18. 1828. 4°. **Or. 3495. 28. a.**

邢昺 HING PING. 爾雅註疏 *Urh ya choo soo.* "The Literary Expositor." With Kŏ Pŏ's Commentary, and a Paraphrase by the Editor Hing Ping. 11 keuen. 1745. 8°. **15318. c. 5.**

行文劄 HING WǍN CHA. 行文劄諭 *Hing wǎn cha yu.* "Despatches, etc." MS. 1842. 8°.
15297. d. 9.

HIRTH (F.). *See* RUHSTRAT (E.). Index of the characters in Dr. Hirth's "Text Book of Documentary Chinese," etc. 1892. 4°.
11099. d. 37.

—— Chinesische Malereien auf Papier und Seide aus den Sammlung des Herrn Professor F. Hirth. pp. 20. *Dresden*, 1897. 8°. 11099. b. 38.

—— Hsin-kuan wên-chien-lu. Text Book of Documentary Chinese, with a Vocabulary, for the special use of the Chinese Customs Service. Edited by F. H. 2 vols. *Shanghai* [printed]. *P. S. King & Son: London*, 1885. 4°. 11100. f. 7.

貨 Ho. 貨則條例 *Ho tsih teaou le.* "Trade Regulations." MS. [1840 ?] 8°. 15241. b. 4.

和 Ho [i.e.   ]. 聖教要理 *Shing keaou yaou le.* "A Catechism on the most important doctrines of the Roman Catholic Faith." pp. x, 182. *Hongkong*, 1893. 8°. 15200. d. 61.

HOANG (PIERRE). Notices techniques sur la Propriété en Chine, avec un choix d'actes et de Documents officiels par P. H. pp. ii, 200. *Shanghai*, 1897. 8°. 11098. a. 15.

—— Variétés Sinologiques, No. 14: Le Mariage Chinois au point de vue legal. Par le P. P. H. pp. liv, 259, 46. *Shanghai*, 1898. 8°. 11095. b. 3.

HOBSON (BENJAMIN). *See* 合信 HOSIN.

賀長齡 Ho CH'ANG-LING. *See* 陶澍 T'AOU CHOO. 江蘇海運全案 *Keang soo hai yun ts'euen gan.* "A discussion on the subject of transporting the Imperial Impost Grain from . . . Keang-soo to the Metropolis." Compiled by . . . Ho Ch'ang-ling, etc. 1826. 8°.
15239. c. 3.

何竹有 Ho CHUH-YEW. 金堂何竹有詩集 *Kin t'ang Ho Chuh-yew she tseih.* "A Collection of the Poems of Ho Chuh-yew." 2 keuen. See 孫澍 SUN SHOO. 古棠書屋叢書 *Koo t'ang shoo wuh ts'ung shoo.* "A Collection of Reprints," etc. 1831–49. 8°. 15315. d. 1.

何芳苡 Ho FANG-E. *See* 張士登 CHANG SZE-TÄNG. 三分夢全傳 *San fun mung ts'euen chuen.* "The Story of a Day-dream." Edited by Ho Fang-e, etc. 1823. 8°.
15334. d. 7.

鶴和堂 Hǒ Ho-T'ANG. 示我周行 *She wo chow hing.* "A Guide to the Roads of the Empire." 6 keuen. 1694. 8°. 15271. a. 14.

—— [Another edition. 3 keuen. 1750 ?] 12°.
15271. a. 22.
Imperfect, containing only Keuen 2, 3.

鶴皋 Ho KAOU. 西陲要略 *Se ch'uy yaou leǒ.* "A short epitomised account of the regions on the western frontiers." By Ho Kaou, who is described as the Poet of Showyang. 4 keuen. 1807. 8°. 15275. c. 9.

何啓 Ho K'E. 新政始基 *Sin ching che ke.* "The foundations of a new system of government" in China. pp. viii, 90. *Hongkong*, 1898. 8°. 15241. b. 14.

—— and 胡禮垣 Hoo LE-YUEN. 中國新政安行 *Chung kwo sin ching ngan hing.* "A Guide to the Reformation of China." pp. iv, 82. *Hongkong*, 1898. 8°. 15297. a. 22.

—— —— 勸學篇書後 *K'euen heǒ p'een shoo how.* "An essay on Chang Che-tung's exhortation to Learning." pp. 126. *Hongkong*, 1899. 8°. 15320. c. 19.

—— —— 新政始基 *Sin ching che ke.* "On the Establishment of Reforms in China." pp. viii, 94. *Hongkong*, 1898. 8°. 15297. a. 23.

何國宗 Ho KWO-TSUNG. *See* 允祿 YUN LUH. 御製律曆淵源 *Yu che leǔh lǐh yuen yuen.* "A Thesaurus of the Exact Sciences . . ." Compiled by Ho Kwo-tsung, etc. 1723. 8°.
15257. c. 4. & d. 1.

何㻞青 Ho LAI-TS'ING. 五經古人典林 *Woo king koo jin teen lin.* "A Forest of Canonical References to Men of Antiquity in the Five Classics." Compiled by Ho Lai-ts'ing. Edited by Ho Tsung-haou. 6 keuen. 1875. 8°.
15225. a. 18.

—— 五經典林 *Woo king teen lin.* "A Forest of Canonical Expressions from the Five Classics." Compiled by Ho Lai-ts'ing. Edited by Ho Tsung-haou. 54 keuen. 1875. 8°.
15225. a. 17.

何 廉 昉 HO LEEN-FANG. See 蘇 軾 SOO SHĬH. 祈 蘇 集 *Nă Soo tseĭh.* "A Collection of Distiches . . ." Compiled by Ho Leen-fang, etc. 1862. 8°. **15323. e. 19.**

—— 悔 餘 菴 尺 牘 *Hwuy-yu gan ch'ĭh tuh.* "Letters from Hwuy-yu's Hut." By Ho Leen-fang. 3 keuen. 1863. 8°. **15319. d. 17.**

—— 悔 餘 菴 詩 稿 *Hwuy-yu gan she kaou.* "A Collection of Poetry from Hwuy-yu's Hut." By Ho Leen-fang. 13 keuen. 1865. 8°. **15323. e. 17.**

—— 悔 餘 菴 文 稿 *Hwuy-yu gan wăn kaou.* "A Collection of Literary Pieces from Hwuy-yu's Hut." By Ho Leen-fang. 9 keuen. 1865. 8°. **15319. d. 18.**

—— 悔 餘 菴 樂 府 *Hwuy-yu gan yŏ foo.* "Songs from Hwuy-yu's Hut." By Ho Leen-fang. 4 keuen. 1865. 8°. **15323. e. 18.**

和 南 HO-NAN. 敎 外 別 傳 *Keaou wai peĭh chuen.* "Supplementary Buddhist Biographies." Compiled by Ho-nan. 16 keuen. 1633. 8°. **15103. d. 1.**

胡 重 HOO CHUNG. 說 文 字 原 韻 表 *Shwo wăn tsze yuen yun peaou.* "Tables showing the original tones of the characters of the *Shwo wăn.*" Compiled by Hoo Chung. Edited by Kin Heaou-pĭh. 2 keuen. 1811. 8°. **15342. b. 5.**

胡 安 國 HOO GANKWO. See 孔 丘 K'UNG K'EW. 春 秋 *Ch'un Ts'ew.* "The Spring and Autumn Annals." With the Commentaries of Hoo Gankwo, etc. 8°. **15212. a. 13.**

—— See 孔 丘 K'UNG K'EW. 春 秋 胡 氏 傳 *Ch'un ts'ew Hoo she chuen.* "The Spring and Autumn Annals," with Hoo Gan-kwo's Commentary, etc. Fol. **16015. c. 4.**

胡 廣 HOO KWANG. See 孔 丘 K'UNG K'EW. 書 傳 大 全 *Shoo chuen ta ts'euen.* "The Book of Historical Documents . . ." Compiled by . . . Hoo Kwang, etc. 8°. **15215. d. 1.**

胡 禮 垣 HOO LE-YUEN. See 何 啓 HO K'E and HOO LE-YUEN. 中 國 新 政 安 行 *Chung kwo sin ching ngan hing.* "A Guide to the Reformation of China . . ." 1898. 8°. **15297. a. 22.**

胡 禮 垣 HOO LE-YUEN. See 何 啓 HO K'E and HOO LE-YUEN. 勸 學 篇 後 *K'euen heŏ p'een how.* "An Essay on Chang Che-tung's Exhortation to Learning," etc. 1899. 8°. **15320. c. 19.**

—— 康 說 書 後 *K'ang shwo shoo how.* "The Views of K'ang," Yew-wei, the Reformers, on the Reform of China. Compiled by Hoo Le-yuen. pp. 48. *Hongkong,* 1898. 8°. **15314. d. 6.**

胡 蘆 HOO LOO. 依 樣 葫 蘆 *E yang hoo loo.* "A Model Letter-Writer." By the Man of the Wei-luy Mountain. 4 keuen. 1813. 8°. **15348. a. 6.**

胡 寶 琳 HOO PAOU-LIN. 武 定 府 志 *Woo-ting foo che.* "A Topography of Woo-ting foo," in Shan-tung. Edited by Hoo Paou-lin, Ch'in T'ing-fang, and others. 38 keuen. 1759. 8°. **15269. b. 9.**

胡 必 相 HOO PEIH-SEANG. 周 禮 貫 珠 *Chow le kwan choo.* "A string of pearls from the *Chow le.*" Compiled by Hoo Peih-seang. 2 keuen. 1821. 8°. **15215. d. 5.**

胡 邵 瑛 HOO SHAOU-YING. See 陳 薲 謨 CH'IN T'SIN-MOO. 五 車 韻 府 *Woo ch'ay yun foo.* "A Phonetic Dictionary . . ." Edited by Hoo Shaou-ying, etc. 8°. **15346. d. 2.**

胡 式 鈺 HOO SHIH-YUH. 竇 存 *Tow ts'un.* "A Collection of Errors in Literature, Poetry, Common Matters, and Conversation." By Hoo Shih-yuh. 4 keuen. *Shanghai,* 1841. 8°. **15317. e. 8.**

胡 德 琳 HOO TIH-LIN. 濟 寧 直 隸 州 志 *Tse-ning chih le chow che.* "A Topography of Tse-ning chow," in Shantung. Compiled by Hoo Tih-lin and others. 34 keuen. 1785. 8°. **15269. a. 12.**

Wanting Keuen 3 and 4.

—— 東 昌 府 志 *Tung-ch'ang foo che.* "A Topography of Tung-ch'ang foo" in Shan-tung. Originally compiled by Hoo Tih-lin and others. Re-edited by Sung Shan and others. 50 keuen. 1808. 8°. **15269. e. 10.**

—— [Another edition.] 50 keuen. 1808. 8°. **15269. a. 13.**

胡 德 邁 Hoo Tih-mai [i.e. T. H. Hudson]. See 柏哲 Pih-chĕ. 經 錄 問 答 *King luh wăn tah.* "A Catechism on Bible Records." Translated into Chinese by Hoo Tih-mai. 15200. c. 3.

—— See 鄱 陽 約 翰 P'oyang Yohan. 勝 旅 景 程 正 編 *Shing leuh king ch'ing ching peen.* "The Pilgrim's Progress." Translated into Chinese by Hoo Tih-mai, etc. 1870. 8°. 15118. d. 4.

—— 指 南 針 *Che nan chin.* "The Compass." A religious tract. pp. 12. 1871. 8°. 15200. c. 51.

—— 主 神 論 *Choo shin lun.* "A discourse on God." A new edition. pp. 20. [*Shanghai?*], 1872. 8°. 15200. c. 44.

—— 主 神 十 條 誡 *Choo shin shih t'eaou keae.* "The Ten Commandments" explained. pp. 14. 1873. 8°. 15200. b. 8.

—— 稽 明 四 終 *Ke ming sze chung.* "The four results of Judgment and Retribution." pp. 18. 1867. 8°. 15200. b. 13.

—— 贖 罪 文 *Shuh tsuy wăn.* "On Redemption." pp. 30. 1867. 8°. 15200. c. 52.

—— 心 覺 論 *Sin keaou lun.* "On Conscience." MS. pp. 30. 1867. 8°. 15200. c. 31.

—— 太 始 傳 *T'ai che chuen.* "On the Creation." pp. 29. 1867. 8°. 15200. c. 7.

—— 清 明 掃 墓 論 *Ts'ing-ming sao moo lun.* "A discussion on the practice of sweeping the tombs at the Tsing-ming festival." pp. 20. 1867. 8°. 15200. b. 16.

胡 子 健 Hoo Tsze-keen. See 李 義 山 Le E-shan. 玉 谿 生 詩 詳 註 *Yuh ke săng she tseang choo.* "Poems from the Jade Valley . . ." Edited by Hoo Tsze-keen, etc. 1780. 8°. 15324. e. 1.

何 炳 Ho Ping. 帝 輿 合 覽 *Te yu ho lan.* "An epitome of the Geography of the Empire." The 1st keuen contains an historical epitome of the geography, and the 2nd keuen describes the geography of each Province. 2 keuen. 1833. 8°. 15261. e. 8.

HOPKINS (Lionel C.). *See* Goh. 官 話 指 南 The Guide to the Kuan hua. A translation. By L. C. H., etc. 1889. 8°. 11098. b. 8.

和 世 太 Ho She-t'ai. See 托 津 T'ŏ Tsin. 欽 定 回 疆 則 例 *K'in ting hwuy keang tsih le.* "Regulations for the Government of the Muhammedan Dependencies of China." Compiled by . . . Ho She-t'ai, etc. 1814. 8°. 15271. b. 6.

和 珅 Ho Shin. See 阿 桂 Ah Kwei. 欽 定 滿 洲 源 流 考 *K'in ting Man chow yuen lew k'aou.* "An Examination into the Origin of the Manchoos." Compiled . . . by . . . Ho Shin, etc. 1777. 8°. 15297. b. 1.

—— See 阿 桂 Ah Kwei. 八 旬 萬 壽 盛 典 *Pă seun wan show shing teen.* "A Memorial of the 80th Birthday of the Emperor Keen-lung." Compiled by . . . Ho Shin, etc. 1792. 8°. 15296. e. 4.

合 信 Hosin [i.e. Benjamin Hobson]. *See* Bible— New Testament: *John, Gospel.* 約 翰 真 經 釋 解 *Yŏhan chin king shih keae.* "The [first 17 chapters of the] true Gospel of St. John, with explanatory comments" by Hosin. 1853. 8°. 15116. a. 12.

—— *See* Bible—New Testament: *John, Gospel.* 約 翰 聖 經 釋 解 *Yŏhan shing king shih keae.* "The Gospel of St. John, with a commentary" by Ho-sin, etc. 1879. 8°. 15200. c. 22.

—— 婦 嬰 新 說 *Foo ying sin shwo.* "A new treatise on Midwifery and the Diseases of Children." Edited by Kwan Mow-ts'ai. pp. xxii, 113, 9. *Shanghai*, 1858. 8°. 15253. b. 9.

—— [Another copy.] 15253. b. 8.

—— 博 物 新 編 *Pŏ wuh sin peen.* "A new treatise on the Natural Sciences." With illustrations. 3 parts. *Shanghai*, 1855. 8°. 15259. g. 8.

—— [Another copy.] 15259. c. 24.

—— 西 醫 略 論 *Se e leŏ lun.* "The first lines of the practice of surgery in the West . . ." With illustrations, and a table of contents in English. 2 keuen. *Shanghai*, 1857. 8°. 15253. b. 7.

—— [Another copy.] 15253. b. 5.

—— 全 體 新 論 *Ts'euen t'e sin lun.* "A new treatise on Anatomy." With illustrations. By Ho-sin, assisted by Ch'in Sew-t'ang. pp. xviii, 142. *Canton*, 1851. 8°. 15255. a. 9.

哈 司 韋 Ho-sze-wei [i.e.   ]. 算 式 集 要 *Swan shih tseih yaou.* "A Collection of Mathematical Problems." Translated into Chinese by Foo-lan-ya [i.e. John Fryer] and transcribed by Keang Hăng. 4 keuen. [*Shanghai*, 1874?] 8°.   **15259. d. 18.**

何 贊 淸 Ho Tsan-ts'ing. 救 劫 金 鑑 *Kew kee kin keen.* "The Golden Mirror of Salvation from Disasters." A collection of five Taouist works, viz.: (1) *Kan ying peen kin keen*; (2) *Wăn wu urh te kew kee chin kin keen*; (3) *Keaou she kin keen*; (4) *Yin chih kin keen*; and (5) *Wăn ch'ing shing heun. Canton,* 1877. 8°.   **15111. e. 11.**

何 秋 濤 Ho Ts'ew-t'aou. *See* 張 穆 Chang Muh. 蒙 古 游 牧 記 *Mung koo yew muh ke.* "A History of the Nomad Mongol Tribes . . ." Edited by Ho Ts'ew-t'aou, etc. 1867. 8°.   **15275. a. 16.**

何 進 善 Ho Tsin-shen. *See* Bible—New Testament. 新 約 全 書 註 釋 *Sin yŏ ts'euen shoo choo shih.* "The New Testament, with a commentary" by Ho Tsin-shen, etc. 1874. 8°.   **15117. b. 11.**

何 宗 鎬 Ho Tsung-haou. *See* 何 㟔 靑 Ho Lai-ts'ing. 五 經 古 人 典 林 "A Forest of Canonical References to Men of Antiquity in the Five Classics . . ." Edited by Ho Tsung-haou, etc. 1875. 8°.   **15225. a. 18.**

—— *See* 何 㟔 靑 Ho Lai-ts'ing. 五 經 典 林 *Woo king teen lin.* "A Forest of Canonical Expressions . . ." Edited by Ho Tsung-haou, etc. 1875. 8°.   **15225. a. 17.**

何 焆 Ho Wei. *See* 岳 飛 Yŏ Fei. 岳 忠 武 王 文 集 *Yŏ chung woo Wang wăn tseih.* "A Collection of the Writings of Yŏ Fei . . ." Edited by Ho Wei, etc. 1770.   **15317. d. 9.**

何 晏 Ho Yen. *See* 四 書 Sze shoo. 正 平 本 論 語 札 解 *Ching p'ing pun lun yu chah keae.* "The true text of the Confucian Analects, with explanatory notes" compiled by Ho Yen, etc. 1813. Fol.   **15201. c. 12.**

火 烟 車 路 Ho yen ch'ay loo. 火 烟 車 路 規 例 *Ho yen ch'ay loo kwei le.* Railway regulations, being a notice issued by the Government of Victoria (Australia) warning Chinamen not to trespass on the railroads. MS. *Victoria,* 1877. A sheet.   **15298. b. 45.**

HUDSON (Thomas Hale). See 胡 德 邁 Hoo Tih-mai.

HUGHES (William). 繪 地 法 原 *Hwuy te fă yuen.* "A treatise on the Construction of Maps" by W. H. Translated into Chinese by Kin-K'eae-le, i.e. C. T. Kreyer. With diagrams. pp. 112, 16. [*Shanghai,* 1864?] 8°. **15271. d. 4.**

弘 晝 Hung Chow. 八 旗 通 志 初 集 *Pă k'e t'ung che ch'oo tseih.* "A Complete Statistical Account of the Eight Banners." Compiled by Hung Chow, Ma Tse, Gŏ Urh-tai, and others. 250 keuen. 1739. 8°.   **15296. c. & d.**

洪 适 Hung Kwŏ. 隸 釋 *Le shih.* "A Collection of Inscriptions in the 'Official' Character," principally of the Han Dynasty. Compiled by Hung Kwŏ in 1168. A new edition. Edited by Wang Jih-sew. 27 keuen. 1778. 8°.   **15299. c. 4.**

—— 隸 續 *Le suh.* "A Supplement to the *Le shih*," or "Collection of Inscriptions in the Official Character." By Hung Kwŏ. Edited by Wang Jih-sew. 21 keuen. 1778. 8°.   **15299. c. 5.**

紅 樓 夢 Hung low mung. 紅 樓 夢 圖 詠 *Hung low mung t'oo yung.* "Portraits of and Odes on the Characters in the Dream of the Red Chamber." 4 vols. 1879. 8°. **15334. f. 1.**

—— 續 紅 樓 夢 *Suh hung low mung.* "A Sequel to the Dream of the Red Chamber." By "the Master of the Marine Garden." 40 keuen. [1800?] 8°.   **15333. a. 5.** Imperfect.

弘 退 思 Hung T'uy-sze. 醫 林 撮 要 *E lin ts'oh yaou.* "An Epitome of Medicine." 13 keuen. [1550?] Fol.   **15253. e. 1.** This work, which was printed in Korea from blocks, was brought from that country by the Japanese invaders at the end of the sixteenth century.

洪 武 Hung-woo, *Emperor.* 御 製 文 集 *Yu che wăn tseih.* "The writings of the Emperor Hung-woo." 20 keuen. 1529. Fol. **15315. d. 5.** Printed in Korea with movable type.

HURLEY (R. C.). Tourists' Map of eight short trips on the mainland of China (neighbourhood of Hongkong). Including the principal places frequented by sportsmen. With vocabulary in Cantonese and Hakka. *Hongkong,* 1896. 8°.   **11099. c. 35.**

HURLEY (R. C.). The Tourists' Map of Hongkong, describing twelve trips on the Island. With short vocabulary in Chinese. Local dialect. *Hongkong*, 1896. 8°.   11099. c. 36.

HUTCHINSON (ARTHUR B.). *See* LITURGIES: ENGLAND, CHURCH OF. The Book of Common Prayer . . . translated into Cantonese by Rev. A. B. H., etc. 1878. 8°.   15118. b. 28.

—— A Harmony of the Four Holy Gospels, according to the Delegates' Version arranged in Parallelisms. By the Rev. A. B. H. *Shanghai*, 1878. 8°.   15118. c. 33.

This work has a Chinese title which runs thus: 福音排偶便覽 *Fuh yin p'ai gow peen lan.*

華湛恩 HWA CHAN-GĂN. *See* 安古琴 GAN KOO-K'IN. 六書韻徵 *Luh shoo yun ching.* "A Dictionary . . ." Edited by Hwa Chan-găn, etc. 1838. 8°.   15344. e. 9.

花之安 HWA CHIH-GAN [i.e. D. E. FABER]. 經學不厭精 *King heŏ pu yen tsing.* "The result of an untiring study of the Classics." 2 keuen. 1896. 8°.   15225. b. 3.

華夷 HWA E. 華夷譯語 *Hwa E yih yu.* "Chinese and Barbarian Vocabularies," viz.: the Pih e, Burmese, Tibetan, Ouigur, Pa-pih kwan [? Shan], and Kaou-ch'ang. [1700?] 8°.   15344. d. 10.

華衡芳 HWA HĂNG-FANG. *See* 希理哈 HE-LE-HA [i.e.   ]. 防海新論 *Fang hae sin lun.* "A New Treatise on Coast Defences . . ." Edited by Hwa Hăng-fang, etc. 8°.   15259. g. 3.

—— *See* 華里司 HWA-LE-SZE [i.e.   ]. 代數術 *Tai soo shuh.* "Algebra . . ." Edited by Hwa Hăng-fang, etc. 8°. 15259. f. 7.

—— *See* 華里司 HWA-LE-SZE. 微積溯源 *Wei tseĭh soo yuen.* "The Differential and Integral Calculuses traced to their sources . . ." Transcribed by Hwa Hăng-fang, etc. 1874. 8°.   15259. d. 19.

—— *See* 金楷理 KIN-K'EAE-LE. 測候叢談 *Ts'ih how ts'ung t'an.* "Conversations on Meteorological Science . . ." Transcribed by Hwa Hăng-fang, etc. 8°.   15259. d. 22.

華衡芳 HWA HĂNG-FANG. *See* 雷俠兒 LUY-HĔĔ-URH. 地學淺釋 *Te heŏ ts'een shih.* "On Geology . . ." Transcribed by Hwa Hăng-fang, etc. 8°.   15259. d. 10.

—— *See* 白爾特 PIH-URH-T'IH. 御風要術 *Yu fung yaou shuh.* "Important Laws for ruling the Winds . . ." Transcribed by Hwa Hăng-fang, etc. 8°.   15259. d. 24.

—— *See* 代那 TAINA. 金石識別 *Kin shih shih peih.* "A Manual of Mineralogy . . ." Transcribed by Hwa Hăng-fang, etc. 1868, 1883. 8°.   15259. c. 20.

華其昌 HWA K'E-CH'ANG. 畫禪室隨筆 *Hwa shen shih suy peih* "Literary Notes from the Hwa-shen Dwelling." By Hwa K'e-ch'ang. Compiled by Yang Poo, and edited by Ch'in Wang-pin. 4 keuen. 1720. 8°. 15320. e. 35.

華里司 HWA-LE-SZE [i.e. WILLIAM WALLACE]. 代數術 *Tai shoo shuh.* "A Treatise on Algebra." Being the article on Algebra in the "Encyclopædia Britannica" (8th edition) by Hwa-le-sze. Translated into Chinese by Foolanya, i.e. J. Fryer. 25 keuen. [*Shanghai*], 1873. 8°.   15259. f. 7.

—— [Another copy.]   15255. d. 20.

—— 微積溯源 *Wei tseĭh soo yuen.* "On the Differential and Integral Calculus." Translated from W. Wallace's article in the "Encyclopædia Britannica" by Foolanya, i.e. J. Fryer. 8 keuen. 1874. 8°.   15259. f. 10.

—— [Another copy.]   15259. d. 19.

惲珍浦 HWĂN CHIN-P'OO. 國朝閨秀正始續集 *Kwŏ ch'aou kwei sew ching che suh tseĭh.* "A Supplement to the *Ching che* Collection of Poems by ladies of the Hareems during the present Dynasty." Compiled by Hwăn Chinp'oo, and edited by his granddaughters Meaou-leen-paou and Fuh-yun-paou. With an appendix compiled by Ch'ing Măng-mei. 8 keuen, with appendix. 1836. 8°.   15327. e. 5.

HWANG (PIERRE). Exposé du Commerce public du Sel. Par P. H. With maps. *Shanghai*, 1898. 8°.   11095. b. 4.

皇朝 HWANG CH'AOU. 皇朝壹統輿地全圖 *Hwang ch'aou yih t'ung yü te ts'euen t'oo.* "A complete map of the whole Empire." 50 sheets. 1832.   15276. e. 3.

HWA

黃正色 HWANG CHING-SIH. See 李昉 LE FANG. 太平御覽 *T'aip'ing yu lan.* "T'aip'ing's Encyclopædia . . ." Reprinted from the original by Hwang Ching-sih, etc. 1892. 8°.
15026. b. 1.

黃正元 HWANG CHING-YUEN. See 顏正 YEN CHING. 文昌帝君繪像寶訓 *Wăn ch'ang te keun hwuy seang paou heun.* "The precious teachings of the God of Literature . . ." With illustrations and notes by Hwang Ching-yuen, etc. 1843. 8°. 15113. a. 26.

皇甫謐 HWANG FOO-MEÏH. 高士傳 *Kaou sze chuen.* "Biographies of 96 eminent scholars." 3 keuen. See 程榮 CH'ING YUNG. 漢魏叢書 *Han Wei ts'ung shoo.* "A collection of works by authors of the Han and Wei Dynasties," etc. 1791. 8°. 15318. a. 1.

黃曉峰 HWANG HEAOU-FUNG. See 王圻 WANG K'E. 三才圖會 *San ts'ae t'oo hwuy.* "An Illustrated Encyclopædia . . ." Edited by Hwang Heaou-fung, etc. 1609. 8°. 15024. a. 1.

黃憲 HWANG HEEN. 外史 *Wai she.* "Un-orthodox History," or rather historical notes. 8 keuen. See 程榮 CH'ING YUNG. 漢魏叢書 *Han Wei ts'ung shoo.* "A collection of works by authors of the Han and Wei Dynasties," etc. 1791. 8°. 15318. a. 1.

黃蕭泳 HWANG HEUN-MUH. 蓮華經普門品 *Leen hwa king p'oo mun p'in.* "Rules for the Guidance of Buddhists from the Saddharma pundarīka Sūtra." Compiled by Hwang Heun-muh. 1828. 8°. 15103. d. 16.

黃鶴齡 HWANG HŎ-LING. 痧證全生 *Sha ching ts'euen săng.* "The Medical Treatment of Cholera." pp. 30. 1863. 8°. 15251. f. 13.

黃虎竀 HWANG HOO-CH'E. 字學舉隅 *Tsze heŏ keu yu.* "A Hint to the Study of the Characters." By Hwang Hoo-ch'e. 1872. 8°. 15342. b. 6.

黃鶴三 HWANG HO-SAN. See 手慶元 YU K'ING-YUEN. 重訂唐詩三百首續選 *Chung ting T'ang she san pih show suh seuen.* "A supplementary selection of three hundred poems of the T'ang Dynasty . . ." Edited by Hwang Ho-san, etc. 1843. 8°. 15324. a. 10.

黃仁 HWANG JIN. 陳忠愍公殉難詩文錄 *Ch'in chung min kung seun nan she wăn luh.* "Records in Verse and Prose of the Death of the Lamented Patriotic Duke Ch'in Hwa-chung." Compiled by Hwang Jin. 4 keuen. 1843. 8°. 15303. d. 2.

黃可垂 HWANG K'O-CH'UY. 呂宋紀畧 *Leu-sung ke lĕŏ.* "Notes on Spain." See 王滭 WANG LEW. 堿外叢書 *Yih wai ts'ung shoo.* "Reprints of Works on Foreign Countries," etc. 1842. 8°. 15271. b. 3.

黃崐圃 HWANG K'UN-POO. See 周禮 CHOW LE. 周禮節訓 *Chow le tsëĕ heun.* "The Chow Ritual. With sectional explanations" by Hwang K'un-poo, etc. 1783. 8°. 15217. a. 8.

黃坤載 HWANG KW'ĂN-TSAI. 昌邑黃先生醫書入種 *Ch'ang yih Hwang Seen-săng E shoo pă chung.* "The Eight Medical Works" of Hwang Kw'ăn-tsae. Edited by San Shoo-ming. 1861. 8°. 15253. b. 1.

—— [Another edition. Imperfect, containing only 5 works. 1865?] 8°.

—— 四聖心源 *Sze shing sin yuen.* "The Foundation of the Systems of the Four Medical Sages," i.e. Hwang-te, K'i-Pih, Yuĕ jin? Chung-king. By Hwang K'wăn-tsai. Edited by Seu Shoo-ming. 10 keuen. 1860. 8°. 15252. b. 29.

皇明 HWANG MING. 皇明英烈傳 *Hwang Ming ying lëĕ chuen.* "Biographies of Heroes under the Ming Dynasty." With illustrations. 4 keuen. [1750?] 8°. 15305. a. 16. Imperfect, containing only Keuen 1.

黃沐三 HWANG MUH-SAN. 小家語 *Seaou kea yu.* "Lesser Family Sayings." A collection of stories. By Hwang Muh-san. 4 keuen. *Shanghai*, 1876. 8°. 15327. e. 6.

黃邦寧 HWANG PANG-NING. See 岳飛 YŎ FEI. 岳忠武王文集 *Yŏ Chung woo Wang wăn tseíh.* "A Collection of the Writings of Yŏ Fei . . ." Compiled by Hwang Pang-ning, etc. 1770. 8°. 15317. d. 9.

黃葆眞 HWANG PAOU-CHIN. 增補事類賦統編 *Tsăng poo sze luy foo t'ung peen.* "A classified literary Encyclopædia in irregular verse. An enlarged edition," with copious notes. Edited by Hwang Paou-chin. 93 keuen. 1849. 8°. 15024. c. 7.

黃伯祿 HWANG PIH-LUH. 正教奉傳 *Ching keaou fung chuen.* "Records of the Spread of the Orthodox Religion" [i.e. Roman Catholicism]. Being a collection of the Edicts and Proclamations which have been issued in connection with that Faith. pp. xxii, 148. *Shanghai,* 1877. 8°. 15118. c. 38.

The date on the title-page [1872] probably refers to an earlier edition, as the work contains a proclamation dated 1883.

黃平曹 HWANG P'ING TSAOU. 處州府志 *Ch'oo-chow-foo che.* "A Topography of Ch'oo-chow-foo." By Hwang P'ing tsaou, a Prefect of Ch'oo-chow-foo. 16 keuen. [1750?] 8°. 15265. a. 2.

Wanting Keuen 1–10.

黃泌秀 HWANG PI-SEW. 達道大全 *Tah taou ta ts'euen.* "A Compendium of the Great Doctrine." 3 keuen. 1873. 8°. 15113. b. 12.
Imperfect, containing only Keuen 1, 2.

黃少瓊 HWANG SHAO-K'EUNG. 字典彙選集成 An English and Chinese Dictionary. Compiled from general miscellaneous important terms, business letters, bills, documents, and to tariff of imports and outports of China, and bills of ladings. By Wong Su King. New edition. pp. 342, 295. *Hongkong,* 1895. 8°. 11098. a. 8.

黃石公 HWANG SHIH-KUNG. 素書 *Soo shoo.* [A work on military affairs.] pp. i, 44. See 程榮 CH'ING YUNG. 漢魏叢書 *Han Wei ts'ung shoo.* "A collection of works by authors under the Han and Wei Dynasties," etc. 1791. 8°. 15318. a. 1.

黃式度 HWANG SHIH-TOO. 積輯漢陽縣志 *Suh tseih Han-yang heen che.* "A revised topographical history of Han-yang heen." Compiled by Hwang Shih-too and others. 28 keuen. 1868. 8°. 15275. b. 15.

黃歲 HWANG SHING. See 顧藹吉 KOO GAI-KEĬH. 隸辨 *Le peen.* "A Dictionary of the 'Official' Character . . ." Edited by Hwang Shing, etc. 1873. 8°. 15344. c. 1.

黃帝 HWANG-TE. 內經靈樞註證發微 *Nuy king Ling ch'oo choo ching fah wei.* "The Ling ch'oo medical treatise (traditionally ascribed to Hwang-te). With a Commentary and confirming evidences" by Ma Yuen-t'ai. 9 keuen. 1609. Fol. 15253. e. 3.
Printed in Japan with movable type.

黃天河 HWANG T'EEN-HO. 金壺弋墨 *Kin hoo ts'ih mih.* "The Seven Collections of Tales of the Golden Jug." By Hwang T'een-ho. *Sung-keang Foo,* 1873. 8°. 15331. c. 14.

黃挺華 HWANG T'ING-HWA. See 呂應奎 LEU YING-K'WEI. 惠州府志 *Hwuy-chow Foo che.* "A Topography of Hwuy-chow Foo . . ." Compiled by . . . Hwang T'ing-hwa, etc. 1687. 8°. 15267. a. 1.

黃庭堅 HWANG T'ING-KEEN. 山谷詩集注 *Shan-kuh she tseih choo.* "The Poems of Shan-kuh [i.e. Hwang T'ing-keen]. With notes." A Japanese edition. 20 keuen [1600?]. 4°. 15324. d. 2.

—— [Another edition.] 20 keuen. [1610?] 4°. 15324. d. 3.

黃佐 HWANG TSO. 革除遺事節本 *Kih ch'oo e sze tseĕ pun.* "Records of meritorious persons who assisted in rooting out" the Ming Dynasty. 6 keuen. [1800?] 8°. 15297. b. 4.

黃左田 HWANG TSO-T'EEN. See 韓愈 HAN YU. 韓詩增註証訛 *Han she tsăng choo ching go.* "The Poems of Han Yu. With Corrective Notes" by Hwang Tso-t'een, etc. 1827. 8°. 15324. e. 2.

黃崇蘭 HWANG TS'UNG-LAN. 增補貢舉考畧 *Tsăng poo kung keu k'aou leŏ.* "An enlarged List of Graduates who have achieved literary success" from the year 1371 to 1847. Compiled by Hwang Ts'ung-lan. 5 keuen. 1847. 8°. 15319. e. 6.

黃維觀 HWANG WEI-KWAN. 錦字箋 *Kin tsze tseen.* "A Dictionary of Elegant Expressions. With Notes." Compiled by Hwang Wei-kwan. Edited by Hwang Yu-he and Wăn Tăng-e. 4 keuen. 1689. 8°. 15346. a. 21.

黃裕燕 HWANG YU-HE. See 黃維觀 HWANG WEI-KWAN. 錦字箋 *Kin tsze tseen.* "A Dictionary of Elegant Expressions . . ." Edited by Hwang Yu-he, etc. 1689. 8°. 15346. a. 21.

黃永發 HWANG YUNG-FĂ. 新增華英通語 *Sin tsăng Hwa Ying t'ung yü.* "A New and Enlarged Chinese and English Vocabulary." 2 vols. *Hongkong,* 1893. 8°. 11098. a. 11.

桓 寬 HWAN KWAN. 鹽 鐵 論 *Yen t'ĕĕ lun.* "Discourses on Salt and Iron." 12 keuen. See 程 榮 CH'ING YUNG. 漢 魏 叢 書 *Han Wei ts'ung shoo.* "A collection of works by authors of the Han and Wei Dynasties," etc. 1791. 8°. **15318. a. 1.**

婚 喪 HWĂN SANG. 婚 喪 公 禮 *Hwăn sang kung le.* "The Christian Forms of the Marriage and Funeral Services." pp. 26. *Shanghai,* 1881. 8°. **15118. a. 34.**

環 字 HWAN TSZE. 環 字 簿 *Hwan tsze poo.* "A Register of the Importation and Exportation of Tea" [to and from Ningpo?]. 1843. 8°. **15241. b. 5.**

圜 悟 大 師 HWAN-WOO TA-SZE. 圜 悟 碧 嚴 集 *Hwan-woo Pih-yen tseih.* "The Jade-peak collection" of treatises on Buddhism by Hwan-woo ta-sze. 10 keuen. 1341. 8°. **15103. e. 10.** Printed in Japan from blocks.

花 撒 賴 HWA SA-LAI [i.e. MRS. HOLMES]. *See* PEEP. 訓 兒 真 言 *Heun urh chin yen.* . . . The Peep of Day, translated into Chinese by Hwa Sa-lai, etc. 1882. 8°. **15200. c. 10.**

華 岫 雲 HWA SEW-YUN. See 葉 天 士 YĔ T'EEN-SZE. 種 福 堂 公 續 選 臨 證 指 南 *Chung-fuh T'ang kung suh seuen lin ching che nan.* "A supplementary verified Guide to Medicine." . . . Edited by Hwa Sew-yun, etc. 1775. 8°. **15252. e. 9.**

—— See 葉 天 士 YĔ T'EEN-SZE. 臨 證 指 南 醫 案 *Lin ching che nan e gan.* "A verified Guide to Medicine . . ." Edited by Hwa Sew-yun, etc. 1844. 8°. **15252. e. 8.**

華 特 HWA-T'IH [i.e. A. WATT]. 電 氣 鍍 金 略 法 *Teen ch'e too kin leŏ fa.* "Electro-metallurgy." Translated into Chinese by Foo-lan-ya, with the assistance of Chow Heun. With diagrams. pp. 170. [1885?] 8°. **15259. e. 11.**

華 得 斯 HWA-TIH-SZE [i.e. H. WATTS]. See 利 稼 孫 LE-KEA-SUN and HWA-TIH-SZE. 製 火 藥 法 *Che ho yaou fa.* "The Manufacture of Gunpowder," etc. 8°. **15259. e. 7.**

畫 圖 HWA T'OO. 畫 圖 緣 *Hwa t'oo yuen.* "The Mystery of a Drawing." Edited by Poo yuĕ choo jin, i.e. The Master of the Travelling Moon. 4 keuen. [1840?] 8°. **15333. b. 11.**

花 影 HWA YING. 花 影 集 *Hwa ying tseih.* "The refections of flowers. A collection" of tales. Compiled by the 'Old Man of the Evening Stream.' A Korean edition. 4 keuen. 1523. Fol. **15334. f. 2.**

慧 照 HWUY-CHAOU, *Priest.* 鎮 州 臨 濟 慧 照 禪 師 語 錄 *Chin-chow Lin tse Hwuy-chaou shen sze yu luh.* "The Discourses of the Priest Hwuy-chaou, of Chin-chow." [1650?] Fol. **15101. d. 13.** Printed in Korea from blocks.

惠 然 HWUY-JEN. See 慧 照 HWUY-CHAOU, *Priest.* 鎮 州 臨 濟 慧 照 禪 師 語 錄 *Chin-chow Lin tse Hwuy-chaou shen sze yu luh.* "The Discourses of . . . Hwuy-chaou." Edited by Hwuy-jen. Fol. **15101. d. 13.**

慧 明 HWUY-MING. 五 燈 會 元 *Woo tăng hwuy yuen.* "A joint compilation of the Five Lamps of Buddhist Biography." Edited by Hwuy-ming. 20 keuen. 1368. Fol. **15103. c. 38.** Printed in Japan from blocks.

惠 頓 HWUY-TUN [i.e. HENRY WHEATON]. 萬 國 公 法 *Wan kwŏ kung fa.* "Wheaton's International Law." Translated into Chinese by Dr. W. A. P. Martin, assisted by a Commission appointed by Prince Kung. 4 keuen. *Peking,* 1864. 8°. **15241. c. 13.**

HYMERS (JOHN). See 海 麻 士 HAI-MA-SZE.

IMBAULT-HUART (CAMILLE). *See* CH'OO YUNG-SHUN. Les Instructions familières du Dr. Tchou Pô-lou. Traité . . . publié . . . par C. I.-H. 1881. 8°. **11099. f. 12.**

INNOCENTIA. Innocentia Victrix, sive sententia Comitiorum Imperii Sinici pro innocentia Christianæ religionis lata juridice per annum 1669, et jussu R. P. Antonij de Gorvea Soc[ia] Jesu ibidem V. Provincialis Sinico-Latine exposita. [The trial and acquittal of certain Jesuit Missionaries.] Chinese and Latin. *In Quăm chĕu metropoliti provinciæ Quăm tŭm in Regno Sinarum.* [Canton], 1671. Fol. **15118. d. 7.** Printed from wooden blocks on forty-five double leaves, on one side only of the paper.

INSLEE (ELIAS B.). 聖 山 諧 歌 *Sing-săn-yiæ-ko.* "Hymns set to music." In this volume the music is printed in the European form, and the words are given both in Chinese characters and in a romanized translation into the Ningpo dialect. pp. x, 80. *Ningpo,* 1858. 8°. **15118. a. 22.**

ITINERARIES. [Itineraries by Land and Water from Peking to the Provinces. 1840?] 8°.
15271. e. 4.

I-TSING. *See* E-TSING.

JAMES (JOHN ANGELL). 救靈先路 *Kew ling seen loo.* "The anxious enquirer after Salvation." Translated into Chinese by W. Muirhead. pp. vi, 47. *Shanghai*, 1882. 8°.
15200. c. 18.

JAMETEL (MAURICE). Inscription gravée sur une stèle élevée dans la salle des exercices militaires de Kiang-tze (Tibet Antérieur). *Ernest Leroux : Paris*, 1889. 8°.
752. f. 27.

饒敦秩 JAOU TUN-CHIH. *See* 楊守敬 YANG SHOW-KING, and JAOU TUN-CHIH. 歷代輿地沿革險要圖 *Leih tai yu te yen kih heen yaou t'oo.* "Important maps to illustrate the chronological geography of the Empire." 1879. Fol.
15276. e. 4.

然藜子 JEN LE-TSZE. *See* 西周生 SE CHOW-SÄNG. 醒世姻緣傳 *Sing she yin yuen chuen.* "A Tale of Fate to arouse the Age." Edited by Jen Le-tsze, etc. 1841. 8°.
15334. e. 7.

JESUS CHRIST. [An illustrated sheet representing the principal events in the life of Christ. With explanatory text.] [1870?]
15118. b. 27.

—— 耶穌降世傳 *Yay-soo keang she chuen.* "A Life of Christ." pp. 120. *Shanghai*, 1870. 8°.
15118. e. 3.

日記 JIH KE. 日記故事 *Jih ke koo sze.* "A collection of ancient records," beginning with the 24 instances of filial piety. 5 keuen. 1688. 8°.
15319. b. 20 (4).

日課 JIH K'O. 日課撮要 *Jih k'o ts'uh yaou.* "A resumé of the Roman Catholic daily prayers." pp. 358, 24. *Hongkong*, 1890. 16°.
15200. aa. 8.

—— [Another edition.] *Hongkong*, 1896. 16°.
15200. aa. 25.

—— [Another edition.] *Hongkong*, 1897. 16°.
15200. d. 24.

日報 JIH PAOU. 日報約選 *Jih paou yoh seuen.* "Extracts from Newspapers." [1889?] 8°.
15298. a. 48.

任昉 JIN FANG. 述異記 *Shuh e ke.* "Notes on curious facts and phenomena." 2 keuen. *See* 程榮 CH'ING YUNG. 漢魏叢書 *Han Wei ts'ung shoo.* "A collection of works by authors of the Han and Wei Dynasties," etc. 1791. 8°.
15318. a. 1.

仁如堂 JIN JOO-T'ANG. 越絕書 *Yuĕ tseuĕ shoo.* "Incidents in the History of the Secession of Yuĕ." Edited by Jin Joo-t'ang. 15 keuen. *See* 程榮 CH'ING YUNG. 漢魏叢書 *Han Wei ts'ung shoo.* "A collection of the works of authors of the Han and Wei Dynasties," etc. 1791. 8°.
15318. a. 1.

JOHN (GRIFFITH). *See* 楊格非 YANG KIH-FEI.

—— *See* 頌主 SUNG CHOO. 頌主聖詩 Two hundred "Hymns in Praise of God." [By G. J.?], etc. 1883. 8°.
15117. a. 35.

—— and FABER (E.). A collection of nineteen Protestant tracts in Chinese, eighteen by G. J. and one by E. F. 19 sheets. [1885?]
15200. e. 1 (1).

JOHNSTON (JAMES FINLAY WEIR). *See* 粲司騰 CHIN-SZE-T'ÄNG.

JOLY (H. BENCRAFT). *See* 曹雪芹 TS'AOU SEUĔ-K'IN. Hung lou meng . . . Translated by H. B. J., etc. 1892. 8°.
11099. d. 25.

JONES (A. G.). *See* 仲均安 CHUNG KEUN-NGAN.

如蓮 JOO LEEN. 反唐全傳 *Fan T'ang ts'euen chuen.* "The History of the Rebellious T'ang Dynasty" (684–705 A.D.). With portraits. By Joo Leen. 10 keuen. 1793. 8°. 15333. c. 5.

—— 說唐後傳 *Shwo T'ang how chuen.* "A later History of the T'ang Dynasty." With portraits. By Joo Leen. 9 keuen. 1735. 8°.
15333. c. 6.

—— [Another edition.] 11 keuen. 1735. 8°.
15333. c. 7.

JOSEPH. 約瑟聖蹟圖說 *Yŏsih shing tsih t'oo shwo.* An illustrated life of Joseph. 1882. 4°.
15117. d. 8.

若瑟 JŎ-SIH. 若瑟聖月 *Jŏsih shing yueh.* "The Holy Month of Joseph." pp. 139. *Hongkong*, 1890. 12°.
15200. c. 62.

—— [Another edition.] *Hongkong*, 1894. 12°.
15118. a. 30.

入學 JUH HEŎ. 入學圖說 *Juh heŏ t'oo shico.* "An illustrated introduction to knowledge." A Korean edition. 1545. 4°. 15229. b. 20.

JULIEN (STANISLAS AIGNAN). *See* SCHLEGEL (GUSTAVE). La Loi du parallélisme en style Chinois . . . la traduction de la Préface du *Si-yü-ki* par feu S. J., etc. 1896. 8°. 11098. b. 24.

—— 要輯鸞桑 Résumé des Principaux Traités Chinois sur la Culture des Muriers et l'éducation des vers à soie. Traduit par Stanislas Julien [principally from "K'in ting show she t'ung k'aou"]. *Paris*, 1837. 8°. 11100. e.

開發 K'AI FX. 開發總登 *K'ai fă tsung tăng.* "A cash credit account book." MS. [1844 ?] Obl. 15297. d. 19.

改琦 KAI K'E. 紅樓夢圖詠 *Hung low mung t'oo yung.* "Verses on the Dream of the Red Chamber. With illustrations." Edited by Kai K'e. A Japanese edition. 4 keuen. 1882. 8°. 15327. d. 32.

KAINZ (C.). Die sogenannten chinesischen Tempelmünzen. Ein Beitrag zur chinesischen Medaillenkunde. Von C. K. *Berlin*, 1895. 8°. 11098. b. 25.

甘芳谷 KAN FANG-SUH. 詩韻含英題解 *She yun han ying t'e keae.* A dictionary arranged according to the tones and sounds of the characters. Compiled by Kan Fang-suh. [With manuscript notes.] 10 keuen? 1803. 8°. 15346. b. 8.

Only first 4 keuen.

耕織 KĂNG CHĬH. 耕織圖 *Kăng chĭh t'oo.* "Engravings illustrating the various processes employed in cultivating rice and manufacturing silk." With a preface by the Emperor K'ang-he. 1696. 4°. 15255. e. 3.

康熙 K'ANG-HE, *Emperor.* See 蔣廷錫 TSEANG T'ING-SEĬH. 欽定古今圖書集成 *K'in ting koo kin t'oo shoo tseĭh ch'ing.* "An Encyclopædia . . ." Compiled by an Imperial Commission . . . appointed by the Emperor K'ang-he, etc. 1726. 8°. 15000, etc.

—— Il Santo Editto de K'añ-hi, e l'Amplificazione di Yuñ-ceñ. Tradotti con note filologiche da Lodovico Nocentini. pp. xix, 76. *Firenze*, 1880. 8°. 11098. c. 1.

康熙 K'ANG-HE, *Emperor.* 康熙字典 *K'ang-he tsze teen.* "K'ang-he's Dictionary." A photolithographed copy. *Shanghai*, 1883. 8°. 15342. b. 11.

—— [Another edition.] *Shanghai*, 1892. 8°. 2115. c.

—— 康熙字典撮要 *K'ang-he tsze teen ts'uh yaou.* "A concise edition of K'ang-he's Dictionary." Compiled by Chin Yŏ-han [i.e. John Chalmers]. Edited by Wang Yang-gan. *Canton*, 1878. 8°. 15341. d. 2.

—— 聖諭廣訓 Le Saint Édit. Étude de littérature Chinoise préparée par A. Théophile Piry. *London : Trübner & Co.; Shanghai* [printed], 1879. 4°. 11098. c. 3.

—— [Another copy.] 11098. c. 18.

—— 聖諭 *Shing yu.* "The First of the 16 Maxims" of the Emperor K'ang-he. With the commentary of the Emperor Yung-ching, paraphrased in the colloquial style. [1800?] 8°. 15229. a. 22.

—— 聖諭像解 *Shing yu seang keae.* "Illustrations to the Maxims of K'ang-he, with explanations." *Tien-shih-chai. Shanghai*, 1879. 8°. 15229. a. 34.

This work has also the following English title-page, *Sheng ü siang chai*, or Chinese Historical Illustrations. Republished in reduced form by the Tien-shih-chai Photo-lithographic Works.

—— The Sacred Edict, with a translation of the colloquial rendering, notes, and vocabulary, by F. W. Baller. Chinese and English. 2 vols. *American Presbyterian Mission Press, Shanghai*, 1892. 8°. 11098. b. 15.

—— 御製耕織圖 *Yu che kăng chih t'oo.* "Drawings of the forty-six various processes in tillage and weaving, imperially executed." With a stanza of poetry to each. Compiled by the direction of the Emperor K'ang-he. 2 vols. 1697. Fol. 15257. d.

—— [Another edition.] With the original text translated into French and English. *Shanghai*, 1879. 8°. 15255. d. 28.

—— 御製避暑山莊詩 *Yu che pe shoo shan chicang she.* "Poems on the beauties of the hills which form the Imperial Summer retreat" at Jehol. By the Emperor K'ang-he. 2 keuen. 1712. 8°. 15321. e. 7.

With a Manchoo version in a separate volume.

庚 肩 吾 KĂNG KEEN-WOO. 書品 *Shoo p'in.*
"On Caligraphers." pp. 18. See 程 榮 CH'ING
YUNG. 漢 魏 叢 書 *Han Wei ts'ung shoo.*
"A collection of works by authors of the Han
and Wei Dynasties," etc. 1791. 8°. 15318. a. 1.

康 僧 鎧 K'ANGTSĂNGK'AI [i.e. SANGHAVĀRMAN].
無 量 壽 經 *Woo leang show king* (Aparimitāyus Sūtra). 2 keuen. See 劉 翰 清 LEW
HAN-TS'ING. 大 乘 法 寶 十 種 *Ta shing fǎ
paou shih chung.* "Ten precious works on the
Law of the Mahayana." 1881. 8°. 15103. b. 13.

—— 佛 説 無 量 壽 經 *Fuh shwo woo leang show
king.* "The Aparimitāyus Sūtra delivered by
Buddha." Translated into China by K'ang
Tsăng - K'ai. 2 keuen. With Japanese
punctuation. [1390?] 8°. 15103. b. 11.
Printed in Japan from blocks.

康 有 爲 K'ANG YEW-WEI. See 胡 禮 垣 HOO LE-
YUEN. 康 説 書 後 *K'ang shwo shoo how.*
"The Views of K'ang" Yew-wei, the reformer,
etc. 1898. 8°. 15314. d. 6.

K'AN-HI. *See* K'ANG-HE.

干 寶 KAN PAOU. 搜 神 記 *Sow shin ke.*
"Marvellous Tales." 8 keuen. 程 榮 CH'ING
YUNG. 漢 魏 叢 書 *Han Wei ts'ung shoo.*
"A collection of works by authors of the Han
and Wei Dynasties," etc. 1791. 8°. 15318. a. 1.

考 K'AOU. 考 搭 逢 年 *K'aou tah fung nëen.*
Select examination essays. Compiled by the
'Master of the Suy garden.' 30 keuen. 1863.
16°. 15315. a. 5.

高 兆 麟 KAOU CHAOU-LIN. See 張 居 正 CHANG
KEU-CHING. 通 鑑 直 解 *T'ung keen chih keae.*
"An explanatory commentary on the Mirror of
History." Edited by Kaou Chaou-lin, etc.
1631. 8°. 15288. e. 1.

高 朝 瓔 KAOU CH'AOU-YING. 漁 古 山 房 詩
經 體 註 *Yu koo shan fang she king t'e choo.*
"The Books of Odes, with a body of comments
from the Fisherman's old mountain hut."
Compiled by Kaou Ch'aou-ying. 8 keuen.
1711. 8°. 15324. b. 7.

高 琸 KAOU CHŎ. See 甯 雲 鵬 NING YUN-P'ĂNG.
蘇 州 府 志 *Soo-chow Foo che.* "A Topography
of Soo-chow Foo." Compiled by . . . Kaou
Chŏ, etc. 1693. 8°. 15265. c. 1.

高 崗 KAOU KANG. 蓬 萊 縣 志 *P'ăng-lai heen che.*
"A Topography of the P'ăng-lai District." By
Kaou Kang. A new and revised edition, by
Wang Wăn-taou and others. 14 keuen. 1839.
8°. 15269. d. 18.

高 錦 庭 KAOU KIN-T'ING. 瘍 科 臨 證 心 得 集
Yang ko lin ching sin tih tseih. "A collection
of Treatises on Sores." By Kaou Kin-t'ing.
Edited by Woo Hŏ-shan. 3 keuen. With
appendix. 1806. 8°. 15253. b. 4.

高 亮 懷 KAOU LEANG-HWAI. 于 公 太 保 演
義 傳 *Yu kung t'ai paou yen e chuen.* "A
popular biography of Yu K'een, Senior Guardian
of the Heir Apparent," born A.D. 1398. By
Kaou Leang-hwai. 10 keuen. 1822. 8°.
15305. b. 12.

告 示 KAOU SHE. 曉 諭 告 示 賞 格 則 列
Heaou yu kaou she shang kih tsih le. "Proclamations, etc." (in some of which rewards are
offered for the capture of English ships). MS.
1842. 8°. 15297. d. 8.

—— 騰 黃 勅 命 告 示 賞 格 *T'ăng hwang kin
ming kaou she shang kih.* "Proclamations issued
by Imperial Order." 1842. 8°. 15297. d. 10.

高 第 丕 KAOU TE P'EI [i.e. TARLETON P. CRAW-
FORD] and 張 儒 珍 CHANG JOO-CHIN. 文 學
書 官 話 *Wăn heŏ shoo kwan hwa.* "A
Mandarin Grammar." pp. vi, 106. 1869. 8°.
15344. a. 9.

高 則 誠 KAOU TSIH-CH'ING. 燈 草 和 尚 傳
Tăng ts'aou Hoshang chuen. "The story of the
Lampwick Priest." An erotic tale. By Kaou
Tsih-ch'ing, a native of Lingnan in Yunnan,
during the Yuen dynasty. Edited by Ts'eu
Chowk'ew, of the Ming Dynasty. MS. 12
chapters. [*Peking*, 1850?] 8°. Or. 4476. 39. B. f.

高 靜 亭 KAOU TSING-T'ING. 正 音 撮 要 *Ching
yin ts'uh yaou.* "The correct pronunciation of
a selected number of characters." 4 keuen?
[1800?] 12°. 15344. a. 8.
Imperfect, containing only Keuen 4.

哈 邦 KA-PANG [i.e. MRS. CAPP]. 心 算 初 學
Sin swan ch'oo heŏ. "An introduction to mental
arithmetic." 7 keuen. 1881. 8°. 15259. h. 8.

家 KEA. 家 畜 玩 物 *Kea ch'uh wan wuh.*
"Domestic Pets." With coloured illustrations.
By, as is stated in a manuscript note on the
cover, Mrs. Williamson. pp. 8. 1883. 4°.
15331. e. 11.

KEA

假 KEA. 樂假歸真論 *K'e kea kwei chin lun.* "A Tract on rejecting Falsehood and returning to the Truth." [By Rev. W. Lobscheid ?] [*Hongkong*, 1870 ?] 12°. 15118. a. 15.

賈誼 KEA E. 新書 *Sin shoo.* "The New Book." A series of essays on the Confucian doctrine. 10 keuen. See 程榮 CH'ING YUNG. 漢魏叢書 *Han Wei ts'ung shoo.* "A collection of works by authors of the Han and Wei Dynasties," etc. 1791. 8°. 15318. a. 1.

家學 KEA HEŎ. 家學淺論 *Kea heŏ ts'een lun.* "A short treatise on domestic instruction." 2 keuen. *Hongkong*, 1889. 8°. 15229. a. 36.

—— [Another edition.] *Hongkong*, 1899. 8°. 15229. a. 37.

嘉興 KEAHING. Eleven letters written by the officers T'ang Yingke, Chang Chaoyung, and Yeh Kwang, of the Left Camp at Keahing in Chĕkeang, with regard to the transport of treasure, during the year 1842. MS. ff. 15. 1842. 8°. 16308. 39. B. e.

家鶴 KEA-HO. 綠野仙踪全傳 *Luh yay seen tsung ts'euen chuen.* "The Footprints of the Genius of the 'Green Wilderness.'" A novel. With portraits. 80 chapters. 1830. 8°. 15331. f. 4.

賈公彥 KEA KUNG-YEN. See 儀禮 E LE. 欽定儀禮義疏 *K'in ting E le e soo.* "The Meaning of the Decorum Ritual. With explanations" by Kea Kung-yen, etc. 8°. 15219. B. 3. & C. 1.

賈密倫 KEA-MEÏH-LUN [i.e. CAMERON ?]. 輪船布陣 *Lun ch'uen poo chin.* "Steamship Manœuvres." Translated into Chinese by Foolanya, i.e. J. Fryer. 12 keuen. With a volume of diagrams. [*Shanghai*, 1880 ?] 8°. 15259. i. 1.

江 KEANG. 渡江書剛部 *Too keang shoo kang poo.* "A Travelling Dictionary." MS. [1840 ?] 8°. 15346. a. 14.

江潮遠 KEANG CH'AOU-YUEN. 玉歷鈔傳警世 *Yuh leih ch'aou chuen king she.* "A valuable succession of reprints to arouse the world." A collection of Buddhist and Taouist pamphlets. With illustrations. 1854. 8°. 15113. b. 10.

江衡 KEANG HĂNG. See 哈司韋 HO-SZE-WEI. 算式集要 *Swan shih tseih yaou.* "A Collection of Mathematical Problems . . ." transcribed by Keang Hăng, etc. 8°. 15259. d. 18.

姜渾 KEANG HWĂN. 五倫行實圖 *Woo lun hing shih t'oo.* "Instances of virtuous conduct in the five human relationships. With illustrations." Compiled by Keang Hwăn. A Korean edition, with a Korean version of the text added. 5 keuen. [1750 ?] 8°. 15113. c. 5.

江瓘 KEANG KWAN. 名醫類案 *Ming e luy gan.* "The Medical Practice of celebrated Physicians." By Keang Kwan. Edited by Wei Yuh-hung, Ch'in Heaou-tsăng, and others. 12 keuen. 1871. 8°. 15252. b. 30.

畺瓦耶舍 KEANGLEANGYAYSHAY [i. e. KĀLAYAÇAS]. 觀無量壽佛經 *Kwan woo leang show Fuh king (Amitāyur-buddha dhyana Sūtra).* See 劉翰清 LEW HAN-TS'ING. 大乘法寶十種 *Ta shing fă paou shih chung.* "Ten precious works on the Law of the Mahayana . . ." 1881. 8°. 15103. b. 13.

—— 佛說觀無量壽經 *Fuh shwo kwan woo leang show king.* "The Buddhabhāsitāmitāyur-buddha-dhyana sūtra." Translated into Chinese by Kālayaças. 1390. 8°. 15103. b. 10.
Printed in Japan from blocks.

江臨泰 KEANG LIN-T'AI. See 張作楠 CHANG TSO-NAN. 揣篇小錄 *Ch'uy yŏ seaou luh.* "Tables of Terrestrial Longitude and Latitude." Edited by Keang Lin-t'ai, etc. 8°. 15255. c. 9.

—— See 張作楠 CHANG TSO-NAN. 弧角設如 *Hoo keŏ she joo.* "Problems on Spherical Trigonometry." Edited by Keang Lin-t'ai, etc. 1832. 8°. 15255. c. 5.

—— 弧三角舉隅 *Hoo san keŏ keu yu.* "The Chief Points in Spherical Trigonometry." 1822. 8°. 15255. c. 6.

江孟亭 KEANG MĂNG-T'ING. See 杜甫 TOO FOO. 杜少陵全集詳註 *Too Shaou ling ts'euen tseih tseang choo.* "A Complete Collection of the Poems of Too Foo . . ." Edited by Keang Măng-t'ing, etc. 1790. 8°. 15324. b. 1.

KEANG-NAN. A map of that portion of Keang-nan which lies between the Yellow River and the Yangtsze keang. [1890 ?] 15276. b. 5.

江 南 KEANG-NAN. 江 南 鄉 試 題 名 錄 *Keang-nan heang she t'e ming luh*. "A List of the successful Candidates at the Keang-nan Examinations" for the year 1844. 1844. 8°.
15320. e. 29.

江 南 海 關 KEANG-NAN HAI KWAN. 江 南 海 關 則 例 *Keang-nan Hai kwan tsih le*. "Keang-nan Customs Regulations" as established in the year 1785. MS. 1785. 8°. 15239. a. 40.

江 西 KEANGSE. 江 西 省 全 圖 *Keangse shing ts'euen t'oo*. "A complete series of maps of the Province of Keangse." The volume begins with a map of the whole Province, which is followed by maps of the thirteen Prefectures. The maps are coloured. MS. [1800?] Fol.
Add. 16356. 28. c.

江 少 虞 KEANG SHAOU-YU. 皇 宋 事 實 類 苑 *Hwang Sung sze paou luy yuen*. "Elegant extracts from the works of authors of the Sung Dynasty." Compiled by Keang Shaou-yu. 78 keuen. *Kiōto*, 1621. 4°. 15288. e. 3.
Printed in metal type at the cost of the Mikado.

江 戴 德 KEANG TAI-TIH [i.e. LYMAN DWIGHT CHAPIN]. 地 理 志 畧 *Te le che leŏ*. "A short work on Geography." With maps and illustrations. By Keang Tai-tih. Edited by Chaou Joo-kwang. pp. iv, 132. *Peking*, 1882. 4°.
15261. e. 9.

江 東 旭 KEANG TUNG-HEU. 臺 灣 外 記 *T'aiwan wai ke*. "An extra History of Formosa," being a biography of the pirate Ching Ch'ing-kung (Coxinga). 10 keuen. 1704. 8°. 15291. a. 12.

—— [Another copy.] 15275. a. 19.

江 耀 亭 KEANG YAOU-T'ING. 新 增 尺 牘 稱 呼 合 解 *Sin tsăng ch'ih tuh ch'ing hoo ho keae*. "A new and enlarged letter-writer. With an explanation of customary epithets." pp. 334. *Hongkong*, 1886. 8°. 15348. a. 21.

江 永 KEANG YUNG. 河 洛 精 蘊 *Ho lŏ tsing yun*. "The Essence of the Diagrams of Fuh-he and Yu." By Keang Yung. 9 keuen. 1774. 8°.
15225. b. 2.

—— 四 書 典 林 *Sze shoo teen lin*. "A Dictionary of Expressions from the Four Books." 30 keuen. With a supplement entitled 四 書 古 人 典 林 *Sze shoo koo jin teen lin*, in 12 keuen. 1735. 1749. 8°. 15348. b. 4.

教 會 KEAOU HWUY. 教 會 政 治 *Keaou hwuy ching che*. "Rules for the Government of the Presbyterian Church." pp. 88. *Shanghai*, 1881. 8°.
15117. d. 31.

—— 教 會 問 答 *Keaou hwuy wăn tă*. "The Assembly's Catechism." [Translated into Chinese by W. Muirhead?] pp. 33. [*Shanghai?*], 1855. 8°. 15200. b. 10.

覺 羅 舒 英 KEAOU LO SHOO YING. See 穆 克 登 頓 MUH-KIH-TĂNG-GIH. 大 清 通 禮 *Ta Ts'ing t'ung le*. "The Rites and Ceremonies of the Ts'ing Dynasty," etc. 1824. 8°.
15239. c. 9.

教 乘 法 KEAOU SHING FĂ. 教 乘 法 數 摘 要 *Keaou shing fă soo chai yaou*. "An epitome of the *Keaou shing fă soo*," or numerical categories found in Buddhist phraseology. 12 keuen. [1860?] 8°. 15103. b. 14.

買 步 緯 KEA POO-WEI. See 穆 尼 閣 MUH-NE-KIH. 對 數 表 *Tuy shoo peaou*. "Logarithm Tables . . ." Revised and edited by Kea Poo-wei, etc. 8°. 15259. h. 4.

—— 恒 星 表 *Hăng sing peaou*. "A Catalogue of the Fixed Stars" for 1864. With maps of the heavens. 1872. 8°. 15259. g. 6.

—— 弦 切 對 數 表 *Heen ts'ĕĕ tuy shoo peaou*. "Logarithm Tables." pp. 6, 270. [1880?] 8°.
15259. g. 7.

—— 量 法 代 算 *Leang fă tai swan*. "On the European System of Calculating Measurements." 1872. 8°. 15255. c. 17.

嘉 祥 KEASEANG. See 武 梁 WOO LEANG. A collection of rubbings from stone sculptures at Keaseang in Shantung, etc. 15300. b. 10.

買 聲 槐 KEA SHING-HWAI. 樂 清 縣 志 *Lŏ-ts'ing heen che*. "A Topography of Lŏ-ts'ing heen," a district in the Province of Chĕ-keang. By Kea Shing-hwai and others. A new edition. 16 keuen. 1826. 8°. 15267. d. 6.

諫 KEEN. 五 諫 夫 *Woo keen foo*. "Five Reproofs to a Husband." [1800?] 8°. 15327. d. 27.

謙 齋 K'EEN CHAI. 謙 齋 畫 帖 *K'een chai hwa t'ĕĕ*. "Sketches from the Humble Study." MS. [1800?] 4°. 15257. e. 21.

KEE—KEN

乾隆 K'EEN-LUNG, *Emperor*. See 朱彝尊 CHOO E-TSUN. 經義考 *King e k'aou.* "An examination into the meaning of the Classics . . ." With a preface by the Emperor K'een-lung, etc. 1777. 8°.　　15225. b. 1.

—— See 方觀承 FANG KWAN-CH'ING. 御題 棉華圖 *Yu t'e kin hwa t'oo.* "Engravings . . . illustrating the various processes employed in the manufacture of cotton. With notes by the Emperor K'een-lung," etc. 1765. 4°.　　15255. e. 2.

—— See 詩 SHE. 御製詩 *Yu che she.* "Poetry." [By the Emperor K'een-lung], etc. Obl.　　15321. a. 17.

—— See 岳飛 YŎ FEI. 岳忠武王文集 *Yŏ Chung woo Wang wăn tseih.* "A Collection of the Writings of Yŏ Fei . . ." With a preface by the Emperor K'een-lung, etc. 1770. 8°.　　15317. d. 9.

—— See 玉斧珮詩 YUH FOO PEI SHE. 御製玉 斧珮詩 *Yu che yuh foo pei she.* "Imperial 'Jade-axe-ornament' Poetry." [By the Emperor K'een-lung], etc. Small 4°.　　15321. a. 18.

—— 欽定清漢對音字式 *K'in ting Ts'ing Han tuy yin tsze shih.* "An Imperially compiled Manchu Syllabary, with the sounds expressed in Chinese." 1772. 8°.　　15354. a. 7.

—— 御製滿漢蒙古西番合璧大藏全咒 *Yu che Man Han Mung-koo Se-fan hŏ peih ta ts'ang ts'euen chow.* "The Prayers of the Maya-pitaka in Manchu, Chinese, Mongolian, and Tibetan." Edited by the Emperor K'een-lung. 1759. Obl.　　15103. a.–c. 1.
Imperfect.

—— 御製西域同文志 *Yu che se yih t'ung wăn che.* A polyglot vocabulary of the languages of the Western territories, viz.: Mongolian, Tibetan, Tohtih, and Ouigour. Compiled by the Emperor K'een-lung. Edited by Foo Hăng. 24 keuen. 1750. 8°.　　15344. b. 11.

—— 御製盛京賦 *Yu che Shing-king foo.* "A Poetical Eulogium on the City of Moukden." By the Emperor K'een-lung. Edited by Gŏ Urh-tai, Chang Ting yuh, and others. [1748?] 8°.　　15321. e. 3.

乾隆 K'EEN-LUNG, *Emperor*. 御製增訂清 文鑑 *Yu che tsăng ting Ts'ing wăn keen.* "An enlarged edition of the Mirror of the Manchu Language." An Imperial Manchu dictionary. 47 keuen. Supplement, 4 keuen. 1771. 8°.　　15354. a. 6.

黔省 K'EEN SHING. 黔省各種苗圖 *K'een shing kih chung Meaou t'oo.* "Coloured drawings of the Meaou Tribes in the Province of K'een, or Kweichow." Opposite each drawing is a fuller description than is usual of the tribes in question. The appearance, manners, customs, and dress of the people are described. MS. 2 vols. [1850?] Fol.　　Or. 2232. 36. a.

簡牘 KEEN TUH. 簡牘精要 *Keen tuh tsing yaou.* "Epitomised Memoranda" on Korean history and customs. Printed in Korea. [1600?] 8°.　　15292. c. 7.

稽含 KE HAN. 南方草木狀 *Nan fang ts'aou muh chwang.* "The Botany of the South." 3 keuen. See 程榮 CH'ING YUNG. 漢魏 叢書 *Han Wei ts'ung shoo.* "A collection of works by authors of the Han and Wei Dynasties," etc. 1791. 8°.　　15318. a. 1.

紀好弼 KE HAOUPIEH [i.e. REV. ROSEWELL HOBART GRAVES]. 猶太地理誌 *Yew-t'ai te le che.* "A Geography of Judæa." With a map and illustrations. pp. 274. 1882. 8°.　　15271. c. 18.

—— 猶太地理擇耍 *Yew-t'ai te le tsih yaou.* "Noteworthy points in the Geography of Judæa." With three maps. 16 chapters. [*Shanghai?*], 1882. 8°.　　15264. a. 2.

稽璜 KE HWANG. See 阿桂 AH-KWEI. 八旬 萬壽盛典 *Pă seun wan show shing teen.* "A Memorial of the 80th Birthday of the Emperor Keen-lung." Compiled by . . . Ke Hwang, etc. 1792. 8°.　　15296. e. 4.

KEMPIS (THOMAS À). *See* HAMMERLEIN (THOMAS) À KEMPIS.

KENMURE (ALEXANDER). A catalogue of the Chinese publications of the Religious Tract Society of London. (With descriptive notes.) Compiled by A. K. pp. 36. *Shanghai*, 1892. 8°.　　11098. a. 38.

覺恒 KEŎHĂNG. 重刊改併五音類聚四聲篇 *Chung k'an kai ping woo yin luy tseu sze shing p'ien.* "A Chinese Dictionary in which the characters are arranged according to the four tones under the five sounds," viz., the Guttural, the Palatal, the Cerebral, the Dental, and the Labial. The present work is based upon the *Yuh p'een* by Koo Yewang (A.D. 535), and is a revised edition of the edition published in 1520 by the Priest Keŏhăng under the above title, and is re-edited by Keŏhăng's great nephew. 15 keuen. 1559. Fol. 15348. d. 2.

KERL (SIMON). See 喀爾氏 KIH-URH-SHE.

KERR (JOHN GLASGOW). *See* FABER (E.). 大德國學校論畧 *Ta Tih kwŏ heŏ keaou lun leŏ.* "A short account of the educational system of the German Empire." Edited by J. G. Kerr. 1873. 8°. 15320. c. 13.

—— 西藥畧釋 *Se yŏ leŏ shih.* "A Manual of Materia Medica." *Canton,* 1871. 8°. 15252. b. 24.

琦善 K'E SHEN. 陶澍 T'AOU CHOO. 江蘇海運全案 *Keang soo hai yun ts'euen gan.* "A discussion on the subject of transporting the Imperial Impost Grain from the Province of Keang-soo to the Metropolis." Compiled by ... K'e Shen, etc. 1826. 8°. 15239. c. 3.

己巳 KESZE. 己巳進表裏進饌儀軌 *Kesze tsin peaou le tsin chuen e kwei.* "The Rites and Regulations to be observed at the presentation of gifts and congratulations to the Queen of Corea on the occasion of her being 'capped' in the year 1869, and the feast given at the same time." With coloured illustrations. 1868. Fol. 15287. b. 1.

紀大山 KE TA SHAN. 紀大山銘 *Ke ta shan ming.* The rubbing of an inscription on Ke ta shan [in Shantung?]. 15204. a. 2.

勸誡社 K'EUEN KEAE SHAY. 勸誡社彙選 *K'euen keae shay wei seuen.* "Papers in support of the formation of Anti-Opium Associations." Compiled by the Old Man of the Southern Sea. *Canton,* 1876. 8°. 15239. b. 20.

菊 KEŬH. 節義奇綠金葉菊 *Tsëĕ e k'e luh kin yĕ keŭh.* The chaste, pure, and rare green and golden leaved chrysanthemum. [A collection of short popular poems.] 4 keuen. 1855. 8°. 15327. d. 12 (13).

櫉中逸叟 KEŬH CHUNG YIH SOW, *pseud.* 來生福 *Lai săng fuh.* "Happiness in a future life." An allegorical work inculcating virtue. The greater portion is in irregular verse. 36 chapters. [1840?] 8°. 15113. a. 18.

菊部 KEŬH POO. 菊部羣英 *Keuh poo k'eun ying.* "A list of notable actors." 1873. 8°. 15305. a. 15.

屈大均 K'EŬH TA-KEUN. 道援堂詩集 *Taou yuen T'ang she tseĭh.* "A Collection of Poetry from the Taou-yuen Hall." By K'eŭh Ta-keun. 13 keuen. [1713?] 8°. 15324. b. 3.

屈翁山 K'EŬH UNG-SHAN. 廣東新語 *Kwang tung sin yü.* "New Records of Kwang tung." 28 keuen. 1700. 8°. 15263. d. 3.

屈原 K'EŬH YUEN. 楚辭 *Ts'oo ts'ze.* "Elegies of Ts'oo." By K'eŭh Yuen. Edited by Lew Yun-yih. 7 keuen. 1789. 8°. 15323. d. 23.

畿湖 KEUI HO. 畿湖圖 *Keui ho to.* "Coloured Maps of the Provinces of Kyeng-keui-to and Chyoung-chyeng-to." [*Seoul,* 1840?] Fol. Or. 5715. 15276. e. 5.

君臣 KEUN CH'IN. 圖像合璧君臣故事句解 *T'oo seang ho pih keun ch'in ku sze keu keae.* "Historical notices of Princes and Ministers," with illustrations and notes. 2 keuen. [1610?] 8°. 15297. b. 15.
Printed in Korea from blocks.

瞿申之 K'EU SHIN-CHE. See 吳樓圖 WOO P'Ŏ-YUEN. 勝朝遺事 *Shing ch'aou e sze.* "Supplementary Records of the Conquering Dynasty ..." Edited by K'eu Shin-che, etc. 1842. 8°. 15297. b. 11.

瞿祐宗 K'EU YEW-TSUNG. 三燈叢話合刻 *San tăng ts'ung hwa hŏ kih.* "The Three-lamp Collection of Tales," viz.: "The New Tales of the Snuffed Lamp," by the Editor; "The Additional Tales of the Snuffed Lamp," by Le Ching; and "Consequential Tales of the Seeking Lamp," by Shaou she. Edited by K'eu Yew-tsung. 1847. 8°. 15331. d. 14.

述 K'EW. 好逑傳 *Hao-khieou-tchouan.* Ou, La Femme Accomplie. Roman Chinois, traduit sur le texte original par M. Guillaud D'Arcy. *Paris,* 1842. 8°. 11100. e.

KEW

述 K‘EW. 好逑傳 *Haou k‘ew chuan.* "The Fortunate Union." Chapter i. Translated by Robert K. Douglas. pp. 59. *Kegan Paul, Trench, Trübner, & Co.: London,* 1900. 4°.
11095. c. 1.

邱長春 K‘EW CH‘ANG-CH‘UN. 西遊記 *Se yew ke.* "An Account of the Adventures of Heuen Tsang in the West." [1750 ?] 8°. **15271. c. 13.**
Imperfect, containing only Keuen 3, 5, 8, 13.

—— 西遊原旨 *Se yew yuen che.* "The Object of Western Travel." The travels of Heuen Tsang in India, embellished with many fabulous details. With illustrations. 100 chapters. *Ch‘angtih Foo,* 1819. 8°. **15331. f. 1.**

仇兆鰲 K‘EW CHAOU-GAOU. See 杜甫 Too Foo. 杜少陵全集詳註 *Too Shaou-ling ts‘euen tseih tseang choo.* "A Complete Collection of the Poems of Too Foo. With explanatory Notes" by K‘ew Chaou-gaou, etc. 1790. 8°.
15324. b. 1.

求放心齋 K‘EW FANG SIN CHAE, *pseud.* 天下路程 *T‘een hea loo ch‘ing.* "The Roads of the Empire." 6 keuen. 1738. 8°. **15271. a. 15.**

九皇 KEW HWANG. 九皇延生錫禰寶懺 *Kew Hwang yen săng tsze fuh paou ts‘an.* "The Life-long Happiness-giving Tantra of the Nine Emperors." 9 keuen. 1823. 8°. **15101. a. 12.**

鳩摩羅什 KEWMOLOSHIH [i.e. KUMĀRAJĪVA]. (1) 佛說阿彌陀經 *Fuh shwo Omet‘o king* (*Amitābha Vyūha*). Translated by Kewmoloshih. (2) 金剛般若波羅密經 *Kinkang panjŏ polomieh king* (*Diamond pragnāpāramitā Sūtra*). Translated by Kewmoloshih. (3) 維摩詰所說經 *Weimok‘eih so shwo king* (*Vimalakīrtti-nirdesa Sūtra*). Translated by Kewmoloshih. 3 keuen. (4) 妙法蓮華經 *Meaou fă leen hwa king* (*Saddharmapundarīka Sūtra*). Translated by Kewmoloshih. 7 keuen. See 劉翰清 LEW Han-ts‘ing. 大乘法寶十種 *Ta shing fă paou shih chung.* "Ten precious works on the Law of Mahayana," etc. 1881. 8°.
15103. b. 13.

—— 佛說阿彌陀經 *Fuh shwo O-me-t‘o king.* "The Amitābha Vyūha delivered by Buddha." Translated into Chinese by Kumārajīva. [1390 ?] 8°. **15103. e. 12.**
Printed in Japan from blocks.

鳩摩羅什 KEWMOLOSHIH [i.e. KUMĀRAJĪVA]. 妙法蓮華經 *Meaou fă leen hwa king.* The Saddharmapundarīka Sūtra. Translated into Chinese by Kumārajīva. 3 rolls. 1643.
15103. a. 1.
Printed in Japan with movable type. The last line partly cut away.

—— 妙法蓮華經觀世音菩薩普門品 *Meaou fă leen hwa king kwan she yin P‘oosa p‘oo mun p‘in.* The Sūtra of the (25th) chapter on the Samantamukha of the Bodhisattva Avalokiteshvara in the Saddharmapundarīka Sūtra. Translated into Chinese by Kumārajīva. With illustrations. A folded volume. 1331. 8°.
15103. b. 19.
This volume contains the earliest specimens known of wood engravings.

—— [Another edition.] 1504. A roll. **15103. a. 3.**
Printed in Japan from blocks.

—— [Another edition. 1700 ?] 8°. **15103. b. 20.**
A facsimile of the Chinese edition of 1433. Printed in Japan from blocks.

—— [Another edition.] 1792. Obl. **15103. d. 18.**

—— 妙法蓮經 *Meaou fă leen king.* "The Saddharmapundarīka Sūtra." Translated into Chinese by Kumārajīva. 8 rolls. [1650 ?]
15103. a. 2.
Printed in Japan from blocks.

求那跋陀羅 K‘EWNAPŎTOLO [i.e. GUṆABHADRA]. 楞伽阿跋多羅寶經 *Langkea apotolo paou king* (*Lankāvatāra Sūtra*). Translated by K‘ewnapŏtolo. 4 keuen. See 劉翰清 LEW HANTS‘ING. 大乘法寶十種 *Ta shing fă paou shih chung.* "Ten precious works on the Law of the Mahayana . . ." 1881. 8°.
15103. b. 13.

丘濬 K‘EW SEUN. See 真德秀 CHIN TIH-SEW. 大學衍義補 *Ta heŏ yen e poo.* "The Doctrines of the *Ta heŏ* . . ." Enlarged by K‘ew Seun, etc. 1837. 8°. **15223. d. 1.**

—— 成語考 *Ch‘ing yu k‘aou.* "Correct Phraseology." A work of general instruction for the young. 2 keuen. [1700 ?] 8°.
15022. e. 8.

—— A Manual of Chinese Quotations, being a translation of the *Ch‘êng yü k‘ao* (成語考). [By K‘ew Seun.] With the Chinese text, notes, explanations, and an index for easy reference. By J. H. Stewart Lockhart. pp. iv, 425, 83. *Kelly & Walsh: Hongkong,* 1893. 8°.
11098. a. 2.

邱 菽 園 K'ew Shuh-yuen. 菽園著書三種 *Shuh-yuen choo shoo san chung.* "Three Works," viz.: *Shuh-yuen chuy t'an,* "Shuh-yuen Conversations," 14 keuen; *Kăng yin gow ts'un,* "Chance Literary Relics of the year Kăng yin"; and *Jin ch'in tung hing,* "Winter Pleasures of the year Jin ch'in." 8 vols. 1897. 8°.
15313. a. 3.

九 雲 Kew yun. 九雲夢 *Kew yun mung.* "The Dream of the Nine Clouds." A Buddhist story. A Korean edition. 6 keuen. [1600?] 8°.
15201. c. 15.

紀 昀 Ke Yun. See 蘇軾 Soo Shih. 蘇文忠 公詩集 *Soo Wăn chung kung she tseih.* "The Collected Poems of Soo Shih . . ." Annotated and punctuated by Ke Yun, etc. 1834. 8°.
15324. d. 4.

—— 國朝重訂庚辰集 *Kwo ch'aou chung ting kăng shin tseih.* "A Collection of Examination Poetry, with Notes." Compiled by Ke Yun. 5 keuen. 1822. 8°. 15323. d. 15.

—— 二程全書 *Urh Ch'ing ts'euen shoo.* "The Writings of Ch'ing Haou and Ch'ing E." Compiled by Ke Yun and others. 25 keuen. 1787. 8°.
15318. c. 1.

祁 韻 士 K'e Yun-sze. 皇朝藩部要略 *Hwang ch'aou fan poo yaou leŏ.* "Epitomized Histories of the Frontier Dependent Tribes." Edited by Maou Yŏ-săng. 22 keuen. 1846. 8°.
15271. b. 10.

—— 西陲要略 *Se ch'uy yaou leŏ.* "A Brief Account of the Countries on the Western Frontier." 4 keuen. 1837. 8°. 15271. b. 4.

KHÁNH, Cô. *See* Ravier ( ).

格 致 Kih che. 格致釋器 *Kih che shih k'e.* "An Explanation of Utensils used in Natural Science." With plates, to which are added in some cases explanations in English. A translation by J. Fryer of J. J. Griffin's "Chemical Handicraft." Sections 2, 8, 9. [*Shanghai?* 1864?] 8°.
15257. d. 26.

隔 簾 Kih leen. 隔簾花影 *Kih leen hwa ying.* "Flowery Shadows on the Partition Screen." A novel, the scene of which is laid at the end of the Sung Dynasty (A.D. 1126). 48 keuen. [1800?] 8°.
15327. e. 2.

—— [Another copy.] 15333. b. 12.

喀 爾 氏 Kih-urh-she [i.e. Simon Kerl]. 英文 舉隅 *Ying wăn keŭh yu.* "An English Grammar" epitomized from S. Kerl's work. Translated into Chinese by Tsăng Ke-tsih [i.e. the Marquis Tsêng]. pp. vi, 108. *Peking,* 1879. 8°.
15344. b. 13.

金 Kin. 金監督誌畧 *Kin Keentuh che leŏ.* "A Short Biography of (the American) Bishop 'Kin.'" ff. 20. *Foochow,* 1871. 12°.
15118. a. 27.

—— 金瓶梅 *Kin P'ing Mei.* "The Story of Kin, P'ing, and Mei." Translated into Manchu, and entitled in that language Gin Phing Mei bitkhe. 40 keuen. 1707. 8°. 15354. b. 1.

—— 金石緣全傳 *Kin Shih yuen ts'euen chuen.* "The Story of the Relationship between Kin and Shih." By "Tsing-t'een Choo-jin." 8 keuen. 1865. 8°. 15331. d. 12.

金 之 俊 Kin Che-tseun. 息齋集 *Seih chai tseih.* "Literary Collections from the Restful Study." 12 vols. 1666. 8°. 15315. c. 6.

經 King. 寶命真經 *Paou ming chin king.* "The Precious, Ordained, and Veritable Scriptures." Being readings from the Koran in the Arabic character, to which is added a volume of Mahommedan prayers in the same language. Edited by the Che sze kung or Superintendent of the Tsing-ching Mosque at Canton. *Canton,* 1874. 8°. 14507. b. 14.

慶 常 K'ing Ch'ang. See 馬爾頓 Ma-erh-tun. 星軺指掌 *Sing Yaou che chang.* "A Guide for the Chariots of Imperial Envoys . . ." Translated into Chinese by . . . K'ing Ch'ang, etc. 1876. 8°. 15298. a. 44.

—— [Another copy.] 15239. a. 48.

京 房 King Fang. 易傳 *Yih chuen.* "A Commentary on the Book of Changes." 3 keuen. See 程榮 Ch'ing Yung. 漢魏叢書 *Han Wei ts'ung shoo.* "A collection of works by authors of the Han and Wei Dynasties," etc. 1791. 8°.
15318. a. 1.

景 煥 King Hwan. See 穆克登頓 Muh-kih-táng-gih. 大清通禮 *Ta Ts'ing t'ung le.* "The Rites and Ceremonies of the Ts'ing Dynasty," etc. 1824. 8°. 15239. c. 9.

KING (John W.). See 金約朝 Kin Yŏhan.

KIN

慶 吉 祥 K‘ING-KEĬH-TSEANG. 法 寶 勘 同 總 錄 *Fă paou k‘an t‘ung tsung luh.* "A Complete Catalogue of the Treasures of the Law," i.e. Buddhist Literature. Compiled by the Priest K‘ing-keĭh-tseang. 10 keuen. 1360. 8°.
15103. d. 6.

KING (PAUL). See 慶 丕 K‘ING P‘EI.

慶 丕 K‘ING P‘EI [i.e. PAUL KING]. *See* BLAIKIE (WILLIAM). 幼 學 操 身 *Yew heŏ ts‘aou shin.* "Sound Bodies for our Boys and Girls." Translated into Chinese by K‘ing P‘ei, etc. 1890. 8°.
15344. e. 17.

景 淨 KINGTSING. See 大 秦 景 敎 TA TS‘IN KING KEAOU. 大 秦 景 敎 流 行 中 國 碑 *Ta Ts‘in king keaou lew hing Chung kwo pei.* The rubbing of a Tablet set up at Se-ngan Fu . . . Written by the Priest Kingts‘ing, etc.
15300. b. 9.

經 文 KING WĂN. 經 文 求 是 *King wăn k‘ew she.* "Select essays on texts from the Five Classics." 1859. 12°.
15315. a. 4.

經 韻 KING YUN. 經 韻 集 字 析 解 *King yun tseĭh tsze seĭh keae.* "The Characters of the Classics arranged according to their final sounds. With explanations." 1822. 8°.
15225. e. 1.

經 畬 氏 KING YU-SHE. 新 刻 小 試 策 論 格 式 *Sin k‘ih seaou she ts‘ih lun kih shih.* "A new issue of model essays for the preliminary examination for degrees." Compiled by King Yu-she. 2 keuen. *Hongkong,* 1898. 8°.
15320. a. 23.

金 孝 柏 KIN HEAOU-PIH. See 胡 重 HOO CHUNG. 說 文 字 原 韻 表 *Shwo wăn tsze yuen yuen peaou.* "Tables showing the original tones of the characters of the Shwo wăn . . ." Edited by Kin Heaou-pih, etc. 1811. 8°. 15342. b. 5.

金 楷 理 KIN-K‘EAE-LE [i.e. CARL T. KREYER]. *See* HUGHES (WILLIAM). 繪 地 法 原 *Hwuy te fă yuen.* "A treatise on the construction of maps . . ." Translated into Chinese by Kin-k‘eae-le, etc. 8°.
15271. d. 4.

—— *See* PERIODICAL PUBLICATIONS: *Shanghai.* 西 國 近 事 彙 編 *Se kwo kin sze wei peen.* "A quarterly summary of foreign events." Dictated by Kin-k‘eae-le, etc. 1873, etc. 8°.
15298. b. 42.

金 楷 理 KIN-K‘EAE-LE [i.e. CARL T. KREYER]. See 那 麗 NA-LE. 航 海 簡 法 *Hang hai keen fă.* "The Laws of Navigation . . ." Translated into Chinese by Kin-k‘eae-le, etc. 8°.
15259. i. 3.

—— [Another copy.] 15259. c. 19.

—— See 伯 里 牙 芒 PIH-LE-YA-MANG. 營 壘 圖 說 *Ying lui t‘oo shwo.* "La fortification improvisée . . ." Translated into Chinese by Kin-k‘eae-le, etc. 8°.
15259. e. 8.

—— [Another copy.] 15259. d. 7.

—— See 白 爾 特 PIH-URH-TIH. 御 風 要 術 *Yu fung yaou shuh.* "Important Laws for Ruling the Winds . . ." Translated into Chinese by Kin-k‘eae-le, etc. 8°. 15259. d. 24.

—— *See* PRUSSIA, DEPARTMENTS OF STATE, ETC.: *Army.* 克 虜 伯 船 礮 操 法 *Kih-loo-pih ch‘uen p‘aou ts‘aou fă.* "On Krupp-naval-gun Drill . . ." Translated into Chinese by Kin-k‘eae-le, etc. 15259. d. 11 (4).

—— —— 克 虜 伯 礮 準 心 法 *K‘o-loo-pih p‘aou chun sin fă.* "On the trajectory of Krupp's projectiles." Translated by Kin-k‘eae-le, etc. 15259. e. 9.

—— —— [Another edition.] 8°. 15259. d. 14.

—— —— 克 虜 伯 礮 架 說 *Kih-loo-pih p‘aou kea shwo.* "On the Krupp Gun-carriage." Translated into Chinese . . . by Kin-k‘eae-le, etc. 8°. 15259. d. 11 (3).

—— —— 克 虜 伯 礮 說 *Kih-loo-pih p‘aou shwŏ.* "A Description of Krupp Guns . . ." Translated into Chinese by Kin-k‘eae-le, etc. 8°.
15259. h. 6.

—— —— [Another copy.] 15259. d. 15.

—— —— 克 虜 伯 礮 彈 造 法 *Kih-loo-pih p‘aou tan tsaou fă.* "On the Manufacture of Shot and Shell for Krupp Guns." Translated into Chinese by Kin-k‘eae-le, etc. 8°.
15259. g. 1.

—— —— 克 虜 伯 腰 箍 礮 說 *Kih-loo-pih yaou koo p‘aou shwo.* "On Krupp's Rifled Guns." Translated into Chinese . . . by Kin-k‘eae-le, etc. 8°. 15259. d. 11 (2).

—— —— 攻 守 礮 法 *Kung show paou fă.* "On Guns in Battery." Translated into Chinese . . . by Kin-k‘eae-le, etc.
15259. d. 11 (1).

金楷理 Kin-k'eae-le [i.e. Carl T. Kreyer]. See 斯拉弗司 Sze-la-fuh-sze. 臨陣 管見 Lin chin kwan keen. "Tactical Deductions . . ." Translated into Chinese by Kin-k'eae-le, etc. 1873. 8°. **15259. g. 2.**

—— See 田大里 T'een-ta-le. 光學 Kwang heŏ. "Notes on a course of nine Lectures on Light . . ." Translated into Chinese by Kin-k'eae-le, etc. 8°. **15259. h. 2.**

—— *See* United States of America: *Naval Department.* 兵船礮法 Ping ch'uen p'aou fă. "Naval Gunnery." Translated into Chinese by Kin-k'eae-le, etc. 8°. **15259. e. 6.**

—— [Another copy.] **15259. d. 12.**

—— 繪地法原 Hwuy te fă yuen. "On the Elements of Map Drawing." Translated into Chinese by Kin-k'eae-le, and transcribed by Wang Tih-keun. [*Shanghai*, 1874?] 8°. **15259. d. 20.**

—— 測候叢談 Ts'ih how ts'ung t'an. "A Treatise on Meteorology." Being an adapted translation by Kin-k'eae-le, i.e. C. T. Kreyer, of the article on the subject in the Encyclopædia Britannica. With plates. 4 keuen. [*Shanghai*, 1875?] 8°. **15255. f. 2.**

—— [Another copy.] **15259. d. 22.**

金慶門 Kin K'ing-mun. 通文館志 T'ung wăn kwan che (Korean, Htong moun koan tji). "The History of the Court of Interpreters" in Korea. Compiled under the direction of Kin K'ing-mun (Korean, Kim Kyeng-moun). A new edition. 11 keuen. [*Seoul?*], 1778. Fol. **15287. d. 1.**

Wanting Keuen 7–9.

KIN-KOO-K'E-KWAN. Mai-yu-lang-toú-tchen-hoa-koueï. Le Vendeur-d'huile qui seul possède la Reine-de-beauté, ou, Splendeurs et misères des courtisanes chinoises. Roman chinois [from the collection entitled Kin-koo-k'e-kwan], traduit pour la première fois sur le texte original par G. Schlegel. pp. xvii, 140, 79. Chinese and French. *Leyde, Paris*, 1877. 8°. **11100. b. 6.**

金簡 Kin Leen. See 永瑆 Yung Seuen. 皇清 職貢圖 Hwang Ts'ing chih kung t'oo. "Drawings of the Peoples tributary to China . . ." Edited by . . . Kin Leen, etc. 1751. 8°. **15296. b. 11.**

金三俊 Kin San-tseun. 十七史蒙求 Shih ts'eih she mung k'ew. "An Aid to the Study of the Seventeen Histories." In verse, consisting of two works, one by Le Han and the other by Wang How-chai. Edited with commentaries by Kin San-tseun. Keuen 6 and 16. 1848. 8°. **15291. a. 8.**

錦繡叚 Kin sew Twan. 續錦繡叚 Suh kin sew twan. "A supplementary collection of elegant poetical pieces." Compiled by Hwan yun laou jin, "The old man of the magical cloud." A Japanese edition. 1531. 8°. **15321. d. 20.**

金聖嘆 Kin Shing-t'an. 西廂記 Se seang ke. "The Story of the Western Chamber," or The Book of the Scholar of the Sixth Degree. Edited by Kin Shing-t'an. With illustrations. 8 keuen. 1720. 12°. **15333. d. 2.**

—— 才子古文 Ts'ai tsze koo wăn. "The Ancient Literature of Geniuses," beginning with the *Tso chuen* and ending with the publications of the Sung Dynasty. Compiled by Kin Shing-t'an. 15 keuen, with a supplementary keuen. [1650?] 8°. **15318. c. 7.**

—— 玉嬌梨 Yuh keaou le. The novel known as the "Two Cousins." By "The Dissipated Man of Teïh-gan." Edited by Kin Shing-t'an. 4 keuen. [1800?] 8°. **15333. b. 16.**

靳文襄 Kin Wăn-seang. 治河方略 Che ho fang leŏ. "Plans for Regulating the Rivers (notably the Yellow River and the Grand Canal) of the Empire." Edited by Tsuy Ying-keae. 10 keuen. 1767. 8°. **15275. c. 2.**

金幼孜 Kin Yew-tsze. See 孔丘 K'ung K'ew. 書傳大全 Shoo chuen ta ts'euen. "The Book of Historical Documents . . ." Compiled by . . . Kin Yew-tsze, etc. 8°. **15215. d. 1.**

金約翰 Kin Yŏhan [i.e. John W. King]. 海道 圖說 Hai taou t'oo shwo. "The China Pilot," by Commander J. W. K. Translated into Chinese by J. Fryer. 15 keuen. With an appendix. [1875?] 8°. **15235. b. 2.**

—— [Another copy.] **15259. d. 9.**

KLAPROTH (Heinrich Julius von). Chinesische Grammatic nach Fourmont. Copied in manuscript by H. J. v. K. [1830?] Fol. **Add. 18105.**

KNOWLTON (A. L.), MRS. *Hyüing-mong Sing-kying Kong-k'o.* "A Child's Catechism." With illustrations. In the Romanized Ningpo Dialect. pp. 107, 18. *Ningpo,* 1860. 8° 15200. c. 9.

KNOWLTON (MILES JUSTUS). See 那爾敦 NA-URH-TUN.

課 K'o. 早晚課 *Tsaou wan k'o.* "Roman Catholic Morning and Evening Prayers." pp. 64. *Hongkong,* 1896. 12° 15200. aa. 22.

—— 早晚課 *Tsaou wan k'o.* "Roman Catholic Morning and Evening Prayers." pp. 80. *Hongkong,* 1894. 12° 15200. aa. 23.

—— [Another edition.] *Hongkong,* 1897. 12° 15200. d. 19.

—— [Another edition.] *Hongkong,* 1898. 12° 15200. aa. 26.

—— 早晚課 *Tsaou wan k'o.* "Roman Catholic Morning and Evening Prayers." pp. 60. *Hongkong,* 1896. 12° 15200. d. 20.

KŌ - BAU DAI - SI. 實語敎 *Zitu-go kyau.* L'enseignement des verités. See ROSNY (LÉON DE). 蓮花集 Le Lotus Recueil, etc. 1878, etc. 8° 11100. d. 6.

科塲 K'o CH'ANG. 科塲事疑 *K'o ch'ang sze k'wan.* "Memoranda of the Procedure of the (Canton) Examination Hall." [*Canton,* 1840?] 8° 15320. c. 14.

各府州 Kŏ FOO CHOW. 各府州清冊 *Kŏ Foo Chow ts'ing ts'ih.* "A Register of Office Holders in every Prefecture and Sub-Prefecture." MS. 1840. 8° 15239. d. 11.

Imperfect.

萬福根 Kŏ-FUH-KĂN [i.e.]. See 馬爾頓 MA-ERH-TUN. 星軺指掌 *Sing yaou che chang.* "A Guide for the Chariots of Imperial Envoys . . ." Edited by Kŏ-fuh-kăn, etc. 1876. 8° 15298. a. 44.

各號 Kŏ HAOU. 各號出口查驗各貨 *Kŏ haou ch'uh k'ow cha yen kŏ ho.* "An account of goods exported in each ship." MS. 1844. Obl. 15297. d. 14.

—— 各號驗貨 *Kŏ haou yen ho.* "A Ship Pass Book" [containing entries of goods brought by certain ships]. MS. 1844. Obl. 15297. d. 15.

郭憲 Kŏ HEEN. 洞冥記 *Tung ming ke.* "Mysterious Records." 4 keuen. See 程榮 CH'ING YUNG. 漢魏叢書 *Han Wei ts'ung shoo.* "A collection of works by authors of the Han and Wei Dynasties," etc. 1791. 8° 15318. a. 1.

郭顯德 Kŏ HEEN-TIH [i.e. HUNTER CORBETT]. 孝敬父母 *Heaou king foo moo.* "On Filial Piety." With illustrations. pp. iii, 36. *Shanghai,* 1883. 8° 15229. c. 47.

—— 聖會史記 *Shing hwuy she ke.* "Church History." 2 keuen. *Shanghai,* 1876. 8° 15200. b. 2.

—— [Another edition.] *Shanghai,* 1881. 8° 15118. a. 2.

萬學禮 Kŏ HEŎ-LE. 寄郵居時文初集 *Ke ts'un keu she wăn ch'oo tseih.* "Occasional Essays from a Village Lodging." By Kŏ Heŏ-le. Edited by Koo Leen and others. *Nanking,* 1869. 8° 15319. e. 2.

萬洪 Kŏ HUNG. 枕中書 *Chin chung shoo.* "The inside of a pillow." pp. 20. See 程榮 CH'ING YUNG. 漢魏叢書 *Han Wei ts'ung shoo.* "A collection of works by authors of the Han and Wei Dynasties," etc. 1791. 8° 15318. a. 1.

—— 神仙傳 *Shin seen chuen.* "Biographical Notices of Ninety-two Immortals." 10 keuen. See 程榮 CH'ING YUNG. 漢魏叢書 *Han Wei ts'ung shoo.* "A collection of works by authors of the Han and Wei Dynasties," etc. 1791. 8° 15318. a. 1.

郭居靜 Kŏ KEU-TSING. 袖珍日課 *Sew chin jih k'o.* "Daily Christian Religious Exercises. A Pocket Edition." Compiled by Kŏ Keu-tsing and others. 3 keuen. 1849. 12° 15118. a. 14.

各口章程 Kŏ K'OW CHANG CH'ING. 粗定各口章程 *Tsoo ting kŏ k'ow chang ch'ing.* "Provisional Foreign Trade Regulations." MS. [1840?] 8° 15241. c. 3.

郭禮堂 Kŏ LE-T'ANG. See 秦霞峰 TS'IN HEA-FUNG, and Kŏ LE-T'ANG. 詩料詳註 *She leaou tseang choo.* "Poetical Expressions." Compiled by Ts'in Hea-fung and Kŏ Le-t'ang, etc. 1762. 8° 15346. a. 20.

郭 濯 貴 Kǒ Lo-kwei. See 譚 達 軒 T'an Ta-heen. 華 英 字 典 彙 集 An English and Chinese Dictionary . . . Revised by Kwok Lo Kwai, etc. 1897. 8°. **11098. a. 9.**

—— An interlinear translation of the first book of lessons for the use of schools. Fifth edition. pp. 56. *Hongkong*, 1897. Sm. 4°. **11099. a. 16.**

—— 新 增 華 英 尺 牘 The Chinese and English Letter-writer. Compiled by Kwok Lo Kwai. 3rd edition. pp. 125. *Hongkong*, 1893. 8°. **11099. c. 37.**

—— 通 商 須 知 *T'ung shang seu chih.* Useful Manual for the Use of Traders in China. Compiled by Kwok Lo Kwai. pp. xiv, 442, 814, 125. With map. *Hongkong*, 1895. 8°. **11098. c. 8.**

顧 Koo, and 李 Le. 浙 江 魁 卷 *Chě-keang k'wei keuen.* "A Volume of Select Essays from the Chě-keang Examinations." Edited by the examiners Koo and Le. 1816. 8°. **15320. e. 11.**

顧 赤 方 Koo Ch'ih-fang. See 邵 子 湘 Shaou Tsze-seang. 邵 子 湘 全 集 *Shaou Tsze-seang ts'euen tseth.* "The complete Works of Shaou Tsze-seang . . ." Edited by Koo Ch'ih-fang, etc. 1693. 8°. **15318. b. 3.**

古 正 Koo-ching. See 阿 字 無 A-tsze-woo. 光 宣 臺 集 *Kwang seuen t'ai tseth.* "The Kwang seuen Gallery Collection of Buddhist Writings . . ." Edited by Koo-ching, etc. 8°. **15101. b. 26.**

鼓 吹 Koo ch'uy. 鼓 吹 續 編 *Koo ch'uy suh peen.* "A Concert" of poetry. "Supplementary Series." 3 keuen. [1610?] 8°. **15324. b. 5.** Printed in Korea with movable type.

顧 伊 人 Koo E-jin. See 吳 梅 村 Woo Mei-ts'un. 吳 詩 集 覽 *Woo she tseth lan.* "The Collected Poems of Woo Mei-ts'un . . ." Edited by Koo E-jin, etc. 1781. 8°. **15323. e. 13.**

顧 藹 吉 Koo Gai-keïh. 隸 辨 *Le peen.* "A Dictionary of the 'Official' Character." Arranged according to the Finals. By Koo Gai-keïh. Edited by Hwang Shing. 8 keuen. 1873. 8°. **15344. c. 1.**

顧 俠 君 Koo Heě-keun. See 韓 愈 Han Yu. 韓 詩 增 註 証 訛 *Han she tsǎng choo ching go.* "The Poems of Han Yu . . ." Edited by Koo Heě-keun, etc. 1827. 8°. **15324. e. 2.**

顧 康 禑 Koo K'ang-fuh. See 顧 嵐 Koo Lan. 小 石 山 房 叢 書 *Seaou shih shan fang ts'ung shoo.* "A Collection of Reprints . . ." Edited by Koo K'ang-fuh, etc. 1874. 8°. **15316. e. 16.**

顧 起 元 Koo K'e-yuen. See 楊 慎 Yang Shin. 楊 升 菴 外 集 *Yang Shing-gan wai tseth.* "An Additional Collection of the Writings of Yang Shin . . ." Edited by Koo K'e-yuen, etc. 1844. 8°. **15319. e. 9.**

顧 嵐 Koo Lan. 小 石 山 房 叢 書 *Seaou shih shan fang ts'ung shoo.* "A Collection of Reprints from the House on the Seaou-shih Mountains." Compiled by Koo Lan. Edited by Koo Tsung-fuh and Koo K'ang-fuh. 14 parts. 1874. 8°. **15316. e. 16.**

顧 蓮 Koo Leen. See 葛 學 禮 Kǒ Heǒ-le. 寄 郵 居 時 文 初 集 *Ke ts'un keu she wǎn ch'oo tseth.* "Occasional Essays . . ." Edited by Koo Leen, etc. 1869. 8°. **15319. e. 2.**

顧 尚 之 Koo Shang-che. 九 數 外 錄 *Kew shoo wai luh.* "An extra treatise on Arithmetic." With a biographical notice of the author. pp. ii, 102, 12. [1835?] 8°. **15259. h. 13.**

姑 蘇 癡 情 士 Koosoo ch'i ts'ingsze, *pseud.* 鬧 花 叢 *Nao hwa ts'ung.* "A miscellany of bustling pleasure." By Koosoo ch'i ts'ingsze, or the Lustful Lover of Soochow. MS. 4 keuen. [*Peking*, 1870?] 8°. **Or. 4477. 39. B. f.**

顧 俊 Koo Tseun, and 王 燮 Wang Sěě. 小 題 清 新 集 *Seaou t'e ts'ing sin tseth.* "A New Collection of Classical Essays." Compiled by Koo Tseun and Wang Sěě. 1872. 12°. **15319. a. 12.**

顧 祖 禹 Koo Tsoo-yu. 方 輿 紀 要 簡 覽 *Fang yu ke yaou keen lan.* "A Conspectus of the Historical Geography of the Empire." With maps. Edited by P'wan To. 34 keuen. 1858. 8°. **15275. e. 8.**

KOO—KOS

顧 祖 禹 Koo Tsoo-yu. 讀 史 方 輿 紀 要 *T'uh she fang yu ke yaou.* "A Record of Geographical Changes which have taken place in China from the earliest times down to the seventeenth century, intended as a guide to the perusal of the native histories." By Koo King-fan. Edited by P'ăng Yun-mei. 130 keuen. 1774. 8°. **15275. e. 1.**

—— [Another edition.] 9 keuen. 1805. 8°. **15275. b. 14.**

顧 崇 福 Koo Tsung-fuh. See 顧 嵐 Koo Lan. 小 石 山 房 叢 書 *Seaou shih shan fang ts'ung shoo.* "A Collection of Reprints from the House on the Seaou-shih Mountains . . ." Edited by Koo Tsung-fuh, etc. 1874. 8°. **15316. e. 16.**

古 文 Koo wăn. 詳 說 古 文 真 寶 大 全 *Tseang shwo koo wăn chin paou ta ts'euen.* "Gems from Ancient Literature." With explanatory notes. In two parts. Part i, 12 keuen; Part ii, 10 keuen. [1650?] Fol. **15315. e. 4.**
Printed in Korea from blocks. Wanting Keuen 6 and 7 of Part ii.

顧 野 王 Koo Yay-wang. 大 廣 益 會 玉 篇 *Ta kwang yih hwuy yuh p'ien.* "An enlarged and improved edition of the *Yuh p'ien*" Dictionary by Koo Yay-wang (A.D. 519–581). Enlarged and improved by Sun K'eang (A.D. 674). Reprinted in Japan. 30 keuen. 1601. 8°. **15348. c. 3.**

顧 炎 武 Koo Yen-woo. 天 下 郡 國 利 病 書 *T'een hea keun kwo le ping shoo.* "A Work on the Geography of the Empire." By Koo Yen-woo. Edited by Lung Wan-yuh. 120 keuen. 1811. 8°. **15271. e. 6.**

顧 有 孝 Koo Yew-heaou, and 趙 澐 Chaou Yun. 江 左 三 大 家 詩 鈔 *Keang tso san ta kea she ch'aou.* "The Works of the three Poets, Tseen Keen-yih, Kung Ting-tsze, and Woo Wei-něě, on the north of the Yang-tsze keang." Edited by Koo Yew-heaou and Chaou Yun. 1st part, 3 keuen; 2nd part, 3 keuen; and 3rd part, 3 keuen. [1850?] 8°. **15323. e. 9.**

顧 沅 Koo Yuen. See 文 昌 帝 君 Wăn chang te keun. 文 昌 化 書 *Wăn chang hwa shoo.* "Wăn chang te keun's Book of Transformations." Edited by Koo Yuen, etc. 1823. 8°. **15113. b. 4.**

古 雲 Koo-yun. See 阿 字 無 A-tsze-woo. 光 宣 臺 集 *Kwang-seuen t'ai tseih.* "The Kwang-seuen Gallery Collection of Buddhist Writings . . ." Edited by . . . Koo-yun, etc. 8°. **15101. b. 26.**

郭 璞 Kŏ Pŏ. 穆 天 子 傳 *Muh T'een tsze chuen.* "A Narrative of the Adventures of the Emperor Muh." 6 keuen. See 程 榮 Ch'ing Yung. 漢 魏 叢 書 *Han Wei ts'ung shoo.* "A collection of works by authors of the Han and Wei Dynasties," etc. 1791. 8°. **15318. a. 1.**

—— See 邢 昺 Hing Ping. 爾 雅 註 疏 *Urh ya choo soo.* "The Literary Expositor." With Kŏ Pŏ's commentary, etc. 1745. 8°. **15318. c. 5.**

—— See 爾 雅 Urh ya. 爾 雅 *Urh ya.* "The Literary Expositor." With Kŏ Pŏ's commentary, etc. 1829. Fol. **15344. e. 18.**

KO PO-YI [i.e. Robert Henry Cobbold]. See Mŏ-ti-meh. Jih-tsih-yüih-le . . . Translated into Chinese by Ko Po-yi, etc. 1868. 8°. **15118. d. 8.**

KOREAN WORDS AND PHRASES. Corean Words and Phrases. A handbook and pocket dictionary for visitors to Corea and new arrivals in the country. pp. v, 145. *Seoul*, 1897. 8°. **11099. c. 39.**

各 省 Kŏ săng. 各 省 地 名 *Kŏ săng te ming.* "The Names of the Towns in each Province" throughout the Empire. MS. [1850?] 8°. **15271. e. 3.**

—— 各 省 輿 圖 便 覽 *Kŏ săng yu t'oo peen lan.* "Maps of every Province in the Empire." [1826?] 8°. **15271. a. 5.**

郭 象 Kŏ Seang. 莊 周 Chwang Chow. 南 華 真 經 *Nan hwa chin king.* "The Nan-hwa Classic." With comments by Kŏ Seang, etc. 8°. **15212. e. 9.**

郭 善 鄰 Kŏ Shen-lin. 商 邱 史 記 *Shang k'ew she ke.* "Historical Records." 10 keuen. See 孫 澍 Sun Shoo. 古 棠 書 屋 叢 書 *Koo t'ang shoo wuh ts'ung shoo.* "A Collection of Reprints," etc. 1831–1849. 8°. **15315. d. 1.**

各 式 Kŏ shih. 各 式 聖 歌 *Kŏ shih shing ko.* "Hymns appropriate to each service." pp. 78. *Hongkong*, 1892. 12°. **15200. aa. 29.**

歌 頌 KO SUNG. 歌 頌 詩 章 *Ko sung she chang.*
"A Collection of Hymns." *Canton*, 1863. 8°.
15118. c. 35.

The last (35th) hymn is added in manuscript.

柯 士 賓 KO-SZE-PIN [i.e.   ]. 紅 十 字 會
救 傷 第 一 法 *Hung shih tsze hwuy kew shang
te yih fa.* "The Red-Cross Society's First Aid
to the Wounded." Translated into Chinese by
Sun Yih-seen [Sun Yat-sen], who adds a preface.
With illustrations. pp. xii, 141. *London*, 1897.
8°. 15253. a. 14.

匋 子 源 Kŏ TSZE-YUEN. 皇 朝 經 世 文 續 編
Hwang ch'aou king she wǎn suh peen. "A
supplementary collection of State Papers of the
present dynasty." Compiled by Kŏ Tsze-yuen.
120 keuen. 1888. 8°. 15241. b. 13.

郭 雨 三 Kŏ YU-SAN. 詩 韻 類 錦 *She yun luy
kin.* "A Poetical Dictionary arranged according
to subjects." Compiled by Kŏ Yu-san. Edited
by Ch'in Ming-chang. 12 keuen. 1852. 8°.
15346. a. 22.

KREYER (CARL T.). See 金 楷 理 KIN K'EAE-LE.

KRUPP. *See* PRUSSIA, DEPARTMENTS OF STATE,
ETC.: *Army.* 克 虜 伯 礮 彈 造 法 *Kih-loo-
pih paou tan tsaou fǎ.* "On Krupp's Manufacture of Shot," etc. 8°. 15259. d. 13.

穀 梁 赤 KUH-LEANG CH'IH. 春 秋 穀 梁 經 傳
補 注 *Ch'un ts'ew Kuh-leang king chuen poo choo.*
"Kuh-leang's Commentary on the Spring and
Autumn Annals. With supplementary notes"
by Fan Ning. With additional explanations
by Chung Wǎn-ching. 25 keuen. 1875. 8°.
15212. e. 1.

KÜHNERT (FRANZ). Syllabar des Nanking-
Dialectes oder der correcten Aussprache (正 音)
sammt Vocabular zum Studium der Hoch-
chinesischen Umgangssprache von F. K. pp.
472. *Wien*, 1898. 8°. 11098. a. 12.

穀 且 浣 KUH TAN-HWAN. 官 話 彙 解 *Kwan
hwa wei keae.* "A Vocabulary of the Mandarin
Dialect." 3 keuen. 1794. 8°. 15344. d. 1.

孔 晁 K'UNG CHAOU. 汲 冢 周 書 *Keih mung
chow shoo.* "An Introductory History of the
Chow Dynasty." 10 keuen. See 程 榮 CH'ING
YUNG. 漢 魏 叢 書 *Han Wei ts'ung shoo.*
"A collection of works by authors of the Han
and Wei Dynasties," etc. 1791. 8°. 15318. a. 1.

孔 鮒 K'UNG FOO. 孔 叢 子 *K'ung ts'ung tsze.*
"Confucian Miscellanies." 2 keuen. See 程 榮
CH'ING YUNG. 漢 魏 叢 書 *Han Wei ts'ung
shoo.* "A collection of works by authors of the
Han and Wei Dynasties," etc. 1791. 8°.
15318. a. 1.

—— 小 爾 雅 *Seaou Urh ya.* "The lesser Literary
Expositor." pp. ii, 14, 1. See 程 榮 CH'ING
YUNG. 漢 魏 叢 書 *Han Wei ts'ung shoo.*
"A collection of works by authors of the Han
and Wei Dynasties," etc. 1791. 8°. 15318. a. 1.

—— [Another edition. 1800?] 8°. 15346. b. 6 (3).

龔 顯 曾 KUNG HEEN-TSĂNG. See 陳 允 錫 CH'IN
YUN-SEIH. 二 十 一 史 緯 *Urh shih yih she
wei.* "The Woof of the Twenty-one Histories
. . . ." Edited by Kung Heen-tsăng, etc. 1870.
8°. 15292. a-c. 1.

孔 丘 K'UNG K'EW. See 孫 星 衍 SUN SING-YEN.
孔 子 集 語 *K'ung tsze tseih yu.* "A collection
of the Sayings of Confucius," etc. 1815. 8°.
15303. c. 13.

—— See 虞 潘 府 YU P'AN-FOO. 孔 子 通 紀
K'ung tsze t'ung ke. "Biographical Records of
Confucius," etc. Fol. 15303. c. 15.

—— 書 經 *Chou king.* Texte Chinois, avec une
double traduction en Français et en Latin, des
Annotations, et un Vocabulaire. Par S.
Couvreur. pp. 464. *Imprimerie de la Mission
Catholique : Hokien Fu*, 1897. 8°. 11098. a. 31.

—— 春 秋 *Ch'un ts'ew.* "The Spring and Autumn
Annals." With the commentaries of Hoo
Gan-kwo and others. 30 keuen. [1850?] 8°.
15212. a. 13.

—— 春 秋 正 文 *Ch'un ts'ew ching wǎn.* "The
Text of the Spring and Autumn Annals."
[1870?] 32°. 16202. a. 11.

—— 春 秋 胡 氏 傳 *Ch'un ts'ew Hoo she chuen.*
"The Spring and Autumn Annals, with Hoo
Gan-kwo's Commentary." 30 keuen. [1620?]
Fol. 16015. c. 4.

Printed in Korea from movable blocks.

—— 春 秋 經 傳 集 解 *Ch'un ts'ew king chuen
tseih keae.* "The Spring and Autumn Annals,
with Tso K'ew-ming's Narrative. With a collection of Comments." Compiled by Too Yu.
An enlarged edition. 30 keuen. [1620?] Fol.
16015. c. 3.

Printed in Korea from blocks. At the end of the last
keuen is a note giving an account of the invention of
printing with movable types in Korea.

孔 丘 K'ung K'ew (*continued*). [Another edition. 1625?] Fol.   **15212. e. 7.**

—— 春秋左傳 *Ch'un ts'ew Tso chuen.* "The Spring and Autumn Annals, with Tso's Narrative." 30 keuen. 1868. Fol. **15212. e. 6.**

—— 孝 經 *Heaou king.* "The Book of Filial Piety." In Manchoo and Chinese. 8°.   **15229. a. 3.**

—— 孝 經 *Heaou king.* "The Book of Filial Piety." [1700?] A roll.   **15229. c. 42.**
         Printed in Korea.

—— 監本書經 *Keen pun shoo king.* "The Original Text of the Book of Historical Documents." With Ts'ai Ch'in's commentary. 6 keuen. 1790. 8°.   **15215. a. 5.**

—— Kong tze Kia-yu. Les Entretiens familiers de Confucius [K'ung K'ew]. Traduits pour la 1re fois par C. de Harlez. pp. 196. *E. Leroux: Paris*, 1899. 8°.   **11098. a. 22.**

—— 古文孝經 *Koo wăn Heaou king.* "The Ancient Text of the Classic of Filial Piety." Being a conversation on the subject between Confucius and his disciple Tsăng Tsan. [1610?] Fol.   **15229. c. 41.**
     Printed in Japan with movable type.

—— 古文孝經 *Koo wăn Heaou king.* "The Ancient Text of the Classic of Filial Piety." See 四 書 *Sze shoo.* "The Four Books," to which is prefixed the *Koo wăn Heaou king*, etc. 1599. Fol.   **15210. e. 11.**

—— 尙 書 *Shang shoo.* "The Book of Historical Documents." Compiled and edited by K'ung K'ew. 13 keuen. [1610?] Fol. **15215. d. 1.**

—— 書傳大全 *Shoo chuen ta ts'euen.* "The Book of Historical Documents. With a complete collection of Commentaries." Compiled by an Imperially appointed Commission consisting of Hoo Kwang, Yang Yung, Kin Yew-tsze, and others. With illustrations. 10 keuen. [1600?] 8°.   **15215. d. 1.**

—— [Another edition.] [1620?] **15215. e. 10.**
         Printed in Korea.

—— 書 經 *Shoo king.* "The Book of Historical Documents," said to have been compiled by K'ung K'ew (Confucius). Edited with a commentary by Ts'ai Ch'in. 6 keuen. 1209. 8°.   **15215. d. 3.**

孔 丘 K'ung K'ew. 書經正文 *Shoo king ching wăn.* "The Text of the Book of History." 4 keuen. [1870?] 32°.   **15202. a. 13.**

空觀主人 K'ung kwan choo jin, *pseud.* 綉像拍案驚奇 *Sew seang pih ngan king k'e.* "Stories of Striking Wonders." 36 keuen. [1800?] 8°.   **15331. d. 19.**

礦路商務總局 *Kung loo shang woo tsung keu.* A proclamation issued by the above Board explaining the nature of petroleum, and inviting information as to where it is to be found in Shansi. 1899.   **M.P.C.**

公 孫 宏 Kung Seun-hung. 風后握奇經 *Fung How wuh k'i king.* "Fung How's Treatise on the Art of War." pp. 17. See 程 榮 Ch'ing Yung. 漢魏叢書 *Han Wei ts'ung shoo.* "A collection of works by authors of the Han and Wei Dynasties," etc. 1791. 8°.   **15318. a. 1.**

公 禱 Kung taou. 公 禱 書 *Kung taou shoo.* "The Book of Common Prayer." Translated into Chinese by, as is stated in a manuscript note on the cover, the Rev. G. E. Moule. [1870?] 8°.   **15118. a. 50.**

龔 鼎 孳 Kung Ting-tsze. See 顧 有 孝 Koo Yew-heaou, and 趙 澐 Chaou Yun. 江 左三大家詩鈔 *Keang tso san ta kea she ch'aou.* "The Works of . . . Kung Ting-tsze," etc. 8°.   **15323. e. 9.**

KUŎ (Giuseppe M.). 華學進境 Saggio di un Corso di lingua Cinese per G. M. K. Parte quinta. Crestomazia, fascicolo primo. *Napoli*, 1869. 8°.   **11099. d. 33.**

廣 州 府 Kwang-chow Foo. 廣州府屬歷案賢宮題名錄 *Kwang-chow Foo shuh leih gan hung kung t'e ming luh.* "A List of Canton Graduates" from the year 1821 to 1843. *Canton*, 1843. 8°.   **15320. e. 30.**

廣 府 Kwang foo. 廣府十四縣正案題名錄 *Kwang foo shih sze heen ching gan t'e ming luh.* "A List of the Successful Candidates from the Fourteen Districts in the Prefecture of Kwang-chow Foo" at the Canton Examination of 1843. 1843. 8°.   **15320. e. 28.**

廣 寒 子 Kwang Han-tsze. 評註淵海子平大全 *P'ing choo yuen hai tsze p'ing ta ts'euen.* "A Work on Astrology." 4 keuen. 1828. 8°.   **15257. a. 4.**

鄺 其 照 KWANG K'E-CHAOU. 華英字典 *Hwa Ying tsze teen.* English and Chinese Dictionary. From W. H. Medhurst and other authors, and photo-lithographed from Kwong Ki-chiu's edition. pp. 334. *Shanghai*, 1879. 12°.
15342. a. 4.

曠 敏 本 KW'ANG MIN-PUN. 鑑撮 *Keen ts'o.* "Scraps from the Mirror" of history. 4 keuen. With an appendix on the reading of history. [1860?] 8°.
15291. a. 10.

廣 東 KWANG-TUNG. 廣東現任官名 *Kwang-tung heen jin kwan ming.* "A List of Officers in the Province of Kwang-tung." MS. [1850?]
15241. c. 14.

—— 廣東探報 *Kwang-tung t'an paou.* "Reports from Kwang-tung." MS. 1843. 8°. **15298. c. 1.**

—— 廣東歷科拔貢壹等題名錄 *Kwang-tung leih k'o pa kung yih tăng t'e ming luh.* "A List of Selected Sew-ts'ai of the First Class chosen from the Canton Examinations for the years 1813, 1825, and 1837." *Canton*, 1837. 8°.
15320. e. 33.

廣 韻 KWANG YUN. 廣韻 *Kwang yun.* "A Dictionary in which the characters are arranged in accordance with their tones and final sounds." A reprint of the Sung Dynasty edition. 5 keuen. [1800?] 8°.
15346. b. 27.

KWAN HWA. Koan-Hoa Tche-Nan. Boussole du langage mandarin, traduite et annotée par H. Boucher. [With the original text in Chinese characters accompanied by a transliteration.] 2 vols. *Mission Catholique: Zi-Ka-Wei*, 1887. 8°.
11099. f. 9.

關 槐 KWAN HWAI. See 厲荃 LE TS'EUEN. 事物異名錄 *Sze wuh e ming luh.* "An Encyclopædic Dictionary of Terms . . ." Enlarged and re-edited by Kwan Hwai, etc. 1788. 8°.
15344. d. 11.

關 朗 KWAN LANG. 易傳 *Yih chuen.* "A Commentary of the Book of Changes." pp. ii, 27, 3. See 程榮 CH'ING YUNG. 漢魏叢書 *Han Wei ts'ung shoo.* "A collection of works by authors of the Han and Wei Dynasties," etc. 1791. 8°.
15318. a. 1.

観 世 音 KWAN-SHE-YIN. 高王観世音經 *Kaou wang Kwan-she-jin king.* "The Abhyudgada raja Avalōkitēsvara Sūtra." With a portrait of the goddess. pp. 41. *Canton*, 1872. 8°.
15101. d. 7.

關 帝 KWAN-TE. 覺世經 *Keaou she king.* "A Tract to arouse the World." 8°. 15111. d. 7 (2).

—— 關帝明聖眞經 *Kwan-te ming shing chin king.* "The True Sutra of Kwan-te," the God of War. With illustrations. pp. viii, 50. *Hongkong*, 1898. 4°. **15113. a. 30.**

—— 聖帝寶訓 *Shing te paou heun.* "The Precious Teachings of Kwan-te," the God of War. With illustrations, and with notes by Păng He-soo. 4 keuen, with an appendix entitled *Shing te ling ts'ien*, "Kwan-te's Prognostics." 1836. 8°. **15113. b. 11.**

關 天 培 KWAN T'EEN-PEI. 籌海初集 *Chow hai ch'oo tseih.* "On the Coast Defences." 4 keuen. 1837. 8°. **15271. e. 2.**

關 東 KWAN-TUNG. 關東關比圖 *Kwan-tung Kwan-peuk to.* "Coloured Maps of the Provinces of Kang-wăn and Ham-kyeng." MS. [*Seoul*, 1840?] Fol. **15276. e. 5.**

冠 洋 子 KWAN YANG-TSZE. 聖賢像贊 *Shing heen seang tsan.* "Portraits of Sages, with laudatory odes." Compiled by Kwan Yang-tsze. Edited by the gentry of Meen-chuh in Sze ch'uen. 2 vols. 1809. 8°. **15303. c. 17.**

観 弈 道 人 KWAN-YIH TAOU-JIN, *pseud.* See 閱微草堂 YUĔ-WEI-TS'AOU T'ANG. 閱微草堂筆記五種 *Yuĕ-wei-ts'aou T'ang peih ke woo chung.* "Five Collections of Tales . . ." Compiled by Kwan-yih Taou-jin, etc. 1835. 8°.
15331. e. 5.

KWAN-YIN. A collection of twenty-one vignettes painted on ovate leaves cut to the required shape, and pasted on blue paper, representing Bodhisattva and Buddhist Saints, the first being Kwan-yin, the Avalōkitēsvara of the Indian Buddhists. Each vignette is accompanied by a short description, written in gold letters on a blue ground, describing the personage represented, as well as by a slip or slips of paper of later date, containing a popular account of the same. The manuscript is without title, author's name, or date. Early nineteenth century?
Or. 14423.

観 音 KWAN-YIN. 九品観音經 *Kew p'in Kwan-yin king.* "The Sūtra of Kwan-yin." 1856. 8°.
15103. d. 9.

爪爾佳巴尼瑯 KWA-URH-KEA-PA-NE-HWĂN. 清漢文海 *Ts'ing Han wăn hai.* "A Dictionary of Manchoo and Chinese Phrases." By Kwa-urh-kea-pa-ne-hwăn, assisted by Poo-Show-fung, etc. 40 keuen. 1821. 8°.
15354. b. 2.

—— [Another copy.] 15354. b. 3.

奎章 KW'EI CHANG. 御定奎章全韻 *Yu ting kw'ei chang ts'euen yun.* "A complete Imperially edited Chinese Vocabulary arranged according to the Rhymes." A Korean edition. 2 keuen. [1750?] Fol. 15113. e. 4.

葵鄉 KW'EI HEANG. 異談可信錄 *E t'an k'o sin luh.* "Credible Records of Strange Events." Compiled by Kw'ei Heang. 23 keuen. 1796. 8°.
15334. d. 15.

歸熙甫 KWEI HE-FOO. 歸震川文選 *Kwei Chin-chuen wăn seuen.* See 李欽之 LE K'IN-CHE. 金元明八家文選 *Kin, Yuen, Ming pa kea wăn seuen.* "Selections from the Writings of eight authors who wrote during the Kin, Yuen, and Ming Dynasties," etc. 1845. 8°.
15318. e. 1.

葵花 KW'EI HWA. 葵花記全本 *Kw'ei hwa ke ts'euen pun.* "The Tale of the Althea Rosea." In verse. 4 keuen. [1850?] 8°. 15327. d. 21.

規禮 KWEI LE. 節規禮 *Tsëě kwei le.* "An Account of Periodical Payments" [made by some house of business?]. MS. [1844?] 8°.
15297. d. 13.

桂萬榮 KWEI WAN-YING. 棠陰比事 *T'ang yin pe sze.* "Obscure Criminal Cases." Compiled by Kwei Wan-ying. Edited by Teen Tseĭh. A Japanese edition. 2 keuen. [1600?] 4°.
15237. c. 7.

貴榮 KWEI YUNG. See 丁韙良 TING WEI-LEANG. 西學考畧 *Se heŏ k'aou leŏ.* "A short survey of Western learning . . ." Edited by Kwei Yung, etc. 1883. 8°. 15348. e. 2.

KWOK CHAN-SANG. 文法初階 Chinese and English Grammar for Beginners, being an Introduction to Allen and Cornwell's English School Grammar. Translated by Kwok Chan-sang. Second edition. pp. 254. *Hongkong,* 1895. Sm. 4°. 11099. a. 17.

KWOK LO KWAI. See 郭濯貴 Kŏ LO-KWEI.

KWONG KI CHIU. See 廣其照 KWANG K'E-CHAOU.

LAIDLEY (J. W.). *See* FĂ-HEEN. The Pilgrimage of Fa Hian, from the French edition of the Foe Koue Ki of MM. Rémusat, Klaproth, and Landresse. With additional notes and illustrations. [By J. W. L.], etc. 1848. 8°.
11100. e.

賴以矜 LAI E-PIN. 填詞圖譜 *T'een tsze t'oo poo.* "A Register of Ancient Rhymes," with a supplementary section. See 查繼超 CH'A KE-CHAOU. 詞學全書 *Tsze heŏ ts'euen shoo.* "A complete Work on the Art of Rhyming," etc. 1746. 8°. 15321. d. 14.

來保 LAI PAOU. See 傅恒 FOO HĂNG. 欽定皇輿西域圖志 *K'in ting Hwang yu se yih t'oo che.* "An illustrated topography of the Imperial western frontier countries. Compiled by Imperial Order" by Lai Paou, etc. 1782. 8°.
15271. a. 21.

—— See 傅恒 FOO HĂNG. 御批歷代通鑑輯覽 *Yu p'e leih tai t'ung keen tseĭh lan.* "An Imperially revised Survey of Choo He's Mirror of the History of Successive Generations." Compiled by . . . Lai Paou, etc. 1768. 8°.
15290. e. 3.

—— See 詩經 SHE KING. 御纂詩義折中 *Yu tswan She e che chung.* "Well-weighed Decisions on the Meaning of the Book of Odes." Compiled by . . . Lai Paou, etc. 1755. 8°.
15212. e. 2.

賴修仁 LAI SEW-JIN [i.e. JOSEPH RACE?]. 食齋指迷 *Shih chai che me.* "On the errors of religious vegetarianism." pp. iv, 16. *Hankow,* 1880. 8°. 15200. b. 17.

郎仁寶 LANG JIN-PAOU. 七修類藁 *Ts'ih sew luy kaou.* "An Encyclopædia arranged under seven sections." Compiled by Lang Jin-paou. 51 keuen. 1775. 8°. 15026. a. 1.

冷諫庵 LĂNG LEEN-GAN. See 朱梅谿 CHOO MEI-KE, and LĂNG LEEN-GAN. 宋元明詩約鈔三百首 *Sung Yuen Ming she yŏ ch'aou san pih show.* "Three Hundred Pieces of Poetry . . ." Compiled by Choo Mei-ke and Lăng Leen-gan, etc. 1841. 8°. 15323. d. 21.

冷笑焞 Lăng Seaou-k'eu. See 朱梅谿 Choo Mei-ke, and 冷諫庵 Lăng Leen-gan. 朱元明詩約鈔三百首 *Sung Yuen Ming she yŏ ch'aou san pih show*. "Three Hundred Pieces of Poetry . . ." Edited by Lăng Seaou-k'eu, etc. 1841. 8°.   15323. d. 21.

浪子 Lang tsze. 浪子回頭 *Lang tsze hwuy t'ow*. "The Return of the Prodigal Son." Translated into Chinese, according to a manu-script note on cover, by Mrs. Williamson. With coloured illustrations. pp. 8. 1882. 4°.   15118. e. 8.

老君 Laou-keun. 感應篇直講 *Kan ying peen chih keang*. "The Book of Rewards and Punish-ments clearly explained" by Hwang Te-twan. A reprint. *Keang-ning*, 1831. 8°. 15111. d. 14.

—— [Another copy.]   15111. d. 15.

—— [Another copy.]   15111. d. 16.

—— [Another copy.]   15111. d. 17.

—— 老子廬齋口義 *Laou tsze keu ch'ai k'ow e*. "The writings of Laou-keun, with the verbal interpretations" of Lin He. 2 keuen. 1570. Fol.   15113. c. 8.
    Printed in Korea from blocks.

—— [Another edition. 1650?] Fol. 15113. c. 4.
    Printed in Japan from blocks.

—— Lao-Tsze's Tao-Teh-King, Chinese-English. With introduction, transliteration, and notes. By Dr. P. Carus. *Open Court Publishing Co.*: *Chicago*, 1898. 8°.   11099. c. 40.

—— L'Esprit des races jaunes. Le Tao de Laotseu traduit du Chinois par Matgioi (Albert de Pouvourville). pp. 46. *Paris*, 1894. 8°.   11100. b. 31.

—— 太上感應篇詩 *T'ai shang kan ying peen she*. "Poems on Laou-keun's Work on Rewards and Punishments." *Shanghai*, 1843. 8°.   15111. d. 25.

—— 太上感應篇圖說 *T'ai shang kan ying peen t'oo shwŏ*. "The Book of Rewards and Punishments. With illustrations and expositions." Edited by Taou Hung-ke. *Canton*, 1731. 8°.   15111. d. 20.

—— 太上靈寶朝天謝罪懺 *T'ai shang ling paou ch'aou t'ien seay tsui ts'an*. "Laou-keun's ritual for the daily confession of sins." MS. 8 keuen. [1800?] 8°.   15217. a. 11.

老君 Laou-keun. 道德經 *Taou tih king*. "The Classic of Reason and Virtue." 2 keuen. [1300?] 8°.   15210. e. 10.

—— 道德寶章 *Taou tih paou chang*. "The precious treatise on Reason and Virtue." With notes by Pih Yuh-chen. *Canton*, 1838. Fol.   15113. e. 3.

—— Theosophie in China. Betrachtungen über das Tao-teh-king (Der Weg, die Wahrheit, und das Licht). Aus dem Chinesischen des Lao-tze übersetzt von Franz Hartmann. pp. 135. *Leipzig*, [1897?]. 8°.   11099. b. 39.

理 Le. A Proclamation issued on the 14th of the 11th month of the year 1857, in the names of the French and English Admirals Le and Se [i.e. Sir Michael Seymour], and the English General Sze [i.e. Sir C. T. van Straubenzee], before the taking of Canton, explaining the origin of the war and telling the people that they had nothing to fear from the allied troops. *Canton*, 1857. A sheet.   15241. a. 9.

LEAMAN (Charles). General Romanization of the Mandarin Dialect. A primer for schools and self-instruction. By C. L. pp. 100. *Shanghai*, 1897. 8°.   11098. a. 13.

梁章鉅 Leang Chang-keu. 歸田瑣記 *Kwei t'een so ke*. "Occasional Pieces by an Ex-Official." By Leang Chang-keu. 8 keuen. 1845. 8°.   15331. b. 9.

—— 浪跡續談 *Lang tseih suh t'an*. "Sup-plementary Notes of a Wanderer." By Leang Chang-keu. 8 keuen. [1845?] 8°. 15331. b. 11.

—— 浪跡叢談 *Lang tseih ts'ung t'an*. "Notes of a Wanderer." By Leang Chang-keu. 11 keuen. [1845?] 8°.   15331. b. 10.

瓦方 Leang fang. 濟世瓦方 *Tse she leang fang*. "Excellent medical prescriptions for the salvation of the age." 4 keuen. 1839. 8°.   15253. a. 15.

梁安德 Leang Gan-tih. 敬禮耶穌聖心月 *King le Yay-soo Shing sin yueh*. "Services for the Month of the Sacred Heart of Jesus." Compiled by Leang Gan-tih. pp. xiv, 176. *Hongkong*, 1893. 12°.   15200. c. 56.

瓦馬 Leang ma. 瓦馬圖說 *Leang ma t'oo shwo*. "An illustrated account of some quiet horses." By, as is stated on the cover, Mrs. Williamson. 2 keuen. 1883. 4°.   15331. e. 9.

梁 邦 俊 Leang Pang-tseun. See 梁 遠 文 Leang Yuen-wăn. 無 怠 解 齋 詩 稿 *Woo tai heae chai she k'aou.* "Poems . . ." Edited by . . . Leang Pang-tseun, etc. 1848. 8°.
15323. c. 13.

梁 詩 正 Leang She-ching. 欽 定 錢 錄 *K'in ting ts'een luh.* "A record of Chinese coins, compiled by Imperial Order," by a commission consisting of Leang She-ching and nine other Ministers of State in the year 1750. A reprint. With an English preface. 16 keuen. *Ningpo,* 1880. 8°.
15300. b. 6.

梁 詩 拔 Leang She-pa. 愧 齋 遺 詩 *Kw'ei chai e she.* "The bequeathed poems of Leang She-pa, also known as Kw'ei chai." 32 pp. 1846. 8°.
15321. c. 13.

梁 清 標 Leang Ts'ing-peaou. 息 影 軒 畫 譜 *Sieh ying heen hwa poo.* "The Sieh-ying studio drawing-book" of sages and heroes. A new edition. pp. xii, 84. 1863. 8°.
15303. d. 15.

梁 文 煜 Leang Wăn-yuh. 鳳 山 縣 志 *Fung-shan heen che.* "A Topography of Fung-shan heen," a district in the Province of Fuh-kien. Compiled by Leang Wăn-yuh and others, and re-edited by Lo Sze-ming and others. 12 keuen. 1764. 8°.
15267. e. 7.

梁 武 帝 Leang Woo te. 梁 武 帝 全 傳 *Leang Woo te ts'euen chuen.* "The Story of the Emperor Woo te of the Leang Dynasty" (502–550 A.D.). A historical novel which is otherwise known as *Sew seang se lai yen e.* With portraits. 40 chapters. 1819. 8°.
15331. e. 7.

梁 應 來 Leang Ying-lai. 兩 般 秋 雨 盦 隨 筆 *Leang pan ts'ew yu gan suy peih.* "Occasional Essays." By Leang Ying-lai. 8 keuen. 1837. 8°.
15320. a. 20.

梁 遠 文 Leang Yuen-wăn. 無 怠 解 齋 詩 稿 *Woo tai heae chai she k'aou.* "Poems from the study of a diligent man." Edited by his son Leang Pang-tseun. 32 pp. 1842. 8°.
15321. c. 14.

—— [Another edition.] *Canton,* 1848. 8°.
15323. c. 13.

廖 百 子 Leaou Pih-tsze. 正 字 通 *Ching tsze t'ung.* "A complete Dictionary of the correct character." By Leaou Pih-tsze. 1673. 8°.
15342. c. 3.

—— [Another copy.]
15342. d. 3.

—— [Another edition.] 1734.
15342. d. 1.

禮 齋 Le chai, *pseud.* 雲 南 夷 類 圖 *Yunnan e luy t'oo.* "An illustrated description of the 44 Aboriginal Tribes of Yunnan." The illustrations, which are coloured, are very descriptive of the people, and profess to have been taken from life. The work is preceded by a preface by 白 儕 賀 Pih Ts'ai-ho. MS. 1810. 4°.
Or. 4152. 28. a.

李 昌 祺 Le Ch'ang-k'e. 剪 燈 餘 話 *Tseen táng yu hwa.* "Stories for lamp light." Compiled by Le Ch'ang-k'e. A Japanese edition. 5 keuen. [1600?] 4°.
15331. e. 6.

李 兆 洛 Le Chaou-lŏ. 皇 朝 文 典 *Hwang ch'aou wăn teen.* "The Sacrificial Canons of the present Dynasty." Compiled by Le Chaou-lŏ. 74 keuen. 1815. 8°.
15241. d. 1.

李 贄 Le Che. 墨 子 批 選 *Mih-tsze p'e seuen.* Selections from the writings and sayings of the philosopher Mih-tsze on religion and politics. Compiled by Le Che. 4 keuen. 1750? 8°.
15314. e. 8.

李 芝 泉 Le Che-ts'euen. See 李 棨 阿 Le P'an-ah, and Le Che-ts'euen. 本 朝 試 賦 新 硎 *Pun ch'aou shih foo sin hing.* "A new whetstone supplied by the examination odes of the present Dynasty . . ." Compiled by Le P'an-ah and Le Che-ts'euen, etc. 1764. 8°.
15324. b. 10.

李 禎 Le Ching. "The Additional Tales of the Snuffed Lamp." See 瞿 祐 宗 Keu Yew-tsung. 三 燈 叢 話 合 刻 *Sun táng ts'ung hwa ho kih.* "The Three-lamp Collection of Tales," etc. 1847. 8°.
15331. d. 14.

李 周 翰 Le Chow-han. See 蕭 統 Seaou T'ung. 六 臣 註 文 選 *Luh ch'in choo wăn seuen.* "Elegant extracts . . . with the commentaries" of . . . Le Chow-han, etc. 1607. Fol.
15320. e. 39.

李 州 俟 Le Chow-hou. 李 州 俟 家 訓 *Le Chow-hou kea heun.* "Le Chow-hou's Family Instructions." pp. 44. *Hongkong,* 1886. 8°.
15229. a. 35.

李春芳 Le Chun-fang. 海瑞大紅袍全傳 *Hai Shwuy ta hung paou ts'euen chuen.* "Hui Shwuy's Red Coat. A Novel." 60 keuen. 1813. 8°. **15334. d. 3.**

—— [Another edition.] 1853. 8°. **15334. d. 4.**

裂敎 Lĕĕ Keaou. 裂敎原委問答 *Lĕĕ keaou yuen wei wăn ta.* "A Roman Catholic Catechism on the beginning and end of Protestantism." pp. 26. *Hongkong*, 1899. 8°. **15200. d. 16.**

聯芳 Leen Fang. See 馬爾頓 Ma-erh-tun. 星軺指掌 *Sing yaou che chang.* "A Guide for the Chariots of Imperial Envoys . . ." Translated into Chinese by Leen Fang, etc. 1876. 8°. **15298. a. 44.**

—— [Another copy.] **15239. a. 48.**

蓮社 Leen shay. 蓮社高賢傳 *Leen shay kaou heen chuen.* "Biographies of the Saints of the Lily Society." pp. 52, 2. See 程榮 Ch'ing Yung. 漢魏叢書 *Han Wei ts'ung shoo.* "A collection of works by authors of the Han and Wei Dynasties," etc. 1791. 8°. **15318. a. 1.**

練恕 Leen Shoo. 五代地理考 *Woo tai te le k'aou.* "The Geography of the Empire under the Five Dynasties examined." 1838. 8°. **15275. b. 9.**

連提 Leen-t'e [i.e. Auguste Frédéric Lendy]. 行軍測繪 *Hing keun ts'ih hwuy.* "A practical course of Military Surveying." By Leen-t'e. Translated into Chinese by Foolanya, i.e. John Fryer. With plates. 10 keuen. [*Shanghai*, 1880?] 8°. **15259. f. 1.**

—— [Another copy.] **15259. d. 6.**

李義山 Le E-shan. 樊南文集詳註 *Fan-nan wăn tseih tseang choo.* "A collection of writings from Fan-nan by Le E-shan. With explanations and notes." Compiled by Fung Măng-ting. Edited by Choo Chow-wang and others. 8 keuen. 1765. 8°. **15318. b. 5.**

—— 李義山詩集 *Le E-shan she tseih.* "A collection of the Poetry of Le E-shan." Edited with notes by Choo Hŏ-ling. 3 keuen. 1659. 8°. **15323. e. 16.**

—— 玉谿生詩詳註 *Yuh k'e săng she tseang choo.* "Poems from the Jade Valley. By Le E-shan. With explanations and notes." Compiled by Fung Măng-ting. Edited by Hoo Tsze-keen. 3 keuen. 1780. 8°. **15324. e. 1.**

李義山 Le E-shan. 玉谿生詩箋註 *Yuh k'e săng she tseen choo.* "Poems from the 'Jade Valley.' With notes." By Le E-shan, otherwise Le Shang-yin [A.D. 813–858]. Edited by Fung Haou. 8 keuen. 1767. 8°. **15324. d. 5.**

列禦冦 Lĕĕ Yu-k'ow. 沖虛眞經 *Ch'ung heu chin king.* "The true classic of the deep void." With a commentary by Chang Chan. 8 keuen. [1300?] 8°. **15210. e. 9.**

李昉 Le Fang. 太平御覽 *T'ai ping yu lan.* "T'aiping's (A.D. 976–984) Encyclopædia." Compiled by Le Fang and others in 983. The original work, of which only one imperfect printed copy existed, was reprinted from this and from manuscript copies by Hwang Chingsih in 1572. A new edition was published by Yuen Yuen in 1812, and of this edition his present copy is a reprint. 1000 keuen. 1892. 8°. **15026. b. 1.**

李芳普 Le Fang-poo. 水石緣 *Shwuy Shih yuen.* "The Union of Shwuy and Shih." 6 keuen. 1794. 8°. **15331. d. 13.**

李富孫 Le Foo-sun. See 李敬堂 Le King-t'ang. 鶴徵錄 *Ho ching luh.* "Biographical Records." Compiled by . . . Le Foo-sun, etc. 1797. 8°. **15305. b. 2.**

—— 鶴徵後錄 *Ho ching how luh.* "A Later Collection of Biographical Records of Celebrities." Compiled by Le Foo-sun. 12 keuen. 1809. 8°. **15305. b. 3.**

李鳳苞 Le Fung-paou. See 林樂知 Lin-lo-che, and 嚴瓦勤 Yen Leang-heun. 四裔編年表 *Sze e peen neen peaou.* "Comparative Chronological Tables . . ." Arranged by Le Fung-paou, etc. 8°. **15298. c. 23.**

—— [Another copy.] **15298. a. 42.**

—— See 伯里牙芒 Pih-le-ya-mang. 營壘圖說 *Ying lui t'oo shwo.* "La fortification improvisée . . ." Translated into Chinese . . . with the assistance of Le Fung-paou, etc. 8°. **15259. e. 8.**

—— [Another copy.] **15259. d. 7.**

—— *See* Prussia, Departments of State, etc.: *Army.* 克虜伯礮準心法 *Kih-loo-pih p'aou chun sin fa.* "On the Regulation of Krupp Guns . . ." Transcribed by Le Fung-paou, etc. 8°. **15259. d. 14.**

LEF—LEH

李鳳苞 LE FUNG-PAOU. *See* PRUSSIA, DEPARTMENTS OF STATE, ETC. : *Army.* 克虜伯礮架說 *Kih-loo-pih p'aou kea shwo.* "On the Krupp Gun Carriage . . ." Transcribed by Le Fung-paou, etc. 8°.   **15259. d. 11 (3).**

—— —— 克虜伯礮說 *Kih-loo-pih p'aou shwo.* "On Krupp Guns . . ." Transcribed by Le Fung-paou, etc. 8°.   **15259. d. 15.**

—— —— 克虜伯礮彈造法 *Kih-loo-pih p'aou tan tsaou fa.* "On Krupp's Manufacture of Shot . . ." Transcribed by Le Fung-paou, etc. 8°.   **15259. d. 12.**

—— —— 克虜伯礮操法 *Kih-loo-pih p'aou ts'aou fa.* "Krupp Gun Drill . . ." Transcribed by Le Fung-paou, etc. 8°.   **15259. d. 15.**

—— —— 克虜伯腰箍礮說 *Kih-loo-pih yaou koo p'aou shwo.* "On Krupp's Rifled Guns . . ." Transcribed by Le Fung-paou, etc. 8°.   **15259. d. 11 (2).**

—— —— 攻守礮法 *Kung show p'aou fa.* "On Attacking and Defensive Gunnery . . ." Transcribed by Le Fung-paou, etc. 8°.   **15259. d. 11 (1).**

—— *See* UNITED STATES OF AMERICA : *Admiralty.* 兵船礮法 *Ping ch'uen p'aou fa.* "On Naval Gunnery . . ." Edited by Le Fung-paou, etc. 8°.   **15259. d. 12.**

LEGGE (JAMES), D.D.   *See* BAKER (CHARLES). 智環啟蒙塾課 *Che hwan k'e mung shuh k'o.* "Graduated Reading . . ." Translated into Chinese by J. L., etc. 1856. 8°. **11099. c. 6.**

—— [Another copy.]   **11099. c. 42.**

—— [Another edition.] *Shanghai,* 1873. 8°.   **15229. a. 34.**

—— [Another edition.] *Hongkong,* 1895. 8°.   **11098. a. 34.**

—— The Chinese Classics : with a translation, critical and exegetical notes, prolegomena, and copious indexes. Second edition revised. Vol. i. Chinese and English. *The Clarendon Press : Oxford,* 1893.   **11098. a. 1.**

—— The notions of the Chinese concerning God and Spirits : with an examination of the defence of an essay on the proper rendering of the words *Elohim* and *Theos* into the Chinese language by William J. Boone, D.D. . . . By the Rev. J. L. *Hongkong,* 1852. 8°. **12910. bb. 12.**

李瀚 LE HAN.   *See* 金三俊 KIN SAN-TSEUN. 十七史蒙求 *Shih ts'ih she mung k'ew.* "An aid to the study of the seventeen histories." In verse . . . by Le Han, etc. 1848. 8°.   **15291. a. 8.**

—— 標題徐狀元補注蒙求 *Peaou t'e Seu Chwang-yuen poo choo mung k'ew.* "Information for beginners" by Le Han, "edited with a commentary by the Chwang-yuen, Seu Tsze-kwang." 3 keuen. 1596. 4°.   **15229. d. 5.** Printed in Japan.

李瀚章 LE HAN-CHANG.   *See* 曾國藩 TSĂNG KWO-FAN. 曾文正公雜著 *Tsăng Wăn ching kung tsa choo.* "Miscellaneous Publications . . ." Edited by Le Han-chang, etc. 1874. 8°.   **15313. d. 2.**

—— 曾文正公年譜 *Tsăng Wăn-ching kung neen p'oo.* "A life of Tsăng Kwŏfan," canonised as Wăn-ching kung. Edited by "his pupil" Le Han-chang, from materials compiled by Le Shuh-ch'ang. 12 keuen. 1877. 8°. **15305. a. 14.**

李翰圖 LE HAN-POO.   *See* 葉天士 YĔ T'EEN-SZE. 臨證指南醫案 *Lin ching che nan e gan.* "A Verified Guide to Medicine . . ." Edited by . . . Le Han-poo, etc. 1844. 8°.   **15252. e. 8.**

李希賢 LE HE-HEEN. 沂州府志 *E-chow Foo che.* "A Topography of E-chow Foo" in Shantung." Compiled by Le He-heen and others. 36 keuen. 1760. 8°.   **15267. a. 9.**

李鶴年 LE HO-NEEN. 豫軍紀略 *Yu keun ke leŏ.* "A short history of the campaigns of the armies of Honan" against the T'aip'ings, the Hwuy-fei, the T'oo-fei, and the Hwan-fei, during the reigns of Taou-kwang (1820–1850) and Heen-fung (1851–1861). Edited by Le Ho-neen. 12 keuen. 1877. 8°.   **15297. b. 20.**

李鴻章 LE HUNG-CHANG.   *See* 曾國藩 TSĂNG KWO-FAN. 十八家詩鈔 *Shih pa kea she ch'aou.* "Poems by eighteen Poets . . ." Critically edited by Le Hung-chang, etc. 1874. 8°.   **15313. b. 2.**

—— Celebration of the seventieth birthday of Le Hung-chang . . . at Tientsin, February, 1892. [With photographs and plan of the Hall where the celebration took place.] Accompanying this English version is the Chinese text of the address presented by Chang Chih-tung and others, translated by C. H. Brewitt-Taylor, and a series of Chinese drawings representing the Gordon Hall. *Tientsin*, 1892. 8°. **15305. b. 11.**

李 鴻 章 LE HUNG-CHANG. A letter addressed to Colonel Gordon and General Le Hăng-sung regarding the preparations for the attack on Leyang, and asking whether it would be possible to send help for the attack on Chang Chow. Dated the 1st of the 2nd month of the 3rd year of T'ungche, i.e. 1864. MS. 1864. **Or. 3534.**

—— A letter addressed to Colonel Gordon in reply to two letters of his, on the subject of stores and rations to be forwarded to the force before Soochow. The letter, which ends by expressing a hope that advantage will be taken of the fine weather to push on the siege, is dated the 16th day of the 8th month of the 2nd year of T'ungche, i.e. 1863, and is addressed to "General Ko, i.e. Gordon, of the ever victorious army." MS. 1863. **Or. 3534.**

—— A letter in reply addressed to Colonel Gordon regarding the rewards to be given to the "Braves," presumably after the capture of Soochow. Le says that it is impossible to exceed much the regulation remunerations, but that on this occasion he has given orders to pay what Gordon desires, and urges economy for the future. Dated the 9th of the 1st month of the 3rd year of T'ungche, i.e. 1864. MS. 1864. **Or. 3534.**

—— A letter addressed to Colonel Gordon by Le Hung-chang accompanying four suits of complimentary clothing presented to Colonel Gordon by the Emperor's command for his services in command of the Ever Victorious Army. Accompanied by a detailed list of the clothing. Dated the 20th of the 8th month [of presumably the 3rd year of T'ungche, i.e. 1864]. MS. **Or. 3534.**

—— A letter addressed to Colonel Gordon by Le Hung-chang forwarding to him a medal of the highest order and 10,000 taels of silver for his energy and skill in the capture of Soochow. Dated the 15th of the 11th month of the 2nd year of T'ungche, i.e. December 25, 1863. MS. 1863. **Or. 3534.**

李 鴻 章 LE HUNG-CHANG. A letter addressed to Colonel Gordon on the subject of a gratuity which Colonel Gordon had given to the crew of the " Hyson" (Haisăng). Le states that the giving of such additional pay is inconvenient; that he gives it this time as an encouragement to attack Quinsan (Kwansăng) and Soochow; but has told the paymasters that the regulation pay is not to be exceeded. He adds that he has ordered the ship people to buy 100 tons of coal for the use of General Le's troops, and sends to him a vessel to take them to Quinsan. Dated the 27th of the 6th month of the 2nd year of T'ungche, i.e. 1863. MS. 1863. **Or. 3534.**

—— A proclamation issued by Le Hung-chang in explanation of the execution by his orders of the T'aip'ing leaders, the Na Wang and others, who surrendered the city of Soochow to the Imperialists on the promise given them by Colonel Gordon that their lives would be spared. The proclamation is dated the 7th day of the 1st month of the 3rd year of the reign of T'ungche, i.e. 1864. MS. 1864. A sheet, 4 ft. 2 in. by 5 ft. 5½ in. **Or. 3534.**

—— Verbal discussions during peace negotiations between the Chinese plenipotentiary Viceroy Li Hung Chang and the Japanese plenipotentiaries Count Ito and Viscount Mutsu at Shimonoseki, Japan, March–April, 1895. (pp. iv, 27.) Translated from the original Chinese records. Reprinted from *The Peking and Tientsin Times*, etc. *The Tientsin Press: Tientsin*, 1895. 4°. **11100. e. 26.**

曆 法 LEIH FĂ. 曆 法 問 答 *Leih fa wăn ta.* "A Catechism on Astronomy." Evidently written under the influence of the Jesuit missionaries. At the end are a few pages on astronomical calculation in the handwriting of a Portuguese Missionary (?). With illustrations. ff. 663. 8°. **Add. 16634. 39. B. d.**

歷 代 LEIH TAI. 歷 代 序 畧 *Leih tai seu leŏ.* "Outlines of the History of the successive Chinese Dynasties," to the Yuen Dynasty. 1554. **15275. a. 20.**
Printed in Japan from blocks.

立 德 LEIH-TIH. *See* LITTLE (ARCHIBALD).

LE ING-PAH. *Ts'u 'öh di-li veng-teh.* "A Catechism of Geography." Translated into the Romanized Ningpo Dialect by Le Ing-pah, i.e. Rev. J. A. Leyenbergen. With illustrations. pp. 126. *Shanghai,* 1873. 4°. 15271. c. 19.

—— [Another copy.] 15275. a. 3.

李壬叔 LE JIN-SHUH. 算學課藝 *Swan heö k'o e.* "Mathematical Problems." Based on the European system. Compiled by Le Jin-shih. 4 keuen. 1880. 8°. 15255. d. 32.

李若望 LE JO-WANG. 裂敎原委問答 *Lëe keaou yuen wei wăn ta.* "A Catechism on the beginning and end of Protestantism." pp. 26. *Hongkong,* 1897. 8°. 15200. d. 38.

李銳 LE JUY. See 李冶 LE YAY. 測圓海鏡 *Ts'ih yuen hai king.* "On Trigonometrical Calculation." With notes by Le Juy, etc. 1876. 8°. 15255. e. 29.

李凱 LE K'AI. 塞香亭傳奇 *Han heang t'ing chuen k'e.* "The Story of the Cool and Fragrant Pavilion." Edited by Fan Woo. 4 keuen. 1777. 8°. 15327. b. 13.

禮記 LE KE. 禮記 *Le ke.* "The Book of Rites." With a commentary by Ching K'ang-ch'ing. 20 keuen. [1620?] Fol. 15217. b. 7.
Printed in Japan with movable type.

—— 禮記 *Le ke.* "The Book of Rites." With a collection of comments compiled by Ch'in Haou. Edited by Le Han-chang. 10 keuen. 1868. Fol. 15217. e. 7.

—— 禮記正文 *Le ke ching wăn.* "The Text of the Book of Rites." [1870?] 32°. 15202. a. 12.

—— 禮記省度 *Le ke săng too.* "The Book of Rites examined and tested." By P'ăng Kwankeïh. 4 keuen. 1672. 8°. 15217. b. 7.

—— 禮記集說 *Le ke tseïh shwo.* "The Book of Rites. With a collection of comments" compiled by Ch'in Haou. 10 keuen. [1850?] 8°. 15217. b. 8.

—— 禮記集說大全 *Le ke tseïh shwo ta ts'euen.* "The Book of Rites. With a complete collection of comments." ? keuen. [*Korea,* 1700?] Fol. 15220. c. 1.
Imperfect, wanting Keuen 1–6.

禮記 LE KE. 禮記讀本 *Le ke tuh pun.* "The Text of the Book of Rites." With an interlinear commentary. 6 keuen. [1800?] 8°. 15217. a. 7.

—— Li ki, ou Mémoires sur les bienséances et les cérémonies. Texte Chinois, avec une double traduction en Français et en Latin. Par S. Couvreur. 2 vols. *Ho-kien Fou,* 1899. 8°. 11098. b. 39.

李鍇 LE K'EAE. 尚史 *Shang she.* "Archaic History." By Le K'eae. 70 keuen. 1773. 8°. 15297. c. 7.

利稼孫 LE-KEA-SUN, and 華得斯 HWA-TIH SZE [i.e. T. RICHARDSON and H. WATTS?]. 製火藥法 *Che ho yaou fa.* "The Manufacture of Gunpowder." Translated into Chinese by Foolan-ya assisted by Ting Shoo-t'ang. With diagrams. 3 keuen. [1880?] 8°. 15259. e. 7.

—— [Another copy.] 15252. d. 13.

李巨來 LE-KEU-LAI. See 吳廷華 WOO T'INGHWA. 儀禮章句 *E le chang keu.* "The Decorum Ritual . . ." Edited by . . . Lekeu-lae, etc. 1757. 8°.

李欽之 LE K'IN-CHE. 金元明八家文選 *Kin Yuen Ming pa kea wăn seuen.* "Selections from the Writings of eight Authors who wrote during the Kin, Yuen, and Ming Dynasties," viz.: the *Yuen E-shan wăn seuen,* by Yuen Tihming, 7 keuen; the *Yaou Muh-gan wăn seuen,* by Yaou Twan-foo, 5 keuen; the *Woo Tsaou-leu wăn seuen,* by Woo Yew-tsing, 6 keuen; the *Yu Taou-yuen wăn seuen,* by Yu Pih-săng, 8 keuen; the *Sung King-leen wăn seuen,* by Sung King-leen, 7 keuen; the *Wang Yangming wăn seuen,* by Wang Pih-gan, 7 keuen; the *T'ang King-chuen wăn seuen,* by T'ang Ying-tih, 7 keuen; and the *Kwei Chin-chuen wăn seuen,* by Kwei He-foo, 6 keuen. Edited by Le K'in-che. 1845. 8°. 15318. e. 1.

—— 國朝文錄 *Kwo ch'aou wăn luh.* "The Writings of forty Authors under the present Dynasty." Compiled by Le K'in-che. 1837. 8°. 15318. e. 2.

—— 國朝文錄續編 *Kwo ch'aou wăn luh suh peen.* "A Supplementary Collection of the Writings of fifty Authors under the present Dynasty." Compiled by Le K'in-che. 1868. 8°. 15318. e. 3.

李 欽 之 LE K'IN-CHE. 邁 堂 文 畧 *Mai T'ang wăn leŏ*. " A few Writings from the ' Old ' Hall." By Le K'in-che. 1835. 8°. 15317. d. 12.

—— 邁 堂 文 畧 *Mai T'ang wăn leŏ*. "A few Writings from the ' Old ' Hall." By Le K'in-che. 4 keuen. 1868. 8°. 15317. d. 13.
A separate work from the above, with the same title.

—— 史 論 五 種 *She lun woo chung*. "Five Works on History," viz.: *Tseen Han show seth tuh*, 4 keuen ; *How Han shoo chuy yu*, 3 keuen ; *San kwo che shoo how*, 1 keuen ; *Ming she tsa choo*, 1 keuen ; *Poo shang she lun tsan*, 2 keuen. By Le K'in-che. 1871. 8°. 15292. c. 5.

李 敬 堂 LE KING-T'ANG. 鶴 徵 錄 *Ho ching luh*. " Biographical Records of Celebrities." Compiled by Le King-t'ang, Le Foo-sun, and Le Yu-sun. 8 keuen. 1797. 8°. 15305. b. 2.

李 光 昭 LE KWANG-CHAOU. 禊 帖 類 聯 *He t'ĕ luy leen*. "Mottoes" appropriate for occasions of rejoicing. Compiled by Le Kwang-chaou. 1832. 8°. 15348. a. 19.

李 光 地 LE KWANG-TE. See 張 玉 書 CHANG YUH-SHOO. 佩 文 韻 府 *Pei wăn yun foo*. "A Lexicon . . ." Compiled by . . . Le Kwang-te, etc. 1711. 8°.

李 光 廷 LE KWANG-T'ING. 漢 西 域 圖 考 *Han se yih t'oo k'aou*. "An Examination of the Frontier Countries of China during the Han Dynasty." With maps. 7 keuen. 1870. 8°. 15296. b. 12.

—— 吉 金 志 存 *Keth kin che ts'un*. "A collection of lucky and other coins." 4 keuen. 1859. 8°. 15300. b. 2.

李 圭 LE KWEI. 環 遊 地 球 新 錄 *Hwan yew te k'ew sin luh*. " A Voyage round the World." Being an account of a visit to the Philadelphian Exhibition and of short stays in London and Paris, with the return voyage. With a preface by Le Hung-chang, a table of errata, and a map. 4 keuen. 1878. 8°. 15291. b. 1.

李 軌 LE KWEI. See 楊 雄 YANG HEUNG. 新 纂 門 目 五 臣 音 註 揚 子 法 言 *Sin tswan mun muh woo ch'in yin choo yang tsze fa yen* . . . Discourses on Law, with notes by . . . Le Kwei, etc. 8°. 15237. c. 6.

李 國 龍 LE KWO-LUNG. 李 躍 門 百 蝶 圖 *Le Yo-mun pih tieh t'oo*. "Drawings of ' a hundred ' butterflies." With appropriate odes. 4 parts. 1849. Fol. 15257. d. 31.

—— [Another copy.] 15257. d. 32.

李 龍 LE LUNG. 聖 賢 讚 像 圖 *Shing heen tsan seang t'oo*. Likeness of celebrated sages and worthies, copied from the drawings of Le Lung by Wang Yuen-tsai. [MS.] 1652. 8°. 15303. d. 1.

利 瑪 竇 LE MA-TOW [i.e. MATTEO RICCI]. 畸 人 十 篇 *Ke jin shih p'een*. "Ten conversations with eminent men." A reprint. 2 keuen. *Hongkong*, 1896. 8°. 15320. c. 17.

—— 天 主 實 義 *T'een choo shih e*. "A Treatise on the Character and Attributes of God." By Le Ma-tow. A new edition. 2 keuen. *Hongkong*, 1894. 8°. 15118. a. 39.

LEMIÈRE (J. E.). See 張 之 洞 CHANG CHE-TUNG. 勸 學 篇 *K'ien-hio p'ien*. . . . Ouvrage traduit du Chinois . . . et précédé d'une notice biographique par J. E. L., etc. 1898. 4°. 11098. d. 4.

LENDY (AUGUSTE FRÉDÉRIC). See 連 提 LEEN-T'E.

禮 拜 LE PAI. 禮 拜 模 範 *Le pai moo fan*. " Forms of Worship." pp. 36. *Shanghai*, 1881. 8°. 15200. c. 39.

李 槃 阿 LE P'AN-AH, and 李 芝 泉 LE CHE-TS'EUEN. 本 朝 試 賦 新 硎 *Pun ch'aou shih foo sin hing*. " A new whetstone supplied by the examination odes of the present Dynasty." With commentaries and notes. Compiled by Le P'an-ah and Le Che-ts'euen. 5 keuen. 1764. 8°. 15324. b. 10.

利 步 條 LE POO-T'EAOU. See 錢 氏 TS'EEN SHE. 胎 產 秘 書 *T'ai ch'an pe shoo*. "On Midwifery." Edited by Le Poo-t'eaou, etc. 1860. 8°. 15252. b. 17.

李 省 惢 LE SĂNG-K'IEN. 至 寶 錄 *Che paou luh*. "Most valuable moral precepts." By "The Master of the Ningshwuy [coldly felicitous] Hall." A new edition. Edited by Le Săng-k'ien. In 6 parts. 1849. 8°. 15225. a. 21.

李 小 湖 LE SEAOU-HOO. 鍾 山 課 藝 彙 鈔 *Chung-shan ko e wei ch'aou*. "The Chung-shan Library Collection of Examination Essays" on Texts from the Four Books. Compiled by Le Seaou-hoo. *Nanking*, 1873. 8°. 15320. c. 11.

李 秀 芳 LE SEW-FANG. 若瑟聖月 *Jo-sih shing yueh.* "The Month of St. Joseph." pp. xxii, 90. *Hongkong,* 1899. 12°. **15200. d. 12.**

李 修 善 LE SEW-SHEN [i.e. DAVID HILL]. 戒烟醒世圖 *Keae yin sing she t'oo.* "Warnings against Opium Smoking." By Le Sew-shen, Yang Kih-fei [i.e. Griffith John], and Tih-ching [i.e. John Dudgeon]. With illustrations. pp. xiv, 20. *Hankow,* 1883. 8°. **15200. b. 21.**

李 時 珍 LE SHE-CHIN. 重刊證類本草 *Chung k'an ching luy pun ts'aou.* "A revised edition of the preface to Le She-chin's Materia Medica." 1603. Fol. **15255. a. 8.**
    Printed in Japan with movable type.

—— 本草綱目 *Pun ts'aou kang muh.* "The Materia Medica" of Le She-chin. Edited by Chang Yun-chung. With illustrations. 52 keuen. 1826. 8°. **15252. e. 1.**

李 善 LE SHEN. See 蕭統 SEAOU T'UNG. 六臣註文選 *Luh ch'in choo wǎn seuen.* "Elegant Extracts ... with the Commentaries" of Le Shen, etc. 1607. Fol.

李 善 蘭 LE SHEN-LAN. See 艾約瑟 GAI YO-SIH. 重學 *Chung heǒ.* "On the Science of Weight ..." Transcribed by Le Shen-lan, etc. 1866. 8°. **15259. e. 1.**

—— See 艾約瑟 GAI YO-SIH. 圜錐曲線 *Hwan chuy keǔh seen.* "On Conic Sections ..." Transcribed by Le Shen-lan, etc. 8°. **15259. e. 3.**

—— 則古昔齋算學 *Tsih-koo-seǐh Chai swan heǒ.* "Mathematical Treatises from the Tsih-koo-seǐh Study." By Le Shen-lan. [*Shanghai?*], 1867. 8°. **15259. e. 2.**

—— 李淳風 LE SHUN-FUNG. 增補萬法歸宗 *Tsǎng poo wan fa kwei tsung.* "A Collection of Prayers and Charms." By Le Shun-fung. Edited and enlarged by Yuen T'een-kang. 5 keuen. [1800?] 8°. **15113. b. 6.**

黎 庶 昌 LE SHOO-CH'ANG. See 李瀚章 LE HAN-CHANG. 曾文正公年譜 *Tsǎng Wǎn-ching kung neen p'oo.* "A Life of Tsǎng Kwo-fan ..." Edited ... from materials compiled by Le Shoo-ch'ang, etc. 1877. 8°. **15305. a. 14.**

—— 拙尊園叢稿 *Cho tsun yuen ts'ung kaou.* "A collection of writings from the Cho tsun Garden." By Le Shoo-ch'ang. 6 keuen. 1893. 8°. **15315. d. 5.**

李 舜 臣 LE SHUN-CH'IN. 李忠武公全書 *Le Chung-woo-kung ts'euen shoo* (or in Korean, *Ri chyung mou kong tjyen sze*). "The complete works of the Patriotic Military Duke, Le Shun-ch'in (Korean, Ri Syun sin), a Korean General." 14 keuen. [*Seoul?*], 1795. Fol. **15287. d. 2.**

李 惺 LE SING. See 張熙宇 CHANG HE-YU. 硃批增註七家詩選 *Choo p'e tsǎng choo ts'ih kea she seuen.* "Imperially endorsed Poems" by ... Le Sing, etc. 1857. 8°. **15323. c. 14.**

—— See 張熙宇 CHANG HE-YU. 七家詩輯註彙鈔 *Ts'ih kea she tseǐh choo wei ch'aou.* "A collection of the writings of" ... Le Sing, etc. 1870. 8°. **15324. a. 12.**

李 星 池 LE SING-CH'E. 澹香閣詩鈔 *Tan-heang ko she ch'aou.* "Poems from the Tan-heang Pavilion," and other short collections by Le Sing-ch'e and others. 1878. 8°. **15324. a. 14.**

李 士 達 LE SZE-TA. 功過格輯要 *Kung kwo kih tseǐh yaou.* "A Mirror of Righteous and Wicked Deeds." Compiled by Le Sze-ta. 16 keuen. *Shanghai,* 1717. 8°. **15111. d. 31.**

李 太 白 LE T'AI-PIH. La Pêche à la ligne et son influence sur la Civilisation et le Progrès. Traduit de K. Li-Tai-Pé [?]. *Paris,* [1878?]. 12°. **11099. a. 1.**

—— 李太白文集輯註 *Le Tae-pih wǎn tseǐh tseǐh choo.* "The writings of Le Tae-pih. Edited with a collection of notes" by Wang Ke. 36 keuen. 1758. 8°. **15321. d. 4.**

李 坦 夫 LE T'AN-FOO. 宋鑑節要 *Sung keen tsëě yaou.* "An epitome of the History of the Sung Dynasty." 7 keuen. 1559. Fol. **15288. e. 5.**

李 筌 LE TS'EUEN. 神機制敵太白陰經 *Shin ke che tih t'ai pih yin king.* "An illustrated treatise on military tactics" by Le Ts'euen of the eighth century. MS. 10 keuen. ff. 115. [1800?] 4°. **16302. 39. B. d.**
    Imperfect, containing only Keuen 3–10.

—— 事物異名錄 *Sze wuh e ming luh.* "An Encyclopædic Dictionary of Terms." Compiled by Le Ts'euen. Enlarged and re-edited by Kwan Hwai. 40 keuen. 1788. 8°. **15344. d. 11.**

李 宗 昉 Le Tsung-fang. See 文 慶 Wăn K'ing. 欽定國子監志 *K'in ting kwo tsze keen che.* "The History of the Imperial College ..." By ... Le Tsung-fang, etc. 1834. 8°.
15297. e. 1.

李 次 青 Le Ts'ze-ts'ing. 國朝先正事略 *Kwo ch'aou seen ching sze leŏ.* "Short Notices of Celebrities during the earlier years of the present Dynasty." By Le Ts'ze-ts'ing. Edited by Tseang Tung-kwan and others. 60 keuen. 1869. 8°.
15305. a. 13.

李 童 山 Le Tung-shan. 童山詩選集 *Tung-shan she seuen tseih.* "A Collection of the Poems of Le Tung-shan." 5 keuen. See 孫 澍 Sun Shoo. 古棠書屋叢書 *Koo t'ang shoo wuh ts'ung shoo.* "A Collection of Reprints," etc. 1831-1849. 8°. 15315. d. 1.

李 東 陽 Le Tung-yang. 西涯擬古樂府 *Se yai e koo yo foo.* "An Examination of Ancient Music." Edited by Seay Ming-che and others. A Korean edition. 2 keuen. 1504. Fol.
15257. e. 16.

呂 安 世 Leu Gan-she. 三才一貫圖 *San ts'ai yih kwan t'oo.* "An Illustrated Panorama of the Three Powers of Nature," i.e. Heaven, Earth, and Man. 1722. A sheet. 15024. a. 3.

呂 向 Leu Heang. See 蕭 統 Seaou T'ung. 六臣註文選 *Luh ch'in choo wăn seuen.* "Elegant Extracts ... with the Commentaries" of ... Leu Heang, etc. 1607. Fol.
15320. e. 39.

呂 坤 Leu Kw'ăn. 居官刑戒 *Keu kwan hing keae.* "Reasons why officials should forego punishments." pp. 5. [1870?] 8°.
15241. a. 11.

呂 廷 濟 Leu T'ing-tse. See 蕭 統 Seaou T'ung. 六臣註文選 *Luh ch'in choo wăn seuen.* "Elegant Extracts ... with the Commentaries of ... Leu T'ing-tse," etc. 1607. Fol.
15320. e. 39.

呂 祖 謙 Leu Tsoo-k'een. See 朱 熹 Choo He, and Leu Tsoo-k'een. 近思錄 *Kin sze luh.* "A record of nearly agreeing philosophies," etc. Fol.
15315. e. 9.

—— [Another copy.] 15315. e. 10.

—— 晉書詳節 *Tsin shoo tseang tsëĕ.* "Explanatory Notes on the History of the Tsin Dynasty." A Korean edition. 30 keuen. [1700?] Fol.
15292. c. 8.

呂 祖 謙 Leu Tsoo-k'een. 東萊博議 *Tung-lai po e.* "The writings of Leu Tsoo-k'een, Tung-lai, fully discussed." Edited by Chang Wăn-ping. 4 keuen. 1790. 8°. 15317. c. 11.

—— 東萊先生東漢詳節 *Tung-lai seen săng tung Han tseang tsëĕ.* "Leu Tsoo-k'een's Explanations of the History of the Eastern Han Dynasty." 30 keuen. [1250?] 8°. 15292. c. 8.
Imperfect, containing only Keuen 1-9.

呂 維 祺 Leu Wei-k'e. 正韻通 *Ching yun t'ung.* "A Dictionary in which the Characters are arranged under their Final Sounds." Edited by Leu Wei-keĭh. 30 keuen. 1634. 8°.
15346. e. 2.

呂 維 吉 Leu Wei-keĭh. See 呂 維 祺 Leu Wei-k'e. 正韻通 *Ching yun t'ung.* "A Dictionary in which the Characters are arranged under their Final Sounds." Edited by Leu Wei-keĭh, etc. 1634. 8°. 15346. e. 2.

呂 耀 曾 Leu Yaou-tsăng. 盛京通志 *Shing king t'ung che.* "A Topography of the Province of Sheng king" [Mukden]. Compiled by Leu Yaou-tsăng, Wang Ho, and others. 48 keuen. [1736?] 8°. 15275. e. 3.
Imperfect, containing only Keuen 1-12, 15-26, 28-33, and 42-46.

呂 品 Leu Yen. See 蔡 一 聲 Ts'ai Yih-tsun. 九皇新經註解 *Kew Hwang sin king choo keae.* "The New Sūtra of the Nine Emperors. With Notes" by Leu Yen, etc. 1824. 8°.
15113. b. 3.

—— A reproduction in black and white of an inscription in the Cursive hand which is said to have been traced by Leu Yen (A.D. 755), and which is now in the San sze Temple at Jooning Foo in Honan. 15300. b. 11 (1).

—— 壽 *Show.* A rubbing of the character 'Show' inscribed by Leu Yen on a stone in the Shwuy tsing Temple outside the city of Woochow in the Province of Kwang si. 1514.
15300. b. (11) 2.

呂 應 奎 Leu Ying-k'wei. 惠州府志 *Hwuy-chow Foo che.* "A Topography of Hwuy-chow Foo" in the Province of Kwang-tung. Compiled by Leu Ying-k'wei, Yu Kew-ching, Hwang Ting-hwa, and others. 20 keuen. 1687. 8°.
15267. a. 1.

LEW

劉 Lew. 劉 大 將 軍 平 倭 戰 記 *Lew ta tseang keun p'ing Wei chen ke.* "A History of the Campaign conducted by General Lew against the Japanese" in Formosa. With illustrations. 3 parts. [1895?] 12°.　　　　15296. b. 13.

李 問 漁 Le Wăn-yu. 辯 惑 巵 言 *Peen hwo chih yen.* "An overflowing discourse in explanation of religious doubts." pp. 4, 47. *Hongkong,* 1889. 8°.　　　　15200. d. 55.

劉 智 Lew Che. 天 方 典 禮 擇 要 解 *T'een fang teen le tsih yaou keae.* "A Work on the Doctrines, Rites, and Customs of the Mahommedan Religion." 20 keuen. 1740. 8°.
15200. a. 6.

—— 天 方 性 理 *T'een fang sing le.* "Mahommedan Philosophy." 5 keuen. 1760. 8°.
15200. a. 7.

劉 辰 翁 Lew Ch'in-ung. See 陳 與 義 Ch'in Yu-e. 間 齋 詩 集 *Keen-chai she tseih.* "Keen-chai's Poems." Edited with notes by Lew Ch'in-ung. 1545. 8°.　　15324. c. 5.

—— See 蘇 軾 Soo Shih. 增 刊 校 正 王 狀 元 集 註 分 類 東 坡 先 生 詩 *Tsăng k'an keaou ching Wang Chwang yuen tseih choo fun luy Tung-p'o Seen săng she.* "A revised edition of Soo Shih's Poems . . ." Edited by Lew Ch'in-ung, etc. 4°.　　　　15313. f. 2.

劉 安 Lew Gan. 淮 南 子 *Hwae nan tsze.* "The Treatise of Lew Gan, the Prince of Hwae nan." 21 keuen. See 程 榮 Ch'ing Yung. 漢 魏 叢 書 *Han Wei ts'ung shoo.* "A collection of works by authors of the Han and Wei Dynasties," etc. 1791. 8°.　　15318. a. 1.

劉 翰 淸 Lew Han ts'ing. 大 乘 法 寶 十 種 *Ta shing fa paou shih chung.* "Ten precious works on the Law of the Mahayana," consisting of—(1) Woo leang show king (Aparimitāyus Sūtra). Translated by K'ang tsăng k'ai (i.e. Sanghavarman). 2 keuen. (2) Kwan woo leang show Fuh king (Amitāyur - buddha - dhyāna Sūtra). Translated by Keang leang yay shay (i.e. Kālayaças). (3) Fuh shwo Ometo king (Amitābha Sūtra). Translated by Kewmoloshih (i.e. Kumārajīva). (4) Tafang kwang Fuh hwa yen king p'oo heen hing yuen p'in (chapter on the practice and prayer of the Bodhisattva Samantabhadra in the Mahāvaipulya-buddhāvatamsaka Sūtra). Translated by Panjo (i.e.

Prajna). (5) Tafang kwang yuen keaou sew tolo leaou e king (Mahāvaipulya-pūrnabuddha Sūtra-prasannārtha Sūtra). Translated by Fuh-totolo (i.e. Buddhatrāta). 2 keuen. (6) Kin-kang panjo polomeih king (Diamond prajnā-pāramitā Sūtra). Translated by Kewmoloshih (i.e. Kumārajīva). (7) Ta Fuh ting Joolae meih yin sew ching leaou e choo P'oosa wan hing show lăng yen king (Maha-buddhoshnisha-tāthāgata-gúhyahetu-sākshātkrita-prasannārtha-sarvabodhisattvakaryā-sūrāngama Sūtra). Translated by Panlameihte and Mek'ieshihkea (i.e. Pāramiti and Mikasākya). 10 keuen. (8) Wei-mok'eih so shwo king (Vimalakīrtta-nirdesa Sūtra). Translated by Kewmoloshih (i.e. Kumārajīva). 3 keuen. (9) Langkea apotolo paou king (Lankāvatāra Sūtra). Translated by K'ewnapŏtolo (i.e. Gunabhadra). 4 keuen. (10) Meaou fa leen hwa king (Saddharma pundarīka Sūtra). Translated by Kewmoloshih (i.e. Kumārajīva). 7 keuen. 1881. 8°.
15103. b. 13.

劉 灝 Lew Haou. See 王 象 晉 Wang Seang-tsin. 廣 羣 芳 譜 *Kwang k'eun fang poo.* "A Herbarium." Enlarged and revised by Lew Haou, etc. 1708. 8°.　　15255. a. 2.

劉 熙 Lew He. 釋 名 *Shih ming.* "Phrases explained." 4 keuen. See 程 榮 Ch'ing Yung. 漢 魏 叢 書 *Han Wei ts'ung shoo.* "A collection of works by authors of the Han and Wei Dynasties," etc. 1791. 8°.　　15318. a. 1.

劉 向 Lew Heang. 說 苑 *Shwo yuen.* "A Garden of Discourses" on the principles of Government, etc. 20 keuen. See 程 榮 Ch'ing Yung. 漢 魏 叢 書 *Han Wei ts'ung shoo.* "A collection of works by authors of the Han and Wei Dynasties," etc. 1791. 8°.　　15318. a. 1.

—— 新 序 *Sin seu.* "A new arrangement" of historical incidents. 10 keuen. See 程 榮 Ch'ing Yung. 漢 魏 叢 書 *Han Wei ts'ung shoo.* "A collection of works by authors of the Han and Wei Dynasties," etc. 1791. 8°.
15318. a. 1.

劉 勰 Lew Hĕĕ. 新 論 *Sin lun.* "New discourses" on moral duties. 10 keuen. See 程 榮 Ch'ing Yung. 漢 魏 叢 書 *Han Wei ts'ung shoo.* "A collection of works by authors of the Han and Wei Dynasties, etc." 1791. 8°.
15318. a. 1.

劉勰 LEW HËĔ. 文心雕龍 *Wăn sin teaou lung.* A critique on poetry and literature. 10 keuen. See 程榮 CH'ING YUNG. 漢魏叢書 *Han Wei ts'ung shoo.* "A collection of works by authors of the Han and Wei Dynasties," etc. 1791. 8°.   15318. a. 1.

劉昫 LEW HEU. 舊唐書 *Kew T'ang shoo.* "The earlier history of the T'ang Dynasty," A.D. 618–907. 200 keuen. 1872. 8°.   15291. c. 1.

劉歆 LEW HIN. 西京雜記 *Se king tsa ke.* "The Miscellaneous Records of Chang-gan, the Western Capital." 5 keuen. See 程榮 CH'ING YUNG. 漢魏叢書 *Han Wei ts'ung shoo.* "A collection of works by authors of the Han and Wei Dynasties," etc. 1791. 8°. 15318. a 1.

劉會孟 LEW HWUY-MĂNG. See 杜甫 TOO FOO. 集千家註批點杜工部文詩集 *Tseih ts'een kea choo p'e teen Too Kung-poo wăn she tseih.* "The writings of Too Foo . . ." Edited by Lew Hwuy-măng, etc. 8°.   15324. e. 5.

劉仁初 LEW JIN-CH'OO. 三場文選 *San ch'ang wăn seuen.* "Elegant Extracts from Examination Halls." Compiled by Lew Jin-ch'oo. A Korean edition. 8 keuen. 1454. 8°. 15315. e. 6.

—— 文選對策 *Wăn seuen tuy ts'ih.* "Elegant Extracts from Examination Halls in the form of answers to questions." Compiled by Lew Jin-ch'oo. A Korean edition. 8 keuen. 1548. Fol.   15315. e. 8.

劉蓉霞 LEW JUNG-HEA. 思辨錄疑義 *Sze peen luh e e.* "The meaning of doubtful passages in the record of thoughtful discriminations." pp. i, 68. 1877. 8°.   15223. b. 5.

—— 養晦堂詩集 *Yang hwei t'ang she tseih.* "A collection of poems from the Yang-hwei Hall." By Lew Jung-hea. 2 keuen. 1877. 8°.   15324. a. 13.

—— 養晦堂文集 *Yang hwei t'ang wăn tseih.* "A collection of literary pieces from the Yang-hwei Hall." By Lew Jung-hea. 10 keuen. 1877. 8°.   15318. c. 2.

劉嘉謨 LEW KEA-MOW. See 曹維藩 TS'AOU WEI-FAN. 鑑撮蒙求 *Keen ts'o mung k'ew.* "A Resumé of Historical Events . . ." Edited by Lew Kea-mow, etc. 1815. 8°. 15297. b. 13.

劉麒瞻 LEW K'E-CHAN. 增輯書法殼 *Tsăng tseih shoo fa kou.* "The full rules of penmanship." Edited by Lew K'e-chan. With a supplement entitled *Peih fa tsing keae,* "The rules of penmanship minutely explained." 1778. 8°.   15342. b. 10.

劉季昭 LEW KE-CHAOU. See 諸葛亮 CHOOKO LEANG. 諸葛忠武侯文集 *Chooko chung woo how wăn tseih.* "The collected writings of Chooko . . ." Edited by Lew Ke-chaou, etc. 1873. 8°.   15317. a. 7.

—— See 宗澤 TSUNG TSIH. 宋宗忠簡公文集 *Sung Tsung Chung keen kung wăn tseih.* "The collected writings of Tsung Tsih . . ." Edited by Lew Ke-chaou, etc. 1873. 8°.   15315. c. 4.

—— See 岳飛 YO FEI. 岳忠武王文集 *Yo Chung woo wang wăn tseih.* "The collected writings of Yo Fei . . ." Edited by Lew Ke-chaou, etc. 1873. 8°.   15315. c. 5.

劉球 LEW K'EW. 隸韻 *Le yun.* "A Dictionary of the 'Official' Character arranged according to the Finals." By Lew K'ew. With an appendix by Ung Fang-kang. 12 keuen. 1810. 8°.   15344. c. 2.

劉墾 LEW KWĂN. 各省輿地 *Ko sing yu te.* "A Series of Maps of the Provinces of the Empire." With manuscript notes in English. 1805. 8°.   15271. a. 6.

—— [Another copy.]   15271. d. 3.

—— [Another copy.]   15276. e. 2.

劉瓦 LEW LEANG. See 蕭統 SEAOU T'UNG. 六臣註文選 *Luh ch'in choo wăn seuen.* "Elegant Extracts . . . with the Commentaries" of . . . Lew Leang, etc. 1607. Fol.   15320. e. 39.

劉謐 LEW ME. 三教平心論 *San keaou p'ing sin lun.* "Disquisitions on the pacifying effect on the mind of the Three Religions," viz.: Confucianism, Taouism, and Buddhism. 2 keuen. [1804 ?] 8°.   15111. a. 21.

劉豹君 LEW PAOU-KEUN. 詩學含英 *She heŏ han ying.* "Elegant Expressions for the use of Students of Versification." Compiled by Lew Paou-keun. A new edition. 14 keuen. 1772. 8°.   15346. a. 17.

劉 璧 山 LEW PIH-SHAN. See 吳 少 雲 Woo SHAOU-YUN, and LEW PIH-SHAN. 避 難 竹 枝 詞 *Pi nan chuh che ts'ze.* "Light Odes," etc. 1863. 8°. 15327. d. 31.

劉 雪 坡 LEW SEŬH-PO. 鄧 齊 嵋 T'ĂNG TS'E-MEI. 佩 文 韻 府 約 編 *Pei wăn yun foo yo peen.* "An Epitomised Lexicon . . ." Edited by . . . Lew Seŭh-po, etc. 1759. 8°. 15348. b. 3.

劉 邵 LEW SHAOU. 人 物 志 *Jin wuh che.* "A Philosophical Treatise on Mankind." 2 keuen. See 程 榮 CH'ING YUNG. 漢 魏 叢 書 *Han Wei ts'ung shoo.* "A collection of works by authors of the Han and Wei Dynasties," etc. 1791. 8°. 15318. a. 1.

劉 守 眞 LEW SHOW-CHIN. 劉 河 間 傷 寒 三 書 *Lew Ho-keen shang han san shoo.* "Three Works by Lew Show-chin, otherwise Lew Ho-keen, on Diseases arising from Cold." *Singan Foo,* 1431. 8°. 15253. b. 2.

劉 松 年 LEW SUNG-NEEN. See 龍 大 淵 LUNG TA-YUEN. 古 玉 圖 譜 *Koo yuh t'oo p'oo.* "An Illustrated Work on Antiquities . . ." Illustrated by Lew Sung-neen, etc. 1779. 8°. 15299. c. 2.

劉 嗣 綰 LEW SZE-WAN. See 張 熙 宇 CHANG HE-YU. 硃 批 增 註 七 家 詩 選 *Choo p'e tsăng choo ts'ih kea she seuen.* "Imperially endorsed Poems" by . . . Lew Sze-wan, etc. 1857. 8°. 15323. c. 14.

—— See 張 熙 宇 CHANG HE-YU. 七 家 詩 輯 註 彙 鈔 *Ts'ih kea she tsĕih choo wei ch'aou.* "A collection of the writings of" . . . Lew Sze-wan, etc. 1870. 8°. 15324. a. 12.

劉 體 恕 LEW T'E-SHOO. See 文 昌 帝 君 WĂN CH'ANG TE KEUN. 文 帝 全 書 *Wăn te ts'euen shoo.* "The complete works of Wăn ch'ang te keun," the God of Literature, etc. 1835. 8°. 15113. b. 8.

—— 文 帝 全 書 *Wăn te ts'euen shoo.* "A complete record of the God of Literature." 6 keuen. 1845. 8°. 15113. a. 27.

劉 藻 LEW TSAOU. 曹 州 府 志 *Ts'aou-chow Foo che.* "A Topography of Ts'aou-chow Foo" in Shan-tung. Compiled by Lew Tsaou and others. 22 keuen. 1756. 8°. 15269. c. 14.

柳 宗 LEW TSUNG. See 揚 雄 YANG HEUNG. 新 篡 門 目 五 臣 音 註 揚 子 法 言 *Sin tsuan mun muh woo ch'in yin choo Yang tsze fa yen . . .* "Discourses on Law, with Notes" by . . . Lew Tsung, etc. 8°. 15237. c. 6.

劉 文 澂 LEW WĂN-CHE. See 宋 如 林 SUNG JOO-LIN. 松 江 府 志 *Sung keang foo che.* "A Topography of the Prefecture of Sung-keang . . ." Compiled by . . . Lew Wăn-che, etc. 1818. 8°. 15265. e. 6.

劉 晚 榮 LEW WAN-YUNG. 述 古 叢 鈔 *Shuh koo ts'ung ch'aou.* "A Collection of Reprints." Edited by Lew Wan-yung. In two series. 1870, 1874. 8°. 15314. a. 3.

劉 耀 微 LEW YAOU-WEI. See 楊 有 慶 YANG YEW-K'ING. 大 成 通 志 *Ta ch'ing t'ung che.* "A complete record of the 'Great Perfection' . . ." Edited by Lew Yaou-wei, etc. 1669. 8°. 15225. e. 2.

劉 像 巷 LEW YU-GAN. 詳 訂 古 文 評 註 全 集 *Tseang ting koo wăn p'ing choo ts'euen tseih.* "Extracts from Ancient Literature." Compiled by Lew Yu-gan. "With critical notes and comments" by Kwo Kung and Hwang Yuĕ. This collection begins with extracts from the Narrative of Tso K'ew-ming, and is continued down to works of authors of the present Dynasty. 10 keuen. 1807. 8°. 15312. d.

留 雲 居 士 LEW-YUN KEU-SZE, *pseud.* See 明 MING. 明 季 稗 史 彙 編 *Ming ke pai she wei peen.* "Records of the closing struggles of the Ming Dynasty." Compiled by "Lew-yun Keu-sze," etc. 8°. 15296. b 10.

劉 蘊 德 LEW YUN-TIH. See 南 懷 仁 NAN-HWAI-JIN. 新 製 靈 臺 儀 象 志 *Sin che ling t'ai seang che.* "A New Work on Astronomy . . ." Edited by Lew Yun-tih, etc. 1674. 8°. 15256. b. 1.

劉 雲 翼 LEW YUN-YIH. See 屈 原 K'ŬH YUEN. 楚 辭 *Ts'oo tsze.* "Elegies of Tsoo . . ." Edited by Lew Yun-yih, etc. 1789. 8°. 15323. d. 23.

理 雅 各 LE YA-KIH [i.e. JAMES LEGGE, D.D.]. *See* BIBLE: *New Testament.* 新 約 全 書 註 釋 *Sin yo ts'euen shoo choo shih.* "The New Testament, with a Commentary . . ." Revised by Le Ya-kih, etc. 1874. 8°. 15117. b. 11.

李 冶 Le Yay. 測圓海鏡 *Ts'ih yuen hai king.* "On Trigonometrical Calculation." With notes by Le Juy. With a diagram. 12 keuen. 1876. 8°. **15255. e. 29.**

LEYENBERGER (Joseph Anderson). See 雷 應 百 Luy-ying-pih.

—— *See* Le Ing-pah.

—— *See* Bible: *New Testament—Galatians.* 加 拉 太 書 註 釋 *Kea-la-t'ai shoo choo shih.* The Epistle to the Galatians, with a Commentary. [Translated by Rev. J. A. Leyenberger], etc. 1878. 8°. **15117. d. 4.**

李 延 基 Le Yen-ke. 清文彙書 *Ts'ing wǎn wei shoo.* A Manchoo and Chinese Dictionary. By Le Yen-ke. 12 keuen. 1751. 8°. **15354. b. 4.**

—— [Another copy.] **15354. c. 1.**

李 延 壽 Le Yen-show. 南北史捃華 *Nan pih she keun hwa.* "An Anthology from the Histories of the South and North." Compiled by Chow Kea-yew. 8 keuen. [1850?] 8°. **15291. a. 5.**

李 遇 孫 Le Yu-sun. See 李 敬 堂 Le King-t'ang. 鶴徵錄 *Ho ching luh.* "Biographical Records." Compiled by . . . Le Yu-sun, etc. 1797. 8°. **15305. b. 2.**

林 楨 Lin Ching. 聯新事備詩學大成 *Leen sin sze pe she heǒ ta ch'ing.* "A complete aid to Poetry. With parallel sentences added." 30 keuen. [1250?] 8°. **15324. a. 8.**

LIN CHOU-MIN. Iaó-lì kiàng lén, seu Explicatio Catechismi Provinciæ Su-tchuen. Auctore Lin Choú-min. pp. 255. *Hongkong,* 1894. 8°. **15200. d. 64.**

LIND (Abram). A Chapter of the Chinese Penal Code. Proef-schrift-ten verkrigging van den graad van Doctor in de Rechtswetenschap aan de Ryks-Universiteit le Leiden . . . Door A. L. *E. J. Brill: Leiden,* 1887. 8°. **11098. b. 35.**

林 以 正 Lin E-ching. 諸儒箋解古文真寶 *Choo joo tween keae koo wǎn chin pau.* "Elegant extracts from ancient literature, with annotations by numerous scholars." Compiled by Lin E-ching. A Japanese edition. 10 keuen. [1600?] Fol. **15315. e. 5.**

夔 以 棟 Ling E-tung. 五車韻瑞 *Woo ch'ay yun suy.* A Dictionary of expressions in which the characters are arranged under the 106 finals. 160 keuen. [1502?] 8°. **15346. d. 1.**
The first part of the Preface is supplied in manuscript.

—— [Another edition.] 1592. 8°. **15346. d. 3.**

—— [Another copy.] **15346. e. 1.**

靈 魂 Ling hwan. 靈魂之糧 *Ling hwan che leang.* "Food for the Soul." By A. W. Douthwaite, as stated by a manuscript note on the cover. pp. 120. *Shanghai,* 1880. 8°. **15200. c. 4.**

靈 操 竹 Ling Ts'aou-chuh. 瑜伽集要施食壇儀應門 *Yu-kea tseih yaou she shih tan e ying mun.* "A Manual of the Rites of the Yoga Sect." With critical Note by Yu Paou. Edited by Ch'in Tsai-te. 2 keuen. [1700?] 8°. **15103. d. 13.**

伶 元 Ling Yuen. 飛燕外傳 *Fei yen wai chuen.* "The Story of Chaou Fei-yen," the Empress of Ching Te of the Han Dynasty. pp. 15, 2. See 程 榮 Ch'ing Yung. 漢魏叢書 *Han Wei ts'ung shoo.* "A collection of works by authors of the Han and Wei Dynasties," etc. 1791. 8°. **15318. a. 1.**

林 衡 南 Lin Hǎng-nan. 華夷通語 *Hwa e t'ung yu.* "A Chinese and Barbarian [i.e. English] Vocabulary." A new edition. Edited by Le Ts'ing-hwuy. 2 keuen. *Singapore,* 1883. 8°. **15346. b. 30.**

林 希 Lin He. See 莊 周 Chwang Chow. 莊子廬齋口義 *Chwang-tsze keu chai k'ow e.* "The writings of Chwang Chow with the verbal interpretations" of Lin He, etc. 1629. Fol. **15113. c. 6.**

—— See 老 君 Laou keun. 老子廬齋口義 *Laou tsze keu chai k'ow e.* "The writings of Laou keun, with the verbal interpretations" of Lin He, etc. Fol. **15113. c. 8.**

麟 見 亭 Lin Keen-t'ing. 鴻雪因緣圖 *Hung seŭh yin yuen t'oo.* "Fate-directed footprints on the snows of travel, illustrated." Edited by Ts'ung Shih and Ts'ung How. *Tien-shih-chai Photo-lithographic Works: Shanghai,* 1879. 8°. **15297. a. 14.**
This work also bears the following English title-page: "Selections from the Hung-sueh Sketches by Ling Chien-ling. First series. Photo-lithographed from the original Chinese edition, with brief translations in English."

麟見亭 LIN KEEN-T'ING. 鴻雪圖緣 *Hung seŭh t'oo yuen.* "Selections from the Hung seŭh Sketches." 1st series. *Shanghai*, 1879. 8°. **11100. a. 38.**

林君復 LIN KEUN-FUH. 林和靖集 *Lin Ho-tsing tseĭh.* "A collection of the Poetry of Lin Keun-fuh." Edited by Choo Kung-chang. 4 keuen. With appendix. *Changchow*, 1873. 8°. **15323. e. 12.**

林溥 LIN POO. See 宋如林 SUNG JOO-LIN. 松江府志 *Sung keang foo che.* "A Topography of the Prefecture of Sung-keang . . ." Compiled by . . . Lin Poo, etc. 1818. 8°. **15265. e. 6.**

林西仲 LIN SE-CHUNG. 古文析義合編 *Koo wăn seĭh e ho peen.* "Extracts from Ancient Literature. With Explanatory Notes." Compiled by Lin Se-chung. A new edition. 6 keuen. 1716. 8°. **15312. b. 5.**
Imperfect, containing only Keuen 1.

—— 古文析義二編 *Koo wăn seĭh e urh peen.* "Extracts from Ancient Literature. With Explanations." Second series. Compiled by Lin Se-chung. Edited by Ye Teen-tsze. 8 keuen. 1687. 8°. **15312. a. 6.**

林氏 LIN SHE. 欽定萬年書 *K'in ting wan nien shoo.* "A chronology of ten thousand years; printed by Imperial order." Practically a chronology of the present dynasty, and brought down by prophetic foresight to the 41st year of the reign of the present Emperor, i.e. A.D. 1915. A reprint with additions to the original work published in 1727. 2 keuen. [1880?] 8°. **15298. a. 43.**

林殿颺 LIN TEEN-YANG. 性理體註大全旁訓要解 *Sing le t'e choo ta ts'euen pang heun yaou keae.* "A collection of standard works on mental philosophy, with commentaries and explanations." Compiled by Lin Teen-yang and others. 8 keuen. [1840?] 8°. **15202. c. 27.**

林楊廷 LIN YANG-T'ING. 代疑編 *Tai e peen.* "A treatise for the suppression of religious doubts." pp. xiv, 108. *Hongkong*, 1894. 8°. **15200. d. 49.**

林堯叟 LIN YAOU-SOW. See 左邱明 TSO K'EW-MING. 左繡 *Tso sew.* "The Elegancies of Tso K'ew-ming's Commentary . . ." With notes by Lin Yaou-sow, etc. 1720. 8°. **15212. e. 3.**

林樂知 LIN YOH-CHE [i.e. Y. J. ALLEN]. See GREAT BRITAIN AND IRELAND: *Admiralty.* 水師章程 *Shwuy sze chang ch'ing.* "Admiralty Regulations." Translated into Chinese by Lin Yoh-che, etc. 8°. **15235. b. 1.**

—— See 羅斯古 LO-SZE-KOO. 格致啟蒙 *Kih che k'e mung.* "Chemistry . . ." Translated into Chinese by Lin Yoh-che, etc. 8°. **15259. h. 1.**

—— See 麥丁富得力 MIH-TING FOO-TIH-LE. 列國歲計政要 *Lĕĕ kwo suy ke ching yaou.* "The Statesman's Year Book . . ." Translated into Chinese by Lin Yoh-che, etc. 1875. 8°. **15233. d. 7.**

—— See 麥高爾 MIH-KAOU-URH. 歐洲東方交涉記 *Gow chow tung fang keuou she ke.* "The European Eastern Question." Translated into Chinese by Lin Yoh-che, etc. 1880. 8°. **15296. a. 30.**

—— and 嚴瓦勳 YEN LEANG-HEUN. 四裔編年表 *Sze e peen neen peaou.* "Comparative Chronological Tables of the principal countries in the world." Translated into Chinese by Lin Yoh-che and Yen Leang-heun. Arranged by Le Fung-paou. 4 keuen. [*Shanghai*, 1874?] 8°. **15298. c. 23.**

—— [Another copy.] **15298. a. 42.**

LI-TAI-PÉ. See 李太白 LE TAI-PIH.

LITTLE (ARCHIBALD). 老鼠告狀 *Laou shoo kaou chwang.* The Rat's Plaint. With illustrations. *Sampson, Low, Marston, & Co.: London*, 1878. 8°. Obl. **11100. a. 16.**

—— [Another edition.] 1891. 8°. Obl. **16100. a. 28.**

LITURGIES: CHINA—*Basel Mission Communities.* Liturgie zum Gebrauch in den Basler Missions-Gemeinder in China . . . Hak-ka, syuk-wà. (Das Wurttembergische Confirmationsbuchlein in den Umgangssprache der Hakka-Chinesen) pp. 138, 19. *Basel*, 1878-75. 8°. **15118. b. 43.**

LITURGIES: ENGLAND, *Church of.* The Book of Common Prayer . . . according to the use of the Church of England; the Psalter or Psalms of David, etc. Translated into Cantonese by the Rev. Arthur B. Hutchinson. *Hongkong*, 1878. 8°. **15118. b. 28.**
This work has also the following Chinese title: 聖會禱文 *Shing hwuy taou wăn.*

LITURGIES: ENGLAND, *Church of.* 禱告文全書 *Taou kaou wăn ts'euen shoo.* "The Book of Common Prayer." [Translated into Chinese by Dr. Walter Henry Medhurst.] 14 keuen. *Hongkong*, 1855. 8°.   **15118. b. 42.**

—— 耶穌聖教禱告文 *Yay-soo shing keaou taou kaou wăn.* "The Morning and Evening Prayers of the Church of England." 1854. 8°.   **15118. c. 7.**

LOBSCHEID (WILHELM). See 假 KEA. 樂假歸異論 *K'e kea kwei chin lun.* "A Tract . . ." [By Rev. W. L. ?], etc. 12°.   **15118. a. 15.**

—— 英華字典 "English and Chinese Dictionary," with the Punti and Mandarin pronunciation. By the Rev. W. L. *Hongkong*, 1866. 4°.

—— Grammar of the Chinese Language. *Hongkong*, 1864. 8°.   **11099. c. 41.**

—— [Another copy.]   **12910. bb.**

羅傳炳 LO CHUEN-PING. 通書 *T'ung shoo.* "A Thorough Work" on Divination. 1842. 8°.   **15257. b. 20.**

LOCKHART (J. H. STEWART). See 邱瀓 K'EW SEUN. A Manual of Chinese Quotations, being a translation of the Ch'êng yü k'ao . . . By J. H. S. L., etc. 1893. 8°.   **11098. a. 2.**

駱賓王 LOH PIN-WANG. 駱賓王文集 *Loh Pin-wang wăn tseih.* "The writings of Loh Pin-wang." 10 keuen. [1600?] 8°. **15315. c. 2.** Printed in Korea from blocks.

羅貫中 LO KWAN-CHUNG. 三國志 *San kwo che.* "The History of the Three Kingdoms." Edited by Hăng Tsze-năng. 60 keuen. 1850. 8°.   **15334. e. 9.**

—— 三國志全圖演義 *San kwo che ts'euen t'oo yen e.* "The History of the Three Kingdoms. Completely illustrated, and with explanatory comments." By Lo Kwan-chung. Edited by Kin Shing-tan. 60 keuen. 1883. 8°.   **15333. f. 1.**

—— 繡像平妖全傳 *Sew seang p'ing yaou ts'euen chuen.* "The Pacification of the 'Imps.'" A book of wonders. Edited by Fung Yew-lung. With illustrations. 18 chapters. [1840?] 8°.   **15331. b. 14.**

羅貫中 LO KWAN-CHUNG. 殘唐五代全傳 *Tsan T'ang Woo tai ts'euen chuen.* "A complete account of the Fall of the T'ang and the Five Dynasties." By Lo Kwan-chung. 6 keuen. 1783. 8°.   **15333. d. 1.**

—— [Another edition.] Edited by T'ang Jo-sze. 6 keuen. 1866. 8°.   **15331. d. 8.**

樂蓮裳 LO LEEN-SHANG. 耳食錄 *Urh shih luh.* "Food for the Ears. A Collection of Tales." Compiled by Lo Leen-shang. 12 keuen. 1792. 8°.   **15331. b. 8.**

羅密士 LO-MEIH-SZE [i.e. ELIAS LOOMIS]. 代微積拾級 *Tai wei tseih shih keih.* "Analytical Geometry and Differential and Integral Calculus." By Lo-meih-sze. Translated into Chinese by Wei-lĕĕ-a-leih, i.e. A. Wylie, and transcribed by Le Shen-lan. 18 keuen. 1859. 8°.   **15259. f. 6.**

羅茗香 LO MING-HEANG. See 朱世傑 CHOO SHE-KEĚ. 算學啟蒙 *Swan heŏ k'e mung.* "A General Treatise on Arithmetic . . ." With the emendations of Lo Ming-heang, etc. 1839. 8°.   **15259. h. 3.**

羅懋登 LO MOW-TĂNG. 西洋記 *Se yang ke.* An apocryphal "Account of the Expedition made to the Southern (*lit.* Western) Ocean" by the Eunuch Ching Ho. With illustrations. 20 keuen. 1597. 8°.   **15331. f. 2.**

路程 LOO CH'ING. 路程第一書 *Loo ch'ing te yih shoo.* "The best book on the roads of China." 2 parts. 1694. 12°.   **15271. a. 25.**

路潤生 LOO JUN-SĂNG. See 許雲嶠 HEU YUN-KEAOU. 六觀樓北曲六種 *Lŭh kwan low pih k'eŭh luh chung.* "Six Plays . . ." Edited by . . . Loo Jun-săng, etc. 1874. 8°.   **15327. d. 29.**

鴛江寄迹人 LOO-KEANG KE TSEĬH JIN (*pseud.*). 我國志畧 *Wo kwo che leŏ.* "A Short History of Russia." By Loo-keang ke tseĭh jin, i.e. a visitor at Amoy. With a map. [*Shanghai?*], 1880. 8°.   **15291. a. 14.**

路德 LOO TIH. See 張熙宇 CHANG HE-YU. 七家詩輯註彙鈔 *Ts'ih kea she tseih choo wei ch'aou.* "A collection of the writings of . . ." Loo Tih, etc. 1870. 8°. **15324. a. 12.**

—— 路得事蹟圖說 *Loo-tih sze tseih t'oo shwo.* "The Story of Ruth. With coloured illustrations." pp. 8. [*Shanghai?*], 1882. 4°.   **15118. e. 7.**

LOO—LOU

路 德 閏 Loo Tihjun. See 張 熙 宇 Chang He-yu. 硃 批 增 註 七 家 詩 選 *Choo p'e tsáng choo ts'ih kea she seuen.* "Imperially endorsed Poems" by . . . Loo Tihjun, etc. 1857. 8°.
15323. c. 14.

羅 伯 聃 Lo-pih Tan [i.e. Robert Thom]. 華 英 通 用 雜 話 *Hwa Ying t'ung yung tsa hwa.* "A Chinese and English Vocabulary." Part i. *Canton*, 1843. 8°. 15346. b. 29.

—— [Another copy.] 15344. c. 27.

羅 博 Lo poh. See 鹿 兆 甲 Luh Chaou-keǎ. 福 山 縣 志 *Fuh-shan heen che.* "A Topography of Fuh-shan heen . . ." Edited by Lo Poh, etc. 1763. 8°. 15269. c. 13.

LORD (Edward Clemens). See 羅 爾 梯 Lo Urh-te.

—— *See* Bible—Old Testament : *Psalms.* The Book of Psalms in Chinese. Ningpo Colloquial. Translated by E. C. L., etc. 1877. 8°.
15117. b. 36.

—— *See* Goddard (Josiah). 耶 穌 登 山 教 衆 體 註 *Yay-soo táng shan keaou chung t'e choo.* "Christ's Sermon on the Mount, with Notes" by E. C. L., etc. 1851. 8°. 15200. b. 9.

—— 讚 神 樂 章 *Tsan shin lo chang.* Hymns and tunes. Compiled by E. C. L. On one page is given the text of each hymn in Chinese characters and in Romanized Chinese, and on the opposite page the music. pp. 31. *Ningpo*, 1856. 8°. 15118. a. 21.

羅 森 鐸 Lo Sǎn-to [i.e.]. 聖 女 羅 洒 行 實 *Shing nu Lo-se hing shih.* "The Life of Saint Rose." pp. vi, 116. *Hongkong*, 1896. 8°. 15200. d. 18.

樂 說 今 辯 Lo-shwo-kin-peen. See 阿 字 無 Ah-tsze woo. 海 幢 阿 字 無 禪 師 語 錄 *Hai chwang Ah-tsze woo shen sze yu luh.* "The Sayings of the Priest Ah-tsze woo . . ." Edited by . . . Lo-shwo-kin-peen, etc. 8°. 15101. b. 27.

LO SING-LAU. See 羅 星 樓 Lo Sing-low.

羅 星 樓 Lo Sing-low. English self-taught for Chinese. By Lo Sing-lau. 2 keuen. *Hongkong*, 1896. 8°. 11098. b. 18.

—— [Another edition.] *Hongkong*, 1898. 8°.
11098. a. 56.

羅 星 樓 Lo Sing-low. 司 梳 淺 譯 *Sze shoo ts'een yih.* A free translation of the Royal Readers. No. 1. By Lo Sing-lau. pp. 142. *Hongkong*, 1900. 8°. 11099. c. 43.

羅 斯 古 Lo-sze-koo [i.e. Sir Henry Enfield Roscoe]. 格 致 啟 蒙 *Kih che k'e mung.* "Chemistry." Science Primer. No. 2. By Lo-sze-koo. With plates. Translated into Chinese by Lin Yoh Che [i.e. Y. J. Allen]. 4 keuen. [*Shanghai*, 1885 ?] 8°. 15259. h. 1.

羅 四 明 Lo Sze-ming. See 梁 文 煜 Leang Wǎn-yuh. 鳳 山 縣 志 *Fung shan heen che.* "A Topography of the District of Fung shan . . ." Edited by Lo Sze-ming, etc. 1764. 8°. 15267. e. 7.

羅 大 經 Lo Ta-king. 鶴 林 玉 露 *Ho lin yuh loo.* "Precious dew from the Crane Forest." A collection of essays. 16 keuen. [1610 ?] Fol. 15320. d. 38.

Printed in Korea with movable type.

—— [Another edition. Incorrectly divided into keuen.] 18 keuen. [1620 ?] Fol. 15320. d. 39.
Printed in Japan with movable type.

羅 丹 臣 Lo Tan-ch'in. See 馮 楚 瞻 Fung Ts'oo-chen. 痘 疹 全 集 *Tow chin ts'euen tseth.* "A complete collective Treatise on Small-pox . . ." Edited by Lo Tan-ch'in, etc. 8°. 15252. b. 28.

駱 坦 軒 Lo Tan-heen. See 四 書 Sze shoo. 四 書 襯 *Sze shoo tsin.* "The Four Books. With an inner garment" of comments by Lo Tan-heen, etc. 8°. 15202. b. 19.

羅 通 Lo T'ung. See 趙 普 Chaou Poo. 煙 波 釣 叟 歌 *Yen po t.aou sow ko.* "Verses on Military Tactics . . ." Edited with notes by Lo Tung, etc. 8°.

羅 爾 梯 Lo Urh-te [i.e. E. C. Lord]. *See* Bible—New Testament : *Ephesians.* 使 徒 保 羅 寄 以 弗 所 聖 會 書 註 *She t'oo Pao-lo ke E-fuh-so shing hwuy shoo choo.* "The Epistle . . . to the Ephesians, with Notes" by Lo Urh-te, etc. 1855. 8°. 15200. b. 14.

—— 真 道 問 答 *Chin taou wǎn ta.* "A Catechism on the true doctrine." A Christian tract. pp. 50. *Ningpo*, 1868. 8°. 15200. c. 50.

鹿兆甲 Luh Chaou-keă. 禑山縣志 *Fuh-shan heen che.* "A Topography of Fuh-shan heen" in Shantung. Compiled by Luh Chaou-keă, Wang Chih, and others, and edited by Lo Poh. 12 keuen. 1763. 8°. **15269. c. 12.**

六壬 Luh Jin. 六壬眎斯 *Luh jin she sze.* "A Book on Fortune-telling." 4 keuen? [1750?] 8°. **15257. a. 6.**
Imperfect, containing only Keuen 3 and 4.

陸璣 Luh Ke. 詩草木蟲魚疏 *She ts'aou muh chung yu soo.* "Notes on the Botany and Zoology of the Book of Odes." 2 keuen. See 程榮 Ch'ing Yung. 漢魏叢書 *Han Wei ts'ung shoo.* "A collection of works by authors of the Han and Wei Dynasties," etc. 1791. 8°. **15318. a. 1.**

陸賈 Luh Kea. 新語 *Sin yu.* "New Discourses" on philosophical and other subjects. 2 keuen. See 程榮 Ch'ing Yung. 漢魏叢書 *Han Wei ts'ung shoo.* "A collection of works by authors of the Han and Wei Dynasties, etc." 1791. 8°. **15318. a. 1.**

陸喬木 Luh K'eaou-muh. 玉歷鈔傳警世 *Yuh leih ch'aou chuen king she.* "Excerpta from Buddhist Literature to arouse the World." Compiled by Luh K'eaou-muh. *Canton*, 1814. 8°. **15101. e. 13.**

陸稼書 Luh Kea-shoo. 三魚堂文集 *San-yu T'ang wăn tseth.* "Literary piece from the Hall of the 'Three Fishes.'" By Luh Kea-shoo. Edited by Seïh Yung-seun and Seïh Tseen-seïh. 12 keuen. With appendix in 6 keuen. [1840?] 8°. **15317. a. 6.**

陸拒石 Luh Keu-shih. 善卷堂四六 *Shen keuen T'ang sze lŭh.* "The Writings of Lŭh Keu-shih of the Shen-keuen Hall." Edited by Ch'in Fuh-chen. With notes by Woo Jo-shan. A reprint. 10 keuen. 1875. 8°. **15319. d. 21.**

陸九如 Luh Kew-joo. 應酬彙選新集 *Ying ch'ow wei seuen sin tseth.* "A new collection of selected letters relating to social entertainments," etc. 4 vols. 1864. 8°. **15315. c. 9.**

陸敬安 Luh King-gan. 冷廬雜識 *Lăng leu tsa shih.* "Miscellanies from the 'Cold Cottage.'" By Luh King-gan. 8 keuen. 1826. 8°. **15331. c. 13.**

陸敬科 Luh King-k'o. An English Grammar for Chinese Students, with concurrent explanation in Chinese. pp. vi, 141. *Hongkong*, 1896. 8°. **11098. a. 35.**

—— [Another edition.] *Hongkong*, 1898. 8°. **11098. a. 36.**

陸朗甫 Luh Lang-foo. 皇朝經世文鈔 *Hwang ch'aou king she wăn ch'aou.* "Essays on Classical Subjects by writers of the present Dynasty." Compiled by Luh Lang-foo. Edited by Tsung Kwo-ching. 30 keuen. 1869. 8°. **15320. e. 36.**

六部 Luh Poo. 六部成語 *Luh Poo ch'ing yu (Ninggun Churyan i toktoho gisun).* "The Phraseology of the Six Boards." 6 keuen. *Peking*, 1795. 8°. **15236. d. 12.**

陸小峯 Luh Seaou-fung. 禑音講臺 *Fuh yin keang t'ai.* "The Gospel Pulpit." A collection of sermons. Begun by Luh Seaou-fung and completed by Too Poo-se. pp. viii, 442. *Shanghai*, 1889. 8°. **15117. c. 8.**

陸西星 Luh Se-sing. 方壺外史 *Fang hoo wai she.* "Minor Taouist Works," including the Taou tih king. Compiled with commentaries by Luh Se-sing. 8 keuen. [1850?] 8°. **15113. b. 5.**

—— 金丹就正篇玄膚論 *Kin tan tsew ching peen heuen foo lun.* "Enquiries about the Philosopher's Stone. Discussions on the profound and great" powers of Nature. MS. 1576. 8°. **15111. c. 22.**

六十七 Luh-shih-ts'ih. 番社采風圖考摘畧 *Fan shay ts'ai fung t'oo k'aou tsih leŏ.* "Notes on Foreign Customs." See 王流 Wang Lew. 域外叢書 *Yih wai ts'ung shoo.* "Reprints of Works on Foreign Countries," etc. 1842. 8°.

陸士珍 Luh Sze-chin. 說唱繡香襄全傳 *Shwo ch'ang sew heang nang ts'euen chuen.* "The Complete Story of the Embroidered Fragrant Bag." A drama. 7 parts. 1814. 8°. **15327. b. 14.**

陸太淑 Luh T'ai-shuh. 馮母陸太淑人傳 *Fung moo Luh T'ai-shuh jin chuen.* "The Life of Luh T'ai-shuh." [1850?] 8°. **15303. d. 3.**

陸 德 明 LUH TIH-MING. See 周 禮 CHOW LE.
周 禮 *Chow le.* "The Chow Ritual . . ."
with explanatory notes by Luh Tih-ming, etc.
1868. Fol.   15220. b. 7.

—— See 莊 周 CHWANG CHOW. 南 華 眞 經
Nan hwa chin king. "The Nan-hwa Classic . . ."
with notes on the sounds of the characters by
Luh Tih-ming, etc. 8°.   15212. e. 9.

—— See 儀 禮 E LE. 儀 禮 *E le.* "The
'Decorum Ritual' . . ." With explanatory
notes by Luh Tih-ming, etc. 1868. Fol.
      15220. b. 2.

—— See 爾 雅 URH YA. 爾 雅 *Urh ya.* "The
Literary Expositor . . ." With notes on the
sounds by Luh Tih-ming, etc. 1868. Fol.
      15344. e. 16.

鹿 樵 LUH TS'EAOU. 滇 寇 紀 畧 *Tien k'ow ke leo.*
"An Account of the War in Yunnan," during
the Wars of the Three Kingdoms in the third
century before Christ. MS. 8 keuen. [*Peking,*
1850?] 8°.   Or. 4475. 39. B. f.

陸 奏 LUH TSOW. 御 定 陸 奏 約 選 *Yu ting
luh tsow yo seuen.* "A Collection of State
Memorials." A Korean edition. 2 keuen.
[1600?] 4°.   15236. c. 10.

陸 二 疋 LUH URH-P'EIH. See 張 餘 圃 CHANG
YU-POO. 佩 文 韻 篆 *Pei wan yun chuen.*
"A Dictionary of the Seal Character arranged
according to the finals . . ." Edited by Luh
Urh-p'eih, etc. 1797. 8°.   15344. b. 7.

陸 應 陽 LUH YING-YANG. 重 訂 廣 輿 記 *Chung
ting Kwang yu ke.* "A General Geography of
the Empire" by Luh Ying-yang, at the
beginning of the seventeenth century. Revised
and edited by Ts'ai Fang ping. With maps.
24 keuen. 1668. 8°.   15261. e. 7.
Imperfect, containing only Keuen 1, 2, 18–19, 24.

陸 元 朗 LUH YUEN-LANG. See 左 邱 明 TSO
K'EW-MING. 左 傳 *Tso sew.* "The Elegancies
of Tso K'ew-ming's Commentary . . ." explained
by Luh Yuen-lang, etc. 1720. 8°. 15212. e. 3.

LUK KING FO. See 陸 敬 科 LUH KING-K'O.

LUND (THOMAS). See 倫 德 LUN-TIH.

隆 中 LUNG-CHUNG. 隆 中 圖 *Lung-chung t'oo.*
"Rubbings from Lung-chung" [in Shensi?],
representing topographical plans and inscriptions. 10 sheets.

LUNG SHU. Suh-ki-li-lih-kiu. The Suhṛillekha
or 'Friendly Letter,' written by Lung shu
(Nâgârjuna), and addressed to King Sadvaha.
Translated [with the text] from the Chinese
edition of I-tsing. By the Rev. Samuel Beal.
pp. 51, 12. *Luzac & Co.: London,* 1892. 8°.
      11100. b. 27.

龍 大 淵 LUNG TA-YUEN. 古 玉 圖 譜 *Koo yuh
t'oo poo.* "An Illustrated Work on Antiquities."
Compiled by Lung Ta-yuen. Illustrated by
Lew Sung-neen. 100 keuen. 1779. 8°.
      15299. c. 2.

龍 萬 育 LUNG WAN-YUH. See 顧 炎 武 KOO
YEN-WOO. 天 下 郡 國 利 病 書 *T'een hea
keun kwo le ping shoo.* "A Work on the
Geography of the Empire" by Lung Wan-yuh,
etc. 1811. 8°.   15271. e. 6.

龍 嚴 LUNG-YEN. 眞 言 集 *Chin yen tseih.* "A
collection of true sayings," i.e. Buddhist Charms,
in Sanskrit, Chinese, and Korean. By Lung-
yen, assisted by his pupil Pih-yen. Re-edited
by Ying-yuĕ. 2 keuen. [1600?] Fol.
      15313. f. 1.

倫 德 LUN-TIH [i.e. THOMAS LUND]. 代 數 難 題
Tai shoo nan t'e. Lund's "Companion to
Wood's Algebra." Translated into Chinese by
Foolanya. 16 keuen. [*Shanghai,* 1876?] 8°.
      15259. f. 9.

雷 俠 兒 LUY-HËĔ-URH [i.e. Sir CHARLES LYELL,
Bart.]. 地 學 淺 釋 *Te heŏ ts'een shih.*
"Elements of Geology." Translated into
Chinese by Ma-kaou-wăn [i.e. D. J. Macgowan].
With plates drawn by Chaou Hung. 38 keuen.
1873. 8°.   15259. f. 4.

—— [Another copy.] 1873. 8°.   15259. d. 10.

雷 琳 LUY LIN. 漁 磯 漫 鈔 *Yu ke man ch'aou.*
"A collection of Tales from the Fishing Pier."
Compiled by Luy Lin, Wang Shaou-hoo, and
Mŏ Yay-tang. 10 keuen. 1871. 8°. 15331. d. 17.

磊 砢 山 房 主 人 LUY-LO SHAN FANG CHOO JIN,
pseud. 蟫 史 *Yin she.* "Miscellaneous Records"
of marvels. By the Master of the Dwelling on
Mount Luy-lo. With illustrations. 20 keuen.
[1800?] 8°.   15327. e. 9.

雷應百 Luy Ying-pih, and 浦德立 P'oo Tih-leĭh. 讚美詩 *Tsan mei she.* "Christian Hymns." Translated into the Ningpo dialect. Edited by Luy Ying-pih and P'oo Tih-leĭh. pp. xiv, 465. *Shanghai,* 1874. 8°.　**15118. a. 42.**

—— [Another copy.]　**15118. b. 32.**

LYELL (Sir Charles), Bart.　See 雷俠兒 Luy-hĕĕ-urh.

McCARTEE (Divie Bethune).　See 麥嘉締 培端 Mih Kea-te Pei-twan.

—— 西士來意畧論 *Se sze lai e leŏ lun.* "The reasons why Western scholars come to China." ff. 8. [*Tăngchow?*], 1863. 12°.　**15118. a. 24.**

—— 耶穌敎要旨 *Yaysoo keaou yaou che.* "The Fundamental Truths of Christianity." A revised edition of the *Yaysoo keaou yaou keue* by the same author, published at Ningpo in 1849. p. 22. *Ningpo,* 1858. 12°. **15118. a. 25.**

McCARTEE (Mrs.).　See 麥耐氏 Mih Nai she.

MACGOWAN (Daniel Jerome).　See 馬高溫 Ma-kaou-wăn.

—— 救溺死烟毒編 *Kew ne sze yin tuh peen.* Directions for resuscitating the apparently drowned, for recovering from opium-poisoning, and for the treatment of opium-smokers. With a preface in English and with plates. pp. ii, 19. *Shanghai,* 1877. 8°.　**15253. a. 17.**

—— [Another copy.]　**15118. b. 26.**

MACGOWAN (John).　A History of China from the earliest days down to the present. By J. M. pp. ix, 622. *London: Kegan Paul, Trench, Trübner, & Co.,* 1897. 8°.　**11098. b. 38.**

MACQUIRE (　).　See 麥高爾 Mih-kaou-urh.
15296. a. 30.

MAIN (Thomas J.).　See 美以納 Mei-e-na.

瑪高溫 Ma-kaou-wăn [ie. D. J. Macgowan]. See 雷俠兒 Luy-hĕĕ-urh. 地學淺釋 *Te heŏ ts'een shih.* "Elements of Geology." Translated into Chinese by Ma-kaou-wăn, etc. 1873. 8°.　**15259. f. 4.**

—— [Another copy.]　**15259. d. 10.**

瑪高溫 Ma-kaou-wăn.　See 代那 Taina. 金石識別 *Kin shih shih pĕĕ.* "A Manual of Mineralogy . . ." Translated into Chinese by . . . D. J. Macgowan, etc. 1868, 1883.
15259. c. 23.

—— [Another copy.]　**15259. c. 20.**

—— 航海金針 *Hang hai kin chin.* "A Treatise on Cyclones," chiefly taken from Colonel Reid's work on Typhoons. With diagrams. 3 keuen. *Ningpo,* 1853. 8°.　**15259. g. 11.**

—— [Another copy.]　**15259. g. 22.**

馬駧 Ma Kung.　儀禮章句易讀 *E le chang keu yih tuh.* "The Decorum Ritual made easy to read, paragraph by paragraph and sentence by sentence." Compiled by Ma Kung. With illustrations. 17 keuen. 1773. 8°. **15217. a. 9.**

馬葵齊 Ma Kwei-chai.　See 沈約 Ch'in Yo. 竹書紀年統箋 *Chuh shoo ke neen t'ung tseen.* "The Record of the Bamboo Books . . ." Edited by Ma Kwei-chai, etc. 1750. 8°.
15292. c. 4.

馬鳴菩薩 Ma-ming P'oo-sa.　大乘起信論纂註 *Ta shing k'e sin lun tsuan choo.* "The Mahāyāna-shraddhotpāda-shāstra. With a Commentary" by the Shamun Chin-keae. 2 keuen. 1876. 8°.　**15101. b. 29.**

MANDARIN DIALECT.　A first reader in the Mandarin Dialect. Being the first two chapters of John's Gospel, printed in clear type, with space opposite each character for manuscript notes. *China Inland Mission: Shanghai,* 1887. 8°.　**11099. d. 36.**

孟姜 Măng Keang.　孟姜女萬里尋夫 *Măng Keang neu wan le sin foo.* "Măng Keang goes ten thousand miles in search of her husband." A ballad. 1868. 8°.　**15323. b. 33.**

—— 孟姜女萬里尋夫全部 *Măng-keang neu wan le sin foo ts'euen pu.* "The complete story, represented on two sheets of coloured illustrations, of Măng-keang travelling ten thousand miles in search of her husband." 2 sheets. [1900?]　**M.P.C.**

孟經國 Măng King-kwo.　禍綠善慶集 *Fuh luh shen k'ing tseth.* "The happy, prosperous, good, and blessed collection" of medical prescriptions. 6 keuen. [1850?] 8°. **15252. a. 29.**
Imperfect, containing only Keuen 3.

MAN—MAT

孟 保 Măng Paou. See 朱 熹 Choo He. 合 壁 小 學 Ho peih seaou heŏ. "The Youth's Instructor . . ." Edited by Măng Paou, etc. 1850. 8°. **15229. b. 9.**

孟 子 Măng tsze. 孟 子 大 題 萃 Măng tsze ta t'e ts'uy. "A Collection of Essays on Texts from Măng tsze." Edited by the Master of the Seaou yun Pavilion. 1821. 24°.
15202. c. 19.

Imperfect.

滿 漢 Man Han. 滿 漢 類 書 全 集 Man Han luy shoo ts'euen tseïh. "A Manchu and Chinese Vocabulary arranged according to subjects." 30 keuen. [1735?] 8°.
Much torn.

毛 昶 熙 Maou Ch'ang-he. 科 名 金 鍼 K'o ming kin chin. "A guide for competitors at the public examinations." 1875. 8°. **15239. a. 47.**

毛 先 舒 Maou Seen-shoo. 塡 詞 名 解 T'een tsze ming keae. "A Critical Treatise on Rhyming." See 查 繼 超 Ch'a Ke-chaou. 詞 學 全 書 Tsze heŏ ts'euen shoo. "A Complete Work on the Art of Rhyming," etc. 1746. 8°. **15321. d. 14.**

毛 對 山 Maou Tuy-shan. 對 山 書 屋 墨 餘 錄 Tuy-shan shoo wuh mih yu luh. "Literary Miscellanies from Tuy-shan's Study." 16 keuen. 1870. 12°. **15316. b. 3.**

—— [Another edition.] 1871. 12°. **15331. d. 10.**

毛 嶽 生 Maou Yo-săng. See 祁 韻 士 K'e Yun-sze. 皇 朝 藩 部 要 略 Hwang ch'aou fan poo yaou leŏ. "Epitomized Histories of the Frontier Dependent Tribes." Edited by Maou Yo-săng, etc. 1846. 8°. **15271. b. 10.**

毛 雲 翼 Maou Yun-yih. See 徐 位 山 Seu Wei-shan. 經 言 拾 遺 King yen shih e. "Resuscitated Notes on the Classics . . ." Edited by Maou Yun-yih, etc. 1756. 8°.
15223. c. 11.

MARTIN (Frederick). See 麥 丁 富 得 力 Mih-ting Foo-tih-le.

MARTIN (William A. P.), D.D. See 丁 韙 良 Ting Wei-leang.

—— See Richard (Bonhomme). La science du Bonhomme Richard . . . With a Chinese version by Dr. W. A. P. M., etc. 1884. 12°.
11099. a. 12.

MARTIN (William A. P.), D.D. The Analytical Reader. A short method for learning to read and write Chinese. By W. A. P. M. pp. 204. *Shanghai*, 1897. 8°. **11098. a. 14.**

—— 三 要 錄 San yaou luh. "The Three Principles." A Christian tract. pp. 60. *Shanghai*, 1882. Sm. 4°. **15200. b. 34.**

—— 雙 千 字 文 Shwang ts'een tsze wăn. "The Two Thousand Character Classic." [*Peking?* 1870?] 8°. **15118. c. 36.**

—— [Another copy.] **15118. c. 1.**

馬 信 道 Ma Sin-taou. 延 年 要 訣 Yen neen yaou keuĕ. "Important secrets on protracting years." A collection of moral tracts. Compiled by Ma Sin-taou. 3 keuen. 1875. 8°.
15113. a. 29.

MASSON ( ), Monseigneur. See 要 理 Yaou le. 肆 原 要 理 Sze yuen yaou le. "The Original Doctrines" of Christianity . . . [By Mgr. Masson?], etc. 1898. 8°. **15200. b. 25.**

馬 太 Ma-t'ai. 馬 太 福 音 書 問 答 Ma-t'ai fuh yin shoo wăn ta. "A Catechism on the Gospel of St. Matthew." [By A. P. Happer.] pp. ii, 116. *Shanghai*, 1874. 8°. **15117. d. 25.**

MATEER (Calvin W.). See 狄 考 文 T'ieh K'aou-wăn.

—— A course of Mandarin Lessons, based on idiom. pp. xlix, 714. *American Presbyterian Mission Press: Shanghai*, 1892. 4°. **11098. c. 2.**

—— [A new and revised edition.] 2 vols. *Shanghai*, 1898. 4°. **11098. c. 16.**

MATEER (Julia B.). See 狄 就 烈 T'ieh Tsew-lĕĕ.

—— 西 國 樂 法 啟 蒙 Se kwo yo fa k'e mung. "The Laws of Western Music." *Shanghai*, 1872. 8°. **15257. e. 17.**

—— 鉛 字 揀 法 集 全 Yuen tsze peen fa tseïh ts'euen. "List of Chinese Characters in the Fonts" of the Presbyterian Mission Press. *Shanghai*, 1873. 8°. **15344. c. 19.**

馬 頭 Ma t'ow. 新 馬 頭 Sin ma t'ow. "The new landing-place." A play. pp. 8. [1860?] 8°. **15327. d. 33 (3).**

馬會 MA TS‘E. See 弘晝 HUNG CHOW. 八旗通志初集 *Pa k‘e t‘ung che ch‘oo tseih.* "A Complete Statistical Account of the Eight Banners." Compiled by . . . Ma Ts‘e, etc. 1739. 8°.   15296. c. & d.

馬俊瓦 MA TSEUN-LEANG. See 鄭方坤 CHING FANG-KWĂN. 本朝名家詩鈔小傳 *Pun ch‘aou ming kea ch‘aou seaou chuen.* Poems . . . Edited by Tseun-leang, etc. [1741?] 8°.   15323. b. 30 (4).

—— 龍威祕書 *Lung wei pi shoo.* A collection of reprints. A kind of literary encyclopædia. In ten parts. Edited by Ma Tseun-leang. [1840?] 8°.   15316. b. 5.
Imperfect, containing only Part 5.

馬端臨 MA TWAN-LIN. 文獻通考 *Wăn heen t‘ung k‘aou.* "A general examination of records and scholars." 348 keuen. [1600?] 4°.   15019. a. & b.
A Korean reprint of an edition dated 1266. Printed with movable type. Wanting preface and index. Keuen 115–118, 138–140, 148–150, 235–237 supplied in manuscript.

MAUNG GYI (J. A.) and CHEAH (TOON HOON). The Hokkien Library Series. Vol. i. The Celestial Mirror, an English translation by J. A. M. G. and T. H. C. of Pó Kàm, or extracts from *Liau chai* [*Leaou chai che e*], *Pau Kong an* [*Paou Kung an*], etc. pp. ii, 127, viii. *Rangoon,* 1894. 8°.   11100. c. 32.

馬爾頓 MA-URH-TUN. 星軺指掌 *Sing yaou che chang.* "A guide for Ministers going abroad," being notes on the forms of foreign governments. Edited by Kŏ-fuh-kăm. Translated by Leen Fang and King Ch‘ang. 3 keuen, with a supplement. 1876. 8°.   15239. a. 48.

—— [Another copy.]   15298. a. 44.

MAY (ALFRED J.). *See* ÆSOP. Æsop's Fables. Compiled [by R. Thom, and adapted and arranged by A. J. M.] for the use of Chinese studying English, etc. 1891, etc. 8°.   11100. c. 9.

—— [Another edition.] *Hongkong,* 1899. 1898. 8°.   11098. a. 30.

—— 訓蒙指南 A Guide to Knowledge. By A. J. M. First edition. 54 pp. *Hongkong,* 1897. 8°.   11098. b. 34.

—— [Another edition.] 1898. 8°. 11098. a. 28.

MAYERS (WILLIAM FREDERICK). The Chinese Government. A manual of Chinese titles, categorically arranged and explained, with an appendix. By W. F. M. Third edition. Revised by G. M. H. Playfair. pp. vi, 196. *Kelly & Walsh: Shanghai,* etc. ; and *Kegan Paul, Trench, Trübner, & Co.: London,* 1897. 8°.   11099. d. 39.

馬元臺 MA YUEN-T‘AI. See 黃帝 HWANG-TE. 內經靈樞註證發微 *Nuy king Ling ch‘oo choo ching fa wei.* "The Ling ch‘oo . . . With a Commentary and confirming evidences" by Ma Yuen-t‘ai, etc. 1609. Fol. 15253. e. 3.

馬融 MA YUNG. 忠經 *Chung King,* "The Classic on Patriotism." pp. vii, 16, 2. See 程榮 CH‘ING YUNG. 漢魏叢書 *Han Wei ts‘ung shoo.* "A collection of works by authors of the Han and Wei Dynasties," etc. 1791. 8°.   15318. a. 1.

—— 忠孝經讀本 *Chung heaou king tuh pun.* "The Classics on Patriotism by Ma Yung, and on Filial Piety." With a commentary by Wang Seang. [1800?] 8°.   15225. a. 23.

麻榮 MA YUNG. 天后傳 *T‘een-how chuen.* "A Biography of the Queen of Heaven." With illustrations. Edited by Ma Yung. 1838. 8°.   15111. a. 23.

苗 MEAOU. 苗圖 *Meaou t‘oo.* "Illustrated Descriptions of the Meaou Tribes" of South-Western China. The illustrations are coloured and on silk. No author's name is given. MS. [1750?] 4°.   Or. 4153. 28. a.

妙蓮保 MEAOU-LEEN-PAOU. See 惲珍浦 HWĂN CHINP‘OO. 國朝閨秀正治續集 *Kwo ch‘aou kwei sew ching che suh tseih.* "A supplement to the *Ching che* collection of Poems . . ." Edited by . . . Meaou-leen-paou, etc. 1836. 8°.   15327. e. 5.

MEDHURST (WALTER HENRY). See 尚德 SHANG TIH.

—— *See* BIBLE — NEW TESTAMENT: *Romans.* 羅馬書註解 *Lo-ma shoo choo keae.* "The Epistle to the Romans. With an explanatory Commentary." [Translated into Chinese by W. H. M.], etc. 1857. 8°.   15117. d. 28.

—— *See* BIBLE—NEW TESTAMENT: *First Epistle to the Corinthians.* 哥林多書註解 *Ko-lin-to shoo choo keae* . . . Translated by W. H. Medhurst, etc. 1858. 8°.   15117. b. 12.

MEDHURST (WALTER HENRY). See 聖經 SHING KING. 聖經史記 *Shing king she ke.* "Bible History." A manuscript note on the cover attributes this work to W. H. M., etc. 1846. 8°. **15200. c. 37.**

—— See 字 TSZE. 三字經 *San tsze king.* "A Three-character Classic" [. . . by W. H. M.], etc. 1843. 8°. **15225. a. 22.**

—— See 耶穌 YAY-SOO. 耶穌教畧 *Yay-soo keaou leŏ.* "A condensed statement of Christianity." [By W. H. M.], etc. 1879. 8°. **15200. c. 45.**

綿忻 MEEN HIN. 欽定新疆識畧 *K'in ting sin keang shih leŏ.* "An account of the newly-acquired Muhammedan Districts to the West of China." Compiled by an Imperial Commission consisting of Meen Hin, He Găn, Wang Ting-chin, and others. 12 keuen. 1820. 8°. **15271. b. 12.**

緬甸 MEENTIEN. 緬甸譯語 *Meentien yih yu.* "A Classified Burmese and Chinese Vocabulary," in which the Burmese word or words, written in a square cursive character, come first, then the equivalent in Chinese, followed by the sound expressed in Chinese characters. MS. [1700?] 8°. **Or. 11710. 39. B. f.**
Imperfect, containing only six out of the fifteen headings into which the work is divided.

MEI. 二度梅 *Erh-tou-Mei*, ou les pruniers merveilleux. Roman Chinois, traduit et accompagne de notes philologiques par A. T. Piry. 2 tom. *Paris*, 1880. 12°. **11099. b. 2.**

美以納 MEI-E-NA, and 白勞那 PIH-LAOU-NA [i.e. THOMAS J. MAIN and THOMAS BROWN]. 汽機發軔 *K'e ke fa jin.* "The Marine Steam Engine." By Mei-e-na and Pih-laou-na. Translated into Chinese by Wei-lĕĕ, i.e. A. Wylie. With diagrams. 9 keuen. With an appendix. [*Shanghai*, 1870?] 8°. **15259. f. 2.**

—— [Another copy.] **15259. d. 5.**

梅毅成 MEI KOW-CH'ING. See 程大位 CH'ING TA-WEI. 增刪算法統宗 *Tsăng shan swan fa t'ung tsung.* "A Work on Mathematics . . ." Enlarged and critically edited by Mei Kow-ch'ing, etc. 1877. 8°. **15259. b. 5.**

玫瑰經 MEI KWEI KING. 玫瑰經小問答 *Mei kwei king seaou wăn ta.* "A Catechism on the Rosary." pp. 30. *Hongkong*, 1890. 12°. **15200. c. 54.**

美國水雷局 MEI KWO SHWUY LUI KEU [i.e. The Department of Fulminates and Explosives of the United States]. 爆藥記要 *Paou yo ke yaou.* "On Fulminates and Explosives." Translated into Chinese by Shoo-kaou-te, assisted by Chaou Yuen-yih. With drawings. 6 keuen. 1875. 8°. **15259. e. 10.**

梅庭氏 MEI-T'ING-SHE. 繪像八仙綠 *Sew seang pa seen luh.* "An illustrated record of the Eight Genii." 4 keuen. 1829. 8°. **15101. c. 39.**

梅膺祚 MEI YING-TSOO. 字彙 *Tsze wei.* "A Chinese Dictionary." Compiled by Mei Ying-tsoo. 8°. **15344. b. 5.**
Very imperfect.

—— 玉堂字彙 *Yuh t'ang tsze wei.* "The Jade Hall Dictionary." Edited by Ch'in Haou-tsze. 4 parts. *Canton*, 1676. 8°. **15344. d. 6.**

—— [Another edition.] 1807. 8°. **15344. d. 7.**

—— 韻法 *Yun fa.* "Rules for Rhyming." By Mei Ying-tsoo. [1750?] 8°. **15344. e. 12 (1).**

—— [Another edition. 1840?] 8°. **15344. e. 12 (2).**

MÉLY (FERNAND DE). Les Lapidaires de l'Antiquité et du moyen âge. Ouvrage publié sous les auspices du Ministère de l'instruction publique et de l'Académie des Sciences. Par F. de M. Tome i : Les Lapidaires Chinois : Introduction, texte, et traduction, avec la collaboration de M. H. Courel. pp. lxvi, 300, 144. *Ernest Leroux : Paris*, 1896. 4°. **11098. b. 28.**

彌撒經 ME-SA KING. 輔彌撒經 *Foo Me-sa king.* "Aids to the Mass." Sinico-Annamite. pp. 10. *Hongkong*, 1889. 16°. **15200. aa. 30.**

MESNY (WILLIAM). See PERIODICAL PUBLICATIONS, SHANGHAI. Mesny's Chinese Miscellany. A textbook of notes on China and the Chinese. 1896, etc. 4°. **11094. b. 1.**

繆蓮仙 MEW LEEN-SEEN. 塗說 *T'oo shwo.* "Dull Notes" on historical and literary subjects. By Mew Leen-seen. 4 keuen. 1828. 8°. **15331. c. 11.**

繆襲 MEW SHIH. 尤射 *Yew shay.* "Strange Archery." pp. 25. See 程榮 CH'ING YUNG. 漢魏叢書 *Han Wei ts'ung shoo.* "A collection of works by authors of the Han and Wei Dynasties," etc. 1791. 8°. **15318. a. 1.**

MICHEL. Quelques observations au sujet du sens de mot Chinois *Giao chè,* nom des Ancêtres du peuple Annamite. *Ernest Leroux: Paris,* 1889. 8°. **752. f. 27.**

墨憨齋 MIH HAN-CHAI, *pseud.* 今古奇觀 *Kin koo k'e kwan.* "Strange Tales of ancient and modern times." Edited by Mih Han-chai. 40 keuen. [1800 ?] 8°. **15331. c. 2.**

麥高爾 MIH-KAOU-URH [i.e MACGUIRE?]. 歐洲東方交涉記 *Gow chow tung fang keaou she ke.* "The European Eastern Question." Translated into Chinese by Lin Lo-chih, i.e. G. J. Allen, assisted by Keu Gang-lai. 12 keuen. 1880. 8°. **15296. a. 30.**

麥嘉締培端 MIH-KEA-TE P'EITWAN [i.e. D. B. McCARTEE]. 悔改信耶穌說畧 *Hwuy kai sin Yay soo shwo leŏ.* "A short discourse on Repentance and Faith in Christ." pp. 18. *Shanghai,* 1874. 8°. **15118. a. 31.**

—— 勸解鴉片論 *K'euen keae ya-peen lun.* "Warnings against Opium." 7 leaves. *Shanghai,* 1867. 8°. **15116. e. 64.**

—— 靈魂貴於身體論 *Ling hwan kwei yu shin t'e lun.* "The Worth of the Soul." A brief discourse on Matthew, x, 28. 11th edition. pp. 12. *Shanghai,* 1862. 12°. **15113. a. 21.**

—— [Another copy.] **15118. a. 26.**

—— [Another edition.] *Shanghai,* 1867. 8°. **15116. e. 65.**

—— 靈魂總論 *Ling hwan tsung lun.* "A Brief Discourse on the Soul." 11th edition. pp. 10. *Shanghai,* 1862. 12°. **15113. a. 19.**

—— [Another edition.] *Shanghai,* 1867. 8°. **15116. e. 66.**

—— 聖經類書 *Shing king luy shoo.* "Quotations from the Bible, arranged according to subjects." 2 keuen. *Ningpo,* 1856. 8°. **15118. d. 5.**

—— 耶穌教例言 *Yay-soo keaou le yen.* "On Christian Beliefs and Customs." 11th edition. pp. 21. *Shanghai,* 1862. 12°. **15113. a. 20.**

—— [Another copy.] **15118. a. 16.**

墨湨子 MIH-LANG-TSZE, *pseud.* 西湖佳話 *Se hoo kea hwa.* "Notes on the Beauties of the Western Lake." By a writer styling himself Mih-lang-tsze. 16 keuen. 1785. 8°. **15276. b. 4.**

墨磨主人 MIH MO CHOO JIN. See 秘苑 PE YUEN. 古今秘苑 *Koo kin pe yuen.* "A Collection of Recipes . . ." Compiled by Mih mo choo jin, etc. 1846. 12°. **15333. b. 20.**

麥耐氏 MIH NAI -SHE [i.e. Mrs. McCARTEE]. 舊約節錄啓蒙 *Kew yo tsëë luh k'e mung.* "Old Testament History." With illustrations. pp. ii, 384. *Shanghai,* 1868. 8°. **15118. d. 9.**

默想 MIH SEANG. 六十三默想 *Luh shih san mih seang.* "The Sixty-three Subjects for Meditation." pp. 58. *Hongkong,* 1893. 12°. **15200. aa. 32.**

—— 默想指掌 *Mih seang che chang.* "A Guide to Meditation." pp. vi, 118. *Hongkong,* 1894. 12°. **15200. d. 23.**

麥丁富得力 MIH-TING FOO-TIH-LE [i.e. FREDERICK MARTIN]. 列國歲計政要 *Lëë kwo suy ke ching yaou.* "The Statesman's Year Book," by F. Martin. Translated into Chinese by Lin Lŏ Che, i.e. Y. J. Allen. 12 keuen. 1875. 8°. **15233. d. 7.**

墨子 MIH-TSZE. See 李贄 LE-CHE. 墨子批選 *Mih-tsze p'e seuen.* Extracts from the writings and sayings of . . . Mih-tsze, etc. 8°. **15314. e. 8.**

MILINDAPAÑHO. *See* SPECHT (É.). Deux traductions Chinoises du Milindapañho. 1893. 8°. **11100. b. 28.**

MILNE (THOMAS), M.A., F.R.G.S. See 托馬斯米爾納 T'OMASZE ME-URH-NA. **15291. b. 1.**

MILNE (WILLIAM), D.D. See 學善居士 HŎ SHEN KEU SZE.

—— See 張 CHANG. 張遠兩友相論 *Chang Yuen leang yew seang lun.* "Discussions between the two friends Chang and Yuen." [By Dr. W. M.], etc. 1882. 8°. **15200. c. 26.**

—— See 長 CH'ANG. 長遠兩友相論 *Ch'ang Yuen leang yew seang lun.* "Discussions between the two friends Ch'ang and Yuen." [By Dr. W. M.], etc. 1883. 8°. **15200. c. 5.**

MIL—MOO

MILNE (William), D.D. See 二 友 Urh yew. 二 友 相 論 *Urh yew seang lun.* "Discussions between two friends." [By Dr. W. M.], etc. 1864. 8°. **15200. c. 6.**

—— Some account of a secret association in China entitled the Triad Society. By the late Dr. Milne. Communicated by the Rev. Robert Morrison. From the Transactions of the Royal Asiatic Society of Great Britain and Ireland, vol. i. *London*, 1825. 4°.

明 Ming. 明 季 稗 史 彙 編 *Ming ke pai she wei peen.* "Records of the closing struggles of the Ming Dynasty." Compiled by "Lew-yun keu sze." [1830?] 8°. **15296. b. 10.**

MING DYNASTY. 大 明 會 典 *Ta Ming hwuy teen.* "A comprehensive description of the System of Government under the Ming Dynasty." [1600?] Fol. **15233. e. 2.** Very imperfect. Without either head-title or title-page.

—— 大 明 會 典 節 錄 *Ta Ming hwuy teen tseih luh.* "Extracts from the *Ta Ming hwuy teen.*" These extracts, which were copied for the Jesuit Missionary Fouquet, relate to the State worship of China, and are taken from Books 81–88, 91–93, and 95. The volume is interleaved, but contains only one European annotation. 2 vols. [1700?] 8°. **15233. d. 3.**

名 義 Ming e. 翻 譯 名 義 *Fan yih ming e.* "An explanation of the meaning of Sanskrit names and terms" which occur in Buddhist literature. pp. 59. [1860?] 8°. **15103. b. 13.**

—— 翻 譯 名 義 集 選 *Fan yih ming e tseih seuen.* "The Meanings of Sanskrit names and terms which occur in Buddhist Literature." [1800?] 8°. **15103. d. 14.**

名 犬 Ming k'euen. 名 犬 圖 說 *Ming k'euen t'oo shwo.* "An illustrated account of noted dogs." By, as is stated in a manuscript note on the cover, Mrs. Williamson. 2 keuen. 1883. 4°. **15331. e. 10.**

名 班 Ming pan. 名 班 抄 出 新 演 *Ming pan ch'aou ch'uh sin yen.* "Manuscript copies of 41 celebrated plays, lately acted" at Tientsin. ff. 38. [1875?] 8°. **Or. 4466. 39. B. f.**

閔 含 貞 Min Han-ching. See 閔 齊 伋 Min Ts'e-keih. 六 書 通 *Luh shoo t'ung.* "A Dictionary of the six forms of characters . . ." Edited by Min Han-ching, etc. 1824. 8°. **15342. e. 9.**

閔 齊 伋 Min Ts'e-keih. 六 書 通 *Luh shoo t'ung.* "A Dictionary of the six forms of characters." By Min-ts'e-keih. Edited by Min Han-ching and Ch'ing-Ch'ih-wăn. 10 keuen. 1795. 8°. **15342. d. 4.**

—— [Another edition.] 1824. 8°. **15342. e. 12.**

MOK LAI CHI. See 莫 禮 智 Mo Le-che.

MOK MAN-CHEUNG. The "Tah ts'z" (達 辭), Anglo-Chinese Dictionary. 2 vols. *Hongkong*, 1898. 8°. **11098. a. 25.**

莫 禮 智 Mo Le-che. English simplified for Chinese beginners. By Mok Lai Chi. pp. 58, 36. *Hongkong*, 1897. 8°. **11099. a. 18.**

慕 稒 德 Moo-a-tih [i.e. Archdeacon A. E. Moule]. 聖 公 會 大 綱 *Shing kung hwuy ta kang.* "The Great Institutions of the Church." A commentary on the thirty-nine articles. pp. ii, 158. *Shanghai*, 1877. 8°. **15117. b. 13.**

—— 信 徒 格 言 *Sin t'oo kih yen.* "Maxims for Christian Disciples." pp. viii, 50. *Shanghai*, 1875. 8°. **15200. c. 33.**

—— 大 倫 圖 說 *Ta lun t'oo shwo.* "A work on the great principles of conduct. With illustrations." pp. xii, 155. 1879. 8°. **15117. d. 29.**

慕 稼 穀 Moo Kea-kuh [i.e. George Evans Moule]. 讚 美 詩 *Tsan mei she.* "Christian Hymns." pp. 176. *Hangchow*, 1871. 8°. **15118. d. 21.**

慕 德 Moo-tih [i.e.]. See Bible—New Testament: *John, Gospel.* 約 翰 聖 經 釋 解 *Yohan shing king shih keae.* "The Gospel of St. John, with a Commentary" by . . . Moo-tih, etc. 1879. 8°. **15200. c. 22.**

慕 維 廉 Moo Wei-leen [i.e William Muirhead]. See Bunyan (John). 人 靈 戰 紀 *Jin ling chen ke.* "The Holy War." Translated into Chinese by Moo Wei-leen, etc. 1884. 8°. **15118. d. 27.**

—— *See* Periodical Publications, Shanghai. 益 智 新 錄 *Yih che sin luh* "A Miscellany of useful knowledge." Edited by Moo Wei-leen, etc. 1876, 1877. 8°. **15298. b. 39.**

慕維廉 MOO WEI-LEEN [i.e. WILLIAM MUIRHEAD]. 眞理尋繹 *Chin le sin yih.* "A search for the true principles" of religion. pp. ii, 56. *Shanghai*, 1880. 8°. **15200. c. 14.**

—— 竭力事主 *Keĕ leĭh sze choo.* "Serve the Lord with all your might." A Christian tract. pp. 34. *Shanghai*, 1877. 8°. **15200. c. 49.**

—— 古聖任罪 *Koo shing jin tsuy.* "The Confession of an Ancient Saint," i.e. St. Augustine. Abridged and translated into Chinese by Moo Wei-leen. pp. ii, 34. *Shanghai*, 1884. 8°. **15200. b. 19.**

—— 析疑辨謬 *Seih e peen meu.* "The explanation of doubtful points and the discrimination of falsehood" in the controversy between Protestants and Roman Catholics in China. pp. 46. *Shanghai*, 1881. 8°. **15200. c. 15.**

—— 天儒並論 *T'een joo ping lun.* "Christianity and Confucianism compared." pp. ii, 38. *Shanghai*, 1879. 8°. **15200. c. 41.**

—— 耶穌合稿 *Yay-soo ho kaou.* "Evidences of Christianity." pp. 30. *Shanghai*, 1877. 8°. **15200. c. 11.**

—— 耶穌言行綱目 *Yay-soo yen hing kang muh.* "An abstract of the Sayings and Doings of Christ." pp. 78, 34. *Shanghai*, 1868. 8°. **15118. d. 6.**

MORRISON (ROBERT), D.D. See 英國 YING KWO. 大英國人事略說 *Ta ying kwo jin sze leŏ shwo.* "A short treatise on English affairs." [By Dr. R. M.] 1832. 8°.

—— A Dictionary of the Chinese Language. In one volume. Photo-lithographed. *Shanghai*, 1879. 8°. **15342. a. 5.**

—— Some account of charms, talismans, and felicitous appendages worn about the person or hung up in houses, etc., used by the Chinese. By R. M. From the Transactions of the Royal Asiatic Society of Great Britain and Ireland, vol. iii. *London*, 1832. 4°.

MORTIMER (FAVELL LEE), MRS. See MÔ-TI-MEH.

摩西 MO-SE. 摩西聖蹟圖說 *Mo-se shing tse t'oo shwo.* "An Illustrated Life of Moses." By, as is stated in a manuscript note on the cover, Mrs. Williamson. pp. 36. 1882. 4°. **15118. e. 4.**

MÔ-TI-MEH [i.e. Mrs. F. L. MORTIMER]. Jih-tsih-yüih-le [Line upon Line]: ziu-z Gyu-iah djün-shü-li tsah-c'ih-læ yüong-yi ming-bah go shih-wo: feng tso zông-'ô liang-kyün. Translated into Chinese by Ko Po-yi [i.e. R. H. Cobbold]. 2 vols. *London*, 1868. 8°. **15118. d. 8.**

MOULE (ARTHUR EVANS), ARCHDEACON. See 慕極德 MOO A-TIH.

—— *Kông-ka.* "Sermons." Vol. ii. *Shanghai*, 1872. 8°. **15118. a. 53.**

MOULE (GEORGE EVANS). *See* BIBLE — NEW TESTAMENT: *John, Gospel.* An Sen Jah-'an dzun foh-in sö. Translated by G. E. M., etc. 1878. 8°. **15117. b. 35.**

—— *See* HANGCHOW. Hangchow Primer. Translation and notes. [By G. E. M. ?], etc. 1876. 8°. **11098. a. 31.**

—— See 公禱 KUNG TAOU. 公禱書 *Kung taou shoo.* "The Book of Common Prayer." Translated into Chinese by . . . G. E. M., etc. **15118. a. 50.**

—— Kong tao sö, or Book of Common Prayer. In Romanized Hangchow colloquial. pp. vii, 99. *London*, 1876. 8°. **15117. d. 34.**

MOULE (   ), MRS. *See* VÆN-TS'ÆN. *Yü-be væn-ts'æn zi dzo-ts'ah zi.* "On self-examination . . ." [By Mrs. M. ?], etc. 1866. 8°. **15200. b. 11.**

莫冶堂 MO YAY-T'ANG. See 雷琳 LUY LIN. 漁礁漫鈔 *Yu ke man ch'aou.* "A Collection of Tales . . ." Compiled by . . . Mo Yay-t'ang, etc. 1871. 8°. **15331. d. 17.**

穆克登頓 MUH-KIH-TĂNG-GIH. 大淸通禮 *Ta Ts'ing T'ung le.* "The Rites and Ceremonies of the Ts'ing Dynasty." [Edited by Muh-kih-tăng-gih and others under the sanction of the Emperor Taou-kwang.] 2 vols. 1824. 8°. **15239. c. 9.**

穆尼閣 MUH-NE-KIH [i.e.   ]. 對數表 *Tuy shoo peaou.* "Logarithm Tables." Based on the instruction of the "Western Scholar" Muh-ne-kih during the reign of Shun-che [1644–1662]. Revised and edited by Kea Poo-wei. 3 keuen. [1850?] 8°. **15259. h. 4.**

MUIRHEAD (WILLIAM). See 慕 維 廉 Moo
WEI-LEEN.

—— *See* BIBLE — NEW TESTAMENT: *Colossians.*
哥 羅 西 書 註 釋 *Ko-lo-se shoo choo shih.*
"The Epistle to the Colossians. Commented
on and explained." [By W. M.?], etc. 1878.
8°.   15200. c. 38.

—— See 福 音 FUH YIN. 福 音 聖 詩 *Fuh yin
shing she.* "Gospel Hymns." Stated in a
manuscript note on cover to be by W. M., etc.
1881. 8°.   15200. c. 1.

—— *See* JAMES (JOHN ANGELL). 救 靈 先 路
Kew ling seen loo. "The anxious enquirer after
Salvation." Translated into Chinese by W. M.,
etc. 1882. 8°.   15220. c. 18.

—— See 敎 會 KEAOU HWUY. 敎 會 問 答
Keaou hwuy wǎn ta. "The Assembly's Catechism." [Translated . . . by W. M.?], etc.
1855. 8°.   15200. b. 10.

—— See 聖 神 SHING SHIN. 聖 神 降 臨 *Shing
shin keang lin.* "The Descent of the Holy
Ghost" [By W. M.?], etc. 1883. 8°.
                                        15200. b. 20.

—— See 聖 書 SHING SHOO. 聖 書 綱 目 *Shing
shoo kang muh.* "A Scripture Textbook with
commentary." By . . . W. M. 1882. 8°.
                                        15118. a. 49.

—— See 頌 主 SUNG CHOO. 頌 主 聖 篇 *Sung
choo shing p'een.* "A Christian Hymnbook."
A manuscript note attached states that this
work is by the Rev. W. M., etc. 1876. 12°.
                                        15118. a. 47.

—— See 托 馬 斯 米 爾 納 T'OMASZE ME-URHNA.
大 英 國 志 *Ta ying kwo che.* "The History
of England . . ." Translated into Chinese by
W. M., etc. 1881. 8°.   15291. b. 1.

—— 地 理 全 志 *Tele ts'euen che.* "A work on
universal geography," being the second edition
of a work published by the author in 1853.
With maps. pp. 286. *Shanghai,* 1883. 8°.
                                        15271. c. 20.

蒙 古 MUNGKOO. 蒙 古 律 例 *Mungkoo leŭh le.*
"The Mongol Penal Code." 12 keuen. [1840?]
8°.   15239. c. 12.

NÂGÂRJUNA. *See* LUNG SHU.

耶 麗 NA-LE [i.e Sir GEORGE STRONG NARES,
K.C.B.]. 航 海 簡 法 *Hang hai keen fa.*
"On Seamanship." By Sir G. S. Nares.
Translated into Chinese by Kin-k'eae-le [i.e.
C. T. Kryer], and revised by Wang Tih-keun.
4 keuen. [1874?] 8°.   15259. c. 19.

—— [Another copy.]   15259. i. 3.

耶 連 提 耶 舍 NA-LIEN-T'E-YAY-SHAY [i.e. NAREN-
DRAYASAS]. 大 雲 輪 請 雨 經 *Ta yün lun
ts'ing yü king.* "The Great Cloud-wheel Sutrā
for praying for rain." Translated into Chinese
by Indian Priest Narendrayasas. 2 keuen.
[1840?] 8°.   15111. c. 19.

南 懷 仁 NAN-HWAI-JIN [i.e. FERDINAND VERBIEST].
敎 要 序 論 *Keaou yaou seu lun.* "An
Exposition of the Doctrines" of Roman
Catholicism. A new edition. pp. ii, x, 109.
Hongkong, 1889. 8°.   15200. d. 50.

—— A reprint. pp. xiv, 110. *Hongkong,* 1900. 8°.
                                        15200. b. 33.

—— 靈 臺 儀 象 圖 *Ling t'ai e seang t'oo.*
"Astronomical and Mechanical Drawings."
By Nan-hwai-jin. 2 vols. 1674. 4°.
                                        15257. d. 29.

—— [Another copy.]   15257. d. 30.

—— 新 製 靈 臺 儀 象 志 *Sin che ling t'ai e
seang che.* "A New Work on Astronomy."
By Nan-hwai-jin. Edited by Lew Yun-tih,
Sun Yew-pun, and others. 16 keuen. 1674. 8°.
                                        15255. b. 5.
Imperfect, Keuen 15 and 16, containing the plates, being
wanting.

南 北 宋 NAN PIH SUNG. 南 北 宋 志 傳 *Nan
pih Sung che chuen.* "The History of the
Southern and Northern Sung Dynasties." An
historical novel. Compiled by *Yen shih shan
ts'eaou,* or "The Woodman of the Yen shih
Mountain." With illustrations. The period
embraced in this work is from the year 926 to
975. 10 keuen. [1800?] 8°.   15286. c. 71.

瑙 挨 德 NAOU-AI-TIH [i.e. HENRY M. NOAD].
電 學 *Luy heŏ.* "A Manual of Electricity."
Being an adaptation of a work under that title
by H. M. Noad, and translated into Chinese by
Foolanya, i.e. J. Fryer. With plates. 10 keuen.
[*Shanghai,* 1875?] 8°.   15259. f. 15.

NARENDRAYASAS. See 那連提耶舍 NA-LEEN-T‘E-YAY-SHAY.

NARES (Sir GEORGE STRONG), K.C.B. See 那麗 NA-LE.

那清安 NA TS‘ING-NGAN. See 張熙宇 CHANG HE-YU. 硃批增註七家詩選 *Choo p‘e tsăng choo ts‘ih kea she seuen.* "Imperially endorsed Poems" by . . . Na Ts‘ing-ngan, etc. 1857. 8°. 15323. c. 14.

—— See 張熙宇 CHANG HE-YU. 七家詩輯註彙鈔 *Ts‘ih kea she tseth choo wei ch‘aou.* "A collection of the writings of . . ." Na Ts‘ing-ngan, etc. 1870. 8°. 15324. a. 12.

那爾敦 NA-URH-TUN [i.e. MILES JUSTUS KNOWLTON]. 聖經許諭 *Shing king heu yu.* "The Promises of the Bible." 3 keuen. *Ningpo*, 1867. 8°. 15118. b. 49.

—— 聖經問答 *Shing king wăn ta.* "A Scripture Catechism." pp. viii, 295, 10. [*Ningpo*], 1861. 8°. 15118. d. 10.

納延泰 NA YEN-T‘AI. See 允祿 YUN-LUH. 欽定同文韻統 *K‘in ting t‘ung wăn yun t‘ung.* The primary Sanskrit . . . characters . . . represented in Chinese . . . by . . . Na Yen-t‘ai, etc. 1750. 8°. 15354. a. 5.

NEAL (JAMES B.). *See* NORRIS (WILLIAM F.), A.M., M.D., and OLIVER (CHARLES A.). 眼科證治 *Yenko ching che.* The more important parts of the "Text-book of Ophthalmology . . ." Translated into Chinese by J. B. N., 1895. 8°. 15252. a. 30.

念常 NEEN-CHANG. 佛祖歷代通載 *Fuh tsoo leth tai t‘ung tsai.* "A History of Buddhism chronologically arranged." Published in 1344. 22 keuen. [1800 ?] 8°. 15103. d. 5.
Imperfect, containing only Keuen 1–10.

年希堯 NEEN HE-YAOU. See 樊騰鳳 FAN TĂNG-FUNG. 新增五方元音全書 *Sin tsăng woo fang yuen yin ts‘euen shoo.* "The original universal sounds of the characters . . ." Edited by Neen He-yaou, etc. 1835. 8°.
15346. b. 22.

—— See 樊騰鳳 FAN TĂNG-FUNG. 五方元音 *Woo fang yuen yin . . .* A Tonic Dictionary. . . . Edited by Neen He-yaou, etc. 1698. 8°.
15346. b. 24.

倪戈氏 NE KO SHE [i.e. MRS. NEVIUS]. 梅奠氏行畧 *Mei Mo she hing leŏ.* "A short Biography of Mrs. Mills." pp. 32. *Shanghai*, 1875. 8°. 15200. b. 6.

—— 耶穌教官話問答 *Yay-soo keaou kwan hwa wăn ta.* "A Protestant Catechism in the Mandarin Dialect." pp. 42. *Shanghai*, 1866. 8°. 15118. a. 37.

NESTORIAN TABLET. See 大秦景教 TA TS‘IN KING KEAOU.

NEVIUS (JOHN L.). See 倪維思 NE-WEI-SZE.

—— *See* BIBLE—NEW TESTAMENT: *Mark.* 馬可傳福音書畧解 *Ma-k‘o chuen fuh yin shoo leŏ keae.* St. Mark's Gospel, with notes [edited by J. L. Nevius], etc. 1878. 8°. 15117. b. 7.

—— *T‘in-lu ts nen.* "A Guide to Heaven." pp. 84. *Shanghai*, 1868. 8°. 15118. a. 54.

NEVIUS ( ), MRS. See 倪戈氏 NE KO SHE.

—— See 耶穌教 YAY-SOO KEAOU. 耶穌教官話問答 *Yay-soo keaou kwan hwa wăn ta.* "A Christian Catechism . . ." By Mrs. Nevius, etc. 1883. 8°. 15200. c. 24.

—— 孩童故事 *Hait‘ung koo sze.* The Swiss Boy; or the Story of Sah-pe. Translated by Mrs. Nevius. pp. 22. *Shanghai*, 1883. 8°.
15118. a. 33.

—— *Ju-dong ts‘u-hyiao.* "The Peep of Day," translated into the Ningpo Dialect by Mrs. N., and printed in the Roman character. With some hymns. pp. 155, 23. *Shanghai*, 1881. 8°.
15118. a. 44.

倪維思 NE-WEI-SZE [i.e. JOHN L. NEVIUS]. *See* BIBLE—NEW TESTAMENT: *Acts.* 使徒行傳註解 *She t‘oo hing chuen choo keae.* "The Acts of the Apostles, with a Commentary" by Ne-wei-sze, etc. 1868. 8°.

—— 宣道指歸 *Seuen taou che kwei.* "A Manual for Native Evangelists." pp. iv, 98. *Shanghai*, 1873. 8°. 15117. d. 30.

—— 神道總論 *Shin taou tsung lun.* "A Compendium of Theology." 3 keuen. *Shanghai*, 1872. 8°. 15200. b. 11.

—— 頌揚眞神歌 *Sung yang chin shin ko.* "Hymns of Praise." Compiled by Ne-wei-sze. *Shanghai*, 1871. 8°. 15118. b. 34.

倪 維 思 NE-WEI-SZE [i.e. JOHN L. NEVIUS]. 天 路 指 南 *T'een loo che nan.* "A Guide to Heaven." pp. 84, 7. *Shanghai*, 1882. 8°.
15118. d. 9.

—— *T'in-lu ts-nen.* "A Guide to Heaven." In Romanized Ningpo dialect. pp. 100. *London*, 1868. 8°. 15118. a. 52.

—— and 狄 考 文 T'EIH K'AOU WĂN [i.e. Rev. CALVIN W. MATEER]. 讚 神 聖 詩 *Tsan shin shing she.* "Christian Hymns." By J. L. Nevius and C. W. Mateer. With a preface and index of first lines in English. pp. xviii, 244, 6. *Shanghai*, 1877. 8°. 15117. b. 37.

牛 奐 NEW HWAN. See 吳 任 臣 WOO JIN-CH'IN. 十 國 春 秋 *Shih kwo ch'un ts'ew.* "The Spring and Autumn Annals of the Ten States . . ." Edited by New Hwan, etc. 1672. 8°.
15292. c. 6.

NEWLAND (A. G. E.). A practical handbook of the language of the Lais as spoken by the Hakas and other allied tribes of the Chin Hills. pp. ii, 687. *Rangoon: Superintendent, Government Printing*, 1897. 8°. 11098. b. 32.

愛 漢 者 NGAI HAN CHAY [i.e. K. F. A. GÜTZLAFF]. 福 音 之 箴 規 *Fu yin che chin kwei.* "Gospel Precepts." pp. ii, 34. *Singapore*, 1836. 8°.
15118. a. 41.

安 氏 NGAN SHE. 竊 憤 錄 *Ts'eih fun luh.* "Secret Records" of the Court during the reign of Shao Hing of the Southern Sung Dynasty (1131–1163), followed by a supplement and a biographical notice of Ahket'e. MS. ff. 37. [1800?] 8°. Add. 16345. 39. B. e.

NINGPO. *Nying-po kyiao-we-li sô yüong go tsæn-me s.* "Hymns in the Romanized Ningpo Dialect." pp. xii, 243. *London*, 1868. 12°. 15200. c. 47.

—— *Nying-po t'u-wô ts'u-'ôh.* "A Romanized Primer of the Ningpo Dialect." [By H. van V. Rankin.] pp. 26. *Shanghai*, 1883. 4°.
15229. b. 22.

寗 雲 鵬 NING YUN-P'ĂNG. 蘇 州 府 志 *Soo-chow Foo che.* "A Topography of Soo-chow Foo." Compiled by Ning Yun-p'ăng, Kaou Cho, and others. 82 keuen. 1693. 8°. 15265. c. 1.

NOAD (HENRY M.). See 瑙 挨 德 NAOU-AI-TIH.

NOCENTINI (LODOVICO). See K'ANGHE. Il Santo editto . . . Tradotti con note filologiche da L. N., etc. 1880. 8°. 11098. c. 1.

諾 格 德 NO-KIH-TIH [i.e.]. 西 藝 知 新 *Se e che sin.* "On Western Mechanical Science." Translated into Chinese by Foo-lan-ya [i.e. John Fryer], and transcribed by Seu Taou. 3 keuen. [*Shanghai*, 1875?] 8°. 15259. d. 17.

NORRIS (WILLIAM F.), A.M., M.D., and OLIVER (CHARLES A.). 眼 科 證 治 *Yen ko ching che.* The more important parts of the "Textbook of Ophthalmology," by W. F. Norris and C. A. Oliver. Translated into Chinese by James B. Neal. 3 keuen. *Shanghai*, 1895. 8°.
15252. a. 30.

NOTES. A volume of literary and historical notes. Without title. MS. ff. 59. [1750?] 8°.
16374. 39. B. e.

阿 發 滿 O-FA-MAN [i.e. FREDERICK OVERMAN]. 冶 金 錄 *Yay kin luh.* "The Moulder's and Founder's Pocket Guide." By O-fa-man. Translated into Chinese by Foolanya, i.e. J. Fryer. Revised by Chaou Yuen-yih. With plates. 3 keuen. [*Shanghai*, 1875?] 8°.
15259. h. 5.

—— [Another copy.] 15259. d. 3.

OLIVER (CHARLES A.). *See* NORRIS (WILLIAM F.) and OLIVER (CHARLES A.). 眼 科 證 治 *Yenko ching che.* The more important parts of the "Textbook of Ophthalmology," by W. F. N. and C. A. O., etc. 1895. 8°. 15252. a. 30.

OSBORN (SAMUEL). See 柯 士 賓 KO-SZE-PIN.

OSGOOD (D. W.). 全 體 闡 微 *Ts'euen t'e shen wei.* Gray's "Anatomy, descriptive and surgical," adapted and translated into Chinese by D. W. O. With plates, and an Anatomical Vocabulary in English and Chinese. 6 keuen. *Foochow*, 1881. 8°. 15253. e. 5.

OVERMAN (FREDERICK). See 阿 發 滿 O-FA-MAN.

OWEN (GEORGE SYDNEY). See 文 敎 治 WĂN KEAOU-CHE.

彭 芝 庭 P'ĂNG CHE-T'ING. See 四 書 SZE SHOO. 四 書 襯 *Sze shoo ch'in.* "The Four Books . . ." Edited by P'ăng Che-t'ing, etc. 8°.
15202. b. 19.

龐 鍾 璐 P'ANG CHUNG LOO. 文 廟 祀 典 考 *Wăn meaou sze teen k'aou.* "An Examination of the Religious Rites observed at Confucian Temples." With illustrations. 50 keuen. 1879. 8°.   15223. c. 12.

彭 希 涑 P'ANG HE-SOO. See 關 帝 KWAN TE. 聖 帝 寶 訓 *Shing te paou heun.* "The precious teachings of Kwan-te . . ." With notes by P'ăng He-soo, etc. 1836. 8°.
                                    15113. b. 11.

彭 觀 吉 P'ANG KWAN-KEĬH. See 禮 記 LE KE. 禮 記 省 度 *Le ke săng too.* "The Book of Rites examined and tested." By P'ăng Kwan-keĭh, etc. 1672. 8°.   15217. b. 7.

彭 紹 升 P'ANG SHAOU-SHING. 測 海 集 *Ts'ih hai tseĭh.* "A Collection from the Ocean" of literature. Compiled by P'ăng Shaou-shing. 6 keuen. 1779. 8°.   15321. d. 11.

彭 定 求 P'ANG TING-K'EW. See 曹 寅 TSAOU YEN. 全 唐 詩 *Ts'euen T'ang she.* "A complete Collection of the Poems of the Tang Dynasty." Compiled by P'ăng Ting-k'ew, etc. 1707. 8°.

彭 蘊 璨 P'ANG WĂN-TS'AN. 畫 史 彙 傳 *Hwa she wei chuen.* "Biographical Notices of Celebrated Artists." Compiled by P'ăng Wăn-ts'an. 72 keuen. 1825. 8°.   15305. b. 6.

彭 芸 楣 P'ANG YUN-MEI. See 顧 景 范 KOO KING-FAN. 讀 史 方 輿 紀 要 *Tuh she fung yu ke yaou.* "A Record of Geographical Changes . . ." Edited by P'ăng Yun-mei, etc. 1774. 8°.   15275. e. 1.

般 若 PANJO [i.e. PRAJNA]. 大 方 廣 佛 華 嚴 經 普 賢 行 願 品 *Tafang kwang Fuh hwa yen king p'oo heen hing yuen p'in.* Chapter on the practice and prayer of the Bodhisattva Samantabhadra in the Mahavaipulya-buddhavatamsaka Sūtra. Translated by Panjo. See 劉 翰 淸 LEW HANTS'ING. 大 乘 法 寶 十 種 *Ta shing fa paou shih chung.* "Ten precious works on the Law of the Mahayana . . ." 1881. 8°.
                                    15103. b. 13.

般 若 波 羅 蜜 多 PANJO PO-LO-MEĬH-TO. 般 若 波 羅 蜜 多 心 經 *Panjo po-lo-meĭh-to sin king.* "On the Prajnâ Pâramita Sûtra." *Canton,* [1800?]. 8°.   15103. d. 10.

班 固 PAN KOO. 漢 武 內 傳 *Han Wu nuy chuen.* "A history in the events of the reign of the Emperor Woo of the Han Dynasty." pp. 33, 2. See 程 榮 CH'ING YUNG. 漢 魏 叢 書 *Han Wei ts'ung shoo.* "A collection of works by authors of the Han and Wei Dynasties," etc. 1791. 8°.   15318. a. 1.

—— 白 虎 通 *Pih hoo t'ung.* The report of a "Conversation held in the Pih hoo kwan." 4 keuen. See 程 榮 CH'ING YUNG. 漢 魏 叢 書 *Han Wei ts'ung shoo.* "A collection of works by authors of the Han and Wei Dynasties," etc. 1791. 8°.   15318. a. 1.

—— 前 漢 書 *Ts'een Han shoo.* "The History of the Former Han Dynasty" (B.C. 206–A.D. 24), by Pan Koo. With a commentary by Yen Szekoo. The work is divided into four parts: Part I, *Te ke,* 13 keuen; Part II, *Neen peaou,* 10 keuen; Part III, *Che,* 10 keuen; and Part IV, *Leĕ chuen,* 79 keuen. [1850?] 8°.
                                    15296. c. 1.

般 刺 密 帝 PAN-LA-MEĬH-TE [i.e. PARAMITI]. 大 佛 頂 首 楞 嚴 經 會 解 *Ta Fuh ting show Lăng yen king hwuy keae.* "The Mahabuddhoshnisha-Sūrāngama Sūtra," translated into Chinese by Pan-la-meĭh-te. With interpretorial notes by Me-k'ie-shih-kea. 10 keuen. 1342. 8°.   15101. e. 12.

—— and 彌 伽 釋 迦 ME-K'IE-SHIH-KEA [i.e. MIKASĀKYA]. 大 佛 頂 如 來 密 因 修 證 了 義 諸 菩 薩 萬 行 首 楞 嚴 經 *Ta Fuh ting joolai meĭh yin sew ching leaou e choo P'oosa wan hing show lăng yen king* (Maha-buddhoshnisha-tāthāgata-guh yahetu-sākshātkrita-prasannārthā-sarvabodhisattvakaryā-Sūrāngama Sūtra). Translated by Paulameĭhte and Me-k'ieshihkea. 10 keuen. See 劉 翰 淸 LEW HANTS'ING. 大 乘 法 寶 十 種 *Ta shing fa paou shih chung.* "Ten precious works on the Law of the Mahayana . . ." 1881. 8°.
                                    15103. b. 13.

包 琭 PAOU YU. See 陰 時 夫 YIN SHE-FOO. 增 續 會 通 韻 府 群 玉 *Tsăng suh hwuy t'ung yun foo k'eun yuh.* "A Complete Tonic Dictionary . . ." Edited with additions by Paou Yu, etc. 1625. 4°.   15341. c. 4.

PARKER (EDWARD HARPER). Digest of the Yungch'ang Annals of Burma. By E. H. P. pp. 7. *Simla,* 1894. Fol.   11098. d. 2.

PAS—PER

八線 PA SEEN. 八線簡表 *Pa seen keen peaou.*
"Abridged Trigonometric Tables." pp. 180.
[1713 ?] 8°. 15259. h. 10.

八線對數簡表 *Pa seen tuy shoo keen peaou.*
See 買步緯 KEA POO-WEI. 15259. g. 20.

PAVIE (AUGUSTE). Mission Pavie Indo-Chine,
1879–1895. Études diverses: 1, Recherches sur
la littérature du Cambodge, du Laos, et du
Siam; (2, Recherches sur l'histoire du Cambodge, du Laos, et du Siam). Par A. P. 2 vols.
Ernest Leroux: Paris, 1898. 4°. 11098. c. 17.

票據 PEAOU KEU. 票據會要 *Peaou keu hwuy
shing.* "A Banker's Account Book." MS.
[1840 ?] 4°. 15297. d. 12.

PEARSE (MARK GUY), the Younger. 紅侏
儒傳 *Hung choo joo chuen.* "The Terrible
Red Dwarf." Translated into Chinese by Yang
Kih-fei [i.e. Griffith John]. With illustrations.
pp. vi, 30. *Hankow*, 1882. 8°. 15200. b. 18.

卜潤甫 PEEN YUEN-FOO. 山水真蹟 *Shan
shwuy chin tseih.* "Sketches of mountain and
river scenery from Nature." [1820 ?] 4°.
15255. e. 4.

PEEP. 訓兒真言 *Heun urh chin yen.* "True
words of instruction for children," i.e. the Peep
of Day, translated into Chinese by Hwa Sa-lai,
i.e. Mrs. Holmes. With illustrations. pp. vi,
117. *Shanghai*, 1882. 8°. 15200. c. 10.

—— Iu-dong ts'u-hyiao. "The Peep of Day."
Translated into the Ningpo Dialect by
Mrs. Nevius, etc. 1881. 8°. 15118. a. 44.

畢利幹 PEIH-LE-KAN [i.e. A. BILLEQUIN]. 法國
律例 *Fa kwo leuh le.* "The French Penal
Code." Dictated by A. B., and transcribed by
She Yü-hwa. ? keuen. *Peking*, 1880. 8°.
15241. c. 10.

—— 化學指南 *Hwa heŏ che nan.* "A Guide
to Chemistry." With plates, and vocabularies
in Chinese and French. 10 keuen. 1873. 8°.
15259. g. 1.

—— [Another copy. Imperfect.] 15259. d. 9.

—— 化學闡原 *Hwa heŏ shen yuen.* "The
elements of chemistry explained." With plates.
Translated into Chinese by Peïh-le-kan. 15
keuen. *Peking*, 1882. 8°. 15253. d. 3.

璧星泉 PEÏH SING-TS'EUEN. 守邊輯要 *Show
peen tseih yaou.* "On the National Defences."
MS. 1839. 8°. 15259. c. 13.

碧桃錦帕 PEÏH T'AOU KIN PA. 新碧桃
錦帕全本 *Sin peih t'aou kin pa ts'euen pun.*
"The Story of the Green Peach embroidered
Kerchief." In verse. 4 keuen. [1850 ?] 8°.
15327. d. 24.

裴路 P'EI-LOO [i.e.   ]. 輪船布陣 *Lun
ch'uen poo ch'in.* "Steamship Manœuvres."
With an introduction. Translated into Chinese
by Foo-lan-ya [i.e. Fryer], and transcribed by
Seu Keen-yin. 12 keuen. With a volume of
plans. [1872 ?] 8°. 15259. c. 18.

PEKING: TUNGWEN COLLEGE. Calendar of the
Tungwen College. First issue. *Peking*, 1879.
8°. 11099. c. 29.

PERIODICAL PUBLICATIONS: *Hongkong.*
醫學報 *E heŏ paou.* The Chinese Medical
Journal. A monthly journal of medicine,
surgery, and hygiene. Edited by Wan Tun-mo
(Yin Twan-moo). Vol. i, No. 1. *Hongkong*,
1898, etc. 8°. 15253. a. 18.

—— 避邇貫珍 *Hea urh kwan chin.* "A Serial
of Foreign and Domestic News." Containing
only vol. iii, Nos. 3, 7, 9–12, and vol. iv,
Nos. 1, 2, 4, 5. *Hongkong*, 1855–1856. 8°.
15298. b. 43.

—— 華番和合通書 *Hwa Fan ho ho t'ung
shoo.* "The Anglo-Chinese Concord Almanac"
for the year 1847. [Edited by Dr. Dyer Ball.]
[*Hongkong*], 1847. 8°. 15298. a. 38.
This magazine was first published in 1843 and was
continued until 1854, when Dr. Ball resigned the
editorship to Mr. French, who changed the title to
Ho ho t'ung shoo.

—— *London.* 中英商工機器時報 The
Chinese, Corean, and English Journal of
Commerce and Engineering. Vol. i, No. 4;
vol. ii, Nos. 5, 6, 7, 8, 9; vol. iii, Nos. 10, 11, 12.
The Eastern Press: London, 1896. 4°.
15255. f. 3.
Incomplete, wanting Nos. 1–3.

—— *Ningpo* 甬報 *Yung paou.* "The Ningpo
Magazine," also entitled "The Child's Paper."
. . . *Shanghai*, 1881, etc. 8°. 15298. b. 41.
In progress.

PERIODICAL PUBLICATIONS: *Peking.* 京報 *King paou.* "The Peking Gazette." 1841, etc. 8°. **15232, etc.**

Imperfect.

—— Translation of the Peking Gazette for 1872, 1873, 1875, etc. *Shanghai*, 1873, etc. 8°. **11098. a. 1.**

In progress.

—— 大清中樞備覽 *Ta Ts'ing chung shu pei lan.* "A View of the Government of the Empire," for the year 1876. 2 keuen. 1876. 8°. **15239. b. 22 (2).**

—— 大清搢紳全書 *Ta Ts'ing tsin shin ts'euen shoo.* "A complete Official Directory of the Empire" for the years 1834 [imperfect], 1835 [2 copies, one imperfect], 1836 [? imperfect], 1838 [2 copies], 1840 [4 copies, one imperfect], 1859, 1861, 1862, 1876, 1887. 1834, etc. 8°. **15239. d. 7–10, 13, 15, b. 22 (1).**

—— *San Francisco.* 舊金山唐人新聞帋 *Kew kin shan T'ang jin sin wǎn chih.* The San Francisco China News. 1874, etc. Nos. 1–46, July 4, 1874, to May 29, 1875. **15298. a. 47.**

—— *Shanghai.* The Celestial Empire. 華洋通聞 *Hwa yang t'ung wǎn. Shanghai*, 1877, etc. **PP. 9990. b.**

In progress.

—— The Chinese, Corean, and English Journal of Commerce and Engineering. *See supra*, London. **15255. f. 3.**

—— The Chinese Illustrated News. Vol. iv, No. 10. *Shanghai*, 1884. 8°. **15298. a. 50.**

—— 中國教會新報 *Chung kwo keaou hwuy sin paou.* "A Chinese Church Magazine." With illustrations. *Shanghai*, 1868, etc. 8°. Vol. i, 1–50; vol. ii, 51–100; vol. iii, 101–151; vol. iv, 153, 155, 158–172, 174, 175, 177–182, 184–200; vol. v, 201–218, 221, 224–238, 240–250; vol. vi, 251–259, 261–300. **15298. c. 27.**

—— 中西聞見錄 *Chung se wǎn keen luh.* "A Chinese and Foreign Magazine." 1875. **15298. a. 46.** Containing only Nos. 11, 27–34, 36.

—— 中外新報 *Chung wai sin paou.* "A Chinese and Foreign Magazine." 1855–57. 8°. **15298. b. 5.** Only Nos. 2, 3, 19 of vol. ii, Nos. 2, 12 of vol. iii, and No. 1 of vol. iv.

PERIODICAL PUBLICATIONS: *Shanghai.* 格致彙編 *Kih che wei peen.* The Chinese Scientific Magazine: a monthly journal of popular scientific information, with which is incorporated the Peking Magazine. With illustrations. Edited by John Fryer. Second edition. *Shanghai*, 1876, etc. 8°. **15298. c. 26.** Containing the first four years, viz. 1876–1879.

—— 六合叢談 *Luh ho ts'ung t'an.* "A Magazine of General Literature." With illustrations. Edited by A. Wylie. Nos. 1 to 13. *Shanghai*, 1857. 8°. **15298. a. 45.**

—— Mesny's Chinese Miscellany. A text-book of notes on China and the Chinese. *Chinese Gazette Office : Shanghai*, 1896, etc. 4°. **11094. b. 1.**

In progress.

—— 西國近事彙編 *Se kwo kin sze wei peen.* "A quarterly summary of foreign events." Dictated by Kin Kea-le, i.e. C. T. Kreyer, and transcribed by Ts'ai Seïh-ling. Parts 1–4 of 1873, 1–4 of 1874, 1–4 of 1876, and 1–4 of 1877. *Shanghai*, 1873, etc. 8°. **15298. b. 42.**

In progress.

—— 新報 *Sin paou.* "The New Gazette." *Shanghai*, 1877, etc. **15230, etc.**

In progress.

—— 點石齋畫報 *Teen-shih chai hwa paou.* "The Teen-shih chai Illustrated News." Vols. i–vii, No. 301, etc. 1892, etc. 8°. **15298. e.**

In progress.

—— 七日鏡覽 *Ts'ih jih king lan.* "A Weekly Mirror" of News. *Shanghai*, 1870. 8°. **15298. b. 6.** Only numbers for the 29th of the eighth month and for the 5th of the ninth month.

—— 萬國公報 *Wan kwo kung paou.* "An Universal Gazette." *Shanghai*, 1874, etc. 8°. **15298. a. 51.**

In progress.

—— 益智新錄 *Yih che sin luh.* "A Miscellany of Useful Knowledge." Edited by Moo Wei-leen, i.e. Rev. William Muirhead, with the help of Dr. J. Edkins and Y. J. Allen. With an English title-page and table of contents in each number. Vol. i, Nos. 1–12; vol. ii, Nos. 1–12. *Shanghai*, 1876, 1877. 8°. **15298. b. 39.**

PERIODICAL PUBLICATIONS : *Singapore*. 東 西 洋 考 毎 月 統 記 傳 *Tung se yang k'aou mei yueh t'ung ke chuen.* "A monthly periodical of foreign and domestic news." Edited by Gai-Han-chay, i.e. Rev. K. F. A. Gützlaff. [1837 ?] 8°.   **15298. b. 4.**
An odd part without any indication as to its number in the serial.

—— *Taiwan Fu*. Tâi-oân-hú-siâⁿ Kàu-hōe-pò. [The Taiwan Fu Church News.] Vol. i, 1885–1886. *Taiwan Fu*, 1887. 4°. **15298. a. 41.**

彼 得 羅 PE-TIH-LO. 彼 得 羅 言 行 全 傳 *Pe-tih-lo yen hing ts'euen chuen.* "The Life of Saint Peter." [By K. F. A. Gützlaff.] 2 keuen. [1838 ?] 8°.   **15118. d. 12.**

PETILLON (CORENTIN). Variétés Sinologiques, No. 13: Allusions littéraires. Première série. Par Le P. C. P. Second fascicule. *Shanghai*, 1898. 8°.   **11095. b. 2.**

秘 苑 PE YUEN. 古 今 秘 苑 *Koo kin pe yuen.* "A collection of Recipes of ancient and modern times." Compiled by Mih mo choo jin, i.e. The Master of an Ink Mill. 15 keuen. With a supplement in 13 keuen. 1846. 12°.   **15333. b. 20.**

柏 哲 PIH-CHĔ [i.e. J. G. PIKE]. 經 錄 問 答 *King luh wăn ta.* "A Catechism on Bible Records." Translated into Chinese by Hoo Tih-mai [i.e. T. H. Hudson]. pp. iv, 107. 1868. 8°.   **15200. c. 3.**

白 潢 PIH HWANG. 西 江 志 *Se keang che.* "A Topography of the Province of Keang se." Compiled by Pih Hwang, Cha Shin-hing, Luh Kwei-heun, and others. 206 keuen. 1720. 8°.   **15264. b. 2. & c.**

柏 衣 文 PIH I-WĂN [i.e. BARRETT ?]. 祈 禱 慎 思 *K'e taou shin sze.* "Careful Reflections on Prayer." pp. iv, 38. *Shanghai*, 1882. 8°.   **15200. c. 8.**

伯 仁 PIH JIN. 竹 波 軒 樣 冊 *Chuh po heen mei shan.* "A Model Drawing Book" by Pih Jen, edited by T'ang Yun-woo (?). 1838. 4°.   **15255. e. 20.**

伯 仁 滑 PIH JIN-HWA. 正 人 明 堂 圖 *Ching jin ming t'ang t'oo.* "An anatomical plate of the full-face human figure." 1577. A scroll.   **15253. c. 6 (1).**

白 起 德 PIH-K'E-TIH [i.e.   ]. 運 規 約 指 *Yun kwei yo che.* "A Work on Practical Geometry." Translated into Chinese by Foolanya [i.e. J. Fryer]. Edited by Seu Keen-yin. 3 keuen. [*Shanghai*, 1870 ?] 8°. **15255. d. 19.**

—— [Another copy.]   **15259. g. 18.**

白 居 易 PIH KEU-YIH. 白 氏 文 集 *Pih she wăn tseth.* "The Writings of Pih Keu-yih." Compiled by Yuen Wei-che. 71 keuen. [1618 ?] Fol.   **15315. d. 2.**
Printed in Japan from blocks.

白 勞 那 PIH-LAOU-NA [i.e. THOMAS BROWN]. See 美 以 納 MEI-E-NA and PIH-LAOU-NA. 汽 機 發 靭 *K'e ke fa jin.* "The Marine Steam Engine," etc. 8°.   **15259. f. 2.**

—— [Another copy.]   **15259. d. 1.**

白 力 蓋 PIH LEÏH-KAI [i.e. V. LE BLANC ?]. 器 象 顯 真 *K'e seang heen chin.* "Drawings for Engineers and Machinists. With atlas of engravings." Adapted from the work of V. Le Blanc and Jacques Eugène Armengaud. Translated into Chinese by Foolanya [i.e J. Fryer]. 4 keuen, with atlas. [1880 ?] 8°.   **15259. h. 2.**

—— [Another copy.]   **15259. c. 15.**

伯 里 牙 芒 PIH-LE-YE-MANG [i.e. H. BRIALMONT]. 營 壘 圖 說 *Ying lui t'oo shuo.* "La fortification improvisée, illustrated and explained." Translated into Chinese by Kin-k'eae-le, with the assistance of Le Fung-paou. pp. 56, 16. [1880 ?] 8°.   **15259. e. 8.**

—— [Another copy.]   **15259. d. 7.**

百 鳥 PIH NEAOU. 百 鳥 圖 說 *Pih neaou t'oo shuo.* "Notes on Birds." By Mrs. Williamson, as stated in a manuscript note on cover. pp. 58. 1882. 8°.   **15255. e. 31.**

白 多 瑪 PIH TO-MA. 四 終 畧 意 *Sze chung leŏ e.* "A short explanation of the four ends," i.e. Death, Judgment, Hell, and Paradise. 4 keuen. *Hongkong*, 1889. 8°.   **15200. d. 52.**

柏 靜 濤 PIH TSING-T'AOU. 奉 使 朝 鮮 驛 程 日 記 *Fung she ch'aou-seen yih ch'ing jih ke.* "A Diary of an Embassy to Corea." 1844. 8°.   **15275. a. 10.**

白爾格 PIH-URH-KIH [i.e. NICHOLAS PROCTOR BURGH?]. 汽機新制 K'e ke sin che. "New Rules for the Steam Engine." Translated into Chinese by Foolanya [i.e. John Fryer]. 8 keuen. [*Shanghai*, 1880?] 8°. **15259. i. 4.**

—— [Another copy.] **15259. d. 16.**

白爾捺 PIH-URH-NA [i.e. OLIVER BYRNE]. 井礦工程 Tsing hwang kung ch'ing. "Methods of sinking wells and of boring for sulphur," based on the article Boring and Blasting in Spon's Dictionary of Engineering, edited by O. Byrne. Translated into Chinese by Foolanya, i.e. J. Fryer. With plates. 3 keuen. [*Shanghai*, 1878?] 8°. **15259. i. 2.**

白爾特 PIH-URH-T'IH [i.e. WILLIAM RADCLIFF BIRT]. 御風要術 Yu fung yaou shuh. "Important Laws for Managing the Wind." Translated into Chinese by Kin-k'eae-le [i.e. C. T. Kreyer], and transcribed by Hwa Hangfang. 3 keuen. [*Shanghai*, 1874?] 8°. **15259. d. 24.**

—— [Another copy.] **15259. g. 19.**

白巖 PIH-YEN. See 龍巖 LUNG-YEN. 真言集 Chin yen tseïh. "A collection of true sayings," i.e. Buddhist Charms. By . . . Pih-yen, etc. Fol. **15313. f. 1.**

白玉蟾 PIH YUH-CHEN. See 老君 LAOU KEUN. 道德寶章 Taou tih paou chang. "The precious treatise on Reason and Virtue." With notes by Pih Yuh-chen, etc. 1838. Fol. **15113. e. 3.**

白雲道人 PIH-YUN TAOU-JIN, pseud. 玉樓春 Yuh low ch'un. A Novel. With illustrations. 4 keuen. 1860. 8°. **15334. c. 8.**

PIKE (J. G.). See 柏哲 PIH-CHĔ.

稟 PIN. 稟批簿 Pin p'e po. "Petitions." MS. 1844. 8°. **15241. b. 10.**

馮培 PING PEI. See 延豐 YEN-FUNG. 欽定重修兩浙鹽法志 K'in ting chung sew leang Che yen fa che. A Record of the Laws on the Salt Monopoly for the Province of Chĕkeang. By Ping Pei, etc. 1801. 8°. **15239. e. 1.**

PIRY (A. THÉOPHILE). See 康熙 K'ANG-HE, *Emperor.* 聖諭廣訓 Le Saint Édit. Étude de littérature Chinoise préparée par A. Théophile Piry, etc. 1879. 4°. **11098. c. 3.**

—— [Another copy.] **15229. b. 18.**

—— See MEI. 二度梅 Erh-tou-Mei . . . traduit et accompagné de notes philologiques par A. T. P., etc. 1880. 12°. **11099. b. 2.**

PLAYFAIR (GEORGE MACDONALD HOME). See MAYERS (WILLIAM FREDERICK). The Chinese Government . . . Third edition. Revised by G. M. H. P., etc. 1897. 8°. **11099. d. 39.**

PLAYS. A collection of seventeen Plays from Tientsin, without general title. Some of them are described as belonging to the repertoire of Chungk'ing companies, and others to that of Ngank'ing companies. They consist of comedies and farces. 2 vols. Vol. i, ff. 194; vol. ii, ff. 179. [*Tientsin*, 1880?] 8°. **Or. 4465. 40. B. e.**

—— A collection of 32 short plays from Peking. 3 vols. Vol. i, ff. 497; vol. ii, ff. 375; vol. iii, ff. 470. [*Peking*, 1880?] **Or. 4468. 39. B. f.**

博愛者 PO-GAI-CHAY [i.e. WILLIAM MILNE, D.D.]. 鄉訓五十二則 Heang heun woo shih urh tsih. "Twelve village sermons, for weekly use." Keuen 1. *Shanghai*, 1874. 8°. **15200. c. 19.**

POLETTI (P.). 華英萬字典 A Chinese and English Dictionary, arranged according to Radicals and Sub-Radicals. New and enlarged edition containing 12,650 Chinese characters, with the pronunciation in the Peking dialect according to Sir T. Wade's system, and the pronunciation in the general language of China in Dr. Williams' spelling. By P. P. pp. cvii, 307. *Shanghai*, 1896. 8°. **11098. b. 30.**

—— 華英字錄 Hwa Ying tsze luh. "Analytic Index of Chinese Characters . . . with the concise meaning in English." By P. P. *Tientsin*, 1881. 8°. **15344. c. 28.**

哺乳 POO JOO. 哺乳須知 Poo joo seu che. "How to use condensed milk." [*Hongkong*, 1898?] 12°. **15253. a. 19.**

POO—PRU

蒲 陸 山 P'oo-luh-shan [i.e. Charles Loudon Bloxam]. 化 學 分 原 *Hwa heŏ fun yuen.* "On Practical Chemistry." Translated into Chinese by Foolanya [i.e. Fryer]. Edited by Seu Keen-yin. 8 keuen. [*Shanghai*, 1870?] 8°. **15252. d. 11.**

—— [Another copy.] **15259. g. 15.**

—— 化 學 鑑 原 續 編 *Hwa heŏ keen yuen suh peen.* "An Examination of the Principles of Chemistry. A supplementary work." Being an adaptation of the organic portion of Bloxam's "Chemistry, Inorganic and Organic." Translated into Chinese by Foolanya, i.e. J. Fryer. With plates. 22 keuen. [*Shanghai*, 1880?] 8°. **15259. g. 5.**

步 倫 Poo-lun [i.e. Johann Caspar Bluntschli]. 公 法 會 通 *Kung fa hwuy t'ung.* "International Law," being a translation into Chinese of Bluntschli's "Das moderne Völker recht der civilisirten Staten als Rechtsbuch dargestellt," by Ting Wei-leang, i.e. Dr. W. A. P. Martin. 10 keuen. 1880. 8°. **15241. c. 11.**

—— [Another copy.] **15241. c. 12.**

補 相 子 Poo Seang-tsze. 透 膽 寒 *T'ow tan han.* "Courage-chilling Records." A lawyer's guide. 4 keuen. 1812. 8°. **15241. a. 3.**

浦 惺 廔 P'oo Sing-chan. See 四 書 Sze shoo. 四 書 合 讀 *Sze shoo ho keang.* "The Four Books . . ." Edited by P'oo Sing-chan, etc. 1865. 8°. **15202. b. 20.**

薄 德 立 P'oo Tih-leih. See 雷 應 百 Luy Ying-pih and P'oo Tih-leih. 讚 美 詩 *Tsan mei she.* "Christian Hymns," etc. 1874. 8°. **15118. a. 42.**

—— 總 會 記 錄 成 章 摘 譯 *Tsung hwuy ke luh ch'ing chang chai yih.* "A Digest of the Acts of the General Assembly of the (American) Presbyterian Church" from 1710 to 1873. Translated into Chinese by P'oo-tih-leih. pp. 34. *Shanghai*, 1884. 8°. **15118. a. 20.**

蒲 而 捺 Poo-urh-na [i.e. John Bourne]. 汽 機 *K'e ke.* "Handbook of the Steam Engine." By J. Bourne. Translated into Chinese by Foolanya [i.e. J. Fryer], and revised by Seu Keen-yih. 13 keuen. *Shanghai* [1874?]. 8°. **15259. d. 4.**

蒲 而 捺 Poo-urh-na [i.e. John Bourne]. 汽 機 必 以 *K'e ke pe e.* "A Catechism of the Steam Engine." Adapted and translated into Chinese by Foolanya, i.e. J. Fryer. With plates. 12 keuen. With supplement. *Shanghai* [1874?]. 8°. **15259. f. 8.**

步 月 主 人 Poo yuĕ choo jin. See 畫 圖 Hwa t'oo. 畫 圖 緣 *Hwa t'oo yuen.* "The Mystery of a Drawing." Edited by Poo yuĕ choo jin, etc. 8°.

PORTER (Mary A.). See Gwen. 閨 娜 傳 *Kwei-no chuen.* . . . Little Gwen's story. Translated into Chinese by Miss Porter, etc. 1882. 8°. **15200. c. 2.**

—— See Walton (Catherine Augusta). 安 樂 家 *Gan yo kea* . . . Christie's Old Organ . . . Translated into Chinese by M. A. P., etc. 1882. 8°. **15200. c. 16.**

啵 哫 官 Po-urh kwan. 啵 哫 官 的 問 答 話 *Po-urh kwan ti wăn ta hwa.* "Mr. B.'s Dialogues." MS. ff. 30. [1850?] **15318. d. 2.**

POUVOURVILLE (Albert de). See Laou-tsze. L'Esprit des races jaunes. Le Tao de Laotseu, traduit . . . par Matgioi (A. de Pouvourville). 1894. 8°. **11100. b. 31.**

博 文 居 士 Po wăn keu sze, *pseud.* See Æsop. 伊 娑 菩 喻 言 *E-so-p'oo yu yen.* "Æsop's Fables." Translated into Chinese by Po wăn keu sze, etc. 1890. 12°. **15331. b. 17.**

郡 陽 約 翰 P'oyang Yohan [i.e. John Bunyan]. 勝 旅 景 程 正 編 *Shing leuh king ch'ing ching peen.* "The Pilgrim's Progress." Translated into Chinese by Hoo Tih-mai, i.e. Thomas Hall Hudson. 2 vols. *Ningpo*, 1870. 8°. **15118. d. 4.**

PRUSSIA: Departments of State, etc.—*Army.* 攻 守 礮 法 *Kung show p'aou fa.* "On Attacking and Defensive Gunnery." Issued in the original by the Prussian War Office. Translated into Chinese by Kin K'eae-le and transcribed by Le Fung-paou. pp. 44. [1874?] 8°. **15259. d. 11 (1).**

—— 克 虜 伯 船 礮 操 法 *K'ih-lŭo-pih ch'uen p'aou tsaou fa.* "On Krupp Naval Gun Drill." Translated into Chinese from a work published by the Prussian War Office, by Kin-k'eae-le, and transcribed by Le Fung-paou. [*Shanghai*, 1874?] 8°. **15259. d. 11 (4).**

—— [Another copy.] **15259. d. 15 (2).**

PRUSSIA: DEPARTMENTS OF STATE, ETC.—*Army*. 克虜伯礮準心法 *K'ih-loo-pih p'aou chun sin fa.* "On the Trajectory of Krupp's Projectiles." Translated by Kin K'eae-le, with the assistance of Le Fung-paou. With a volume of plans. [1880?] 8°. **15259. e. 9.**

—— [Another copy.] **15259. d. 14.**

—— 克虜伯礮架說 *K'ih-loo-pih p'aou kea shwo.* "On the Krupp Gun Carriage." Translated into Chinese from a work published by the Prussian War Office, by Kin-k'eae-le, and transcribed by Le Fung-paou. [*Shanghai,* 1874?] 8°. **15259. d. 11 (3).**

—— [Another copy.]

—— 克虜伯礮說 *K'ih-loo-pih p'aou shwo.* "A Description of Krupp Guns." With drill and tables. Translated into Chinese by Kin-k'eae-le. With plates. 8 keuen. With a volume of tables. [*Shanghai,* 1880?] 8°. **15259. h. 6.**

—— [Another edition.] 4 keuen. **15259. d. 15 (1).**

—— 克虜伯礮彈造法 *K'ih-loo-pih p'aou tan tsaou fa.* "On Krupp's Manufacture of Shot." Translated into Chinese by Kin K'eae-le and transcribed by Le Fung-paou. 2 keuen. With appendix. [*Shanghai,* 1875?] 8°. **15259. d. 13.**

—— [Another copy.] **15259. g. 1.**

—— 克虜伯腰箍礮說 *K'ih-loo-pih yaou koo p'aou shwo.* "On Krupp's Rifled Guns." Translated into Chinese from a work published by the Prussian War Office, by Kin K'eae-le, and transcribed by Le Fung-paou. [*Shanghai,* 1874?] 8°. **15259. d. 11 (2).**

—— [Another copy.] **15259. d. 26.**

PSALMANAZAR (GEORGE). *See* CAMPBELL (WILLIAM). The Articles of Christian Instruction in Favorlang-Formosan . . . With Psalmanazar's Dialogue between a Japanese and a Formosan, etc. 1896. 4°. **11098. b. 17.**

不空 PUH-K'UNG [i.e. AMOGHAVAJRA]. 仁王護國般若波羅密多經 *Jin wang hoo kwo pan jo po lo me to king.* "The Prajnā pāramitā sūtra of a benevolent King who protects his country." Translated by Amoghavajra. 2 rolls. 1590. **15103. a. 6.**
Printed in Japan from blocks.

本分 PUN FUN. 本分規條 *Pun fun kwei t'eaou.* "Rules for each Service" of the Roman Catholic Church. pp. ii, 40. *Hongkong,* 1896. 12°. **15200. d. 9.**

本草圖 PUN TS'AOU T'OO. 沼興按定本草圖 *Chaou hing keaou ting pun ts'aou t'oo.* "Coloured Botanical Drawings of Chinese Aquatic Plants." MS. 2 keuen. [1600?] 8°. **Or. 911. 39. B. g.**

本字 PUN TSZE. 抄本字彙 *Ch'aou pun tsze wei.* "A List of the Characters" arranged under the Radicals. MS. [1840?] 8°. **15344. c. 15.** Imperfect, containing characters under Radicals 1–94, 147–214.

—— 抄本字彙 *Ch'aou pun tsze wei.* "A List of the Characters" arranged under the Radicals. MS. [1850?] 8°. **15344. c. 16.**

潘鐸 P'WAN TO. *See* 顧祖禹 KOO TSOO-YU. 方輿紀要簡覽 *Fang yu ke yaou keen lan.* "A Conspectus of the Historical Geography of the Empire . . ." Edited by P'wan To, etc. 1858. 8°. **15275. e. 8.**

RABOUIN (P.). Dictionnaire Français-Chinois. Dialecte de Chang-hai, Song-kiang, etc. Par le P. P. R. 2 vols. *Shanghai,* 1894. 8°. **11094. d. 2.**

RANKIN (HENRY VAN VLECK). *See* BIBLE: OLD TESTAMENT — *Miscellaneous Parts.* Ts'ông-shü kyi (C'ih yiæ-gyih kyi) . . . A Romanized version by H. V. V. Rankin, etc. 1871. 8°. **15117. d. 27.**

—— *See* NINGPO. *Nying-po t'u-wô ts'u'-ôh.* "A Romanized Primer of the Ningpo Dialect." [By H. V. V. R.], etc. 1883. 4°. **15229. b. 22.**

RAVIER (M. H.). *See* FAUTRAT ( ). Elementa litteraturæ . . . Cô Khánh (M. R.) dã xem lai, etc. 1880. 8°. **11100. b. 25.**

RELIGIOUS LEAFLETS. A collection of 22 Christian leaflets. **15200. d 37.**

RELIGIOUS TRACTS. A collection of 10 Christian tracts. 16°. **15200. d. 32.**

—— A collection of 10 Christian tracts. 16°. **15200. d. 33.**

—— A collection of 10 Christian tracts. 12°. **15200. d. 34.**

—— A collection of 13 Christian tracts. 8°. **15200. d. 35.**

—— A collection of 6 Christian tracts. 8°. **15200. d. 36.**

RICCI (Matteo). See 利瑪竇 Le Ma-tow.

RICHARD (Bonhomme). La Science du Bonhomme Richard, ou le chemin de la Fortune. Tel qu'il est clairement indiqué dans un vieil almanach de Pennsylvanie intitulé L'Almanach du Bonhomme Richard. With a Chinese version by Dr. Martin. pp. 32. *Peking*, 1884. 12°.
11099. a. 12.

RIPA (Matthæus). See 伊都立 E Too-leih. A circular letter . . . in Latin, Chinese, and Manchoo . . . subscribed by M. Ripa, etc. 1716.
15200. e. 2.

RISTRETTO. Breve R. delle Notizie gia dedotte circa l'uso delle Tabelle colle parole Cinesi King-tien. [1699?] 12°. 11100. a. 14 (2).

—— R. delle Notizie circa l'uso della voce Cinese Xam-ti. [1699?] 12°. 11100. a. 14 (1).

ROSCOE (Sir Henry Enfield). See 羅斯古 Lo-sze-koo.

RUDLAND (William). See Sing iah shü. *Sing iah shü jü-veng-teh Foh-ing ts'æn-di* . . . [By W. R.?], etc. 1881. 8°. 15200. b. 3.

—— See Sing-shü. *Sing-shü veng-teh.* "A Christian Catechism." [By W. R.?], etc. 1882. 8°. 15200. c. 34.

—— See T'ai-chow. *T'e-tsiu Tsæn mi s.* "Sixty-two Hymns . . ." [By W. R.?], etc. 1880. 12°. 15200. c. 42.

—— See T'ai-chow. *T'e-tsiu t'u wa ts'u ôh.* "A Primer . . ." [By W. R.], etc. 1880. 8°. 15229. b. 24.

RUHSTRAT (E.). Index of the Characters in Dr. Hirth's "Text Book of Documentary Chinese." Arranged by their Radicals. With a list giving the Tones. By E. R. pp. 41. *Kelly & Walsh: Shanghai*, 1892. 4°. 11099. d. 37.

RULES OF WAR. 今將大英與西方成化各國交戰之例藝條 *Kin tseang ta Ying yü se fang ch'ing hwa koh kwo keaou chan che le shoo t'eaou.* "The Rules of War as recognized by England and the other European Nations," in five clauses. Contained in an envelope addressed to Hoo Tsinkwan, the Danish (?) Compradore at Whampoa. MS. [1840?] Or. 3534.

RUSSELL. See 曾紀澤 Ts'äng Ke-tsih. 中西合㽸 *Chung Se ho leih.* "A Chinese and Foreign Comparative Calendar . . ." Compiled by Professor . . . Russell, etc. 1877. 8°.
15298. b. 40.

兩西 Ryang sye. 兩西圖 *Ryang sye to.* "Coloured Maps of the Two Western Provinces of Hwanghai to and Phyöng-an to." MS. [*Seoul*, 1840?] Fol. 15276. e. 5.

SAFFORD (A. C.). See 師 Sze.

—— See 帥萬誼 Sze Gai-e.

—— See 師小棋 Sze Seaou-k'e.

SAFFORD (A. E.) See 帥溫誼 Sze A. E.

SAINT FRANCIS XAVIER'S SCHOOL, SHANGHAI. See Shanghai: Saint Francis Xavier's School.

賽倘阿 Saishangah. 蒙文晰義 *Mung wăn seih e.* "Mongol phrases clearly explained." 4 keuen. 1848. 8°. 15348. c. 5.

三輔黃圖 *San foo hwang t'oo.* "A Description of the Public Buildings in Chang-gan." 6 keuen. See 程榮 Ch'ing Yung. 漢魏叢書 *Han Wei ts'ung shoo.* "A collection of works by authors of the Han and Wei Dynasties," etc. 1791. 8°. 15318. a. 1.

桑欽 Sang K'in. 水經 *Shwuy king.* "The Water Classic." 2 keuen. See 程榮 Ch'ing Yung. 漢魏叢書 *Han Wei ts'ung shoo.* "A collection of works by authors of the Han and Wei Dynasties," etc. 1791. 8°. 15318. a. 1.

生地獄 Säng te yo. 生地獄圖說 *Säng te yo t'oo shwo.* "A Living Hell. With Illustrations." Being an account of the miseries endured by Chinese coolies in Peru and Cuba. *Canton*, 1874. 8°. 15298. b. 38.

三合 San ho. 三合劍全傳 *San ho keen ts'euen chuen.* "The Swords of the Three Confederates. A Novel." 6 keuen. 1844. 8°. 15334. d. 1.

三綱 San kang. 三綱行實 *San kang hing shih.* "Instances of virtuous performance of the 'three bonds,' i.e. the personal and relative duties of a prince, a father, and a husband." A Korean edition, with a Korean version of the text added. With supplement. 4 vols. [1650?] Fol. 15113. e. 2.

—— [Another edition. 1680?] 4°. 15113. e. 1.

三綱 SAN KANG. 三綱行實孝子圖 *San kang hing shih heaou tsze t'oo.* "Drawings illustrating the 'three bonds' (between sovereign and subject, father and son, husband and wife) and the conduct of dutiful sons." With Korean and Chinese texts. Printed in Korea. [1500?] Fol.
15303. d. 16.

三氏 SAN SHE. 西域紀要 *Se yih ke yaou.* "An epitomised account of the Western Frontier Territories." 8 keuen. 1826. 8°.
15291. a. 5.

三書院 SAN SHOO YUEN. 三書院正外付課 *San choo yuen, ching wai fu, ko.* "A List of the Successful Candidates in the Three Courts at the Canton Examination" of 1843. *Canton,* 1843. 8°.
15320. e. 26.

SAN-TSZE-KING. *See* WANG TSIN-SHING. Le commentaire du San-ze-king, etc. 1894. 8°.
11100. b. 30.

三要 SAN YAOU. 三要錄 *San yaou luh.* "Treatises on the three essential subjects" of the Christian Faith, viz., God, man, and Jesus Christ. pp. ii, 58. *Shanghai,* 1862. 8°.
15116. d. 45.

三元 SAN YUEN. 御定三元甲子萬年書 *Yu ting san yuen kea tsze wan neen shoo.* "A Chronological List of the Emperors of China from the Accession of Hwang-te [B.C. 2697] to the thirteenth year of the Emperor Taou-kwang" [A.D. 1833]. *Peking,* 1833. 8°.
15297. b. 12.

SAN-YU-LOW. 三與樓 San-yu-low: or the three dedicated rooms. A tale, translated from the Chinese. By J. F. Davis. *Canton,* 1815. 8°.
11099. c. 1 (2).

SAN-ZE-KING. *See* SAN-TSZE-KING.

SCARBOROUGH (WILLIAM). Four Scripture Parables translated into Chinese under the titles: (1) 浪子之喻 *Lang tsze chih yü,* "The Parable of the Prodigal Son"; (2) 無花菓樹之喻 *Woo hwa kwo shoo chih yü,* "The Parable of the Barren Fig-tree"; (3) 播種之喻 *Po chung chih yü,* "The Parable of the Sower"; and (4) 麵酵之喻 *Mien chiao chih yü,* "The Parable of the Leaven." With illustrations. 2 sheets. *Hankow,* [1885?].
15200. e. 1 (2).

SCHAANK (S. H.). Het Loeh-foeng-Dialect, door S. H. S. pp. 226. *E. J. Brill: Leiden,* 1897. 8°.
11098. a. 10.

SCHERESCHEWSKY (JOSEPH J.), Bishop. *See* BIBLE—OLD TESTAMENT: *Genesis.* 創世記 *Ch'wang she ke.* [Translated into the Mandarin dialect by Bishop S.?], etc. 1883. 12°.
15117. d. 35.

SCHLEGEL (GUSTAVE). Die Chinesische Inschrift auf dem Uigurischen Denkmal in Kara Balgassun. Übersetzt und erläutert von Dr. G. S. pp. xv, 141. *Société Finno-Ougrienne: Helsingfors,* 1896. 8°.
11098. b. 27.

—— *See* KIN-KOO-K'E-KWAN. Mai-yu-lang-tou-tchen-hoa-koueï. Le Vendeur d'huile qui seul possède la Reine-de-beauté . . . Roman chinois traduit . . . par G. Schlegel. 1877. 8°.
11100. b. 6.

Appended is the Chinese text of this and another tale entitled 女秀才移花接木 *Neu sew tsai e hwa tsëë muh.*

—— La Loi du parallélisme en style Chinois, démontrée par la Préface de *Si-yü-ki* (西域記). La traduction de cette Préface par feu Stanislas Julien, défendue contre la nouvelle traduction du Père A. Gueluy, par G. S. *Leide,* 1896. 8°.
11098. b. 24.

—— Supplément au Catalogue des Livres Chinois qui se trouvent dans la Bibliothèque de l'Université de Leyde. pp. 11. *E. J. Brill: Leide,* 1886. 4°.
11098. a. 6.

—— The secret of the Chinese method of transcribing foreign sounds. By Dr. G. S. pp. ix, 103. *E. J. Brill: Leyden,* 1900. 8°. **11095. c. 4.**

—— and CORDIER (HENRI). 通報 *T'oung pao.* Archives pour servir à l'étude de l'histoire, des langues, de la géographie, et de l'ethnographie de l'Asie orientale. Rédigées par MM. G. S. et H. C. Extrait du vol. i. pp. 8. *E. J. Brill: Leide,* 1890. 8°.
11098. b. 2.

SCHMIDT ( ). See 斯米德 SZE-ME-TIH.

SCHULENBURG (ALBRECHT GRAF VON DER). Fürstin Chiang und ihre beiden Söhne. Eine Erzählung aus dem Tso-chuan. Von A. G. von der S. pp. 48. *E. J. Brill: Leiden,* 1895. 8°.
11098. b. 33.

西 SE [i.e. SIR MICHAEL SEYMOUR]. See 理 LE. A Proclamation issued . . . in the names of the English and French Admirals Le and Se, etc. 1857. A sheet. 15241. a. 9.

相 輪 SEANG LUN. 相輪陀羅尼 *Seang lun t'o-lo-ne.* An extract from "The Dharani of Association with the Wheel." [8th century?] A roll.

Printed in Japan.

象 山 縣 SEANG-SHAN HEEN. 象山縣志 *Seang-shan Heen che.* "A Topography of Seang-shan Heen." 22 keuen. With appendix. [1800?] 8°. 15267. a. 8.

Imperfect, containing only Keuen 19–22, and Appendix, Keuen 1.

蕭 煥 袞 SEAOU HWANG-LE. 詩賦駢字類珠 *She foo p'een tsze luy foo.* "A Classified Lexicon of Elegant Poetical Expressions." 8 keuen. 1814. 8°. 15346. a. 8.

蕭 家 蕙 SEAOU KEA-HWUY. 河內縣志 *Ho nuy heen che.* "A Topography of Ho nuy heen" in Honan. Compiled by Seaou Kea-hwuy and other officials. 5 keuen. 1693. 8°. 15267. a. 10.

小 吉 羅 庵 主 SEAOU-KEIH-LO GAN CHOO. 瀛寰瑣紀 *Ying hwan so ke.* "Miscellaneous Records." By the Master of the Seaou-keih-lo Cottage. pp. 48. 1872. 8°. 15298. a. 49.

蕭 瓦 有 SEAOU LEANG-YEW. 龍文鞭影 *Lung wăn peen ying.* "The shadow of a whip for a willing horse." An educational work in verse, with notes. Edited by Yang Ch'in-ching. 2 keuen. [1850?] 8°. 15323. a. 19.

蕭 騰 驎 SEAOU T'ĂNG-LIN. 西藏見聞錄 *Se Ts'ang keen wăn luh.* "Notes on what is to be seen and heard in Tibet." With a map. 2 keuen. 1770. 8°. 15297. a. 17.

小 題 SEAOU T'E. 小題靈秀集 *Seaou t'e ling sew tseih.* "Elegant Essays on Texts from the Four Books." 1872. 12°. 15315. a. 3.

—— 小題文綜 *Seaou t'e wăn tsung.* "A collection of Essays on Texts from the Four Books." 54 keuen. 1866. 12°. 15315. a. 1.

蕭 統 SEAOU T'UNG. 六臣註文選 *Luh ch'in choo wăn seuen.* Elegant extracts from polite literature. Compiled by Prince Seaou T'ung with the Commentaries of the six Ministers, Le Shen, Leu Yen-tse, Lew Leang, Chang Seen, Le Chow-han, and Leu Heang. An enlarged edition, edited by Ch'in Jin-tsze. 60 keuen. 1607. Fol. 15320. e. 39.

A facsimile of a Korean edition printed in Japan with movable type.

蕭 硯 精 SEAOU YEN-TSING. 清文典要 *Ts'ing wăn teen yaou.* "A Book of Phrases in Manchoo." By Seaou Yen-tsing. [In this work the Chinese phrases translated into Manchoo consist of four characters, and are arranged under the radical of the initial character.] 1738. 8°. 15354. c. 2.

謝 兆 申 SEAY CHAOU-SHIN. 古文奇字輯解 *Koowăn k'e tsze tseih keae.* "Curious Characters in the Koowăn writing, compiled and explained." By Seay Chaou-shin, of Suygan in Fuhkien. MS. 4 keuen. ff. 63. 1612. 8°. Or. 2282. 39. B. e.

薛 傳 源 SEAY CH'UEN-YUEN. 防海備覽 *Fang hai pei lan.* "Preventive measures for the protection of the coast." With maps. 10 keuen. 1811. 8°. 15239. a. 46.

謝 枋 得 SEAY FANG-TIH. 謝疊山先生文章軌范 *Seay Tëe-shan Seen-săng wăn chang kwei fan.* "Literary Models." Compiled by Seay Fang-tih. Edited by Wang Pih-gan. 7 keuen. 1868. 8°. 15312. d. 11.

薛 禑 保 SEAY FUH-PAOU. 青萍軒詩錄 *Ts'ing p'ing heen she luh.* "Poems from the 'Green Duckwood Study.'" pp. 30. [1882?] 8°. 15323. a. 21.

—— 青萍軒文錄 *Ts'ing p'ing heen wăn luh.* "Literary notes from the 'Green Duckwood Study.'" 2 keuen. 1882. 8°. 15323. a. 21.

薛 湘 SEAY SEANG. 滌非齋制藝僅存 *Te-fei chai che e kin ts'un.* "Essays from the Study for wiping out wrongs." Edited with notes by Tsăng Kwo-fan. pp. xx, 86, vi. 1879. 8°. 15317. a. 8.

謝 敦 倫 SEAY TUN-LUN. 昔 時 賢 文 Chhien jū bûn and Sam jū keng. Excellent ancient adages, together with notes on the writings of Chinese romanized in the Hokkien Dialect. Edited with an alphabetical index of different Chinese characters. Metrically translated and arranged by Cheah Toon Hoon. *Rangoon*, 1890. 8°.
11098. b. 10.

西 周 生 SE CHOW-SĂNG. 醒 世 姻 緣 傳 *Sing she yin yuen chuen.* "A Tale of Marriage Affinities to Arouse the Age." Edited by Jen Le-tsze. 100 chapters. 1841. 8°. **15334. e. 7.**

薛 SËË. 薛 院 判 醫 書 二 十 四 種 *Sëë yuen pan e shoo urh shih sze chung.* "Reprints of Twenty-four Medical Works issued by Sëë." Edited by Woo Kwan. [1800?] 8°.
15253. c. 1.

薛 福 成 SËË FUH-CH'ING. See 曾 國 書 TSĂNG KWO-FAN. 曾 文 正 公 奏 議 *Tsăng wăn ching kung tsow e.* "The Memorials of Tsăng Kwo-fan." Compiled by Sëë Fuh-ch'ing, etc. 1873. 8°. **15241. c. 9.**

暹 羅 SËEN-LO. 暹 羅 譯 語 *Sëen-lo yih yu.* "A Siamese and Chinese Vocabulary." [1800?] 8°. **15346. b. 27.**

仙 尼 華 四 SEEN-NE-HWA-SZE (i.e. P. STREENE-VASSA). 英 華 仙 尼 華 四 雜 字 文 *Ying Hwa Seen-ne-hwa-sze tsa tsze wăn.* An English and Chinese Vocabulary (in the Ningpo dialect) by Seen-ne-hwa-sze (a native of Madras). *Ting hai*, 1846. 8°. **11100. e. 16.**
Has also an English title-page.

薛 平 貴 SËË P'ING-KWEI. 平 貴 別 窰 *P'ing-kwei pëë yaou.* "Sëë P'ing-kwei leaves a Brothel" for the field. A Drama. [1840?] 8°. **15327. d. 28.**

薛 慰 農 SËË WEI-NUNG. 中 鋒 集 初 編 *Chung fung tseih ch'oo peen.* "The Chung-fung Collection of Examination Essays on Texts from the Four Books." First series. Edited by Sëë Wei-nung. 1869. 8°. **15320. c. 10.**

—— 薛 氏 五 種 *Sëë she woo chung.* "The Five Poetical Works of Sëë Wei-nung." 1868. 8°.
15323. d. 22.

—— 五 經 鴻 裁 *Woo king hung ts'ai.* "Learned Essays on Texts from the Five Classics." Edited by Sëë Wei-nung. 1873. 12°.
15319. c. 21.

西 番 SE-FAN. 西 番 譯 語 *Se-fan yih yu.* "A Tibetan and Chinese Vocabulary." The Tibetan is written in the cursive hand, and in each case is followed by the meaning in Chinese, and below that by a transcription of the sound of the Tibetan. MS. ff. 102. [1870?]
Or. 4473. 39. B. f.

—— [A printed edition of the same work. 1840?] 8°. **15344. d. 9.**

西 番 碧 玉 帶 SE-FAN PEÏH YUH TAI. 西 番 碧 玉 帶 全 本 *Se-fan peih yuh tai ts'euen pun.* "The Story of the Tibetan Serpentine Girdle." In verse. 2 keuen. [1850?] 8°. **15327. d. 22.**

西 湖 居 士 SE HOO KEU SZE, *pseud.* 玉 釧 緣 *Yuh ch'uen yuen.* "The destiny of a jade bracelet." With portraits. 32 keuen. *Peking*, 1842. 8°. **15327. f. 8.**

西 湖 漁 隱 主 人 SE HOO YÜ YIN CHOO JIN. See 貪 歡 T'AN HWAN. 貪 歡 報 *T'an hwan paou.* "Records of excessive pleasure-seeking." By Se hoo yü yin choo jin, etc. 8°. **15331. f. 5.**

錫 璜 SEÏH HWANG. 掣 鯨 堂 詩 選 *Che k'ing t'ang she seuen.* "A Selection of Poetry from the Che-k'ing-t'ang." 9 keuen. See 孫 澍 SUN SHOO. 古 棠 書 屋 叢 書 *Koo t'ang shoo wuh ts'ung shoo.* "A Collection of Reprints from the Koo-t'ang-shoo Dwelling," etc. 1831–1849. 8°. **15315. d. 1.**

席 前 席 SEÏH TS'EEN-SEÏH. See 陸 稼 書 LUH KEA-SHOO. 三 魚 堂 文 集 *San yu T'ang wăn tseih.* "The 'Three-fishes Hall' Collection of Literary Pieces . . ." Edited by Seïh Ts'een-seïh, etc. 8°. **15317. a. 6.**

席 永 恂 SEÏH YUNG-SEUN. See 陸 稼 書 LUH KEA-SHOO. 三 魚 堂 文 集 *San-yu T'ang wăn tseih.* "The 'Three-fishes Hall' Collection of Literary Pieces . . ." Edited by Seïh Yung-seun, etc. 8°. **15317. a. 6.**

SELBY (THOMAS G.). See 師 多 馬 SZE TOMA.

西 泠 狂 者 SELING KWANG CHE, *pseud.* 載 花 船 *Tsai hwa ch'uen.* "The Pleasure-laden Vessel." An historical tale of Court life during the reign of the Empress Woo How in the latter half of the seventh century. By the Madman of Seling. Revised by the "Intelligent Man of Soosing." MS. ff. 81. [*Peking*, 1860?]
Or. 4475. 39. B. f.

SE-MA TS'IEN. See 司馬遷 SZEMA TS'IEN.

SERCEY (DE), Comte. *See* VITALE (GUIDO), Baron, and SERCEY (DE), Comte. Grammaire et Vocabulaire de la langue Mongole, etc. 1897. 8°. **11099. a. 19.**

西 山 異 氏 SE SHAN CHIN SHE. 心 經 附 註 *Sin King foo choo.* "The Heart Sutra with Notes." 4 keuen. 1566. Fol. **15103. e. 15.**
Printed in Japan.

西 士 SE SZE. 西 士 酬 中 國 人 書 *Se sze ch'ow Chung kwo jin shoo.* "A Western Scholar's reply to Chinese" objections to Christianity. A manuscript note on cover states that this work is by Dr. A. Williamson. 50 pp. *Shanghai*, 1875. 8°. **15118. c. 40.**

西 天 SE T'EEN. 西 天 異 寶 名 經 *Se t'een chin shih ming king.* "A Sūtra containing the three names of the Western Heaven." Sanskrit characters in the seal form with transliteration in Chinese characters. MS. ff. 45. [1850 ?] 8°. **Or. 2894. 39. B. d.**

SEU (ETIENNE). Variétés Sinologiques. No. 5. Pratique des Examens littéraires en Chine. Par Le P. Etienne Zi (Seu), S.J. *Shanghai*, 1894. 8°. **11100. b. 34.**

徐 朝 後 SEU CH'AOU-TSEUN. 高 厚 蒙 求 摘 畧 *Kaou how mung k'ew tsih leŏ.* "Notes for Students." See 王 塗 WANG LEW. 域 外 叢 書 *Yih wai ts'ung shoo.* "Reprints of Works on Foreign Countries," etc. 1842. 8°. **15271. b. 3.**

徐 郙 SEU FOO. 三 江 邁 倫 集 *San keang mai lun tseih.* "A Collection of Superior Essays from the Three Keang Provinces." Edited by Seu Foo, Tung Hwa, and others. 1876. 8°. **15320. a. 22.**

徐 鳳 輝 SEU FUNG-HWUY. 國 朝 二 十 四 家 文 鈔 *Kwo ch'aou urh shih sze kca wăn ch'aou.* "The Writings of Twenty-four Authors of the Present Dynasty." Compiled by Seu Fung-hwuy. Edited by Seu Kung-săng and others. 24 keuen. 1830. 8°. **15320. e. 37.**

徐 幹 SEU HAN. 中 論 *Chun lun.* "Central Discourses" on Government, Morals, etc. 2 keuen. See 程 榮 CH'ING YUNG. 漢 魏 叢 書 *Han Wei ts'ung shoo.* "A collection of works by authors of the Han and Wei Dynasties," etc. 1791. 8°. **15318. a. 1.**

徐 勳 右 SEU JANG-YEW. 彙 纂 詩 法 度 針 *Wei tswan she fa too chin.* "The Laws of Poetry. With Model Examples." Compiled by Seu Jang-yew. 10 keuen. 1758. 8°. **15321. d. 12.**

徐 鍇 傳 SEU K'EAE-CHUEN. See 許 愼 HEU SHIN. 說 文 解 字 通 釋 *Shwo wăn keae tsze t'ung shih.* "The explanations of characters in the *Shwo wăn* thoroughly expounded" by Seu K'eae-chuen, etc. 1839. 8°. **15346. d. 4.**

徐 建 益 SEU KEEN-YIH. See 蒲 而 捺 POO-URH-NA. 汽 機 *K'e ke.* "Handbook of the Steam Engine . . ." Revised by Seu Keen-yih, etc. *Shanghai*, 8°. **15259. d. 4.**

徐 建 寅 SEU KEEN-YIN. See ENGLAND: ADMIRALTY. 永 師 操 練 *Shwuy sze ts'aou leen.* "Naval Drill . . ." Edited by Seu Keen-yin, etc. 8°. **15259. e. 5.**

—— See 裴 路 P'EI-LOO [i.e.]. 輪 船 布 陣 *Lun ch'uen poo ch'in.* "Steamship Manœuvres," . . . transcribed by Seu Keen-yin, etc. 8°. **15259. c. 18.**

—— See 白 起 傷 PIH-K'E-TIH. 運 規 約 指 *Yun kwei yo che.* "A Work on Practical Geometry . . ." Edited by Seu Keen-yin, etc. 8°. **15255. d. 19.**

—— See 白 力 蓋 PIH-LEIH-KAI. 器 象 顯 異 *K'e seang heen chin.* "Engineering Drawing . . ." Edited by Seu Keen-yin, etc. 8°. **15259. h. 2.**

—— See 白 爾 格 PIH-URH-KIH. 汽 機 新 制 *K'e ke sin che.* "On Planning Steam Engines . . ." Transcribed by Seu Keen-yin, etc. 8°. **15259. d. 16.**

—— See 蒲 陸 山 POO-LUH-SHAN. 化 學 分 原 *Hwa heŏ fun yuen.* "On Practical Chemistry . . ." Edited by Seu Keen-yin, etc. 8°. **15252. d. 11.**

—— See 田 大 里 T'EEN-TA-LE. 聲 學 *Shing heŏ.* "On Sound." Revised by Seu Keen-yin, etc. 8°. **15259. d. 1.**

徐 居 仁 SEU KEU-JIN. See 杜 預 TOO YU. 集 千 家 分 類 杜 工 部 詩 *Tseih ts'een fun luy Too Kung-poo she.* "A classified collection of the poems of Too Yu." Edited by Seu Keu-jin, etc. 8°. **15324. c. 3.**

徐 金 生 SEU KIN-SĂNG. See 吳 其 濬 WOO K'E-SEUN. 滇 南 礦 廠 輿 程 圖 畧 *Teen nan kwang ch'ang yu ch'ing t'oo leŏ.* "The Mines of Yunnan . . ." Edited by Seu Kin-sǎng, etc. 8°.   15271. e. 5.

徐 恭 生 SEU KUNG-SĂNG. See 徐 鳳 輝 SEU FUNG-HWUY. 國 朝 二 十 四 家 文 鈔 *Kwo ch'aou urh shih sze kea wǎn chaou.* "The Writings of Twenty-four Authors . . ." Edited by Seu Kung-sǎng, etc. 1830. 8°. 15320. e. 37.

徐 光 啟 SEU KWANG-K'E. 闢 妄 *P'e wang.* "A treatise exposing the follies" of Buddhism. A new edition. pp. i, 33. *Hongkong*, 1888. 8°.   15200. d. 56.

—— [Another edition.] *Hongkong*, 1896. 8°.   15200. b. 24.

徐 陵 孝 SEU LING-HEAOU. 玉 臺 新 詠 箋 註 *Yuh t'ai sin yung tseen choo.* "New Songs from the Beautiful Tower." Compiled by Seu Ling-heaou. "With Notes" by Woo Chaou-e. Edited by Ching Tse-shing. 10 keuen. 1774. 8°.   15323. c. 12.

徐 靈 胎 SEU LING-T'AI. 徐 氏 醫 書 六 種 *Seu she E shoo luh chung.* Six Medical Works, viz.: *Nan king king shih, E lun, Shin nung pun ts'aou, E kwan peen, Shang han luy fang,* and *San tai kwei fan.* Edited by Seu Ling-t'ai. 1873. 8°.   15252. d. 16.

荀 況 SEUN HWANG. 荀 子 *Seun tsze.* "The writings of the Philosopher Seun Hwang." With a commentary by Yang Leang. 20 keuen. [1300?] 8°.   15113. b. 7.

苟 悅 SEUN YUĔ. 申 鑒 *Shin keen.* "An Explanatory Mirror." An essay on Government, etc. 5 keuen. See 程 榮 CH'ING YUNG. 漢 魏 叢 書 *Han Wei ts'ung shoo.* "A collection of works by authors of the Han and Wei Dynasties," etc. 1791. 8°. 15318. a. 1.

徐 三 省 SEU SAN-SĂNG. 新 增 萬 寶 元 龍 通 考 *Sin tsǎng wan paou yuen lung t'ung k'aou.* "An Encyclopædia." Compiled by Seu San-sǎng. Edited by Tai Ke-ta. 3 keuen. [1800?] 8°.   15024. c. 5.

徐 錫 壽 SEU SEIH-SHOW. See 王 梗 敬 WANG HWAI-KING. An illuminated genealogy of the Chan Family . . . A manuscript copy made by Seu Seih-show in 1774. A scroll. 15296. e. 5.

徐 樹 銘 SEU SHOO-MING. See 黃 坤 載 HWANG K'WĂN-TSAI. 昌 邑 黃 先 生 醫 書 入 種 *Ch'ang yih Hwang Seen-sǎng e shoo pa chung.* "The Eight Medical Works" of Hwang K'wǎn-tsai. Edited by Seu Shoo-ming, etc. 1861. 8°.   15253. b. 1.

—— See 黃 坤 載 HWANG K'WĂN-TSAI. 四 聖 心 源 *Sze shing sin yuen.* "The Foundation of the Systems of the Four Medical Sages . . ." Edited by Seu Shoo-ming, etc. 1860. 8°.   15252. b. 29.

—— 徐 壽 SEU SHOW. See 儲 意 比 CHOO-E-PE. 營 城 揭 要 *Ying ch'ing këĕ yaou.* "On Fortifications . . ." Transcribed by Seu Taou, etc. 8°.   15259. d. 8.

—— See 富 路 瑪 FOO-LOO-MA. 測 地 繪 圖 *T'sih te hwuy t'oo.* "On Land Measurement . . ." Transcribed by Seu Show, etc. 8°.   15259. d. 21.

—— See 美 以 納 MEI-E-NA and 白 勞 那 PIH-LAOU-NA. 汽 機 發 軔 *K'e ke fa jen.* "The Marine Steam Engine . . ." Revised by Seu Show, etc. 8°.   15259. d. 1.

—— See 諾 格 偽 NO-KIH-TIH. 西 藝 知 新 *Se e che sin.* "On Western Mechanical Science . . ." Transcribed by Seu Show, etc. 8°.   15259. d. 17.

—— See 韋 而 司 WEI-URH-SZE. 化 學 鑑 原 *Hwa heŏ keen yuen.* "Inorganic Chemistry . . ." Edited by Seu Show, etc. 8°.   15252. d. 12.

徐 星 伯 SEU SING-PIH. 徐 星 伯 先 生 著 書 三 種 *Seu Sing-pih Seen-sǎng choo shoo san chung.* "The Three Works of Seu Sing-pih," viz.: (1) *Se yih shwuy taou ke,* "The water-ways of the countries on the Western Frontiers," 5 keuen, with maps; (2) *Sin keang foo,* "A poetical description of the new Frontier countries"; and (3) *Han shoo se yih chuen poo choo,* "The account of the Western Frontiers from the Han Shoo, with notes," 2 keuen. 1829. 8°.   15275. e. 2.

徐 松 星 SEU SUNG-SING. 唐 兩 京 城 坊 考 *T'ang leang king ch'ing fang k'aou.* "An Examination of the Sites of the two Capitals [Chang-gan Heen and Lo-yang Heen] of the T'ang Dynasty." Edited by Chang Muh-sung. 5 keuen. 1848. 8°.   15296. e. 2.

SEU—SEY

徐士業 SEU SZE-YEH. 徐氏三種 *Seu she san chung.* "The Works of Seu Sze-yeh," viz.: the *San tsze king heun koo,* "The Three Character Classic, with expositions"; the *Pih kea sing k'aou leŏ,* "The Hundred Surnames, with short explanations"; and the *Ts'een tsze wăn shih e,* "The Thousand Character Classic, with explanatory comments." 1866. 8°. 15223. b. 4.

—— [Another edition.] 1875. 8°. 15202. b. 21.

徐衜 SEU TAOU. 歷代神仙通鑑 *Leih tai shin seen t'ung keen.* "Biographical Notices of Taouist Saints chronologically arranged." With illustrations. By Seu Taou, assisted by Le Le. Edited by Hwang Chang-lun. 22 keuen. 1712. 8°. 15303. e. 1.

—— 神仙鑑 *Shin seen keen.* "Biographical Notices of Saints and Sages." By Seu Taou and Le Le. 22 keuen. [1700?] 8°. 15303. d. 13.

徐子光 SEU TSZE-KWANG. See 李瀚 LE HAN. 標題徐狀元補注蒙求 *Peaou t'e Seu Chwang-yuen poo choo mung k'ew.* "Information for beginners . . . Edited by . . . Seu Tsze-kwang," etc. 1596. 4°. 15229. d. 5.

徐子拐 SEU TSZE-LĂNG. See 湯芷鄉 T'ANG CHE-KING. 翼駉稗編 *Yih kung pai peen.* "A collection of racy and rich stories . . ." Edited by Seu Tsze-lăng, etc. 1869. 8°. 15331. c. 15.

徐文長 SEU WĂN-CHANG. 英烈全傳 *Ying lëĕ ts'euen chuen.* "A Complete History of Heroes." Another edition of the *Hung woo ts'euen chuen.* By Seu Wăn-chang. 10 keuen. 1833. 8°. 15334. a. 11.

徐渭仁 SEU WEI-JIN. 隨軒金石文字 *Suy Heen kin shih wăn tsze.* "A Collection of Inscriptions of the time of the Chow and Han Dynasties." Edited by Seu Wei-jin. *Shanghai,* 1841. 8°. 15299. c. 3.

徐位山 SEU WEI-SHAN. See 沈約 CH'IN YO. 竹書紀年統箋 *Chuh shoo ke neen t'ung tseen.* "The Record of the Bamboo Book . . . With Notes" by Seu Wei-shan, etc. 1750. 8°. 15292. c. 4.

—— 經言拾遺 *King yen shih e.* "Resuscitated Notes on the Classics." Compiled by Seu Wei-shan. Edited by Maou Yun-yih. 14 keuen. 1756. 8°. 15223. c. 11.

徐位山 SEU WEI-SHAN. 管城硯記 *Kwan ch'ing shih ke.* "Pencil Notes" on classical subjects. By Seu Wei-shan. Edited by Seu Yung-ch'oo. 30 keuen. 1744. 8°. 15223. c. 10.

—— 詩賦全集 *She foo ts'euen tseih.* "A complete collection of Poems and Odes." By Seu Wei-shan. 1735. 8°. 15323. d. 24.

—— 天下山河兩戒考 *T'een hea shan ho leang keae k'aou.* "An Examination of the Limits of the Mountains and Rivers of the Empire." By Seu Wei-shan. A reprint. 14 keuen. 1876. 8°. 15269. b. 8.

—— 禹貢會箋 *Yu kung hwuy tseen.* "The Tribute of Yu. With Notes" by Seu Wei-shan. Edited by Chaou Wăn-meen. 12 keuen. 1848. 8°. 15292. c. 3.

徐榮椐 SEU YUNG-CH'OO. See 徐位山 SEU WEI-SHAN. 管城碩記 *Kwan ch'ing shih ke.* "Pencil Notes . . ." Edited by Seu Yung-ch'oo, etc. 1744. 8°. 15223. c. 10.

繡鞋 SEW HEAE. 繡鞋記醒貴新書 *Sew heae ke king kwei sin shoo.* "The Story of the Embroidered Shoes. A fresh warning for the upper classes." 4 keuen. [1850?] 8°. 15331. b. 16.

繡球 SEW K'EW. 繡球綠 *Sew k'ew yuen.* "The Union brought about by the Embroidered Ball. A Novel." 4 keuen. 1851. 8°. 15334. d. 2.

繡戈袍 SEW KO P'AOU. 繡戈袍全傳 *Sew ko p'aou ts'euen chuen.* "The Complete Story of the Embroidered Spear-coat." By "the Master of the Suy Garden." 8 keuen. [1750?] 8°. 15333. b. 13.

秀升 SEW SHING. 三合便覽 *San ho peen lan.* "A Chinese Grammar of the Manchu and Mongolian Languages, followed by a Manchu-Mongolian and Chinese Vocabulary." Compiled by Sew Shing. 1780. 8°. 15354. c. 3.

—— [Another edition.] 1792. 8°. 15354. e. 1.

SEYMOUR (SIR MICHAEL), *Admiral.* See 西 SE.

西嶽 SE YO. 西嶽華山廟 *Se yo Hwa-shan meaou.* "Rubbings of the Inscriptions at the Hwa-shan Temple on the Western Sacred Mountain in Shensi" commemorating the restoration of the Temple in 1778. 11 sheets. 15204. a. 4.

沙 木 SHA MUH. See 吳 毅 人 WOO KUH-JIN. 藝 文 備 覽 E wăn pei lan. "A ready synopsis of discriminated characters." A dictionary. With notes by Sha Muh. Edited by Woo Seih-k'e. 12 parts. 1806. 8°. **15346. e. 3.**

上 海 SHANG-HAI. 上 海 徽 寧 思 恭 堂 徵 信 錄 Shang-hai Hwuy Ning sze kung T'ang ching sin luh. "The Report of the Hwuy Chow and Ning-kwo Foo Society for providing shelter for coffins awaiting interment at Shanghai" for the year 1844. Shanghai, 1844. 8°. **15298. c. 12.**

—— [Another copy.] **15298. c. 13.**

—— 上 海 大 關 則 例 謹 遵 木 榜 抄 錄 Shang-hai ta kwan tsih le kin tsun muh pang ch'aou luh. "Shanghai Customs Regulations and Tariff." 1785. 8°. **15239. a. 43.**

—— 上 海 同 仁 堂 徵 信 錄 Shang-hai t'ung jin T'ang ching sin luh. "The Report of the Shanghai Benevolent Society" for the year 1843. Shanghai, 1843. 8°. **15298. c. 10.**

—— 上 海 同 仁 堂 義 學 條 規 Shang-hai t'ung jin T'ang e heŏ t'eaou kwei. "The Rules of the School attached to the Shanghai Benevolent Society." Shanghai, 1843. 8°. **15298. c. 11.**

—— 上 海 育 嬰 堂 徵 信 錄 Shang-hai yuh ying T'ang ching sin luh. "The Report of the Shanghai Foundling Hospital" for the year 1843. Shanghai, 1843. 8°. **15298. c. 14.**

—— A Chinese Map of the City and District of Shanghai. Without title. [Shanghai, 1890 ?] **15261. c. 3 (2).**

—— SAINT FRANCIS XAVIER's SCHOOL. A method of learning to read, write, and speak English, for the use of Chinese pupils. Two parts. Catholic Mission Press: Zi-Ka-Wei, 1882-83. 8°. **11099. f. 10.**

—— —— Introduction to the method of learning to read, write, and speak English, for the use of Chinese pupils. pp. 24. Catholic Mission: Zi-Ka-Wei, 1882. 8°. **11099. f. 11.**

—— 上 海 格 致 書 院 第 一 次 記 錄 Shanghai kih che shoo yuen te yih t'sze ke luh. "The First Report of the Polytechnic Institution at Shanghai." By, according to a manuscript note on cover, J. Fryer. Shanghai, 1875. 8°. **15229. b. 26.**

上 海 SHANG-HAI. The Desk Hong List; a general and business directory for Shanghai and the Northern and River Ports, Japan, etc., January, 1876. Shanghai, 1876. Obl. **15298. c. 24.**

—— 上 海 大 關 則 例 Shanghai ta kwan tsih le. "Shanghai Customs' Regulations and Tariff." 1785. 8°. **15239. a. 42.**

伺 德 SHANG-TIH [i.e. W. H. MEDHURST]. 中 華 諸 兄 慶 賀 新 禧 文 Chung hwa choo heung k'ing ho sin he wăn. "A congratulatory [and admonitory] address to Chinamen on the New Year." pp. 12. Singapore [1836 ?]. 8°. **15118. c. 46.**

—— 福 音 調 和 Fuh yin t'eaou ho. "A Harmony of the Gospels." 2 keuen. Malacca, 1835. 8°. **15116. d. 50.**
Imperfect, containing only Keuen 1.

—— 上 帝 生 日 之 論 Shang-te săng jih che lun. "A Discourse on the Birthday of the Deity Shang-te." Singapore [1850 ?]. 8°. **15116. e. 48 (4).**

—— 清 明 掃 墓 之 論 Ts'ing ming sao moo che lun. "On the Feast at the Tombs on the Ts'ing ming term day." pp. 12. Singapore [1836 ?]. 8°. **15118. c. 45.**

伺 德 者 SHANG TIH CHAY [i.e. W. H. MEDHURST]. 創 世 歷 代 書 Ch'wang she leih tai shoo. "A Genealogy from the Creation," being an epitome of the first 11 chapters of Genesis, with a commentary. pp. 66. [1840 ?] 8°. **15118. d. 17.**

—— 神 理 總 論 Shin le tsung lun. "Discourses on Theology." pp. 209. Malacca, 1833. 8°. **15116. d. 49.**

—— [Another copy.] **15118. b. 48.**

山 左 SHAN TSO. 山 左 闈 墨 Shan tso wei mih. Shan-tung [?] examination essays. [1800 ?] 8°. **15320. e. 4.**

山 右 SHAN YEW. 山 右 闈 墨 Shan yew wei mih. Shan-se [?] examination essays. [1800 ?] 8°. **15320. e. 5.**
A fragment.

邵 長 蘅 SHAOU CH'ANG-HĂNG. See 蘇 軾 SOO SHIH. 蘇 文 忠 公 詩 合 註 Soo Wăn-chung kung she ho choo. "The Poems of Soo Shih consistently explained" by the Commentators . . . Shaou Ch'ang-hăng, etc. 1870. 8°. **15324. b. 2.**

SHA—SHE

邵 荀 慈 SHAOU SEUN-TS'ZE. 玉芝堂文集 *Yuh che t'ang wăn tseïh.* "A collection of Literary Pieces from the Hall of the Jade Che." See 吳 錫 麒 WOO SEÏH-KE. 八 家 四 六 *Pa kea sze luh.* "A collection of some of the works of eight authors," etc. 1805. 8°.   15317. a. 4.

邵 氏 SHAOU SHE. "Tales of the Seeking Lamp." See 瞿 祐 宗 KEU YEW-TSUNG. 三 燈 叢 話 合 刻 *San tăng ts'ung hwa ho kih.* "The Three-lamp Collection of Tales," etc. 1847. 8°.   15331. d. 14.

邵 新 甫 SHAOU SIN-FOO. See 葉 天 士 YE T'EEN-SZE. 臨 證 指 南 醫 案 *Lin ching che nan e gan.* "A verified Guide to Medicine . . ." Edited by . . . Shaou Sin-foo, etc. 1844. 8°.   15252. e. 8.

邵 子 湘 SHAOU TSZE-SEANG. 邵 子 湘 全 集 *Shaou Tsze-seang ts'euen tseïh.* "The Complete Works of Shaou Tsze-seang." Edited by Koo Chih-fang. In three parts. 1st part, 16 keuen ; 2nd part, 6 keuen ; 3rd part, 8 keuen. 1693. 8°.   15318. b. 3.

沙 守 信 SHA SHOW-SIN. 真 道 自 證 *Chin taou tsze ching.* "The self-witness of the true doctrine." 4 keuen. *Hongkong,* 1887. 8°.   15200. c. 66.

沙 勿 畧 SHA WUH-LEŎ. 七 克 真 訓 *Ts'ih koh chin heun.* "The True Roman Catholic Teachings of the Seven Abstinences." 2 keuen. *Hongkong,* 1891. 8°.   15200. d. 42.

史 SHE. 史 要 聚 選 *She yaou tseu seuen.* "Historical Biographical Extracts." 9 keuen. [1650 ?] 8°.   15305. b. 10.
Printed in Korea from blocks.

詩 SHE. 御 製 詩 *Yu che she.* "Poetry." [By the Emperor K'een-lung.] [1780 ?] Obl.   15321. a. 17.

世 昌 SHE-CH'ANG. 誠 心 痛 悔 前 過 *Ch'ing sin t'ung hwuy ts'een kwo.* "With a true heart earnestly to repent of former sins," and other Christian treatises. By the Disciple She-ch'ang. MS. [1850 ?] 8°.   15117. b. 38.

SHEFFIELD (D. Z.). Outlines of General History, in Easy Wen-li. Illustrated with thirteen large double-page mounted and coloured maps. And in addition an English index. By D. Z. S. 4 keuen, with a volume of maps. The Chinese title is 萬 國 通 鑑 *Wan kwo t'ung keen. Shanghai,* 1882. 8°.   15292. c. 11.

—— [Another copy.]   15296. b. 15.

施 閏 章 SHE JUN-CHANG. 登 州 府 志 *T'ăng-chow Foo che.* "A Topography of T'ăng-chow Foo" in Shantung. Compiled by She Jun-chang and others. 22 keuen. With a supplementary topography in 12 keuen. 1660. 1742. 8°.   15269. a. 14.

詩 經 SHE KING. The Book of Chinese Poetry. Being the collection . . . known as the Shih Ching or Classic of Poetry, metrically translated by C. F. R. Allen. pp. xl, 528. *Kegan Paul & Co.: London,* 1891. 8°.   11099. c. 4.

—— "The Books of Odes." With a Manchoo translation. 8 keuen. 1768. 8°.   15210. c. 9.

—— Cheu king. Texte Chinois, avec une double traduction en Français et en Latin, une introduction, et un vocabulaire. Par S. Couvreur. pp. xxxii, 556. *Ho-kien Fou,* 1896. 8°.   11098. c. 20.

—— 監 本 詩 經 *Keen pun she king.* "The Original Text of the Book of Odes." With Choo He's Commentary. The Keae-tsze Yuen edition. 8 keuen. *Nanking,* 1790. 8°.   15210. a. 12.

—— 毛 詩 *Maou She.* "Maou Ch'ang's Version of the Book of Odes." 20 keuen. [1620 ?] Fol.   15324. d. 1.
Printed in Japan with movable type.

—— 詩 經 *Schï-king.* Das kanonische Liederbuch der Chinesen. Aus dem Chinesischen übersetzt und erklärt von V. von Strauss. pp. 528. *Heidelberg,* 1880. 8°.   11100. d. 3.

—— 詩 傳 大 全 *She chuen ta ts'euen.* "The Book of Odes. With a complete collection of Commentaries." Edited by Choo He. With manuscript notes. 5 (?) keuen. [*Korea,* 1650 ?] Fol.   15201. c. 18.
Imperfect, containing only Keuen 1–5.

—— 詩 經 *She king.* "The Book of Odes." With Choo He's preface, commentary, and notes. 8 keuen. [1800 ?] 8°.   15215. a. 8.

—— [Another edition.] Edited by Le Han-chang. 1868. Fol.   15210. c. 17.

—— 御 纂 詩 義 折 中 *Yu tswan She e che chung.* "Well-weighed Decisions on the Meaning of the Book of Odes." Compiled by Imperial order by a commission consisting of Foo Hăng, Lai Paou, Wang Yew-tun, and others. 20 keuen. 1755. 8°.   15212. e. 2.

善終 SHEN CHUNG. 善終已亡經 *Shen chung e wang king.* "[Roman Catholic] Services for the dying and the dead." pp. 110. *Hongkong,* 1894. 12°.　　15200. aa. 15.

禪門 SHEN MUN. 禪門日誦 *Shen mun jih sung.* "Daily Recitations for the Contemplative School" of Buddhists. pp. 224. 1785. 8°.　　15103. d. 23.

善生 SHEN SĂNG. 善生福終 *Shen săng fuh chung.* "The happy end of a good life." pp. vi, 83. *Hongkong,* 1888. 8°.　15200. c. 67.

善俤 SHEN-TIH [i.e K. F. A. GÜTZLAFF]. 異道自證 *Chin taou tsze ching.* "Proofs of the Truth." pp. i, 53. *Singapore* [1838?]. 8°.　　15118. d. 16.

—— 約色弗言行錄 *Yo-sih-fuh yen hing luh.* "The Life of Joseph." pp. 46. *Singapore* [1838?]. 8°.　　15118. d. 11.

—— [Another copy.]　　15118. a. 9.

施嬰夏 SHE PEI-HEA. 奕妙 *Yih meaou.* "On Chess." [1800?] 8°.　　15257. d. 4.

施少峯 SHE SHAOU-FUNG. See 宋小茗 SUNG SEAOU-MING. 耐冷譚 *Nae lăng t'an.* "Notes" on Poetry ... Edited by She Shaou-fung, etc. 1829. 8°.　　15323. b. 31.

施宿 SHE SUH. See 蘇軾 SHOO SHIH. 蘇文忠公詩合註 *Soo Wăn-chung kung she ho choo.* "The Poems of Soo Shih consistently explained by the Commentators" She Suh, etc. 1870. 8°.　　15324. b. 2.

試策 SHE TS'IH. 試策補要 *She ts'ih poo yaou.* "Supplementary Notes" on literary subjects. By "Chuh-yin Choo-jin." 8 keuen. 1876. 8°.　　15319. a. 14.

氏族 SHE TSUH. 氏族大全 *She tsuh ta ts'euen.* "A Complete Biographical Dictionary." A Korean edition of the Chinese work. 10 parts. [1600?] 8°.　　15301. c. 6.

施躍衢 SHE YO-KEU. 鄧霽幗 T'ĂNG TSE-MEI. 佩文韻府約編 *Pei wăn yun foo yo peen.* "An Epitomised Lexicon ..." Edited by She Yo-keu, etc. 1759. 8°.　　15348. b. 3.

示諭 SHE YU. 示諭抄本 *She yu ch'aou pun.* "Proclamations." MS. [1840?] 8°.　　15297. d. 1.

施元倩 SHE YUEN-TS'EEN. See 張路玉 CHANG LOO-YUH. 傷寒緒論 *Shang han seu lun.* "Successive Discourses on Diseases arising from Cold ..." Edited by She Yuen-ts'een, etc. 8°.　　15252. a. 28.

時雨化 SHE YÜ-HWA. See 畢利幹 PEIH-LE-KAN. 法國律例 *Fa kwo leuh le.* "The French Penal Code ..." Transcribed by She Yü-hwa, etc. 1880. 8°.　　15241. c. 10.

—— See 丁韙瓦 TING WEI-LEANG. 西學考畧 *Se heŏ k'aou leŏ.* "A short survey of Western learning ..." Edited by ... She Yü-hwa, etc. 1883. 8°.　　15348. e. 2.

施永圖 SHE YUNG-T'OO. 海運要畧 *Hai yun yaou leŏ.* "Important directions for coast defence." [1840?] 8°.　　15259. c. 22.

—— 武備秘書 *Woo pe pe shoo.* "A Work on the Art of War." [1800?] 8°. 15259. c. 14.

施禹泉 SHE YÜ-TS'EUEN. 養生錄 *Yang săng luh.* Taouist "Remedies for Preserving Life." pp. 76, 22. 1841. 8°.　　15111. a. 22.

實叉難陀 SHIH-CHA-NAN-TO [i.e. ṢIKSHANANDA]. 大方廣佛華嚴經 *Ta fang kwang Fuh hwa yen king.* "The Mahāvaipulya-buddhāvatamsaka Sūtra." Translated into Chinese by Ṣikshananda. 80 keuen. [1700?] 8°.　　15103. e. 14.

A fragment of a Korean manuscript, containing only Keuen 32.

十竹齋 SHIH CHUH CHAI. 十竹齋書畫冊 *Shih chuh chai shoo hwa tsih.* "A (polychromatic) drawing-book from the Ten-bamboos study." In eight parts. 16 vols. [1700?] 8°.　　15255. c. 18.

十房 SHIH FANG. 十房薦卷同門錄 *Shih fang tseen keuen t'ung mun luh.* "A List of the Successful Candidates at the Canton Examination" in 1840. *Canton,* 1840. 8°. 15320. e. 25.

石函氏 SHIH-HAN SHE. 品花寶鑒 *P'in hwa paou keen.* "The precious mirror of classified 'flowers.'" A novel. 60 chapters. 1848. 8°.　　15331. f. 3.

十九史 SHIH KEW SHE. 十九史略諺鮮 *Shih kew she leŏ yen keae.* "An epitome of the nineteen histories of China popularly explained," in Chinese and Korean. 4 keuen. 1804. Obl. 8°.　　15292. c. 10.

SHI

石閭居士 SHIH-LEU KEU SZE. See 杜甫 TOO FOO. 杜律詳解大全集 *Too leu heang keae ta ts'euen tseih.* "A complete collection of the Eight Stanza Poems of Too Foo, explained in detail . . ." Edited by Shih-leu keu sze, etc. 1875. 8°.　　　**15324. d. 6.**

石申 SHIH SHIN. 星經 *Sing king.* "The Astronomical Classic." 2 keuen. See 程榮 CH'ING YUNG. 漢魏叢書 *Han Wei ts'ung shoo.* "A collection of works by authors of the Han and Wei Dynasties," etc. 1791. 8°. **15318. a. 1.**

石鐸琭 SHIH TO-LUH. 默想神功 *Mo seang shin kung.* "The divine merit of contemplation." pp. iii, xx, 98. *Hongkong,* 1893. 12°.　　　**15200. c. 57.**

十五音 SHIH WOO YIN. 彙集雅俗通十五音 *Wei tseih ya suh t'ung shih woo yin.* "A Phonetic Dictionary of the Dialect of Chang Chow in Fuh-keen, arranged according to the 15 initials." 8 keuen. 1861. 12°. **15346. a. 27.**

—— [Another copy.]　　　**15344. d. 8.**

省察 SHING CH'A. 省察規式 *Shing ch'a kwei shih.* "Directions for Self-examination." 2 keuen. *Hongkong,* 1893. 12°.　　　**15200. aa. 17.**

聖學 SHING HEŎ. 聖學十圖 *Shing heŏ shih t'oo.* "Ten diagrams illustrative of the sacred learning." 1569. Square fol.　　**15103. e. 13.**
　　Printed in Korea from movable blocks.

聖會 SHING HWUY. 聖會勸懲條例 *Shing hwuy k'euen ch'ing t'eaou le.* "The Rules of Church Discipline." pp. 56. *Shanghai,* 1881. 8°.　　　**15118. a. 19.**

聖人 SHING JIN. 聖人言行 *Shing jin yen hing.* "The lives of Saints" of the sixth month. pp. vi, 406, 10. *Hongkong,* 1899. 8°.　　　**15200. b. 29.**

—— 聖人言行 *Shing jin yen hing.* "The Lives of the Saints" whose festival days fall in March and April. 2 vols. *Hongkong,* 1898. 8°.　　　**15118. c. 43.**

聖綱鑑 SHING KANG KEEN. 聖綱鑑小畧 *Shing kang keen seaou lŏ.* "An Epitome of Bible History." pp. 196. *Hongkong,* 1892. 8°.　　　**15200. d. 62.**

聖家會 SHING KEA HWUY. 聖家會規 *Shing kea hwuy kwei.* "The Rules of the Society of the Holy Family." pp. 24. *Hongkong,* 1893. 12°.　　　**15200. aa. 36.**

聖教 SHING KEAOU. 聖教主日法 *Shing keaou choo jih fa.* "Rules for the Observance of the Christian Sunday." pp. x, 161. *Nazareth: Hongkong,* 1893. 8°.　　**15351. a. 1.**

—— [Another edition.] 1894. 8°. **15200. d. 28.**

—— [Another edition.] 1897. 8°. **15200. d. 43.**

—— 聖教日課 *Shing keaou jih k'o.* "Roman Catholic Daily Prayers." 3 keuen. *Hongkong,* 1890. 12°.　　　**15200. aa. 11.**

—— [Another edition.] *Hongkong,* 1892. 12°.　　　**15200. aa. 12.**

—— [Another edition.] 1896. 12°. **15200. d. 5.**

—— [Another edition.] 1898. 12°. **15200. d. 7.**

—— 聖教經課 *Shing keaou king k'o.* "Roman Catholic Canonical Prayers." 2 keuen. *Hongkong,* 1889. 12°.　　　**15200. d. 47.**

—— [Another edition.] 1891. 12°. **15200. aa. 13.**

—— 聖教理證 *Shing keaou le ching.* "Reasonable Evidence of the Roman Catholic Faith." pp. xii, 87. *Hongkong,* 1889. 8°.　　　**15200. c. 65.**

—— [Another edition.] 1896. 8°. **15200. d. 30.**

—— 聖教禮規 *Shing keaou le kwei.* "The Ceremonials of the Roman Catholic Religion." 5 keuen. *Hongkong,* 1892. 12°. **15200. aa. 21.**

—— [Another edition.] 1898. 12°. **15200. d. 4.**

—— 聖教切要 *Shing keaou ts'ĕĕ yaou.* "The Main Doctrines of the Roman Catholic Religion." pp. ii, 147. *Hongkong,* 1889. 8°. **15200. d. 40.**

—— 聖教要理 *Shing keaou yaou le.* "A Catechism on the Essential Doctrines of Roman Catholicism." pp. 182. *Hongkong,* 1890. 8°.　　　**15200. c. 58.**

—— [Another edition.] 1894. 8°. **15200. b. 27.**

—— 聖教要理國語 *Shing keaou yaou le kwo yü.* "A Catechism on the Essential Doctrines of Roman Catholicism." In Sinico-Annamite. pp. ii, 50, 6. *Hongkong,* 1892. 8°. **15200. d. 57.**

—— [Another edition.] *Hongkong,* 1897. 8°.　　　**15200. d. 58.**

聖 教 SHING KEAOU. 聖 教 要 理 問 答 *Shing keaou yaou le wăn ta.* "A Catechism on the Essential Doctrines of Roman Catholicism." pp. vi, 99. *Hongkong*, 1889. 12°. **15200. aa. 6.**

—— [Another edition.] *Hongkong*, 1890. 12°. **15200. aa. 7.**

—— [Another edition.] 1896. 12°. **15200. aa. 18.**

—— [Another edition.] 1897. 12°. **15200. d. 22.**

聖 經 SHING KING. 聖 經 廣 益 *Shing king kwang yih.* "The wide advantages of the Bible." 2 keuen. *Hongkong*, 1891. 12°. **15200. d. 46.**

—— 聖 經 史 記 *Shing king she ke.* "Bible History." A manuscript note on the cover attributes this work to W. H. Medhurst. pp. 32. *Shanghai*, 1846. 8°. **15200. c. 37.**

聖 歌 SHING KO. 各 式 聖 歌 *Ko she shing ko.* "Canticles for all occasions." pp. 78. *Hongkong*, 1898. 12°. **15200. d. 11.**

陞 官 SHING KWAN. 陞 官 圖 說 *Shing kwan t'oo shwo.* "A Sketch of the System of Official Promotion." MS. [1850?] 8°. **15241. b. 3.**

盛 冠 寶 SHING KWAN-PAOU. 滿 漢 合 璧 三 字 經 註 解 *Man Han hoh peih San tsze king choo keae.* "A Manchu-Chinese Edition of the Three-character Classic." With explanatory notes. Edited by Shing Kwan-paou. The Manchu version is by T'aou Kih. 2 keuen. 1735. 8°. **15210. e. 8.**

聖 羅 閣 SHING LOH-KIH. 聖 羅 閣 九 日 敬 禮 *Shing Loh-kih kew jih king le.* "A nine-day meditation on events in the life of Saint Luke" of "Mang-pih-le" in France (A.D. 1295–1327). pp. 23. *Hongkong*, 1900. 12°. **15200. b. 35.**

聖 路 SHING LOO. 聖 路 善 工 *Shing loo shen kung.* "The Stations of the Cross." pp. 42. *Hongkong*, 1894. 12°. **15200. d. 6.**

—— [Another edition.] 1898. 12°. **15200. d. 10.**

—— [Another edition.] 1900. 12°. **15200. aa. 45.**

聖 母 SHING MOO. 聖 母 行 實 *Shing moo hing shih.* "Events in the Life of the Virgin Mary." 3 keuen. *Hongkong*, 1893. 8°. **15200. d. 48.**

—— 聖 母 玫 瑰 經 十 五 端 *Shing moo mei kwei king shih woo twan.* "The fifteen sections of the Rosary of the Holy Mother." pp. 18. *Hongkong*, 1893. 12°. **15200. aa. 19.**

—— [Another edition.] 1894. 12°. **15200. d. 21.**

—— [Another edition.] *Hongkong*, 1895. 12°. **15200. aa. 20.**

聖 母 SHING MOO. 聖 母 小 日 課 *Shing moo seaou jih k'o.* "Prayers to the Holy Mother" (of God). pp. 126, 26. *Hongkong*, 1898. 12°. **15200. d. 13.**

—— 聖 母 聖 月 *Shing moo shing yueh.* "The Sacred Month of the Holy Mother" [i.e. the Virgin Mary]. pp. 166. *Hongkong*, 1899. 12°. **15200. aa. 38.**

—— 聖 母 聖 月 *Shing moo shing yueh.* "The Sacred Month of the Holy Mother." pp. 82. *Hongkong*, 1899. 12°. **15200. aa. 44.**

—— 聖 母 聖 月 *Shing moo shing yueh.* "The Sacred Month of the Holy Mother." pp. xiii, 119. *Hongkong*, 1889. 12°. **15200. c. 60.**

—— 聖 母 七 苦 籍 規 略 *Shing moo ts'ih k'oo tseih kwei leŏ.* "Rules of the Register of the Seven Dolors of the Holy Mother." pp. ii, 26. *Hongkong*, 1894. 12°. **15200. aa. 31.**

聖 母 善 導 會 SHING MOO SHEN TAOU HWUY. 聖 母 善 導 會 直 指 *Shing moo shen taou hwuy chih che.* "The Objects of the Society of Notre Dame de bons Secours." pp. viii, 126. *Hongkong*, 1896. 12°. **15200. d. 3.**

—— [Another edition.] 1896. 12°. **15200. d. 1.**

—— 聖 母 善 導 會 公 規 *Shing moo shen taou hwuy kung kwei.* "The General Rules of the Society of Notre Dame de bons Secours." pp. 22. *Hongkong*, 1896. 12°. **15200. d. 2.**

聖 安 多 尼 SHING NGAN-TO-NE. 聖 安 多 尼 行 實 *Shing Ngan-to-ne hing shih.* "The Life of St. Anthony." pp. iv, 54, 10. *Hongkong*, 1898. 12°. **15200. d. 14.**

盛 百 二 SHING PIH-URH. 晉 山 樓 吟 稿 *Keae shan low yin kaou.* "Ballads from the Keae-shan Pavilion." 4 keuen. 1792. 8°. **15323. d. 25.**

—— 尚 書 釋 天 *Shang shoo shih t'een.* "An Explanation of the Astronomy of the Shoo king." 6 keuen. 1753. 8°. **15215. b. 13.**

—— 增 訂 教 稼 書 *Tsăng ting keaou kea shoo.* "A Work on Agriculture. An enlarged edition." 2 keuen. 1772. 8°. **15253. d. 2.**

—— 柚 堂 筆 談 *Yew t'ang peih t'an.* "Notes from the 'Pumelo' Hall." 4 keuen. 1769. 8°. **15215. c. 14.**

SHI—SHU

盛 百 二 SHING PIH-URH. 柚堂文存 *Yew t'ang wǎn ts'un.* "Miscellaneous Writings from the 'Pumelo' Hall." 4 keuen. 1792. 8°.
15215. c. 13.

盛 世 SHING SHE. 盛世芻蕘 *Shing she ch'oo jao.* "A Treatise on various details of Roman Catholicism." 2 keuen? *Hongkong,* 1889. 8°.
15200. c. 64.

Imperfect, containing only Keuen 2.

聖 善 薰 沐 SHING-SHEN-HEUN-MUH. 大悲神咒心經 *Ta pei shin chow sin king.* "The Great-Compassionate-Deities' Prayer-heart Sûtra." Edited by Shing-shen-heun-muh. *Canton,* 1809. Obl.
15103. d. 17.

聖 神 SHING SHIN. 聖神降臨 *Shing shin keang lin.* "The Descent of the Holy Ghost." [By W. Muirhead?] pp. 31. [*Shanghai?*], 1883. 8°.
15200. b. 20.

聖 書 SHING SHOO. 聖書綱目 *Shing shoo kang muh.* "A Scripture Text-book with Commentary." By, as is stated in a manuscript note on cover, the Rev. W. Muirhead. 12 keuen. *Shanghai,* 1882. 8°.
15118. a. 49.

聖 心 SHING SIN. 聖心月新編 *Shing sin yueh sin peen.* "The Month of the Sacred Heart." A new edition. pp. xvi, 134. *Hongkong,* 1891. 12°.
15200. aa. 9.

—— [Another edition.] *Hongkong,* 1895. 12°.
15200. aa. 10.

聖 體 SHING T'E. 領聖體要經 *Ling Shing t'e yaou king.* "The Service of the Mass in the Roman Catholic Church." pp. ii, 40. *Hongkong,* 1892. 12°.
15200. aa. 3.

—— [Another edition.] *Hongkong,* 1893. 12°.
15200. aa. 4.

—— [Another edition.] 1894. 12°. 15200. aa. 14.

—— [Another edition.] *Hongkong,* 1895. 12°.
15200. aa. 5.

昇 寅 SHING YIN. 使喀爾喀䢑程草 *She Kih-urh-kih ke ch'ing ts'aou.* "Odes on Incidents in the Embassy to the Goorkhas." 1820. 8°.
15323. e. 2.

SHING YU. Sheng ü siang chai, or Chinese Historical Illustrations. Republished in reduced form by the Tien shih chai Photo-lithographic Works. 20 keuen. 1879. 8°. 11100. a. 20.

聖 願 SHING YUEN. 聖願問答 *Shing yuen wǎn ta.* "A Catechism on the Sacred Vows." pp. 22. *Hongkong,* 1896. 12°. 15200. d. 8.

申 培 SHIN PEI. 詩說 *She shwo.* "Remarks on the Book of Odes." pp. ii, 54, 2. See 程榮 CH'ING YUNG. 漢魏叢書 *Han Wei ts'ung shoo.* "A collection of works by authors of the Han and Wei Dynasties," etc. 1791. 8°.
15318. a. 1.

神 詩 SHIN SHE. 養心神詩 *Yang sin shin she.* "Hymns." 2 keuen. 1851. 8°. 15118. c. 14.

神 道 SHIN TAOU. 神道總論 *Shin taou tsung lun.* "Discussions on Sacred Doctrines." 3 keuen. *Shanghai,* 1872. 8°. 15116. d. 44.

神 天 SHIN-T'EEN. 神天十條聖誡 *Shin t'een shih t'eaou shing keae.* "The Ten Commandments." pp. 7. *Hongkong,* 1844. 8°.
15118. a. 48.

慎 微 SHIN WEI. 經史證類大觀本草 *King she ching luy ta kwan pun ts'aou.* "A classified general view of Botany substantiated by references to classical and historical works." 31 keuen. 1302. Fol. 15253. e. 4.

Printed in Korea from blocks. Keuen 1, 13, and 14, together with preface, supplied in very fine MS.

壽 SHOW. The hundred forms of the Character 'Show.' [1800?] 15204. a. 3.

守 謙 氏 SHOW-K'EEN-SHE, *pseud.* 增訂驗方新編縮本 *Tsǎng ting yen fang sin peen so pun.* "An enlarged new collection of medical prescriptions." 18 keuen. 1889. 8°. 15253. a. 16.

SHUCK (JEHU LEWIS). See 叔 SHUH.

贖 SHUH. 救贖何義 *Kew shuh ho e.* "The Theory of Redemption." [By C. F. A. Gützlaff.] pp. 4. [1836?] 8°. 15118. d. 19.

叔 SHUH [i.e. JEHU LEWIS SHUCK]. 卜卦之論 *Po kwa che lun.* "A Discourse on Divination." pp. 8. [1845?] 8°. 15257. a. 27.

舒 高 第 SHU KAOU-TE [i.e. SUVOONG?]. See 美國水雷局 MEI KWO SHWUY LUI KEU. 爆藥記要 *Paou yoh ke yaou.* "On Fulminates and Explosives." Translated into Chinese by Shu Kaou-te, etc. 1875. 8°.
15259. e. 10.

純 陽 氏 SHUN-YANG SHE, *pseud.* 證道經 *Ching taou king.* "The Sûtra in proof of Taou." pp. xxvi, 46, 4. *Canton,* 1811. 8°. 15111. a. 24.

雙 太 宗 SHWANG T'AI-TSUNG. See 四書 SZE SHOO. 四書讀本辨義 *Sze shoo tuh pun peen e.* "The Text of the Four Books . . ." Edited by Shwang T'ai-tsung, etc. 1747. 8°.
15202. e. 14.

雙 釘 SHWANG TING. 雙釘記 *Shwang ting ke.* "The Story of the Pair of Nails." In verse. [1840?] 8°.
15327. d. 23.

SIEBOLD (PHILIPP FRANZ VON). 類合 Lui ho, sive vocabularium sinense in Koraïanum conversum; opus Sinicum origine in peninsula Kôraï impressum, in lapide exaratum a Sinensi Ko Tsching Dschang, et redditum curante P. F. von S. (Annexa appendice vocabulorum Koraïnorum, Japonicorum, et Sinensium comparativa.) *Lugduni Batavorum*, 1838. 4°.
11099. g. 2.

SILSBY (J. A.). Shanghai Syllabary arranged in phonetic order. By J. A. S. *American Presbyterian Mission Press : Shanghai*, 1897. 8°.
11099. c. 45.

SING IAH SHÜ. *Sing iah shü jü-veng : teh Foh-ing ts'æn-di.* "An introduction to the New Testament, with a synopsis of the Gospels." In the Romanized T'ai chow dialect. [By W. Rudland?] pp. 78. *T'ai chow Foo*, 1881. 8°.
15200. b. 3.

姓 名 SING MING. 姓名總冊 *Sing ming tsung ts'ih.* "A General List of Names" [probably of the customers at some house of business?]. MS. [1844?] Obl.
15297. d. 17.

SING-SHÜ. *Sing-shü Veng-teh.* "A Christian Catechism." In the Romanized T'ai chow dialect. [By W. Rudland?] pp. 13. *T'ai chow Foo*, 1882. 8°.
15200. c. 34.

新 疆 SINKEANG. 新疆則例便覽 *Sinkeang tsih le peen lan.* "A synopsis of the laws and regulations of Eastern Turkestan," passed during the reign of K'eenlung, 1736–1795. 8 keuen, in 2 vols. Vol. i, ff. 73 ; vol. ii, ff. 77. [1880?]
Or. 4471. 39. B. f.

信 道 SIN TAOU. 信道撮要書 *Sin taou keae yaou shoo.* "A Confession of the Christian Faith." pp. 92. *Shanghai*, 1881. 8°.
15118. a. 18.

心 總 SIN-TSUNG. See 佛 FUH. 佛說摩利支天陀羅尼經 *Fuh shwo Mo-le-che t'een T'o-lo-ne king.* "The Dharani of the Mo-le-che t'een . . ." Edited by . . . Sin-tsung, etc. Obl.
15103. d. 19.

信 從 SIN TS'UNG. 信從相約文 *Sin ts'ung seang yo wăn.* "A Confession of Christian Faith, and a Covenant of Christian Conduct." Issued by the American Baptist Mission. pp. 12. *Ningpo*, 1869. 8°.
15118. a. 32.

新 約 SIN-YO. 新約史記條問 *Sin yo she ke t'eaou wăn.* "A Catechism on the New Testament History." pp. iv, 30. *Shanghai*, 1874. 8°.
15118. a. 45.

SMITH (FREDERICK PORTER). See 師惟善 SZE-WEI-SHEN.

SMYTH (WARRINGTON W.). See 士密德 SZE-MEĬH-TIH.

SONGS. [Twenty-two recitative songs, many of them "Boatmen's Songs."] 1868, etc. 12°.
15327. b. 18.

蘇 如 蓮 SOO JOO-LEEN. 繡像薛仁貴征東全傳 *Sew seang Seay Jin-kwei ching tung ts'euen chuen.* "An Illustrated History of the Pacification of the Eastern Provinces" during the T'ang Dynasty. An historical novel. 6 keuen. [1850?] 8°.
15297. b. 19.

蘇 洵 SOO SEUN. 蘇老泉先生全集 *Soo Laou-ts'euen Seen-săng ts'euen tseih.* "The Complete Writings of Soo Seun." 16 keuen. [1800?] 8°.
15315. d. 4.
Printed in Japan with movable type.

蘇 軾 SOO SHIH. 枘蘇集 *Na Soo tseih.* "A Collection of Distiches taken from Soo Shih's Poetry." Compiled by Ho Leen-fang. 2 keuen. 1862. 8°.
15323. e. 19.

—— 蘇文忠公詩合註 *Soo Wăn-chung Kung she ho choo.* "The Poems of Soo Shih, canonised as Soo Wăn-chung Kung, with a collection of Commentaries." Edited by Fung Ying-lew. With a portrait. 50 keuen. 1795. 8°.
15322. a. 1.

—— [Another edition.] 1870. 8°. 15324. b. 2.

—— 蘇文忠公詩集 *Soo Wăn-chung Kung she tseih.* "The collected poems of Soo Shih, canonised as Wăn-chung Kung." Annotated and punctuated by Ke Yun. 50 keuen. 1834. 8°.
15324. d. 4.

頌主 Sung choo. 頌主聖篇 *Sung choo shing p'een.* "A Christian Hymn-book." A manuscript note attached states that this work is by the Rev. William Muirhead. pp. 210. *Shanghai*, 1876. 12°. 15118. a. 47.

—— 頌主聖詩 *Sung choo shing she.* Two hundred "Hymns in Praise of God." [By the Rev. Griffith John?] *Hankow*, 1883. 8°. 15117. a. 35.

宋遺民 Sung E-min, *pseud.* 水滸後傳 *Shwuy hoo how chuen.* "A further Story of the River's Banks." Edited by Yen-t'ang Shan Ts'eaou, i.e. The Woodman of Mount Yen-t'ang. 8 keuen. 1608. 8°. 15334. e. 3.

宗咸 Sung Heen. See 揚雄 Yang Heung. 新纂門目五臣音註揚子法言 *Sin tswan mun muh woo ch'in yin choo Yang tsze fa yen.* "Discourses on Law, with notes by . . . Sung Heen," etc. 8°. 15237. c. 6.

宋如林 Sung Joo-lin. 松江府志 *Sung keang foo che.* "A Topography of the Prefecture of Sung-keang," in the Province of Keang-nan. Compiled by Sung Joo-lin, Lin Poo, Lew Wǎn-che, and others. 84 keuen. 1818. 8°. 15265. e. 6.

宋景濂 Sung King-leen. 宋景濂文選 *Sung King-leen wǎn seuen.* See 李欽之 Le K'in-che. 金元明八家文選 *Kin, Yuen, Ming, pa kea wǎn seuen.* "Selections from the Writings of Eight Authors who wrote during the Kin, Yuen, and Ming Dynasties," etc. 1845. 8°. 15318. e. 1.

宋廣業 Sung Kwang-něě. 羅浮山志會編 *Lo-fow shan che hwuy peen.* "An Illustrated Topography of the Lo-fow Hills." [1716?] 8°. 15269. c. 10.

Only the illustrations.

宋鳴琦 Sung ming-k'e. 嘉定府志 *Kea ting foo che.* "A Topography of Kea-ting Foo." Compiled by Sung ming-k'e, Chang Sin-king, Yuen Fung-sun, and others. 48 keuen. 1803. 8°. 15267. a. 2.

宋小茗 Sung Seaou-ming. 耐冷譚 *Nai lǎng t'an.* "Notes" on Poetry. By Sung Seaou-ming. Edited by She Shaou-fung and others. 16 keuen. 1829. 8°. 15323. b. 31.

嵩山 Sung Shan. See 胡德琳 Hoo Tih-lin. 東昌府志 *Tung-ch'ang foo che.* "A Topography of Tung-ch'ang foo . . ." Re-edited by Sung Shan, etc. 1808. 8°. 15269. e. 10.

松筠 Sung Yun. 鎮撫事宜 *Chin foo sze e.* "Records of the guarding, soothing, and harmonizing processes adopted towards neighbouring countries." Compiled by Sung Yun. 5 keuen. 1823. 8°. 15239. b. 1.

孫高亮 Sun Kaou-leang. 萃忠全傳 *Tsuy chung ts'euen chuen.* "A Complete Record of the Patriotic Deeds" of Duke Yu Shaou-paou. 6 keuen. [1840?] 8°. 15331. b. 1.

孫鑛 Sun Ke. 學宮禮器圖 *Heŏ kung le k'e t'oo.* "Drawings of Ceremonial Utensils proper to Colleges." See 孫澍 Sun Shoo. 古棠書屋叢書 *Koo t'ang shoo wuh ts'ung shoo.* "A Collection of Reprints," etc. 1831–1849. 8°. 15315. d. 1.

—— 蜀破鏡 *Shuh p'o king.* "The P'o-king [i.e. Rebels] of Shuh." 3 keuen. See 孫澍 Sun Shoo. 古棠書屋叢書 *Koo t'ang shoo wuh ts'ung shoo.* "A Collection of Reprints," etc. 1831–1849. 8°. 15315. d. 1.

—— 孫瘦石文鈔 *Sun Sow-shih wǎn ch'aou.* "The Writings of Sun Ke." 15 keuen. See 孫澍 Sun Shoo. 古棠書屋叢書 *Koo t'ang shoo wuh ts'ung shoo.* "A Collection of Reprints," etc. 1831–1849. 8°. 15315. d. 1.

—— 杜主開明後志 *Too choo K'ai ming how che.* "A Later Account of Too Yu." 8 keuen. See 孫澍 Sun Shoo. 古棠書屋叢書 *Koo t'ang shoo wuh ts'ung shoo.* "A Collection of Reprints," etc. 1831–1849. 8°. 15315. d. 1.

孫強 Sun K'eang. See 顧野王 Koo Yay-wang. 大廣益會玉篇 *Ta kwang yih hwuy yuh p'ien.* "An enlarged and improved edition of the *Yuh p'ien* . . ." Enlarged . . . by Sun K'eang, etc. 1601. 8°. 15348. c. 3.

孫馮 Sun P'ing. 小方壺試律詩 *Seaou fang hoo she leuh she.* "A Collection of Examination Odes." 3 keuen. See 孫澍 Sun Shoo. 古棠書屋叢書 *Koo t'ang shoo wuh ts'ung shoo.* "A Collection of Reprints," etc. 1831–1849. 8°. 15315. d. 1.

孫詩樵 Sun She-ts'eaou. 餘墨偶談 *Yu mih gow t'an.* "Miscellaneous Literary Notes." 8 keuen. 1873. 8°. 15316. b. 4.

SUN—SZE

孫 澍 Sun Shoo. 古 棠 書 屋 叢 書 *Koo t'ang shoo wuh ts'ung shoo.* " A Collection of Reprints from the Koo-t'ang-shoo Dwelling." Compiled by Sun Shoo. [A Japanese edition.] 1831–1849. 8°. **15315. d. 1.**

—— 孫 春 皋 外 集 *Sun Ch'un-kaou wai tseih.* " A further Collection of the Writings of Sun Shoo." 4 keuen. See 孫 澍 Sun Shoo. 古 棠 書 屋 叢 書 *Koo t'ang shoo wuh ts'ung shoo.* " A Collection of Reprints," etc. 1831–1849. 8°. **15315. d. 1.**

—— 杜 主 開 明 前 志 *Too choo k'ai ming ts'een che.* " An Early Account of Too Yu," a legendary ruler of Shuh. 4 keuen. See 孫 澍 Sun Shoo. 古 棠 書 屋 叢 書 *Koo t'ang shoo wuh ts'ung shoo.* " A Collection of Reprints," etc. 1831–1849. 8°. **15315. d. 1.**

孫 星 衍 Sun Sing-yen. 孔 子 集 語 *K'ung tsze tseih yu.* " A Collection of the Sayings of Confucius." Compiled by Sun Sing-yen. 17 keuen. 1815. 8°. **15303. c. 13.**

孫 顏 Sun Yen. 玉 堂 芽 *Yuh T'ang ya.* " Sprouts from the Jade Hall." A dictionary of literary expressions arranged according to subjects. 4 keuen. 1841. 8°. **15342. a. 3.**

孫 逸 仙 Sun Yih-seen. See 柯 士 賓 Ko-sze-pin. 紅 十 字 會 救 傷 第 一 法 *Hung shih tsze hwuy kew shang te yih fa.* " The Red Cross Society's First Aid to the Wounded." Translated into Chinese by Sun Yih-seen, etc. 1897. 8°. **15253. a. 14.**

孫 玉 田 Sun Yuh-t'een. 鑄 史 駢 言 *Choo she p'een yen.* " Notes from History on Classified Subjects." Compiled by Sun Yuh-t'een. 12 keuen. 1876. 12°. **15297. a. 11.**

逐 日 Suy jih. 逐 日 驗 貨 *Suy jih yen ho.* " A Daily Pass-book " [of goods received]. MS. [1844?] Obl. **15297. d. 16.**

隨 園 戲 Suy-yuen-he, *pseud.* 新 齊 諧 *Sin ts'e heae.* " A new collection of stories." 24 keuen. [1820?] 8°. **15327. f. 7.**

算 法 Swan fa. 算 法 指 掌 *Swan fa che chang.* " A Guide to Arithmetic." 1823. 8°. **15255. d. 6.**

西 南 Sye nam. 西 南 圖 *Sye nam to.* " Coloured Maps of the South - Western Provinces of Tjyen-ra to and Kyeng-syang to." [*Seoul*, 1840?] Fol. **15276. e. 5.**

士 Sze. 士 農 工 商 *Sze nung kung shang.* A child's book on the results of the labours of " Scholars, Farmers, Mechanics, and Tradesmen." In verse. [1870?] 8°. **15323. d. 20.**

事 Sze. 雜 事 祕 辛 *Tsa sze pe sin.* " Miscellaneous Records." pp. 18, 1. See 程 榮 Ch'ing Yung. 漢 魏 叢 書 *Han Wei ts'ung shoo.* " A collection of works by authors of the Han and Wei Dynasties," etc. 1791. 8°. **15318. a. 1.**

斯 Sze [i.e. Sir C. T. van Straubenzee]. See 理 Le. A Proclamation issued . . . in the names of . . . the English General Sze, etc. 1857. A sheet. **15241. a. 9.**

帥 Sze [i.e. Miss A. C. Safford]. 聖 書 典 論 *Shing shoo teen lun.* " An Outline of Old Testament History " to the end of Esther. In the Soochow Dialect. With illustrations. 2 keuen. *Shanghai*, 1880–81. 8°. **15118. c. 40.**

帥 蒭 誼 Sze A. E. [i.e. Miss A. E. Safford]. 真 道 略 論 *Chin taou leo lun.* " Talks about the True Doctrine," in the Soochow Dialect. 2 keuen. *Shanghai*, 1883. 8°. **15118. d. 3.**

—— 靈 魂 略 論 *Ling hwan leo lun.* " A short treatise on the Soul." pp. ii, 32. 1882. 8°. **15200. c. 36.**

四 季 Sze ke. 四 季 想 思 *Sze ke seang sze.* " Thoughts on the four Seasons." In irregular verse. pp. 9. [1860?] 8°. **15327. b. 33 (4).**

斯 拉 弗 司 Sze-la-fuh-sze [i.e. A. von Boguslawski]. 臨 陣 管 見 *Lin chin kwan keen.* " Tactical Deductions " from the German and Austrian War of 1866, and from the German and French War of 1870–71. Translated into Chinese by Kin-k'eae-le, i.e. C. S. Kreyer. With a plan. 9 keuen. 1873. 8°. **15259. g. 2.**

司 馬 光 Sze-ma Kwang. 司 馬 公 詩 *Sze-ma kung she.* " Sze-ma Kwang's Poetry." See 孫 澍 Sun Shoo. 古 棠 書 屋 叢 書 *Koo t'ang shoo wuh ts'ung shoo.* " A Collection of Reprints from the Koo-t'ang-shoo Dwelling," etc. 1831–1849. 8°. **15315. d. 1.**

—— See 揚 雄 Yang Heung. 新 纂 門 目 五 臣 音 註 揚 子 法 言 *Sin tswan mun muh woo ch'in yin choo yang tsze fa yen.* . . . . " Discourses on Law, with notes " by . . . Sze-ma Kwang, etc. 8°. **15237. c. 6.**

司 馬 遷 SZEMA TS'EEN. Les Mémoires de Se-ma Ts'ien. Traduits et annotés par Édouard Chavannes. 3 vols. *Ernest Leroux: Paris,* 1895. 8°. 11094. b. 2.

—— [Another copy.] Vols. i and iii. 11094. b. 2.

—— 史 記 菁 華 錄 *She ke tsing hwa luh.* "The Essences and Flowers of Sze-ma Ts'een's Historical Record." Compiled by Choo Teen. 6 keuen. 1824. 8°. 15286. a. 6.

—— [Another copy.] 1824. 8°. 15296. b. 7.

士 密 德 SZE-MEÏH-TIH [i.e. WARINGTON W. SMYTH]. 開 煤 要 法 *K'ai mei yaou fa.* "A treatise on Coal and Coal-mining." With diagrams. Translated into Chinese by Foolanya, i.e. J. Fryer. 12 keuen. [*Shanghai,* 1875?] 8°. 15259. h. 3.

—— [Another copy.] 15252. d. 14.

斯 米 德 SZE-ME-TIH [i.e. SCHMIDT?]. 得 救 要 法 *Tih kew yaou fa.* "The Way of Salvation." With a map. 2 keuen. [*Shanghai?*], 1883. 8°. 15200. b. 7.

師 小 棋 SZE SEAOU-K'E, i.e. MISS A. C. SAFFORD. 訓 兒 眞 言 *Heun urh chin yen.* "True words of instruction for children." In the Soochow Dialect. With illustrations. 51 chapters. *Shanghai,* 1879. 8°. 15200. c. 12.

四 書 SZE SHOO. The Chinese Classical work commonly called the Four Books: I, Ta Heŏ . . . compiled by Tsăng-tsze; II, Chung-yung . . . compiled by Kung-keïh; III, Lun-yu . . . conversations between Confucius and his disciples, . . . collected and committed to writing by the latter; IV, Shang Mung and Hea Mung . . . the production of Mung tsze (i.e. Mencius). Translated and illustrated with notes by the late Rev. David Collie. *Malacca,* 1828. 8°. 11100. b. 1.

—— 正 平 本 論 語 札 解 *Ching p'ing pun lun yu chah keae.* "The true text of the Confucian Analects, with explanatory notes" compiled by Ho Yen. With a bibliographical appendix. 10 keuen. 1813. Fol. 15201. c. 12.
Printed in Japan from blocks.

—— 中 西 四 書 *Chung Se Sze shoo.* The Four Books or the Chinese Classics in English. Compiled from the best previous works. With a preface signed L. Y. T. pp. ii, 617 *Hongkong,* 1898. 8°. 11098. a. 29.

四 書 SZE SHOO. 中 庸 章 句 *Chung yung chang keu.* "The Doctrine of the Mean, explained sentence by sentence by Choo He." [1620?] Fol. 15202. c. 26.
Printed in Japan from blocks.

—— 中 庸 章 句 本 義 匯 參 *Chung yung chang keu pun e hwuy ts'an.* "The Doctrine of the Mean, explained sentence by sentence. With the various commentaries." [8 keuen? 1800?] 8°. 15215. e. 9.
Imperfect, containing only Keuen 4 and 5.

—— 中 庸 指 南 *Chung yung che nan.* "A Guide to the Doctrine of the Mean." [1650?] Fol. 15202. c. 25 (2).
Printed in Korea with movable type.

—— "The Four Books," to which is prefixed the *Koo wăn Heaou king,* or "The ancient text of the classic of filial piety." 1599. Fol. 15210. e. 11.
Printed in Japan with movable type by order of the Mikado.

—— Les Quatre Livres, avec un commentaire abrégé en Chinois, un double traduction en Français et en Latin, et un vocabulaire des Lettres et des noms propres. Par S. Couvreur. pp. vii, 748. *Ho-kien Fou,* 1895. 8°. 11098. c. 19.

—— 學 庸 *Heŏ Yung.* "The Great Learning and the Doctrine of the Mean." With a collection of comments arranged sentence by sentence by Choo He. Edited by Le Hanchang and others. 1867. Fol. 15202. d. 21.

—— 論 語 *Lun yu.* "The Confucian Analects." With comments collected by Choo He. 10 keuen. 1868. Fol. 15202. d. 19.

—— 論 語 *Lun yu.* "The Confucian Analects." With comments compiled by Ho Yen. 10 keuen. 1368. Fol. 15202. d. 20.
The earliest Japanese edition, containing variations from the received text. Printed from blocks.

—— [Another copy, without date.] 15202. d. 21.

—— [Another edition.] 10 keuen. 1499. Fol. 15202. c. 23.

—— [Another edition of the text only.] 10 keuen. 1533. Fol. 15202. c. 21.

—— [Another edition. 1610?] Fol. 15201. c. 10.
Printed in Japan with movable type.

—— [A facsimile reprint of the edition of 1533.] 10 keuen. [1650?] Fol. 15202. c. 22.

SZE

四書 SZE SHOO. 論語 *Lun yu.* "The Confucian Analects." With Choo He's commentary, and with notes. 10 keuen. *Changchow* [1870?]. 8°.
15103. b. 14.

—— 論語集註 *Lun yu tseih choo.* "The Confucian Analects." With Choo He's collection of comments. 10 keuen. [1650?] Fol.
15201. c. 11.
Printed in Japan from blocks.

—— 孟子 *Măng tsze.* "The Sayings of Mencius." With comments collected by Choo He. 7 keuen. 1868. Fol.
15202. d. 20.

—— 孟子 *Măng tsze.* "The Sayings of Mencius." With Choo He's Commentary, and with notes. 7 keuen. *Changchow* [1870?]. 8°. **15201. c. 16.**

—— 孟子集註 *Măng tsze tseih choo.* "The Sayings of Mencius. With a collection of comments" compiled by Choo He. 7 keuen. [1600?] Fol.
15323. d. 27.
Printed in Japan from blocks.

—— Seu Chou, ou Les Quatre Livres, traduits par un Missionnaire de la Congrégation du Cœur immaculé de Marie. pp. 379. *Hongkong*, 1897. 8°.
11099. b. 34.

—— 四書正文 *Sze shoo ching wăn.* "The Correct Text of the Four Books." Edited by Chin Kŏ-hwan. [1818?] 8°. **15202. b. 15.**

—— 四書正文 *Sze shoo ching wăn.* "The Correct Text of the Four Books." Sleeve edition. [1870?] 32°. **15202. a. 14.**

—— 四書正文 *Sze shoo ching wăn.* "The Correct Text of the Four Books." The *San-yuen T'ang* edition. [1750?] 8°. **15202. b. 16.**
Imperfect, containing only the *Lun yu* and the first part of the *Măng tsze.*

—— 四書合講 *Sze shoo ho keang.* "The Four Books jointly explained." With a collection of comments compiled by Choo He. Edited by Poo Sing-chan and Chang Ching. 1865. 8°.
15202. b. 20.

—— 四書便蒙 *Sze shoo peen mung.* "The Four Books for the use of Children." With Choo He's commentary. 1878. 8°. **15201. a. 8.**
Imperfect, containing only the Ta heŏ and the Chung yung.

四書 SZE SHOO. 四書不二字音義撮要 *Sze shoo puh urh tsze yin i ts'uh yaou.* Recueil de tous les Caractères contenus dans les Classiques Chinois. Prononciation et sens en langue Annamite. pp. 65. *Hongkong*, 1897. 8°.
15344. a. 11.

—— 四書集註 *Sze shoo tseih choo.* "The Four Books with a collection of explanations," being those of Choo He, Ch'ing tsze, and others. *Nanking*, 1872. 8°. **15201. a. 7.**

—— 四書全注 *Sze shoo ts'euen choo.* "The Four Books with complete Commentaries." [1850?] 16°. **15201. a. 9.**

—— [Four other copies of this work.]
15201. a. 10–13.

—— 四書襯 *Sze shoo ts'in.* "The Four Books. With an inner garment" of comments. By Lo Tan-heen. Edited by T'ăng Tung-ch'ang and P'ăng Che-ting. [1863?] 8°. **15202. b. 19.**

—— 四書讀本辨義 *Sze shoo tuh pun peen e.* "The Text of the Four Books, with Choo He's Gloss." And with Lexicographical Notes. Edited by Shwang T'ai-tsung. 1747. 8°.
15202. e. 14.

—— 四書味根錄 *Sze shoo wei kăn luh.* "The Four Books, with notes on their flavour and roots drawn from the works of numerous commentators." *Ta heŏ*; *Chung yung*; *Lun yü*, 20 keuen; *Măng tsze*, 14 keuen. 1860. 8°.
15201. a. 6.

—— 大學 *Ta heŏ.* "The Great Learning." With comments compiled by Choo He. A Japanese edition, with manuscript notes and a portrait of Choo He. pp. vi, 30. [1700?] 8°.
15201. b. 3.

—— 大學章句 *Ta heŏ chang keu.* "The Great Learning, explained sentence by sentence" by Choo He. [1610?] Fol. **15202. c. 24.**
Printed in Japan from blocks.

—— 大學通旨 *Ta heŏ t'ung che.* "The Complete Scope of the Great Learning." [1650?] Fol. **15202. c. 25.**
Printed in Korea with movable type.

—— 大學諺解 *Ta heŏ yen keae.* "The Great Learning with the traditional explanations." [1600?] 8°. **15202. c. 20.**
Some few pages are supplied in manuscript.

師 多 馬 SZE TOMA [i.e. SELBY?]. 耶 穌 事
蹟 考 *Yay Soo-sze tseih k'aou.* "A Life of
Christ." With illustrations. 9 keuen. 1887. 8°.
15116. e. 41.

四 字 經 SZE TSZE KING. 四 字 經 文 *Sze tsze
king wăn.* "The text of the four-character
classic." A Roman Catholic work. [Said to
have been written by Julio Aleni.] pp. 65.
Hongkong, 1893. 12°.　15200. c. 53.

—— [Another edition.] *Hongkong*, 1898. 12°.
15200. aa. 1.

師 惟 善 SZE-WEI-SHEN [i.e. FREDERICK PORTER
SMITH]. 勸 戒 詳 烟 *K'euen keae yang yen.*
"Advice against Opium Smoking." *Hankow*
[1870?]. A sheet.　15298. c. 22.

—— 保 冤 攔 除 *Paou meen lan ch'oo.* On the
means of protecting oneself against disease.
15252. b. 27.

—— 相 造 居 室 扼 要 論 *Seang tsaou keu shih
gih yaou lun.* "On the Construction of Houses."
Hankow [1870?]. A sheet.　15257. d. 2.

TABERD (JEAN LOUIS), *Bishop of Isauropolis.*
Documenta rectæ rationis, seu forma instructionis
ad usum alumnorum Sinensium, Annamitarum,
necnon et catechistarum concinnata à J. L. T.
pp. 298. *Hongkong*, 1893. 8°.　11100. a. 22.

—— Logicæ institutiones quæ in Collegio urbano
de propaganda fide traduntur necnon documenta
rationis editum . . . à J. L. T. *Hongkong*,
1849. 8°.　8467. bb. 20.

達 洪 阿 TA HUNG-AH. 臺 灣 奏 摺 上 諭
T'ai-wan tsow che shang yu. "Memorials from
Ta Hung-ah and others, and Decrees on the
subject of the Foreign War in Formosa" in
the year 1842. MS. 1842. 8°.　15297. d. 3.

大 婚 TA HWAN. 大 婚 禮 節 *Ta hwan le tsëë.*
"Ceremonies to be observed on the occasion
of the Marriage" of the Emperor T'ung-che.
1871. 8°.　15229. c. 36.

T'AI-CHOW. *T'e-tsiu Tsæn-mi s.* "Sixty-two Hymns
in the Romanized T'ai-chow dialect." [By
W. Rudland?] *T'ai-chow Foo*, 1880. 12°.
15200. c. 42.

戴 凱 之 TAI KAI-CHE. 竹 譜 *Chuh p'oo.* "A
botanical work on the different kinds of
Bamboo." pp. 28. See 程 榮 CH'ING YUNG.
漢 魏 叢 書 *Han Wei ts'ung shoo.* "A collection of works by authors of the Han and
Wei Dynasties," etc. 1791. 8°.　15318. a. 1.

戴 啟 達 TAI K'E-TA. See 徐 三 省 SEU SAN-
SĂNG. 新 增 萬 寶 元 龍 通 考 *Sin tsăng
wan paou yuen lung t'ung k'aou.* "An Encyclopædia . . ." Edited by Tai K'e-ta, etc. 8°.
15024. c. 5.

代 那 TAINA [i.e. J. D. DANA]. 金 石 識 別 *Kin
shih shih peih.* "A Manual of Mineralogy."
With illustrations, and with a vocabulary of
mineralogical terms. Translated into Chinese
by Makaouwăn, i.e. D. J. Macgowan, and
transcribed by Hwa Hăng-fang. 12 keuen.
1868, 1883. 8°.　15259. c. 23.

—— [Another copy.]　15259. c. 20.

太 平 天 國 T'AIP'ING T'EEN KWO. 抄 各 詔
Ch'aou k'ih chaou. "Copies of the Edicts of the
T'een wang and other Princes" issued during
the end of 1860 and the beginning of 1861.
MS. [1861?] 4°.　15297. a. 21.

—— 詔 書 蓋 璽 頒 行 論 *Chaou shoo kai se
pan hing lun.* "On affixing the Imperial Seal
and disseminating Edicts." pp. iv, 30. 1853.
8°.　15297. d. 26.

—— 行 軍 總 要 *Hsing keun tsung yaou.* "The
Elements of Military Tactics." pp. viii, 52.
1855. 8°.　15297. d. 30.

—— 建 天 京 於 金 陵 論 *K'een t'een king yü
Kin ling lun.* "A discussion on establishing
the 'Heavenly' Capital at Nanking." pp. iv, 58.
1853. 8°.　15297. d. 31.

—— 救 世 異 聖 幼 主 詔 書 *Kew she chin
shing yew choo chaou shoo.* "An Edict issued
by the truly sacred youthful Monarch, the
Saviour of the World." 1861. 15297. d. 20 (2).

—— 欽 定 士 階 條 例 *K'in ting sze keae t'eaou li.*
"Imperially ordained rules for regulating the
ranks of Scholars." pp. 63. 1861. 8°.
15297. d. 29.

Folios i, xvii, and xviii are wanting.

—— 貶 妖 穴 爲 罪 隸 論 *Pien yaou heue wei
tsuy le lun.* "On degrading the name of the
Imp's cave (i.e. Chih le) into Tsuy le" (i.e.
criminal jurisdiction). pp. vi, 36. 1853. 8°.
15297. d. 23.

—— A Proclamation issued by the Heavenly King.
[1861?]　15297. d. 20 (1).

—— A Proclamation on the Principles of T'ai-
p'ingdom issued by the Princes Mung and
Hung and General Le. 1861. 15297. d. 20 (3).

太平天國 T'aip'ing t'een kwo. 太平天國
辛酉拾壹年新曆 T'aip'ing t'een kwo sin
yew shih yih neen sin leih. "A new almanac for
the 11th year of the T'aip'ing Dynasty," 1861,
or rather the 10th year having regard to the
contents. pp. xviii, 50. 1861. 8°. 15297. d. 33.

—— 太平天國 … 楊奏准頒行詔書
T'aip'ing t'een kwo … Yang tsow chun pan
hing chaou shoo. "Memorials presented by
Yang for the dissemination of Edicts." pp.
iv, 20. 1853. 8°. 15297. d. 24.

—— 天朝田畝制度 T'een ch'aou t'een mow
che too. "Regulations regarding agriculture
issued by the Heavenly Dynasty." pp. iv, 15.
1853. 8°. 15297. d. 25.

—— 天父詩 T'een Fu she. "Hymns to God."
Issued by the T'aip'ing rebels. 5 keuen. 1857.
8°. 15297. d. 34.

—— 天情道理書 T'een ts'ing taou le shoo.
"The Doctrine of the Love of Heaven." Issued
by the T'aip'ing Rebels. pp. iv, 102. 1854. 8°.
15297. d. 32.

—— 天王詔旨 T'een wang chaou chih. "Five
Edicts issued by the Heavenly King." 1861.
15297. d. 20 (4).

—— 王長次兄親目親耳共証福音書
Wang chang ts'ze heung ts'in muh ts'in erh kung
ching fuh yin shoo. "The authoritative gospel
of what the King's brothers saw and heard with
their eyes and ears." pp. iv, 18. 1860. 8°.
15297. d. 28.

—— 武畧 Woo leŏ. "Military Tactics." A
collection of extracts from the writings of
ancient authors. [1855?] 8°. 15297. d. 22.

—— 幼主詔書 Yew choo chaou shoo. "The
Edicts of the youthful Monarch" of the
T'aip'ing Dynasty. pp. ii, 10. [1855?] 8°.
15297. d. 27.

—— 御製千字文 Yu che ts'een tsze wăn.
"An Imperially arranged 'Thousand Character
Classic.'" pp. iv, 28. 1854. 8°. 15297. d. 21.

戴德 TAI TIH. 大戴禮記 Ta Tai le ke. "The
Ritual of the Senior Tai." 13 keuen. See
程榮 CH'ING YUNG. 漢魏叢書 Han Wei
ts'ung shoo. "A collection of works by authors
of the Han and Wei Dynasties," etc. 1791. 8°.
15318. a. 1.

太祖 T'AI TSOO. 宋太祖三下南唐 Sung
T'ae Tsoo san hea Nan T'ang. "The History
of the Three Conquests of the Southern T'ang
Dynasty by the Emperor T'ai Tsoo, of the Sung
Dynasty." By "Haou koo choo jin." 8 keuen.
1874. 8°. 15331. c. 10.

太宗 T'AI-TSUNG. 大唐三藏聖教序 Ta
T'ang san tsang shing keaou seu. "A Preface
to the Holy Religion of the Tripitaka." By
the Emperor T'ai-tsung of the T'ang Dynasty,
written in 648 A.D. Reproduced by lithography
at the Teen shih ch'ai, Shanghai. 15204. a. 5.

TALMAGE (JOHN VAN NEST). See BIBLE—NEW
TESTAMENT: John, Epistles. Sù-tô Iok-hān ê
sam-su. … [Translated by J. van N. T. ?],
etc. 1870. 8°. 15117. d. 36.

TAM TAH HIN. See 覃達軒 T'AN TA-HEEN.

但以理 TAN-E-LE. 但以理聖蹟圖說 Tan-e-le
shing tseih t'oo shwo. "An illustrated life of the
Prophet Daniel." By, as it is stated in a
manuscript note on the cover, Mrs. Williamson.
pp. 42. 1882. 4°. 15118. e. 5.

單復 TAN FUH. See 杜甫 Too Foo. 讀杜詩
愚得 Tuh Too she yu tih. "A guide to reading
Too's poetry," by Tan Fuh, etc. 1501. Fol.

唐 T'ANG. 說唐全傳 Shwo T'ang ts'euen chuen.
"A complete history of the T'ang Dynasty."
With portraits. 14 keuen, with a supplementary
keuen. 1736. 8°. 15291. a. 9.
Imperfect, wanting Keuen 1–3, 7–10.

湯芷卿 T'ANG CHE-KING. 翼駉稗編 Yih
kung pai peen. "A collection of racy and rich
Stories." By T'ang Che-king. Edited by Seu
Tsze-lăng. 8 keuen. 1869. 8°. 15331. c. 15.

湯義仍 T'ANG E-JĂNG. 玉茗新詞四積
Yuh-ming sin ts'ze sze chung. "Four Plays
from the Yuh-ming Hall," by T'ang E-jăng,
viz.: (1) Hwan hun ke, 2 keuen; (2) Tsze
ch'ai ke, 2 keuen; (3) Nan ko ke, 2 keuen;
(4) Han tan ke, 2 keuen. Edited by Tsang
Tsin-shuh. With illustrations. [1600?] 8°.
15333. f. 2.

唐衡銓 T'ANG HĂNG-TS'EUEN. 文房肆考
圖說 Wăn fang sze k'aou t'oo shwo. "An
illustrated treatise on the four (necessaries) for
a study," viz.: inkstones, ink, paper, and
pencils. By T'ang Hăng-ts'euen. Edited by
Chin Yun-pai. 8 keuen. 1778. 8°. 15317. e. 2.

揚若士 T'ANG JO-SZE. See 羅貫中 LO KWAN-CHUNG. 殘唐五代全傳 *Tsan T'ang Woo tai ts'euen chuen.* "A complete History of the Fall of the T'ang and of the 'Five Dynasties.'" ... Edited by T'ang Jo-sze, etc. 1866. 8°.
15331. d. 8.

唐介軒 T'ANG KEAE-HEEN. 古文翼 *Koo wǎn yih.* "Extracts from Ancient Literature." Compiled by T'ang Keae-heen. Edited by Chang Ying-joo and others. 8 keuen. 1873. 8°.
15312. b. 7.

唐荊川 T'ANG KING CH'UEN. See 戚繼光 TSEIH KE-KWANG. 紀效新書 *Ke heaou sin shoo.* "A new work on the Stratagems of War ..." With an extract ... from a work entitled *Woo peen,* by T'ang King ch'uen, etc. 8°.
15259. c. 12.

唐夢容 T'ANG MUNG-YUNG. 濟南府志 *Tsenan foo che.* "A Topography of Tsenan fu," in the Province of Shantung. Compiled by T'ang Mung-yung and others With plates. 38 keuen. 1690. 8°.
15276. b. 3.
Imperfect, containing only Keuen 4–7, 9–16, 18–38.

揚南溪 T'ANG NAN-K'E. See 張浦山 CHANG POO-SHAN. 國朝畫徵錄 *Kwŏ ch'aou hwa ching luh.* "Biographical Notices of Artists ..." Edited by T'ang Nan-k'e, etc. 1739. 8°.
15305. b. 1.

鄧士憲 TĂNG SZE-HEEN. 南海縣志 *Nan-hai heen che.* "A Topography of Nan-hai heen," forming part of the city of Canton. Compiled by Tăng Sze-heen and others. 44 keuen. With appendix. 1835. 8°.
15276. a. 2.

揚祥瑟 T'ANG TSEANG-PE. 詩韻合璧 *She yun ho peih.* "A complete Rhyming Dictionary." 5 keuen. With an appendix. 1875. 8°.
15346. a. 18.

鄧霽嶒 TĂNG TSE-MEI. 佩文韻府約編 *Pei wǎn yun foo yo peen.* "An Epitomized Lexicon arranged according to the 106 Finals." By Tăng Tse-mei. Edited by She Yo-keu and Lew Seuĕ-po. 24 keuen. 1759. 8°. 15348. b. 3.

鄧東長 TĂNG TUNG-CH'ANG. See 四書 SZE SHOO. 四書襯 *Sze shoo ts'in.* "The Four Books ..." Edited by Tăng Tung-ch'ang, etc. 8°.
15202. b. 19.

揚文潞 T'ANG WĂN-LOO. 校補詩韻合璧 *Keaou poo she yun ho pe.* "An enlarged and improved dictionary of poetical expressions," arranged under the 106 final syllables distributed among the five tones. Compiled by T'ang Wăn-loo. 5 keuen, with a supplement. *Shanghai,* 1879. 8°.
15348. c. 4.

唐惟懋 T'ANG WEI-MOW. 發蒙小品二集 *Fa mung seaou p'in urh tseih.* "A collection of Model Essays for beginners." Compiled by T'ang Wei-mow. 1743. 8°. 15319. a. 8.
Imperfect, wanting the first essays on the Shang lun.

唐應德 T'ANG YING-TIH. 唐荊川文選 *T'ang King-ch'uen wǎn seuen.* See 李欽之 LE K'IN-CHE. 金元明八家文選 *Kin, Yuen, Ming, pa kea wǎn seuen.* "Selections from the Writings of Eight Authors who wrote during the Kin, Yuen, and Ming Dynasties," etc. 1845. 8°.
15318. e. 1.

揚雲霧 T'ANG YUN-WOO. See 伯仁 PIH JEN. 竹波軒楳册 *Chuh po heen mei shan.* "A Model Drawing Book ..." Edited by T'ang Yun-woo, etc. 1838. 8°. 15255. e. 20.

貪歡 T'AN HWAN. 貪歡報 *T'an hwan paou.* "Records of excessive pleasure-seeking." By *Se hoo yü yin choo jin,* or "The retired fishing master of the western lake." With illustrations. 24 chapters. [1840?] 8°. 15331. f. 5.

譚乾初 T'AN KAN-CH'OO. 古巴雜記 *Koo-pa tsa ke.* "Miscellaneous Records concerning Cuba." pp. 76. 1887. 8°. 15275. a. 22.

譚伯玉 T'AN PIH-YUH. See 趙子昂 CHAOU TSZE-GANG. 趙子昂詩集 *Chaou Tsze-gang she tseih.* "Chaou Tsze-gang's poetry." Edited by T'an Pih-yuh, etc. 8°. 15324. a. 6.

譚心翼 T'AN SIN-YIH. 武帝寶訓像註 *Woo te paou heun seang choo.* "The precious instructions of the God of War." Illustrated and with a commentary. 4 keuen. *Canton,* 1845. 8°.
15113. a. 25.

譚達軒 T'AN TA-HEEN. 華英字典彙集 An English and Chinese Dictionary with English meaning or expression for every English word. By Tam Tah Hin. Revised by Kwok Lo Kwai. Third edition. pp. 917. *Hongkong,* 1897. 8°. 11098. a. 9.

TAO

TAO-KAO-GO. *Tao-kao-go ing-ny iæn* "The Power of Prayer." In the Ningpo dialect. A manuscript note on the cover states that the work is by Butler. pp. 34. *Shanghai, 1875.* 8°.
15118. a. 55.

TAO SU. See 老君 LAOU KEUN.

道綽 TAOU-CH'O. 安樂集 *Gan lo tseïh.* "A peaceful and pleasurable collection of Buddhist essays." 2 keuen. 1386. 8°. 15103. b. 6.
Printed in Japan from blocks.

陶澍 T'AOU CHOO. 江蘇海運全案 *Keang soo hai yun ts'euen gan.* "A discussion on the subject of transporting the Imperial Impost Grain from the Province of Keang - soo to the Metropolis." Compiled by a Commission consisting of T'aou Choo, Ke Shen, Ho Changling, and others. 12 keuen. 1826. 8°.
15239. c. 3.

陶宏景 T'AOU HUNG-KING. 刀劍錄 *Taou keen luh.* "An account of (ancient and modern) swords." pp. 22. See 程榮 CH'ING YUNG. 漢魏叢書 *Han Wei ts'ung shoo.* "A collection of works by authors of the Han and Wei Dynasties," etc. 1791. 8°. 15318. a. 1.

桃花女 T'AOU HWA NEU. 桃花女陰陽鬥傳 *T'aou hwa neu yin yang tow chuen.* "The Story of the Peach Blossom Maiden, or the fight between the male and female principles of nature." 4 keuen. 1848. 8°. 15331. c. 16.

陶然 T'AOU JEN. 味閒堂課鈔 *Wei heen t'ang ko ch'aou.* "The Wei-heen T'ang Collection of Essays" on Texts from the Four Books, together with Poetical Pieces. Compiled by T'aou Jen. 1860. 8°. 15320. c. 12.

陶格 T'AOU KIH. See 盛冠寳 SHING KWAN-PAOU. 滿漢合璧三字經註解 *Man Han hoh peïh San tsze king choo keae.* "A Manchu-Chinese edition of the Three-character Classic . . ." The Manchu translation is by T'aou Kih, etc. 1735. 8°. 15210. e. 8.

陶錫祈 T'AOU SEÏH-K'E [i.e. S. DODD]. *See* BIBLE — NEW TESTAMENT: *Corinthians, 2nd Epistle.* 哥林多後書註釋 *Ko-lin-to how shoo choo shih.* "The 2nd Epistle to the Corinthians. Translated with a Commentary" by T'aou Seïh-k'e, etc. 1882. 8°. 15200. c. 21.

陶錫祈 T'AOU SEÏH-K'E [i.e. S. DODD]. *See* BIBLE — NEW TESTAMENT: *Hebrews.* 希伯來書註釋 *He pih-lai shoo choo shih.* Translated by T'aou Seïh-k'e, etc. 1882. 8°.
15117. b. 9.

—— 使徒雅各暨彼得前後書註釋 *She t'oo Yakih ke Pe-tih ts'een how shoo choo shih.* "A Commentary on the Epistles of St. James and St. Peter." By T'aou Seïh-k'e. 2 keuen. *Shanghai, 1881.* 8°. 15117. d. 24.

道宣 TAOU-SEUEN. 釋迦方誌 *Shih kea fang che.* "An Account of the Country of Sakya Muni." By the Priest Taou-seuen. 3 keuen. MS. [1850?] 8°. 15103. d. 4.

陶遜亭 T'AOU SUN-T'ING. 草韻彙編 *Ts'aou yun wei p'een.* "A Dictionary of the Grass Character arranged according to the Finals." By Ts'aou Sun-t'ing. Edited by Choo Kang-se, Yu Tung-kaou, and others. 26 keuen. 1755. 8°. 15344. b. 8.

陶潛 T'AOU TSEEN. 孝傳 *Heaou chuen.* "Stories of Filial Piety." pp. i, 13, 2. See 程榮 CH'ING YUNG. 漢魏叢書 *Han Wei ts'ung shoo.* "A collection of works by authors of the Han and Wei Dynasties," etc. 1791. 8°.
15318. a. 1.

—— 羣輔錄 *Keun foo luh.* "A Record of Celebrities," down to the fourth century of our era. pp iv, 50, 2. See 程榮 CH'ING YUNG. 漢魏叢書 *Han Wei ts'ung shoo.* "A collection of works by authors of the Han and Wei Dynasties," etc. 1791. 8°. 15318. a. 1.

—— 積搜神記 *Suh sow shin ke.* "A sequel to the *Sow shin ke.*" 2 keuen. See 程榮 CH'ING YUNG. 漢魏叢書 *Han Wei ts'ung shoo.* "A collection of works by authors of the Han and Wei Dynasties," etc. 1791. 8°.
15318. a. 1.

—— 靖節先生集 *Tsing tsëë Seen-săng tseïh.* "The Poems of the Elder of Tsing-tsëë," i.e. T'aou Ts'een. 10 keuen. 1583. Fol.
15324. c. 7.
Printed in Korea from blocks.

道原 TAOU-YUEN. 景德傳燈錄 *King-tih chuen tăng luh.* "Buddhist Biographies during the Reign of Kingtih" (1004–1008). A Japanese edition. 30 keuen. 1348. 4°. 15103. c. 37.
Keuen 3–6, 15, 16, 21, 25, 26 supplied in manuscript.

大鬧王 TA-P'EĬH WANG. 大鬧王聖蹟圖說 *Ta-p'eĭh wang shing tseĭh t'oo shwo.* "An Illustrated Life of King David." By, as is stated in a manuscript note on the cover, Mrs. Williamson. 1882. 4°. **15118. e. 6.**

達生 TA SĂNG. 達生編 *Ta săng peen.* "A work on Midwifery." 1813. 8°. **15252. b. 19.**

大達塔 *Ta-ta t'a.* The reproduction of the inscription memorialising the building of the Ta-ta Pagoda, in 841. 8°. **15113. b. 13.**

大藏 TA TS'ANG. 大藏目錄 *Ta ts'ang muh luh.* "A Catalogue of the Chinese Version of the Buddhist Canon." 3 keuen. [1620 ?] Fol. **15103. e. 9.**

Printed in Korea from blocks.

TA TS'ING YIH T'UNG YÜ T'U. Nord-Tibet und Lob-Nur-Gebiet in der Darstellung des Ta-Thsing i Thung yü Thu . . . unter Mitwirkung des Herrn K. Himly . . . herausgegeben von Dr. G. Wegener. Mit einer Tafel. Sonderabdruck aus der Zeitschrift der Gesellschaft für Erdkunde zu Berlin, etc. pp. 201–242. *Berlin*, 1893. 8°.

大秦景敎 TA TS'IN KING KEAOU. 大秦景敎流行中國碑 *Ta Ts'in king keaou lew hing Chung kwo pei.* "The rubbing of a Tablet set up in Se-ngan Fu to commemorate the spread of the Religion of Ta Ts'in [Nestorian Christianity] in China" in the year 781 A.D. Written by the Priest Kingtsing. Reset up in the year 1859 by Han T'ai-hwa. Chinese and Syriac. A sheet. **15300. b. 9.**

大東 TA TUNG. 大東輿地圖 *Ta tung yü te t'oo.* "A Map of Korea," in 22 sheets, according to the political divisions. [1810 ?] Folio. **15261. c. 2.**

大英國 TA YING KWO. 大英國統志 *Ta Ying kwo t'ung che.* "A History of England." [By K. F. A. Gützlaff.] With maps and portraits of the Georges. 5 keuen. 1834. 8°. **15291. a. 13.**

TAYLOR (JAMES HUDSON). *See* BIBLE — NEW TESTAMENT: *Gospels and Acts.* Ah-lah Kyiu-cü Yiæsu kyi-toh-go Sing jah Shü . . . [Translated into the Romanized Ningpo dialect by J. H. T.], etc. 1870. 4°. **15117. e. 17.**

TCHOU PÔ-LOU. *See* CH'OO PIH-LOO.

條約 T'EAOU YO. 善後條約 *Shen how t'eao u yo* "Additional Treaty Regulations." MS. [1842?] 8°. **15241. c. 4.**

鐵麟 T'EĔ LIN. *See* 文慶 WĂN K'ING. 欽定國子監志 *K'in ting kwo tsze keen che.* "The History of the Imperial College . . ." By . . . T'eĕ Lin, etc. 1834. 8°. **15297. e. 1.**

天主 T'EEN CHOO. 天主經 *T'een choo king.* "The Lord's Prayer." To which is added the Apostles' Creed. [1890 ?] 4°. **15117. d. 43.**

—— 天主十戒勸論聖蹟 *T'een choo shih keae k'euen lun shing tseĭh.* "The Ten Commandments, with explanations and examples from religious history." MS. [1840 ?] 8°. **15118. d. 18.**

天主聖敎 T'EEN CHOO SHING KEAOU. 天主聖敎日課 *T'een choo shing keaou jih k'o.* "Roman Catholic daily Prayers." 3 keuen. *Hongkong*, 1897. 12°. **15200. d. 44.**

—— 天主聖敎日課 *T'een choo shing keaou jih k'o.* "Roman Catholic Daily Prayers." In Sinico-Annamite. pp. iv, 198. *Hongkong*, 1892. 8°. **15200. c. 59.**

—— [Another edition.] 1894. 8°. **15200. d. 29.**

—— 天主聖敎日課 *T'een choo shing keaou jih k'o.* "Roman Catholic Daily Prayers." 3 keuen. *Hongkong*, 1899. 12°. **15200. aa. 37.**

天下 T'EEN HEA. 天下路程 *T'een hea loo ch'ing.* "The Roads of the Empire." *Nanking* [1800 ?]. 8°. **Gren : 15683.**

天花藏主人 T'EEN-HWA-TS'ANG KEU-JIN, *pseud.* 醉菩提全傳 *Tsuy P'u t'i ts'euen chuen.* The Story of the "Drunken Intelligence." 4 keuen. 1847. 8°. **15327. f. 5.**

天然 T'EEN-JEN. 石點頭 *Shih teen t'ow.* "The Stone bows its Head." A Buddhist tale by the Priest T'een-jen. 14 keuen. [1750 ?] 8°. **15103. d. 3.**

天官 T'EEN KWAN. 天官賜福 *T'een kwan ts'ze fuh.* "The Officials of Heaven bestow happiness." A fortune-telling book. *Canton*, 1871. 8°. **15257. a. 26.**

田類思 T'EEN-LUY-SZE [i.e.   ]. 聖敎鑑略 *Shing keaou keen leŏ.* "An abridged exposition of Christianity." By T'een-luy-sze. 2 keuen. *Hongkong*, 1894. 8°. **15118. a. 29.**

TEE—TIH

天象 T‘EEN SEANG. 天象列次分野之圖 *T‘een seang lëë ts‘ze fun yay che t‘oo.* "A Chart of the Heavenly Constellations," with explanations. [1700?] A sheet. **15259. f. 13.**

天神會 T‘EEN SHIN HWUY. 天神會課 *T‘een shin hwuy k‘o.* "Lessons on the Doctrines of the (Roman Catholic) Church." [1750?] 8°. **15118. c. 32.**

田大里 T‘EEN-TA-LE [i.e. JOHN TYNDALL]. 光學 *Kwang heŏ.* "Notes on a course of nine Lectures on Light." With diagrams. Translated into Chinese by Kin-k‘eae-le, i.e. C. T. Kreyer. 2 keuen. [*Shanghai*, 1875?] 8°. **15259. h. 2.**

—— [Another copy.] **15259. d. 2.**

—— 電學綱目 *Luy heŏ kang muh.* "Notes on Electricity." Translated into Chinese by Foo-lan-ya, i.e. John Fryer. pp. 140. [1870?] 8°. **15259. h. 9.**

—— 聲學 *Shing heŏ.* "On Sound." Translated into Chinese by Foolanya, i.e. John Fryer. With plates. 8 keuen. [*Shanghai*, 1880?] 8°. **15259. h. 4.**

—— [Another copy.] **15259. d. 1.**

天堂 T‘EEN T‘ANG. 天堂直路 *T‘een t‘ang chih loo.* "The straight road to Heaven." pp. iv, 41. *Hongkong*, 1889. 8°. **15200. d. 53.**

—— [Another edition.] *Hongkong*, 1899. 8°. **15200. b. 30.**

天道 T‘EEN TAOU. 天道溯原直解 *T‘een taou soo yuen chih keae.* "The evidences of Christianity explained." 3 keuen. 1881. 8°. **15118. d. 23.**

天文 T‘EEN WĂN. 天文須知 *T‘een wăn seu che.* "Elements of Astronomy." By J. Fryer, according to a manuscript note on cover. pp. 24. [*Shanghai?*] 1881. 8°. **15257. a. 28.**

—— [Another copy.] **15200. b. 34.**

狄考文 T‘EĬH K‘AOU-WĂN [i.e. REV. CALVIN W. MATEER]. 創世記問答 *Ch‘wang she ke wăn ta.* "A catechism on the Book of Genesis." pp. iv, 378. *Shanghai*, 1875. 8°. **15118. d. 8.**

—— 孩子受洗禮論 *Hai-tsze show se le lun.* "On infant baptism." pp. ii, 43. *Shanghai*, 1871. 8°. **15118. a. 23.**

狄就烈 T‘EĬH TSEW-LËË [i.e. MRS. JULIA B. MATEER]. 西國樂法啓蒙 *Se kwo yo fa k‘e mung.* "The laws of Western Music for beginners." With songs set to music. 3 keuen. *Shanghai*, 1872. 8°. **15118. a. 48.**

—— [Another edition.] *Shanghai*, 1879. 8°. **15257. e. 20.**

地理 TE LE. 地理輯要 *Te le tseĭh yaou.* "An abstract of (chiromantic and) geomantic lore." MS. ff. 73. [1860?] 8°. **Or. 1304. 308. c. 4.**

—— 地理問荅 *Te le wăn ta.* "A catechism of geography." A manuscript note attached to the title-page describes this work as having been written by 'Wong.' With illustrations. 1865. 4°. **15271. c. 17.**

棣麼甘 TE MO-KAN [i.e. A. DE MORGAN]. 數學理 *Shoo heŏ le.* "The Elements of Arithmetic." 6th edition, 1876. By Te Mo-kan. Translated into Chinese by Foolanya, i.e. J. Fryer. 10 keuen. [*Shanghai*, 1880?] 8°. **15259. h. 3.**

地藏菩薩 TE TS‘ANG POO-SA. 地藏菩薩本願經 *Te tsang P‘oo-sa pun yuen king.* "The Original Sûtra of the Soul-saving Bodhisattwa." In Manchoo and Chinese. 2 keuen. [1820?] 8°. **15103. d. 15.**

T‘E-TSIU. *T‘e-tsiu t‘u wa ts‘u-ôh.* "A Primer in the Romanized dialect of T‘ai-chow." [By W. Rudland.] pp. 62. *T‘ai chow*, 1880. 8°. **15229. b. 24.**

THEATRICAL SCENE. A sheet representing the scene of the capture of Kwan Kung and the ladies Kan and Mi by Ts‘ao Ts‘ao in the third century. [1900?] **15301. d. (8).**

THOM (ROBERT). *See* ÆSOP. Æsop's Fables. Compiled [by R. T.], etc. 1891, etc. 8°. **11100. c. 9.**

惪貞 TIH-CHING [i.e. JOHN DUDGEON, M.D.]. *See* 李修善 LE SEW-SHEN. 戒烟醒世圖 *Keae yin sing she t‘oo.* "Warnings against opium smoking." By . . . Tih-ching, etc. 1883. 8°. **15200. b. 21.**

惪成 TIH-CH‘ING. A rubbing of an inscription in an arch at Kew-yung kwan in six languages, viz., Sanskrit, Tibetan, Mongolian, Ouigur, Nüchih, and Chinese. A Chinese legend in the nature of a colophon by Tih-ch'ing, a priest of the Paou-tseih sze at Ch'ingtu, states that the inscription was finished in the year 1345. Just a century later we are told that it was restored with funds given by the meritorious and believing official Lin P'oo-heen. This rubbing omits the Sanskrit part of the inscription. For a full account of the inscription see an article on the subject by Alexander Wylie in the 5th volume of the Journal of the Royal Asiatic Society. 7 sheets. **Or. 1095. 36. d.**

瞿 汝 丹 TIH JOO-TAN. *See* BLAIKIE (WILLIAM). 幼 學 操 身 *Yew heŏ ts'aou shin.* "Sound bodies for our boys and girls." Translated into Chinese . . . with the assistance of Tih Joo-tan, etc. 1890. 8°. **15344. e. 17.**

荻 岸 散 人 TIH NGAN SAN JIN, *pseud.* 平 山 冷 燕 *P'ing-shan lăng yen.* "The Cold Swallow of P'ing-shan." A novel. With illustrations. 4 keuen. [1850?] 8°. **15333. f. 6.**

丁 樹 棠 TING SHOO-T'ANG. See 利 稼 孫 LE-KEA-SUN, and 華 得 斯 HWA-TIH-SZE. 製 火 藥 法 *Che ho yo fa.* "On the Manufacture of Gunpowder." Edited by Ting Shoo-t'ang, etc. 8°. **15259. e. 7.**

丁 韙 良 TING WEI-LEANG [i.e. DR. W. A. P. MARTIN]. See 步 倫 POO-LUN. 公 法 會 通 *Kung fa hwuy t'ung.* "International Law," . . . a translation into Chinese . . . by Ting Wei-leang, etc. 1880. 8°. **15236. e. 7.**

—— See 吳 氏 WOO SHE. 公 法 便 覽 *Kung fa peen lan.* "An Introduction to the Study of International Law . . . ." Translated into Chinese by . . . Dr. W. A. P. Martin, etc. 1877. 8°. **15239. c. 11.**

—— *Di-li shü.* "A work on Geography" in the Romanized Ningpo dialect. With a map and illustrations. pp. 52. *Ningpo,* 1859. 8°. **15263. b. 4.**

—— 富 國 策 *Foo kwo ts'ih.* "A statement of the economic principles carried out in the most advanced Western countries." 3 keuen. 1880. 8°. **15233. d. 5.**

—— [Another edition.] *Shanghai,* 1882. 8°. **15235. d. 6.**

丁 韙 良 TING WEI-LEANG [i.e. DR. W. A. P. MARTIN]. 格 物 入 門 *Kih wuh juh mun.* "An Introduction to Natural Philosophy." With plates. 7 keuen. *Peking,* 1868. 8°. **15255. c. 20.**

—— 陸 地 戰 例 新 選 *Luh te chen le sin seuen.* "The Rules of War." A new edition. pp. x, 31. *Peking,* 1883. 8°. **15259. b. 5.**

—— 保 羅 垂 訓 *Paou lo ch'uy heun.* "Paul's Discourse" at Athens. 12 pp. *Shanghai,* 1866. 8°. **15118. a. 38.**

—— 西 學 考 畧 *Se heŏ k'aou leŏ.* "A report on Education in the West," including Japan. With an additional title-page and table of contents in English. 2 keuen. *Peking,* 1883. 8°. **15348. e. 2.**

—— [Another copy.] **15292. c. 12.**

—— 天 道 溯 原 *T'een taou soo yuen.* "The way of Heaven traced to its source." A Christian tract. 3 keuen. *Shanghai,* 1867. 8°. **15118. b. 45.**

TIN TUN - LING. Lettre de la province de Chang-Si. 倫 小 鞋 La Petite Pantoufle (Thou-sio-sié). Traduction de . . . C. Aubert. Avec six eaux-fortes originales reproduites par F. Chevalier. [" Édition Franco-Chinoise."] [*Paris,*] *Meaux* [printed 1875]. 8°. **11100. f. 3.** Printed on one side only of paper, in Chinese fashion.

TOBAR (JEROME). See 張 之 洞 CHANG CHE-TUNG. 勸 學 篇 K'ien-hio p'ien . . . Ouvrage traduit du Chinois par J. T., etc. 1898. 4°. **11098. d. 4.**

譯 林 TO LIN. 要 理 講 論 *Yaou le keang lun.* "A catechism on essential points of the Christian doctrine." 4 keuen. *Hongkong,* 1896. 8°. **15200. d. 26.**

托 馬 斯 米 爾 納 T'OMASZE ME-URNA [i.e. THOMAS MILNER]. 大 英 國 志 *Ta ying kwo che.* "The History of England." To which is added a chapter on the British Constitution taken from Chambers' "Information for the People." Translated into Chinese by William Muirhead. With illustrations, maps, and a preface in English. 8 keuen. *Shanghai,* 1881. 8°. **15291. b. 1.**

TOO—TSA

杜甫 Too Foo. 杜律詳解大全集 *Too leu seang keae ta ts'euen tseïh.* "A complete collection of the eight-stanza poems of Too Foo explained in detail." With a biography of the poet. Edited by *Shih-leu keu sze,* or the retired scholar of Shih-leu [i.e. the stone village]. 6 keuen. With a supplement in 2 keuen. 1875. 8°. **15324. d. 6.**

—— 杜少陵全集詳註 *Too Shaou-ling ts'euen tseïh seang choo.* "A complete collection of the poems of Too Foo. With explanatory notes" by K'ew Chaou-gaou. Edited by Keang Măng-ting. 20 keuen. With appendix. 1790. 8°. **15324. b. 1.**

—— 杜詩會稡 *Too she hwuy tsuy.* "A collection of the poems of Too Foo" [A.D. 712–770]. Edited with notes by Chang Yuen. 24 keuen. 1688. 8°. **15324. e. 7.**

—— 杜詩鏡銓 *Too she king ts'euen.* "The Poems of Too Foo, illustrated and expurgated." Edited by Yang Se-ho. 20 keuen. 1872. 8°. **15324. e. 3.**

Appended to this work is a volume entitled *Too wăn choo keae.* "The Writings of Too Foo. With comments and explanations." Edited by Chang Shang-jo. 2 keuen.

—— 杜詩七言律 *Too she ts'ih yen leuh.* "A collection of Too Foo's heptameter poems." With Yu Tseïh-pih's commentary. A Korean edition. 1470. 8°. **15324. c. 4.**

—— 集千家註批點杜工部文詩集 *Tseïh ts'een kea choo p'e t'een Too Kung-poo wăn she tseïh.* The writings of Too Foo, with the notes of numerous commentators. Edited by Lew Hwuy-măng. 15 keuen. [1600?] 8°. **15324. e. 5.**

Printed in Japan from blocks.

—— 集千家分類杜工部詩 *Tseïh ts'een kea fun luy Too Kung-poo she.* "A classified collection of the poems of Too Foo." Edited by Seu Keu-jin. A Korean edition. 25 keuen. [1650?] 8°. **15324. c. 3.**

—— 讀杜詩愚得 *Tuh Too she yu tih.* "A guide to reading Too's poetry," by Tan Fuh. 18 keuen. 1501. Fol. **15324. e. 4.**

Printed in Korea from movable type.

杜聯 Too Leen. 龍山課藝二集 *Lung shan k'o e urh tseïh.* "Essays from the Dragon Hill. Second series." Compiled by Too Leen. 1873. 8°. **15319. e. 3.**

杜步西 Too Poo-se. See 陸小峯 Luh Seaou-fung. 福音講臺 *Fuh yin keang t'ai.* "The Gospel Pulpit . . ." Completed by Too Poo-se, etc. 1889. 8°. **15117. c. 8.**

徐宗瀛 T'oo Tsung-ying. 敬業蓉珠書院課藝合編 *King nëe e choo Shoo yuen k'o e ho peen.* "Examination Essays by Scholars from the King-nëe-e-choo College" on texts from the Classics. With notes. Compiled by T'oo Tsung-ying. In two parts. 1870–73. 8°. **15319. e. 4.**

杜預 Too Yu. See 左邱明 Tso K'ew-ming. 左繡 *Tso sew.* "The Elegancies of Tso K'ew-ming's Commentary . . ." By Too Yu, etc. 1720. 8°. **15212. e. 3.**

脫脫 T'o-t'o. 宋史 *Sung she.* "A History of the Sung Dynasty" (A.D. 960–1278). A reprint. 496 keuen. 1875. 8°. **15287. a. .**

托津 To Tsin. 欽定回疆則例 *K'in ting hwuy keang tsih le.* "Regulations for the Government of the Muhammedan Dependencies of China." Compiled by an Imperial Commission consisting of To Tsin, Ho She-tai, Fuh Choo, and others. 1814. 8°. **15271. b. 6.**

TREATY REGULATIONS. Treaty Regulations for the Five Ports of Canton, Foochow, Amoy, Ningpo, and Shanghai, with tariffs. Preceded by a proclamation issued by K'eying and others, and a dispatch from Sir Henry Pottinger. MS. 1843. **15241. e. 3.**

財 Ts'ai. 橫財玉尺圖 *Hăng ts'ai yuh ch'ih t'oo.* "Rules for fortune-telling." 1855. 8°. **15257. b. 13.**

蔡方炳 Ts'ai Fang-ping. See 陸應陽 Luh Ying-yang. 重訂廣輿記 *Chung ting Kwang yu ke.* "A general geography of the Empire . . ." Revised and edited by Ts'ai Fang-ping, etc. 1668. 8°. **15261. e. 7.**

—— 廣治平畧 *Kwang che p'ing leŏ.* "A short chronological account of the Chinese system of government." 36 keuen. [1870?] 8°. **15239. b. 21.**

—— [Another copy.] **15239. a. 45.**

蔡逢年 Ts'ai Fung-neen. 處分則例圖要 Ch'oo fun tsih le t'oo yaou. "A tabulated epitome of the regulations concerning the punishment of officials for errors in administration." 6 keuen. 1865. 8°.   15334. e. 10.

蔡九霞 Ts'ai Kew-hea. 正續廣治平畧 Ching suh kwang-che p'ing leŏ. "A correct enlarged epitome of the Imperial system of government. With a supplement." By Ts'ai Kew-hea, who based his work on the Che p'ing leŏ of Choo He. 36 keuen. Supplement, 8 keuen. [1850?] 12°.   15239. d. 14.

蔡烈先 Ts'ai Lĕĕ-seen. 萬方鍼線 Wan fang chin seen. "A collection of 10,000 Medical Prescriptions." 8 keuen. [1827?] 8°.   15252. a. 21.

蔡錫貞 Ts'ai Seang-ching. 醫書滙恭輯成 E shoo hwuy tsan tseih ch'ing. "Extracts from Medical Works. With complete commentaries." Compiled by Ts'ai Seang-ching. Edited by Wang Ming-keu. 24 keuen. 1807. 8°.   15251. f. 12.

蔡錫齡 Ts'ai Seïh-ling. See Periodical Publications : Shanghai. 西國近事彙編 Se kwo kin sze wei peen. "A quarterly summary of foreign events ..." Transcribed by Ts'ai Seïh-ling, etc. 1876, etc. 8°.   15298. b. 42.

蔡沈 Ts'ai Shin. See 孔丘 K'ung K'ew. 書經 Shoo king. "The Book of Historical Documents ..." Edited with a commentary by Ts'ai Shin, etc. 1209. 8°.   15215. d. 3.

蔡廷猷 Ts'ai T'ing-yew. 二十四山秘訣 Urh shih sze shan pi keue. "The secret craft of the four and twenty mountains." A book on fortune-telling, mainly transcribed by Ts'ai T'ing-yew, the last 32 folios being in another hand. MS. ff. 91. [1750?] 8°.   Or. 3229. 39. B. c.

蔡一聾 Ts'ai Yih-tsun. 九皇新經註解 Kew Hwang sin king choo keae. "The New Sûtra of the Nine Emperors. With notes" by Leu Yen, "and with explanations." Edited by Ts'ai Yih-tsun and others. 3 keuen. 1824. 8°.   15113. b. 3.

蔡邕 Ts'ai Yung. 獨斷 Tuh twan. "The Book of Decisions" on matters of court etiquette, etc. pp. 66, 2. See 程榮 Ch'ing Yung. 漢魏叢書 Han Wei ts'ung shoo. "A collection of works by authors of the Han and Wei Dynasties," etc. 1791. 8°.   15318. a. 1.

臟腑 Tsang foo. 臟腑明堂圖 Tsang foo ming t'ang t'oo. "An anatomical plate representing the human intestines." [1782?] A scroll.   15253. c. 6 (2).

曾紀澤 Tsăng Ke-tsih. See 喀爾氏 Kih-urh-she. 英文舉隅 Ying wăn keuh yu. "An English Grammar ..." Translated into Chinese by Tsăng Ke-tsih, etc. 1879. 8°.   15344. d. 13.

—— 中西合曆 Chung Se ho leĭh. "A Chinese and foreign comparative calendar" for the years 1879–1884, based on the Nautical Almanac. (Compiled by Professors Harrington, Fritsche, and Russell.) Edited by Ts'ang Ke-tsih. 5 vols. 1879, etc. 8°.   15298. b. 40.
    In progress.

曾國藩 Tsăng Kwo-fan. See 朱熹 Choo He. 孟子要畧 Măng tsze yaou leŏ. "An important epitome of the doctrines of Mencius." With notes by Tsăng Kwo-fan, etc. 1849. 8°.   15101. b. 30.

—— See 薛湘 Seay Seang. 滌非齋制藝僅存 Te-fei chai che e kin ts'un. "Essays ..." Edited with notes by Tsăng Kwo-fan, etc. 1879. 8°.   15316. b. 3.

—— 求闕齋日記類鈔 K'ew-k'eue chai jih ke luy ch'aou. "Daily jottings from the K'ew-k'eue Study, arranged according to subjects." 2 keuen. 1876. 8°. See 曾國藩 Tsăng Kwo-fan. 曾文正公全集 Tsăng wăn ching kung ts'euen tseĭh. "A complete collection of the works of Tsăng Kwo-fan," etc. 1876. 8°.   15313. d. 4.

—— 求闕齋讀書錄 K'ew k'eue chai tuh shoo luh. "Literary notes from the K'ew k'eue study." 10 keuen. 1876. 8°. See 曾國藩 Tsăng Kwo-fan. 曾文正公全集 Tsăng wăn ching kung ts'euen tseĭh. "A complete collection of the works of Tsăng Kwo-fan," etc. 1876. 8°.   15313. d. 3.

TSA

曾 國 藩 Tsăng Kwo-fan. 經 史 百 家 簡 編 *King she pih kea heen peen.* "Notes on the classics and histories by a hundred writers." Edited by Tsăng Kwo-fan. 2 keuen. 1874. 8°. See 曾 國 藩 Tsăng Kwo-fan. 曾 文 正 公 全 集 *Tsăng wăn ching kung ts'euen tseih.* "A complete collection of the works of Tsăng Kwo-fan," etc. 1876. 8°. **15313. c. 2.**

—— 經 史 百 家 雜 鈔 *King she pih kea tsa ch'aou.* "Miscellaneous writings of a hundred authors on the classics and histories." 26 keuen. 1876. 8°. See 曾 國 藩 Tsăng Kwo-fan. 曾 文 正 公 全 集 *Tsăng wăn ching kung ts'euen tseih.* "A complete collection of the works of Tsăng Kwo-fan," etc. 1876. 8°. **15313. c. 1.**

—— 嗚 原 堂 論 文 *Ming Yuen t'ang lun wăn.* "Literary Disquisitions from the Ming Yuen Hall." 2 keuen. 1873. 8°. See 曾 國 藩 Tsăng Kwo-fan. 曾 文 正 公 全 集 *Tsăng wăn ching kung ts'euen tseih.* "A complete collection of the works of Tsăng Kwo-fan," etc. 1876. 8°. **15313. c. 3.**

—— 十 八 家 詩 鈔 *Shih pa kea she ch'aou.* "Poems by eighteen poets." Compiled by Tsăng Kwo-fan, and critically edited by Li Hung-chang. 28 keuen. 1874. 8°. See 曾 國 藩 Tsăng Kwo-fan. 曾 文 正 公 全 集 *Tsăng wăn ching kung ts'euen tseih.* "The complete works of Tsăng Kwo-fan," etc. 1876. 8°. **15313. b. 2.**

—— 曾 文 正 公 年 譜 *Tsăng wăn ching kung neen p'oo.* "A biography of the author," 1811–1872. 12 keuen. 1876. 8°. See 曾 國 藩 Tsăng Kwo-fan. 曾 文 正 公 全 集 *Tsăng wăn ching kung ts'euen tseih.* "A complete collection of the works of Tsăng Kwo-fan," etc. 1876. 8°. **15313. d. 5.**

—— 曾 文 正 公 批 牘 *Tsăng wăn ching kung p'e tuh.* "Critical official documents." 6 keuen. 1876. 8°. See 曾 國 藩 Tsăng Kwo-fan. 曾 文 正 公 全 集 *Tsăng wăn ching kung ts'euen tseih.* "A complete collection of the works of Tsăng Kwo-fan," etc. 1876. 8°. **15313. d. 1.**

曾 國 藩 Tsăng Kwo-fan. 曾 文 正 公 詩 集 *Tsăng wăn ching kung she tseih.* "A collection of poems." 4 keuen. 1874. 8°. See 曾 國 藩 Tsăng Kwo-fan. 曾 文 正 公 全 集 *Tsăng wăn ching kung ts'euen tseih.* "A complete collection of the works of Tsăng Kwo-fan," etc. 1876. 8°. **15313. c. 4.**

—— 曾 文 正 公 書 札 *Tsăng wăn ching kung shoo cha.* "Letters." 33 keuen. 1876. 8°. See 曾 國 藩 Tsăng Kwo-fan. 曾 文 正 公 全 集 *Tsăng wăn ching kung ts'euen tseih.* "A complete collection of the works of Tsăng Kwo-fan," etc. 1876. 8°. **15313. c. 6.**

—— 曾 文 正 公 雜 著 *Tsăng wăn ching kung tsă choo.* "Miscellaneous publications." Edited by Li Han-chang. 4 keuen. 1874. 8°. See 曾 國 藩 Tsăng Kwo-fan. 曾 文 正 公 全 集 *Tsăng wăn ching kung ts'euen tseih.* "A complete collection of the works of Tsăng Kwo-fan," etc. 1876. 8°. **15313. d. 2.**

—— 曾 文 正 公 全 集 *Tsăng wăn ching kung ts'euen tseih.* "A complete collection of the works of Tsăng Kwo-fan," consisting of—(1) An Introduction, 1 vol.; (2) *Tsow kaou*, Memorials, 30 keuen; (3) *Shih pa kea she ch'aou*, Poems of eighteen poets, 28 keuen; (4) *King she pih kea tsă ch'aou*, Miscellaneous writings of a hundred authors on the classics and histories, 26 keuen; (5) *King she pih kea heen peen*, Notes on the classics and histories, 2 keuen; (6) *Ming Yuen t'ang lun wăn*, Literary disquisitions, 2 keuen; (7) *She tseih*, Poems, 4 keuen; (8) *Wăn tseih*, Literary pieces, 4 keuen; (9) *Shoo cha*, Letters, 33 keuen; (10) *P'i tu*, Official documents, 6 keuen; (11) *Tsă choo*, Miscellaneous writings, 2 keuen; (12) *K'ew k'eue chai tu shoo luh*, Literary notes, 4 keuen; (13) *K'ew k'eue chai jih ke luy ch'aou*, Daily jottings, 2 keuen; (14) *Neen p'oo*, Biography, 12 keuen. 156 keuen 1876. 8°. **15313. b. 1, 2; c. 1-6; d. 1-5.**

—— 曾 文 正 公 奏 議 *Tsăng wăn ching kung tsow e.* "The Memorials of Tsăng Kwŏ-fan." Compiled by Sëë Fuh-ching, and edited by Chang Ying. 11 keuen. *Soochow*, 1873. 8°. **15241. c. 9.**

—— 曾 文 正 公 奏 議 補 編 *Tsăng wăn ching kung tsow e poo peen.* "A supplementary collection of the Memorials of Tsăng Kwŏ-fan." Compiled by Sëë Fuh-ching. Edited by Chang Ying, etc. 4 keuen. 1874. 8°. **15317. d. 11.**

曾 國 藩 TSĂNG KWO-FAN. 曾文正公奏稿 *Tsăng wăn ching kung tsow kaou.* "Memorials to the Throne," beginning from the year 1850. 30 keuen. 1876. 8°. See 曾 國 藩 TSĂNG KWO-FAN. 曾文正公全集 *Tsăng wăn ching kung ts'euen tseĭh.* "The complete works of Tsăng Kwo-fan," etc. 1876. 8°. **15313. b. 1.**
Imperfect, wanting Keuen 22, 23.

—— 曾文正公文鈔 *Tsăng Wăn-ching kung wăn ch'aou.* "The Literary Productions of Tsăng Kwŏ-fan," who was canonised as the Duke Tsăng Wăn-ching. Edited by Chang Ying. 4 keuen. [*Canton*?], 1873. 8°.
15317. d. 10.

—— 曾文正公文集 *Tsăng wăn ching kung wăn tseĭh.* "A collection of writings." 4 keuen. 1874. 8°. See 曾 國 藩 TSĂNG KWO-FAN. 曾文正公全集 *Tsăng wăn ching kung ts'euen tseĭh.* "A complete collection of the works of Tsăng Kwo-fan," etc. 1876. 8°.
15313. c. 5.

曾先之 TSĂNG SEEN CHE. 古今歷代標題註釋十九史略通考 *Koo kin leĭh tai p'iao t'e choo shih kew she leŏ t'ung k'ao.* An abridgment of the nineteen histories of ancient and modern times commented and explained, with a thorough criticism by Chuh Woyu. Compiled and edited by Tsăng Seen-che. A Corean edition. 8 keuen. [1600?] Fol.
15292. e. 3.

—— 十九史略通考 *Shih kew she leŏ t'ung k'aou.* "An epitome of the nineteen histories, thoroughly examined." Edited by Tsăng Seen-che. A Korean edition. 8 keuen. 1582. Fol.
15292. b. 1.

—— [Another edition.] 1616. Fol. **15292. c. 9.**
Printed in Japan with movable type.

臧晉叔 TSANG TSIN-SHUH. See 湯義仍 T'ANG E-JĂNG. 玉茗新詞四種 *Yuh ming sin ts'ze sze chung.* "Four Plays . . ." Edited by Tsang Tsin-shuh, etc. 8°. **15333. f. 2.**

—— 元人百種曲 *Yuen jin pih chung k'euh.* "The Hundred Plays of the Yuen Dynasty." Edited by Tsang Tsin-shuh of the Ming Dynasty. [1700?] 8°. **15327. d. 1.**
Imperfect, containing only 42 Plays.

—— [Another edition. With illustrations. 1750?] 8°. **15327. e. 11.**
Imperfect, containing only 10 Plays.

臧晉叔 TSANG TSIN-SHUH. 元人雜劇 *Yuen jin tsa keĭh.* "Plays of the Yuen Dynasty." Edited by Tsang Tsin-shuh. [1600?] 8°.
15333. f. 5.
Imperfect, containing only "Chaou she hoo urh," "Tow go yuen," "Too lew ts'uy," "Woo juh t'aou yuen," "Mo ho lo," "P'un urh kwei," "Wang keang t'ing," "Jin fung tsze," "Peih t'aou hwa," "Chang sang choo hai," "Sang kin ko," "Fung yuh lan," "Hwan laou mo," "Lew e chuen," "Hwo lang tan," "Lo Le lang," "K'an ts'een nu."

—— 元人雜劇百種 *Yuen jin tsa keĭh pih chung.* "The Hundred Plays of the Yuen Dynasty." With illustrations. In ten Parts, with five Plays to a Part. Edited by Tsang Tsin-shuh. This edition contains only a selection of the Hundred Plays. [1600?] 8°. **15333. f. 3.**
Imperfect, wanting parts 5 and 6.

—— 元曲選 *Yuen k'euh seuen.* "Selections from the Plays of the Yuen Dynasty." Edited by Tsang Tsin-shuh. With illustrations. [1600.] 8°. **15333. f. 4.**

曹 TS'AOU. 曹洞宗 *Ts'aou tung tsung.* "Biographical notices of members of the Ts'aou and Tung Buddhist Sects." 1349. 8°. **15103. b. 2.**
Imperfect, printed in Japan from blocks.

曹之升 TS'AOU CHE-SHING. 四書摭餘說 *Sze shoo chih yu shwo.* "A collection of notes on the Four Books." Compiled by Ts'aou Che-shing. Edited by Chang Poo-shan. 1832. 8°.
15202. b. 18.

曹振鏞 TS'AOU CHIN-YUNG. 欽定平定回疆剿捦逆裔方略 *K'in ting p'ing ting hwuy keang tseaou k'in ne e fang leŏ.* A short account of the Mahommedan frontiers, and the attack on and capture of the rebellious districts during the period from the 25th year of Kea k'ing (1820) to the 9th year of Taou kwang (1829). Published by Imperial order and with an Imperial preface, by Ts'aou Chin-yung and other officials. 80 keuen. 1830. 8°. **15259. e. 4.**

曹珖 TS'AOU HEUEN. See 魏源 WEI YUEN. 皇朝經世文編 *Hwang ch'aou king she wăn peen.* "Essays . . ." Edited by Ts'aou Heuen, etc. 1826. 8°. **15318. d. 1.**

曹驊 TS'AOU HWA. 鄉試硃卷 *Heang she choo keuen.* "Essays written at the examination for the degree of Keu-jin." [*Nanking*?], 1840. 8°.
15346. a. 24.

曹鏵 Ts'aou Hwa. 會試硃卷 *Hwuy she choo keuen.* "Essays written at the examination for the degree of Tsin-sze." [*Nanking?*], 1845. 8°. **15346. b. 26.**

曹雪芹 Ts'aou Seuĕ-k'in. Hung lou meng; or The Dream of the Red Chamber. A Chinese novel. Translated by H. Bencraft Joly. Book i. *Kelly & Walsh : Hongkong, Shanghai, Yokohama, and Singapore*, 1892. 8°. **11099. d. 25.**

曹樹翹 Ts'aou Shoo-keaou. 苗蠻合志 *Meaou Man ho che.* "An Account of the Meaou-tsze and Man Barbarians." 4 keuen. MS. *Canton* [1840 ?]. 8°. **15297. b. 3.**

曹維灜 Ts'aou Wei-fan. 鑑撮叢求 *Keen ts'ŏ mung k'ew.* "A resumé of Historical Events for children." By Ts'aou Wei-fan. With notes by Wang Wei. Edited by Lew Kea-moo. 1815. 8°. **15297. b. 13.**

曹寅 Ts'aou Yen. 全唐詩 *Ts'euen T'ang she.* "A complete collection of the Poems of the T'ang Dynasty." Compiled by Imperial order by Ts'aou Yen, P'ăng Ting-k'ew, and others. 12 parts. 1707. 8°. **15321. b. & c. 1.**

雜字 Tsă tsze. 校正日用雜字 *Keaou ching jih yung tsa tsze.* "A Colloquial Vocabulary." [*Canton*, 1850 ?] 8°. **15344. c. 20.**

蔣季眉 Tseang Ke-mei. 增訂蔣季眉四書稿 *Tsăng ting Tsëang Ke-mei sze shoo kaou.* An enlarged edition of Tseang Ke-mei's essays on the Four Books. Edited by Wang-kew-ching. 1725. 8°. **15319. a. 9.**

蔣瓵騏 Tseang Leang-ke. 東華錄 *Tung hwa luh.* "Records from the Tung-hwa Gate." A summary of events from the origin of the present dynasty down to the year 1735. 32 keuen. 1765. 8°. **15297. b. 2.**

蔣大鴻 Tseang Ta-hung. 挨星秘窮 *Ai sing pe k'eaou.* "A work on Astrology." 1834. 8°. **15257. b. 22.**

蔣太史 Tseang T'ai-she. See 車萬育 Ch'ay Wan-yuh. 聲律啟蒙撮要 *Shing leu k'e mung ts'o yaou.* "A guide for beginners to the Laws of Sound." Edited by Tseang T'ai-she, etc. 1857. 8°. **15346. a. 13.**

蔣廷錫 Tseang T'ing-seĭh. 欽定古今圖書集成 *K'in ting koo kin t'oo shoo tseĭh ch'ing.* "An Encyclopædia in which the subjects are illustrated by quotations from all works of recognized value from the Yih king downwards. With Illustrations." Compiled by an Imperial Commission consisting of Tseang T'ing-seĭh and others, appointed by the Emperor K'ang-he. With a preface by the Emperor Yung-ching. 10,000 keuen. *Peking*, 1726. 8°. **15000. etc.**

蔣敦復 Tseang Tun-fuh. 嘯古堂文集 *Seaou koo T'ang wăn tseĭh.* "A Collection of Writings from the Seaou-koo Hall." 8 keuen. 1860. 8°. **15317. b. 6.**
Imperfect, containing only Keuen 1–4.

蔣東觀 Tseang Tung-kwan. See 李次青 Le Ts'ze-ts'ing. 國朝先正事略 *Kwo ch'aou seen ching sze leŏ.* "Short notices of worthies during the earlier years of the present Dynasty . . ." Edited by Tseang Tung-kwan, etc. 1869. 8°. **15305. a. 13.**

蔣无妄 Tseang Woo-wang. See 張浦山 Chang Poo-shan. 國朝畫徵錄 *Kwo ch'aou hwa ching luh.* "Biographical Notices of Artists . . ." Edited by Tseang Woo-wang, etc. 1739. 8°. **15305. b. 1.**

焦竑 Tseaou Hung. See 楊慎 Yang Shin. 楊升菴外集 *Yang Shing-gan wai tseĭh.* "An additional collection of the writings of Yang Shin." Compiled by Tseaou Hung, etc. 1844. 8°. **15319. e. 9.**

樵南陽 Ts'eaou Nan-yang. 紅樓復夢 *Hung low fuh mung.* "A new Dream of the Red Chamber." Edited by Ch'in She-wăn. With portraits. 100 keuen. 1805. 8°. **15333. a. 3.**

焦延壽 Tseaou Yen-show. 易林 *Yih lin.* "A Forest of Changes." 4 keuen. See 程榮 Ch'ing Yung. 漢魏叢書 *Han Wei ts'ung shoo.* "A collection of works by authors of the Han and Wei Dynasties," etc. 1791. 8°. **15318. a. 1.**

千佛 Ts'een Fuh. 賢刧千佛號 *Heen keĭh ts'een fuh haou.* "The names of the Thousand Buddhas of the Bhadrakalpa" in Tibetan, Mongolian, and Manchu. [1750 ?] 8°. **15101. a. 11.**
Imperfect, containing only Maki 2.

錢 日 壽 Ts'een Jih-show. See 錢 梅 溪 Ts'een Mei-k'e. 履 園 叢 話 *Le yuen ts'ung hwa.* "The *Le yuen* Collection of Tales . . ." Edited by Ts'een Jih-show, etc. 1870. 8°. **15331. d. 7.**

錢 梅 溪 Ts'een Mei-k'e. 履 園 叢 話 *Le yuen ts'ung hwa.* "The *Le yuen* Collection of Tales." Compiled by Ts'een Mei-k'e. Edited by Ts'een Jih-show. 24 keuen. 1870. 8°. **15331. d. 7.**

錢 恂 Ts'een Seun. 韻 目 表 *Yun muh peaou.* "A tabulated index to the rhyming syllables." pp. 62. 1879. 8°. **15321. c. 12.**

錢 氏 Ts'een she. 胎 產 秘 書 *T'ai ch'an pe shoo.* "On Midwifery." Edited by Le Poo-t'eaou. 3 keuen, with appendix. *Canton,* 1860. 8°. **15252. b. 17.**

錢 恕 齊 Ts'een Shoo-ts'e. 幼 學 句 解 *Yew heŏ keu keae.* The youth's instructor. With explanations. By Ts'een Shoo-ts'e. 4 keuen. 1838. 8°. **15229. b. 15.**

錢 德 蒼 Ts'een Tih-ts'ang. 新 訂 解 人 頤 廣 集 *Sin ting keae jin e kwang tseih.* "A new edition of a large collection of witticisms." Compiled by Ts'een Tih-ts'ang. 8 keuen. [1820 ?] 8°. **15327. e. 8.**

千 字 文 Ts'een tsze wăn. 雙 千 字 文 *Shwang ts'een tsze wăn.* "Another Thousand Character Classic." A Christian tract. [1870 ?] 8°. **15229. c. 39.**

錢 東 生 Ts'een Tung-săng. 文 獻 徵 存 錄 *Wăn heen ching ts'un luh.* "A Record of Literary Biography." By Ts'een Tung-săng. Edited by Wang Shuh-yuen. 10 keuen. *Hang-chow,* 1858. 8°. **15305. b. 4.**

錢 元 龍 Ts'een Yuen-lung. See 程 允 升 Ch'ing Yun-shing. 幼 學 須 知 句 解 *Yew heŏ seu che keu keae.* "General Knowledge . . ." Edited by Ts'een Yuen-lung, etc. 8°. **15022. e. 19.**

棲 霞 氏 Ts'e Hea-she. 尺 牘 分 類 *Ch'ih tuh fun luy.* "A letter-writer arranged according to subjects." 2 keuen. *Hongkong,* 1896. 8°. **15348. b. 5.**

—— 尺 牘 分 類 補 遺 *Ch'ih tuh fun luy poo i.* "A supplemental letter-writer." 2 keuen. *Hongkong,* 1897. 8°. **15348. b. 6.**

戚 繼 光 Tseih Ke-kwang. 紀 效 新 書 *Ke keaou sin shoo.* "A new work on the Stratagems of War." 1804. 8°. **15259. c. 12.**
Imperfect, containing only Keuen 17 and 18.

—— 紀 交 新 書 *Ke heaou sin shoo.* "A new work on the Stratagems of War," by Tseih Ke-kwang, or rather, an excerpt from that work consisting of Keuen 10 and 12. With illustrations, and with an extract at the end of Keuen 10 from a work entitled *Woo peen* by T'ang King-chuen. ff. 65. [1840 ?] 8°.
Or. 1305. 39. B. c.

七 十 一 Ts'eih Shih-yih. 西 域 瑣 談 *Se yih so tan.* "Things heard and seen on the Western Frontiers." 4 keuen. MS. 1777. 8°.
15271. b. 5.

濟 顛 大 師 Tse teen ta sze. See 醉 菩 提 Tsuy P'oo-te. 醉 菩 提 全 傳 *Tsuy P'oo-te ts'euen chuen.* "The Story of the Drunken bodhi." By Tse-teen-ta-sze, etc. 1874. 8°.
15331. d. 9.

齊 子 冶 Ts'e Tsze-yay. 見 聞 續 筆 *Keen wăn suh peih.* "Supplementary notes on things I have seen and heard." By Ts'e Tsze-yay. 24 keuen. 1876. 8°. **15297. a. 13.**

—— 見 聞 睦 筆 *Keen wăn suy peih.* "Notes on things I have seen and heard." By Ts'e Tsze-yay. 26 keuen. 1871. 8°. **15297. a. 12.**

趙 周 求 Ts'eu Chow-k'ew. See 高 則 誠 Kaou Tsih-ch'ing. 燈 草 和 尙 傳 *Tăng ts'aou Hoshang chuen.* "The Story of the Lampwick Priest . . ." Edited by Ts'eu Chow-k'ew, etc. 8°. **Or. 4476. 39. B. f.**

全 子 式 Ts'euen Tsze-urh. 說 倭 傳 *Shwo Wei chuen.* "An account of the Japanese War." 2 keuen. [*Hongkong,* 1896 ?] 8°. **15296. b. 16.**

全 韻 Ts'euen yun. 全 韻 玉 篇 *Ts'euen yun yuh p'een.* "A complete Chinese dictionary," with the Korean equivalents of the characters. A Korean edition. 2 keuen. [1600 ?] 8°.
15341. d. 2.

酒 Tsew. 戒 酒 論 *Keae tsew lun.* "On Temperance." [By S. P. Barchet ?] pp. 13. *Ningpo,* 1876. 8°. **15200. c. 48.**

秋 芳 堂 主 人 Ts'ew-fang t'ang choo-jin, *pseud.* 清 文 典 要 *Ts'ing wăn teen yaou.* "A Manchoo and Chinese Vocabulary." Arranged according to the Chinese radicals. Compiled by Ts'ew-fang t'ang choo-jin, 'The Master of the Hall of Autumn Fragrance.' 4 keuen. [1800?] 8°. **15344. d. 12.**

七 克 Ts'ih kih. 七 克 眞 訓 *Ts'ih kih chin heun.* "A true instruction on the seven victories" over sins. 2 keuen. *Hongkong*, 1899. 8°. **15200. b. 31.**

則 克 Tsih k'ih. 則 克 錄 *Tsih k'ih luh.* "A Treatise on the Military Art." 3 keuen. [1840?] 8°. **15259. b. 4.**

積 慶 堂 Tsih-k'ing t'ang. 積 慶 堂 試 藝 *Tsih-k'ing t'ang she e.* "The Tsih-k'ing Hall collection of prize essays," written for the examinations held at Shanghai in 1871. [*Shanghai*, 1871?] 8°. **15346. a. 25.**

TS'ING DYNASTY. 欽 定 大 清 會 典 *K'in ting ta Ts'ing hwuy teen.* "A comprehensive description of the system of government under the Ts'ing Dynasty." Compiled by an Imperial Commission consisting of Prince Yun-to and others. 100 keuen. 1764. 8°. **15231. e. 3.**

—— [Another edition.] 1818. 8°. **15231. d. 3.**

—— 欽 定 大 清 律 例 *K'in ting Ta Ts'ing leŭh le.* "The Fundamental Laws and Subordinate Statutes of the Ts'ing Dynasty." An Imperial publication. Compiled by Imperial order by a Commission consisting of Tang Shaou-tsoo and others. 1740. 8°. **15236. b. 2.**
This copy is very imperfect; it contains only Books 1–6, 8, 10, 11. 16, 17, 19–21, 23, 25, 27–30, 36–39 out of the 46 forming the whole work.

—— 大 清 會 典 *Ta Ts'ing hwuy teen.* "Extracts from the *Ta Ts'ing hwuy teen.*" These extracts were copied for the Jesuit Fouquet during his residence in China about the end of the seventeenth century [from 1690]. It contains Keuen 55–58 and 63–66. MS. With notes. 2 vols. [1700.] 8°. **15231. e. 4.**

—— 大 清 會 典 *Ta Ts'ing hwuy teen.* "A comprehensive description of the System of Government under the Ts'ing Dynasty." [250 keuen. 1820?] 8°. **15231. e. 1.**
Imperfect, containing only Keuen 38, 39, 46–48, 131–133, 181, 182.

TS'ING DYNASTY. 大 清 律 例 統 纂 集 成 *Ta Ts'ing leuh le tung tswan tseth ch'ing.* "The Fundamental Laws and Subordinate Statutes of the Ts'ing Dynasty." 1820. 8°. **15236. b. 1.**

—— 大 清 律 纂 修 條 例 *Ta Ts'ing leuh tswan sew t'eaou le.* Laws and Regulations of the Ts'ing Dynasty. A revised edition. [This supplementary work was published by order of the Emperor *Kea-k'ing.*] 1814. 8°. **15236. c. 2.**

青 霆 子 Ts'ing fei-tsze. 韻 府 萃 音 *Yun foo ts'uy yin.* "A Rhyming Dictionary." Compiled by Ts'ing Fei-tsze. 12 parts. *Canton*, 1810. 8°. **15348. b. 2.**

青 河 髮 Ts'ing-ho-fa. 神 僧 傳 *Shin tsăng chuen.* "Biographies of Sacred Buddhist Personages and Priests." A Japanese edition. 9 keuen. 1659. 8°. **15303. a. 3.**

清 溪 道 人 Ts'ing k'e taou jin, *pseud.* 禪 眞 後 史 *Shen chin how shih.* "Later stories of Buddhist 'Pure Ones.'" Compiled by Ts'ing k'e taou jin. With illustrations. 60 chapters. 1629. 8°. **15103. b. 14.**

清 三 Ts'ing-san. 笑 雲 和 尙 古 文 眞 寶 之 抄 *Seaou-yun Hoshang ku wăn chin paou che ch'aou.* "A copy of gems from ancient literature compiled by the Priest of the Laughing Cloud," i.e. Ts'ing-san and others. A Japanese edition. 9 keuen. [1610?] Fol. **15315. e. 3.**
Printed in Japan with movable type.

靜 嘯 齋 主 人 Tsing seaou chai choo jin, *pseud.* 西 遊 補 *Se yew poo.* "A supplementary account of western travel." A fanciful account of an expedition of Buddhist priests to the west during the T'ang Dynasty. 16 chapters. 1875. 8°. **15291. a. 4.**

清 心 道 人 Ts'ing sin taou jin [*pseud.*]. 禪 眞 逸 史 *Shen chin yih she.* An illustrated popular history of the period from A.D. 543 to about 618. Compiled by an author calling himself Ts'ing sin taou jin. 40 chapters. [1830?] 8°. **15292. a. 2.**

靜 恬 主 人 Tsing-teen choo-jin. See 金 Kin. 金 石 緣 全 傳 *Kin shih yuen ts'euen chuen.* "The story of the relationship between Kin and Shih." By "Tsing-teen Choo-jin," etc. 1865. 8°. **15331. d. 12.**

精蘊 Tsing wăn. 崇修精蘊 *Ts'ung sew tsing wăn.* "On Spiritual Meditation." pp. xiv, 212. *Hongkong,* 1890. 8°. **15200. d. 39.**

—— 清文指要 *Ts'ing wăn che yaou.* "A Guide to Manchu (and Chinese) Conversations." 3 keuen. With supplement in 2 keuen. 1789. 8°. **15354. e. 3.**

—— [Another edition.] 1809. 8°. **15354. e. 4.**

—— 御製四體清文鑑 *Yu che sze t'e Ts'ing wăn keen.* "The Mirror of the Manchu language (an Imperial Manchu dictionary), in four languages," viz., Manchu, Tibetan, Mongolian, and Chinese. 32 keuen, with a supplement in 4 keuen. [1790?] 8°. **15353. a. 2.**
Imperfect, containing only Keuen 1-6, 31, 32, and the four supplementary keuen.

—— 御製五體清文鑑 *Yu che woo t'e Ts'ing wăn keen.* "The Mirror of the Manchu language (an Imperial Manchu dictionary), in five languages," viz., Manchu, Tibetan, Mongolian, Eastern Turkish, and Chinese. [Compiled by the Emperor K'een-lung?] 32 keuen, with a supplement in 4 keuen. [1790?] Fol. **15353. a. 1.**

秦漢 Ts'in Han. 秦漢圖章 *Ts'in Han t'oo chang.* "Seals of the Ts'in and Han Dynasties" [1700?] 8°. **15299. a. 1.**

秦霞峰 Ts'in Hea-fung, and 郭禮堂 Ko Le-t'ang. 詩料詳註 *She leaou tseang choo.* "Poetical expressions. With explanations and notes." Compiled by Ts'in Hea-fung and Ko Le t'ang. With explanations by Ch'in Kwan-min. 4 keuen. 1762. 8°. **15346. a. 20.**

秦淮墨客 Ts'in hwai mih kih, *pseud.* 楊家將演義 *Yang kea tseang yen e.* "A popular history of the Generals of the Yang Family" during the Sung Dynasty. With illustrations. 10 keuen. 1618. 8°. **15291. a. 11.**

秦嘉謨 Ts'in Kea-moo. 月令粹編 *Yuĕ ling suy peen.* "Historical Memoranda for every day in the year." 24 keuen. 1812. 8°. **15255. b. 3.**

秦元君 Tsin Yuen-keun. 坤寧妙經 *K'wăn ning meaou king.* "The excellent Sūtra on the repose of earth." A Taouist work. 2 keuen. *Canton* [1840?]. 8°. **15111. c. 21.**

秦玉 Ts'in Yuh. Drawings of the Cultivation and Manufacture of Silk. MS. [1840?] Fol. **15255. e. 30.**

左邱明 Tso K'ew-ming. 春秋綱目左傳句解 *Ch'un ts'ew kang muh Tso chuen keu keae.* "Tso's Commentary on the text of the *Ch'un ts'ew,* explained sentence by sentence." Edited by Han T'an. 6 keuen. [1870?] 8°. **15348. e. 1.**

—— Selections from the Tso chün [by Tso K'ew-ming] and Ku man, translated for the use of Queen's College, Hongkong. pp. 40. *Hongkong,* 1894. 8°. **11100. a. 21.**

—— 左繡 *Tso sew.* "The Elegancies of Tso K'ew-ming's Commentary" on the Spring and Autumn Annals, which work fills the lower half of each page. By Too Yu. With notes by Lin Yaou-sow and explanations by Luh Yuen-lang. 30 keuen. 1720. 8°. **15212. e. 3.**

鄒迪光 Tsow Tih-kwang. 勸戒圖說 *K'euen keae t'oo shwo.* "Moral warnings. With illustrations." A Japanese edition. 4 keuen. 1594. 8°. **15113. c. 3.**

作印 Tso Yin. 作印集字 *Tso yin tseih tsze.* "A Selection of (three thousand of the most important) Characters in the Chinese Language." *Malacca,* 1834. 8°. **15344. c. 23.**
With an English title-page and preface.

崇厚 Ts'ung How. See 麟見亭 Lin Keen-t'ing. 鴻雪因緣圖 *Hung sueh yin yuen t'oo.* "Fate-directed footprints on the snows of travel, illustrated." Edited by . . . Ts'ung How, etc. 1879. 8°. **15297. a. 14.**

崇敎者 Ts'ung-keaou-chay. 進敎要理問答 *Tsin keaou yaou le wăn ta.* "The Convert's Catechism." By Ts'ung-keaou-chay, i.e. Bishop Boone. 2 keuen. *Shanghai* [1846?]. 12°. **15116. e. 39.**

崇國貞 Ts'ung Kwo-ching. See 陸朗甫 Luh Lang-foo. 皇朝經世文鈔 *Hwang ch'aou king she wăn ch'aou.* "Essays on classical subjects by writers of the present Dynasty . . ." Edited by Ts'ung Kwo-ching, etc. 1869. 8°. **15320. e. 36.**

宗懍 Tsung Lin. 荊楚歲時記 *King ts'oo suy she ke.* "A calendar of the popular customs in Hookwang." pp. 37. See 程榮 Ch'ing Yung. 漢魏叢書 *Han Wei ts'ung shoo.* "A collection of works by authors of the Han and Wei Dynasties," etc. 1791. 8°. **15318. a. 1.**

宗密 Tsung-meih. 禪源諸詮集 *Shen yuen choo ts'euen tseih.* "Discourses on deep (Buddhist) subjects of meditation." By the Priest Tsung-meih. 2 keuen. [1600?] 8°. **15103. b. 5.**

Printed in Korea from blocks.

崇實 Ts'ung Shih. See 麟見亭 Lin Keen-t'ing. 鴻雪因緣圖 *Hung sueh yin yuen t'oo.* "Fate-directed footprints on the snows of travel, illustrated." Edited by Ts'ung Shih, etc. 1879. 8°. **15297. a. 14.**

宗澤 Tsung Tsih. 宋宗忠簡公文集 *Sung Tsung chung keen kung wăn tseih.* "The collected writings of Tsung Tsih canonised as Chung-Keen-Kung." Edited by Lew Ke-chaou. 4 keuen, with a supplementary volume. 1873. 8°. **15315. c. 4.**

崔鴻 Ts'uy Hung. 十六國春秋 *Shih lew kwo ch'un ts'ew.* "The Annals of the sixteen independent Dynasties," which existed contemporaneously with the Tsin and the Sung Dynasties. See 程榮 Ch'ing Yung. 漢魏叢書 *Han Wei ts'ung shoo.* "A collection of works by authors of the Han and Wei Dynasties," etc. 1791. 8°. **15318. a. 1.**

崔豹 Ts'uy Paou. 古今注 *Koo kin choo.* "An examination of historical antiquities." 3 keuen. See 程榮 Ch'ing Yung. 漢魏叢書 *Han Wei ts'ung shoo.* "A collection of works by authors of the Han and Wei Dynasties," etc. 1791. 8°. **15318. a. 1.**

醉菩提 Tsuy P'oo-te. 醉菩提全傳 *Tsuy P'oo-te ts'euen chuen.* "The Story of the Drunken *bodhi.*" By Tse-teen-ta-sze. 4 keuen. 1874. 8°. **15331. d. 9.**

崔郁岑 Ts'uy Yuh-ch'in. See 沈約 Ch'in Yo. 竹書紀年統箋 *Chuh shoo ke neen t'ung tseen.* "The Record of the Bamboo Books . . ." Edited by Ts'uy Yuh-ch'in, etc. 1750. 8°. **15292. c. 4.**

字 Tsze. Chinese School-books. Sam-tsz-king. Translated by E. J. Eitel. pp. 22. *Hongkong,* 1892. 8°. **11099. c. 31.**

—— 三字經 *San tsze king.* A precise translation [into English] of the Three-character Classic. *Rangoon,* 1831. 8°. **11098. a. 3.**

—— [Another copy.] **11098. b. 6.**

—— 三字經 *San tsze king.* "A Three-character Classic." [A Christian imitation of the original work by W. H. Medhurst?] *Hongkong,* 1843. 8°. **15225. a. 22.**

—— 三字經 *San tsŭ ching.* Translated and annotated by Herbert A. Giles. pp. v, 178. *Kelly & Walsh: Shanghai,* 1900. 8°. **11095. c. 2.**

—— 字類標韻 *Tsze luy peaou yun.* "A List of the Characters arranged under the Radicals." MS. [1844?] 8°. **15344. c. 21.**

自誠氏 Tsze-ch'ing she, *pseud.* 列仙傳 *Lëe seen chuen.* "Lives of [Taouist] 'Immortals.'" 4 keuen. 1833. 8°. **15303. b. 15.**

字部 Tsze poo. 字部緝解 *Tsze poo tseih keae.* "The Radicals, with their meanings explained." *Macao,* 1840. 8°. **15344. c. 24.**

子思 Tsze sze. 四書便蒙 *Sze shoo peen mung.* "The Four Books for Beginners." Containing only the text of the Chung yung, or the "Doctrine of the Mean." By Tsze-sze. The Lun yu and Măng-tsze. The San-yuen Hall edition. [1800?] 8°. **15202. e. 6.**

紫陽 Tsze-yang. 紫陽正誼兩書院課藝合選 *Tsze-yang Ching-e leang Shoo yuen k'o e ho seuen.* "Prize Essays from the Tsze-yang and Ching-e Colleges." In three parts. 1848. 8°. **15319. b. 17.**

讀體 Tuh-t'e. 三壇傳戒正範 *San t'an chuen keae ching fan.* "The correct rules relating to the vows to be taken at the three Altars," viz., at the initiation of Buddhist novices, Bhikshus, and Bôdhisatvas. 4 keuen. 1879. 8°. **15217. b. 9.**

Evidently printed in Japan.

咄咄夫 Tuh-tuh-foo, *pseud.* 增補一夕話 *Tsăng poo yih seih hwa.* "An evening's tales. An enlarged edition." A miscellany. By "Tuh-tuh-foo." 6 keuen. 1865. 8°. **15333. e. 12.**

東 TUNG. A rubbing of a Memorial Tablet erected by Tung to the memory of his father, mother, and stepmother. 1750. 8°.　　15305. a. 11.

T‘UNG CHE, *Emperor.* An Imperial Decree issued in response to the memorial presented by Le Hung-chang announcing the capture of Soochow, and ordering that a medal of the highest grade and 10,000 taels of silver should be presented to Colonel Gordon. The decree is dated the 26th day of the 10th month of the 2nd year of the reign of T‘ung che [1863].　　Add. 33,222.

童 貞 T‘UNG CHING. 童 貞 修 規 *T‘ung ching sew kwei.* "Rules for Chinese Nuns" pp. 76. *Hongkong*, 1894. 12°.　　15200. aa. 16.

董 中 和 TUNG CHUNG-HO. 耶 穌 異 教 四 牌 *Yay-soo chin keaou sze p‘ai.* "The four warrants of the true religion of Jesus." A controversial work to prove that Roman Catholicism is the true religion, and Protestantism the false. pp. xiv, 152. *Hongkong*, 1898. 8°. 15118. b. 50.

董 仲 舒 TUNG CHUNG-SHOO. 春 秋 繁 露 *Ch‘un ts‘ew fun loo.* "Dewdrops from the Spring and Autumn Annals." 17 keuen. See 程 榮 CH‘ING YUNG. 漢 魏 叢 書 *Han Wei ts‘ung shoo.* "A collection of works by authors of the Han and Wei Dynasties," etc. 1791. 8°.　　15318. a. 1.

董 方 立 TUNG FANG-LEIH. 董 方 立 算 書 *Tung Fang-leih swan shoo.* "Tung Fang-leih's work on Mathematics." 3 keuen. 1830. 8°.　　15259. h. 15.

東 方 朔 TUNG FANG-SO. 十 洲 記 *Shih chow ke.* "An account of the Ten Islands." pp. 26. See 程 榮 CH‘ING YUNG. 漢 魏 叢 書 *Han Wei ts‘ung shoo.* "A collection of works by authors of the Han and Wei Dynasties," etc. 1791. 8°.　　15318. a. 1.

—— 神 異 經 *Shin e king.* "The book of supernatural wonders." pp. 32. See 程 榮 CH‘ING YUNG. 漢 魏 叢 書 *Han Wei ts‘ung shoo.* "A collection of works by authors of the Han and Wei Dynasties," etc. 1791. 8°. 15318. a. 1.

童 華 TUNG HWA. See 徐 郙 SEU FOO. 三 江 邁 倫 集 *San keang mai lun tseih.* "A Collection of Superior Essays . . ." Edited by . . . Tung Hwa, etc. 1876. 8°.　　15320. a. 22.

通 潤 T‘UNG-JUN. 大 佛 頂 首 楞 嚴 經 合 轍 *Ta Fuh ting show lăng yen king ho ch‘ay.* "The Mahabuddhoshngisha Sūrangama Sūtra explained according to tradition." By T‘ung-jun. 10 keuen. 1621. 8°.　　15101. b. 28.

董 其 昌 TUNG K‘E-CH‘ANG. 瓊 宮 五 帝 內 思 上 法 *K‘eung kung woo te nuy sze shang fa.* "The ritual of contemplation on the Five Emperors in the K‘eung Palace." White characters on black ground. 1607. 8°.　　15217. a. 10.

東 閣 TUNG KO. 東 閣 散 錄 *Tung ko san luh.* "Records from the Eastern Pavilion" with reference to events in China between the years 1602 and 1623. MS. 4 keuen. [1750 ?] 8°.　　15291. a. 16.

同 館 T‘UNG KWAN. 同 館 賦 鈔 *T‘ung kwan foo ch‘aou.* "A collection of Odes by Scholars from the same College." 2 keuen. [1800 ?] 8°.　　15323. d. 6.

董 明 鐸 TUNG MING-TO. 音 漢 清 文 鑑 *Yin Han Ts‘ing wăn keen.* "A mirror-like vocabulary of the Chinese and Manchu Languages." 20 keuen. 1735. 8°.　　15354. e. 5.

—— [Another edition.] 20 keuen. 1735. 8°.　　15354. e. 6.

—— 清 文 鑑 *Ts‘ing wăn keen.* "A mirror of the Manchu Language." A Manchu and Chinese dictionary arranged according to subjects. Compiled by Tung Ming-to. 20 keuen. 1735. 8°.　　15354. c. 8.

—— [Another edition.] 20 keuen. [1740 ?] 8°.　　15354. c. 9.

Imperfect, containing only Keuen 6 to 20.

同 門 T‘UNG MUN. 同 門 錄 *T‘ung mun luh.* "A List of the Successful Candidates" at the Canton examination of 1840. *Canton*, 1840. 8°.　　15320. e. 31.

There are two copies of this work.

東 史 TUNG SĂ. 東 史 會 綱 *Tung să hoi kang.* "An Epitome of the Annals of Korea" from B.C. 57 to the fifteenth century. 12 keuen. [1700 ?] 8°.　　15287. c. 1.

The last keuen is supplied in manuscript.

佟 世 男 Tung She-nan. 篆 字 彙 *Chuen tsze wei.* "A Dictionary of the Seal Character," arranged under the Radicals. Edited by Leang-Pei-lan. 1691. 8°. **15344. b. 3.**

—— [Another copy.] **15344. b. 4.**

—— [Another copy.] **15344. b. 5.**

通 瑞 T'ung Shwuy. 吏 治 輯 要 *Le che tseih yaou.* "A Manual on Government." Translated into Manchoo by T'ung Shwuy. Edited by Yew-poo-ming-seu, a Mongol. 1823. 8°. **15241. b. 1.**

東 隅 逸 士 Tung yu yih sze [*pseud.*]. 飛 龍 全 傳 *Fei lung ts'euen chuen.* "The complete story of the Flying Dragon." An account of events during the reign of T'ai-tsu, 960–975. With portraits. 60 chapters. 1767. 8°. **15292. b. 2.**

敦 顯 德 Tun Heen-tih [i e. Hunter Corbett]. 十 誡 問 答 *Shih keae wăn ta.* "A Catechism on the Ten Commandments." With illustrations. pp. ix, 149. *Shanghai*, 1883. 8°. **15118. d. 20.**

TURRETTINI (François). See 王 晉 升 Wang Tsin-shing. Le commentaire du San-ze-king . . . Avec notes et variantes par F. T., etc. 1892–1894. 8°. **11100. e. 30.**

—— [Another copy.] **11100. b. 30.**

段 長 基 Tw'an Ch'ang-ke. 歷 代 二 十 四 史 統 紀 全 表 *Leih tai urh shih sze she t'ung ke ts'euen peaou.* "Chronological Tables of the Twenty-four Histories," beginning from P'an-ku, the creator of the world, down to the close of the Ming Dynasty (A.D. 1644). 13 keuen. 1817. 4°. **15291. d. 1.**

段 成 式 Tw'an Ch'ing-shih. 酉 陽 雜 俎 *Yew-yang tsah tsoo.* "Miscellanies from Yew-yang." Notes on antiquarian matters and marvels. A new edition. 20 keuen. 1849. 8°. **15297. b. 14.**

端 恩 Twan Găn. 簪 花 閣 集 *Tsanhwa ko tseih.* "The Tsanhwa Pavilion Collection of Poems." By Twan Găn. pp. 64. With a supplement in 28 pages. 1886. 8°. **15324. a. 11.**

端 木 賜 Twan Muh-sze. 詩 傳 *She chuen.* "A Commentary on the Book of Odes." pp. ii, 32, 5. See 程 榮 Ch'ing Yung. 漢 魏 叢 書 *Han Wei ts'ung shoo.* "A collection of works by authors of the Han and Wei Dynasties," etc. 1791. 8°. **15318. a. 1.**

段 大 令 Tw'an Ta-ling. 段 氏 說 文 注 訂 *Tw'an she Shwo wăn choo ting.* "Tw'an Ta-ling's edition of the *Shwo wan* revised by Woo Shoo-yuh." 8 keuen. *Soo-chow*, 1866. 8°. **15342. b. 4.**

TYNDALL (John). See 田 大 里 T'een-ta-le.

翁 方 綱 Ung Fang-kang. See 劉 璵 Lew K'ew. 隸 韻 *Le yun.* "A Dictionary of the 'Official' Character . . ." With an appendix by Ung Fang-kang, etc. 1810. 8°. **15344. c. 2.**

UNITED STATES OF AMERICA: Naval Department. 兵 船 礮 法 *Ping ch'uen p'aou fa.* "On Naval Gunnery." Published by the Naval Department of the United States of America. Translated into Chinese by Kin-k'eae-le, i.e. C. T. Kreyer. Transcribed by Choo Găn-seïh. Edited by Le Fung-paou. 6 keuen. [*Shanghai*, 1875?] 8°. **15259. d. 12.**

—— [Another copy.] **15259. e. 6.**

兒 Urh. 訓 兒 眞 言 *Heun urh chin yen.* "True words for the instruction of children." A Christian tract. *Shanghai*, 1867. 8°. **15116. d. 46.**

二 倫 Urh lun. 二 倫 行 實 圖 *Urh lun hing shih t'oo.* "An illustrated record of virtuous conduct." With a Korean version of the text added. [1542?] Fol. **15260. a. 1.**

二 十 四 孝 Urh shih sze heaou. 二 十 四 孝 圖 解 *Urh shih sze heaou t'oo keae.* "The twenty-four instances of filial piety illustrated and described." [1850?] 8°. **15229. c. 46.**

爾 雅 Urh ya. 爾 雅 *Urh ya.* "The literary expositor." With Ko P'o's commentary. 3 keuen. 1829. Fol. **15344. e. 18.** A facsimile reprint of the illustrated Chinese edition. Printed in Japan from blocks.

—— [Another edition.] With notes on the sounds of the characters by Luh Tih-ming. Edited by Le Han-chang and others. 3 keuen. 1868. Fol. **15344. e. 16.**

二 友 Urh yew. 二 友 相 論 *Urh yew seang lun.* "Discussion between two friends." [By Dr. William Milne.] A new edition. pp. 59. *Ningpo*, 1864. 8°. **15200. c. 6.**

VÆN-TS'ÆN. *Yü-be væn-ts'æn zi-dzo-ts'ah zi.* "On self-examination preparatory to the Lord's Supper." [By Mrs. Moule?] pp. 38. *Ningpo,* 1866. 8°. **15200. b. 11.**

VAL D'EREMAO (José P.). *See* YIH-KING. The Yih-king. A new translation from the original Chinese. . . . Translated from the French by J. P. Val d'Eremao, etc. 8°. **11098. b. 20.**

VANG PE HEU. *See* WANG PIH-HOW. **11100. c. 31.**

VERTRECHT (JACQUES). *See* CAMPBELL (WILLIAM). The Articles of Christian Instruction in Favorlang-Formosan . . . from Vertrecht's Manuscript of 1650, etc. 1896. 4°. **11098. b. 17.**

VISITING CARDS. A collection of twelve visiting cards bearing the names of Le Hungtsaou, Choo Kihjin, Tăng Ch'ingchung, Lew Szek'i, Lin Shoo, Wang Wănshaou, Woo T'ingfun, Tsung Le, Hea Keahaou, Ch'in Kweifun, King Leen, and Paou Yun. MS. [1863?] **Or. 3534.**

VITALE (GUIDO), *Baron.* Chinese Rhymes first collected and edited with notes and translation by Baron G. V. pp. xvii, 220. *Peking,* 1896. 8°. **11098. a. 16.**

—— and SERCEY (DE), *Comte.* Grammaire et Vocabulaire de la langue Mongole (Dialecte des Khalkhas). Par le Baron Vitale et le Comte de Sercey. pp. viii, 68. *Peking,* 1897. 8°. **11099. a. 19.**

A VOLUME of essays on texts from the classics. Without title. MS. [1840?] 8°. **15113. a. 31.**

WADE (SIR THOMAS FRANCIS), K.C.B. *See* 威妥瑪 WEI T'O-MA.

—— *See* CHINA: KWANG-SEU, *Emperor.* 中英新增條議 *Chung Ying sin tsäng t'eaou e.* "The Chefoo Convention . . . made between Le Hung-chang . . . and Sir T. W.," etc. 1876. 8°. **15297. b. 16.**

—— The Lun yü; being utterances of Kung Tzŭ, known to the Western world as Confucius. Translated by T. F. W. Privately printed. 1869. 4°. **11098. c. 13.**

—— NOTE on the condition and government of the Chinese Empire in 1849. 1849. 8°. **11100. a. 23.**

WADE (SIR THOMAS FRANCIS), K.C.B. 語言自邇集 *Yü-yen Tzŭ-erh Chi.* A progressive course designed to assist the student of colloquial Chinese, as spoken in the Capital and the Metropolitan Department. In eight parts, with key, syllabary, and writing exercises. By T. F. W. 5 vols. *London,* 1867. 4°. **12910. k.**

WALLACE (WILLIAM). *See* 華里司 HWA-LE-SZE.

WALTON (CATHERINE AUGUSTA). 安樂家 *Gan yo kea,* or according to the English title-page "Christie's Old Organ; or Home, Sweet Home." Translated into Chinese by Mary A. Porter. With illustrations. 14 chapters. *Shanghai,* 1882. 8°. **15200. c. 16.**

文 WĂN. 佩文韻府 *Pei wăn yun foo.* "A Lexicon arranged according to the usual system of one hundred and six finals distributed among the five tones." 106 keuen. [1711?] 8°. **15348. b. 7.**
Imperfect, containing only Keuen 14 and part of 16.

—— 同文玉海 *T'ung wăn yuh hai.* "A Treasury of Characters." A dictionary. 20 keuen. 8°. **15344. e. 13.**
Imperfect, containing only Keuen 12–20.

文昌帝君 WĂN-CH'ANG TE-KEUN. 文昌化書 *Wăn-ch'ang hwa shoo.* "Wăn-ch'ang te-keun's Book of Transformations." Edited by Koo Yuen. With illustrations by Yew Sze-fung. 4 keuen. With appendix. 1823. 8°. **15113. b. 4.**

—— 文昌聖典內函 *Wăn-ch'ang shing teen nuy han.* "Some of the contents of the Sacred Canon of Wăn-ch'ang te-keun." [1750?] 8°. **15111. e. 1.**
Imperfect.

—— 文帝全書 *Wăn te ts'euen shoo.* "The complete works of Wăn-ch'ang te-keun." Edited by Lew T'e-shoo. 50 keuen. With appendix. 1835. 8°. **15113. b. 8.**

—— 陰騭文 *Yin chih wăn.* Le Livre de la Récompense des bienfaits secrets. Traduit sur le texte Chinois, par L. Léon de Rosny. *Paris,* 1856. 8°. **11100. d. 28.**

文職 WĂN CHIH. 文職, 武職 *Wăn chih, Woo chih.* "A list of Civil and Military Official Ranks." [1840?] A sheet. **15298. b. 44.**

WAN

問竹主人 WĂN CHUH CHOO JIN, *pseud.* 忠烈 俠義傳 *Chung lëĕ hëĕ e chuen.* "A story of patriotic, loyal, brave, and righteous men." A tale of the Sung Dynasty, based on the adventures of Paou Kung. 120 chapters. 1879. 8°. **15331. f. 7.**

王昶 WANG CH'ANG. 湖海詩傳 *Hoo hai she chuen.* "A collection of Poems from the Lakes and Seas. With short biographical notices of the different authors." Compiled by Wang Ch'ang. Edited by Wang Sze-kow. 46 keuen. 1865. 8°. **15323. e. 20.**

—— 湖海文傳 *Hoo hai wăn chuen.* "A Collection of Literature from the Lakes and Seas." Compiled by Wang Ch'ang. 75 keuen. 1837. 8°. **15320. e. 38.**

—— 金石萃編 *Kin shih ts'uy peen.* "A Collection of Inscriptions." Edited by Wang Ch'ang. 160 keuen. [1805?] 8°. **15300. a. 1.**

汪芝田 WANG CHE-T'EEN. See 陳澄泉 CH'IN CH'ING-TS'EUEN, and WANG CHE-T'EEN. 草書 習慎 *Ts'aou shoo seth shin.* "Carefully selected exercises in the 'Grass' Character." By Ch'in Ch'ing-ts'euen and Wang Che-t'een, etc. 1749. 8°. **15342. b. 8.**

王醫 WANG CHIH. See 鹿兆甲 LUH CHAOU-KĔĂ. 福山縣志 *Fuh-shan heen che.* "A Topography of Fuh-shan heen . . ." Compiled by . . . Wang Chih, etc. 1763. 8°. **15269. c. 13.**

王植桂 WANG CHIH-KWEI. See 張熙宇 CHANG HE-YU. 七家詩輯註彙鈔 *Ts'ih kea she tseth choo wei ch'aou.* "A collection of the writings of seven poets . . ." With notes and comments by Wang Chih-kwei, etc. 1870. 8°. **15324. a. 12.**

王充 WANG CH'UNG. 論衡 *Lun hăng.* "Discourses by means of Comparisons" on philosophical and scientific subjects. 30 keuen. See 程榮 CH'ING YUNG. 漢魏叢書 *Han Wei ts'ung shoo.* "A collection of works by authors of the Han and Wei Dynasties," etc. 1791. 8°. **15318. a. 1.**

王懿榮 WANG E-YUNG. 字學三種 *Tsze heŏ san chung.* "Three works on the Study of the Characters," viz., *Kan luh tsze shoo,* by Yen Yuen-sun; *Suh shoo ch'ing woo,* by Yen Min-ts'oo; and *Tsze shoo woo tuh,* by Wang Fun. Edited by Wang E-yung. 1874. 8°. **15342. b. 7.**

汪昉 WANG FANG. 書經 *Shoo king.* "Essays on Texts from the Shoo king" by Wang Fang and others. [1800?] 12°. **15225. a. 14.**

王符 WANG FOO. 潛夫論 *Ts'een foo lun.* "The discourses of an unknown scholar." 10 keuen. See 程榮 CH'ING YUNG. 漢魏 叢書 *Han Wei ts'ung shoo.* "A collection of works by authors of the Han and Wei Dynasties," etc. 1791. 8°. **15318. a. 1.**

王夫之 WANG FOO-CHE. See 許慎 HEU SHIN. 說文廣義 *Shwo wăn kwang e.* "Extended Meanings of Heu Shin's *Shwo wăn.*" By Wang Foo-che, etc. 1865. 8°. **15344. c. 3.**

王復齋 WANG FUH-CHAI. 宋王復齋鐘鼎 款識 *Sung Wang Fuh-chai chung ting ku'an shih.* "Facsimiles of Inscriptions on Bells and Tripods collected by Wang Fuh-chai of the Sung Dynasty." Edited by Yuen Yuen. 1802. Fol. **15299. d. 2.**

王雰 WANG FUN. 字書誤讀 *Tsze shoo woo luh.* See 王懿榮 WANG E-YUNG. 字學三種 *Tsze heŏ san chung.* "Three works on the Study of the Characters," etc. 1874. 8°. **15342. b. 7.**

王鏠預 WANG FUNG-YU. 大明廣輿考 *Ta Ming kwang yu k'ao.* "The Geography of China during the Ming Dynasty" (1368–1644). With maps. 2 vols. 1610. Fol. **15275. d. 11.**

汪昂 WANG GAN. 圖註本草醫方合編 *T'oo choo pun ts'aou e fang ho peen.* "A Materia Medica. With Prescriptions. Illustrated and Annotated." By Wang Gan. Edited by Hoo Heŏ-fung. 6 keuen. [*Nanking*], 1800. 8°. **15253. a. 11.**

—— [Another edition.] 6 keuen. 1830. 8°. **15251. f. 3.**

—— 增訂圖註本草脩要 *Tsăng ting t'oo choo pun ts'aou pei yaou.* "A Brief Epitome of the *Pun ts'aou kang mŭh.*" With illustrations and comments. By Wang Gan. Edited by Wang Twan, Wang Hwan, and others. 4 keuen. With supplement. *Nanking*, 1694. 8°. **15253. a. 12.**

王羲 WANG HE. 王羲之筆陣圖 *Wang He che pŭh ch'in t'oo.* "Wang He's illustrated work on caligraphy." *Canton* [1860?]. 8°. **15320. c. 15.**

王羲之 WANG HE-CHE. 新鐫興草篆隸千家詩 *Sin tseuen chin ts'aou chuen le ts'een kea she.* "A collection of poems by a thousand authors in the grass, the seal, and the official writings." Edited by Wang He-che. [1688?] 8°.   15319. b. 20 (2).

Wanting the introductory matter.

王厚齋 WANG HOW-CHAI. See 金三俊 KIN SAN-TSEUN. 十七史蒙求 *Shih ts'ih she mung k'ew.* "An aid to the study of the seventeen histories." In verse . . . by Wang How-chai, etc. 1848. 8°.   15291. a. 8.

王槐敬 WANG HWAI-KING. An illuminated genealogy of the Chan Family, the descendants of King Seuen of the Chow Dynasty (B.C. 827). Originally compiled by Wang Hwaiking in 1677. This is a manuscript copy made by Seu Seïhchow in 1774. A scroll.   15296. e. 5.

汪庚 WANG KĂNG. 列女傳 *Lĕĕ neu chuen.* "Biographical notices of celebrated women." Edited by Wang Kăng. Illustrated by Kew Ying-shih. 16 keuen. 1778. 8°. 15303. d. 14.

王圻 WANG K'E. 三才圖會 *San ts'ai t'oo hwuy.* "An Illustrated Encyclopædia." Compiled by Wang K'e. Edited by Hwang Heaoufung. In fourteen sections. 1609. 8°.   15024. a. 1.

王嘉 WANG KEA. 拾遺記 *Shih e ke.* "Lost pages of history." 10 keuen. See 程榮 CH'ING YUNG. 漢魏叢書 *Han Wei ts'ung shoo.* "A collection of works by authors of the Han and Wei Dynasties," etc. 1791. 8°. 15318. a. 1.

王嬌鸞 WANG-KEAOU-LÏWAN. 王嬌鸞百年長恨 *Wang-keaou-lïwan pih nĕen ch'ang hăn,* or the lasting resentment of Miss Keaou-lïwan-Wang. A Chinese tale, founded on fact. Translated from the original by "Sloth." *Canton,* 1839. 8°.   825. a. 13.

汪汲葵 WANG KE-K'WEI. 詞名集解 *Ts'ze ming tseïh keae.* "A collection of Chinese phrases and epithets, with explanations." Compiled by Wang Ke-k'wei. 6 keuen. With a supplementary volume in 2 keuen. 1794. 8°.   15348. c. 2.

王芑孫 WANG K'E-SUN. 大清一統志表 *Ta Ts'ing yih t'ung che peaou.* "Geographical tables, historically arranged, to the *Ta Ts'ing yih t'ung che.*" 1793. 8°.   15261. e. 6.

王俅 WANG K'EW. 嘯堂集古錄考異 *Seaou t'ang tseïh koo luh k'aou e.* "A Catalogue of the Antiquities collected at the Seaou T'ang." Compiled by Wang K'ew. "With an Examination of the different readings" of the Inscriptions by Chang Yung-king. 4 keuen. 1812. 8°.   15299. b. 5.

—— [Another copy.]   15299. b. 8.

王景猷 WANG KING-YEW. 標題句解孔子家語 *Peaou t'e keu keae K'ung tsze kea yu.* "The Family Sayings of Confucius." Edited with a commentary by Wang King-yew. 2 keuen. 1324? Fol.   15201. c. 13.

Printed in Korea with movable wooden type. The first sheet in each volume has been supplied in manuscript facsimile.

—— [Another edition.] 3 keuen. 1599. Fol.   15201. c. 14.

Printed in Japan with movable type.

汪立名 WANG LEÏH-MING. 鐘鼎字源 *Chung ting tsze yuen.* "The Characters on Bells and Tripods, with the places where they occur." Edited by Wang Leïh-ming. 1716. 8°.   15344. b. 9.

王塈 WANG LEW. 域外叢書 *Yih wai ts'ung shoo.* "Reprints of works on foreign countries," consisting of *Hai luh,* "Records of the Sea," by Yang Ping; *Hai taou yih che tsih leŏ,* "Notes on foreign countries," by Wang Ta-hai; *Kaou how mung kew tsih leŏ,* "Notes for Students," by Seu Chaou-tseun; *Fan shay tsai fung too k'aou tsih leŏ,* "Notes on foreign customs," by Luh-shih-tseïh; *Hung maou fan Ying-keïh-le k'aou leŏ,* "Notes on England," by Wang Wăn-tai; and *Leu sung ke leŏ,* "Notes on Spain," by Hwang Ko-chuy. 1842. 8°. 15271. b. 3.

王鳴衡 WANG MING-KEU. See 蔡象貞 TS'AI SEANG-CHING. 醫書滙恭輯成 *E shoo hwuy tsan tseïh ch'ing.* "Extract from Medical Works . . ." Edited by Wang Ming-keu, etc. 1807. 8°.   15251. f. 12.

王鳴盛 WANG MING-SHING. 尚書後案 *Shang shoo how gan.* "Latest Decisions on the Shang Shoo." 30 keuen, with appendix. 1782. 8°.   15215. b. 14.

王棻 WANG NĔĔ. See 吳錫麒 WOO SEÏH-K'E. 有正味齋駢體文 *Yew ching wei chai peen t'e wăn.* "A collection of literary pieces . . ." With notes by Wang Nĕĕ, etc. 1859. 8°.   15319. e. 7.

WAN

王 弼 WANG PEÏH. See 易 經 YIH KING. 周易 *Chow yih.* "The Chow Changes." With a commentary by Wang Peïh, etc. 1605. 4°.

—— 易 略 例 *Yih leŏ le.* "Short generalizations on the Book of Changes." pp. iv, 32, 2. See 程 榮 CH'ING YUNG. 漢魏 叢 書 *Han Wei ts'ung shoo.* "A collection of works by authors of the Han and Wei Dynasties," etc. 1791. 8°.
15318. a. 1.

王 伯 安 WANG PIH-GAN. 王 陽 明 文 選 *Wang Yang-ming wăn seuen.* See 李 欽 之 LE K'IN-CHE. 金 元 明 八 家 文 選 *Kin, Yuen, Ming, pa kea wăn seuen.* "Selections from the Writings of Eight Authors of the Kin, Yuen, and Ming Dynasties," etc. 1845. 8°. 15318. e. 1.

—— See 謝 枋 得 SEAY FANG-TIH. 謝 疊 山 先生 文 章 軌 范 *Seay Tëĕ-shan Seen-sang wăn chang kwei fan.* "Literary Models . . ." Edited by Wang Pih-gan, etc. 1868. 8°.
15312. d. 11.

—— 王 陽 明 先生 全 集 *Wang Yang-ming Seen săng ts'euen tseĭh.* "The Complete Works of Wang Pih-gan." 16 keuen. 1826. 8°.
15318. b. 2.

王 伯 厚 WANG PIH-HOW. Il Libro delle tre parole secondo la versione Mangese di Tooghe. Pubblicato per cura di E. Teza. (Estratto dagli Annali delle Università Toscane.) *Manchu and Ital.* pp. 22. *Pisa*, 1880. 8°. 11100. c. 33.

—— 三 字 經 訓 詁 *San tsze king heun koo.* "The Three-character Classic, with explanations." See 徐 建 勳 SEU KEEN-HEUN. 徐 氏 三 種 *Seu she san chung.* "Seu reprints," etc. 1875. 8°. 15202. b. 21.

王 炳 堃 WANG PING-K'UN. 眞 理 課 選 *Chin le k'o seuen.* "Exhortations on the True Christian Doctrine." By Wang Ping-k'un and others. Parts i, ix. *Hankow*, 1881. 8°.
15200. b. 15.

王 炳 耀 WANG PING-YAO. 中 日 戰 輯 *Chung Jih chen chi.* "An account of the War between China and Japan." With six maps. 6 keuen. *Hongkong*, 1895. 8°. 15296. b. 14.

王 勃 WANG PO. 成 道 記 *Ch'ing taou ke.* "The perfect (Buddhist) way." By Wang Po of the T'ang Dynasty. With notes by the Monk Taou Ch'ing. This is a modern copy of an edition published in 1578. MS. ff. 36. [1870?] 8°. Or. 4542. 39. B. f.

王 步 青 WANG POO-TS'ING. 塾 課 小 題 分 編 *Shuh k'o seaou t'e fun peen.* "Scholastic essays methodically arranged." 1801. 8°. 15319. a. 6.

徃 生 WANG SĂNG. 徃 生 拾 因 *Wang săng shih yin.* "The causes of going to be born [in Buddha's country?]." 1248. 8°. 16006. e. 18.
Printed in Japan from blocks.

王 相 WANG SEANG. See 馬 融 MA YUNG. 忠孝 經 讀 本 *Chung heaou king tuh pun.* "The Classics on Patriotism . . . and on Filial Piety." With a commentary by Wang Seang, etc. 8°.
15225. a. 23.

王 繢 堂 WANG SEANG-T'ANG. 通 天 曉 *T'ung t'een-heaou.* "A book of General Information." By Wang Seang-t'ang. 18 keuen. 1816. 8°.
15026. a. 7.

王 象 晉 WANG SEANG-TSIN. 廣 羣 芳 譜 *Kwang keun fang p'oo.* "A Herbal." Enlarged and revised by Lew Haou, under Imperial patronage. 100 keuen. 1708. 8°. 15255. a. 2.

王 燮 WANG SĔĔ. See 顧 俊 KOO TSEUN, and WANG SĔĔ. 小 題 清 新 集 *Seaou t'e ts'ing sin tseĭh.* "A New Collection of Classical Essays." Compiled by Koo Tseun and Wang Sĕĕ, etc. 1872. 12°. 15319. a. 12.

汪 西 亭 WANG SE-T'ING. 白 香 山 詩 集 *Pih heang shan she tseĭh.* "A Collection of Poetry from the Pih-heang Mountain." By Wang Se-t'ing. In four parts. 40 keuen. 1703. 8°.
15323. e. 15.

汪 少 溯 WANG SHAOU-HOO. See 雷 琳 LUY LIN. 漁 磯 漫 鈔 *Yu ke man ch'aou.* "A Collection of Tales . . ." Compiled by . . . Wang Shaou-hoo, etc. 1871. 8°. 15331. d. 17.

王 十 朋 WANG SHIH-P'ĂNG. See 蘇 軾 SOO SHIH. 蘇 文 忠 公 詩 合 註 *Soo Wăn-chung kung she ho choo.* "The Poems of Soo Shih consistently explained by the Commentators . . ." Wang Shih-p'ăng, etc. 1870. 8°. 15324. b. 2.

—— See 蘇 軾 SOO SHIH. 增 刊 校 正 王 狀 元 集 註 分 類 東 坂 先生 詩 *Tsăng k'an keaou ching Wang chwang yuen tseĭh choo fun luy Tung-p'o seen săng she.* "A revised edition of Soo Shih's Poetry . . ." Compiled by Wang Shih-p'ăng, etc. 4°. 15313. f. 2.

王 慎 初 WANG SHIN-CH'OO. See 馮 楚 瞻 FUNG
TS'OO-CHEN. 馮氏錦囊秘錄 *Fung she kin
nang pe luh.* "Fung's Repertoire of Medical
Works." Edited by Wang Shin-choo, etc.
1813. 8°. 15253. c. 2.

王 菽 原 WANG SHUH-YUEN. See 錢 東 生 TS'EEN
TUNG-SĂNG. 文獻徵存錄 *Wăn heen ching
ts'un luh.* "A Record of Literary Biography
. . ." Edited by Wang Shuh-yuen, etc. 1858.
8°. 15305. b. 4.

王 士 禎 WANG SZE-CHING. 漁洋山人古詩選
Yu yang shan jin koo she seuen. "A Selection
of Ancient Poems." Edited by Wang Sze-ching.
Part i, 17 keuen; Part ii, 15 keuen. 1868. 8°.
15321. d. 19.

王 嗣 周 WANG SZE-CHOW. See 袁 中 立 YUEN
CHUNG-LEĬH. 黃縣志 *Hwang heen che.* "A
Topography of the District of Hwang." Edited
by Wang Sze-chow, etc. 1755. 8°. 15269. e. 12.

王 司 寇 WANG SZE-KOW. See 王 昶 WANG
CH'ANG. 湖海詩傳 *Hoo hai she chuen.* "A
Collection of Poems . . ." Edited by Wang
Sze-kow, etc. 1865. 8°. 15323. e. 20.

王 大 海 WANG TA-HAI. 海島逸誌 *Hai taou
yih che.* "Notes on Foreign Countries." Edited
by Wang Ting-shan. 6 keuen. 1806. 8°.
15271. a. 16.

—— [Another edition.] 6 keuen. 1860. 8°.
15291. a. 6.

—— 海島逸誌摘畧 *Hai taou yih che tsih lĕŏ.*
"Notes on Foreign Countries." See 王 蟶
WANG LEW. 域外叢書 *Yih wai ts'ung shoo.*
"Reprints of Works on Foreign Countries,"
etc. 1842. 8°. 15271. b. 3.

王 岱 與 WANG TAI-YU. 正敎眞詮 *Ching keaou
chin ts'euen.* "A Work on the Mahommedan
Religion." 4 keuen. 1795. 8°. 15200. a. 5.

王 大 娘 WANG TA NEANG. 王大娘補缸 *Wang
ta neang poo kang.* "Mrs. Wang mends an
earthen jar." A drama. pp. 7. [1860?] 8°.
15327. d. 33 (2).

汪 登 原 WANG TĂNG-YUEN. 中詮 *Chung Ts'euen.*
"Central Discourses" on the Confucian system.
With portrait of the author. 6 keuen. 1630. 8°.
15202. b. 22.

王 丹 麓 WANG TAN-LU. 檀几叢書 *T'an-ke
ts'ung shoo.* "The T'an-ke Collection of
Reprints." Compiled by Wang Tan-lu and
edited by Chang Shan-lai. In three series.
Series i, 50 keuen; Series ii, 50 keuen;
Supplementary Series, 2 keuen. 1695. 8°.
15315. b. 2.

王 韜 WANG T'AOU, and 張 宗 瓦 CHANG
TSUNG-LEANG. 普法戰紀 *P'oo Fa chen ke.*
"A History of the Franco-German War,"
1870-71. Compiled from the English newspapers and other sources by Wang Taou and
Chang Tsung-leang. 14 keuen. 1872. 8°.
15298. d. 1.

—— [Another edition.] 4 keuen. *Hongkong,*
1898. 8°. 15297. a. 18.

—— 遯窟讕言 *T'un k'uh lan yen.* A collection
of tales. Compiled by Wang T'aou. 12 keuen.
1875. 8°. 15331. c. 9.

汪 道 鼎 WANG TAOU-TING. 坐花誌果 *Tso hwa
che kwo.* "The records of one sitting among
the flowers." A collection of stories. 8 keuen.
1873. 8°. 15327. e. 3.

王 大 同 WANG TA-T'UNG. 上海縣志 *Shang
hai heen che.* "A Topography of Shang-hai
Heen." Compiled by Wang Ta-t'ung, Chin
Wăn-shuh, Fang Tso, and others. 20 keuen.
1814. 8°. 15269. b. 5.

汪 體 齋 WANG T'E-CHAI. 天下有山堂墨
竹蘭石譜 *T'een hea yew shan t'ang mih chuh
lan shih p'oo.* "Sketches of Bamboos, Flowers,
and Rocks." By Wang T'e-chai. Edited by
Fang Hwa-po. 1724. 8°. 15255. e. 22.

王 德 均 WANG TIH-KEUN. See 金 楷 理 KIN-
K'EAE-LE. 繪地法原 *Hwuy te fa yuen.*
"On the Elements of Map Drawing . . ."
Transcribed by Wang Tih-keun, etc. 8°.
15259. d. 20.

—— See 士 密 德 SZE-MEĬH-TIH. 開煤要法
K'ai mei yaou fa. "On Coal-mining . . ."
Edited by Wang Tih-keun, etc. 8°.

王 德 寬 WANG TIH-K'WAN. 臙脂牡丹 *Yen
chih mutan.* "The painted peony." A collection
of model letters arranged in the usual way
according to subjects. Compiled by Wang Tih-
k'wan. 6 keuen. 1839. 12°. 15348. a. 20.
Imperfect, wanting Keuen 4.

WAN

王葦 WANG T‘ING. 詒晉齋法帖 *E tsin chai fa t‘ëĕ.* "Black paper copy of Poems from the E tsin Study." By Wang T‘ing. 1804. 8°.
15324. e. 4.

汪廷珍 WANG T‘ING-CHIN. See 綿忻 MEEN HIN. 欽定新疆識畧 *K‘in ting sin keang shih leŏ.* "An account of the newly acquired Muhammedan Districts . . ." Compiled by Wang T‘ing-chin, etc. 1820. 8°. 15271. b. 12.

王廷珊 WANG T‘ING-SHAN. See 王大海 WANG TA-HAI. 海島逸誌 *Hai taou yih che.* "Notes on Foreign Countries." Edited by Wang T‘ing-shan, etc. 1806. 8°. 15271. a. 16.

王廷紹 WANG T‘ING-SHAO. See 張熙宇 CHANG HE-YU. 硃批增註七家詩選 *Choo p‘e tsăng choo ts‘ih kea she seuen.* "Imperially endorsed Poems" by . . . Wang T‘ing-shao, etc. 1857. 8°. 15323. c. 14.

—— See 張熙宇 CHANG HE-YU. 七家詩輯註彙鈔 *Ts‘ih kea she tseĭh choo wei ch‘aou.* "A collection of the writings of" . . . Wang T‘ing-shaou, etc. 1870. 8°. 15324. a. 12.

王粲 WANG TSAN. 英雄記 *Ying heung ke.* "Records of Heroes." pp. vi, 52, 2. See 程榮 CH‘ING YUNG. 漢魏叢書 *Han Wei ts‘ung shoo.* "A collection of works by authors of the Han and Wei Dynasties," etc. 1791. 8°.
15318. a. 1.

王清任 WANG TS‘ING-JIN. 醫林改錯 *E lin kai ts‘o.* "Medical errors corrected." By Wang Ts‘ing-jin. 2 keuen. *Nanking,* 1849. 8°.
15253. b. 3.

王晉升 WANG TSIN-SHING. 百家姓考略 *Pih kea sing k‘aou leŏ.* "A short account of the family names of China." See 徐建勛 SEU KEEN-HEUN. 徐氏三種 *Seu she san chung.* Seu's reprints, etc. 1875. 8°. 15202. b. 21.

—— Le Commentaire du San-ze-king, le Recueil des Phrases de trois mots. Version Mandchoue, avec notes et variantes par François Turrettini. *H. Georg: Geneva,* 1892–1894. 8°. 11100. e. 30.

—— [Another copy.] 11100. b. 30.

王宗貴 WANG TSUNG-KWEI. [A document purporting to be a deed of sale of a Bamboo House in Formosa to foreigners for the sum of 127 dollars. 1752. 15297. c. 3.

王通 WANG T‘UNG. 中說 *Chung shwo.* "Central Discourses" on legislation, etc. 2 keuen. See 程榮 CH‘ING YUNG. 漢魏叢書 *Han Wei ts‘ung shoo.* "A collection of works by authors of the Han and Wei Dynasties," etc. 1791. 8°.
15318. a. 1.

—— 元經 *Yuen king.* "The Early History" of China, from A.D. 290 to 618. 8 keuen. See 程榮 CH‘ING YUNG. 漢魏叢書 *Han Wei ts‘ing shoo.* "A collection of works by authors of the Han and Wei Dynasties," etc. 1791. 8°.
15318. a. 1.

汪文芳 WANG WĂN-FANG. 增訂尺牘見 *Tsăng ting ch‘ih tuh keen.* "A collection of letters. An enlarged edition." 3 keuen. [1860 ?] 8°. 15315. c. 8.

王文璧 WANG WĂN-PEĬH. See 周德清 CHOW TIH-TS‘ING. 中原音韻 *Chung yuen yin yun.* "A Pronouncing Dictionary of the Mandarin Dialect . . ." With notes by Wang Wăn-peĭh, etc. 8°. 15346. b. 21.

汪文泰 WANG WĂN-T‘AI. 紅毛番嘆咭唎考畧 *Hung maou fan Ying-keih-le k‘aou leŏ.* "Notes on England." See 王塗 WANG LEW. 域外叢書 *Yih wai ts‘ung shoo.* "Reprints of works on foreign countries," etc. 1842. 8°.
15271. b. 3.

王文燾 WANG WĂN-TAOU. See 高崗 KAOU KANG. 蓬萊縣志 *Păng-lai heen che.* "A Topography of the Păng-lai District . . ." A new and revised edition by Wang Wăn-taou, etc. 1839. 8°. 15269. d. 18.

汪由敦 WANG YEW-TUN. See 詩經 SHE KING. 御纂詩義折中 *Yu tswan She e che chung.* "Well-weighed Decisions on the Meaning of the Book of Odes." Compiled by . . . Wang Yew-tun, etc. 1755. 8°. 15212. e. 2.

—— See 允祿 YUN-LUH. 欽定同文韻統 *Kin ting tung wăn yun tung.* The primary Sanskrit . . . characters . . . represented in Chinese . . . by Wang Yew-tun, etc. 1750. 8°.
15354. a. 5.

王翼雲 WANG YIH-YUN. See 王阮亭 WANG YUEN-T‘ING. 唐詩合解箋註 *T‘ang she ho keae chien choo.* "A selection of poems by the most celebrated authors of the T‘ang Dynasty . . ." With a commentary by Wang Yih-yun, etc. 1732. 8°. 15324. b. 9.

王 源 WANG YUEN. 文章練要 *Wăn chang leen yaou.* "Select literary extracts" from the *Tso chuen.* Edited with notes by Wang Yuen. 10 keuen. [1750?] 8°. 15318. c. 6.

王 元 貞 WANG YUEN-CHING. See 陰 時 夫 YIN SHE-FOO. 韻府羣玉原本 *Yun foo keun yuh yuen pun.* "A Dictionary . . ." Edited by Wang Yuen-ching, etc. 1590. 8°. 15348. c. 1.

王 阮 亭 WANG YUEN-T'ING. 唐 詩 合 解 箋 註 *T'ang she ho keae tseen choo.* "A selection of poems by the most celebrated authors of the T'ang Dynasty." Compiled by Wang Yuen-t'ing. With a commentary by Wang Yih-yun. Part i, 12 keuen ; Part ii, 4 keuen. 1732. 8°. 15324. b. 9.

王 元 宰 WANG YUEN-TSAI. See 李 龍 LE LUNG. 聖賢讚像圖 *Shing heen tsan seang t'oo.* "Likeness of celebrated Sages and Worthies." Compiled by Wang Yuen-tsae, etc. 1652. 8°. 15303. d. 1.

王 裕 豐 WANG YÜ-FUNG. See 熏 沐 HEUN-SHUH. 釋迦如來應化事蹟 *Shih kea joo lai ying hwa sze tse.* "The Transformations of Sākya Tathāgata . . ." Edited by Wang Yü-fung, etc. 1808. 4°. 15113. e. 5.

王 永 祺 WANG YUNG-KE. See 張 景 星 CHANG KING-SING. 宋 詩 別 裁 集 *Sung she pĕĕ tsai tseih.* "A collection of the Poetry of the Sung Dynasty." Compiled by . . . Wang Yung-ke, etc. 1761. 8°. 15324. a. 2.

—— See 張 景 星 CHANG KING-SING. 元 詩 別 裁 集 *Yuen she pĕĕ tsai tseih.* "A collection of the Poetry of the Yuen Dynasty." Compiled by . . . Wang Yung-ke, etc. 1764. 8°. 15324. a. 3.

玩 花 主 人 WAN-HWA CHOO-JIN, *pseud.* 審 音 鑑 古 錄 *Shin yin keen koo luh.* "Operas illustrative of the past," consisting of the *Pepa ke, King ch'ai ke, Hung le ke, Urh sun fuh, Ch'ang săng teen, Mowtan t'ing, Se seang ke, Ming fung ke, T'eih kwan t'oo*; with supplements to the *Se seang ke,* the *Hung le ke,* the *Mowtan t'ing,* the *Ch'ang săng teen,* and the *T'eih kwan t'oo.* With illustrations. Compiled by a man calling himself Wan-hwa Choo-jin. 1834. 8°. 15257. e. 18.

文 澂 治 WĂN KEAOU-CHE [i.e. GEORGE SYDNEY OWEN]. 地學指要 *Te heŏ che yaou.* "Elements of Geology." With illustrations. Translated into Chinese by Wăn Keaou-che. 3 keuen. 1881. 8°. 15259. h. 7.

文 慶 WĂN K'ING. 欽定國子監志 *K'in ting kwo tsze keen che.* "The History of the Imperial College (at Peking)." By an Imperially appointed Commission consisting of Wăn K'ing, Le Tsung-fang, T'ĕĕ Lin, and others. 82 keuen. 1834. 8°. 15297. e. 1.

萬 空 大 師 WANK'UNG TASZE. 金臺華嚴禪寺請經沙門萬空大師重修記 *Kint'ai Hwayen ch'en sze keang king Shamum Wank'ung Tasze chung siu ke.* "A rubbing of an inscription giving an account of the restoration in 1491 of the Hwayen temple outside the Tsungwăn gate at Peking, by the Priest Wank'ung." Followed by a rubbing of a long Sanskrit inscription, to which is appended a statement in Chinese that the temple was built in the 5th year of the reign of T'een hwuy of the Kin Dynasty, i.e. 1127. 1491. A roll. Or. 1095.

萬 蓮 山 WAN LEEN-SHAN. See 張 小 浦 CHANG SEAOU-POO. 十三經集字摹本 *Shih san king tseih tsze moo pun.* "The Characters of the Thirteen Classics . . ." Edited by Wan Leen-shan, etc. 1849. 8°. 15344. a. 6.

萬 邦 維 WAN PANG-WEI. 萊 陽 縣 志 *Laiyang heen che.* "A Topography of Lai-yang heen," in Shantung. By Wan Pang-wei and others. 10 keuen. 1678. 8°. 15269. d. 14.

文 壁 WĂN PEÏH [i.e.   ]. 天道正統 *T'ien taou ching t'ung.* "The correct clue to Christianity." pp. i, 142. *Shanghai,* 1879. 8°. 15200. c. 20.

萬 蓬 山 WAN P'UNG-SHAN. See 張 小 浦 CHANG SEAOU-P'OO. 十三經集字摹本 *Shih san king tseih moo pun.* "The Characters of the Thirteen Classics." . . . Edited by Wan P'ung-shan, etc. 1850. 8°. 15344. b. 10.

文 書 WĂN SHOO. 文書字數 *Wăn shoo tsze soo.* "An Index of Characters." MS. [1844?] 8°. 15344. c. 22.

文 書 WĂN SHOO. 來 往 文 書 *Lai wang wăn shoo.* "Copies of Despatches" from the Chinese authorities to the British Consuls at Canton and Shanghai (?) during the years 1842 and 1843. MS. 2 vols. 1842–43. 8°. **15297. d. 5.**

文 書 封 WĂN SHOO FUNG. 文 書 封 *Wăn shoo fung.* "Official Envelopes" from Ke Kung, Ke Ying, and Shoo Kung-show. 1840. 1843. **15297. d. 7.**

萬 壽 WAN SHOW. 萬 壽 盛 典 *Wan show shing teen.* Panoramic illustrations representing the rejoicings at Peking on the occasion of the 60th birthday of the Emperor K'ang-he, in 1721. Tien-shih-chai Photo-lithographic Works. *Shanghai,* 1879. 12°. **15297. a. 15.**
This work has also the following English title-page: "Panorama of Peking during the celebrations of the sixtieth anniversary of the Chinese Emperor K'ang-he's birthday. Photo-lithographed from the Chinese original, etc."

文 燈 伊 WĂN TĂNG-E. See 黃 維 觀 HWANG WEI-KWAN. 錦 字 箋 *Kin tsze tseen.* "A Dictionary of Elegant Expressions . . ." Edited by Wăn Tăng-e, etc. 1689. 8°. **15346. a. 21.**

萬 濟 國 WAN TSE-KWO. 聖 敎 明 徵 *Shing keaou ming ching.* "The Holy Religion clearly explained." By Wan Tse-kwo. 8 keuen. *Hongkong,* 1894. 8°. **15118. a. 36.**

萬 靑 銓 WAN TS'ING-TS'EUEN. 三 字 鑑 勘 本 *San tsze keen k'an pun.* "The Three-character Classic critically annotated." pp. xii, 80. 1849. 8°. **15202. c. 28.**

萬 字 WAN TSZE. 萬 字 典 *Wan tsze teen.* "A dictionary of ten thousand characters." A concise Chinese dictionary. pp. iii, 400. *Shanghai* [1880?]. 8°. **15342. a. 7.**

WAN-TUN-MO. See 尹 端 模 YIN TWAN-MOO.

文 端 公 WĂN-TWAN KUNG. 吏 治 輯 要 *Le che tseĭh yaou.* "A digest of rules of administration." 1875. 8°. **15241. a. 12.**

萬 物 WAN WUH. 萬 物 眞 原 *Wan wuh chin yuen.* "The true source of all things." pp. ii, 51. *Hongkong,* 1888. 8°. **15200. b. 26.**

WAR SCENES. Thirteen coloured engravings representing scenes in the war of 1900. **M.P.C.**

凹 凸 丈 夫 WA TEĬH CHANGFU, *pseud.* 詩 僊 *She seen.* "Poetical Geniuses." Coloured portraits of Chinese poets, with in each case a specimen of their works. The collection, which consists of eighteen poets, begins with Soo Woo, second century B.C., and ends with Lew Tsung-yuen, A.D. 773–819. A Japanese edition. MS. ff. 18. 1684. 4°. **Or. 985. 28. a.**

WATT (ALEXANDER). See 華 特 HWA-T'IH.

—— 電 氣 鍍 金 *Teen k'e too kin.* "Electro Metallurgy." By A. Watt. Translated into Chinese by Foo-lan-ya. With illustrations. 8 keuen. [*Shanghai?*] 1880. 8°. **15259. g. 13.**

WATTERS (THOMAS). Stories of Every-day Life in Modern China. Told by Chinese and done into English by T. Watters. pp. vii, 226. *D. Nutt : London,* 1896. 8°. **11100. a. 24.**

WAY (RICHARD QUARTERMAN). See 褘 理 哲 WEI LE-CHE.

WEGENER (GEORG). *See* TA TS'ING YIH T'UNG YÜ T'U. Nord-Tibet und Lob-Nur-Gebiet in der Darstellung des Ta-Thsing i Thung yü Thu . . . herausgegeben von Dr. G. Wegener, etc. 1893. 8°. **Pam. 88.**

韋 昭 WEI CHAOU. 重 訂 國 語 國 策 合 註 *Chung ting kwo yu kwo ts'ih ho choo.* "'The Story of the Contending States' and the 'Narrative of the Contending States,' together annotated" by Wei Chaou. 1870. 8°. **15334. d. 16.**
Imperfect, containing only the "Story of the Contending States," 21 keuen.

魏 徵 WEI CHING. 羣 書 治 要 *K'eun shoo che yaou.* "An epitome of the contents of (classical and historical) works." 50 keuen. [*Suruga,* 1618.] 4°. **15297. e. 2.**
Printed with Japanese metal type. Wanting Keuen 4, 13, 20.

韋 更 斯 WEI-KĂNG-SZE [i.e.   ]. 海 塘 輯 要 *Hai t'ang tseĭh yaou.* "On building Sea-dikes." By Wei-kăng-sze. Translated into Chinese by Foo-lan-ya, i.e. J. Fryer. Transcribed by Chaou Yuen-yih. 10 keuen. [*Shanghai,* 1874?] 8°. **15259. d. 23.**

—— [Another copy.] **15259. d. 27.**

威基謁 Wei Ke-ye [i.e.   ]. 電報新書
Luy paou sin shoo. "A New System for
Telegraphing in Chinese." 1872. 8°.
15252. b. 26.

褘理哲 Wei Le-che [i.e. R. Q. Way]. 地球
說畧 *Te k'ew shwo leŏ.* "A short geography."
With maps and illustrations. 114 ff. An
enlarged edition of an original work entitled
地球圖說 *Te k'ew t'oo shwo.* *Ningpo,* 1856.
8°. 15263. d. 2.
On the title-page occur the initials R. Q. W.

—— [Another edition.] *Shanghai,* 1871. 8°.
15275. a. 2.

—— [Another edition.] *Shanghai,* 1878. 8°.
15264. a. 1.

—— 耶穌門徒金針 *Yay-soo mun t'oo kin
chin.* "The Disciple's Guide." pp. ix, 28.
Shanghai, 1871. 12°. 15200. c. 43.

偉烈 Wei-lĕĕ [i.e Alexander Wylie]. See
美以納 Mei-e-na, and 白勞那 Pih-laou-
na. 汽機發軔 *K'e ke fa jin.* "The
Marine Steam Engine . . ." Translated into
Chinese by Wei-lĕĕ, etc. 8°. 15259. f. 2.

韋廉臣 Wei-leen-ch'in [i.e. Alexander
Williamson]. 格物探元 *Kih wuh t'an yuen.*
"An enquiry into the principles of the
philosophy of nature." 1876. 8°. 15257. b. 29.

—— [Another edition.] With illustrations. 3 keuen.
1880. 8°. 15259. g. 17.

—— 二約釋義叢書 *Urh yo shih e ts'ung
shoo.* "Aids to understanding the Old and
New Testaments." With maps. By Wei-leen-
ch'in. *Shanghai,* 1882. 8°. 15118. c. 39.

—— [Another copy.] 15118. d. 28.

惟明 Wei Ming. 皇越地輿誌 *Hwang yueh
te yu che.* "A Geography of Annam." 2 keuen.
1812. 8°. 15271. b. 18.

—— 南圻六省地輿誌 *Nan k'e luh shing te
yu che.* "A Geography of the Six Provinces
of the Southern Borders," i.e. Annam. 1812.
8°. 15271. b. 17.

韋明珠 Wei Ming-choo [i.e. Miss Williamson].
動物類編 *Tung wuh luy peen.* "Zoology"
in Chinese and English, with coloured plates.
1882. 12°. 15255. a. 10.

韋門道氏 Wei-mun-taou She. 百獸圖說
Pih show t'oo shwo. "Illustrative Notes on
Animals." By Wei-mun-taou she (? Mrs.
Williamson). pp. 61. 1882. 8°. 15331. e. 8.

維寗 Wei Ning. 字類標韻 *Tsze luy peaou
yun.* "A Dictionary of the Characters with
their Rhyming Sounds." 6 keuen. 1841. 8°.
15346. a. 12.

魏伯陽 Wei Pih-yang. 參同契 *Ts'an t'ung
kĕĕ.* "A work on Alchemy." xvi, 40, 2.
See 程榮 Ch'ing Yung. 漢魏叢書 *Han
Wei ts'ung shoo.* "A collection of works by
authors of the Han and Wei Dynasties," etc.
1791. 8°. 15318. a. 1.

—— 參同契 *Ts'an tung kĕĕ.* "A work on
Alchemy." See 彭好古 Păng Haou-koo.
道言內外秘訣全書 *Taou yen nuy wai
pe keuĕ ts'euen shoo.* "A Complete Collection of
Taouist Works," etc. 8°. 15111. b. 3.

威妥瑪 Wei T'o-ma [i.e. Sir Thomas Wade,
K.C.B.]. 登瀛篇 *Tăng ying p'een.* "Pro-
gressive Exercises" in Chinese. By Sir T.
Wade. *Shanghai,* 1860. Fol. 15229. b. 19.

韋而司 Wei-urh-sze [i.e. D. A. Wells]. 化學
鑑原 *Hwa heŏ keen yuen.* "Inorganic
Chemistry." Translated into Chinese by Foo-
lan-ya [i.e. J. Fryer]. Edited by Seu Show.
6 keuen. [*Shanghai,* 1870?] 8°. 15252. d. 12.

—— [Another copy.] 15259. f. 16.

魏源 Wei Yuen. 皇朝經世文編 *Hwang
ch'aou king she wăn peen.* "A collection of
State Papers of the present Dynasty." Compiled
by Wei Yuen. 120 keuen. 1826. 8°.
15291. b. 3.

—— [Another copy.] 15318. d. 1.

—— 聖武記 *Shing woo ke.* "A History of the
Wars of the present Dynasty." By Wei Yuen.
14 keuen. 1842. 8°. 15296. b. 9.

魏玉橫 Wei Yuh-hung. See 江瓘 Keang
Kwan. 名醫類案 *Ming e luy gan.* "The
Medical Practice of celebrated Physicians . . ."
Edited by Wei Yuh-hung, etc. 1871. 8°.
15252. b. 30.

魏玉麟 Wei Yuh-lin. 側人明堂圖 *Ts'ih jin
ming t'ang t'oo.* "An anatomical drawing of
the side view of a man's figure." 1782. A
scroll. 15253. c. 6 (3).

WELLS (DAVID AMES). See 韋而司 WEI-URH-SZE.

WIEGER (LÉON). 漢語入門 Rudiments de parler Chinois. Dialecte du 河間府. Par le P. L. W. *Hokien Fu*, 1899. 8°. **11094. d. 1.**
In progress.

WILKINSON (WILLIAM HENRY). *See* YUEN SEANG FOO. "Those Foreign Devils." Translated by W. H. W. 1891. 8°. **11099. b. 28.**

—— THE COREAN GOVERNMENT: Constitutional changes, July, 1894, to October, 1895. With an appendix on subsequent enactments to 30th June, 1896. With a map. pp. xi, 192. *P. S. King & Son: London*, 1897. 4°. **11098. c. 14.**

WILLIAMSON (ALEXANDER). See 西士 SE SZE. 西士酬中國人書 *Se sze ch'ow Chung kwŏ jin shoo.* "A Western scholar's reply to Chinese" objections to Christianity. A manuscript note on cover states that this work is by A. W., etc. 1875. 8°. **15118. c. 40.**

—— ANCIENT RELIGIONS AND PHILOSOPHIES: their origin, aim, and issue. (In Chinese, with the Chinese title 古教彙參 *Koo keaou wei ts'an.*) With illustrations. 3 keuen. *Shanghai*, 1882. 8°. **15118. c. 39.**

WILLIAMSON (MISS). See 韋明珠 WEI MING-CHOO.

WILLIAMSON (MRS.). See 箴言 CHIN YEN. 箴言摘錄 *Chin yen tsih luh.* "Extracts from the Book of Proverbs . . ." By . . . Mrs. Williamson. 1882. 4°. **15117. d. 23.**

—— See 家 KEA. 家畜玩物 *Kea chuh wan wuh.* "Domestic Pets . . ." By . . . Mrs. Williamson, etc. 1883. 4°. **15331. e. 11.**

—— See 浪子 LANG TSZE. 浪子回頭 *Lang tsze hwuy t'ou.* "The Return of the Prodigal Son." Translated into Chinese . . . by Mrs. W., etc. 1882. 4°. **15118. e. 8.**

—— See 瓦馬 LEANG MA. 瓦馬圖說 *Leang ma t'oo shwo.* "An illustrated account of some quiet horses." By . . . Mrs. Williamson, etc. 1883. 4°. **15331. e. 9.**

WILLIAMSON (MRS.). See 名犬 MING K'EUEN. 名犬圖說 *Ming k'euen t'oo shwo.* "An illustrated account of noted dogs." By . . . Mrs. Williamson, etc. 1883. 4°. **15331. e. 10.**

—— See 摩西 MO-SE. 摩西聖蹟圖說 *Mo-se shing tse t'oo shwo.* "An illustrated life of Moses." By . . . Mrs. Williamson, etc. 1882. 4°. **15118. e. 4.**

—— See 百鳥 PIH NEAOU. 百鳥圖說 *Pih neaou t'oo shwo.* "Notes on Birds." By Mrs. W., etc. 1882. 8°. **15255. e. 31.**

—— See 但以理 TAN-E-LE. 但以理聖蹟圖說 *Tan-e-le shing tse t'oo shwo.* "An illustrated life of the Prophet Daniel." By . . . Mrs. Williamson, etc. 1882. 4°. **15118. e. 5.**

—— See 大闢王 TA-P'EIH WANG. 大闢王聖蹟圖說 *Ta-p'eih wang shing tseih t'oo shwo.* "An illustrated life of King David." By . . . Mrs. Williamson, etc. 1882. 4°. **15118. e. 6.**

—— See 韋門道氏 WEI-MUN-TAOU SHE.

WONG LU-HING. See 黃履卿 HWANG LE-K'ING.

WONG SU KING. See 黃少瓊 HWANG SHAO-K'EUNG.

吳 WOO. 吳中平寇記 *Woo chung p'ing k'ow ke.* "The Suppression of the T'aip'ing Rebellion in the Province of Woo," i.e. Kiangsu. 8 keuen. 1875. 12°. **15297. a. 20.**

吳長元 WOO CHANGYUEN. 宸垣讖畧 *Ch'in yuen shih leŏ.* "A short account of the Imperial City in Peking." With plans. 16 keuen. 1788. 8°. **15327. e. 7.**

吳兆宜 WOO CHAOU-E. See 徐陵孝 SEU LING-HEAOU. 玉臺新詠箋註 *Yuh tai sin yung tseen choo.* "New Songs from the Beautiful Tower . . ." "With Notes" by Woo Chaou-e, etc. 1774. 8°. **15323. c. 12.**

吳中孚 WOO CHUNG-FOO. 商賈便覽 *Shang koo peen lan.* "The Merchant's Guide." 8 keuen. 1792. 8°. **15229. c. 27.**

—— [Another copy.] **15229. c. 44.**

WOOD (J.), *Dean of Ely.* See 倫德 LUN-TIH. 代數難題 *T'ai shoo nan t'e.* "Lund's Companion to Wood's Algebra," etc. 8°. **15259. f. 9.**

吳 攙 斥 Woo Heang-han. 客窗閒話 *Kih chwang heen hwa.* "Leisure Jottings from the 'Guests' Window.'" By Woo Heang-han. 8 keuen. 1875. 8°. **15331. d. 15.**

—— 續客窗閒話 *Suh kih chwang heen hwa.* "Supplementary Leisure Jottings from the 'Guests' Window.'" By Woo Heang-han. 8 keuen. 1875. 8°. **15331. d. 16.**

五虎 Woo Hoo. 五虎平南後傳 *Woo Hoo ping nan how chuen.* "The subsequent account of the pacification of the South by the 'Five Tigers'" during the reign of Jin - Tsung, A.D. 1023–1064. 6 keuen. 1822. 8°. **15334. b. 5.**

—— 五虎平西前傳 *Woo Hoo ping se ts'een chuen.* "The Pacification of the West by the 'Five Tigers.'" 1805. 8°. **15334. b. 4.**

吳鶴山 Woo Ho-shan. See 高錦庭 Kaou Kin-t'ing. 瘍科臨證心得集 *Yang ko lin ching sin tih tseih.* "A Collection of Treatises on Sores . . ." Edited by Woo Ho-shan, etc. 1806. 8°. **15253. b. 4.**

吳會清 Woo Hwuy-ts'ing. 版圖圩號冊 *Pan t'oo yu haou ts'ih.* "A list of the proprietors of the land employed in making the defensive dikes" [in the Province of Che keang?] in the year 1782. Compiled by Woo Hwuy-ts'ing. 2 vols. 1835. Obl. **15241. b. 7.**

吳任臣 Woo Jin-ch'in. 十國春秋 *Shih kwo ch'un ts'ew.* "The Spring and Autumn Annals of the Ten States" which existed between the time of the T'ang and Sung Dynasties. By Woo Jin-ch'in. Edited by New Hwan. 116 keuen. 1672. 8°. **15292. c. 6.**

吳若山 Woo Jo-shan. See 陸拒石 Luh Keu-shih. 善卷堂四六 *Shen-keuen T'ang sze luh.* "The Writings of Luh Keu-shih . . ." With notes by Woo Jo-shan, etc. 1875. 8°. **15319. d. 21.**

吳謙 Woo Keen. 金鑑外科 *Kin keen wai ko.* "The Golden Mirror of Medicine for the Cure of External Complaints." Published by Imperial Order. 16 keuen. 1742. 8°. **15251. a. 3.**

吳謙 Woo Keen. 御纂醫宗金鑑 *Yu tswan e tsung kin keen.* "The Golden Mirror of Medicine." Compiled by Imperial Order by Woo Keen, Lew Yu-to, and other officers of the Medical Hall, under the supervision of Prince Hung Chow. 90 keuen. 1742. 8°. **15251. b. 1. & c. 1.**

—— [Another edition.] 90 keuen. 1742. 8°. **15253. b. 6.**

吳其濬 Woo K'e-seun. 植物名實圖考 *Chih wuh ming shih t'oo k'aou.* "An illustrated work on botany." Part i, 38 keuen; Part ii, 22 keuen. 1848. 8°. **15253. d. 1.**

—— 滇南礦廠興程圖畧 *Teen nan kung ch'ang yu ch'ing t'oo leŏ.* "The Mines of Yunnan. With maps." By Woo K'e-seun. Edited by Seu Kin-săng. 8°. **15271. e. 5.**

舞格 Woo Kih. 清文啟蒙 *Ts'ing wăn k'e mung.* A book for students of Manchu. Revised by Ching Ming-yuen. 4 keuen. 1730. 8°. **15354. c. 4.**

—— [Another edition.] 1730. 8°. **15354. c. 5.**

—— [Another edition. 1750 ?] 8°. **15354. c. 6.**

—— [Another edition. 1750 ?] **15354. c. 7.** Imperfect, containing only Keuen 1 and 2.

吳兢 Woo King. 貞觀政要 *Ching-kwan ching yaou.* "The essence of government, illustrated by the history of the reign of Ching-kwan" (A.D. 627–649). 10 keuen. 1465. Fol. **15297. c. 10.**

—— 貞觀政要 *Ching-kwan ching yaou.* "The essence of government illustrated by the reign of Ching-kwan," A.D. 627–650. 10 keuen. With manuscript notes in Japanese. 1600. Fol. **15297. c. 8.** Printed in Japan with movable type.

—— [Another edition.] *Kiôto,* 1623. Fol. **15297. c. 9.** Printed in Japan with movable type.

五經 Woo king. 五經句解 *Woo king keu keae.* "The Five Classics explained Sentence by Sentence." Edited by Chang-she. 1817. 8°. **15210. a. 4.**

—— 五經讀本 *Woo king tuh pun.* "The Texts of the Five Classics." 1786. 8°. **15210. a. 2.**

—— 五經讀本 *Woo king tuh pun.* "The Texts of the Five Classics." 1823. 8°. **15210. a. 1.**

WOO

吳 毅 人 WOO KUH-JIN. 執 文 備 覽 *E wǎn pei lan.* A ready synopsis of discriminated characters. Compiled by Woo Kuh-jin. With notes by Sha Muh. 10 keuen. 1806. 8°.
15346. e. 3.

吳 聾 WOO KUNG. See 余 笠 湖 YU LEÏH-HOO. 吟 風 閣 *Yin fung ko.* Plays ... edited by Woo Kung, etc. 1820. 8°. 15331. f. 6.

吳 瑄 WOO KWAN. See 薛 SÉÉ. 薛 院 判 醫 書 二 十 四 種 *Sëë yuen pan e shoo urh shih sze chung.* "Reprints of Twenty-four Medical Works ..." Edited by Woo Kwan, etc. 8°.
15253. c. 1.

五 老 WOO LAOU. 五 老 集 *Woo laou tseih.* "Collections of the writings of five literary elders." 2 keuen. [1620?] Fol. 15315. d. 3. Printed in Japan with movable type.

武 梁 WOO LEANG. 漢 武 梁 石 室 *Han Woo Leang shih shih.* "Rubbings of the Sculptures in the house of Woo Leang of the Han Dynasty," at Kea-seang Heen in the Province of Shantung. These sculptures were put up by the two sons of Woo Leang in A.D. 147. By a change in the course of the Yellow River the building was overwhelmed, and it was not until the reign of K'ienlung (A.D. 1736–1795) that the sculptures were recovered. 44 rolls.
Box 1. 2.

—— Another collection of rubbings of sculptures ... at Kea-seang in Shantung. 15300. b. 10.

吳 畱 村 WOO LEW-TS'UN. 增 訂 古 文 觀 止 善 本 *Tsǎng ting koo wǎn kwan chih shen pun.* "An enlarged edition of a survey of ancient literature." Edited by Woo Lew-ts'un. 6 keuen. 1698. 8°. 15318. c. 3.

武 林 祝 WOO LIN-CHOW. 香 山 縣 志 *Heang-shan Heen che.* "A Topography of Heang-shan Heen." Edited by Woo Lin-chow. 8 keuen. 1827. 8°. 15267. e. 9.

WOOLSEY (THEODORE D.). See 吳 氏 WOO SHE. 公 法 便 覽 *Kung fa peen lan.* "An Introduction to the Study of International Law." By T. D. W., etc. 1877. 8°. 15239. c. 11.

五 美 WOO MEI. 五 美 緣 *Woo mei yuen.* "The Union of the Five Beauties." A novel. 12 keuen. 1824. 8°.
15334. c. 6.

吳 梅 村 WOO MEI-TS'UN. 吳 詩 談 歡 *Woo she tan sow.* "Notes on the Poetry of Woo Mei-ts'un." By Fan Keae-jin. 20 keuen. [1781?] 8°.
15323. e. 14.

—— 吳 詩 集 覽 *Woo she tseih lun.* "The Collected Poems of Woo Mei-ts'un reviewed" by Fan Keae-jin. Edited by Koo E-jin and Heu Kew-jih. 20 keuen. With supplement in 20 keuen. 1781. 8°. 15323. e. 13.

無 名 WOO MING. 無 名 淨 光 經 *Woo ming tsing kwang king.* "The nameless, pure, bright Sūtra." [Eighth century?] A roll.
Printed in Japan.

—— [Another edition. Twelfth century?] A roll.
Printed in Japan.

吳 牧 騶 WOO MUH-TSOW. 小 題 扷 輯 *Seaou t'e pah ch'e.* "Successful Essays on Classical Subjects." First series. Compiled by Woo Muh-tsow. 1860. 12°. 15315. a. 2.

吳 訥 WOO NOH. See 朱 熹 CHOO HE. 小 學 大 全 *Seaou heǒ ta ts'euen.* "The complete Youth's Instructor ..." Edited by Woo Noh, etc. Fol. 15229. d. 4.

吳 祕 WOO PE. See 揚 雄 YANG HEUNG. 新 纂 門 目 五 臣 音 註 揚 子 法 言 *Sin tswan mun muh woo ch'in yin choo Yang tsze fa yen ...* "Discourses on Law, with notes" by ... Woo Pe, etc. 8°. 15237. c. 6.

吳 樸 園 WOO P'O-YUEN. 勝 朝 遺 事 *Shing ch'aou e sze.* "Supplementary Records of the Conquering, i.e. Ming, Dynasty." Compiled by Woo P'o-yuen. Edited by Keu Shin-che and others. In two parts. 1st part, 6 keuen; 2nd part, 8 keuen. 1842. 8°. 15297. b. 11.

吳 錫 麒 WOO SEÏH-K'E. See 吳 毅 人 WOO KUH-JIN. 執 文 備 覽 *E wǎn pei lan.* "A ready synopsis of discriminated characters ..." Edited by Woo Seïh-k'e, etc. 1806. 8°.

—— 八 家 四 六 *Pa kea sze luh.* "A collection of Odes of eight authors," viz.: *Yew ching wei tsai suh tseih,* by the editor Woo Seïh-k'e; *Yuh che t'ang wǎn tseih,* by Shaou Seun-tsze; *Seaou tsang shan fang wai tseih,* by Yuen Mei; *Wǎn tsze t'ang wai tseih; Se ke yu yin wai tseih; E ching t'ang e k'aou; Keuen she ko wǎn yih tseih;* and *Sze poo t'ang wǎn tseih.* Edited by Woo Seïh-k'e. 1805. 8°. 15317. a. 4. Imperfect, containing only the first three works.

154

吳 錫 麒 Woo Seĭh-k'e. 有 正 味 齋 駢 體 文 *Yew ching wei chai p'een t'e wăn.* "A collection of literary pieces from the Study of 'Correct Taste.'" By Woo Seĭh-k'e. With notes by Wang Nëĕ. 24 keuen. 1859. 8°. 15319. e. 7.

吳 璿 Woo Seuen. 繡 像 飛 龍 全 傳 *Sew seang Fei lung ts'euen chuen.* "The History of the Flying Dragon." A story of the adventures of Chaou Kw'ang-yin, the founder of the Sung Dynasty. With illustrations. Edited by Woo Seuen. 12 keuen. 1874. 8°. 15291. a. 3.

吳 修 Woo Sew. 昭 代 名 人 尺 牘 小 傳 *Chaou tai ming jin ch'ih tuh seaou chuen.* "Short Biographies of Celebrated Men of the present Dynasty." By Woo Sew. 24 keuen. 1826. 8°. 15305. b. 5.

吳 少 雲 Woo Shaou-yun, and 劉 璧 山 Lew Pih-shan. 避 難 竹 枝 詞 *Pi nan chuh che ts'ze.* "Light odes on avoiding the [political] disturbances" [i.e. the T'ai-p'ing rebels?]. pp. iv, 46. 1863. 8°. 15327. d. 31.

吳 氏 Woo She [i.e. Theodore D. Woolsey]. 公 法 便 覽 *Kung fa peen lan.* "An Introduction to the Study of International Law." By T. D. Woolsey. Translated into Chinese by Ting Wei-leang, i.e. Dr. William A. P. Martin. 5 keuen. *Peking,* 1877. 8°. 15239. c. 11.

吳 樹 玉 Woo Shoo-yuh. See 段 大 令 Twan Ta-ling. 段 氏 說 文 注 訂 *Twan she Shwo wăn choo ting.* "Twan Ta-ling's edition of the *Shwo wăn* revised by Woo Shoo-yuh, etc. 1866. 8°. 15342. b. 4.

—— 說 文 新 附 考 *Shwo wăn sin foo k'aou.* "A new and supplementary examination of the *Shwo wăn.*" By Woo Shoo-yuh. 6 keuen, with appendix. *Soo-chow,* 1868. 8°. 15342. b. 3.

吳 瑛 Woo Ting. See China, *Empire of.* 乾 隆 欽 定 入 旗 則 例 *K'een lung k'in ting pa k'e tsih le.* Regulations for the Bannermen. An Imperial publication, etc. 1742. 8°. 15237. d. 9.

吳 廷 鉁 Woo T'ing-chin. 館 課 賦 稿 *Kwan k'o foo kaou.* "A collection of Foo Poems." By Woo T'ing-chin. pp. viii, iv, 130. 1831. 8°. 15324. b. 8.

吳 進 之 Woo Tsin-che. See 馮 冶 堂 Fung Yay-t'ang. 國 朝 畫 識 *Kwo ch'aou hwa shih.* "Biographical Notices of Artists . . ." Edited by Woo Tsin-che, etc. 1831. 8°. 15305. b. 7.

悟 清 子 Woo Ts'ing-tsze. 仙 佛 宗 指 *Seen Fuh tsung che.* "A Guide to Genii and Buddhas." A collection of religious writings. Compiled by Woo Ts'ing-tsze. 2 keuen. 1851. 8°. 15103. b. 17.

吳 遵 程 Woo Tsun-ch'ing. 成 方 切 用 *Ch'ing fang ts'ëĕ yung.* "Medical Prescriptions of Value." By Woo Tsun-ch'ing. Edited by his pupils Chow Lan-kew and Yin Haou-joo. 13 keuen. 1761. 8°. 15252. e. 7.

吳 幼 清 Woo Yew-ts'ing. 吳 草 廬 文 選 *Woo Ts'aou-leu wăn seuen.* See 李 欽 之 Le K'in-che. 金 元 明 八 家 文 選 *Kin, Yuen, Ming pa kea wăn seuen.* "Selections from the writings of eight authors who wrote during the Kin, Yuen, Ming Dynasties," etc. 1845. 8°. 15318. e. 1.

吳 源 起 Woo-yuen-k'e. 正 字 通 *Ching tsze t'ung.* A complete dictionary of the correct character. Edited by Woo-yuen-k'e, assisted by Chang-tsze-lëĕ and Leaou-pih-tsze. 4 vols. 1685. 8°. 15342. d. 2.

吳 元 泰 Woo Yuen-t'ai. 東 遊 八 仙 記 出 身 傳 *Tung yew pa seen ke ch'uh shin chuen.* "The Story of the travels of the Eight Taouist Immortals in the East." 4 keuen. [1800?] 8°. 15113. a. 28.

悟 元 道 人 Woo-yuen taou-jin, *pseud.* 道 書 十 二 種 *Taou shoo shih urh chung.* "A collection of twelve Taouist works" forming an Encyclopædia of Taouism. Compiled by Woo-yuen taou-jin. 14 vols. *Ch'ăngtih Foo,* 1816. 8°. 15111. e. 10.

吳 踰 龍 Woo Yu-lung. 詳 註 文 範 初 編 *Tseung choo wăn fan ch'oo peen.* "Model Essays. With Notes. First Series." Compiled by Woo Yu-lung. 1757. 8°. 15319. c. 20.

吳 榮 光 Woo Yung-kwang. 吾 學 錄 *Woo heŏ luh.* "Notes on things within my knowledge," consisting of rites, ceremonies, etc. By Woo Yung-kwang. 24 keuen. 1832. 8°. 15312. d. 10.

WOO—YAN

吳 榮 光 Woo Yung-kwang. 筠 清 館 金 石 *Yunts'ing kwan kinshih.* "Inscriptions from the Yunts'ing Hall." 5 keuen. 1842. 8°.
15300. b. 7.

WYLIE (Alexander). *See* Periodical Publications: *Shanghai.* 六 合 叢 談 *Luh ho ts'ung t'an.* "A Magazine . . ." Edited by A. W., etc. 1857. 8°.
15298. a. 45.

牙 行 Ya hing. 私 充 牙 行 埠 頭 *Sze ch'ung ya hing fow tow.* "Regulations to suppress unauthorized brokers and harbour masters." [*Canton*, 1840?] 8°.
15241. b. 9.

山 本 龍 Yamamoto Riū. *See* 孔 丘 K'ung K'ew. 古 文 孝 經 孔 氏 傳 *Koo wăn Heaou king K'ung she chuen.* "The ancient text of the Book of Odes . . ." Edited by Yamamoto Riū, etc. 1800. 8°.
15229. b. 28.

楊 昌 濬 Yang Ch'angseun. 平 浙 紀 略 *P'ing Che ke leŏ.* "A short account of the pacification of Chekeang" during the T'aip'ing rebellion. Compiled from official documents by Yang Ch'angseun. 16 keuen. 1875. 8°.
15297. b. 17.

楊 貞 頤 Yang Ching-e. 本 草 述 鉤 元 *Pun ts'aou shuh kow yuen.* "Notes on Materia Medica, and investigations into its origin." 32 keuen. 1842. 8°.
15252. e. 6.

楊 衒 之 Yang Heuen-che. 洛 陽 伽 藍 記 *Lo-yang kea lan ke.* "A description of the Buddhist monasteries at Lo-yang." 5 keuen. *See* 程 榮 Ch'ing Yung. 漢 魏 叢 書 *Han Wei ts'ung shoo.* "A collection of works by authors of the Han and Wei Dynasties," etc. 1791. 8°.
15318. a. 1.

揚 雄 Yang Heung. 方 言 *Fang yen.* "On Dialects." 13 keuen. *See* 程 榮 Ch'ing Yung. 漢 魏 叢 書 *Han Wei ts'ung shoo.* "A collection of works by authors of the Han and Wei Dynasties," etc. 1791. 8°. 15318. a. 1.

—— 方 言 *Fang yen.* "On Dialects." Compiled and arranged by Yang-heung, of the Han Dynasty. With explanatory notes by K'o-po, of the Tsin Dynasty. [A reprint.] 13 keuen. [1750?] 8°.
15346. b. 18.

揚 雄 Yang Heung. 法 言 *Fa yen.* "Discourses on Law." 10 keuen. *See* 程 榮 Ch'ing Yung. 漢 魏 叢 書 *Han Wei ts'ung shoo.* "A collection of works by authors of the Han and Wei Dynasties," etc. 1791. 8°. 15318. a. 1.

—— 新 纂 門 目 五 臣 音 註 揚 子 法 言 *Sin tswan mun muh woo Ch'in yin choo Yang tsze fa yen.* "A new edition of Yang Heung's Discourses on Law, with notes by the five ministers," Le Kwei, Lew Tsung, Sung Heen, Woo Pe, and Sze-ma Kwang. 10 keuen. [1300?] 8°.
15237. c. 6.

—— 太 玄 集 注 *T'ai heuen tseĭh choo.* "The Great Deep Classic" by Yang Heung. With a collection of comments. 4 keuen. *See* 孫 淵 Sun Shoo. 古 棠 書 屋 叢 書 *Koo t'ang shoo wuh ts'ung shoo.* "A Collection of Reprints," etc. 1831–1849. 8°.
15315. d. 1.

楊 庚 Yang Kăng. *See* 張 熙 宇 Chang Heyu. 硃 批 增 註 七 家 詩 選 *Choo p'e tsăng choo ts'ih kea she seuen.* "Imperially endorsed Poems" by . . . Yang Kăng, etc. 1857. 8°.
15323. c. 14.

—— *See* 張 熙 宇 Chang He-yu. 七 家 詩 輯 註 鈔 *Ts'ih kea she tseĭh choo ch'aou.* "A collection of the writings of" . . . Yang Kăng, etc. 1870. 8°.
15324. a. 12.

楊 甲 Yang Keă. 六 經 圖 *Luh king t'oo.* "Illustrations to accompany the Six Classics." Edited by Maou Pang-han and others. 1165. Fol.
15223. d. 2.

楊 格 非 Yang Kih-fei [i.e. Dr. Griffith John]. *See* Bible: *New Testament.* 新 約 全 書 *Sin yo ts'euen shoo.* . . . Translated into the *Wăn le,* or literary style, by Yang Kih-fei, etc. 1890. 8°.
15116. a. 7.

—— *See* Bible: *New Testament.* 新 約 全 書 . . . Translated into the *Kwan hwa,* or Mandarin Dialect, by Yang Kih-fei, etc. 1892. 8°.
15116. a. 8.

—— *See* 李 修 善 Le Sew-shen. 戒 烟 醒 世 圖 *Keae yin sing she t'oo.* "Warnings against opium smoking." By . . . Yang Kih-fei, etc. 1883. 8°.
15200. b. 21.

—— *See* Pearse (Mark Guy), *the Younger.* 紅 硃 儒 傳 *Hung choo joo chuen.* "The terrible red dwarf." Translated into Chinese by Yang Kih-fei, etc. 1882. 8°. 15200. b. 18.

156

楊 格 非 YANG KIH-FEI [i.e. DR. GRIFFITH JOHN]. 眞理八篇 Chin le pa p'een. "Eight chapters of orthodox Christian doctrine." pp. 62. [Hankow?], 1880. 8°. 15200. c. 29.

—— 眞理便讀三字經 Chin le peen tuh San tsze king. "Orthodox Christian Principles arranged after the model of the 'Three-character Classic.'" pp. 41. [Hankow?], 1883. 8°. 15200. c. 28.

—— 眞道入門問答 Chin taou juh mun wǎn ta. "A Catechism of Christian Doctrine." pp. 47. Hankow, 1882. 8°. 15118. a. 43.

—— 天路指明 T'een loo che ming. "A Guide to Heaven." pp. iv, 61. Hankow, 1884. 8°. 15200. c. 23.

—— 德慧入門 Tih hwuy juh mun. "The Gate of Virtue and Wisdom." pp. vi, 71. Hankow, 1883. 8°. 15200. c. 46.

—— 引家當道 Yin kea tang taou. "On leading the family in the right way." pp. iv, 69. Hankow, 1882. 8°. 15200. c. 27.

—— 引道三章 Yin taou san chang. "Right guidance, in three chapters." With illustrations. pp. 39. Hankow, 1882. 8°. 15200. c. 25.

楊 景 索 YANG KING-SOO. See 岳飛 YO FEI. 岳忠武王文集 Yo Chung woo Wang wǎn tseih. "A Collection of the Writings of Yo Fei . . ." Edited by Yang King-soo, etc. 1770. 8°. 15317. d. 9.

陽 新 賢 YANG KIN-HEEN. 鍼灸大成 Chin kew ta ch'ing. "A Complete System of Acupuncture." Edited by Le Yuě-kwei. 10 keuen. 1798. 8°. 15252. a. 4.

楊 光 憲 YANG KWANG-HEEN. 省心畜德編 讀本 Sing sin ch'uh tih pien tuh pun. "A collection of essays for searching the heart and cultivating virtue." Compiled by Yang Kwangheen. 5 keuen. Canton, 1840. 8°. 15113. c. 2.

陽 瑪 諾 YANG MA-NO [i.e. EMMANUEL DIAZ]. See HAEMMERLEIN (THOMAS) À KEMPIS. 輕世金書 K'ing she kin shoo. The Imitation of Christ . . . Translated into Chinese by Yang Ma-no, etc. 1890. 8°. 15200. d. 60.

陽 瑪 諾 YANG MA-NO [i.e. EMMANUEL DIAZ]. See 瞿西滿 KEU-SE-MWAN, and 聶伯多 NĚĚ-PIH-TO [i.e. ADRIANUS GRELON]. 天主降生出像經解 T'een choo keang sǎng ch'uh seang king keae. "An illustrated life of Christ, with explanations." [Canton?], 1637. Fol. 15118. d. 7.

楊 炳 YANG PING. 海錄 Hai luh. "Records of the Sea." See 王塋 WANG LEW. 域外叢書 Yih wai ts'ung shoo. "Reprints of Works on Foreign Countries," etc. 1842. 8°. 15271. b. 3.

楊 補 YANG POO. See 華其昌 HWA K'E-CH'ANG. 畫禪室隨筆 Hwa shen shih suy peih. "Literary Notes . . ." Compiled by Yang Poo, etc. 1720. 8°. 15320. e. 35.

楊 西 河 YANG SE-HO. See 杜甫 TOO FOO. 杜詩鏡銓 Too she king ts'euen. "The Poems of Too Foo . . ." Edited by Yang Se-ho, etc. 1872. 8°. 15324. e. 3.

楊 紹 和 YANG SHAOU-HO. 臨文便覽 Lin wǎn peen lan. "A guide to the composition of literary essays" for the examinations. Edited by Yang Shaou-ho. Peking, 1874. 8°. 15320. e. 34.

楊 愼 YANG SHIN. See 禹 YÜ. 禹碑 Yü pei. "The Inscription of Yü . . ." With Yang Shin's interpretation, etc. 1864. 15300. c. 3 (2).

—— 升菴全集 Shing gan ts'euen tseih. "A complete collection of the writings of Yang Shin." Edited by Chow Sau-yuen. With notes by Yang Yew. 81 keuen. 1795. 8°. 15317. e. 9.

—— 楊升菴外集 Yang Shing-gan wai tseih. "An additional collection of the writings of Yang Shin." Compiled by Tseaou Hung. Edited by Koo K'e-yuen. 81 keuen. 1844. 8°. 15319. e. 9.

楊 升 菴 YANG SHING-GAN. 繡像安邦定國全傳 Sew seang gan pang ting kwo ts'euen chuen. "The story of the pacifying of the States and the settlement of the country" from the reign of the Emperor Seuen-tsung to that of Chaou-tsung (847–905) of the T'ang Dynasty. With portraits. An historical novel written in poetry, in lines of seven characters. In two parts. Gan pang, 20 keuen; Ting kwo, 20 keuen. Canton, 1850. 8°. 15334. f. 3.

楊 守 敬 Yang Show-king, and 饒 敦 秩 Jaou Tun-chih. 歷 代 與 地 沿 革 險 要 圖 *Leih tai yü te yen kih heen yaou t'oo.* "Important maps to illustrate the chronological geography of the Empire." 1879. Fol. **15276. e. 4.**

養 心 詩 Yang sin she. 養 心 詩 調 叙 *Yang sin she teaou seu.* "Hymn Tunes." [1870?] 8°. **15118. b. 53.**

楊 椒 山 Yang Tseaou-shan. 楊 椒 山 先 生 家 訓 *Yang Tseaou-shan seen săng kea heun.* "The Family Teachings of Yang Tseaou-shan." Edited by Chin Keun. 1856. 8°. **15103. d. 12.**

洋 錢 Yang-ts'een. 恭 訂 洋 錢 鬼 字 全 法 各 疑 倒 後 *Ts'an ting yang ts'een kwei tsze ts'euen fa koh k'wan le how.* "A treatise on foreign coins with their inscriptions." [1840?] 8°.

楊 靜 亭 Yang Tsing-t'ing. 都 門 紀 略 *Too mun ke leŏ.* "A Short Guide to Peking" for the use of Provincials. With a plan of the city. ? keuen. *Peking,* 1875. 8°. **15239. d. 16.** Imperfect, containing only Keuen 1.

楊 彥 合 Yang Yen-ho. 臨 文 便 覽 *Lin wăn peen lan.* "A Survey of the Alphabet of Literature." Edited by Yang Yen-ho. 2 keuen. 1874. 8°. **15319. d. 20.**

楊 有 慶 Yang Yew-k'ing. 大 成 通 志 *Ta ch'ing t'ung che.* "A complete record of the 'Great Perfection,'" i.e. Confucius. By Yang Yew-k'ing. Edited by Lew Yaou-wei and others. 18 keuen. 1669. 8°. **15225. e. 2.**

楊 榮 Yang Yung. See 孔 丘 K'ung K'ew. 書 傳 大 全 *Shoo chuen ta ts'euen.* "The Book of Historical Documents . . ." Compiled by . . . Yang Yung, etc. 8°. **15215. d. 1.**

姚 學 甲 Yaou Heŏkea. 鳳 臺 縣 志 *Fungt'ai heen che.* "A Topography of Fungt'ai heen" in Shanse. With maps and plans. Compiled by Yaou Heŏkea, the magistrate of the district, and other officials. 20 keuen. 1784. 8°. **15261. d. 4.**

要 理 Yaou le. 肆 原 要 理 *Sze yuen yaou le.* "The Original Doctrines" of Christianity. In Sino-Annamite. [By Mgr. Masson?] 2 vols. *Hongkong,* 1898. 8°. **15200. b. 25.**

要 理 Yaou le. 要 理 六 端 *Yaou le lew twan.* "The Six Articles of Important Christian Doctrines." pp. 8. [*Hongkong,* 1890?] 12°. **15200. aa. 35.**

—— 要 理 辯 正 邪 自 證 *Yaou le peen ching seay tsze ching.* "Arguments on the orthodoxy and heterodoxy of the essential doctrines" of Roman Catholicism. In Sino-Annamite. Keuen i. *Hongkong,* 1895. 8°. **15200. d. 51.**

姚 璉 Yaou Leen. See 張 考 夫 Chang K'aou-foo. 楊 園 先 生 全 集 *Yang yuen seen săng ts'euen tseih.* "The complete writings of the Doctor of the Aspen Garden . . ." Compiled by Yaou Leen, etc. 1869. 8°. **15315. c. 1.**

姚 鼐 Yaou Nai. 古 文 辭 類 纂 *Koo wăn ts'ze luy tsuan.* "Extracts from ancient literature arranged according to subjects." Compiled by Yaou Nai. 74 keuen. [1810?] 8°. **15312. d. 12.**

姚 鼐 姬 Yaou Nai-ke. 惜 抱 軒 集 *Seih-paou heen tseih.* "Literary collections from the Seih-paou Study." By Yaou Nai-ke. 88 keuen. [*Canton?*], 1866. 8°. **15317. d. 8.**

姚 培 謙 Yaou P'ei-k'een. See 張 景 星 Chang King-sing. 宋 詩 別 裁 集 *Sung she pĕĕ ts'ai tseih.* "A collection of the Poetry of the Sung Dynasty." Compiled by . . . Yaou P'ei-k'een, etc. 1761. 8°. **15324. a. 2.**

—— See 張 景 星 Chang King-sing. 元 詩 別 裁 集 *Yuen she pĕĕ ts'ai tseih.* "A collection of the Poetry of the Yuen Dynasty." Compiled by . . . Yaou P'ei-k'een, etc. 1764. 8°. **15324. a. 3.**

—— and 張 景 星 Chang King-sing. 綱 鑑 擧 要 *Kang keen lan yaou.* "An epitome of Choo He's Condensation of the General Mirror of History." Compiled by Yaou P'ei-k'een and Chang King-sing. 4 parts. Part i, 2 keuen; Part ii, 19 keuen; Part iii, 8 keuen; and Part iv (the History of the Ming Dynasty), 8 keuen. *Peking,* 1850. 12°. **15291. a. 1.**

姚 邵 瑛 Yaou Shaou-ying. 九 十 二 法 *Kew shih urh fa.* "The Ninety-two Rules" for the formation of the characters. 1844. 8°. **15344. c. 17.**

姚端甫 YAOU TWAN-FOO. 姚敬巷文選 *Yaou Muh-gan wăn seuen.* See 李欽之 LE K'IN-CHE. 金元明八家文選 *Kin, Yuen, Ming pa kea wăn seuen.* "Selections from the writings of eight authors who wrote during the Kin, Yuen, and Ming Dynasties," etc. 1845. 8°. 15318. e. 1.

姚韞鋙 YAOU WĂN-YU. 浙江鄉試硃卷 *Che-keang heang she choo keuen.* "Essays written for the Che-keang Examination" in 1832. 1832. 8°. 15320. e. 23.

耶穌 YAY-SOO. 耶穌降世傳 *Yay-soo keang she chuen.* "The Life of Christ on Earth." pp. 120. *Shanghai*, 1870. 8°. 15118. a. 15.

—— 耶穌教畧 *Yay-soo keaou leŏ.* "A condensed statement of Christianity." [By W. H. Medhurst.] A new edition. pp. 38. *Shanghai*, 1879. 8°. 15200. c. 45.

—— 耶穌論 *Yay-soo lun.* "A Discourse on Jesus." Said on the wrapper to be by McIlvaine. [1870?] A sheet. 15305. c.

—— 耶穌比喻註說 *Yay-soo pe yu choo shwo.* "The Parables of Jesus, with explanatory notes." [By K. F. A. Gützlaff?] pp. iv, 58. [1841?] 8°. 15118. d. 15.

—— 耶穌言行紀畧 *Yay-soo yen hing ke leŏ.* "A short life of Christ." 4 keuen. *Hongkong*, 1893. 8°. 15200. d. 65.

耶穌教 YAY-SOO KEAOU. 耶穌教官話問答 *Yay-soo keaou kwan hwa wăn ta.* "A Christian Catechism in the Mandarin Dialect." By Mrs. Nevius. pp. i, 40. *Shanghai*, 1883. 8°. 15200. c. 24.

—— 耶穌教消罪集福眞言 *Yay-soo keaou seaou tsuy tseĭh fuh chin yen.* "An Epitome of Christian Doctrine." pp. 12. *Ningpo*, 1861. 12°. 15200. b. 34.

—— 耶穌教要旨 *Yay-soo keaou yaou chih.* "The Fundamental Principles of Christianity." A tract based on the 耶穌教要訣 by Dr. D. B. McCartee. pp. 22. 1858. 8°. 15200. d. 34.

—— 耶穌教要理大問答 *Yay-soo keaou yaou le ta wăn ta.* "The Larger Catechism." pp. 124. *Shanghai*, 1881. 8°. 15118. d. 22.

耶穌教 YAY-SOO KEAOU. 耶穌教要理問答 *Yay-soo keuen yaou le wăn ta.* "A Catechism on the important doctrines of Christianity." The Shorter Catechism. pp. 36. *Shanghai*, 1881. 8°. 15200. b. 22.

葉正則 YE CHING-TSIH. 水心文集 *Shwuy sin wăn tseĭh.* "A collection of the writings of Ye Ching-tsih," *alias* Shwuy-sin. 29 keuen. 1755. 8°. 15318. b. 4.

葉以霑 YE E-CHIN. See 周德清 CHOW TIH-TS'ING. 中原音韻 *Chung yuen yin yun.* "A Pronouncing Dictionary of the Mandarin Dialect . . ." Edited by Ye E-chin, etc. 8°.

葉九升 YE KEW-SHING. 山法全書 *Shan fa ts'euen shoo.* "A complete work on the Laws of Mountains." 2 keuen. 1741. 8°. 15257. a. 12.

顏之推 YEN CHE-TUY. 還寃記 *Hwan yuen ke.* "Instances of retributive justice." pp. 36. See 程榮 CH'ING YUNG. 漢魏叢書 *Han Wei ts'ung shoo.* "A collection of works by authors of the Han and Wei Dynasties," etc. 1791. 8°. 15318. a. 1.

—— 家訓 *Kea heun.* "Domestic Instructions." 2 keuen. See 程榮 CH'ING YUNG. 漢魏叢書 *Han Wei ts'ung shoo.* "A collection of works by authors of the Han and Wei Dynasties," etc. 1791. 8°. 15318. a. 1.

胭脂 YEN CHIH. 賣胭脂 *Mai yen chih.* "The Rouge-seller." A play. pp. 4. [1860?] 8°. 15327. d. 33 (1).

顏正 YEN CHING. 文昌帝君繪像寶訓 *Wăn ch'ang te keun hwuy seang paou heun.* "The precious teachings of the God of Literature illustrated and explained." Edited by Yen Ching, with illustrations and notes by Hwang Ching-yuen. 2 keuen. *Canton*, 1843. 8°. 15113. a. 26.

兗州府 YEN-CHOW FOO. 兗州府志 *Yen-chow Foo che.* "A Topography of Yen-chow Foo," in Shantung. 32 keuen. 1756. 8°. 15269. c. 12. Imperfect, wanting Keuen 3.

延豐 YEN FUNG. 欽定重修兩浙鹽法志 *K'in ting chung sew leang che yen fa che.* A Record of the Laws on the Salt Monopoly for the Province of Che-keang. An Imperial republication. By Yen Fung and others. 4 vols. 1801. 8°. 15239. e. 1.

YEN—YEW

嚴瓦勳 YEN LEANGHEUN. See 林樂知 LIN LO-CHE. 四裔編年表 *Sze e peen neen peaou.* "Comparative Chronological Tables . . ." Translated by Y. J. Allen, assisted by Yen Leangheun, etc. 4°. **15298. a. 42.**

鴈翎媒 YEN LING MEI. 奇緣鴈翎媒新選 *K'e yuen yen ling mei sin seuen.* "The Story of the Goose-feather Match-Maker." In verse. 4 keuen. [1850?] 8°. **15327. d. 18.**

鴈翎扇墜 YEN LING SHAN CHUY. 新鴈翎扇墜全本 *Sin yen ling shan chuy ts'euen pun.* "The Story of the Goose-feather Fan-pendants." In verse. 2 keuen. [1850?] 8°. **15327. d. 20.**

顏悶楚 YEN MIN-TS'OO. 俗書證誤 *Suh shoo ch'ing woo.* See 王懿榮 WANG E-YUNG. 字學三種 *Tsze heŏ san chung.* "Three works on the study of the characters," etc. 1874. 8°. **15342. b. 7.**

顏茂猷 YEN MOW-YEW. See 四書 SZE SHOO. 四書正文 *Sze shoo ching wăn.* The Le-joo T'ang edition . . . of the Four Books. [Edited by Yen Mow-yen, etc.] 8°. **15201. a. 1.**

—— See 四書 SZE SHOO. 四書正文 *Sze shoo ching wăn.* The Tsuy-king Low edition of the . . . Four Books. [Edited by Yen Mow-yew, etc.] 8°. **15202. b. 3.**

研石山樵 YEN SHIH SHAN TS'EAOU. See 南北宋 NAN PIH SUNG. 南北宋志傳 *Nan pih Sung che chuen.* "The History of the Southern and Northern Sung Dynasties." Compiled by Yen shih shan ts'eaou, etc. 8°. **15286. c. 7.**

嚴樹森 YEN SHOO-SAN. 皇朝中外壹統輿圖 *Hwang chaou chung wai yih t'ung yu t'oo.* "An Atlas of the Chinese Empire under the Ts'ing Dynasty." 1864. 8°. **15275. b. 12.**

顏師古 YEN SZEKOO. See 班固 PAN KOO. 前漢書 *Ts'een Han shoo.* "A History of the Former Han Dynasty . . ." With a commentary by Yen Szekoo, etc. 8°. **15296. c. 1.**

嚴從簡 YEN TS'EEN-KUNG. 殊域周咨錄 *Choo yih chow tsze luh.* "Official Records of the Surrounding Countries." Compiled by Yen Ts'ung-keen. 20 keuen. 1583. 8°. **15271. b. 7.**

艷艷生 YEN YEN SĂNG, *pseud.* 昭陽趣史 *Chaouyang ts'eu she.* "The pleasant history of Chaouyang," or the Empress's Palace. A novel on the life of Feiyen the concubine of Ch'êng Ti, B.C. 32 to A.D. 6. MS. 4 keuen. [*Peking*, 1870?] 8°. **Or. 4479. 39. B. f.**

顏元孫 YEN YUEN-SUN. 干祿字書 *Kan luh tsze shoo.* See 王懿榮 WANG E-YUNG. 字學三種 *Tsze heŏ san chung.* "Three works on the Study of the Characters," etc. 1874. 8°. **15342. b. 7.**

鹽運司 YEN YUN SZE. 鹽運司出入文書偶錄 *Yen yun sze ch'uh juh wăn shoo gow luh.* "Certain Despatches received and written by the Salt Commissioner" [at Canton?] during the years 1835–41. MS. 1835–41. 8°. **15297. d. 6.**

葉天士 YE T'EEN-SZE. 積福堂公積選臨證指南 *Chung-fuh T'ang Kung suh seuen lin ching che nan.* "A Supplementary verified Guide to Medicine." By Ye T'een-sze. Edited by Hwa Sew-yun. 4 keuen. 1775. 8°. **15252. e. 9.**

—— 臨證指南醫案 *Lin ching che nan e gan.* "A verified Guide to Medicine." By Ye T'een-sze. Edited by Hwa Sew-yun, Le Han-poo, and Shaou Sin-foo. 10 keuen. *Soo-chow,* 1844. 8°. **15252. e. 8.**

葉殿紫 YE TEEN-TSZE. See 林西仲 LIN SE-CHUNG. 古文析義二編 *Koo wăn seth e urh peen.* "Extracts from Ancient Literature . . ." Edited by Ye Teen-tsze, etc. 1687. 8°. **15312. a. 6.**

葉鼎三 YE TING-SAN. 漢口竹枝詞 *Han k'ow chuh che tsze.* "Light [lit. Bamboo-branch] Odes from Hankow." 6 keuen. 1850. 8°. **15327. d. 30.**

葉文康 YE WĂN-K'ANG. 禮經會元 *Le king hwuy yuen.* "On the Ritual Classics." By Ye Wăn-k'ang. Edited by Luh Kea-shoo. 4 keuen. 1189. 8°. **15220. b. 6.**

葉煒亮 YE WEI-LEANG [i.e.　　　　]. 聖書地理 *Shing shoo te le.* Scripture geography. With maps. 24 pp. *Peking,* 1871. 8°.
15118. c. 42.

遊戲主人 YEW-HE CHOO-JIN, *pseud.* 笑林廣記 *Seaou lin kwang ke.* "A collection of laughable stories." Compiled by Yew-he choo-jin. 4 keuen. 1829. 8°. 15334. c. 9.

攸圃明叙 YEW-POO-MING-SEU. See 通瑞 T'UNG SHWUY. 吏治輯要 *Le che tseih yaou.* "A Manual of Government . . ." Edited by Yew-poo-ming-seu, etc. 1823. 8°. 15241. b. 1.

愛時居士 YEW SHIH KEU SZE. 覷豸雜存 *Kwei paou tsa ts'un.* "Miscellaneous essays within a limited scope." Compiled by a foreigner calling himself Yew shih Keu-sze. pp. ii, 82. 1881. 8°. 15320. c. 16.

游士鳳 YEW SZE-FUNG. See 文昌帝君 WĂN CH'ANG TE KEUN. 文昌化書 *Wăn ch'ang hwa shoo.* "Wăn ch'ang te keun's Book of Transformations . . ." With illustrations by Yew Sze-fung, etc. 1823. 8°. 15113. b. 4.

尤侗 YEW T'UNG. 尤悔菴全集 *Yew Hwuy-gan ts'euen tseih.* "A complete collection of the Poetical Works of Yew T'ung." 1665–1684. 8°. 15321. d. 13.

幼童 YEW T'UNG. 幼童習字法 *Yew t'ung seih tsze fa.* "Reading and copy books for children." [1840?] 8°. 15225. e. 3.

YIÆ-SU SING-DU. Yiæ-su Sing-du ziu-k'wu tsong-leng. Early Christian Martyrs. pp. 105. *Shanghai,* 1883. 8°. 15118. d. 24.

益智 YIH CHE. 益智書彙 *Yih che shoo wei.* "A list of books for the advancement of knowledge." [By J. Fryer?] With a list of subscribers and agents. pp. 18. [1880?] 8°. 15229. b. 27.

易經 YIH KING. 周易 *Chow yih.* "The Chow Changes." With a commentary by Wang Peih. 6 keuen. 1605. 4°. 15211. a. 2.
Printed in Japan with movable type.

—— [Another copy.] 15211. a. 3.

—— [Another edition.] 10 keuen. *Ashikaga,* 1605. Fol. 15211. a. 4.
Printed in Japan with movable type.

易經 YIH KING. 周易 *Chow yih.* "The Chow Changes." With the commentaries of Wang Peih and others. A Japanese manuscript. 1510. Fol. 15211. a. 1.

—— 周易 *Chow yih.* "The Chow Changes." With notes and commentaries. 4 keuen. [1800?] 8°. 15215. d. 4.

—— 周易傳義大全 *Chow yih chuen e ta ts'euen.* The Chow Book of Changes. With a collection of comments. Compiled by Hoo Kwang and others. 24 keuen. [1400?] 8°. 15211. b. 2.

—— 周易讀本 *Chow yih tuh pun.* "The Text of the Chow Changes." 4 keuen. 1789. 8°. 15212. d. 8.
Imperfect, containing only Keuen 1.

—— 芥子園重訂監本易經 *Keae tsze yuen chung ting keen pun yih king.* The Keae-tsze-yuen [the name of a printing press] edition of the Book of Changes. With notes by Choo-le. 4 keuen. *Nanking,* 1818. 8°. 15212. b. 6.

—— L'Interpretation du Yi-king. La version Mandchoue et ma Traduction. Par C. de Harlez. *Bruxelles,* 1896. 8°. 11098. b. 21.

—— The Yih-king. A new translation from the original Chinese. By Mgr. C. de Harlez. Translated from the French by J. P. Val D'eremao. *Oriental University Institute, Woking,* [1895?]. 8°. 11098. b. 20.

—— 易經正文 *Yih king ching wăn.* "The Text of the Book of Changes." [1870?] 32°. 15202. a. 10.

—— 易經真詮 *Yih king chin ts'euen.* "The Book of Changes, with a true interpretation." 4 keuen. 1870. 8°. 15212. c. 13.

—— 易經增訂旁訓 *Yih king tsăng ting pang heun.* "The Book of Changes. With an interlinear commentary." 3 keuen. [1800?] 8°. 15212. b. 5.

一目 YIH MUH. 一目了然 *Yih muh leaou jen.* (The doctrines of Roman Catholicism) "evident at first sight." pp. 39. *Hongkong,* 1895. 8°. 15200. b. 28.

—— [Another edition.] pp. 65. *Hongkong,* 1898. 8°. 15200. d. 15.

陰 中 夫 YIN CHUNG-FOO. See 陰 時 夫 YIN SHE-FOO. 增 積 會 通 韻 府 群 玉 *Tsăng suh hwuy t'ung yun foo k'eun yuh.* "A complete tonic dictionary . . ." With notes by Yin Chung-foo, etc. 1625. 4°.　　15341. c. 4.

—— See 陰 時 夫 YIN SHE-FOO. 韻 府 羣 玉 原 本 *Yun foo k'eun yuh yuen pun.* "A Dictionary . . ." With notes by Yin Chung-foo, etc. 1590. 8°.　　15348. c. 1.

英 YING. 大 英 俗 語 抄 本 *Ta Ying suh yu ch'aou pun.* "A Chinese and English Vocabulary," in which the sounds of the English words are expressed in the Chinese character. [*Canton*, 1850?] 8°.　　15344. d. 4.

英 華 譯 字 YING HWA YIH TSZE. 英 華 譯 字 則 列 類 *Ying Hwa yih tsze tsih le luy.* "An English and Chinese Vocabulary arranged according to subjects." [1840?] Fol.　　15344. c. 18.

嘆 咭 唎 YING-KEÏH-LE. 擬 勦 洗 嘆 咭 唎 策 *E tseaou se ying-keïh-le tsih.* "Notes on England." MS. [1840?] 8°. 15298. c. 25.

英 國 YING KWO. 大 英 國 人 事 略 說 *Ta ying kwo jin sze leŏ shwo.* "A short treatise on English Affairs." [By Dr. Robert Morrison.] [*Malacca?*], 1832. 8°.　　15297. c. 4.

英 廉 YING LEEN. See 永 瑢 YUNG SEUEN. 皇 清 職 貢 圖 *Hwang Ts'ing chih kung t'oo.* "Drawings of the peoples tributary to China . . ." Edited by . . . Ying Leen, etc. 1751. 8°.　　15298. b. 11.

應 劭 YING SHAOU. 風 俗 通 *Fung suh t'ung.* "Popular traditions." 10 keuen. See 程 榮 CH'ING YUNG. 漢 魏 叢 書 *Han Wei ts'ung shoo.* "A collection of works by authors of the Han and Wei Dynasties," etc. 1791. 8°.　　15318. a. 1.

暎 月 YING-YUĔ. See 龍 嚴 LUNG-YEN. 異 言 集 *Chin yen tseïh.* "A collection of true sayings," i.e. Buddhist Charms . . . Re-edited by Ying-yuĕ, etc. Fol.　　15313. f. 1.

殷 浩 如 YIN HAOU-JOO. See 吳 遵 程 WOO TSUN-CH'ING. 成 方 切 用 *Ch'ing fang tsëĕ yung.* "Medical Prescriptions . . ." Edited by Yin Haou-joo, etc. 1761. 8°. 15252. e. 7.

吟 香 社 YIN HEANG-SHAY. 時 聯 選 箋 四 集 *She leen seuen cheen sze tseïh.* "A collection of selected distiches." pp. 184. *Hongkong*, 1898. 8°.　　15320. c. 18.

尹 繼 善 YIN KE-SHEN. See 傅 恒 FOO HĂNG. 御 批 歷 代 通 鑑 輯 覽 *Yu pe leïh tai t'ung keen tseïh lan.* "An Imperially revised survey of Choo He's mirror of the history of successive generations." Compiled by . . . Yin Ke-shen, etc. 1768. 8°.　　15290. e. 3.

陰 時 夫 YIN SHE-FOO. 增 積 會 通 韻 府 群 玉 *Tsăng suh hwuy t'ung yun foo k'eun yuh.* "A complete tonic dictionary" compiled by Yin She-foo. With notes by Yin Chung-foo. Edited with additions by Paou Yu. 38 keuen. *Kioto*, 1625. 4°.　　15341. c. 4. Printed in Japan with movable type.

—— 韻 府 羣 玉 原 本 *Yun foo k'eun yuh yuen pun.* "A Dictionary arranged according to the 106 Finals." By Yin She-foo. With notes by Yin Chung-foo. Edited by Wang Yuen-ching. 20 keuen. 1590. 8°.　　15348. c. 1.

尹 端 模 YIN TWAN-MOO. *See* PERIODICAL PUBLICATIONS: *Hongkong.* 醫 學 報 *E heŏ paou.* The Chinese Medical Journal . . . Edited by Wan Tun-mo (Yin Twan-moo), etc. 1898. 8°.　　15253. a. 18.

尹 文 YIN WĂN. 尹 文 子 *Yin Wăn tsze.* "A treatise on moral science by Yin Wăn," of the fourth century B.C. With other treatises by different authors on the same subject. [1830?] 8°.　　15113. b. 9.

岳 飛 YO FEI. A series of 55 rubbings from the inscriptions and sculptures in the memorial Temple erected in honour of the General Yo Fei (A.D. 1103–1141). 1804.　　15300. c. 2.

—— 岳 忠 武 王 文 集 *Yo Chung woo wang wăn tseïh.* "A collection of the writings of Yo Fei, canonised as Chung woo wang." Compiled by Hwang Pang-ning. Edited by Ho Wei and Yang King-soo. With a preface by the Emperor K'een-lung. 8 keuen. With an appendix. 1770. 8°.　　15317. d. 9.

—— [Another edition.] Edited by Lew Ke-chaou. 8 keuen, with a supplementary keuen. 1873. 8°.　　15315. c. 5.

約瑟 Yo-sih. 約瑟言行全傳 *Yo-sih yen hing ts'euen chuen.* "A complete life of Joseph." [By M. S. Culbertson?] pp. 54. *Shanghai,* 1861. 8°. **15200. b. 4.**

岳東美 Yo Tung-mei. 岳容齋詩集 *Yo Yung-chai she tseih.* "A collection of the Poetry of Yo Yung-chai," otherwise Yo Tung-mei. 4 keuen. See 孫澍 Sun Shoo. 古棠書屋叢書 *Koo t'ang shoo wuh ts'ung shoo.* "A Collection of Reprints," etc. 1831–1849. 8°. **15315. d. 1.**

禹 Yu. A reproduction of the inscription said to have been engraved by the Emperor Yu on Mount Hăng. Imperfect. **15300. c. 3 (1).**

—— 禹碑 *Yu pei.* "The Inscription of Yü." A rubbing said to have been taken from the inscription placed on Mount Hăng by the Emperor Yu (B.C. 2205–2197)! With Yang Shin's interpretation. A modern reproduction. 1864. **15300. c. 3 (2).**

—— *Viceroy of the two Keang.* 行文扎諭 *Hing wăn cha yu.* "Despatches" urging the collection of troops to resist the English. MS. 1841. 8°. **15297. d. 2.**

與 Yu. 與蔵撮要 *Yu tsai ts'ow yaou.* "An Epitome of Geography," with special reference to Korea, and with maps. Printed in Korea. [1800?] 8°. **15351. b. 1.**

YUAN HSIANG FU. *See* Yuen Seang-foo.

諭札 Yu cha. 諭札牌詳示約抄錄 *Yu cha p'ai tseang she yo ch'aou luh.* "Copies of Proclamations." MS. [1840?] 8°. **15297. c. 6.**

余照 Yu Chaou. 詩韻集成 *She yun tseih ch'ing.* "A complete Rhyming Dictionary." Compiled by Yu Chaou. 10 keuen. *Canton,* 1868. 8°. **15346. a. 19.**

于兆元 Yu Chaou-yuen. See 于慶元 Yu K'ing-yuen. 重訂唐詩三百首續選 *Chung ting T'ang she san pih show suh seuen.* "A supplementary selection of three hundred poems of the T'ang Dynasty." Compiled by . . . Yu Chaou-yuen, etc. 1843. 8°. **15324. a. 10.**

粵匪 Yue fei. 平定粵匪紀略 *P'ing ting yuě fei ke leŏ.* "A short account of the suppression of the T'ai-p'ing Rebellion." 18 keuen. With a supplement in 4 keuen. 1870. 8°. **15331. d. 11.**

—— 粵匪起手根由 *Yuě fei k'e show kăn yew.* "The origin of the outbreak of Yuě banditti," being an account of the T'aip'ing rebellion from the beginning of the movement by Hung S'ewtseuen in 1851 to the capture of Soochow and the execution of the Wangs. Written by a rebel who does not give his name. MS. [1864?] Obl. 8°. **Or. 3534.**

月 Yueh. 聽月樓 *T'ing yueh low.* "The Awaiting-the-Moon Pavilion." A story. 20 chapters. 1815. 8°. **15327. f. 6.**

羽衣客 Yu e kih, *pseud.* 鏡花水月 *Ching hwa shwuy yueh.* Notes and tales on subjects which are as unsubstantial as "Flowers in a mirror or the moon in the water." 8 keuen. *Shanghai,* 1860. 8°. **15327. f. 1.**

袁 Yuen. A notice by Yuen, a Custom House Officer at the Bogue Forts, directing all captains of foreign trading vessels to report their ships when passing the Bogue Forts. The notice is addressed to an English Captain 'Aiyaousze,' to whom is enclosed a certificate of his having reported. Enclosed in an envelope addressed to the 'Great Consul.' MS. 1856. **Or. 3534.**

源超溟 Yuen Chaou-ming. 萬法歸心錄 *Wan fa kwei sin luh.* "A record of ten thousand means of restoring the heart." A Buddhist work. 3 keuen. 1676. 8°. **15103. b. 15.**

袁樞 Yuen Ch'oo. 通鑑紀事本末 *T'ung keen ke sze pun moh.* "A Mirror of Chinese History." [A Japanese reprint.] 42 keuen. 8°. **15298. d. 2.**

袁中立 Yuen Chung-leïh. 黃縣志 *Hwang heen che.* "A Topography of the District of Hwang" in Shantung. Edited by Wang Szechow and others. 12 keuen. 1755. 8°. **15269. e. 12.**

—— [Another edition.] With maps and plans. 12 keuen. 1755. 8°. **15276. b. 2.**

袁鳳孫 Yuen Fung-sun. See 宋鳴琦 Sung ming-k'e. 嘉定府志 *Kea ting foo che.* "A Topography of Kea-ting Foo." Compiled by Yuen Fung-sun, etc. 1803. 8°.

YUE—YUF

阮 咸 YUEN HEEN. 三 墳 書 *San fun shoo.* "The history of the three first mythical emperors." pp. vii, 30, 3. See 程 榮 CH'ING YUNG. 漢 魏 叢 書 *Han Wei ts'ung shoo.* "A collection of works by authors of the Han and Wei Dynasties," etc. 1791. 8°. 15318. a. 1.

阮 嘉 志 YUEN KEA-CHE. 大 南 皇 朝 悲 儒 郡 公 芳 蹟 錄 *Ta nan hwang ch'aou pei joo keun kung fang tseih luh.* "The record of the [French] Commander [Bishop Pigneau de Behaine?], who came to the assistance of the Emperors of Cochin China" at the end of the last century. pp. 22. *Hongkong,* 1897. 8°. 15297. a. 24.

袁 君 載 YUEN KEUN-TSAI. 家 訓 世 範 類 編 *Kea heun she fan luy peen.* Familiar instructions for guidance through life. By Yuen Keun-tsai. 12°. 15229. b. 5.

YUEN SEANG-FOO. "Those Foreign Devils." A Celestial on England and Englishmen . . . Translated by W. H. Wilkinson. pp. xxii, 191. *Leadenhall Press: London,* 1891. 8°. 11099. b. 28.

元 德 明 YUEN TIH-MING. 元 遺 山 文 選 *Yuen E-shan wăn seuen.* See 李 欽 之 LE K'IN-CHE. 金 元 明 八 家 文 選 *Kin Yuen Ming pa kea wăn seuen.* "Selections from the writings of eight authors who wrote during the Kin, Yuen, and Ming Dynasties," etc. 1845. 8°. 15318. e. 1.

圓 瀞 YUEN-TSING. 敎 乘 法 數 *Keaou shing fa soo.* "An explanation of the Numerical Expressions used in Buddhist Literature." By the Priest Yuen-tsing. A new edition. 12 keuen. 1735. 8°. 15103. d. 8.

元 微 之 YUEN WEI-CHE. See 白 居 易 PIH KEU-YIH. 白 氏 文 集 *Pih she wăn tseih.* "The writings of Pih Keu-yih." Compiled by Yuen Wei-che, etc. Fol. 15315. d. 2.

阮 元 YUEN YUEN. See 朱 世 傑 CHOO SHE-KEĚ. 算 學 啓 豪 *Swan heŏ k'e mung.* "A general treatise on Arithmetic . . ." Edited by Yuen Yuen, etc. 1839. 8°. 15259. h. 3.

—— See 李 昉 LE FANG. 太 平 御 覽 *T'aip'ing yu lan.* "T'aip'ing's Encyclopædia . . ." A new edition published by Yuen Yuen, etc. 1892. 8°. 15026. b. 1.

阮 元 YUEN YUEN. 欽 定 重 修 兩 浙 鹽 法 志 *Kin ting chung sew leang Che yen fa che.* "A record of the laws on the salt monopoly for the Province of Chĕ-keang." Compiled by Imperial Order by a commission consisting of Yuen Yuen, Yen-fung, and others. 30 keuen. 1801. 8°. 15239. e. 1.

—— 廣 東 通 志 *Kwang-tung t'ung che.* A complete history of the Province of Kwang-tung. 334 keuen. [1750?] 8°. 15271. c. 7. A fragment, containing only Keuen 83-88 and a few pages of 124.

—— 天 一 閣 書 目 *T'een-yih ko shoo muh.* A catalogue (made by Yuen Yuen) of the library collected in the T'een-yih Pavilion (at Ningpo by Fan-sze-ma under the Ming Dynasty, and which was hidden during the reign of Kea-tsing [1520-1565] and for the succeeding 150 years). 44 keuen. 1808. 8°. 15350. e. 5.

—— 積 古 齋 鐘 鼎 彝 器 欵 識 *Tseih koo chai chung ting e k'e k'wan shih.* "A collection of facsimiles of inscriptions on bells, vases, ancient vessels and instruments examined and deciphered." By Yuen Yuen. 10 keuen. 1804. 8°. 15299. a. 2.

—— 揅 經 室 集 *Yen king shih tseih.* "A collection of writings from the Searching-the-Classics House." By Yuen Yuen. 8 series. 1823. 8°. 15318. b. 1.

阮 芸 臺 YUEN YUN-T'AI. See 許 雲 嶠 HEU YUN-KEAOU. 六 觀 樓 北 曲 六 種 *Luh kwan low pih keŭh luh chung.* "Six Plays . . ." Edited by Yuen Yun-t'ai, etc. 1874. 8°. 15327. d. 29.

閱 微 草 堂 YUĚ-WEI-TS'AOU T'ANG. 閱 微 草 堂 筆 記 五 種 *Yuĕ-wei-ts'aou T'ang pih ke woo chung.* "Five collections of Tales from the Yuĕ-wei-ts'aou Hall." Compiled by 'Kwan-yih Taou-jin.' 1835. 8°. 15331. e. 5.

粵 音 YUĚ YIN. 粵 音 指 南 *Yuĕ yin che nan.* "A guide to Chinese conversation in Cantonese orthography." 4 keuen. *Hongkong,* 1895. 8°. 15341. d. 4.

虞 翻 YU FAN. See 周 易 CHOW YIH. 周 易 審 義 *Chow yih shin e.* "The meaning of the Chow Changes examined." By Yu Fan, etc. 1857. 8°. 15212. d. 14.

玉 Yuh. 玉嬌梨平山泠燕 *Yuh keaou le. P'ing shan läng yen.* "The Story of Miss Hung-yuh, surnamed Woo-keaou, and Miss Loo, surnamed Mung-le," and "The Story of P'ing Joo-häng, Shan-tai, Läng-keang-seuě, and Yen Pih-han." [1800?] 8°.   15333. b. 18.
The two tales on the upper and lower parts of the pages respectively.

俞浩 Yu Haou. 西域考古錄 *Se yih k'aou koo luh.* "An examination of the antiquities of the western frontier districts," i.e. the western part of Kansuh, Tibet, Ili, Yarkand, and Kashgar. 18 keuen. 1848. 8°.   15300. b. 8.

玉斧珮詩 Yuh foo p'ei she. 御製玉斧珮詩 *Yu che yuh foo p'ei she.* "Imperial 'Jade-axe-ornament' Poetry." [By the Emperor K'een-lung.] [1780?] Small 4°.
15321. a. 18.

毓桂山 Yuh Kwei-shan. See 恆壽之 Häng Show-che. 知古錄 *Che koo luh.* "On understanding the military system of the ancients." Edited by Yuh Kwei-shan, etc. 1863. 8°.   15259. e. 21.

玉歷 Yuh leïh. 玉歷鈔傳警世 *Yuh leïh ch'aou chuen king she.* "A precious Buddhist record for awakening the age." 1839. 8°.
15103. c. 35.

余虎庭 Yu Hoo-t'ing. See 余自明 Yu Tsze-ming. 古文釋義新編 *Koo wän shih e sin peen.* "Extracts from Ancient Literature . . ." Edited by Yu Hoo-t'ing, etc. 8°. 15312. b. 6.

玉篇 Yuh p'een. 大廣益會玉篇 *Ta kwang yih hwuy yuh p'een.* "An enlarged Chinese dictionary." 30 keuen. [1620?] Fol.
15344. e. 19.
Printed in Korea with movable type.

玉蕭琴 Yuh seaou kin. 新刻玉蕭琴記全本 *Sin kih yuh seaou k'in ke ts'euen pun.* "The Story of the Precious Seaou Guitar." In verse. First series, 4 keuen; second series, 4 keuen. [1850?] 8°.   15327. d. 25.

玉清帝君 Yuh ts'ing te keun. 鎮宅全書 *Chin tsih ts'euen shoo.* The complete work of the Chin tsih. [Taouist charms, etc., against disease, etc.] By the Deity Yuh ts'ing te keun. *Canton,* [1840?] 8°.   15113. a. 15.

瑜伽 Yukea. 瑜伽餤口施食起止規範 *Yukea yenk'ow she shih k'e che kwei fan.* "The Yoga ritual for offering food to feed the hungry souls in Hell." With illustrations. MS. ff. 96. 1636. 8°.   Or. 2179. 39. B. e.

喻嘉言 Yu Kea-yen. 醫門法律 *E mun fa leüh.* "Rules for the Guidance of Medical Students." By Yu Kea-yen. 6 keuen. [1850?] 8°.   15253. a. 2.

—— 尚論篇 *Shang lun p'een.* "Esteemed Discussions" on medical subjects. By Yu Kea-yen. 2 keuen. With a supplement in 4 keuen. 1740. 8°.   15253. a. 1.

—— 寓意草 *Yu e ts'aou.* "Medical Notes." By Yu Kea-yen. 1643. 8°.   15253. a. 3.

于謙 Yu K'een. See 高亮懷 Kaou Leang-hwai. 于公太保演義傳 *Yu kung t'ai paou yen e chuen.* "A popular biography of Yu K'een," etc. 1822. 8°.   15305. b. 12.

俞九成 Yu Kew-ch'ing. See 呂應奎 Leu Ying-kwei. 惠州府志 *Hwuy-chow Foo che.* "A Topography of Hwuy-chow Foo . . ." Compiled by . . . Yu Kew-ch'ing, etc. 1687. 8°.

余金 Yu Kin. 熙朝新語 *He ch'aou sin yu.* "New records of the present Dynasty." 16 keuen. 1822. 8°.   15297. a. 19.

于慶元 Yu K'ing-yuen. 重訂唐詩三百首續選 *Chung ting T'ang she san pih show suh seuen.* "A supplementary selection of three hundred poems of the T'ang Dynasty." Compiled by Yu K'ing-yuen, Yu Ting-yuen, and Yu Chaou-yuen. A new edition. Edited by Hwang Ho-san. 6 keuen. 1843. 8°. 15324. a. 10.

虞荔 Yu Le. 鼎錄 *Ting luh.* "An historical record of the manufacture of metal vases." pp. 18. See 程榮 Ch'ing Yung. 漢魏叢書 *Han Wei ts'ung shoo.* "A collection of works by authors of the Han and Wei Dynasties," etc. 1791. 8°.   15318. a. 1.

余蓮村 Yu Leen-ts'un. 得一錄 *Tih yih luh.* "Treatises on doing one good deed." Compiled by Yu Leen-ts'un. 16 keuen. *Canton,* 1871. 8°.
15113. c. 1.

余笠湖 Yu Leïh-hoo. 吟風閣 *Yin fung ko.* "The Hall of the moaning wind." A collection of thirty-two plays. By Yu Leïh-hoo. 4 keuen. 1820. 8°.   15331. f. 6.

YUL—YUP

YU - LI, *Tunkinischer Mandarin.* Wundersame Begebenheiten des Yu-Li, eines Tunkinischen Mandarins. Aus dem Französischen. 2 Thle. *Augsburg,* 1778. 8°. 11099. a. 23.

于 敏 中 YU MIN-CHUNG. See 阿 桂 AH KWEI. 欽 定 滿 洲 源 流 考 *K'in ting man chow yuen lew k'aou.* "An examination into the origin of the Manchoos." Compiled . . . by . . . Yu Min-chung, etc. 1777. 8°. 15297. b. 1.

俞 夢 蕉 YU MUNG-TSEAOU. 蕉 軒 摭 錄 *Tseaou heen chih luh.* "Tales from The Plaintain Study." Compiled by Yu Mung-tseaou. 12 keuen. 1839. 8°. 15334. d. 8.

韻 YUN. 廣 韻 *Kwang yun.* "A Dictionary with the characters arranged according to their tones and final sounds." 5 keuen. 1666. 15346. b. 16.

YUÑ-CEÑ. *See* YUNGCHING.

允 祉 YUN CHE. See 允 祿 YUN LUH. 御 製 律 曆 淵 源 *Yu che leŭh leth yuen yuen.* "A Thesaurus of the exact sciences . . ." Compiled by . . . Yun Che, etc. 1723. 8°. 15257. c. 4. & d. 1.

雲 中 子 YUN CHUNG TSZE, *pseud.* 生 草 藥 性 *Sǎng ts'aou yo sing.* "The medical properties of plants growing" on the Lo-fow Shan. By Yun chung tsze, i.e. 'The Man in the Clouds.' 2 keuen. [1840 ?] 8°. 15255. a. 7.

YUNG CHING. *See* K'ANGHE. Il Santo Editeo . . . e l'amplificazione di Yuñ-ceñ, etc. 1880. 8°. 11098. c. 1.

雍 正 YUNG-CHING, *Emperor.* 硃 批 諭 旨 *Choo p'e yu che.* "State papers, with notes written with the vermilion pencil" by the Emperor Yung-ching. 1823–1832. 8°. 15241. c. 6.

永 璥 YUNG SEUEN. 皇 清 職 貢 圖 *Hwang Ts'ing chih kung t'oo.* "Drawings (with text) of peoples tributary to the Imperial Ts'ing Dynasty of China," including the European nations. Compiled by Prince Ying Seuen, Ying Leen, Kin Leen, and others. 9 keuen. 1751. 8°. 15236. e. 7.

—— [Another edition. 1780 ?] 8°. 15226. e. 6.

永 珊 熏 沐 YUNG SHAN HEUN MUH. 釋 迦 如 來 應 化 事 蹟 *Shih kea joo lai Ying hwa sze tseih.* "Incidents in the life of Sakyamuni Tathagata." Preceded by the *Ch'ing taou ke,* "The Perfect Way," of Wang P'ŏ. With illustrations, each illustration corresponding to a page of text. Edited by the Imperial Duke Yung shan heun muh. 4 vols. 1808. 4°. 15113. e. 5. Slightly imperfect.

蘊 香 丸 YUN HEANG HWAN. 繡 像 蘊 香 丸 *Sew seang yun heang hwan.* "The Secret Scented Pill. With illustrations." A drama. 4 keuen. 1818. 8°. 15327. b. 10.

允 祿 YUN LUH. 欽 定 同 文 韻 統 *K'in ting t'ung wǎn yun t'ung.* The primary Sanskrit, Tibetan, and Manchoo characters phonetically represented in Chinese. Published by Imperial order (by the four ministers Yun-luh, Foo-hǎng, Wang-yew-tun, Na-yen-tai, and eleven others). With a preface by the Emperor K'een-lung. 6 keuen. 1750. 8°. 15354. a. 5.

—— 御 製 律 曆 淵 源 *Yu che leŭh leth yuen yuen.* "A Thesaurus of the exact Sciences," viz., astronomy, mathematics, and music. Compiled by an Imperial Commission consisting of Yun Luh, Yun Che, Ho Kwo-tsung, and others. 1723. 8°. 15257. c. 4. & d. 1.

韻 字 YUN TSZE. 韻 字 鑑 *Yun tsze keen.* "A mirror of rhyming characters." A poetical dictionary. 4 keuen. [1860 ?] 12°. 15342. a. 8.

虞 潘 府 YU P'AN-FOO. 孔 子 通 紀 *K'ung tsze t'ung ke.* "A Biography of Confucius." A Japanese edition. 8 keuen. 1600. Fol. 15303. c. 15.

俞 寶 YU PAOU. See 靈 操 竹 LING TS'AOU-CHUH. 瑜 伽 集 要 施 食 壇 儀 應 門 *Yu kea tseih yaou she shih tan e ying mun.* "A Manual of the Rites of the Yoga Sect." With critical notes by Yu Paou, etc. 8°. 15103. d. 13.

虞 伯 生 YU PIH-SǍNG. 道 園 全 集 *Taou yuen ts'euen tseih.* "The Taou-yuen Collection of the Writings" of Yu Pih-sǎng. See 孫 澍 SUN SHOO. 古 棠 書 屋 叢 書 *Koo t'ang shoo wuh ts'ung shoo.* "A Collection of Reprints," etc. 1831–1849. 8°. 15315. d. 1.

—— 虞 道 園 文 選 *Yu Taou-yuen wǎn seuen.* See 李 欽 之 LE K'IN-CHE. 金 元 明 八 家 文 選 *Kin, Yuen, Ming, pa kea wǎn seuen.* "Selections from the writings of eight authors who wrote during the Kin, Yuen, and Ming Dynasties," etc. 1845. 8°. 15318. e. 1.

喻 本 元 YU PUN-YUEN, and 喻 本 亨 YU PUN-HĂNG. 療 馬 集 *Leaou ma tseïh.* "A Work on the Veterinary Art." 4 keuen. [1750?] 8°. 15252. e. 4.

Imperfect, containing only Keuen 3.

子 璿 YU-SEUEN. 首 楞 嚴 義 疏 注 經 *Show lang yen e soo choo king.* "The Shūrāngama Sūtra, with its meaning explained" by Yu-seuen. 20 keuen. 1339. 8°. 15103. b. 9.

Imperfect, containing only Keuen 4, 6, 9, 10, and parts of 3 and 5. Printed in Japan from blocks at the cost of Kō no Moronō.

諭 帀 YU SHE. 諭 帀 抄 錄 *Yu she ch'aou luh.* "Copies of Proclamations." MS. [1844?] 8°. 15297. d. 4.

俞 守 義 YU SHOW-E. 皇 清 地 理 圖 *Hwang Ts'ing te le t'oo.* "A Map of the Empire," compiled by Yu Show-e from an earlier map by Hoo Pih-ki, who based his again on one by Tung Fang-leïh. 3 vols. *Canton,* 1871. 8°. 15275. a. 17.

余 德 水 YU TIH-SHWUY. 熙 朝 新 語 *He ch'aou sin yu.* "New Records of the present prosperous Dynasty." By Yu Tih-shwuy. 16 keuen. 1822. 8°. 15297. a. 10.

于 鼎 元 YU TING-YUEN. See 于 慶 元 YU K'ING-YUEN. 重 訂 唐 詩 三 百 首 續 選 *Chung ting T'ang she san pih show suh seuen.* "A supplementary selection of three hundred poems of the T'ang Dynasty." Compiled by ... Yu Ting-yuen, etc. 1843. 8°. 15324. a. 10.

輿 圖 YU T'OO. 輿 圖 要 覽 *Yu t'oo yaou lan.* "A Geography of the Empire." With maps. MS. 4 keuen. [1800?] 8°. 15271. c. 16.

虞 集 伯 YU TSEÏH-PIH. See 杜 甫 TOO FOO. 杜 詩 七 言 律 *Too she ts'ih yen leuh.* "A collection of Too Foo's ... poems." With Yu Tseïh-pih's commentary, etc. 1470. 8°. 15324. e. 4.

俞 俊 YU TSEUN. See 張 作 楠 CHANG TSO-NAN. 倉 田 通 法 續 編 *Ts'ang t'een t'ung fa suh peen.* "Supplementary Rules for Solid and Plane Mensuration." Edited by Yu Tseun, etc. 8°. 15255. c. 2.

余 自 明 YU TSZE-MING. 古 文 釋 義 新 編 *Koo wăn shih e sin peen.* "Extracts from Ancient Literature, with their meanings explained." Compiled by Yu Tsze-ming. Edited by Yu Hoo-ting. 8 keuen. [1750?] 8°. 15312. b. 6.

Imperfect, Keuen 1 wanting.

余 自 明 YU TSZE-MING. 增 訂 古 文 釋 義 *Tsăng ting koo wăn shih e.* "Extracts from ancient literature." An enlarged edition with explanatory notes. 8 keuen. 1840. 8°. 15318. c. 4.

虞 摶 YU TW'AN. 醫 學 正 傳 *E heŏ ching chuen.* "A Treatise on Medicine." 8 keuen. 1531. Fol. 15253. e. 2.

Printed in Korea with movable type.

俞 萬 春 YÜ WAN-CH'UN. 結 水 滸 全 傳 *Keïh Shwuy hoo ts'euen chuen.* "An outcome of the 'Story of the River's Banks.'" A work intended to show up the disloyalty of Sung Keang. 71 keuen. 1857. 8°. 15327. e. 12.

漁 洋 山 人 YU-YANG SHAN JIN [i.e. CHANG TSUNG-NAN]. 帶 經 堂 詩 話 *Tai-king T'ang she hwa.* "Criticisms on Poetry from the Tai-king Hall." By Chang Tsung-nan. 30 keuen. *Canton,* 1873. 8°. 15323. e. 10.

俞 樾 YU YUĚ. 諸 子 平 義 *Choo tsze p'ing e.* "The just meanings of the Philosophers," beginning with Kwan-tsze and ending with the *Fa yen* of Yang-tsze. By Yu Yuě. 35 keuen. 1866. 8°. 15314. d. 5.

—— 春 在 堂 詩 編 *Ch'un tsai t'ang she peen.* "Poetry from the Ch'un-tsai Hall." By Yu Yuě. 6 keuen. With a supplement in 2 keuen. 1868. 8°. 15323. e. 11.

—— 賓 萌 集 *Pin măng tseïh.* "The Pin-măng Collection" of literary notes. By Yu Yuě. 5 keuen. With a supplementary collection in 4 keuen. 1866–70. 8°. 15317. a. 5.

—— See 陳 子 莊 CH'IN TSZE-CHWANG. 庸 閒 齋 筆 記 *Yung-heen chai peïh ke.* "Notes from the Yung-heen Study ..." Edited by Yu Yuě, etc. 1874. 8°. 15331. b. 12.

—— 同 治 上 海 縣 志 *T'ungche Shanghai heen che.* "A topography of Shanghai made during the reign of T'ungche." First published in 1866, and reissued in 1882. With maps. Edited by Yu Yuě and other officials. 33 keuen. 1882. 8°. 15275. a. 21.

喻 元 準 YU YUEN CHUN. See 穆 克 登 額 MUH-KIH-TĂNG-GIH. 大 清 通 禮 *Ta Ts'ing t'ung le.* The Code of the Rites and Ceremonies of the Tsing Dynasty, etc. 1824. 8°.

ZI (ETIENNE). *See* SEU (ETIENNE).

167

ADDENDA

ANC—CHI

ANCIENT CHINA. Five maps of Ancient China, taken from various works. [1750?] **15235. c.**

BAKER (CHARLES), *Headmaster of the Yorkshire Institution for the Deaf and Dumb.* Graduated Reading, comprising a circle of knowledge in 200 lessons. Gradation I. Translated into Chinese by J. Legge. Fourth edition. Revised and improved. pp. viii, 102. *Hongkong*, 1895. 8°. **11098. a. 34.**

BAYER (GOTTLIEB SIEGFRIED). Boussole usitée en Chine dès la plus haute antiquité, tirée de la Dissertation de Bayer sur les heures des Chinois, avec son Cadran solaire vertical. [1740?] A sheet. **M.P.C. (5).**

BIRT (WILLIAM RADCLIFF). See 白爾特 PIH-URH-T'IH.

BLOXAM (CHARLES LOUDON). See 蒲陸山 P'OO-LUH-SHAN.

BONET (JEAN). 大南國音字彙合解大法國音 Dictionnaire Annamite - Français (Langue officielle et langue vulgaire). Par Jean Bonet. 2 vols. *Ernest Leroux : Paris*, 1899. 8°. **11094. b. 9.**

張之洞 **CHANG CHE-TUNG.** China's only Hope. An appeal. By her Greatest Viceroy Chang Chih-tung, with the sanction of the present Emperor, Kwang Sü. Translated from the Chinese edition by Samuel J. Woodbridge. Introduction by Griffith John, D.D. pp. 151. *Fleming H. Revell Company : New York, Chicago, Toronto*, 1900. 8°. **11100. a. 39.**

—— [Another edition.] *Oliphant, Anderson, & Ferrier : Edinburgh & London*, 1901. 8°. **11100. a. 40.**

張之洞 **CHANG CHE-TUNG.** 勸學篇 K'ien-hio p'ien [Exhortations à l'étude]. Ouvrage traduit du Chinois par Jerome Tobar, et précédé d'une notice biographique par J. Em. Lemière. pp. ii, 70. *Shanghai*, 1898. 4°. **11098. d. 4.**

CHANG CHIH-TUNG. See CHANG CHE-TUNG.

倉洞 **CHANG TONG.** 東史綱要 Tong sā kang yo. "An epitome of the Korean annals" in manuscript. By Chang Tong. 9 keuen. [Seoul?], 1884. 4°. **15291. a. 15.**

趙殿最 **CHAOU TEEN-TSUY.** 聖主躬耕耤田頌 *Shing choo kung kăng tseth t'een sung.* "A panegyric on the practice of the Emperor personally ploughing a field" at the vernal equinox. MS. 1738. 8°. **Or. 56. a.**
A beautiful manuscript written on a gold ground.

CHARACTERS. A collection of characters and expressions. MS. [1850?] **15259. h. 14.**

—— A list of characters arranged phonetically according to the English alphabet. MS. [1850?] **15229. a. 40.**

浙江 **CHĔ-KEANG.** Plans of the Suy-an District, the District in charge of the right Brigade of Wăn chow, and the Military Department of Tai-chow Foo, in the Province of Chĕ-keang. [1840?] **15275. d. 12.**

賈步緯 **CHIA POO-WEI.** 開方表 K'ai fang peaou. "Tables of roots of numbers." pp. iv, 60. [1880?] 8°. **15259. g. 21.**

赤道 **CH'IH TAOU.** 赤道南北兩總星圖 *Ch'ih taou nan pih leang tsung sing t'oo.* "The Celestial Globe divided into the Southern and Northern Hemispheres." [1711?] A sheet. **15235. c.**

CHINA. A general map of China, on a blue ground. 6 [?] scrolls. [1800?] 15235. c.
Imperfect, containing only 5 scrolls.

—— Seventeen maps of the Provinces of China, the Province of Kansuh being omitted. [1800?] 15235. c.

—— 大清萬年一統地理全圖 *Ta Ts'ing wan neen yih t'ung te le ts'euen t'oo.* "A complete general map of China under the present Dynasty." 8 scrolls. 1767. 15235. c.

陳以勤 CH'IN E-K'IN. See 永樂 YUNG-LO, *Emperor.* 永樂大典 *Yung-lo ta teen.* "The Great Standard of the Emperor Yung-lo . . ." Collated by Ch'in E-k'in, etc. Fol.

CHINESE. Informatio pro veritate contra iniquiorem famam sparsam per Sinas cum calumnia in P.P. Soc. Jesu, et detrimento Missionis. Communicata Missionariis in Imperio Sinensi. Anno 1717. (*Peking?*) Fol. 11095. b. 14.
Printed from wooden blocks.

CHINESE AND ENGLISH. A Chinese and English vocabulary of phrases, the English words being represented phonetically by Chinese characters. With neither title nor date. MS. [1850?] 8°. M.P.C.

鄭芷畦 CHING CHE-CH'E. 廿一史約編 *Urh shih yih she yo peen.* "A compendium of the Twenty-one Histories," covering a period from the earliest records down to the end of the Ming Dynasty (1644). Compiled by Ching Che-ch'e, and edited by Ch'in Keu-shih. 8 vols. [1816?] 8°. 15287. b. 1.

陳淏子 CH'IN HAOU-TSZE. 花鏡 *Hwa king.* "A mirror of flowers." With illustrations. 6 keuen. 1783. 8°. 15259. g. 23.

陳傑臣 CH'IN KËË-CH'IN. 增廣經驗瓦方 *Tsǎng kwang king yen leang fang.* "An enlarged collection of efficacious prescriptions." Compiled by Ch'in Këë-ch'in. pp. vi, 82. *Hongkong,* 1900. 8°. 15252. d. 17.

陳建 CH'IN KEEN. A petition addressed by Ch'in Keen to Mr. Jackson begging for the intervention of the latter to secure Ch'in Keen's release from the Magistrate's prison at Foochow. MS. 1848. M.P.C.

陳罡石 CH'IN KEU-SHIH. See 鄭芷畦 CHING CHE-CH'E. 廿一史約編 *Urh shih yih she yo peen.* "A compendium of the Twenty-one Histories . . ." Edited by Ch'in Keu-shih, etc. 8°. 15287. b. 1.

沈桂芬 CHIN KWEI-FUN. See 同治 T'UNG-CHE, *Emperor.* 大清穆宗毅皇帝實錄 *Ta Ts'ing moo tsung e Hwang-te shih luh.* "The true record of the reign of the Reverent Ancestor, the Resolute Emperor of the Great Pure Dynasty," i.e. T'ung-che . . . Compiled by . . . Chin Kwei-fun, etc. 1873. Fol. Or. 56. d.

沈壽昌 CHIN SHOW-CH'ANG. 松江府建求忠書院記 *Sung-keang foo keen k'ew chung shoo yuen ke.* "A record of the building of the Chung shoo yuen ('Patriotic Library') at Sung-keang Foo" in 1611. Printed in white characters on black ground. 1611. 8°. 15204. a. 7.

眞言 CHIN YEN. 眞言集 *Chin yen tseih.* "A collection of true [Buddhist] phrases." In Chinese, Korean, and Sanskrit. 1570. 8°. 15103. b. 21.

陳璽 CH'IN YING. 廣東通省水道圖 *Kwang-tung t'ung shing shwuy taou t'oo.* "A complete map of the Province of Kwang-tung, with its water-ways." [1840?] A sheet. 15235. c.

卓歧山 CHO K'E-SHAN. 華英呂應剛撮要 *Hwa Ying Leu Ying ch'ow ts'o yaou.* "A Chinese, English, and Spanish Commercial Vocabulary." pp. viii, 214. [*Hongkong?*], 1899. 8°. 11099. c. 46.

朱熹 CHOO HE. See 詩經 SHE KING. 詩經大全 *She king ta ts'euen.* "The Book of Odes . . ." Edited by Choo He, etc. Fol. 15201. c. 18.

—— See 四書 SZE SHOO. 大學 *Ta heǒ.* "The Great Learning." With comments compiled by Choo He, etc. 8°. 15201. b. 3.

初學 CH'OO HEǑ. 初學文範 *Ch'u heǒ wǎn fan.* "Model essays for beginners." ? keuen. [1850?] 8°. 15229. b. 30.
An odd volume (Keuen 2) containing essays on texts from the Hsia lun and the Chung yung.

周興嗣 CHOW HING-SZE. 滿漢千字文 *Man Han ts'een tsze wǎn.* "The Thousand Character Classic in Manchu and Chinese." pp. 42. *Peking,* [1860?]. 8°. 15201. b. 4.

竹莊 CHUH CHWANG. 晚笑堂畫傳 *Wan seaou t'ang hwa chuen.* "The Evening-laughter Hall collection of illustrated biographies." 2 vols. 1743. 8°. **15301. b. 5.**

CLARK (G. W.). Kwiechow and Yün-nan Provinces. By G. W. C. pp. 296. *Shanghai*, 1894. 8°. **11094. c. 5.**

COURANT (MAURICE). Bibliothèque Nationale, Départment des Manuscrits. Catalogue des livres Chinois, Coréens, Japonais, etc. Par M. C. Premier Fascicule. *Ernest Leroux : Paris*, 1900. 8°. **11095. c. 3.**

COUVREUR (S.). See 禮記 LE KE. Li ki, ou Mémoires sur les bienséances et les cérémonies, etc. 1899. 8°. **11098. b. 39.**

DIALOGUES. Dialogues in English and the Canton dialect of China. Lithographed. Without title. *Canton*, 1850. 4°. **11098. b. 29.**

DURET (THÉODORE). Livres et Albums illustrés du Japon, réunis et catalogués par T. D. pp. ix, 322. *Ernest Leroux : Paris*, 1900. 8°. **11095. a. 8.**

EDKINS (JOSEPH), D.D. *See* EPHEMERIDES. 中西通書 *Chung se t'ung shoo.* "A Chinese and Western Almanac for the year 1857." By J. E., etc. 8°. **15200. b. 34.**

ENGLISH AND CHINESE READERS. 華英進階 English and Chinese Readers (from Primer to fifth Reader). Specially translated and carefully revised by the Commercial Press Book Depôt. *Shanghai*, 1900. 8°. **11094. c. 3.**

EPHEMERIDES. The Anglo-Chinese Kalendar, etc. *Canton*, 1838. 8°. **11095. a. 10.**

—— 中西通書 *Chung se t'ung shoo.* "A Chinese and Western Almanac for the year 1857." By J. Edkins. pp. viii, 69. [1857?] 8°. **15200. b. 34.**

尹斗薈 E TOW-SHOW. 平壤志 *P'ing jang che.* "A Topography of P'ing-jang." In three parts. Part i, 9 keuen; part ii, 5 keuen; part iii, 2 keuen. A reprint. 1855. Fol. **15260. a. 4.**

倚晴樓 E-TS'ING LOW. 倚晴樓七種曲 *E-ts'ing low ts'ih chung k'euh.* "Seven Plays from the E-ts'ing Pavilion." 6 vols. [1870?] 8°. **15325. a. 1.**

FA-HEEN. A record of Buddhistic Kingdoms, being an account by the Chinese Monk Fa-hien of his travels in India and Ceylon (A.D. 399–414) . . . Translated and annotated, with a Corean recension of the Chinese text, by James Legge. pp. xv, 123, 45. *The Clarendon Press : Oxford*, 1886. 4°. **11099. f. 36.**

範荔扉 FAN LE-FEI. 滇繫 *Tien ke.* "A description of Tien" or the Province of Yunnan. By Fan Le-fei. With map. 40 vols. *Yunnan Foo*, 1880. 8°. **15276. b. 6.**

飛雲閣 FEI-YUN KO. 飛雲閣名箋貢扇 *Fei-yun ko ming tseen kung shen.* "Sheets of Chinese notepaper." [1850?] 8°. **15229. a. 41.**

FILIAL PIETY. Four illustrated scrolls representing 18 scenes from the twenty-four instances of filial piety. Without title. [1800?] **15229. e. 1.**

伏人 FOO JIN. 伏人明堂圖 *Foo jin ming t'ang t'oo.* "An anatomical drawing of the back of the human figure." [1782?] A scroll. **15253. c. 6 (4).**

傅蘭雅 FOO-LAN-YA [i.e. J. FRYER]. See 白起德 PIH-K'E-TIH. 鄧規約指 *Yun kwei yo chih.* Practical geometry. Translated into Chinese by Foo-lan-ya, etc. 8°. **15259. g. 18.**

—— See 蒲陸山 P'OO-LUH-SHAN. 化學分原 *Hwa heŏ fun yuen.* "An introduction to practical chemistry." Translated into Chinese by Foo-lan-ya, etc. 8°. **15259. g. 15.**

—— 化學易知 *Hwa heŏ yih chih.* "Chemistry." 2 keuen. *Shanghai*, 1881. 8°. **15259. g. 16.**

FOUCQUET (JOANNES FRANCISCUS). Tabula chronologica historiæ Sinicæ connexa cum cyclo qui vulgo Kia tse dicitur. *Rome*, 1729. A sheet. **15235. c.**

祥 FUH. 祥 *Fuh.* "On happiness." pp. 1. [*Shanghai?* 1870?] 8°. **15200. b. 34.**

婦科 FU K'O. 婦科保嬰三生合編 *Foo k'o paou ying san sǎng ho peen.* "A treatise on the protection of women in childbirth, and of children of all ages." By an author styling himself T'ung-ngan-ko Taou-jin, "The Taouist of the Pavilion of complete rest." A new edition. *Hongkong*, 1898. 8°. **15253. a. 20.**

澳門 GAOU-MUN. A manuscript map of the country round Gaou-mun, or Macao. [1850?] A sheet. **15235. c.**

GÉNIBREL (J. F. M.). Dictionnaire Annamite-Français, comprenant : 1. Tous les caractères de la langue Annamite vulgaire . . . 2. Les caractères Chinois nécessaires à l'étude des . . . Quatre Livres classiques Chinois. 3. La Flore et la Faune de l'Indo-Chine. Deuxième édition. *Imprimerie de la Mission à Tân Dinh: Saigon,* 1898. 4°. **11094. b. 6.**

GOOSE, MOTHER. Chinese Mother Goose Rhymes. Translated and illustrated by J. T. Headland. pp. 157. *F. H. Revell Co.: New York,* [1900]. 4°. **11095. a. 2.**

GOURDIN (F.). Premières études de la Langue Mandarine parlée. Par F. G. pp. 291. *Hongkong,* 1896. 8°. **11095. a. 1.**

GRAINGER (ADAM). 西 蜀 方 言 Western Mandarin, or the spoken language of Western China; with syllabic and English indexes. Compiled by A. G. pp. vi, 803. *American Presbyterian Mission Press: Shanghai,* 1900. 8°. **11094. c. 2.**

恒 星 HĂNG SING. 恒 星 圖 表 *Hăng sing t'oo peaou.* "Tables of the Fixed Stars." Keuen 2. [1880 ?] 8°. **15259. f. 14.**

韓 用 洒 HAN YUNG-SA. 大 清 萬 年 一 統 天 下 全 圖 *Ta Ts'ing wan neen yih t'ung t'een hea ts'euen t'oo.* "A map of the Chinese Empire under the Ta Ts'ing Dynasty." 1767. A sheet. **15235. c.**

HARLEZ (CHARLES DE). Les quarante-deux leçons de Buddha, ou Le King des XLII Sections (Sze-shi-erh-tchang-king). Texte Chinois, avec traduction, introduction, et notes par Ch. de H. pp. 68. [1899 ?] 8°. **11099. c. 47.**

HEADLAND (ISAAC TAYLOR). *See* GOOSE, MOTHER. Chinese Mother Goose Rhymes. Translated and illustrated by I. T. Headland, etc. 4°. **11095. a. 2.**

孝 經 HEAOU KING. Reproductions of celebrated inscriptions, beginning with an Imperial preface to the Heaou king or "Classic of Filial Piety." White characters on black ground. [1800 ?] 8°. **15300. b. 12.**

現 世 HEEN SHE. 現 世 報 應 圖 *Heen she paou ying t'oo.* Recompenses in the present world for evil done. With illustrations. [1850 ?] A sheet. **M.P.C. (6).**

玄 祕 塔 HEUEN-PE TA. A copy of an inscription commemorating the foundation of the Heuen-pi Pagoda. [1750 ?] 8°. **15204. a. 6.**
Imperfect at ends.

HIBBERDINE (W.). "Can see can savey." Hibberdine's Composition Series, Nos. 1–20. *Hongkong,* [1900 ?]. 4°. **11098. d. 18.**

何 克 諫 HO KIH-KEEN. 食 物 本 草 *Shih wuh pun ts'aou.* "A work on edibles." 2 keuen. 1732. 8°. **15259. g. 24.**

胡 蔚 HOO WEI. *See* 楊 慎 YANG SHIN. 南 詔 野 史 *Nan chaou yay she.* "An uncanonical history of Nan chaou . . ." Edited by Hoo Wei, etc. 1880. 8°. **15292. b. 3.**

後 學 者 HOW-HEŎ-CHAY [i.e.]. 節 錄 成 章 幼 學 問 答 *Tseĕ luh ch'ing chang yew heŏ wăn ta.* "A Christian Catechism for the Young." pp. 32. [1850 ?] 8°. **15200. b. 37.**

洪 邁 HUNG MAI. 唐 人 萬 首 絕 句 選 *T'ang jin wan show tseuĕ keu seuen.* "A selection of impromptu verses by poets of the T'ang Dynasty." Compiled by Hung Mai. 7 keuen. [1800 ?] 8°. **15322. a. 2.**

洪 武 HUNG-WOO, *Emperor.* A bank note of the face value of a thousand cash issued during the reign of the Emperor Hung-woo (1368–1398). Printed on a paper made from the bark of the mulberry-tree. [1380 ?] **Or. 56. d.**

—— [Another copy.]

皇 朝 HWANG CH'AOU. 皇 朝 一 統 輿 地 全 圖 *Hwang ch'aou yih t'ung yu te ts'euen t'oo.* "A map of the Chinese Empire under the present Dynasty." 8 rolls. [1800 ?] **15235. c.**
Imperfect, containing only 7 rolls.

黃 履 卿 HWANG LE-K'ING. 英 語 必 讀 *Ying yu pe tuh.* English and Chinese conversation. By Wong Lu-hing. New edition. pp. 170. *Hongkong,* 1899. 8°. **11095. a. 3.**

黃 自 元 HWANG TSZE-YUEN. 讀 書 樂 *Tuh shoo loh.* "The pleasures of reading." pp. 16. [1840 ?] 8°. **15229. a. 38.**

JOHN (GRIFFITH), D.D. *See* CHANG CHE-TUNG. China's only Hope . . . Introduction by G. J., etc. 1901. 8°. **11100. a. 40.**

—— 福 音 大 旨 *Fuh yin ta che.* "The great themes of the Gospel." pp. 19. *Hankow,* 1883. 12°. **15200. b. 34.**

綱鑑 KANG KEEN. 綱鑑甲子圖 *Kang keen kea tsze t'oo.* "A list of the Emperors from the Chow to the 44th year of the reign of K'ang-he of the present Manchu Dynasty." 1705. A sheet. 15292. b. 4.

干寶 KAN PAOU. 三教源流聖帝佛師搜神記 *San keaou yuen lew Shing te Fuh sze sow shin ke.* "Marvellous records of the spiritual world," with an account of the rise and progress of the three religions of China. With illustrations. 1819. 8°. 15296. a. 31.

江南 KEANG-NAN. 江南報恩寺琉璃寶塔全圖 *Keang-nan Paou-ngan sze Lew-le paou ta ts'euen t'oo.* "A complete engraving of the Porcelain Precious Pagoda in the Pao-ngan Temple in Keang-nan." The Porcelain Pagoda at Nanking. 1802. A sheet. 15235. c.
There are a number of duplicate copies.

江甯 KEANG-NING. 江甯省城圖 *Keang-ning shing ch'ing t'oo.* "A map of the city of Keang-ning," i.e. Nanking. 1856. 15351. b. 2.

江蘇 KEANG-SOO. 江蘇現任官名 *Keang-soo heen jin kwan ming.* "A list of officers in the Province of Keang-soo." MSS. [1850?] 15241. c. 15.

買步緯 KEA POO-WEI. 八線對數簡表 *Pa seen tuy shoo keen peaou.* "Abridged Trigonometrical Tables." Edited by Kea Poo-wei. pp. 180. [1880?] 8°. 15259. g. 20.

乾隆 K'EEN-LUNG, *Emperor.* An Imperial Edict issued on the 1st of the 11th month of the 14th year of the reign of the Emperor K'ien-lung [1749] ordering greater attention to, and efficiency in, military matters. Copied in the Yamên of the Viceroy of the two Kiangs by Hwang. 1749. 15235. c.

啓蒙 K'E MUNG. 啓蒙篇 *K'e mung p'een* [Kor. *Kyei mong p'yen*]. "A child's guide to knowledge." In Chinese and Korean. pp. 46. [*Seoul*, 1890?] 8°. 15260. b. 3.

KINBERG (J. G. H.). Novæ literæ Asiæ Orientalis. A new alphabet for China and Japan. By J. G. H. K. pp. 16. *C. E. Fritze's Royal Library: Stockholm*, 1901. 8°. 11094. b. 8.

金華府 KIN-HWA FOO. A coloured map of the city of Kin-hwa Foo in Cheh-keang and the fortifications in its neighbourhood. Without title. MS. [1840?] A sheet. 15235. c.

金楷理 KIN-K'EAE-LE [i.e. C. S. KREYER]. See 白爾特 PIH-URH-T'IH. 御風要術 *Yu fung yaou shuh.* "A handbook of the law of storms." Translated into Chinese by Kin-k'eae-le . . . 1873. 8°. 15259. g. 19.

金炳學 KIN PING-HEŎ. 大典會通 *Ta teen hwuy t'ung.* "A Résumé of the Chief Ordinances" of the Six Boards of China. Compiled by Kin Ping-heŏ. 6 keuen. 1865. Fol. 15260. a. 3.

金泳 KIN YUNG. See 徐浩修 SEU HAOU-SEW. 國朝曆象考 *Kwo ch'aou leih seang k'aou.* "A National Astronomical Almanac . . ." Edited by Kin Yung, etc. Fol. 15260. a. 2.

古潤四山 KOO JUN SZE SHAN. 古潤四山勝境全圖 *Koo jun sze shan shing king ts'euen t'oo.* "A complete map of the Koo jun hills," in Kiangsu [?]. [1840?] 15235. c.

孔安國 K'UNG GAN-KWO. See 孔丘 K'UNG K'EW. 古文孝經孔氏傳 *Koo wăn Heaou king K'ung she chuen.* "The ancient text of the Book of Filial Piety, with K'ung Gan-kwo's Commentary," etc. 1800. 8°. 15229. b. 28.

孔丘 K'UNG K'EW. 古文孝經孔氏傳 *Koo wăn Heaou king K'ung she chuen.* "The ancient text of the Book of Filial Piety, with K'ung Gan-kwo's Commentary." A Japanese edition. Edited by Yamamoto Riū. pp. xxx, 40. 1800. 8°. 15229. b. 28.

廣東 KWANG-TUNG. 廣東輿地總圖 *Kwang-tung yu te tsung t'oo.* "A map of the Province of Kwang-tung." With a plan of the city and suburbs of Canton. [1840?] 15235. c.

KWANG-TUNG. A manuscript map of the Province of Kwang-tung, in four sheets. [1850?] 15235. c.

歸極 KWEI KEIH. 歸極總圖 *Kwei keih tsung t'oo.* "A general map of Peking." In nine sheets. [1800?] 15235. c.

桂龍光 KWEI LUNG-KWANG. 字學舉隅 *Tsze heŏ keu yu.* "A step towards the study of the characters." 1881. 8°. 15229. b. 29.

LACROIX (DÉSIRÉ). Numismatique Annamite. Par D. L. *Imprimerie Menard & Legros: Saigon*, 1900. 4°. 11094. b. 5.
With a volume of plates.

LAOU-TSZE. [Another copy.] Lao-Tsze's Tao-Teh-King. *Open Court Publishing Co. : Chicago*, 1898. 8°.   11099. c. 49.

LEAMAN (CHARLES). 無師初學英文字 General Romanization of the Mandarin Dialect . . . By C. L. pp. 100. *American Presbyterian Mission Press : Shanghai*, 1897. 8°. 11094. c. 6.

列女 LĔĔ NEU. 列女傳 *Lĕĕ neu chuen*. "Illustrated biographies of notable women." 14 keuen. [1800?] 8°.   15301. c. 7.
    Wanting title-page and preface.

LEGGE (JAMES). *See* FA-HEEN. A record of Buddhistic Kingdoms . . . Translated and annotated . . . by J. L., etc. 1886. 4°.   11099. f. 36.

歷代帝王 LEĬH TAI TE WANG. 歷代帝王統紀之圖 *Leĭh tai te wang t'ung ke chih t'oo*. "A chronological list of the Emperors of China from the earliest times down to the reign of Taou-kwang" [1821-1850]. [1840?] A scroll.   15235. c.

李明徹 LE MING-CHE. 圜天圖說 *Yuen t'een t'oo shwo*. "A Treatise on Astronomy." By Le Ming-che. Edited by Yuen Yuen. With illustrations. 3 keuen. 1819. 8°. 15259. f. 17.
    Imperfect, containing only Keuen 2 and 3.

李盤 LE P'AN. 金湯十二籌 *Kin t'ang shih urh ch'ow*. "Twelve plans of 'metal and scalding,'" i.e. for the defence of city walls. With illustrations. By Le P'an and others. 12 keuen. [1800?] 8°.   15259. e. 13.
    Imperfect, containing only Keuen 1-11.

呂嵒 LEU YEN. 勅封燮元贊運純陽演正警化孚佑帝君 *Ch'ih fung seĕ yuen tsan yun shun yang yen ching king hwa foo yew te keun*. "The ritual proper to the worship of the Deity" Leu Yen. With illustrations. 1864. 8°.   15111. d. 33.

劉善堂 LEW SHEN-T'ANG. Two complimentary scrolls inscribed by Lew Shen-t'ang. [1850?]   K. S.

李應憲 LE YING-HEEN. 華音啟蒙 *Hwa yin k'e mung*. "Colloquial Chinese for the instruction of (Korean) children." With a volume containing an inter-verbal translation of the contents of the first part. 2 vols. [1883?] Fol.   15260. b. 1.

MOK LAI CHI. See 莫禮智 MO LE-CHE.

莫禮智 MO LE-CHE. 華英應酬撮要 *Hwa Ying ying ch'ow ts'o yaou*. English conversation, including commercial phrases and abbreviations. By Mok Lai Chi. Second edition. *Hongkong*, 1899. 8°.   11100. a. 31.

MORRISON (ROBERT), D.D. Vocabulary of the Canton Dialect. Part I, English and Chinese. (Part II, Chinese and English; Part III, Chinese words and phrases.) 3 parts. *Macao*, 1828. 8°.   11095. a. 9.
    Imperfect, containing only Parts I and II.

蓬蒿子 P'ÄNG-HAOU TSZE. 新史奇觀全傳 *Sin she k'e kwan ts'euen chuen*. A novel. By a scholar styling himself P'äng-haou tsze. 4 keuen. [1870?] 8°.   15325. b. 1.

潘蔚偉 P'AN WEI-WEI. 衛生要術 *Wei săng yaou shuh*. "Important methods for preserving life." A system of postures. With illustrations. pp. 82. 1848. 8°.   15253. d. 4.

寶鋆 PAOU YUN. See 同治 T'UNG-CHE, *Emperor*. 大清穆宗毅皇帝實錄 *Ta Ts'ing moo tsung e Hwang-te shih luh*. "The true record of the reign of the Reverent Ancestor, the Resolute Emperor of the Great Pure Dynasty," i.e. T'ung-che . . . Compiled by Paou Yun, etc. 1873. Fol.   Or. 56. d.

PARAVEY (CHARLES DE). Six lithographed plates, Nos. ii—vii, on the sexagenary cycle and kindred subjects. The first is entitled "Tableau des rapports des deux cycles ce celui des animaux, aux saisons, aux éléments, &ª aux lettres, nombres." [1830?]   15235. c.

裨治文 PE-CHE-WĂN [i.e.   ]. 大美聯邦志畧 *Ta Mei leen pang che leŏ*. "A short account of the United States of America." With maps and illustrations. 2 keuen. 1861. 8°.   15276. a. 3.

PEKING. Chinese Plan of the [Tartar] City of Peking. Lithographed by Major T. B. Jervis. The original document from which this plan was lithographed was brought from Peking by an Italian missionary . . . and purchased by Sir Woodbine Parish at Naples in 1842. 4 sheets. 1843.   15235. c.
    The names of the streets and buildings are transliterated in Roman letters.

PEKING. A coloured plan of the city of Peking. [1850?] 15235. c.

Much torn.

ROSS (DANIEL). Plan of Tihen-pien, or Tien-pack Harbour, on the south coast of China. By Lieut. Daniel Ross. [1840?] A sheet. 15235. c.

小 兒 SEAOU URH. 小 兒 論 *Seaou urh lun.* "Conversations with Children." In Manchu and Korean. [1780?] Fol. 15354. d. 7.

西 番 SE FAN. 西 番 譯 語 *Se fan yih yu.* "A Tibetan and Chinese Vocabulary." pp. 206. [1800?] 8°. 15354. d. 8.

徐 浩 修 SEU HAOU-SEW. 國 朝 曆 象 考 *Kwo ch'aou leih seang k'aou* [Korean, *Kouk tjyo ryek syang ko*]. "A national astronomical Almanac." Compiled by Seu Haou-sew, and edited by Kin Yung and others. 4 keuen. Fol. 15260. a. 2.

徐 桐 SEU T'UNG. See 同 治 T'UNG-CHE, *Emperor.* 大 清 穆 宗 毅 皇 帝 實 錄 *Ta Ts'ing moo tsung e Hwang-te shih luh.* "The true record of the reign of the Reverent Ancestor, the Resolute Emperor of the Great Pure Dynasty," i.e. T'ung-che ... Compiled by ... Seu T'ung, etc. 1873. Fol. Or. 56. d.

Seven prints and drawings of horses and water buffaloes. [1850?] 15235. c.

商 務 書 館 SHANG WOO SHOO KWAN. 商 務 書 館 華 英 字 典 Commercial Press' English and Chinese Dictionary. Revised and enlarged. pp. 394. *Shanghai,* 1899. 8°. 11094. c. 4.

石 鳳 臺 SHIH FUNG-T'AI. 十 法 界 循 業 發 現 圖 *Shih fa keae hiun yay fa heen t'oo.* "An illustrated scroll representing the states of those who follow in the ways of those in the Ten regions of the law." With descriptive letterpress. Drawn by Shih Fung-t'ai. 1821. 15235. c.

聖 人 SHING JIN. 聖 人 言 行 *Shing jin yen hing.* "The sayings and doings of the Roman Catholic Saints" whose days occur in the month of May. pp. xii, 410. *Hongkong,* 1899. 8°. 15200. c. 69.

聖 敎 SHING KEAOU. 聖 敎 要 理 *Shing keaou yaou le.* "The important doctrines of the Holy (Roman Catholic) Religion." pp. x, 182. *Hongkong,* 1899. 8°. 15200. c. 63.

隨 緣 下 士 SUY LUH HEA SZE. 林 蘭 香 *Lin lan heang.* "The scent of the *Magnolia obovata.*" By a scholar calling himself "Suy luh hea sze." A novel. 8 keuen. 1878. 8°. 15325. b. 2.

四 川 SZE-CH'UEN. 四 川 省 會 城 池 全 圖 *Sze-ch'uen shing hwuy ch'ing ch'e ts'euen t'oo.* "A complete map of the city and moat of Ch'ing too, the capital city of Sze-ch'uen." [1800?] 15235. c.

大 極 上 薄 花 TA KEIH SHANG PO HWA. 大 極 上 薄 花 迺 龍 門 壹 端 *Ta keih shang po hwa nai lung mun yih twan.* "A collection of letters by Soo Chĕ and other scholars of the Sung Dynasty." Printed in white on a black ground. A Japanese edition. [1800?] 15313. f. 3.

電 白 TEEN-PIH. *See* ROSS (DANIEL). Plan of Tihen-pien, or Tien-pack Harbour ... By Lieut. Daniel Ross, etc. 15235. c.

天 文 T'EEN WĂN. 京 板 天 文 全 圖 *King pan t'een wăn ts'euen t'oo.* "An astronomical map of the world" in the two hemispheres. With a large coloured map of China appended. *Peking* [1840?]. A scroll. 15235. c.

丁 保 祿 TING PAOU-LUH. 上 宰 相 書 *Shang tsai seang shoo.* "The book of the lofty Prime Minister," i.e. God. pp. 22. *Hongkong,* 1890. 8°. 15200. b. 36.

托 津 T'O-TS'IN. 欽 定 理 藩 院 則 例 *K'in ting Le-fan-yuen tsih le.* "Imperially ordained rules and regulations of the Le-fan-yuen," or Colonial Office. Compiled in 1818, and revised in 1826 by T'o-ts'in and others. 63 keuen. 1826. 8°. 15241. e. 2.

載 齡 TSAI-LING. *See* 同 治 T'UNG-CHE, *Emperor.* 大 清 穆 宗 毅 皇 帝 實 錄 *Ta Ts'ing moo tsung e Hwang-te shih luh.* "The true record of the reign of the Reverent Ancestor, the Resolute Emperor of the Great Pure Dynasty," i.e. T'ung che ... Compiled by ... Prince Tsai-ling, etc. 1873. Fol. Or. 56. d.

郎 處 富 養 塔 *Tseih ch'oo tang yang t'a.* A Buddhist Sūtra printed within the outlines of a Pagoda. [1840?] A scroll. 15235. c.

泉 州 Tsʻᴇᴜᴇɴ-ᴄʜᴏᴡ. A rubbing of an inscription commemorating the erection of the Wan-ngan-too Stone Bridge in the eleventh century at the city of Tsʻeuen-chow in Fuhkien. 4 rolls.

15204. a. 8.

同 治 Tʻᴜɴɢ-ᴄʜᴇ, *Emperor.* 大 淸 穆 宗 毅 皇 帝 實 錄 *Ta Tsʻing moo tsung e Hwang-te shih luh.* "The true record of the reign of the Reverent Ancestor, the Resolute Emperor of the Great Pure Dynasty," i.e. Tʻung-che (1862–1874). Compiled by the high officials Paou Yun, Prince Tsai-ling, Chin Kwei-fun, and Seu Tʻung. MS. *Peking,* 1873. Fol.

Or. 56. d.

Imperfect, containing only vols. 327–330, consisting of records of the 1st, 2nd, and 3rd months of the 11th year of the reign of Tʻung-che, i.e. 1873.

童 蒙 Tʻᴜɴɢ ᴍᴜɴɢ. 童 蒙 先 習 *Tʻung mung seen seih* [Korean, *Tong mong syen seup*]. "A Children's Primer." In Chinese. pp. 34. [*Seoul,* 1890 ?] 8°. 15260. b. 4.

王 羲 之 Wᴀɴɢ Hᴇ-ᴄʜᴇ. 星 鳳 樓 帖 *Sing-fung low tʻeĕ.* "Writings from the Sing-fung tower." Facsimiles of writing by the celebrated calligrapher Wang He-che (ᴀ.ᴅ. 321–379). Engraved on stone in the year 1096. The first piece celebrates the repair of the Lan Pavilion on the Hwuy-che mountain. [1700 ?] 8°. Or. 56. b.

王 文 治 Wᴀɴɢ Wᴀ̆ɴ-ᴄʜᴇ. 南 華 得 大 羅 漢 像 讚 合 璧 *Nan hwa tih ta Lo-han seang tsan ho peih.* Beautifully coloured "Portraits of the eighteen Arhats (or immediate disciples of Buddha), with eulogies on them" written in gold letters on a dark blue ground. The work of Wang Wăn-che. MS. Eighteenth century. 4°.

Or. 6245.

萬 民 Wᴀɴ ᴍɪɴ. 照 萬 民 光 *Chaou wan min kwang.* "A light to lighten the Gentiles." A life of Christ in Chinese and Korean. pp. iv, 116. *English Missionary Society : Hanyang,* 1894. 8°. 15260. b. 2.

WOODBRIDGE (Sᴀᴍᴜᴇʟ I.). See 張 之 洞 Cʜᴀɴɢ Cʜᴇ-ᴛᴜɴɢ. China's only Hope . . . Translated from the Chinese edition by S. I. W., etc. 1900. 8°. 11100. a. 39.

—— [Another edition.] 1901. 8°. 11100. a. 40.

吳 錫 麒 Wᴏᴏ Sᴇɪ̈ʜ-ᴋʻᴇ. 有 正 味 齋 試 帖 詩 註 *Yew ching wei chai she tʻĕĕ she choo.* "A collection of poems, with notes, from the tasteful Study." By Woo Seïh-kʻe. 8 keuen. 1818. 8°. 15322. a. 3.

楊 愼 Yᴀɴɢ Sʜɪɴ. 南 詔 野 史 *Nan chaou yay she.* "An uncanonical history of Nan chaou," i.e. the territories of the Lolos and others in South-Western China. Compiled by Yang Shin, and edited by Hoo Wei. 2 keuen. *Yunnan Foo,* 1880. 8°. 15292. b. 3.

洋 烟 Yᴀɴɢ ʏᴇɴ. 勸 戒 洋 烟 文 *Kʻeuen keae yang yen wăn.* A series of coloured drawings illustrating the evils of opium-smoking. In the first picture a volume is represented bearing the above title, otherwise the collection is without title. MS. *Canton* [1850]. Obl.

15351. c. 1.

邀 月 樓 主 人 Yᴀᴏᴜ-ʏᴜᴇʜ ʟᴏᴡ ᴄʜᴏᴏ-ᴊɪɴ. 繪 具 記 *Hwuy chin ke.* A collection of plays. Compiled by Yaou-yueh low choo-jin, "the Master of the Inviting-moon Pavilion." 40 keuen. 1812. 8°. 15325. a. 2.

YUEN TIEN-KAN. Push him out ! or a Book of Chinese Prophecy. By Yuen Tien-kan (ᴀ.ᴅ. 643). [Translated into English by an anonymous writer.] pp. vii. *Shanghai,* 1895. 8°. 11095. a. 6.

輿 載 Yᴜ̈ ᴛsᴀɪ. 輿 載 撮 要 *Yü tsai tsʻo yaou.* "A resumé of the Geography of Korea." With maps. [1893 ?] 8°. 15270. a. 1.

POST ADDENDA.

王 大 任 Wᴀɴɢ Tᴀ-ᴊɪɴ. See 永 樂 Yᴜɴɢ-ʟᴏ, *Emperor.* 永 樂 大 典 *Yung-lo ta teen.* "The Great Standard of the Emperor Yung-lo . . ." Collated by . . . Wang Ta-jin, etc. Fol. Or. 5982.

永 樂 Yᴜɴɢ-ʟᴏ, *Emperor.* 永 樂 大 典 *Yung-lo ta teen.* "The Great Standard of the Emperor Yung-lo" (1403–1425). MS. A huge encyclopædia consisting of 22,877 keuen, with an index of 60 keuen, in 11,100 volumes. Compiled by a commission appointed for the purpose, and collated by Chʻin E-kʻin and Wang Ta-jin, revisers in chief, and others. It was never printed. The present volume was saved from the destruction by fire of the Han-lin College during the siege of the Legations at Peking in 1900. [1562–1567.] Fol. Or. 5982.

One volume, containing Keuen 19,789–19,790.

INDEX.

[In this Index an Asterisk (*) is prefixed to Titles which appear among the Addenda.]

AES—CHE

浙 江 鄉 試 硃 卷 *Chĕkeang heang shih choo keuen.* See 姚 駣 語 YAOU WĂN-YU.

浙 江 嘉 興 城 守 營 *Chĕkeang keahing ch'ing show ying.* See 浙 江 CHĔKEANG.

浙 江 關 日 徵 還 簿 *Chĕkeang kwan jih ching hwan pu.* See 浙 江 關 CHĔKEANG KWAN.

浙 江 魁 卷 *Chĕkeang k'wei keuen.* See 浙 江 CHĔKEANG.

—— See 顧 KOO, and 李 LE.

知 古 錄 *Che koo luh.* See 恆 壽 之 HĂNG SHOW-CHE.

指 南 針 *Che nan chin.* See 胡 德 邁 HOO TIH-MAI.

至 寶 錄 *Che paou luh.* See 李 省 愆 LE SĂNG-K'EEN.

折 獄 龜 鑑 *Chĕ yo kwei keen.* See 鄭 克 CHING K'IH.

昔 時 賢 文 *Chhien jŭ bŭn.* See 謝 敦 倫 SEAY TUN-LUN.

* 勅 封 燮 元 贊 運 純 陽 演 正 警 化 孚 佑 帝 君 *Ch'ih fung seĕ yuen tsan yun shun yang yen ching king hwa foo yew te keun.* See 呂 品 LEU YEN.

直 省 鄉 墨 *Chih săng heang mih.* See 陳 栻 CHIN CHIH.

* 赤 道 南 北 兩 總 星 圖 *Ch'ih taou nan pih leang tsung sing t'oo.* See 赤 道 CH'IH TAOU.

尺 牘 分 類 *Ch'ih tuh fun luy.* See 樓 霞 氏 TS'E HEA-SHE.

尺 牘 分 類 補 遺 *Ch'ih tuh fun luy poo e.* See 樓 霞 氏 TS'E HEA-SHE.

植 物 名 實 圖 考 *Chih wuh ming shih t'oo k'aou.* See 吳 其 濬 WOO K'E-SEUN.

鎮 州 臨 濟 慧 照 禪 師 語 錄 *Chin-chow Lin tse Hwuy-chaou shen sze yu luh.* See 慧 照 HWUY-CHAOU.

陳 忠 愍 公 殉 難 詩 文 錄 *Ch'in chung min kung seun nan she wăn luh.* See 黃 仁 HWANG JIN.

CHINESE, COREAN, AND ENGLISH JOURNAL OF COMMERCE AND ENGINEERING. See PERIODICAL PUBLICATIONS: *London.*

鎮 撫 事 宜 *Chin foo sze e.* See 楊 筍 SUNG YUN.

鄭 志 *Ching che.* See 粵 雅 堂 YUĔ-YA-T'ANG.

成 方 切 用 *Ch'ing fang tseĕ yung.* See 吳 遵 程 WOO TSUN-CH'ING.

鏡 花 水 月 *Ching hwa shwuy yueh.* See 羽 衣 客 YU E KIH.

正 人 明 堂 圖 *Ching jin ming t'ang t'oo.* See 伯 仁 滑 PIH JIN-HWA.

正 教 異 詮 *Ching keaou chin ts'euen.* See 正 教 CHING KEAOU.

—— See 王 岱 輿 WANG TAI-YU.

正 教 率 傳 *Ching keaou fung chuen.* See 黃 伯 祿 HWANG PIH-LUH.

貞 觀 政 要 *Ching-kwan ching yaou.* See 吳 兢 WOO KING.

正 名 要 論 *Ching ming yaou lun.* See 湛 約 翰 CHAN YOHAN.

呈 報 運 到 茶 葉 件 數 清 冊 *Ch'ing paou yun taou ch'a ye keen soo ts'ing tsih.* See 茶 葉 CH'A YE.

正 平 本 論 語 札 解 *Ch'ing p'ing pun lun yu chah keae.* See 四 書 SZE SHOO.

鄭 氏 易 譜 *Ching she yih poo.* See 鄭 承 袞 CHING CH'ING-KWĂN.

誠 心 痛 悔 前 過 *Ch'ing sin t'ung hwuy ts'een kwo.* See 世 昌 SHE-CH'ANG.

正 積 廣 治 平 畧 *Ching suh kwang che p'ing leŏ.* See 蔡 九 霞 TS'AI KEW-HEA.

成 道 記 *Ch'ing taou ke.* See 王 勃 WANG PO.

證 道 經 *Ching taou king.* See 純 陽 氏 SHUN-YANG SHE.

稱 讚 淨 土 經 *Ch'ing tsan Tsing t'oo king.* See 昌 觀 CH'ANG-KWAN.

正 字 通 *Ching tsze t'ung.* See 廖 百 子 LEAOU PIH-TSZE.

—— See 吳 源 起 WOO YUEN-K'E.

正 音 撮 要 *Ching yin tso yaou.* See 高 靜 亭 KAOU TSING-T'ING.

成 語 考 *Ch'ing yu k'aou.* See 丘 濬 K'EW SEUN.

CHI—CHO

正韻訓蒙增廣 *Ching yun heun mung tsǎng kwang.* See 正韻 CHING YUN.

正韻通 *Ching yun t'ung.* See 呂維祺 LEU WEI-K'E.

箴膏肓評 *Chin kaou mǎng p'ing.* See 劉逢祿 LEW FUNG-LUH.

陳檢討四六 *Ch'in keen-t'aou sze luh.* See 陳維崧 CH'IN WEI-SUNG.

鍼灸大成 *Chin kew ta ch'ing.* See 陽斬賢 YANG KIN-HEEN.

異理課選 *Chin le k'o seuen.* See 王炳堃 WANG PING-K'UN.

異理八篇 *Chin le pa p'een.* See 楊格非 YANG KIH-FEI.

異理便讀三字經 *Chin le peen tuh San tsze king.* See 楊格非 YANG KIH-FEI.

異理尋繹 *Chin le sin yih.* See 慕維廉 MOO WEI-LEEN.

陳修園公餘醫錄十五種合刻 *Ch'in Sew-yuen kung yu e luh shih woo chung ho kih.* See 陳修園 CH'IN SEW-YUEN.

異道入門問答 *Chin taou juh mun wǎn ta.* See 楊格非 YANG KIH-FEI.

異道略論 *Chin taou leǒ lun.* See 帥萬誼 SZE A. E.

異道自證 *Chin taou tsze ching.* See 異道 CHIN TAOU.

—— See 沙守信 SHA SHOW-SIN.

—— See 善德 SHEN-TIH.

異道問答 *Chin taou wǎn ta.* See 羅爾梯 LO URH-TE.

鎮宅全書 *Chin tsih ts'euen shoo.* See 玉清帝君 YUH TS'ING TE KEUN.

彰宗三昧 *Chin tsung san mei.* See 張路玉 CHANG LOO-YUH.

* 異言集 *Chin yen tseǐh.* See 異言 CHIN YEN.

—— See 龍嚴 LUNG-YEN.

箴言摘錄 *Chin yen tsih luh.* See 箴言 CHIN YEN.

湛園札記 *Chin yuen cha ke.* See 姜宸英 KEANG SHIN-YING.

宸垣識畧 *Ch'in yuen shih leǒ.* See 吳長元 WOO CHANGYUEN.

處州府志 *Ch'oo-chow foo che.* See 黃平曹 HWANG P'ING-TS'AOU.

處分則例圖要 *Ch'oo fun tsih le t'oo yaou.* See 蔡逢年 TS'AI FUNG-NEEN.

* 初學文範 *Ch'oo heǒ wǎn fan.* See 初學 CH'OO HEǑ.

初會問答 *Ch'oo hwuy wǎn ta.* See 初會 CH'OO HWUY.

諸儒註解古文異實前集 *Choo joo choo keae koo wǎn chin paou ts'een tseǐh.* See 諸儒 CHOO JOO.

諸儒箋解古文異實 *Choo joo tseen keae koo wǎn chin paou.* See 林以正 LIN E-CHING.

諸儒箋解古文異實後集 *Choo joo tseen keae koo wǎn chin paou how tseǐh.* See 諸儒 CHOO JOO.

諸儒箋解古文異實前集 *Choo joo tseen keae koo wǎn chin paou ts'een tseǐh.* See 諸儒 CHOO JOO.

諸葛忠武侯文集 *Chooko chung woo how wǎn tseǐh.* See 諸葛亮 CHOOKO LEANG.

硃批增註七家詩選 *Choo p'e tsǎng choo ts'ih kea she seuen.* See 張熙宇 CHANG HEYU.

硃批諭旨 *Choo pe yu che.* See 雍正 YUNG-CHING, *Emperor.*

鑄史駢言 *Choo she peen yen.* See 孫玉田 SUN YUH-T'EEN.

註釋入銘塾鈔 *Choo shih pa-ming shuh chaou.* See 吳蘭陔 WOO LAN-KAI.

主神論 *Choo shin lun.* See 胡德邁 HOO TIH-MAI.

主神十條誡 *Choo shin shih t'eaou keae.* See 胡德邁 HOO TIH-MAI.

朱子格言 *Choo tsze kih yen.* See 朱熹 CHOO HE.

諸子平義 *Choo tsze p'ing e.* See 俞樾 YU YUĚ.

朱子大全 *Choo tsze ta ts'euen.* See 朱熹 CHOO HE.

朱文公校昌黎先生集 *Choo wǎn kung keaou Ch'ang-le seen sǎng tseǐh.* See 韓愈 HAN YU.

殊域周咨錄 *Choo yih chow tsze luh.* See 嚴從簡 YEN TS'UNG-KEEN.

朝鮮板頰合 *Chōsen ban ruigŏ.* See 朝鮮 CHŌSEN.

抽尊圖叢稿 *Chotsun yuen ts'ung kaou.* See 黎庶昌 LE SHOO-CH'ANG.

籌海初集 *Chow hai ch'oo tseih.* See 關天培 KWAN T'EEN-PEI.

周官祿田考 *Chow kwan luh t'een k'aou.* See 沈彤 CH'IN T'UNG.

周禮 *Chow le.* See 周禮 CHOW LE.

—— See 姜兆錫 KEANG CHAOU-SEIH.

周禮貫珠 *Chow le kwan choo.* See 胡必相 HOO PEIH-SEANG.

周禮節訓 *Chow le tseih heun.* See 周禮 CHOW LE.

周禮精華 *Chow le tsing hwa.* See 周禮 CHOW LE.

周詩天機釋解婚姻圖 *Chow she t'een ke shih keae hwăn yin t'oo.* See 周 CHOW.

周易 *Chow yih.* See 周易 CHOW YIH.

—— See 易經 YIH KING.

周易傳義大全 *Chow yih chuen e ta ts'euen.* See 易經 YIH KING.

周易衆義集成 *Chow Yih seang e tseih ch'ing.* See 陳藻垣 CH'IN TSAOU-YUEN.

周易審義 *Chow yih shin e.* See 周易 CHOW YIH.

周易讀本 *Chow yih tuh pun.* See 易經 YIH KING.

船山詩草 *Ch'uen shan she ts'aou.* See 張問陶 CHANG WĂN-T'AOU.

篆書唐詩選 *Chuen shoo T'ang she seuen.* See 鳳岡闗 FUNG KANG-KWAN.

篆字彙 *Chuen tsze wei.* See 佟世男 TUNG SHE-NAN.

竹波軒槼冊 *Chuh po heen mei tsih.* See 伯仁 PIH JEN.

竹書紀年統箋 *Chuh shoo ke neen t'ung tseen.* See 沈約 CH'IN YO.

CHU-KIANG OR PEARL RIVER. *See* BROWN (THOMAS MARSH).

種福堂公績選臨證指南 *Chung-fuh T'ang kung suh seuen lin ching che nan.* See 葉天士 YE T'EEN-SZE.

中鋒集初編 *Chung fung tseih ch'oo peen.* See 薛慰農 SËE WEI-NUNG.

忠孝經讀本 *Chung heaou king tuh pun.* See 馬融 MA YUNG.

重學 *Chung heŏ.* See 艾約瑟 GAI YO-SIH.

沖虛眞經 *Ch'ung heu chin king.* See 列禦冠 LËE YU-K'OW.

中華諸兄慶賀新禧文 *Chung hwa choo heung k'ing ho sin he wăn.* See 尙德 SHANG TIH.

中日戰輯 *Chung Jih chen chi.* See 王炳耀 WANG PING-YAO.

重刊證類本草 *Chung k'an ching luy pun ts'aou.* See 李時珍 LE SHE-CHIN.

重刊改併五音類聚四聲篇 *Chung k'an kai ping woo yin luy tseu sze shing p'een.* See 覺恒 KEŎHĂNG.

重刊改併五音集韻 *Chung k'an kai ping woo yin tseih yun.* See 韓道昭 HAN TAOU-CHAO.

中國教會新報 *Chung kwo keaou hwuy sin paou.* See PERIODICAL PUBLICATIONS: *Shanghai.*

中國新政安行 *Chung kwo sin ching ngan hing.* See 何啟 HO K'E, and 胡禮垣 HOO LE-YUEN.

忠烈俠義傳 *Chung lëĕ hëĕ e chuen.* See 問竹主人 WĂN CHUH CHOO JIN, *pseud.*

鍾呂二仙傳道集 *Chung Leu urh seen chuen taou tseih.* See 鍾離權 CHUNG LE-K'EUEN.

中西合歷 *Chung se ho leih.* See 曾紀澤 TS'ĂNG KE-TSIH.

中西四書 *Chung Se Sze shoo.* See 四書 SZE SHOO.

* 中西通書 *Chung se t'ung shoo.* See EPHEMERIDES.

中西聞見錄 *Chung se wăn keen luh.* See PERIODICAL PUBLICATIONS.

—— *See* PERIODICAL PUBLICATIONS: *Shanghai.*

鍾山課藝彙鈔 *Chung shan k'o e wei chaou.* See 李小湖 LE SEAOU-HOO.

CHU—ESH

重訂廣輿記 *Chung ting Kwang yu ke.* See 陸應陽 LUH YINGYANG.

重訂國語國策合註 *Chung ting Kwo-yü kwo ts'ih ho choo.* See 韋昭 WEI CHAOU.

重訂唐詩三百首續選 *Chung ting T'ang she san pih show suh seuen.* See 于慶元 YU K'ING-YUEN.

鐘鼎字源 *Chung ting tsze yuen.* See 汪立名 WANG LEIH-MING.

中詮 *Chung ts'euen.* See 汪登原 WANG TÄNG-YUEN.

中外新報 *Chung wai sin paou.* See PERIODICAL PUBLICATIONS : *Shanghai.*

中英商工機器時報 *Chung Ying shang kung ke k'e she paou.* See PERIODICAL PUBLICATIONS : *London.*

中英新增條議 *Chung Ying sin tsäng t'eaou e.* See CHINA : KWANG-SEU, *Emperor.*

中原音韻 *Chung yuen yin yun.* See 周德清 CHOW TIH-TS'ING.

中庸章句 *Chung yung chang keu.* See 四書 SZE SHOO.

中庸章句本義匯叅 *Chung yung chang keu pun e hwuy ts'an.* See 四書 SZE SHOO.

中庸指南 *Chung yung che nan.* See 四書 SZE SHOO.

春暉堂叢書 *Ch'un hwuy T'ang ts'ung shoo.* See 春暉堂 CH'UN HWUY T'ANG.

春在堂詩編 *Ch'un tsai t'ang she peen.* See 俞樾 YU YUĔ.

春秋 *Ch'un Ts'ew.* See 孔丘 K'UNG K'EW.

春秋正文 *Ch'un Ts'ew ching wăn.* See 孔丘 K'UNG K'EW.

春秋胡氏傳 *Ch'un Ts'ew Hoo she chuen.* See 孔丘 K'UNG K'EW.

春秋綱目左傳句解 *Ch'un Ts'ew kang muh Tso chuen keu keae.* See 左邱明 TSO K'EW-MING.

春秋穀梁經傳補注 *Ch'un Ts'ew Kuh-leang king chuen poo choo.* See 穀梁赤 KUH-LEANG CH'IH.

揣籥小錄 *Ch'uy yo seaou luh.* See 張作楠 CHANG TSO-NAN.

創世記問答 *Ch'wang she ke wăn ta.* See 狄考文 T'EIH K'AOU-WĂN.

創世歷代書 *Ch'wang she leih tai shoo.* See 倘德者 SHANG TIH CHAY.

莊子虛齋口義 *Chwang-tsze keu chai k'ow e.* See 莊周 CHWANG CHOW.

Di-li shü. See 丁韪良 TING WEI-LEANG.

儀徵縣續志 *E-ching Heen suh che.* See 顔希源 YEN HE-YUEN.

沂州府志 *E-chow Foo che.* See 李希賢 LE HE-HEEN.

醫效祕傳 *E heaou pe chuen.* See 吳葉桂 WOO YE-KWEI.

醫學正傳 *E heŏ ching chuen.* See 虞摶 YU TW'AN.

醫學報 *E heŏ paou.* See PERIODICAL PUBLICATIONS : *Hongkong.*

義學新法 *E heŏ sin fa.* See 仲均安 CHUNG KEUN-NGAN.

宜稼堂叢書 *E-kea T'ang ts'ung shoo.* See 宜稼堂 E-KEA T'ANG.

易經增訂旁訓 *E king tsäng ting pang heun.* See 文王 WĂN-WANG, and 周公 CHOW-KUNG, etc.

儀禮 *E le.* See 儀禮 E LE.

儀禮章句易讀 *E le chang keu yih tuh.* See 馬駉 MA KUNG.

以利亞言行傳 *E-le-ya yen hing chuen.* See 以利亞 E-LE-YA.

醫林改錯 *E lin kai ts'o.* See 王清任 WANG TS'ING-JIN.

醫林撮要 *E lin ts'o yaou.* See 弘退思 HUNG T'UY-SZE.

醫門法律 *E mun fa leŭh.* See 喩嘉言 YU KEA-YEN.

Erh-tou-Mei. See MEI.

E shih pe chuen. See ÆSOP.

意拾喩言 *E-shih yu yen.* See ÆSOP.

醫書滙叅輯成 *E shoo hwuy ts'an tseih ch'ing.* See 蔡象貞 TS'AI SEANG-CHING.

伊娑菩喻言 *E-so-p'oo yu yen.* See ÆSOP.

異談可信錄 *E t'an k'o sin luh.* See 葵鄉 KW'EI HEANG.

擬勦洗嘆咭唎策 *E tseaou se Ying-keïh-le ts'ih.* See 嘆咭唎 YING-KEÏH-LE.

詒晉齋法帖 *E tsin chai fa tëě.* See 王亭 WANG T'ING.

* 倚晴樓七種曲 *E-ts'ing low ts'ih chung k'euh.* 倚晴樓 E-TS'ING LOW.

異端總論 *E twan tsung lun.* See 異端 E TWAN.

藝文備覽 *E wǎn pei lan.* See 吳毅人 WOO KUH-JIN.

依樣葫蘆 *E yang hoo loo.* See 葫蘆 HOO LOO.

法顯傳 *Fa heen chuen.* See 法顯 FA HEEN.

法國律例 *Fa kwo leuh le.* See 畢利幹 PEÏH-LE-KAN.

發蒙小品二集 *Fa mung seaou p'in urh tseïh.* See 唐惟懋 T'ANG WEI-MOW.

發蒙小品式集註釋 *Fa mung seaou p'in urh tseïh choo shih.* See 沈鏡涵 CH'IN KING-HAN.

發蒙益慧錄 *Fa mung yih hwuy luh.* See 哈巴禮理 HA-PA LE-LE.

泛槎圖 *Fan ch'a t'oo.* See 張寶 CHANG PAOU.

防海備覽 *Fang hai pei lan.* See 薛傳源 SEAY CHUEN-YUEN.

防海新論 *Fang hai sin lun.* See 希理哈 HE-LE-HA.

方壺外史 *Fang hoo wai she.* See 陸西星 LUH SE-SING.

方田通法補例 *Fang t'een t'ung fa poo le.* See 張作楠 CHANG TSO-NAN.

方言 *Fang yen.* See 揚雄 YANG HEUNG.

方興紀要簡覽 *Fang yu ke yaou keen lan.* See 顧祖禹 KOO TSOO-YU.

梵綱經 *Fan kang king.* See 梵 FAN.

樊南文集詳註 *Fan-nan wǎn tseïh tseang choo.* See 李義山 LE E-SHAN.

反唐女媧鏡全集 *Fan T'ang Neu-kwa king ts'euen tseïh.* See 反唐 FAN T'ANG.

反唐全傳 *Fan T'ang ts'euen chuen.* See 如遴 JOO LEEN.

翻譯名義 *Fan yih ming e.* See 名義 MING E.

翻譯名義集選 *Fan yih ming e tseïh seuen.* See 名義 MING E.

飛龍全傳 *Fei lung ts'euen chuen.* See 東隅逸士 TUNG YU YIH SZE.

飛蛇全傳 *Fei shay ts'euen chuen.* See 飛蛇 FEI SHAY.

* 飛雲閣名箋貢屜 *Fei-yun ko ming tseen kung shen.* See 飛雲閣 FEI-YUN KO.

Foh-ing dao-li ling kying veng-teh. See FOH-ING.

* 伏人明堂圖 *Foo jin ming t'ang t'oo.* See 伏人 FOO JIN.

* 婦科保嬰三生合編 *Foo k'o paou ying san sǎng ho peen.* See 婦科 FU K'O.

富國策 *Foo kwo ts'ih.* See 丁慧瓦 TING WEI-LEANG.

輔彌撒經 *Foo Me-sa king.* See 彌撒經 ME-SA KING.

敷文書院課藝 *Foo wǎn shoo yuen k'o e.* See 沈念農 CH'IN NEEN-NUNG.

賦役全書 *Foo yih ts'euen shoo.* See 賦役 FOO YIH.

婦嬰新說 *Foo ying sin shwo.* See 合信 HO-SIN.

禰 *Fuh.* See FUH.

福建通志 *Fuh-keen t'ung che.* See 福建 FUH-KEEN.

佛國記 *Fuh kwo ke.* See 法顯 FA HEEN.

福綠善慶集 *Fuh luh shen k'ing tseïh.* See 孟經國 MǍNG KING-KWO.

福山縣志 *Fuh-shan heen che.* See 鹿兆甲 LUH CHAOU-KEǍ.

佛說阿彌陀經 *Fuh shwo Amet'o king.* See 鳩摩羅什 KEW-MO-LO-SHIH.

佛說解冤劫神咒 *Fuh shwo keae yuen këě Shin chow.* See 佛 FUH.

佛說觀無量壽經 *Fuh shwo kwan woo leang show king.* See 疊瓦耶舍 KEANG-LEANG YAY-SHAY.

FUH—HAN

佛 說 摩 利 支 天 陀 羅 尼 經 *Fuh shwo Mo-le-che t'een T'o-lo-ne king.* See 佛 FUH.

佛 說 無 量 壽 經 *Fuh shwo woo leang show king.* See 康 僧 鎧 K'ANG TSĂNG-K'AI.

佛 頂 尊 勝 陀 羅 尼 *Fuh ting tsun shing t'o lo ne.* See 佛 頂 FUH TING.

佛 祖 歷 代 通 載 *Fuh tsoo leth tai t'ung tsai.* See 念 常 NEEN-CH'ANG.

福 音 之 箴 規 *Fuh yin chih chin kwei.* See 愛 漢 者 NGAI HAN CHAY.

福 音 講 臺 *Fuh yin keang t'ai.* See 陸 小 峯 LUH SEAOU-FUNG.

福 音 排 偶 便 覽 *Fuh yin p'ai gow peen lan.* See HUTCHINSON (A. B.).

福 音 聖 詩 *Fuh yin shing she.* See 福 音 FUH YIN.

* 福 音 大 旨 *Fuh yin ta che.* See JOHN (GRIFFITH).

福 音 道 問 答 合 講 *Fuh yin taou wǎn ta ho keang.* See 福 音 FUH YIN.

福 音 調 和 *Fuh yin t'eaou ho.* See 尚 德 SHANG TIH.

福 音 讚 美 歌 *Fuh yin tsan mei ko.* See 長 老 公 CH'ANG LAOU-KUNG.

粉 粧 樓 全 傳 *Fun chwang low ts'euen chuen.* See 粉 粧 樓 FUN CHWANG LOW.

鳳 凰 山 *Fung hwang shan.* See 鳳 凰 山 FUNG HWANG SHAN.

馮 母 陸 太 淑 人 傳 *Fung moo Luh T'ai-shuh jin chuen.* See 陸 太 淑 LUH T'AI-SHUH.

鳳 山 縣 志 *Fung shan heen che.* See 梁 文 煜 LEANG WĂN-YUH.

奉 使 朝 鮮 驛 程 日 記 *Fung she Ch'aou-seen yih ch'ing jih ke.* See 柏 靜 濤 PIH TSING-T'AOU.

馮 氏 錦 囊 秘 錄 *Fung she kin nang pe luh.* See 馮 楚 瞻 FUNG TS'OO-CHEN.

鳳 臺 縣 志 *Fungt'ai heen che.* See 姚 學 甲 YAOU HEŏKEă.

分 野 奇 書 *Fun yay k'e shoo.* See 分 野 FUN YAY.

安 樂 集 *Gan lo tseth.* See 道 綽 TAOU-CH'O.

安 樂 家 *Gan yo kea.* See WALTON (CATHERINE AUGUSTA).

歐 洲 東 方 交 涉 記 *Gow chow tung fang keaou she ke.* See 麥 高 爾 MIH-KAOU-URH.

甌 北 集 *Gow pih tseth.* See 趙 翼 CHAOU YIH.

甌 北 全 集 *Gow pih ts'euen tseth.* See 趙 翼 CHAOU YIH.

歐 陽 氏 遺 書 *Gow-yang she e shoo.* See 歐 陽 直 GOW-YANG CHIH.

海 幢 阿 字 無 禪 師 語 錄 *Hai chwang Ah-tsze Woo shen sze yu luh.* See 阿 字 無 AH-TSZE WOO.

海 瑞 大 紅 袍 全 傳 *Hai shwuy ta hung paou ts'euen chuen.* See 李 春 芳 LE CH'UN-FANG.

海 塘 輯 要 *Hai t'ang tseth yaou.* See 韋 更 斯 WEI-KĂNG-SZE.

海 道 圖 說 *Hai taou t'oo shwŏ.* See 金 約 翰 KIN YOHAN.

海 島 逸 誌 *Hai taou yih che.* See 王 大 海 WANG TA-HAI.

孩 子 受 洗 禮 論 *Hai tsze show se le lun.* See 狄 考 文 T'EIH K'AOU WĂN.

孩 童 故 事 *Hait'ung koo sze.* See NEVIUS (MRS.).

海 運 要 畧 *Hai yun yaou leŏ.* See 施 永 圖 SHE YUNG-T'OO.

航 海 簡 法 *Hang hai keen fa.* See 那 麗 NA-LE.

航 海 金 針 *Hang hai kin chin.* See MACGOWAN (DANIEL JEROME).

—— See 馬 高 溫 MA-KAOU-WĂN.

亨 利 實 錄 *Hăng-le shih luh.* See BUTT, afterwards SHERWOOD (MARY MARTHA).

恒 星 表 *Hăng sing peaou.* See 買 步 緯 KEA PU-WEI.

* 恒 星 圖 表 *Hăng sing t'oo peaou.* See 恒 星 HĂNG SING.

橫 財 玉 尺 圖 *Hăng ts'ai yuh ch'ih t'oo.* See 財 TS'AI.

塞 香 亭 傳 奇 *Han heang t'ing chuen k'e.* See 李 凱 LE K'AI.

漢話初階 *Han hwa ch'oo keae.* See 漢話 HAN HWA.

漢儒易義針度 *Han joo Yih e chin too.* See 朱昌壽 CHOO CH'ANG-SHOW.

漢口竹枝詞 *Han k'ow chuh che ts'ze.* See 葉鼎三 YE TING-SAN.

涵三鏡 *Han san king.* See 熏沐 HEUN-MUH.

漢西域圖考 *Han se yih t'oo k'aou.* See 李光廷 LE KWANG T'ING.

韓詩增註証訛 *Han she tsǎng choo ching go.* See 韓愈 HAN YU.

漢魏叢書 *Han Wei ts'ung shoo.* See 程榮 CH'ING YUNG.

漢武梁石室 *Han Woo Leang shih shih.* See 武梁 WOO LEANG.

漢語入門 *Han yu juh mun.* See WIEGER (LÉON).

好逑傳 *Hao k'ew chuen.* See 逑 K'EW.

諧鐸 *Heae to.* See 沈桐威 CH'IN T'UNG-WEI.

鄉訓五十二則 *Heang heun woo shih urh tsih.* See 博愛者 PO-GAI-CHAY.

香山縣志 *Heang-shan Heen che.* See 武林祝 WOO LIN-CHOW.

鄉試硃卷 *Heang she choo keuen.* See 曹驊 TS'AOU HWA.

孝經 *Heaou king.* See 孔丘 K'UNG K'EW.

孝敬父母 *Heaou king foo moo.* See 郭顯德 KO HEEN-TIH.

曉諭告示賞格則列 *Heaou yu kaou she shang kih tsih le.* See 告示 KAOU SHE.

夏商合傳 *Hea Shang ho chuen.* See 鍾惺 CHUNG SING.

遐邇貫珍 *Hea urh kwan chin.* See PERIODICAL PUBLICATIONS : Hongkong.

遐域瑣談 *Hea yuh so t'an.* See 椿園氏 CH'UN-YUEN-SHE.

熙朝新語 *He ch'aou sin yu.* See 余金 YU KIN.

—— See 余徳水 YU TIH-SHWUY.

咸豐八年原定稅則核與同治五六年進出貨物貿易並抽值成數及征稅來源合開清冊 *Heen-fung pa neen yuen ting shwuy tsih ho yu T'ung-che woo lew neen tsin ch'uh hwo wuh maou e ping ch'ow chih ch'ing shoo keih ching shwuy hai yuen ho k'ai ts'ing ts'ih.* See CHINA : Inspectorate General of Customs.

賢刧千佛號 *Heen keih ts'een fuh haou.* See 千佛 TS'EEN FUH.

閑邪公家傳 *Heen-seay kung kea ch'uen.* See 周馳 CHOW CH'E.

* 現世報應圖 *Heen she paou ying t'oo.* See 現世 HEEN SHE.

弦切對數表 *Heen ts'ĕĕ tuy shoo peaou.* See 賈步緯 KEA POO-WEI.

學考 *Heŏ k'aou.* See 學 HEŎ.

學宮圖考 *Heŏkung t'oo k'aou.* See 學宮 HEŎKUNG.

學院大人考取全省遺才題名錄 *Heŏ Yuen ta jin k'aou ts'eu ts'euen sǎng e ts'ai t'e ming luh.* See 學院大人 HEŎ YUEN TA JIN.

學庸 *Heŏ yung.* See 四書 SZE SHOO.

希伯來書註釋 *He-pih-lai shoo choo shih.* See BIBLE—NEW TESTAMENT : Hebrews.

禊帖類聯 *He tĕĕ luy leen.* See 李光昭 LE KWANG-CHAOU.

訓蒙指南 *Heun mung che nan.* See MAY (ALFRED J.).

訓兒臭言 *Heun urh chin yen.* See PEEP.

—— See 師小姬 SZE SEAOU-K'E.

—— See 兒 URH.

省察規矩要理 *Hing ch'a kwei keu yaou le.* See 省察 HING CH'A.

行軍測繪 *Hing keun ts'ih hwuy.* See 連提 LEEN-T'E.

行軍總要 *Hing keun tsung yaou.* See 太平天國 T'AIP'ING T'EEN KWO.

刑部比照加減成案 *Hing Poo pe chaou kea keen ch'ing gan.* See 許槤 HEU LEEN, and 熊莪 HEUNG GO.

行水金鑑 *Hing shwuy kin keen.* See 傅澤洪
Foo Tsih-hung.

行文剳諭 *Hing wăn cha yu.* See 行文剳
Hing wăn cha.

標箋文章航範 *Hiôsen bunshō kihan.* See
謝枋得 Seay Fang-tih, and 鄒守益
Tsow Show-yih.

鶴徵後錄 *Ho ching how luh.* See 李富孫
Le Foo-sun.

鶴徵錄 *Ho ching luh.* See 李敬堂 Le
King-t'ang.

鶴林玉露 *Ho lin yuh loo.* See 羅大經 Lo
Ta-king.

河洛精蘊 *Ho lo tsing yun.* See 江永 Keang
Yung.

The Hông shan or Macao Dialect. *See* Ball
(Dyer), M.D.

河內縣志 *Honuy heen che.* See 蕭家蕙
Seaou Keahwuy.

護法論 *Hoo fa lun.* See 張商英 Chang
Shang-ying.

湖海詿傳 *Hoo hai she chuen.* See 王昶
Wang Ch'ang.

湖海文傳 *Hoo hai wăn chuen.* See 王昶
Wang Ch'ang.

弧角設如 *Hoo keŏ she joo.* See 張作楠
Chang Tso-nan.

弧三角舉隅 *Hoo san kŏ keu yu.* See
江臨泰 Keang Lin-t'ai.

合壁小學 *Ho pĕih seaou heŏ.* See 朱熹
Choo He.

貨則條例 *Ho tsih t'eaou le.* See 貨 Ho.

後漢書贅語 *How Han shoo chuy yu.* See
李欽之 Le K'in-che.

火烟車路規例 *Ho yen ch'ay loo kwei le.*
See 火烟車路 Ho yen ch'ay loo.

和約書 *Ho yo shoo.* See France: Napoleon III,
Emperor.

紅侏儒傳 *Hung choo joo chuen.* See Pearse
(Mark Guy), *the Younger.*

紅樓復夢 *Hung low fuh mung.* See 樵南陽
Ts'eaou Nan-yang.

紅樓夢圖詠 *Hung low mung t'oo yung.* See
改琦 Kai K'e.

—— See 紅樓夢 Hung low mung.

鴻雪圖綠 *Hung seuĕ t'oo yuen.* See 麟見亭
Lin Keen-t'ing.

鴻雪因綠圖 *Hung seuĕ yin yuen t'oo.* See
崇 Ts'ung.

紅十字會救傷第一法 *Hung shih tsze
hwuy kew shang te yih fa.* See 柯士賓 Ko-
sze-pin.

華夷通語 *Hwa e t'ung yu.* See 林衡南
Lin Häng-nan.

華夷譯語 *Hwa E yih yu.* See 華夷 Hwa E.

華番和合通書 *Hwa Fan ho ho t'ung shoo.*
See Periodical Publications: *Hongkong.*

化學指南 *Hwa heŏ che nan.* See 畢利幹
Peïh-le-kan.

化學分原 *Hwa heŏ fun yuen.* See 蒲陸山
P'oo-luh-shan.

化學鑑原 *Hwa heŏ keen yuen.* See 韋而司
Wei-urh-sze.

化學鑑原補編 *Hwa heŏ keen yuen poo peen.*
See Bloxam (Charles Loudon).

化學鑑原續編 *Hwa heŏ keen yuen suh peen.*
See 蒲陸山 P'oo-luh-shan.

化學闡原 *Hwa heŏ shen yuen.* See 畢利幹
Peïh-le-kan.

華學進境 *Hwa heŏ tsin king.* See Kuo
(Guiseppe M.).

化學衛生論 *Hwa heŏ wei săng lun.* See
吳司滕 Chin-sze-t'ăng.

* 化學易知 *Hwa heŏ yih chih.* See 傅蘭雅
Foo-lan-ya.

淮軍平捻記 *Hwai keun p'ing neen ke.* See
趙烈文 Chaou Lĕĕ-wăn.

* 花鏡 *Hwa king.* See 陳溟子 Ch'in Haou-tsze.

圓錐曲線 *Hwan chuy k'eŭh seen.* See 艾約瑟
Gae Yo-sih.

皇朝中外壹統輿圖 *Hwang ch'aou chung
wai yih t'ung yu t'oo.* See 嚴樹森 Yen
Shoo-san.

皇朝藩部要畧 *Hwang ch'aou fan poo yaou leŏ.* See 祁韻士 KE YUN-SZE.

皇朝經世文鈔 *Hwang ch'aou king she wăn ch'aou.* See 陸朗甫 LUH LANG-FOO.

皇朝經世文編 *Hwang ch'aou king she wăn peen.* See 魏源 WEI YUEN.

皇朝經世文續編 *Hwang ch'aou king she wăn suh peen.* See 葛子源 KO TSZE-YUEN.

皇朝文典 *Hwang ch'aou wăn teen.* See 李兆洛 LE CHAOU-LO.

皇朝武功紀盛 *Hwang ch'aou woo kung ke shing.* See 趙翼 CHAOU YIH.

*皇朝一統輿地全圖 *Hwang ch'aou yih t'ung yu te ts'euen t'oo.* See 皇朝 HWANG CH'AOU.

—— See 皇朝 HWANG CH'AOU.

黃縣志 *Hwang heen che.* See 袁中立 YUEN CHUNG-LEĬH.

皇明直文淵閣諸臣表 *Hwang ming chih wăn yuen kih choo ch'in peaou.* See 鄭曉 CHING HEAOU.

皇明英烈傳 *Hwang Ming ying lëĕ chuen.* See 皇明 HWANG MING.

皇宋事實類苑 *Hwang Sung sze paou luy yuen.* See 江少虞 KEANG SHAOU-YU.

皇清職貢圖 *Hwang Ts'ing chih kung t'oo.* See 永珹 YUNG SEUEN.

皇清地理圖 *Hwang Ts'ing te le t'oo.* See 俞守義 YU SHOW-E.

皇越地輿誌 *Hwang yueh te yu che.* See 惟明 WEI MING.

婚喪公禮 *Hwăn sang kung le.* See 婚喪 HWĂN SANG.

環字簿 *Hwan tsze poo.* See 環字 HWAN TSZE.

圜悟碧巖集 *Hwan woo Pih yen tseĭh.* See 圜悟大師 HWAN WOO TA SZE.

環遊地球新錄 *Hwan yew te k'ew sin luh.* See 李圭 LE KWEI.

畫譜一本 *Hwa p'oo yih pun.* See 行明 HING-MING.

畫禪宝隨筆 *Hwa shen shih suy peĭh.* See 華其昌 HWA K'E-CH'ANG.

畫史彙傳 *Hwa she wei chuen.* See 彭遵琛 P'ĂNG WĂN-TS'AN.

蕾圖樣 *Hwa t'oo yuen.* See 蕾圖 HWA T'OO.

華洋通聞 *Hwa yang t'ung wăn.* See PERIODICAL PUBLICATIONS: *Shanghai.*

華嚴一乘教分記 *Hwa yen yih shing keaou fun ke.* See 法藏 FA-TS'ANG.

*華英呂應酬撮要 *Hwa Ying Leu ying ch'ow ts'o yao.* See 卓歧山 CHO K'E-SHAN.

華英類語 *Hwa Ying luy yu.* See 卓歧山 CHO K'E-SHAN.

花影集 *Hwa ying-tseĭh.* See 花影 HWA YING.

*華英進階 *Hwa Ying tsin keae.* See ENGLISH AND CHINESE READERS.

華英字錄 *Hwa Ying tsze luh.* See POLETTI (P.).

華英字典 *Hwa Ying tsze teen.* See 廣其照 KWANG K'E-CHAOU.

華英字典彙集 *Hwa Ying tsze teen wei tseĭh.* See 譚達軒 T'AN TA-HEEN.

華英通用雜話 *Hwa Ying t'ung yung tsa hwa.* See 羅伯朋 LO-PIH TAN.

華英萬字典 *Hwa Ying wan tsze teen.* See POLETTI (P.).

*華英應酬撮要 *Hwa Ying ying ch'ow ts'o yaou.* See 莫禮智 MO LE-CHE.

華英月份 *Hwa Ying yueh fun.* See WATSON (A. S.) & Co.

*華音啓蒙 *Hwa yin k'e mung.* See 李應憲 LE YING-HEEN.

*繪輿記 *Hwuy chin ke.* See 邀月樓主人 YAOU-YUEH LOW-CHOO-JIN.

惠州府志 *Hwuy chow Foo che.* See 呂應奎 LEU YING-K'WEI.

悔改信耶穌說畧 *Hwuy kai sin Yaysoo shwo leŏ.* See 麥嘉締培端 MIH-KEA-TE P'EITWAN.

會試硃卷 *Hwuy she choo keuen.* See 曹驊 TS'AOU HWA.

繪地法原 *Hwuy te fa yuen.* See HUGHES (WILLIAM).

—— See 金楷理 KIN-K'EAE-LE.

HWU—KEA

悔餘菴尺牘 *Hwuy-yu gan ch'ih tuh.* See 何 廉 昉 Ho LEEN-FANG.

悔餘菴詩稿 *Hwuy-yu gan she kaou.* See 何 廉 昉 Ho LEEN-FANG.

悔餘菴文稿 *Hwuy-yu gan wăn kaou.* See 何 廉 昉 Ho LEEN-FANG.

悔餘菴樂府 *Hwuy-yu gan yo foo.* See 何 廉 昉 Ho LEEN-FANG.

Hyüing-mong Sing-kying kong k'o. See KNOWLTON (A. L.), MRS.

Iu-dong ts'u-hyiao. See PEEP.

日記故事 *Jih ke koo sze.* See 日 記 JIH KE.

日課撮要 *Jih k'o ts'o yaou.* See 日 課 JIH K'O.

日報約選 *Jih paou yoh seuen.* See 日 報 JIH PAOU.

Jih-tsih-yüih-le. See MÔ-TI-MEH.

人靈戰紀 *Jin ling chen ke.* See BUNYAN (JOHN).

仁王護國般若波羅密多經 *Jin wang hoo kwo pan jo po lo me to king.* See 不 空 PUH-K'UNG.

儒門醫學 *Joo mun e heŏ.* See 海 得 蘭 HAI-TIH-LAN.

若瑟聖月 *Jo-sih shing yueh.* See HONGKONG, Office of Nazareth.

—— See 若 瑟 JO-SIH.

—— See 李 秀 芳 LE SEW-FANG.

入學圖說 *Juh heŏ t'oo shwo.* See 入 學 JUH HEŎ.

* 開方表 *K'ai fang peaou.* See 買 步 緯 KEA POO-WEI.

開發總登 *K'ai fa tsung tăng.* See 開 發 K'AI FA.

開煤要法 *K'ai mei yaou fa.* See 士 密 德 SZE-MEÏH-TIH.

陔餘叢考 *Kai yu ts'ung k'aou.* See 趙 翼 CHAOU YIH.

耕織圖 *Kăng chih t'oo.* See 耕 織 KĂNG CHIH.

康熙字典 *K'ang-he tsze teen.* See 康 熙 K'ANG-HE, Emperor.

康熙字典撮要 *K'ang-he tsze teen ts'o yaou.* See 康 熙 K'ANG-HE.

綱鑑甲子圖 *Kang keen kea tsze t'oo.* See 綱 鑑 KANG KEEN.

綱鑑擥要 *Kang keen lan yaou.* See 姚 培 謙 YAOU P'EI-K'EEN, and 張 景 星 CHANG KING-SING.

康說書後 *K'ang shwo shoo how.* See 胡 禮 垣 HOO LE-YUEN.

感應篇直講 *Kan ying p'een chih keang.* See 老 君 LAOU-KEUN.

高弧細草 *Kaou hoo se ts'aou.* See 張 作 楠 CHANG TSO-NAN.

巧搭逢年 *K'aou ta fung neen.* See 巧 K'AOU.

高王觀世音經 *Kaou wang Kwan she yin king.* See 觀 世 音 KWAN-SHE-YIN.

家畜玩物 *Kea ch'uh wan wuh.* See 家 KEA.

皆山樓吟稿 *Keae shan low yin kaou.* See 盛 百 二 SHING PIH-URH.

戒酒論 *Keae tsew lun.* See 酒 TSEW.

芥子園重訂監本易經 *Keae tsze yuen chung ting keen pun yih king.* See 易 經 YIH KING.

戒烟醒世圖 *Keae yin sing she t'oo.* See 李 修 善 LE SEW-SHEN.

家學淺論 *Kea heŏ ts'een lun.* See 家 學 KEA HEŎ.

家訓世範類編 *Kea heun she fan luy peen.* See 袁 君 載 YUEN KEUN-TSAI.

加拉太書註釋 *Kea-la-t'ai shoo choo shih.* See BIBLE—NEW TESTAMENT: Galatians.

江南海關則例 *Keang-nan hai kwan tsih le.* See 江 南 海 關 KEANG-NAN HAI KWAN.

江南鄉試題名錄 *Keang-nan heang she t'e ming luh.* See 江 南 KEANG-NAN.

* 江南報恩寺琉璃寶塔全圖 *Keang-nan Paou-ngan sze Lew-le paou ta ts'euen t'oo.* See 江 南 KEANG-NAN.

* 江寗省城圖 *Keang-ning shing ch'ing t'oo.* See 江 寗 KEANG-NING.

江西省全圖 *Keang-se shing ts'euen t'oo.* See 江 西 KEANG-SE.

江蘇海運全案 *Keang-soo hai yun ts'euen gan.* See 陶 澍 T'AOU CHOO.

* 江蘇現任官名 *Keang-soo heen jin kwan ming.* See 江蘇 KEANG-SOO.

江左三大家詩鈔 *Keang tso san ta kea she ch'aou.* See 顧有孝 KOO YEW-HEAOU, and 趙澐 CHAOU YUN.

校正日用雜字 *Keaou ching jih yung tsa tsze.* See 雜字 TSA TSZE.

教會政治 *Keaou hwuy ching che.* See 教會 KEAOU HWUY.

教會問答 *Keaou hwuy wăn ta.* See 教會 KEAOU HWUY.

校補詩韻合璧 *Keaou poo she yun ho pe.* See 湯文潞 T'ANG WĂN-LOO.

覺世經 *Keaou she king.* See 關帝 KWAN-TE.

交食細草 *Keaou shih se ts'aou.* See 張作楠 CHANG TSO-NAN.

數乘法數 *Keaou shing fa soo.* See 圓瀞 YUEN-TSING.

教乘法數摘要 *Keaou shing fa soo chai yaou.* See 效乘法 KEAOU SHING FA.

教外別傳 *Keaou wai peh chuen.* See 和南 HONAN.

教要序論 *Keaou yaou seu lun.* See 南懷仁 NAN-HWAI-JIN.

嘉定府志 *Kea-ting foo che.* See 宋鳴琦 SUNG MING-KE.

竭力事主 *Kĕĕ leh sze choo.* See 慕維廉 MOO WEI-LEEN.

謙齋晝帖 *K'een chai hwa t'ĕĕ.* See 謙齋 K'EEN CHAI.

簡齋詩集 *Keen-chai she tseh.* See 陳與義 CH'IN YU-E.

乾坤法竅 *Keen kw'an fa keaou.* See 范宜賓 FAN E-PIN.

監本詩經 *Keen pun she king.* See 詩經 SHE KING.

監本書經 *Keen pun shoo king.* See 孔丘 K'UNG K'EW.

揀巽勘世要言 *Keen seuen k'euen she yaou yen.* See 學善居士 HEŎ SHIN KEU SZE.

黔省各種苗圖 *K'een shing kih chung Meaou t'oo.* See 黔省 K'EEN SHING.

建天京於金陵論 *Keen t'een king yü Kinling lun.* See 太平天國 T'AIP'ING T'EEN KWO.

鑑撮 *Keen ts'o.* See 曠敏本 KW'ANG MIN-PUN.

鑑撮蒙求 *Keen ts'o mung k'ew.* See 曹維藩 TS'AOU WEI-FAN.

簡牘精要 *Keen tuh tsing yaou.* See 簡牘 KEEN TUH.

見聞續筆 *Keen wăn suh peh.* See 齊子冶 TS'E TSZE-YAY.

見聞隨筆 *Keen wăn suy peh.* See 齊子冶 TS'E TSZE-YAY.

紀交新書 *Ke heaou sin shoo.* See 戚繼光 TSEÏH KE-KWANG.

吉金志存 *Keih kin che ts'un.* See 李光廷 LE KWANG-T'ING.

吉金所見錄 *Keih kin so keen luh.* See 初渭園 CH'OO WEI-YUEN.

結水滸全傳 *Keih Shwuy hoo ts'euen chuen.* See 兪萬春 YÜ WAN-CH'UN.

畸人十篇 *Ke jin shih p'een.* See 利瑪竇 LE MA-TOW.

汽機 *K'e ke.* See 蒲而捺 POO-URH-NA.

樂假歸眞論 *K'e kea kwei chin lun.* See 假 KEA.

紀效新書 *Ke keaou sin shoo.* See 戚繼光 TSEÏH KE-KWANG.

汽機發軔 *K'e ke fa jin.* See 美以納 MEI-E-NA, and 白勞那 PIH-LAOU-NA.

汽機必以 *K'e ke pe e.* See 蒲而捺 P'OO URH-NA.

汽機新制 *K'e ke sin che.* See 白爾格 PIH-URH-KIH.

穆明四終 *Ke ming sze chung.* See 胡德邁 HOO TIH-MAI.

* 啓蒙篇 *K'e mung p'een.* See 啓蒙 K'E MUNG.

器象顯眞 *K'e seang heen chin.* See 白力蓋 PIH LEÏH-KAI.

記事珠 *Ke sze choo.* See 張贊虞 CHANG TSAN-YU.

己巳進表裏進饌儀軌 *Ke sze tsin peaou le tsin chuen e kwei.* See 己巳 KE SZE.

斳禱慎思 *K'e taou shing sze.* See 栢衣文 PIH I-WĂN.

祀大山銘 *Ke ta shan ming.* See 祀大山 KE TA SHAN.

寄邨居時文初集 *Ke ts'un keu she wăn ch'oo tseth.* See 萬學禮 KO HEŏ-LE.

瞅張心法 *Keuĕ chang sin fa.* See 程冲斗 CH'ING CH'UNG-TOW.

* 勸學篇 *K'euen heŏ p'een.* See 張之洞 CHANG CHE-TUNG.

勸學篇書後 *K'euen heŏ p'een shoo how.* See 何啟 HO K'E, and 胡禮垣 HOO LE-YUEN.

勸誠社彙選 *K'euen keae shay wei seuen.* See 勸誠社 K'EUEN KEAE SHAY.

勸戒圖說 *K'euen keae t'oo shwo.* See 鄒迪光 TSOW TIH-KWANG.

勸戒洋烟 *K'euen keae yang yen.* See 師惟善 SZE-WEI-SHEN.

* 勸戒洋烟文 *K'euen keae yang yen wăn.* See 洋烟 YANG YEN.

勸解鴉片論 *K'euen keae Ya-peen lun.* See 麥嘉締培端 MIH-KEA-TE PEI-TWAN.

勸世瓦言 *K'euen she leang yen.* See 學善居士 HEŏ SHEN KEU SZE.

菊部羣英 *Keuh poo k'eun ying.* See 菊部 KEUH POO.

㡬湖圖 *Keui ho to.* See 㡬湖 KEUI HO.

居官刑戒 *Keu kwan hing keae.* See 呂坤 LEU KW'ĂN.

瓊宮五帝內思上法 *K'eung kung woo te nuy sze shang ja.* See 董其昌 TUNG K'E-CH'ANG.

羣書治要 *K'eun shoo che yaou.* See 魏徵 WEI CHING.

求福免禍要論 *K'ew fu meen hwo yaou lun.* See 學善居士 HEŏ SHEN KEU SZE.

九皇新經註解 *Kew Hwang sin king choo keae.* See 蔡一聲 TS'AI YIH-TSUN.

九皇延生錫福寶懺 *Kew Hwang yen săng tsze fu paou ts'an.* See 九皇 KEW HWANG.

救劫金鑑 *Kew kĕĕ kin keen.* See 何贊清 HO TSAN-TS'ING.

求闕齋日記類鈔 *K'ew-k'eue chai jih ke luy ch'aou.* See 曾國藩 TSĂNG KWO-FAN.

求闕齋讀書錄 *K'ew keue chai tuh shoo luh.* See 曾國藩 TSĂNG KWO-FAN.

舊金山唐人新聞帋 *Kew kin shan T'ang jin sin wăn chih.* See PERIODICAL PUBLICATIONS: *San Francisco.*

救靈先路 *Kew ling seen loo.* See JAMES (JOHN ANGELL).

救溺死烟毒編 *Kew ne sze yen too pun.* See MACGOWAN (D. J.).

九品觀音經 *Kew p'in Kwan-yin king.* See 觀音 KWAN-YIN.

救世眞聖幼主詔書 *Kew she chin shing yew choo chaou shoo.* See 太平天國 T'AIP'ING T'EEN KWO.

九十二法 *Kew shih urh fa.* See 姚邵瑛 YAOU SHAOU-YING.

救贖何義 *Kew shuh ho e.* See 贖 SHUH.

九數外錄 *Kew soo wai luh.* See 顧尚之 KOO SHANG-CHE.

舊唐書 *Kew T'ang shoo.* See 劉昫 LEW HEU.

救嬰錄 *Kew ying luh.* See 趙貞清 CHAOU CHING-TS'ING.

舊約史記條問 *Kew yo she ke t'eaou wăn.* See HAPPER (ANDREW PATTON).

舊約史記問答 *Kew yŏ she ke wăn ta.* See 愛孩提女史 GAI HAI T'E NEU SHE.

舊約節錄啓蒙 *Kew yo tsĕĕ luh k'e mung.* See 麥耐氏 MIH NAI SHE.

九雲夢 *Kew yun mung.* See 九雲 KEW YUN.

寄園寄所寄 *Ke yuen ke so ke.* See 趙恒夫 CHAOU HĂNG-FOO.

奇綠鴈翎媒新選 *K'e yuen yen ling mei sin seuen.* See 鴈翎媒 YEN LING MEI.

格致啟蒙 *Kih che k'e-mung.* See 羅斯古 LO-SZE-KOO.

格致鏡原 *Kih che king yuen.* See 陳元龍 CH'IN YUEN-LUNG.

格致釋器 *Kih che shih k'e.* See 傅蘭雅 FOO-LAN-YA.

—— See 格致 KIH CHE.

格致彙編 *Kih che wei peen.* See PERIODICAL PUBLICATIONS: *Shanghai.*

革除遺事節本 *Kih ch'oo e sze tsëë pun.* See 黃佐 HWANG TSO.

客窗閒話 *Kih ch'wang heen hwa.* See 吳熾釬 WOO HEANG-HAN.

隔簾花影 *Kih leen hwa ying.* See 隔簾 KIH LEEN.

克虜伯船礮槔法 *Kih-loo-pih chuen p'aou ts'aou fa.* See PRUSSIA: DEPARTMENTS OF STATE, ETC.—*Army.*

克虜伯礮準心法 *Kih-loo-pih p'aou chun sin fa.* See PRUSSIA: DEPARTMENTS OF STATE, ETC.—*Army.*

克虜伯礮架說 *Kih-loo-pih p'aou kea shwo.* See PRUSSIA: DEPARTMENTS OF STATE, ETC. —*Army.*

克虜伯礮說 *Kih-loo-pih p'aou shwo.* See PRUSSIA: DEPARTMENTS OF STATE, ETC.— *Army.*

克虜伯礮彈造法 *Kih-loo-pih p'aou tan tsaou fa.* See PRUSSIA: DEPARTMENTS OF STATE, ETC.—*Army.*

克虜伯礮槔法 *Kih-loo-pih p'aou ts'aou fa.* See 金楷理 KIN-K'EAE-LE.

克虜伯腰箍礮說 *Kih-loo-pih yaou koo p'aou shwo.* See PRUSSIA: DEPARTMENTS OF STATE, ETC.—*Army.*

格物入門 *Kih wuh juh mun.* See 丁韪良 TING WEI-LEANG.

格物探原 *Kih wuh t'an yuen.* See 韋廉臣 WEI-LEEN-CH'IN.

經義考 *King e, k'aou.* See 朱彝尊 CHOO E-TSUN.

經觚摧 *King e ts'uy.* See 陳駿孫 CH'IN TSEUN-SUN.

經學不厭精 *King heŏ puh yen tsing.* See 花之安 HWA CHIH-NGAN.

鏡花水月 *King hwa shwuy yueh.* See 月 YUEH.

敬禮耶穌聖心月 *King le Yay-soo Shing sin yueh.* See 梁安德 LEANG GAN-TIH.

經籙問答 *King luh wăn ta.* See 柏哲 PIH-CHĔ.

敬業榮珠書院課藝合編 *King nëĕ e choo Shoo yuen k'o e ho peen.* See 徐宗瀛 T'OO TSUNG-YING.

* 京板天文全圖 *King pan t'een wăn ts'euen t'oo.* See 天文 T'EEN WĂN.

京報 *King paou.* See PERIODICAL PUBLICATIONS: *Peking.*

經史證類大觀本草 *King she ching luy ta kwan pun ts'aou.* See 愼微 SHIN WEI.

輕世金書 *K'ing she kin shoo.* See HAEMMERLEIN (THOMAS) A KEMPIS.

經史百家簡編 *King she pih kea heen peen.* See 曾國藩 TSĂNG KWO-FAN.

經史百家雜鈔 *King she pih kea tsa ch'aou.* See 曾國藩 TSĂNG KWO-FAN.

敬勝堂試藝 *King shing t'ang she e.* See 周載坤 CHOW TSAI-K'WĂN.

敬信錄 *King sin luh.* See 周鼎臣 CHOW TING-CH'IN.

景德傳燈錄 *King-tih ch'uen tăng luh.* See 道原 TAOU-YUEN.

經文求是 *King wăn k'ew she.* See 經文 KING WĂN.

經言拾遺 *King yen shih e.* See 徐位山 SEU WEI-SHAN.

經韻集字析解 *King yun tseih tsze seih keae.* See 經韻 KING YUN.

金壺七墨 *Kin hoo ts'ih mih.* See 黃天河 HWANG T'EEN-HO.

金華晷漏中星表 *Kin hwa kwei low chung Sing peaou.* See 張作楠 CHANG TSO-NAN.

金監督誌畧 *Kin Keen tuh che lŏ.* See 金 KIN.

金鑑外科 *Kin keen wai k'o.* See 吳謙 WOO KEEN.

今古奇觀 *Kin koo k'e kwan.* See 墨憨齋 MIH HAN-CHAI.

金匱方歌括 *Kin kwei fang ko kwo.* See 張仲景 CHANG CHUNG-KING.

金瓶梅 *Kin P'ing Mei.* See 金 KIN.

金山寺夢遊錄 *Kin shan sze mung yew luh.* See 金山寺 KIN SHAN SZE.

KIN—KOC

金石識別 *Kin shih shih pĕĕ.* See 代邪 TAI-NA.

金石索 *Kin shih so.* See 馮雲鵬 FUNG YUN-P'ĂNG.

金石萃編 *Kin shih ts'uy peen.* See 王昶 WANG CH'ANG.

金石綠全傳 *Kin shih yuen ts'euen chuen.* See 金 KIN.

近思錄 *Kin sze luh.* See 朱熹 CHOO HE, and 呂祖謙 LEU TSOO-K'EEN.

金臺華嚴禪寺請經沙門萬空大師重修記 *Kint'ai Hwayen ch'en sze keang king shamun Wank'ung Tasze chung sew ke.* See 萬空大師 WANK'UNG TASZE.

金臺書院課士錄 *Kin t'ai Shoo yuen k'o sze luh.* See 張集馨 CHANG TSEĬH-HING.

*金湯十二籌 *Kin t'ang shih urh ch'ow.* See 李盤 LE P'AN.

金丹就正篇玄膚論 *Kin tan tsew ching peen. Heuen foo lun.* See 陸西星 LUH SE-SING.

欽定周官義疏 *K'in ting Chow kwan e soo.* See 周官 CHOW KWAN.

欽定重修兩浙鹽法志 *K'in ting chung sew leang chĕ yen fa che.* See 阮元 YUEN YUEN.

欽定儀禮義疏 *K'in ting E le e soo.* See 儀禮 E LE.

欽定皇輿西域圖志 *K'in ting Hwang yu se yıh t'oo che.* See 傅恆 FOO HĂNG.

欽定回疆則例 *K'in ting hwuy keang tsih le.* See 托津 T'o TS'IN.

欽定古今圖書集成 *K'in ting koo kin t'oo shoo tseĭh ch'ing.* See 蔣廷錫 TSEANG T'ING-SEĬH.

欽定國朝詩別裁集 *K'in ting kwo ch'aou she pĕĕ ts'ai tseĭh.* See 沈德潛 CH'IN TIH-TS'EEN.

欽定國子監志 *K'in ting kwo tsze keen che.* See 文慶 WĂN K'ING.

*欽定理藩院則例 *K'in ting Le-fan-yuen tsih le.* See 托津 T'O-TS'IN.

欽定滿洲源流考 *K'in ting Man chow yuen lew k'aou.* See 阿桂 AH-KWEI.

欽定平定回疆勦捦遞裔方略 *K'in ting p'ing ting hwuy keang tseaou k'in ne e fang leŏ.* See 曹振鏞 TS'AOU CHIN-YUNG.

欽定選擇詳註便覽吉用憲書大清道光二十五年 *K'in ting seuen tsih tseang choo peen lan keĭh yung heen shoo. Ta Ts'ing Taou-kwang urh shih woo neen.* See EPHEMERIDES.

欽定授時通考 *K'in ting show she t'ung k'aou.* See 弘書 HUNG CHOW.

欽定新疆識畧 *K'in ting sin keang shih leŏ.* See 綿忻 MEEN HIN.

欽定士階條例 *K'in ting sze keae t'eaou li.* See 大平天國 T'AIP'ING T'EEN KWO.

欽定四庫全書簡明目錄 *K'in ting sze koo ts'euen shoo keen ming muh luh.* See CHINA: 乾隆 K'EEN-LUNG, *Emperor.*

欽定大清會典 *K'in ting Ta Ts'ing hwuy teen.* See TS'ING DYNASTY.

欽定大清律例 *K'in ting ta Ts'ing leŭh le.* See TS'ING DYNASTY.

欽定錢錄 *K'in ting ts'een luh.* See 梁詩正 LEANG SHE-CHING.

欽定清漢對音字式 *K'in ting Ts'ing Han tuy yin tsze shih.* See 乾隆 K'EEN-LUNG, *Emperor.*

欽定同文韻統 *K'in ting t'ung wăn yun t'ung.* See 允祿 YUN-LUH.

欽定萬年書 *K'in ting wan neen shoo.* See EPHEMERIDES.

—— See 林氏 LIN SHE.

今將大英與西方成化各國交戰之例嫠條 *Kin tseang ta Ying yu se fang ch'ing hwa koh kwo keaou chan che le shoo t'eaou.* See RULES OF WAR.

金七十論 *Kin ts'ih shih lun.* See 眞諦 CHIN-TE.

錦字箋 *Kin tsze tseen.* See 黃維觀 HWANG WEI-KWAN.

金元明八家文選 *Kin Yuen Ming pa kea wăn seuen.* See 李欽之 LE K'IN-CHE.

科塲事欵 *K'o ch'ang sze kwan.* See 科塲 K'O CH'ANG.

各府州清冊 *Ko Foo Chow ts'ing ts'ih.* See 各府州 Ko Foo Chow.

各號出口查騐各貨 *Ko haou ch'uh k'ow cha yen ko ho.* See 各號 Ko HAOU.

各號騐貨 *Ko haou yen ho.* See 各號 Ko HAOU.

哥林多書註解 *Ko-lin-to shoo choo keae.* See BIBLE—NEW TESTAMENT: *1st Epistle to the Corinthians.*

科名金鑑 *K'o ming kin chin.* See 毛昶熙 MAOU CH'ANG-HE.

Kông-ka. See MOULE (ARTHUR EVANS).

Kong tao sö. See MOULE (GEORGE E.).

鼓吹續編 *Koo ch'uy suh peen.* See 鼓吹 KOO CH'UY.

古香齋鑒賞袖珍春明夢餘錄 *Koo heang chai keen shang sew chin ch'un ming mung yu luh.* See 孫承澤 SUN CH'ING-TSIH.

* 古潤四山勝境全圖 *Koo jun sze shan shing king ts'euen t'oo.* See 古潤四山 KOO JUN SZE SHAN.

古教彙參 *Koo keaou wei ts'an.* See WILLIAMSON (ALEXANDER), LL.D.

古經解彙函 *Koo king keae wei han.* See 鍾謙鈞 CHUNG K'EEN-KEUN.

古今歷代標題註釋十九史略通考 *Koo kin leĭh tai p'eaou t'e choo shih shih kew she leŏ t'ung k'ao.* See 曾先之 TSĂNG SEEN CHE.

古今秘苑 *Koo kin pe yuen.* See 秘苑 PE YUEN.

古今俗語 *Koo kin suh yu.* See 陳光臣 CH'IN KWANG-CH'IN.

古巴雜記 *Koo-pa tsa ke.* See 譚乾初 T'AN KAN-CH'OO.

古詩平仄論 *Koo she p'ing tsih lun.* See 翁方綱 UNG FANG-KANG.

古聖任罪 *Koo shing jin tsuy.* See 惠維廉 MOO WEI-LEEN.

古新聖經問答 *Koo sin shing king wǎn ta.* See BIBLE: *Appendix.*

古棠書屋叢書 *Koo t'ang shoo wuh ts'ung shoo.* See 孫澍 SUN SHOO.

古文孝經 *Koo wǎn heaou king.* See 孔丘 K'UNG K'EW.

* 古文孝經孔氏傳 *Koo wǎn Heaou king K'ung she chuen.* See 孔丘 K'UNG K'EW.

古文奇字輯解 *Koo wǎn k'e tsze tseĭh keae.* See 謝兆申 SEAY CHAO-SHIN.

古文析義合編 *Koo wǎn seĭh e ho peen.* See 林西仲 LIN SE-CHUNG.

古文析義二編 *Koo wǎn seĭh e urh peen.* See 林西仲 LIN SE-CHUNG.

古文釋義新編 *Koo wǎn shih e sin peen.* See 余自明 YU TSZE-MING.

古文辭類纂 *Koo wǎn ts'ze luy tswan.* See 姚鼐 YAOU NAI.

古文翼 *Koo wǎn yih.* See 唐介軒 T'ANG KEAE-HEEN.

古玉圖譜 *Koo yuh t'oo poo.* See 龍大淵 LUNG TA-YUEN.

各省地名 *Ko sǎng te ming.* See 各省 KO SĂNG.

各省輿地 *Ko sǎng yu te.* See 劉塾 LEW KWĂN.

各省輿圖便覽 *Ko sǎng yu t'oo peen lan.* See 各省 KO SĂNG.

各式聖歌 *Ko she shing ko.* See 聖歌 SHING KO.

歌頌詩章 *Ko sung she chang.* See 歌頌 KO SUNG.

勾股六術 *Kow koo luh shuh.* See 項名達 HEANG MING-TA.

公法會通 *Kung fa hwuy t'ung.* See 步倫 POO-LUN.

公法便覽 *Kung fa peen lan.* See 吳氏 WOO SHE.

宮闈百詠 *Kung kwei pih yung.* See 陳其泰 CH'IN K'E-T'AI.

功過格輯要 *Kung kwo kih tseĭh yaou.* See 李士達 LE SZE-TA.

攻守礮法 *Kung show p'aou fa.* See PRUSSIA: DEPARTMENTS OF STATE, ETC.—*Army.*

公禱書 *Kung taou shoo.* See 公禱 KUNG TAOU.

孔 子 集 語 *K'ung tsze tseih yu.* See 孫 星 衍 SUN SING-YEN.

孔 子 通 紀 *K'ung tsze t'ung ke.* See 虞 潘 府 YU P'AN-FOO.

管 城 碩 記 *Kwan ch'ing shih ke.* See 徐 位 山 SEU WEI-SHAN.

廣 治 平 畧 *Kwang che p'ing leŏ.* See 蔡 方 炳 TS'AI FANG-PING.

廣 州 府 屬 歷 案 贊 宮 題 名 錄 *Kwang-chow Foo shuh leih ngan hung kung t'e ming luh.* See 廣 州 府 KWANG-CHOW FOO.

光 學 *Kwang heŏ.* See 田 大 里 T'EEN-TA-LE.

廣 羣 芳 譜 *Kwang k'eun fang poo.* See 王 象 晉 WANG SEANG-TSIN.

廣 鈔 海 心 珠 *Kwang meaou hai sin chu.* See 熏 沐 HEUN-MUH.

光 宣 臺 集 *Kwang seuen t'ai tseih.* See 阿 字 無 AH-TSZE-WOO.

光 緒 九 年 通 商 各 關 謷 船 鋥 浮 椿 總 冊 *Kwang-seu kew neen t'ung shang ko kwan king ch'uen tăng fow chwang tsung ts'ih.* See CHINA: *Inspectorate General of Customs.*

光 緒 十 五 年 通 商 各 關 華 洋 貿 易 總 冊 *Kwang-seu shih woo neen t'ung shang ko kwan hwa yang maou e tsung ts'ih.* See CHINA: *Inspectorate General of Customs.*

廣 策 學 纂 要 *Kwang tsih heŏ tswan yaou.* See 閒 鷗 霞 逸 HEEN GOW HEA YIH.

廣 東 現 任 官 名 *Kwang-tung heen jin kwan ming.* See 廣 東 KWANG-TUNG.

廣 東 歷 科 拔 貢 壹 等 題 名 錄 *Kwang-tung leih k'o pa kung yih tăng t'e ming luh.* See 廣 東 KWANG-TUNG.

廣 東 新 語 *Kwang-tung sin yu.* See 屈 翁 山 K'EUH UNG-SHAN.

廣 東 探 報 *Kwang-tung t'an paou.* See 廣 東 KWANG-TUNG.

廣 東 通 志 *Kwang-tung t'ung che.* See 阮 元 YUEN YUEN.

廣 東 通 省 水 道 圖 *Kwang-tung t'ung săng shwuy taou t'oo.* See 陳 刺 史 CH'IN TS'ZE-SHE.

* —— See 陳 鎣 CH'IN YING.

廣 東 輿 地 總 圖 *Kwang-tung yü te tsung t'oo.* See 廣 東 KWANG-TUNG.

廣 輿 古 今 鈔 *Kwang yu koo kin ch'aou.* See 程 氏 CH'ING SHE.

廣 韻 *Kwang yun.* See 廣 韻 KWANG YUN.

官 話 *Kwan hwa.* See COUVREUR (SÉRAPHIN).

官 話 指 南 *Kwan hwa che nan.* See GOH.

官 話 萃 珍 *Kwan hwa ts'uy chin.* See GOODRICH (CHAUNCEY).

官 話 彙 解 *Kwan hwa wei keae.* See 轂 旦 浣 KUH TAN-HWAN.

館 課 賦 稿 *Kwan k'o foo kaou.* See 吳 廷 鉁 WOO T'ING-CHIN.

坤 寧 妙 經 *K'wăn ning meaou king.* See 秦 元 君 TS'IN YUEN-KEUN.

關 帝 明 聖 眞 經 *Kwan-te ming shing chin king.* See 關 帝 KWAN-TE.

關 東 關 比 圖 *Kwan-tung Kwan-peuk to.* See 關 東 KWAN-TUNG.

愧 齋 遺 詩 *Kw'ei chai e she.* See 梁 詩 拔 LEANG SHE-PA.

葵 花 記 全 本 *Kwei hwa ke ts'euen pun.* See 葵 花 KWEI HWA.

* 歸 極 總 圖 *Kwei keih tsung t'oo.* See 歸 極 KWEI KEIH.

閨 娜 傳 *Kwei-no chuen.* See GWEN.

窺 豹 雜 存 *Kwei paou tsa ts'un.* See 憂 時 居 士 YEW SHIH KEU SZE.

歸 田 瑣 記 *Kwei t'een so ke.* See 梁 章 鉅 LEANG CHANG-KEU.

國 朝 重 訂 庚 辰 集 *Kwo ch'aou chung ting kăng shin tseih.* See 紀 昀 KE YUN.

國 朝 畫 徵 錄 *Kwo ch'aou hwa ching luh.* See 張 浦 山 CHANG POO-SHAN.

國 朝 畫 識 *Kwo ch'aou hwa shih.* See 馮 冶 堂 FUNG YAY-T'ANG.

國 朝 閨 秀 正 始 續 集 *Kwo ch'aou kwei sew ching che suh tseih.* See 惲 珍 浦 HWĂN CHIN-P'OO.

* 國 朝 曆 象 考 *Kwo ch'aou leih seang k'aou* [Korean: *Konk tjyo ryek syang ko*]. See 徐 浩 修 SEU HAOU-SEW.

國朝律賦揀金錄 *Kwo ch'aou leŭh foo keen kin luh.* See 朱玉堂 CHOO YUH-T'ANG.

國朝先正事略 *Kwo ch'aou seen ching sze leŏ.* See 李次青 LE T'SZE-TS'ING.

國朝諡法考 *Kwo ch'aou she fa k'aou.* See 趙鉞 CHAOU YUĔ.

國朝二十四家文鈔 *Kwo ch'aou urh shih sze kea wăn ch'aou.* See 徐鳳輝 SEU FUNG-HWUY.

國朝文錄 *Kwo ch'aou wăn luh.* See 李欽之 LE K'IN-CHE.

國朝文錄續編 *Kwo ch'aou wăn luh suh peen.* See 李欽之 LE K'IN-CHE.

來生福 *Lai săng fuh.* See 楊中逸叟 KEŬH CHUNG YIH SOW.

來往文書 *Lai wang wăn shoo.* See 文書 WĂN SHOO.

萊陽縣志 *Laiyang heen che.* See 萬邦維 WAN PANG-WEI.

冷廬雜識 *Lăng leu tsa shih.* See 陸敬安 LUH KING-GAN.

浪跡續談 *Lang tseĭh suh t'an.* See 梁章鉅 LEANG CHANG-KEU.

浪跡叢談 *Lang tseĭh ts'ung t'an.* See 梁章鉅 LEANG CHANG-KEU.

浪子回頭 *Lang tsze hwuy t'ow.* See 浪子 LANG TSZE.

老鼠告狀 *Laou shoo kaou chwang.* See LITTLE (ARCHIBALD).

老子廞齋口義 *Laou tsze keu ch'ai k'ow e.* 老君 See LAOU KEUN.

量法代算 *Leang fa tai swan.* See 賈步緯 KEA POO-WEI.

Leang Kung-fa. See 學善居士 HEŎ SHEN KEU SZE.

輿馬圖說 *Leang ma t'oo shwo.* See 輿馬 LEANG MA.

兩般秋雨盦隨筆 *Leang pan ts'ew yu gan suy peĭh.* See 梁應來 LEANG YING-LAE.

量倉通法 *Leang ts'ang t'ung fa.* See 張作楠 CHANG TSO-NAN.

梁武帝全傳 *Leang Woo te ts'euen chuen.* See 梁武帝 LEANG WOO TE.

療馬集 *Leaou ma tseĭh.* See 喻本元 YU PUN-YUEN, AND 喻本亨 YU PUN-HĂNG.

吏治輯要 *Le che tseĭh yaou.* See 通瑞 T'UNG SHWUY.

李州俟家訓 *Le Chow-hou kea heun.* See 李州俟 LE CHOW-HOU.

李忠武公全書 *Le Chung-woo kung ts'euen shoo.* See 李舜臣 LE SHUN-CH'IN.

裂教原委問答 *Lĕĕ keaou yuen wei wăn ta.* See 裂教 LĔĔ KEAOU.

—— See 李若望 LI JO-WANG.

列國歲計敢要 *Lĕĕ kwo suy ke ching yaou.* See 麥丁富得力 MIH-TING FOO-TIH-LE.

* 列女傳 *Lĕĕ neu chuen.* See 列女 LĔĔ NEU.

—— See 汪庚 WANG KĂNG.

蓮華經普門品 *Leen hwa king p'oo mun p'in.* See 黃薰沐 HWANG HEUN-MUH.

揀選勸世要言 *Leen seuen k'euen she yaou yen.* See 學善居士 HEŎ SHEN KEU SZE.

聯新事備詩學大成 *Leen sin sze pe she heŏ ta ch'ing.* See 林楨 LIN CHING.

連元閣紅字頭新通書 *Leen-yuen-kih hung tsze t'ou sin t'ung shoo.* See EPHEMERIDES.

列仙傳 *Lĕĕ seen chuen.* See 自誠氏 TSZE-CH'ING SHE.

李義山詩集 *Le E-shan she tseĭh.* See 李義山 LE E-SHAN.

隸法彙纂 *Le fa wei tswan.* See 項懷 HEANG HWAI.

曆法問答 *Leĭh fa wăn ta.* See 曆法 LEIH FĂ.

歷覽記畧 *Leĭh lan ke leŏ.* See 傅蘭雅 FOO-LAN-YA.

歷代序畧 *Leĭh tai seu leŏ.* See 歷代 LEĬH TAI.

歷代神仙通鑑 *Leĭh tai shin seen t'ung chien.* See 徐衜 SEU TAOU.

* 歷代帝王統紀之圖 *Leĭh tai te wang t'ung ke chih t'oo.* See 歷代帝王 LEĬH TAI TE WANG.

LEI—LUH

歷代二十四史統紀全表 *Leih tai urh shih sze she t'ung ke ts'euen peaou.* See 段長基 TW'AN CH'ANG-KE.

歷代輿地沿革險要圖 *Leih tai yu te yen kih heen yaou t'oo.* See 楊守敬 YANG SHOW-KING, and 饒敦秩 JAOU TUN-CHIH.

禮記 *Le ke.* See 禮記 LE KE.

禮記正文 *Le ke ching wǎn.* See 禮記 LE KE.

禮記省度 *Le ke sǎng too.* See 禮記 LE KE.

禮記集說 *Le ke tseĭh shwo.* See 禮記 LE KE.

禮記集說大全 *Le ke tseĭh shwo ta ts'euen.* See 禮記 LE KE.

禮記讀本 *Le ke tuh pun.* See 禮記 LE KE.

禮經會元 *Le king hwuy yuen.* See 葉文康 YE WĂN-K'ANG.

禮拜模範 *Le pai moo fan.* See 禮拜 LE PAI.

隸辨 *Le peen.* See 顧藹吉 KOO GAI-KEĬH.

隸釋 *Le shih.* See 洪适 HUNG KWO.

隸續 *Le suh.* See 洪适 HUNG KWO.

李太白文集輯註 *Le T'ai-pih wăn tseĭh tseĭh choo.* See 李太白 LE T'AI-PIH.

律例七言 *Leŭh le ts'ih yen.* See 朱深揚 CHOO SHIN-YANG.

劉河間傷寒三書 *Lew Ho-keen shanghan san shoo.* See 劉守冀 LEW SHOW-CHIN.

六十三默想 *Lew shih san mih seang.* See 默想 MIH SEANG.

劉大將軍平倭戰記 *Lew ta tseang keun p'ing Wei chen ke.* See 劉 LEW.

留青新集 *Lew ts'ing sin tseĭh.* See 陳枚 CH'IN MEI.

李躍門百蝶圖 *Le Yo-mun pih teĭh t'oo.* See 李國龍 LE KWO-LUNG.

履園叢話 *Le yuen ts'ung hwa.* See 錢梅溪 TS'EEN MEI-K'E.

隸韻 *Le yun.* See 劉球 LEW K'EW.

臨證指南醫案 *Lin ching che nan e gan.* See 葉天士 YE T'EEN-SZE.

臨陣管見 *Lin chin kwan keen.* See 斯拉弗司 SZE-LA-FUH-SZE.

靈魂之糧 *Ling hwan che leang.* See 靈魂 LING HWAN.

靈魂貴於身體論 *Ling hwan kwei yu shin t'e lun.* See MCCARTEE (DIVIE BETHUNE).

—— See 培端 P'EI-TWAN.

—— See 麥嘉締培端 MIH-KEA-TE P'EI-TWAN.

靈魂略論 *Ling hwan leŏ lun.* See 帥羅誼 SZE A. E.

靈魂總論 *Ling hwan tsung lun.* See 麥嘉締培端 MIH-KEA-TE P'EI-TWAN.

領聖體要經 *Ling Shing t'e yaou king.* See 聖體 SHING T'E.

靈臺儀象圖 *Ling t'ai e seang t'oo.* See 南懷仁 NAN-HWAI-JIN.

林和靖集 *Lin Ho-tsing tseĭh.* See 林君復 LIN KEUN-FUH.

* 林蘭香 *Lin lan heang.* See 隨緣下士 SUY LUH HEA SZE.

臨清植隸州志 *Lin ts'ing chih le chow che.* See 張度 CHANG TOO.

臨文便覽 *Lin wǎn peen lan.* See 楊紹和 YANG SHAOU-HO.

—— See 楊彥合 YANG YEN-HO.

羅浮山志會編 *Lo-fow shan che hwuy peen.* See 宋廣業 SUNG KWANG-NĚĚ.

駱賓王文集 *Loh Pin-wang wǎn tseĭh.* See 駱賓王 LOH PIN-WANG.

羅馬書註解 *Lo-ma shoo choo keae.* See BIBLE—NEW TESTAMENT: *Romans.*

路程第一書 *Loo ch'ing te yih shoo.* See 路程 LOO CH'ING.

路加福音傳 *Loo kea fuh yin ch'uen.* See BIBLE—NEW TESTAMENT: *Luke, Gospel of.*

路得事蹟圖說 *Loo-tih sze tseĭh t'oo shwo.* See 路得 LOO-TIH.

樂清縣志 *Lo-ts'ing heen che.* See 賈聲槐 KEA SHING-HWAI.

六臣註文選 *Luh ch'in choo wǎn seuen.* See 蕭統 SEAOU T'UNG.

六合叢談 *Luh ho ts'ung t'an.* See PERIODICAL PUBLICATIONS: *Shanghai.*

六壬睟斯 *Luh jin she sze.* See 六壬 LUH JIN.

六經圖 *Luh king t'oo.* See 楊甲 YANG KEA.

六觀樓北曲六種 *Luh kwan low pih keŭh luh chung.* See 許雲嶠 HEU YUN-KEAOU.

六部成語 *Luh Poo ch'ing yu.* See 六部 LUH POO.

六十三默想 *Luh shih san mih seang.* See 默想 MIH SEANG.

六書分類 *Luh shoo fun luy.* See 傅鸞祥 FOO LWAN-TSEANG.

六書通 *Luh shoo t'ung.* See 閔齊份 MIN TS'E-KEĬH.

六書韻徵 *Luh shoo yun ching.* See 安古琴 GAN KOO-K'IN.

陸地戰例新選 *Luh te chen le sin seuen.* See 丁建瓦 TING WEI-LEANG.

六曲條例 *Luh teen t'eaou le.* See CHINA: SIX BOARDS.

綠野仙踪全傳 *Luh yay seen tsung ts'euen chuen.* See 家鶴 KEA HO.

類合 *Lui ho.* See SIEBOLD (PHILIPP FRANZ VON).

輪船布陳 *Lun ch'uen poo ch'in.* See 裴路 P'EI-LOO.

—— See 買密倫 KEA-MEĬH-LUN.

陸中圖 *Lung-chung t'oo.* See 陸中 LUNG-CHUNG.

龍門縣志 *Lung mun heen che.* See 張維屏 CHANG WEI-P'ING.

龍山課藝二集 *Lung shan k'o e urh tseĭh.* See 杜聯 TOO LEEN.

龍文鞭影 *Lung wǎn peen ying.* See 蕭瓦有 SEAOU LEANG-YEW.

龍威祕書 *Lung wei pi shoo.* See 馬俊瓦 MA TSEUN-LEANG.

論語 *Lun yu.* See 四書 SZE SHOO.

Lun yü. See WADE (SIR T. F.), K.C.B.

論語集註 *Lun yu tseĭh choo.* See 四書 SZE SHOO.

邁堂文畧 *Mai T'ang wǎn leŏ.* See 李欽之 LE K'IN-CHE.

賣胭脂 *Mai yen chih.* See 胭脂 YEN CHIH.

埋憂集 *Mai yew tseĭh.* See 朱梅叔 CHOO MEI-SHUH.

馬可傳福音書畧解 *Ma-k'o chuen fuh yin shoo leŏ keae.* See BIBLE—NEW TESTAMENT: Mark.

孟姜女萬里尋夫 *Mǎng-keang neu wan le sin foo.* See 孟姜 MǍNG-KEANG.

孟姜女萬里尋夫全部 *Mǎng-keang neu wan le sin foo ts'euen pu.* See 孟姜 MǍNG-KEANG.

孟子 *Mǎng tsze.* See 四書 SZE SHOO.

孟子大題萃 *Mǎng tsze ta t'e ts'uy.* See 孟子 MǍNG TSZE.

孟子集註 *Mǎng-tsze tseĭh choo.* See 四書 SZE SHOO.

孟子要嗑 *Mǎng tsze yaou leŏ.* See 朱熹 CHOO HE.

滿漢合璧三字經註解 *Man Han ho peĭh San tsze king choo keae.* See 盛冠寶 SHING KWAN-PAOU.

滿漢類書全集 *Man Han luy shoo ts'euen tseĭh.* See 滿漢 MAN HAN.

滿漢千字文 *Man Han ts'een tsze wǎn.* See 周興嗣 CHOW HING-SZE.

* —— See 周興嗣 CHOW HING-SZE.

毛詩 *Maou she.* See 詩經 SHE KING.

馬太福音書問答 *Ma-t'ai fuh yin shoo wǎn ta.* See 馬太 MA-T'AI.

妙法蓮華經 *Meaou fa leen hwa king.* See 鳩摩羅什 KEW-MO-LO-SHIH.

妙法蓮華經觀世音菩薩普門品 *Meaou fa leen hwa king Kwan-she-yin P'oo sa p'oo mun p'in.* See 鳩摩羅什 KEW-MO-LO-SHIH.

妙法蓮經 *Meaou fa leen king.* See 鳩摩羅什 KEW-MO-LO-SHIH.

苗蠻合志 *Meaou Man ho che.* See 曹樹翹 TS'AOU SHOO-KEAOU.

苗圖 *Meaou t'oo.* See 苗 MEAOU.

緬甸譯語 *Meenteen yih yu.* See 緬甸 MEEN-TEEN.

MEI—PAO

玫瑰經小問答 *Mei kwei king seaou wǎn ta.* See 玫瑰經 MEI KWEI KING.

梅莫氏行畧 *Mei Mo she hing leŏ.* See 倪戈氏 NE KO SHE.

墨香居畫識 *Mih heang keu hwa shih.* See 馮治堂 FUNG YAY-T'ANG.

默想指掌 *Mih seang che chang.* See 默想 MIH SEANG.

默想神功 *Mih seang shin kung.* See 石鐸琭 SHIH TO-LUH.

墨子批選 *Mih-tsze p'e seuen.* See 李贄 LE CHE.

墨范緇黃 *Mih yuen tsze hwang.* See 沈催 CH'IN KEŎ.

名醫類案 *Ming e luy gan.* See 江瓘 KEANG KWAN.

明季稗史彙編 *Ming ke pai she wei peen.* See 明 MING.

名犬圖說 *Ming k'euen t'oo shwo.* See 名犬 MING K'EUEN.

名班抄出新演 *Ming pan ch'aou ch'uh sin yen.* See 名班 MING PAN.

明詩別裁集 *Ming she pëě ts'ai tseih.* See 沈德潛 CH'IN TIH-TS'EEN, and 周準 CHOW CHUN.

明史雜著 *Ming she tsa choo.* See 李欽之 LE K'IN-CHE.

嗚原堂論文 *Ming yuen t'ang lun wǎn.* See 曾國藩 TSĂNG KWO-FAN.

每求軒遽記 *Min k'ew heen shuh ke.* See 陳世鎡 CH'IN SHE-CHIN.

摩西聖蹟圖說 *Mo-se shing tse t'oo shwo.* See 摩西 MO-SE.

蒙求 *Mung k'ew.* See 李瀚 LE HAN.

蒙古律例 *Mung koo leŭh le.* See 蒙古 MUNG KOO.

蒙古游牧記 *Mung koo yew muh ke.* See 張穆 CHANG MUH.

蒙文晰義 *Mung wǎn seih e.* See 賽倘阿 SAISHANGAH.

耐冷譚 *Nai lǎng t'an.* See 宋小茗 SUNG SEAOU-MING.

* 南詔野史 *Nan chaou yay she.* See 楊慎 YANG SHIN.

南海縣志 *Nan-hai heen che.* See 鄧士憲 TĂNG SZE-HEEN.

南華眞經 *Nan hwa chin king.* See 莊周 CHWANG CHOW.

* 南華得大羅漢像讚合璧 *Nan hwa tih ta Lo-han seang tsan ho peih.* See 王文治 WANG WĂN-CHE.

南圻六省地輿誌 *Nan k'e luh sǎng te yu che.* See 惟明 WEI MING.

南比史捃華 *Nan pih she keun hwa.* See 李延壽 LE YEN-SHOW.

南北宋志傳 *Nan pih Sung che chuen.* See 南北宋 NAN PIH SUNG.

鬧花叢 *Nao hwa ts'ung.* See 姑蘇窺情士 KOO-SOO CH'E TS'ING-SZE.

祁蘇集 *Na Soo tseih.* See 蘇軾 SOO SHIH.

內經靈樞註證發微 *Nuy king Ling ch'oo choo ching fa wei.* See 黃帝 HWANG-TE.

Nying-po kyiao-we-li sô yüong go tsæn-me S. See NINGPO.

Nying-po t'u-wô ts'u-'ôh. See NINGPO.

八家四六 *Pa kea sze luh.* See 吳錫麒 WOO SEĬH-K'E.

八旗通志初集 *Pa k'e t'ung che ch'oo tseih.* See 弘晝 HUNG CHOW.

蓬萊縣志 *Pǎng-lai heen che.* See 高崗 KAOU KANG.

般若波羅密多心經 *Pan-jo po-lo-meih-to sin king.* See 般若波羅密多 PAN-JO PO-LO-MEĬH-TO.

版圖扦號冊 *Pan t'oo yu haou ts'ih.* See 吳會清 WOO HWUY-TS'ING.

保羅垂訓 *Paoulo ch'uy heun.* See 丁韙良 TING WEILEANG.

保免攔陰 *Paou meen lan ch'oo.* See 師惟善 SZE-WEI-SHEN.

賣命眞經 *Paou ming chin king.* See 經 KING.

197

555

寶 山 縣 志 *Paou shan heen che.* See 趙 酉 CHAOU YEW.

爆 藥 記 要 *Paou yoh ke yaou.* See 美 國 水 雷 局 MEI KWO SHWUY LUI KEU.

八 綫 簡 表 *Pa seen keen peaou.* See 八 綫 PA SËEN.

八 綫 類 編 *Pa seen luy peen.* See 張 作 楠 CHANG TSO-NAN.

*八 綫 對 數 簡 表 *Pa seen tuy shoo keen peaou.* See 買 步 緯 KEA POO-WEI.

八 綫 對 數 類 編 *Pa seen tuy shoo luy peen.* See 張 作 楠 CHANG TSO-NAN.

八 旬 萬 壽 盛 典 *Pa seun wan show shing teen.* See 阿 桂 AH-KWEI.

票 據 會 案 *Peaou keu hwuy shing.* See 票 據 PEAOU KEU.

標 題 句 解 孔 子 家 語 *Peaou t'e keu keae K'ung tsze kea yu.* See 王 景 猷 WANG KING-YEW.

標 題 徐 狀 元 補 註 蒙 求 *Peaou t'e Seu Chwang-yuen poo choo mung k'ew.* See 李 瀚 LE HAN.

遍 照 發 揮 性 靈 集 *Peen chaou fa hwuy sing ling tseih.* See 異 濟 CHIN-TSE.

辯 惑 巵 言 *Peen hwo chih yen.* See 李 問 漁 LE WĂN-YU.

貶 妖 穴 爲 罪 隸 論 *Peen yaou heue wei tsui li lun.* See 太 平 天 國 T'AIP'ING T'IEN KWO.

闢 妄 *P'eih wang.* See 徐 光 啟 SEU KWANG-K'E.

佩 文 韻 篆 *Pei wăn yun chuen.* See 張 鈵 圖 CHANG YU-POO.

佩 文 韻 府 *Pei wăn yun foo.* See 張 玉 書 CHANG YUH-SHOO.

佩 文 韻 府 約 編 *Pei wăn yun foo yo peen.* See 鄧 齊 嵋 T'ĂNG TSE-MEI.

避 難 竹 枝 詞 *Pe nan chuh che ts'ze.* See 吳 少 雲 WOO SHAOU-YUN, and 劉 壁 山 LEW PIH-SHAN.

批 點 春 秋 左 傳 綱 目 句 解 *P'e teen ch'un ts'ew Tso chuen kang muh keu keae.* See 韓 菼 HAN T'AN.

彼 得 羅 言 行 全 傳 *Pe-tih-lo yen hing ts'euen chuen.* See 彼 得 羅 PE-TIH-LO.

白 香 山 詩 集 *Pih heang shan she tseih.* See 汪 西 亭 WANG SE-T'ING.

白 門 新 柳 記 *Pih mun sin lew ke.* See 許 豫 龔 HEU YU-YANG.

百 鳥 圖 說 *Pih neaou t'oo shwo.* See 百 鳥 PIH NEAOU.

白 氏 文 集 *Pih she wăn tseih.* See 白 居 易 PIH KEU-YIH.

百 獸 圖 說 *Pih show t'oo shwo.* See 韋 門 道 氏 WEI-MUN-TAOU SHE.

百 體 千 字 文 *Pih t'e ts'een tsze wăn.* See 周 興 嗣 CHOW HING-SZE.

平 浙 紀 略 *P'ing Cheh ke leŏ.* See 楊 昌 濬 YANG CH'ANG SEUN.

評 註 淵 海 子 平 大 全 *P'ing choo yuen hai tsze p'ing ta ts'euen.* See 廣 塞 子 KWANG HAN-TSZE.

兵 船 礮 法 *Ping ch'uen p'aou fa.* See UNITED STATES OF AMERICA: *Naval Department.*

*平 壤 志 *P'ing-jang che.* See 尹 斗 壽 E TOW-SHOW.

平 貴 別 窰 *P'ing-kwei pĕĕ yaou.* See 薛 平 貴 SËE P'ING-KWEI.

平 山 冷 燕 *P'ing shan lăng yen.* See 荻 岸 散 人 TIH NGAN SAN JIN, *pseud.*

平 定 粵 匪 紀 略 *P'ing ting Yuĕ fei ke leŏ.* See 粵 匪 YUĔ FEI.

品 花 寶 鑑 *P'in hwa paou keen.* See 石 函 氏 SHIH-HAN SHE.

寘 萌 集 *Pin măng tseih.* See 俞 樾 YU YUĔ.

裏 批 簿 *Pin p'e po.* See 裏 PIN.

卜 卦 之 論 *Po kwa che lun.* See 叔 SHUH.

普 法 戰 紀 *P'oo Fa chen ke.* See 王 韜 WANG T'AOU.

哺 乳 須 知 *Poo joo seu che.* See 哺 乳 POO JOO.

哱 哴 官 的 問 答 話 *Po-urh kwan ti wăn ta hwa.* See 哱 哴 官 PO-URH KWAN.

剖 惑 至 言 *P'ow hwo che yen.* See 陳 光 瑩 CH'IN KWANG-YIN.

博物新編 *Po wuh sin peen.* See 合信 HOSIN.

本朝名家詩鈔小傳 *Pun ch'aou ming kea she ch'aou seaou chuen.* See 鄭方坤 CHING FANG-KWĂN.

本朝試賦新硎 *Pun ch'aou shih foo sin hing.* See 李榮阿 LE P'AN-AH, and 李芝泉 LE CHE-TS'EUEN.

本分規條 *Pun fun kwei t'eaou.* See 本分 PUN FUN.

本經逢原 *Pun king fung yuen.* See 張路玉 CHANG LOO-YUH.

本草綱目 *Pun ts'aou kang muh.* See 李時珍 LE SHE-CHIN.

本草綱目拾遺 *Pun ts'aou kang muh shih e.* See 趙恕軒 CHAOU SHOO-HEEN.

本草述鈎元 *Pun ts'aou shuh kow yuen.* See 楊貞頤 YANG CHING-E.

番禺陳氏東塾叢書 *Pwan yu Ch'in she tung shuh ts'ung shoo.* See 陳澧 CH'IN LE.

兩西圖 *Ryang sye to.* See 兩西 RYANG SYE.

Sách Meo Latinh. See MEO LATINH.

Sam-jŭ-keng sin-chōan Pek-oa chù-kái. See EDE (GEORGE).

三塲文選 *San ch'ang wăn seuen.* See 劉仁初 LEW JIN-CH'OO.

三車一覽 *San ch'ay yih lan.* See 方謙之 FANG K'EEN-CHE.

三分夢全傳 *San fun mung ts'euen chuen.* See 張士登 CHANG SZE-TĂNG.

Sanghavarman. See 康僧鎧 K'ANG TSĂNG-K'AI.

生地獄圖說 *Săng te yo t'oo shwo.* See 生地獄 SĂNG TE YO.

生草藥性 *Săng ts'aou yo sing.* See 雲中子 YUN CHUNG TSZE.

三合劍全傳 *San ho keen ts'euen chuen.* See 三合 SAN HO.

三合便覽 *San ho peen lan.* See 秀升 SEW SHING.

三綱行實 *San kang hing shih.* See 三綱 SAN KANG.

三綱行實孝子圖 *San kang hing shih heaou tsze t'oo.* See 三綱 SAN KANG.

三江邁倫集 *San keang mai lun tseih.* See 徐郙 SEU FOO.

三敎平心論 *San keaou p'ing sin lun.* See 劉謐 LEW ME.

* 三敎源流聖帝佛帥搜神記 *San keaou yuen lew shing te Fuh sze sow shin ke.* See 干寶 KAN PAOU.

三角數理 *San keŏ shoo le.* See 海麻士 HAI-MA-SZE.

三國志 *San kwo che.* See 羅貫中 LO KWAN-CHUNG.

三國志書後 *San kwo che shoo how.* See 李欽之 LE K'IN-CHE.

三國志全圖演義 *San kwo che ts'euen t'oo yen e.* See 羅貫中 LO KWAN-CHUNG.

三山論學 *San shan lun heŏ.* See 艾儒畧 GAI JOO-LEŎ.

三十一條思量 *San shih yih t'eaou sze leang.* See 思量 SZE LEANG.

三書院正外付課 *San shoo yuen ching wai foo k'o.* See 三書院 SAN SHOO YUEN.

三壇傳戒正範 *San t'an chuen keae ching fan.* See 讀體 TUH-T'E.

三燈最話合刻 *San tăng ts'ung hwa ho kih.* See 瞿祐宗 KEU YEW-TSUNG.

三才圖會 *San ts'ai t'oo hwuy.* See 王圻 WANG KE.

三才一貫圖 *San ts'ai yih kwan t'oo.* See 呂安世 LEU GAN-SHE.

三字鑑勘本 *San tsze keen k'an pun.* See 萬青銓 WAN TS'ING-TS'EUEN.

三字經 *San tsze king.* See 字 TSZE.

三要錄 *San yaou luh.* See MARTIN (WILLIAM A. P.), D.D.

三與樓 *San-yu-low.* See SAN-YU-LOW.

三魚堂文集 *San-yu T'ang wăn tseih.* See 陸稼書 LUH KEA-SHOO.

相輪陀羅尼 *Seang lun t'o-lo-ne.* See 相輪 SEANG LUN.

象山縣志 *Seang-shan Heen che.* See 象山縣 SEANG-SHAN HEEN.

相造居室挀要論 *Seang tsaou keu shih gih yaou lun.* 師惟善 SZE-WEI-SHEN.

小學註解 *Seaou heŏ choo keae.* See 朱熹 CHOO HE.

小學大全 *Seaou heŏ ta ts'euen.* See 朱熹 CHOO HE.

小學集說 *Seaou heŏ tseǐh shwo.* See 朱熹 CHOO HE.

小家語 *Seaou kea yu.* See 黃沐三 HWANG MUH-SAN.

嘯古堂文集 *Seaou koo T'ang wǎn tseǐh.* See 蔣敦復 TSEANG TUN-FUH.

笑林廣記 *Seaou lin kwang ke.* See 遊戲主人 YEW-HE CHOO-JIN.

小石山房叢書 *Seaou shih shan fang ts'ung shoo.* See 顧嵐 KOO LAN.

嘯堂集古錄考異 *Seaou t'ang tseǐh koo luh k'aou e.* See 王俅 WANG K'EW.

小題靈秀集 *Seaou t'e ling sew tseǐh.* See 小題 SEAOU T'E.

小題拔幟 *Seaou t'e pa ch'e.* See 吳敬騮 WOO MUH-TSOW.

小題清新集 *Seaou t'e ts'ing sin tseǐh.* See 顧俊 KOO TSEUN, and 王燮 WANG SĔĔ.

小題文綜 *Seaou t'e wǎn tsung.* See 小題 SEAOU T'E.

* 小兒論 *Seaou urh lun.* See 小兒 SEAOU URH.

笑雲和尚古文真寶之抄 *Seaou-yun Hoshang ku wǎn chin paou che ch'aou.* See 清三 TS'ING-SAN.

謝疊山先生文章軌范 *Seay Tĕĕ-shan Seen-sǎng wǎn chang kwei fan.* See 謝枋得 SEAY FANG-TIH.

西陲要略 *Se ch'uy yaou leŏ.* See 鶴皋 HO KAOU.

—— See 祁韻士 KE YUN-SZE.

西藝知新 *Se e che sin.* See 傅蘭雅 FOO-LAN-YA.

—— See 諾格德 NO-KIH-TIH.

西醫略論 *Se e leŏ lun.* See 合信 HOSIN.

仙佛宗指 *Seen Fuh tsung che.* See 悟清子 WOO TS'ING-TSZE.

暹羅譯語 *Sëen-lo yih yu.* See 暹羅 SĔEN-LO.

薛氏五種 *Sĕĕ she woo chung.* See 薛慰農 SĔĔ WEI-NUNG.

薛氏判醫書二十四種 *Sĕĕ yuen pan e shoo urh shih sze chung.* See 薛 SĔĔ.

西方公據 *Se fang kung keu.* See 沈清麄 CH'IN TS'ING-CH'IN, and 周遠振 CHOW YUEN-CHIN.

西番碧玉帶全本 *Se fan peǐh yuh tai ts'euen pun.* See 西番碧玉帶 SE FAN PEǏH YUH TAI.

西番譯語 *Se fan yih yu.* See 西番 SE FAN.

* —— See 西番 SE FAN.

西學考畧 *Se heŏ k'aou leŏ.* See 丁韙瓦 TING WEI-LEANG.

西湖佳話 *Se hoo kea hwa.* See 墨浪子 MIH-LANG-TSZE.

西湖拾遺 *Se hoo shih e.* See 陳樹基 CH'IN SHOO-KE.

息齋集 *Seǐh chai tseǐh.* See 金之俊 KIN CHE-TSEUN.

折疑辨譌 *Seǐh e peen meu.* See 慕維廉 MOO WEI-LEEN.

惜抱軒文集 *Seǐh-paou heen wǎn tseǐh.* See 姚鼐姬 YAOU NAI-KE.

息影軒畫譜 *Seǐh ying heen hwa pu.* See 梁清標 LEANG TS'ING-PEAOU.

西江志 *Se keang che.* See 白潢 PIH HWANG.

西國近事彙編 *Se kwŏ kin sze wei peen.* See 金楷理 KIN K'EAE-LE.

—— *See* PERIODICAL PUBLICATIONS : *Shanghai.*

西國樂法啓家 *Se kwo yo fa k'e mung.* See MATEER (JULIA B.).

—— See 狄就烈 T'ĔIH TSEW-LĔĔ.

西廂記 *Se seang ke.* See 金聖嘆 KIN SHING-T'AN.

* 西蜀方言 *Se Shuh fang yen.* See GRAINGER (ADAM).

西士翺中國人書 *Se sze ch'ow Chung kwo jin shoo.* See 西士 SE SZE.

西士來意畧論 *Se sze lai e leŏ lun.* See 麥嘉締培端 MIH-KEA-TE PEI-TWAN.

—— *See* MCCARTEE (DIVIE BETHUNE).

西天眞實名經 *Se t'een chin shih ming king.* See 西天 SE T'EEN.

西藏見聞錄 *Se Ts'ang keen wǎn luh.* See 蕭騰麟 SEAOU T'ĂNG-LIN.

宣道指歸 *Seuen tao che kwei.* See 倪維思 NE-WEI-SZE.

選擇本願念佛集 *Seuen tsih pun yuen neen Fuh tseih.* See 佛 FUH.

雪月梅傳 *Seuĕ Yuĕ Mei chuen.* See 陳朗 CH'IN LANG.

荀子 *Seun tsze.* See 荀況 SEUN HWANG.

徐氏醫書六種 *Seu she e shoo luh chung.* See 徐靈胎 SEU LING-T'AI.

徐氏三種 *Seu she san chung.* See 徐建勳 SEU KEEN HEUN.

—— *See* 徐士橐 SEU SZE-YEH.

徐星伯先生著書三種 *Seu Sing-pih Seen Sǎng choo shoo san chung.* See 徐星伯 SEU SING-PIH.

袖珍日課 *Sew chin jih k'o.* See 郭居靜 KO KEU-TSING.

繡鞋記醫貫新書 *Sew heae ke king kwei sin shoo.* See 繡鞋 SEW HEAE.

繡虎軒尺牘全集 *Sew hoo heen ch'ih tuh ts'euen tseih.* See 張西源 CHANG SE-YUEN.

繡球緣 *Sew k'ew yuen.* See 繡球 SEW K'EW.

繡戈袍全傳 *Sew ko p'aou ts'euen chuen.* See 繡戈袍 SEW KO P'AOU.

繡像義妖傳 *Sew seang e yaou chuen.* See 陳遇乾 CH'IN YU-K'EEN.

繡像飛龍全傳 *Sew seang Fei lung ts'euen chuen.* See 吳璿 WOO SEUEN.

繡像安邦定國全傳 *Sew seang gan pang ting kwo ts'euen chuen.* See 楊升菴 YANG SHING-GAN.

繡像八仙緣 *Sew seang Pa seen luh.* See 梅庭氏 MEI-T'ING-SHE.

繡像拍案驚奇 *Sew seang pih ngan king k'e.* See 空觀主人 K'UNG KWAN CHOO JIN.

繡像平妖全書 *Sew seang p'ing yaou ts'euen chuen.* See 羅貫中 LO KWAN-CHUNG.

繡像薛仁貴征東全傳 *Sew seang Seay Jin kwei ching tung ts'euen chuen.* See 蘇如運 SOO JOO LEEN.

繡像東西漢演義 *Sew seang tung se Han yen e.* See 鍾伯敬 CHUNG PIH-KING.

繡像蘊香丸 *Sew seang yun heang hwan.* See 蘊香丸 YUN HEANG HWAN.

西涯擬古樂府 *Se yai e koo yo foo.* See 李東陽 LE TUNG-YANG.

西洋記 *Se yang ke.* See 羅懋登 LO MOW-TĂNG.

西遊記 *Se yew ke.* See 邱長春 K'EW CH'ANG-CH'UN.

西遊補 *Se yew poo.* See 靜嘯齋主人 TSING SEAOU CHAI CHOO JIN, *pseud.*

西遊原旨 *Se yew yuen che.* See 邱長春 K'EW CH'ANG-CH'UN.

西域考古錄 *Se yih k'aou koo luh.* See 俞浩 YU HAOU.

西域紀要 *Se yih ke yaou.* See 三氏 SAN SHE.

西域瑣談 *Se yih so t'an.* See 七十一 TS'IH SHIH-YIH.

西嶽華山廟 *Se yo Hwa-shan meaou.* See 西嶽 SE YO.

西藥畧釋 *Se yo leŏ shih.* See KERR (JOHN GLASGOW).

痧證全生 *Sha ching ts'euen sǎng.* See 黃鶴齡 HWANG HO LING.

山法全書 *Shan fa ts'euen shoo.* See 葉九升 YE KEW-SHING.

上海醫院述畧十四冊 *Shanghai e yuen shuh leŏ shih sze ts'ih.* See 韓雅各 HAN YA-KOH.

上海縣志 *Shanghai heen che.* See 王大同 WANG TA-T'UNG.

上海徽寧思恭堂徵信錄 *Shanghai hwuy Ning sze kung t'ang ching sin luh.* See 上海 SHANGHAI.

上海格致書院第一次記錄 *Shanghai kih che shoo yuen te yih t'sze ke luh.* See 上海 SHANGHAI.

上海大關則列 *Shanghai ta kwan tsih le.* See 上海 SHANGHAI.

上海大關則例躉遷木榜抄錄 *Shanghai ta kwan tsih le kin tsun muh pang ch'aou luh.* See 上海 SHANGHAI.

上海同仁堂徵信錄 *Shanghai t'ung jin T'ang ching sin luh.* See 上海 SHANGHAI.

上海同仁堂義學條規 *Shanghai t'ung jin T'ang e heŏ t'eaou kwei.* See 上海 SHANGHAI.

上海育嬰堂徵信錄 *Shanghai yuh ying T'ang ching sin luh.* See 上海 SHANGHAI.

傷寒兼證析義 *Shang han keen ching seih e.* See 張飛鳴 CHANG FEI-CHOW.

傷寒緒論 *Shang han seu lun.* See 張路玉 CHANG LOO-YUH.

傷寒舌鑑 *Shang han she keen.* See 張覩先 CHANG TAN-SEEN.

傷寒大成 *Shang han ta ch'ing.* See 張路玉 CHANG LOO-YUH.

商賈便覽 *Shang koo peen lan.* See 吳中孚 WOO CHUNG-FOO.

尙論篇 *Shang lun p'een.* See 喩嘉言 YU KEA-YEN.

尙史 *Shang she.* See 李鍇 LE K'EAR.

尙史論賛 *Shang she lun tsan.* See 李欽之 LE K'IN-CHE.

尙書 *Shang shoo.* See 孔丘 K'UNG K'EW.

尙書後案 *Shang shoo how gan.* See 王鳴盛 WANG MING-SHING.

尙書釋天 *Shang shoo shih t'een.* See 盛百二 SHING PIH-URH.

上帝生日之論 *Shang te săng jih che lun.* See 尙德 SHANG TIH.

* 上宰相書 *Shang tsai seang shoo.* See 丁保祿 TING PAOU-LUH.

* 商務書館華英字典 *Shang woo shoo kwan Hwa Ying tsze teen.* See 商務書館 SHANG WOO SHOO KWAN.

山谷詩集注 *Shan kuh she tseih choo.* See 黃庭堅 HWANG T'ING-KEEN.

山水臭蹟 *Shan shwuy chin tseih.* See 卞潤甫 PEEN YUEN-FOO.

山左闈墨 *Shan tso wei mih.* See 山左 SHAN TSO.

山右闈墨 *Shan yew wei mih.* See 山右 SHAN YEW.

邵子湘全集 *Shaou Tsze-seang ts'euen tseih.* See 邵子湘 SHAOU TSZE-SEANG.

詩鈔 *She chaou.* See 趙翼 CHAOU YIH.

詩傳大全 *She chuen ta ts'euen.* See 詩經 SHE KING.

詩賦駢字類珠 *She foo p'een tsze luy choo.* See 蕭熿藜 SEAOU HWANG-LE.

詩賦全集 *She foo ts'euen tseih.* See 徐位山 SEU WEI-SHAN.

詩學含英 *She heŏ han ying.* See 劉豹君 LEW PAOU-KEUN.

試行蠶桑說 *She hing ts'an sang shwo.* See 陳慶偕 CH'IN K'ING-KEAE.

詩話 *She hwa.* See 趙翼 CHAOU YIH.

史記菁華 *She ke tsing hwa.* See 司馬遷 SZE-MA TS'EEN.

史記菁華錄 *She ke tsing hwa luh.* See 司馬遷 SZE-MA TS'EEN.

使喀爾喀紀程草 *She kih-urh-kih ke ching ts'aou.* See 昇寅 SHING YIN.

詩經 *She king.* See 詩經 SHE KING.

詩料詳註 *She leaou tseang choo.* See 秦霞峰 TS'IN HEA-FUNG, and 郭禮堂 KO LE-T'ANG.

時聯選箋四集 *She leen seuen tseen sze tseih.* See 吟香社 YIN HEANG-SHAY.

史論五種 *She lun woo chung.* See 李欽之 LE K'IN-CHE.

禪眞後史 *Shen chin how shih.* See 清溪道人 TS'ING K'E TAOU JIN.

禪眞逸史 *Shen chin yih she.* See 清心道人 TS'ING SIN TAOU JIN.

善終己亡經 *Shen chung e wang king.* See 善終 SHEN CHUNG.

SHE—SHI

善後條約 *Shen how t'eaou yo.* See 條約 T'EAOU YO.

善卷堂四六 *Shen-keuen T'ang sze luh.* See 墜拒石 LUH KEU-SHIH.

禪林類聚 *Shen lin luy tseu.* See 智境 CHE-KING.

禪門日誦 *Shen mun jih sung.* See 禪門 SHEN MUN.

善生福終 *Shen săng fuh chung.* See 善生 SHEN SĂNG.

禪源諸詮集 *Shen yuen choo ts'euen tseih.* See 宗密 TSUNG-MEIH.

詩僊 *She seen.* See 凹凸丈夫 WA TEIH CHANG FOO.

使徒行傳註解 *She t'oo hing chuen choo keae.* See BIBLE—NEW TESTAMENT: *Acts.*

使徒雅各暨彼得前後書註釋 *She t'oo Ya kih ke Pe-tih ts'een how shoo choo shih.* 陶錫祈 T'AOU SEIH-K'E.

試策補要 *She ts'ih poo yaou.* See 試策 SHE TS'IH.

氏族大全 *She tsuh ta ts'euen.* See 氏族 SHE TSUH.

示我周行 *She wo chow hing.* See 鶴和堂 HO HO-T'ANG.

史要聚選 *She yaou tseu seuen.* See 史 SHE.

示翰抄本 *She yu ch'aou pun.* See 示翰 SHE YU.

詩韻含英題解 *She yun han ying t'e keae.* See 甘芳谷 KAN FANG-SUH.

詩韻合璧 *She yun ho peih.* See 湯祥瑟 T'ANG TSEANG-PE.

詩韻類錦 *She yun luy kin.* See 郭雨三 KO YU-SAN.

詩韻集成 *She yun tseih ch'ing.* See 余照 YU CHAOU.

食齋指迷 *Shih chai che me.* See 賴修仁 LAI SEW-JIN.

十竹齋書畫冊 *Shih chuh chai shoo hwa ts'ih.* See 十竹齋 SHIH CHUH CHAI.

* 十法界循業發現圖 *Shih fa keae heun yay fa heen t'oo.* See 石鳳臺 SHIH FUNG-T'AI.

十房薦卷同門錄 *Shih fang tseen keuen t'ung mun luh.* See 十房 SHIH FANG.

十誡問答 *Shih keae wăn ta.* See 郭顯德 KO HEEN-TIH.

釋迦方誌 *Shih kea fang che.* See 道宣 TAOU-SEUEN.

釋迦如來應化事蹟 *Shih kea joo-lai Ying hwa sze tseih.* See 永珊熏沐 YUNG SHAN HEUN SHUH.

—— See 熏沐 HEUN SHUH.

十九史略通考 *Shih kew she leŏ t'ung k'aou.* See 曾先之 TSĂNG SEEN-CHE.

十九史略諺解 *Shih kew she leŏ yen keae.* 十九史 SHIH KEW SHI.

十國春秋 *Shih kwo ch'un ts'ew.* See 吳任臣 WOO JIN-CH'IN.

十八家詩鈔 *Shih pa kea she ch'aou.* See 曾國藩 TSĂNG KWO-FAN.

十八羅漢 *Shih pa Lo-han.* See 羅漢 LO-HAN.

十三經集字摹本 *Shih san king tseih tsze moo pun.* See 張小浦 CHANG SEAOU-P'OO.

石點頭 *Shih teen t'ow.* See 天然 T'EEN-JIN.

十七史蒙求 *Shih ts'ih she mung k'ew.* See 金三俊 KIN SAN-TSEUN.

適情雅趣 *Shih ts'ing ya ts'eu.* See 陳希夷 CH'IN HE-E.

* 食物本草 *Shih wuh pun ts'aou.* See 何克諫 HO KIH-KEEN.

食物本草會纂 *Shih wuh pun ts'aou hwuy tswan.* See 沈李龍 CH'IN LE-LUNG.

拾雅 *Shih ya.* See 夏味堂 HEA WEI-T'ANG.

省察規式 *Shing ch'a kwei shih.* See 省察 SHING CH'A.

勝朝遺事 *Shing ch'aou e sze.* See 吳樸園 WOO P'O-YUEN.

* 聖主躬耕藉田頌 *Shing choo kung kăng tseih t'een sung.* See 趙殿最 CHAOU TEEN-TSUY.

升菴全集 *Shing gan ts'euen tseih.* See 楊慎 YANG SHIN.

聖賢像贊 *Shing heen seang tsan.* See 冠洋子 KWAN YANG-TSZE.

聖賢讀像圖 *Shing heen tsan seang t'oo.* See 李龍 Le Lung.

聲學 *Shing heŏ.* See 田大里 T'een-ta-le.

聖學十圖 *Shing heŏ shih t'oo.* See 聖學 Shing heŏ.

聖會勸懲條例 *Shing hwuy k'euen ch'ing t'eaou le.* See 聖會 Shing hwuy.

聖會史記 *Shing hwuy she ke.* See 郭顯德 Ko Heen-tih.

聖會禱文 *Shing hwuy taou wăn.* See Liturgies: England, Church of.

* 聖人言行 *Shing jin yen hing.* See 聖人 Shing jin.

—— See 艾儒畧 Gai Joo-leŏ.

聖綱鑑小畧 *Shing kang keen seaou leŏ.* See 聖綱鑑 Shing kang keen.

聖家會規 *Shing kea hwuy kwei.* See 聖家會 Shing kea hwuy.

聖教主日法 *Shing keaou choo jih fa.* See 聖教 Shing keaou.

聖教日課 *Shing keaou jih k'o.* See 聖教 Shing keaou.

聖教鑑畧 *Shing keaou keen leŏ.* See 田類思 T'een-luy-sze.

聖教經課 *Shing keaou king k'o.* See 聖教 Shing keaou.

聖教理證 *Shing keaou le ching.* See 聖教 Shing keaou.

聖教禮規 *Shing keaou le kwei.* See 聖教 Shing keaou.

聖教明徵 *Shing keaou ming ching.* See 萬濟國 Wan Tse-kwo.

聖教切要 *Shing keaou ts'ĕĕ yaou.* See 聖教 Shing keaou.

* 聖教要理 *Shing keaou yaou le.* See 聖教 Shing keaou.

—— See 和 Ho.

聖教要理國語 *Shing keaou yaou le kwo yu.* See 聖教 Shing keaou.

聖教要理問答 *Shing keaou yaou le wăn tă.* See 聖教 Shing keaou.

聖經許輪 *Shing king heu yu.* See 那爾敦 Na-urh-tun.

聖經廣益 *Shing king kwang yih.* See 聖經 Shing king.

聖經類書 *Shing king luy shoo.* See 麥嘉緒培端 Mih Kea-te Pei-twan.

聖經史記 *Shing king she ke.* See 聖經 Shing king.

盛京通志 *Shing king t'ung che.* See 呂耀曾 Leu Yaou-tsăng.

聖經問答 *Shing king wăn ta.* See 那爾敦 Na-urh-tun.

聖公會大綱 *Shing kung hwuy ta kang.* See 慕稚德 Moo-a-tih.

陞官圖說 *Shing kwan t'oo shwo.* See 陞官 Shing kwan.

勝旅景程正編 *Shing leuh king ch'ing ching peen.* See 都陽約翰 P'oyang Yohan.

聲律啟蒙撮要 *Shing leu k'e mung ts'o yaou.* See 車萬育 Ch'ay Wan-yuh.

聖羅閣九日敬禮 *Shing Loh-kih kew jih king le.* See 聖羅閣 Shing Loh-kih.

聖路善工 *Shing loo shen kung.* See 聖路 Shing loo.

聖母行實 *Shing moo hing shih.* See 聖母 Shing moo.

聖母玫瑰經十五端 *Shing moo Mei kwei king shih wu twan.* See 聖母 Shing moo.

聖母小日課 *Shing moo seaou jih k'o.* See 聖母 Shing moo.

聖母善導會直指 *Shing moo shen taou hwuy chih che.* See 聖母善導會 Shing moo shen taou hwuy.

聖母善導會學規 *Shing moo shen taou hwuy heŏ kwei.* See 聖母善導會 Shing moo shen taou hwuy.

聖母善導會公規 *Shing moo shen taou hwuy kung kwei.* See 聖母善導會 Shing moo shen taou hwuy.

聖母聖月 *Shing moo shing yuĕ.* See 聖母 Shing moo.

SHI—SHW

聖 母 七 苦 籍 規 喀 *Shing moo ts'ih k'oo tseih kwei leŏ.* See 聖 母 SHING MOO.

聖 安 多 尼 行 實 *Shing Ngan-to-ni hing shih.* See 聖 安 多 尼 SHING NGAN-TO-NI.

聖 女 羅 洒 行 實 *Shing nu Lo-se hing shih.* See 羅 森 鐸 LO SĂN-TO.

聖 山 諧 歌 *Shing shan heae ko (Sing-sæn-yiæ-ko).* See INSLEE (ELIAS B.).

盛 世 芻 蕘 *Shing she ch'oo jao.* See 盛 世 SHING SHE.

聖 神 降 臨 *Shing shin keang lin.* See 聖 神 SHING SHIN.

聖 書 綱 目 *Shing shoo kang muh.* See 聖 書 SHING SHOO.

聖 書 典 論 *Shing shoo teen lun.* See 帥 SZE.

聖 書 地 理 *Shing shoo te le.* See 葉 韙 瓦 YE WEI LEANG.

聖 書 衍 義 *Shing shoo yen e.* See 哈 巴 安 德 HA-PA NGAN-TIH.

聖 心 月 新 稿 *Shing sin yuĕ sin peen.* See 聖 心 SHING SIN.

聖 帝 寶 訓 *Shing te paou heun.* See 關 帝 KWAN-TE.

聖 體 要 理 *Shing t'e yaou le.* See 艾 儒 喀 GAI JOO-LEŎ.

聖 武 記 *Shing woo ke.* See 魏 源 WEI YUEN.

聖 諭 *Shing yu.* See 康 熙 K'ANG-HE, *Emperor.*

聖 願 問 答 *Shing yuen wăn ta.* See 聖 願 SHING YUEN.

聖 諭 廣 訓 *Shing yu kwang heun.* See 康 熙 K'ANG-HE, *Emperor.*

聖 諭 像 解 *Shing yu seang keae.* See 康 熙 K'ANG-HE, *Emperor.*

神 機 制 敵 太 白 陰 經 *Shin ke che tih t'ai pih yin king.* See 李 筌 LE TS'EUEN.

神 理 總 論 *Shin le tsung lun.* See 俏 德 者 SHANG-TIH-CHAY.

神 仙 鑑 *Shin seen keen.* See 徐 衜 SEU TAOU.

神 道 總 論 *Shin taou tsung lun.* See 倪 維 思 NE-WEI-SZE.

神 天 十 條 聖 誡 *Shin t'een shih t'eaou shing keae.* See 神 天 SHIN T'EEN.

神 僧 傳 *Shin tsăng chuen.* See 青 河 髮 TS'ING-HO-FA.

審 音 鑑 古 錄 *Shin yin keen koo luh.* See 玩 花 主 人 WAN-HWA-CHOO-JIN.

書 傳 大 全 *Shoo chuen ta ts'euen.* See 孔 丘 K'UNG K'EW.

數 學 理 *Shoo heŏ le.* See 棵 麼 甘 TE MOKAN.

書 經 *Shoo king.* See 孔 丘 K'UNG K'EW.

—— See 汪 昉 WANG FANG.

書 經 正 文 *Shoo king ching wăn.* See 孔 丘 K'UNG K'EW.

壽 *Show.* See 呂 喦 LEU YEN.

首 楞 嚴 義 疏 注 經 *Show lang yen e soo choo king.* See 予 璿 YU-SEUEN.

守 邊 輯 要 *Show peen tseih yaou.* See 璧 星 泉 PEÏH SING-TS'EUEN.

述 古 叢 鈔 *Shuh koo ts'ung ch'aou.* See 劉 晚 榮 LEW WAN-YUNG.

塾 課 小 題 分 編 *Shuh k'o seaou t'e fun peen.* See 王 步 青 WANG POO-TS'ING.

贖 罪 之 道 *Shuh tsuy che taou.* See 愛 漢 者 GAI HAN CHAY.

贖 罪 之 道 傳 *Shuh tsuy che taou chuen.* See 愛 漢 者 GAI HAN CHAY.

贖 罪 文 *Shuh tsuy wăn.* See 胡 德 邁 HOO TIH-MAI.

菽 園 箸 書 三 種 *Shuh-yuen choo shoo san chung.* See 邱 菽 園 K'EW SHUH-YUEN.

雙 釘 記 *Shwang ting ke.* See 雙 釘 SHWANG TING.

雙 千 字 文 *Shwang ts'een tsze wăn.* See MARTIN (W. A. P.), D.D.

—— See 千 字 文 TS'EEN TSZE WĂN.

說 唱 繡 香 囊 全 傳 *Shwo ch'ang sew heang nang ts'euen chuen.* See 陸 士 珍 LUH SZE-CHIN.

說 唐 後 傳 *Shwo T'ang how chuen.* See 如 蓮 JOO LEEN.

說 唐 全 傳 *Shwo T'ang ts'euen chuen.* See 唐 T'ANG.

說 文 解 字 通 釋 *Shwo wăn keae tsze t'ung shih.* See 許 慎 HEU SHIN.

說 文 廣 義 *Shwo wăn kwang e.* See 許 慎 HEU SHIN.

說 文 新 附 考 *Shwo wăn sin foo k'aou.* See 吳 樹 玉 WOO SHOO-YUH.

說 文 字 原 韻 表 *Shwo wăn tsze yuen yun peaou.* See 胡 重 HOO CHUNG.

說 文 通 訓 定 聲 *Shwo wăn t'ung heun ting shing.* See 朱 駿 聲 CHOO TSEUN-SHING.

說 偎 傳 *Shwo Wei chuen.* See 全 子 式 TS'EUEN TSZE-URH.

水 滸 後 傳 *Shwuy hoo how chuen.* See 宋 遺 民 SUNG E-MIN.

水 石 綠 *Shwuy Shih yuen.* See 李 芳 普 LE FANG-POO.

水 心 文 集 *Shwuy sin wăn tseih.* See 棄 正 則 YE CHING-TSIH.

水 師 章 程 *Shwuy sze chang ch'ing.* See GREAT BRITAIN AND IRELAND: *Admiralty.*

水 師 操 練 *Shwuy sze ts'aou leen.* See GREAT BRITAIN AND IRELAND: *Admiralty.*

Siao Hyin-li teng gyi-go ti-'ŏ nying bu-zi. See BUTT, afterwards SHERWOOD (MARY MARTHA).

新 製 靈 臺 儀 象 志 *Sin che ling t'ai e seang che.* See 南 懷 仁 NAN-HWAI-JIN.

新 政 始 基 *Sin ching che ke.* See 何 啓 HO K'E.

—— See 何 啓 HO K'E, and 胡 禮 垣 HOO LE-YUEN.

新 政 眞 詮 *Sin ching chin ts'euen.* See 何 啓 HO K'E, and 胡 禮 垣 HOO LE-YUEN.

* 星 鳳 樓 帖 *Sing fung low t'eĕ.* See 王 羲 之 WANG HE-CHE.

Sing iah shü jü-veng: teh Foh-ing ts'æn-di. See SING IAH SHÜ.

性 理 體 註 大 全 旁 訓 要 解 *Sing le t'e choo ta ts'euen pang heun yaou keae.* See 林 殿 颺 LIN TEEN-YANG.

姓 名 總 冊 *Sing ming tsung ts'ih.* See 姓 名 SING MING.

醒 世 姻 緣 集 *Sing she yin luh tseih.* See 西 周 生 SE CHOW-SĂNG.

Sing-shü veng-teh. See SING-SHÜ.

省 心 畜 德 編 讀 本 *Sing sin ch'uh tih peen tuh pun.* See 楊 光 憲 YANG KWANG-HEEN.

星 軺 指 掌 *Sing yaou che chang.* See 馬 爾 頓 MA-ERH-TUN.

新 疆 則 例 便 覽 *Sin keang tsih le peen lan.* See 新 疆 SIN KEANG.

新 疆 外 叛 紀 略 *Sin keang wai Fan ke leŏ.* See 椿 園 氏 CH'UN-YUEN-SHE.

心 覺 論 *Sin keaou lun.* See 胡 德 邁 HOO TIH-MAI.

新 刻 小 試 策 論 格 式 *Sin k'ih seaou she ts'ih lun kih shih.* See 經 舍 氏 KING YU-SHE.

新 刻 玉 簫 琴 記 全 本 *Sin k'ih yuh seaou k'in ke ts'euen pun.* See 玉 簫 琴 YUH SEAOU K'IN.

心 經 附 註 *Sin king foo choo.* See 眞 德 秀 CHIN TIH-SEW.

新 馬 頭 *Sin ma t'ow.* See 馬 頭 MA T'OW.

新 報 *Sin paou.* See PERIODICAL PUBLICATIONS: *Shanghai.*

新 編 古 今 事 文 類 聚 *Sin peen koo kin sze wăn luy tseu.* See 祝 穆 CHUH MUH.

新 碧 桃 錦 帕 全 本 *Sin peĭh t'aou kin pa ts'euen pun.* See 碧 桃 錦 帕 PEĬH T'AOU KIN PA.

* 新 史 奇 觀 全 傳 *Sin she k'e kwan ts'euen chuen.* See 蓬 蒿 子 P'ĂNG-HAOU TSZE.

Šin šu, kai s šit. See BIBLE: *Appendix.*

心 算 初 學 *Sin swan ch'oo heŏ.* See 哈 邦 KA-PANG.

信 道 揭 要 書 *Sin taou keae yaou shoo.* See 信 道 SIN TAOU.

新 訂 解 人 頤 廣 集 *Sin ting keae jin e kwang tseih.* See 錢 德 蒼 TS'EEN TIH-TS'ANG.

信 徒 格 言 *Sin t'oo kih yen.* See 慕 稚 偉 MOO A-TIH.

SIN—SUN

新增智囊補 *Sin tsăng che nang poo.* See 馮夢龍 FUNG MUNG-LUNG.

新增尺牘稱呼合解 *Sin tsăng ch'ih tuh ch'ing hoo ho keae.* See 江耀亭 KEANG YAOU-T'ING.

新增華英尺牘 *Sin tsăng hwa ying ch'ih tuh.* See 郭灑貴 KO LO-KWEI.

新增華英通語 *Sin tsăng hwa ying t'ung yu.* See 黃永發 HWANG YUNG-FA.

新增萬寶元龍通考 *Sin tsăng wan paou yuen lung t'ung k'aou.* See 徐三省 SEU SAN-SĂNG.

新增五方元音全書 *Sin tsăng woo fang yuen yin ts'euen shoo.* See 樊騰鳳 FAN T'ĂNG-FUNG.

新齊諧 *Sin ts'e heae.* See 隨園戲 SUY-YUEN-HE.

新鐫興草篆隸千家詩 *Sin tseuen chin ts'aou chuen le ts'een kea she.* See 王羲之 WANG HE-CHE.

新測中星圖表 *Sin ts'ih chung sing t'oo peaou.* See 張作楠 CHANG TSO-NAN.

新測更漏中星表 *Sin ts'ih kăng low chung sing peaou.* See 張作楠 CHANG TSO-NAN.

信從相約文 *Sin ts'ung seang yo wăn.* See 信從 SIN TS'UNG.

新篡門目五臣音註揚子法言 *Sin tswan mun muh woo ch'in yin choo yang tsze fa yen.* See 揚雄 YANG HEUNG.

新篡聖道備全 *Sin tswan shing taou pe ts'euen.* See 種德者 CHUNG-TIH-CHAY.

新鴈翎扇墜全本 *Sin yen ling shan chuy ts'euen pun.* See 鴈翎扇墜 YEN LING SHAN CHUY.

新約史記絛問 *Sin yo she ke t'eaou wăn.* See 新約 SIN-YO.

新約全書註釋 *Sin yo ts'euen shoo choo shih.* See BIBLE: *New Testament.*

琑蛣雜記 *So keĭh tsa ke.* See 竹勿山石道人 CHUH WUH SHAN SHIH TAOU JIN.

蘇州府志 *Soo-chow Foo che.* See 寗雲鵬 NING YUN-PĂNG.

蘇老泉先生全集 *Soo Laou-ts'euen seen-săng ts'euen tseĭh.* See 蘇洵 SOO SEUN.

蘇松浮糧核議 *Soo Sung fow leang kih e.* See 蘇松 SOO SUNG.

蘇東坡 *Soo Tung-p'o.* See 蘇軾 SOO SHIH.

蘇文忠公詩合註 *Soo Wăn-chung kung she ho choo.* See 蘇軾 SOO SHIH.

蘇文忠公詩集 *Soo Wăn-chung kung she tseĭh.* See 蘇軾 SOO SHIH.

續紅樓夢 *Suh Hung low mung.* See 紅樓夢 HUNG LOW MUNG.

續客窗閒話 *Suh k'ih ch'wang heen hwa.* See 吳獮斥 WOO HEANG-HAN.

續錦綉叚 *Suh Kin sew twan.* See 錦綉叚 KIN SEW TWAN.

續天路歷程土話 *Suh t'een loo leĭh ching t'oo hwa.* See BUNYAN (JOHN).

續輯漢陽縣志 *Suh tseĭh Han-yang heen che.* See 黃式度 HWANG SHIH-TOO.

俗言警敎 *Suh yen king keaou.* See 俗言 SUH YEN.

頌主聖篇 *Sung choo shing p'een.* See 頌主 SUNG CHOO.

頌主聖詩 *Sung choo shing she.* See 頌主 SUNG CHOO.

松江府志 *Sung keang foo che.* See 宋如林 SUNG JOO-LIN.

* 松江府建求忠書院記 *Sung-keang foo keen k'ew chung shoo yuen ke.* See 沈壽昌 CHIN SHOW-CH'ANG.

宋鑑節要 *Sung keen tsëě yaou.* See 李坦夫 LE T'AN-FOO.

宋史 *Sung she.* See 脫脫 T'O-T'O.

宋詩別裁集 *Sung she pëě ts'ai tseĭh.* See 張景星 CHANG KING-SING.

宋太祖三下南唐 *Sung T'ai Tsoo san hea Nan T'ang.* See 太祖 T'AI TSOO.

宋宗忠簡公文集 *Sung Tsung Chung keen kung wăn tseĭh.* See 宗澤 TSUNG TSIH.

宋王復齋鐘鼎款識 *Sung Wang Fuh-chai chung ting kw'an shih.* See 王復齋 WANG FUH-CHAI.

頌揚眞神歌 *Sung yang chin shin ko.* See 倪維思 NE-WEI-SZE.

宋元明詩約鈔三百首 *Sung Yuen Ming she yo ch'aou san pih show.* See 朱梅嶅 CHOO MEI-K'E, and 冷謙庵 LÄNG LEEN-GAN.

隨軒金石文字 *Suy Heen kin shih wǎn tsze.* See 徐渭仁 SEU WEI-JIN.

算法指掌 *Swan fa che chang.* See 算法 SWAN FA.

算學啓蒙 *Swan heŏ k'e mung.* See 朱世傑 CHOO SHE-KEĔ.

算學課藝 *Swan heŏ k'o e.* See 李王叔 LE JIN-SHUH.

算式集要 *Swan shih tseĭh yaou.* See 哈司拿 HO-SZE-WEI.

西南圖 *Sye nam to.* See 西南 SYE NAM.

* 四川省會城池全圖 *Sze ch'uen shing hwuy ch'ing ch'e ts'euen t'oo.* See 四川 SZE CH'UEN.

四終暑意 *Sze chung leŏ e.* See 白多瑪 PIH TO-MA.

私充牙行埠頭 *Sze ch'ung ya hing fow t'ow.* See 牙行 YA HING.

四裔編年表 *Sze e peen neen peaou.* See 林樂知 LIN-LO-CHE, and 嚴瓦勳 YEN LEANG-HEUN.

死候保佑要視書 *Sze how paou yew yaou kwei shoo.* See 死候 SZE HOW.

四季想思 *Sze ke seang sze.* See 四季 SZE KE.

思綺堂文集 *Sze k'e t'ang wǎn tseĭh.* See 章豋積 CHANG K'E-TSIH.

士農工商 *Sze nung kung shang.* See 士 SZE.

思辨錄疑義 *Sze peen luh e e.* See 劉蓉霞 LEW JUNG-HEA.

四史聖經譯註 *Sze she shing king yih choo.* See BIBLE—NEW TESTAMENT: *Mark.*

—— See BIBLE—NEW TESTAMENT: *John, Gospel.*

四聖心源 *Sze shing sin yuen.* See 黃坤載 HWANG K'WǍN-TSAI.

四書攟餘說 *Sze shoo chih yu shwo.* See 曹之升 TS'AOU CHE-SHING.

四書正文 *Sze shoo ching wǎn.* See 四書 SZE SHOO.

四書合講 *Sze shoo ho keang.* See 四書 SZE SHOO.

四書便蒙 *Sze shoo peen mung.* See 子思 TSZE SZE.

四書不二字音義撮要 *Sze shoo puh urh tsze yin i ts'uh yaou.* See 四書 SZE SHOO.

四書典林 *Sze shoo teen lin.* See 江永 KEANG YUNG.

司梳淺譯 *Sze shoo ts'een yih.* See 羅星樓 LO SING-LOW.

四書集注 *Sze shoo tseĭh choo.* See 四書 SZE SHOO.

四書全註 *Sze shoo ts'euen choo.* See 四書 SZE SHOO.

四書襯 *Sze shoo tsin.* See 四書 SZE SHOO.

四書讀本辨義 *Sze shoo tuh pun peen e.* See 四書 SZE SHOO.

四書味根錄 *Sze shoo wei kǎn luh.* See 四書 SZE SHOO.

四述奇 *Sze shuh k'e.* See 張德彝 CHANG TIH-E.

氾水縣志 *Sze shwuy heen che.* See 許勉燉 HEU MEENTUN.

四字經文 *Sze tsze king wǎn.* See 四字經 SZE TSZE KING.

事物異名錄 *Sze wuh e ming luh.* See 厲荃 LE TS'EUEN.

肆原要理 *Sze yuen yaou le.* See 要理 YAOU LE.

大成通志 *Ta ch'ing t'ung che.* See 楊有慶 YANG YEW-KING.

大中國與大亞美利駕合衆國和約章程 *Ta chung kwo yu Ta A-mei-le-kea ho tsung kwo ho yo chang ch'ing.* See CHINA. 咸豐 HEEN-FUNG, *Emperor.*

大方廣佛華嚴經 *Ta fang kwang Fuh hwa yen king.* See 實叉難陀 SHIH-CHA-NAN-TO.

—— See 佛陀跋陀羅 FUH-T'O-PO-T'O-LO.

大佛頂如來密因修證了義諸菩薩萬行首楞嚴經 *Ta Fuh ting joo-lai meïh yin sew ching leaou e choo Poo-sa wan hing show lăng yen king.* See 般剌密帝 PAN-LA-MEÏH-TE.

大佛頂首楞嚴經合轍 *Ta Fuh ting show lăng yen king ho ch'ay.* See 通潤 T'UNG-JUN.

大佛頂首楞嚴經會解 *Ta Fuh ting show Lăng yen king hwuy keae.* See 般剌密帝 PAN-LA-MEÏH-TE.

大學 *Ta heŏ.* See 四書 SZE SHOO.

大學章句 *Ta heŏ chang keu.* See 四書 SZE SHOO.

大學通旨 *Ta heŏ t'ung che.* See 四書 SZE SHOO.

大學衍義 *Ta heŏ yen e.* See 眞德秀 CHIN TIH-SEW.

大學衍義補 *Ta heŏ yen e poo.* See 眞德秀 CHIN TIH-SEW.

大學諺解 *Ta heŏ yen keae.* See 四書 SZE SHOO.

The "*Tah ts'z*" (達辭) *Anglo-Chinese Dictionary.* See MOK MAN-CHEUNG.

大婚禮節 *Ta hwan le tsëě.* See 大婚 TA HWAN.

大會年錄 *Ta hwuy neen luh.* See 大會 TA HWUY.

胎產秘書 *T'ai ch'an pe shoo.* See 錢氏 TS'EEN SHE.

太始傳 *T'ai che chuen.* See 胡德邁 HOO TIH-MAI.

代疑編 *Tai e peen.* See 林楊廷 LIN YANG-T'ING.

帶經堂詩話 *Tai-king T'ang she hwa.* See 漁洋山人 YU-YANG SHAN JIN.

Tâi-oân-hú-siâⁿ Kàu-hōe-pò. See PERIODICAL PUBLICATIONS: *Taiwan Fu.*

太平天國辛酉拾壹年新曆 *T'aip'ing t'een kwo sin yew shih yih neen sin leih.* See 太平天國 T'AIP'ING T'EEN KWO.

太平天國 . . . 楊秦准頒行詔書 *T'aip'ing t'een kwo . . . Yang tsow chun pan hing chaou shoo.* See 太平天國 T'AIP'ING T'EEN KWO.

太平御覽 *T'aip'ing yu lan.* See 李昉 LE FANG.

太上感應篇詩 *T'ai shang kan ying p'een she.* See 老君 LAOU-KEUN.

太上感應篇圖說 *T'ai shang kan ying p'een t'oo shwo.* See 老君 LAOU-KEUN.

太上靈寶朝天謝罪懺 *T'ai shang ling paou ch'aou t'een seay tsui ts'an.* See 老君 LAOU-KEUN.

代數難題 *Tai shoo nan t'e.* See 倫德 LUN-TIH.

代數術 *Tai shoo shuh.* See 華里司 HWA-LE-SZE.

臺灣奏摺上諭 *T'ai-wan tsow che shang yu.* See 達洪阿 TA HUNG-AH.

臺灣外記 *T'ai-wan wai ke.* See 江日昇 KEANG JIH-SHING.

—— See 江東旭 KEANG TUNG-HEU.

代微積拾級 *Tai wei tseih shih keih.* See 羅密士 LO-MEÏH-SZE.

* 大極上薄花迺龍門壹 *Ta keih shang po hwa nai lung mun yih.* See 大極上薄花 TA KEIH SHANG PO HWA.

答客剳言 *Ta k'ih ch'oo yen.* See 沈容齋 CH'IN JUNG-CHAI.

答客問 *Ta k'ih wăn.* See 朱宗元 CHOO TSUNG-YUEN.

大廣益會玉篇 *Ta kwang yih hwuy yuh p'een.* See 顧野王 KOO YAY-WANG.

—— See 玉篇 YUH P'EEN.

大倫圖說 *Ta lun t'oo shwo.* See 慕稚德 MOO A-TIH.

* 大美聯邦志畧 *Ta Mei leen pang che leŏ.* See 裨治文 PE-CHE-WĂN.

大明會典 *Ta Ming hwuy teen.* See MING DYNASTY.

大明會典節錄 *Ta Ming hwuy teen tsëě luh.* See MING DYNASTY.

大明廣輿考 *Ta Ming kwang yu k'ao.* See 王豐預 WANG FUNG-YU.

大南皇朝悲儒郡公芳積錄 *Ta nan Hwang ch'aou pei joo keun kung fang tseih luh.* See 阮嘉志 YUEN KEA-CHE.

* 大南國音字彙合解大法國音 *Ta nan kwo yin tsze wei ho keae ta Fa kwo yin.* See BONET (JEAN).

但以理聖蹟圖說 *Tan-e-le shing tseih t'oo shwo.* See 但以理 TAN-E-LE.

登州府志 *T'ăng-chow Foo che.* See 施閏章 SHE JUN-CHANG.

謄黃勅命告示賞格 *T'ăng hwang kin ming kaou she shang kih.* See 告示 KAOU SHE.

* 唐人萬首絕句選 *T'ang jin wan show keue keu seuen.* See 洪邁 HUNG MAI.

唐鑑 *T'ang keen.* See 范祖禹 FAN TSOO-YU.

唐兩京城坊考 *T'ang leang king ch'ing fang k'aou.* See 徐松星 SEU SUNG-SING.

唐詩合解箋註 *T'ang she ho keae tseen choo.* See 王阮亭 WANG YUEN-T'ING.

唐詩別裁集 *T'ang she pĕĕ ts'ai tseih.* See 沈德潛 CH'IN TIH-TS'EEN, and 周準 CHOW CHUN.

唐詩三百首註疏 *T'ang she san pih show choo soo.* See 蘅塘退士 HĂNG T'ANG T'UY SZE.

—— See 蘅退士 HĂNG T'UY-SZE.

燈草和尚傳 *Tăng ts'aou Hoshang chuen.* See 高則誠 KAOU TSIH CH'ING.

登瀛篇 *Tăng ying p'een.* See 威妥瑪 WEI T'O-MA.

棠陰比事 *T'ang yin pe sze.* See 桂萬榮 KWEI WAN-YING.

澹香閣詩鈔 *Tan-heang ko she ch'aou.* See 李星池 LE SING-CH'E.

貪歡報 *T'an hwan paou.* See 貪歡 T'AN HWAN.

檀几叢書 *T'an ke ts'ung shoo.* See 王丹麓 WANG TAN-LU.

談天 *T'an t'een.* See HERSCHEL (SIR JOHN FREDERICK WILLIAM), Bart.

Tao-kao-go ing-nyiæn. See TAO-KAO-GO.

桃花女陰陽鬥傳 *T'aou hwa neu yin yang tow chuen.* See 桃花女 T'AOU HWA NEU.

桃花源記 *T'aou hwa yuen ke.* See 趙光 CHAOU KWANG.

禱告文全書 *Taou kaou wăn ts'euen shoo.* See LITURGIES : ENGLAND, *Church of.*

道光二十四年日用便覽 *Taou-kwang urh shih sze neen jih yung peen lan.* See EPHEMERIDES.

韜略元機 *T'aou leŏ yuen ke.* See 陳希夷 CH'IN HE-E.

道書十二種 *Taou shoo shih urh chung.* See 悟元道人 WOO-YUEN TAOU-JIN.

道德經 *Taou tih king.* See 老君 LAOU-KEUN.

道德寶章 *Taou Tih paou chang.* See 老君 LAOU-KEUN.

道援堂詩集 *Taou yuen T'ang she tseih.* See 屈大均 K'EŬH TA-KEUN.

大般若波羅密多經 *Ta pan jo po lo mi to king.* See 玄奘 HEUEN-TS'ANG.

大關王聖蹟圖說 *Ta-p'eĭh wang shing tseih t'oo shwo.* See 大關王 TA-P'EĬH WANG.

大悲神咒心經 *Ta pei shin chow sin king.* See 聖善薰沐 SHING-SHEN-HEUN-MUH.

達生編 *Ta săng peen.* See 達生 TA SĂNG.

大乘法寶十種 *Ta shing fa paou shih chung.* See 劉翰清 LEW HAN-TS'ING.

大乘起信論纂註 *Ta shing k'e sin lun tswan choo.* See 馬鳴菩薩 MA-MING P'OO-SA.

大唐三藏聖教序 *Ta T'ang san tsang shing keaou seu.* See 太宗 T'AI-TSUNG.

達道大全 *Ta taou ta ts'euen.* See 黃泌秀 HWANG PE-SEW.

* 大典會通 *Ta teen hwuy t'ung.* See 金炳學 KIN PING-HEŎ.

大德國學校論畧 *Ta Tih kwo heŏ keaou lun leŏ.* See FABER (ERNST).

大藏目錄 *Ta tsang muh luh.* See 大藏 TA TSANG.

TAT—TEE

大清中樞備覽 *Ta Ts'ing chung shu pei lan.* See PERIODICAL PUBLICATIONS.

大清咸豐八年歲次戊午選吉擇日便民通書 *Ta Ts'ing Heen-fung pa neen suy ts'ze woo woo seuen keih tsih jih peen min t'ung shoo.* See EPHEMERIDES.

大清咸豐便民通書 *Ta Ts'ing Heen-fung peen min t'ung shoo.* See EPHEMERIDES.

大清咸豐十年時憲書 *Ta Ts'ing Heen-fung shih neen she heen shoo.* See EPHEMERIDES.

大清咸豐七年歲次丁巳時憲書 *Ta Ts'ing Heen-fung ts'ih neen suy ts'ze ting sze she heen shoo.* See EPHEMERIDES.

大清會典 *Ta Ts'ing hwuy teen.* See TS'ING DYNASTY.

大清律例統纂集成 *Ta Ts'ing leŭh le tung tswan tseih ch'ing.* See TS'ING DYNASTY.

大清律纂修條例 *Ta Ts'ing leŭh tswan sew t'eaou le.* See TS'ING DYNASTY.

* 大清穆宗毅皇帝實錄 *Ta Ts'ing moo tsung e Hwang-te shih luh.* See 同治 T'UNG-CHE, *Emperor.*

大清道光年時憲書 *Ta Ts'ing Taou-kwang neen she heen shoo.* See EPHEMERIDES.

大清道光二十六年丙午便民通書 *Ta Ts'ing Taou-kwang urh shih luh neen ping woo peen min t'ung shoo.* See EPHEMERIDES.

大清道光二十三年癸卯便民通書 *Ta Ts'ing Taou-kwang urh shih san neen kwei maou peen min t'ung shoo.* See EPHEMERIDES.

大清道光二十四年甲辰便民通書 *Ta Ts'ing Taou-kwang urh shih sze neen kea shin peen min t'ung shoo.* See EPHEMERIDES.

大清全書 *Ta Ts'ing ts'euen shoo.* See 沈弘照 CH'IN HUNG-CHAOU.

大清搢紳全書 *Ta Ts'ing tsin shin ts'euen shoo.* See PERIODICAL PUBLICATIONS : *Peking.*

大清通禮 *Ta Ts'ing t'ung le.* See 穆克登額 MUH-KIH-TÄNG-GIH.

* 大清萬年一統天下全圖 *Ta Ts'ing wan neen yih t'ung t'een hea ts'euen t'oo.* See 韓用洒 HAN YUNG-SA.

大清一統志表 *Ta Ts'ing yih t'ung che peaou.* See 王芑孫 WANG K'E-SUN.

大秦景教流行中國碑 *Ta Ts'in King keaou lew hing Chung kwo pei.* See 大秦景教 TA TS'IN KING KEAOU.

大東輿地圖 *Ta tung yu te t'oo.* See 大東 TA TUNG.

大易象數鈎深圖 *Ta yih seang shoo kow shin t'oo.* See 張仲純 CHANG CHUNG-SHUN.

大英國志 *Ta Ying kwo che.* See 托馬斯米爾納 T'OMA-SZE ME-URH-NA.

大英國人事略說 *Ta Ying kwo jin sze leŏ shuo.* See 英國 YING KWO.

大英國統志 *Ta Ying kwo t'ung che.* See 大英國 TA YING KWO.

大英俗語抄本 *Ta Ying suh yu ch'aou pun.* See 英 YING.

大雲輪請雨經 *Ta yun lun ts'ing yu king.* See 那連提耶舍 NA-LEEN-T'E-YAY-SHAY.

條例 *T'eaou le.* See CHINA : 嘉慶 KEA-K'ING, *Emperor.*

地志須知 *Te che seu che.* See 傅蘭雅 FOO-LAN-YA.

天朝田畝制度 *T'een ch'aou t'een mow che too.* See 太平天國 T'AIP'ING T'EEN KWO.

電氣鍍金略法 *Teen ch'e too kin leŏ fa.* See 華特 HWA-T'IH.

天主降生出像經解 *T'een choo keang săng ch'uh seang king keae.* See 陽瑪諾 YANG-MA-NŎ, 瞿西滿 KEU SE-MWAN, and 聶伯多 NĔĔ PIH-TO.

天主經 *T'een choo king.* See 天主 T'EEN CHOO.

天主實義 *T'een choo shih e.* See HONGKONG : *Office of Nazareth.*

—— See 利瑪竇 LE MA-TOW.

天主十誡勸論聖蹟 *T'een choo shih keae k'euen lun shing tseih.* See 天主 T'EEN CHOO.

天主聖教日課 *T'een choo shing keaou jih k'o.* See 天主聖教 T'EEN CHOO SHING KEAOU.

天方性理 *T'een fang sing le.* See 劉智 LEW CHE.

天 方 典 禮 擇 要 解 *T'een fang teen le tsih yaou keae.* See 劉 智 LEW CHE.

天 父 詩 *T'een Fu she.* See 太 平 天 國 T'AIP'ING T'EEN KWO.

天 下 郡 國 利 病 書 *T'een hea keun kwo le ping shoo.* See 顧 炎 武 KOO YEN-WOO.

天 下 路 程 *T'een hea loo ch'ing.* See 求 放 心 齋 K'EW FANG SIN CHAI.

—— See 天 下 T'EEN HEA.

天 下 山 河 兩 戒 考 *T'een hea shan ho leang keae k'aou.* See 徐 位 山 SEU WEI-SHAN.

天 下 有 山 堂 墨 竹 蘭 石 譜 *T'een hea yew shan t'ang mih chuh lan shih p'oo.* See 汪 體 齋 WANG T'E-CHAI.

電 學 *Teen heŏ.* See 瑪 換 德 NAOU-AI-TIH.

電 學 綱 目 *Teen heŏ kang muh.* See 田 大 里 T'EEN-TA-LE.

天 后 傳 *T'een how chuen.* See 麻 槳 MA YUNG.

天 儒 並 論 *T'een joo ping lun.* See 慕 維 廉 MOO WEI-LEEN.

* 滇 繫 *Teen ke.* See 範 荔 扉 FAN LE-FEI.

電 氣 鍍 金 *Teen k'e too kin.* See WATT (ALEXANDER).

天 經 或 問 天 *T'een king hwo wăn t'een.* See 方 密 之 FANG MEĬH-CHE.

滇 蔻 紀 署 *Teen k'ow ke leo.* See 鹿 樵 LUH TS'EAOU.

天 官 賜 福 *T'een kwan tsz'e fuh.* See 天 官 T'EEN KWAN.

天 路 指 明 *T'een loo che ming.* See 楊 格 非 YANG KIH-FEI.

天 路 指 南 *T'een loo che nan.* See 倪 維 思 NE-WEI-SZE.

天 路 歷 程 *T'een loo leĭh ch'ing.* See BUNYAN (JOHN).

滇 南 礦 廠 興 程 圖 署 *Teen nan kwang ch'ang yu ch'ing t'oo leŏ.* See 吳 其 濬 WOO K'E-SEUN.

滇 報 新 書 *Teen paou sin shoo.* See 威 基 謁 WEI KE-YE.

天 象 列 次 分 野 之 圖 *T'een seang lĕĕ ts'ze fun yay che t'oo.* See 天 象 T'EEN SEANG.

天 仙 正 理 *T'een seen ching le.* See 冲 虛 伍 真 人 CHUNG HEU WU CHIN JIN.

點 石 齋 畫 報 *Teen-shih chai hwa paou.* See PERIODICAL PUBLICATIONS: *Shanghai.*

天 神 會 課 *T'een shin hwuy k'o.* See 天 神 會 T'EEN SHIN HWUY.

天 堂 直 路 *T'een t'ang chih loo.* See 天 堂 T'EEN T'ANG.

天 道 正 統 *T'een taou ching t'ung.* See 文 璧 WĂN PEĬH.

天 道 溯 原 *T'een taou soo yuen.* See 丁 韙 瓦 TING WEI-LEANG.

天 道 溯 原 直 解 *T'een taou soo yuen chih keae.* See 天 道 T'EEN TAOU.

天 情 道 理 書 *T'een ts'ing taou le shoo.* See 太 平 天 國 T'AIP'ING T'EEN KWO.

天 王 詔 旨 *T'een wang chaou chih.* See 太 平 天 國 T'AIP'ING T'EEN KWO.

天 文 須 知 *T'een wăn seu che.* See 天 文 T'EEN WĂN.

天 一 閣 書 目 *T'een yih ko shoo muh.* See 阮 元 YUEN YUEN.

滌 非 齋 制 藝 僅 存 *Te-fei chai che e kin ts'un.* See 薛 湘 SEAY SEANG.

地 學 指 要 *Te heŏ che yaou.* See 文 敎 治 WĂN KEAOU-CHE.

地 學 須 知 *Te heŏ seu che.* See 傅 蘭 雅 FOO-LAN-YA.

地 學 淺 釋 *Te heŏ tseen shih.* See 雷 俠 兒 LUY-HĔĔ-URH.

帝 鑑 圖 說 *Te keen t'oo shwo.* See 張 居 正 CHANG KEU-CHING.

地 球 說 署 *Te k'ew shwo leŏ.* See 瑋 理 哲 WEI LE-CHĔ.

地 理 志 署 *Te le che leŏ.* See 江 戴 德 KEANG T'AI-TIH.

地 理 須 知 *Te le seu che.* See 傅 蘭 雅 FOO-LAN-YA.

地 理 輯 要 *Te le tseĭh yaou.* See 地 理 TE LE.

地 理 全 志 *Te le ts'euen che.* See MUIRHEAD (WILLIAM).

扐理問答 *Te le wǎn ta.* See 地理 TE LE.

地藏菩薩本願經 *Te tsang P'oo-sa pun yuen king.* See 地藏菩薩 TE TSANG P'OO-SA.

T'e-tsiu Tsæn-mi s. See T'AI-CHOW.

T'e-tsiu t'u wa ts'u ôh. See T'E-TSIU.

帝輿合覽 *Te yu ho lan.* See 何炳 HO PING.

太極圖 *Thai-kih-thu.* See 周敦頤 CHOW TUN-E.

德慧入門 *Tih hwuy juh mun.* See 楊格非 YANG KIH-FEI.

得救要法 *Tih kew yaou fa.* See 斯米德 SZE-ME-TIH.

得一錄 *Tih yih luh.* See 余蓮村 YU LEEN-TS'UN.

定國志 *Ting kwo che.* See 楊升蓭 YANG SHING-GAN.

瞻月樓 *T'ing yueh low.* See 月 YUEH.

Tin-lu ts-nen. See 倪維思 NE WEI-SZE.

—— See NEVIUS (JOHN L.   ).

* 東史綱要 *Tong sǎ kang yo.* See 倉洞 CHANG TONG.

圖註本草醫方合編 *T'oo choo pun ts'aou e fang ho peen.* See 汪昂 WANG GAN.

渡江書剛部 *Too keang shoo kang poo.* See 江 KEANG.

杜律詳解大全集 *Too leu seang keae ta ts'euen tseih.* See 杜甫 TOO FOO.

都門紀略 *Too mun ke leǒ.* See 楊靜亭 YANG TSING-T'ING.

圖像合璧君臣故事句解 *T'oo seang ho pih keun ch'in ku sze keu keae.* See 君臣 KEUN CH'IN.

杜少陵全集詳註 *Too Shaou-ling ts'euen tseih seang choo.* See 杜甫 TOO FOO.

杜詩會稡 *Too she hwuy tsuy.* See 杜甫 TOO FOO.

杜詩鏡銓 *Too she king ts'euen.* See 杜甫 TOO FOO.

杜詩七言律 *Too she ts'ih yen leuh.* See 杜甫 TOO FOO.

圖書府 *T'oo shoo foo.* See 漢川曹 HAN CH'UEN-TS'AOU.

墊說 *T'oo shwo.* See 繆蓮仙 MEW LEEN-SEEN.

痘疹全集 *Tow chin ts'euen tseih.* See 馮楚瞻 FUNG TS'OO-CHEN.

透膽寒 *T'ow tan han.* See 補相子 POO SEANG-TSZE.

寶存 *Tow ts'un.* See 胡式鈺 HOO SHIH-YUH.

雜症痘疹藥性合恭 *Tsǎ ching tow chin yo sing ho tsan.* See 馮楚瞻 FUNG TS'OO-CHEN.

載花船 *Tsai hwa chuen.* See 西泠狂者 SELING KWANG CHE.

才子古文 *Ts'ai tsze koo wǎn.* See 金聖歎 KIN SHING-T'AN.

增註硃字拾伍音 *Tsǎng choo choo tsze shih woo yin.* See 拾伍音 SHIH WOO YIN.

臟腑明堂圖 *Tsang foo ming t'ang t'oo.* See 臟腑 TSANG FOO.

增福財神告白 *Tsǎng fuh ts'ai shin kaou pih.* See 義和團 E-HO-T'WAN.

增刊校正王狀元集註分類東坡先生詩 *Tsǎng k'an keaou ching Wang Chwang yuen tseih choo fun luy Tung-p'o Seen sǎng she.* See 蘇軾 SOO SHIH.

* 增廣經驗瓦方 *Tsǎng kwang king yen leang fang.* See 陳傑臣 CH'IN KËE-CH'IN.

增補指明算法 *Tsǎng poo che ming swan fa.* See 鄭元美 CHING YUEN-MEI.

增補貢舉考畧 *Tsǎng poo kung keu k'aou leǒ.* See 黃崇蘭 HWANG TS'UNG-LAN.

增補事類賦統編 *Tsǎng poo sze luy foo t'ung peen.* See 黃葆真 HWANG PAOU-CHIN.

增補萬法歸宗 *Tsǎng poo wan fǎ kwei tsung.* See 李淳風 LE SHUN-FUNG.

增補一夕話 *Tsǎng poo yih seih hwa.* See 咄咄夫 TUH TUH FOO.

增刪算法統宗 *Tsǎng shan swan fa t'ung tsung.* See 程大位 CH'ING TA-WEI.

增續會通韻府群玉 *Tsǎng suh hwuy t'ung yun foo k'eun yuh.* See 陰時夫 YIN SHE-FOO.

倉 田 通 法 續 編 *Ts'ang t'een t'ung fa suh peen.* See 張 作 楠 CHANG TSO-NAN.

增 訂 尺 牘 見 *Tsăng ting ch'ih tuh keen.* See 汪 文 芳 WANG WĂN-FANG.

增 訂 教 稼 書 *Tsăng ting keaou kea shoo.* See 盛 百 二 SHING PIH-URH.

增 訂 古 文 觀 止 善 本 *Tsăng ting koo wăn kwan chih shen pun.* See 吳 留 村 WOO LEW-TS'UN.

增 訂 古 文 釋 義 *Tsăng ting koo wăn shih e.* See 余 自 明 YU TSZE-MING.

增 訂 圖 註 本 草 備 要 *Tsăng ting t'oo choo pun ts'aou pei yaou.* See 汪 昂 WANG GAN.

增 訂 蔣 季 眉 四 書 稿 *Tsang ting Tseang Ke-mei sze shoo kaou.* See 蔣 季 眉 TSEANG KE-MEI.

增 訂 驗 方 新 編 縮 本 *Tsăng ting yen fang sin peen so pun.* See 守 謙 氏 SHOW-K'ĔEN-SHE.

增 輯 書 法 轂 *Tsăng tseĭh shoo fa kou.* See 劉 麒 瞻 LEW K'E-CHAN.

曾 文 正 公 年 譜 *Tsăng wăn ching kung neen p'oo.* See 李 瀚 章 LE HAN-CHANG.

—— See 曾 國 藩 TSĂNG KWO-FAN.

曾 文 正 公 批 牘 *Tsăng wăn ching kung p'i tuh.* See 曾 國 藩 TSĂNG KWO-FAN.

曾 文 正 公 詩 集 *Tsăng wăn ching kung she tseĭh.* See 曾 國 藩 TSĂNG KWO-FAN.

曾 文 正 公 書 札 *Tsăng wăn ching kung shoo cha.* See 曾 國 藩 TSĂNG KWO-FAN.

曾 文 正 公 雜 著 *Tsăng wăn ching kung tsa choo.* See 曾 國 藩 TSĂNG KWO-FAN.

曾 文 正 公 全 集 *Tsăng wăn ching kung ts'euen tseĭh.* See 曾 國 藩 TSĂNG KWO-FAN.

曾 文 正 公 奏 議 *Tsăng wăn ching kung tsow e.* See 曾 國 藩 TSĂNG KWO-FAN.

曾 文 正 公 奏 議 補 編 *Tsăng wăn ching kung tsow e poo peen.* See 曾 國 藩 TSĂNG KWO-FAN.

曾 文 正 公 奏 稿 *Tsăng wăn ching kung tsow 'kaou.* See 曾 國 藩 TSĂNG KWO-FAN.

曾 文 正 公 文 鈔 *Tsăng wăn ching kung wăn ch'aou.* See 曾 國 藩 TSĂNG KWO-FAN.

曾 文 正 公 文 集 *Tsăng wăn ching kung wăn tseĭh.* See 曾 國 藩 TSĂNG KWO-FAN.

簪 花 閣 集 *Tsan-hwa ko tseĭh.* See 端 恩 TWAN GĂN.

讚 美 詩 *Tsan mei she.* See 雷 應 百 LUY YING-PIH, and 蒲 德 立 P'OO TIH-LĔIH.

—— 慕 稼 穀 MOO KEA-KUH.

讚 神 樂 章 *Tsan shin lo chang.* See LORD (EDWARD CLEMENS).

讚 神 聖 詩 *Tsan shin shing she.* See 倪 維 思 E WEI-SZE, and 狄 考 文 T'IEH K'AOU-WĂN.

殘 唐 五 代 全 傳 *Tsan T'ang Woo tai ts'euen chuen.* See 羅 貫 中 LO KWAN-CHUNG.

恭 訂 洋 錢 鬼 字 全 法 各 欵 列 後 *Ts'an ting yang ts'een kwei tsze ts'euen fa koh k'wan le how.* See 洋 錢 YANG TS'EEN.

曹 州 府 志 *Ts'aou-chow Foo che.* See 劉 藻 LEW TSAOU.

草 書 習 愼 *Ts'aou shoo seĭh shin.* See 陳 澄 泉 CH'IN CH'ING-TS'ĔUEN, and 汪 芝 田 WANG CHE-T'EEN.

曹 洞 宗 *Ts'aou tung tsung.* See 曹 TS'AOU.

早 晚 課 *Tsaou wan k'o.* See 課 K'O.

草 韻 彙 編 *Ts'aou yun wei p'een.* See 陶 遜 亭 T'AOU SUN-T'ING.

詳 註 文 範 初 編 *Tseang choo wăn fan ch'oo peen.* See 吳 踰 龍 WOO YU-LUNG.

詳 說 古 文 真 寶 大 全 *Tseang shwo koo wăn chin paou ta ts'euen.* See 古 文 KOO-WĂN.

詳 訂 古 文 評 註 全 集 *Tseang ting koo wăn p'ing choo ts'euen tseĭh.* See 劉 繆 萇 LEW YU-GAN.

蕉 軒 摭 錄 *Tseaou heen chih luh.* See 俞 夢 蕉 YU MUNG-TSEAOU.

節 義 奇 緣 金 葉 菊 *Tsĕĕ e k'e luh kin ye keŭh.* See 菊 KEŬH.

節 規 禮 *Tsĕĕ kwei le.* See 規 禮 KWEI LE.

* 節 錄 成 章 幼 學 問 答 *Tsĕĕ luh ch'ing chang yew heŏ wăn ta.* See 後 學 者 HOW-HEŎ-CHAY.

TSE—TSI

籤註唐賢絕句三體詩法 *Tseen choo T'ang heen tseue keu san t'e she fa.* See 周弼 CHOW PIH.

前漢書細讀 *Tseen Han shoo seih tuh.* See 李欽之 LE K'IN-CHE.

剪燈餘話 *Tseen tăng yu hwa.* See 李昌祺 LE CH'ANG-K'E.

千字文 *Ts'een tsze wăn.* See 周興嗣 CHOW HING-SZE.

千字文釋句 *Ts'een tsze wăn shih keu.* See 周興嗣 CHOW HING-SZE.

竊憤錄 *Ts'eih fun luh.* See 安氏 NGAN SHE.

積慶堂試藝 *Tseih-k'ing t'ang she e.* See 積慶堂 TSEIH-K'ING T'ANG.

積古齋鐘鼎彝器欵識 *Tseih koo chai chung ting e k'e k'wan shih.* See 阮元 YUEN YUEN.

集千家註批點杜工部文詩集 *Tseih ts'een kea choo p'e teen Too Kung-poo wăn she tseih.* See 杜甫 TOO FOO.

集千家分類杜工部詩 *Tseih ts'een kea fun luy Too Kung-poo she.* See 杜甫 TOO FOO.

濟南府志 *Tsenan foo che.* See 唐夢容 T'ANG MUNG-YUNG.

濟寧直隸州志 *Tse-ning chih le chow che.* See 胡德琳 HOO TIH-LIN.

濟世瓦方 *Tse she leang fang.* See 瓦方 LEANG FANG.

全唐詩 *Ts'euen T'ang she.* See 曹寅 TS'AOU YEN.

全體闡微 *Ts'euen t'e shen wei.* See OSGOOD (D. W.).

全體新論 *Ts'euen t'e sin lun.* See 合信 HO-SIN.

全韻玉篇 *Ts'euen yun yuh p'een.* See 全韻 TS'EUEN YUN.

測海集 *Ts'ih hai tseih.* See 彭紹升 P'ĂNG SHAOU-SHING.

測候叢談 *Ts'ih how ts'ung t'an.* See 金楷理 KIN-K'EAE-LE.

七日鏡覽 *Ts'ih jih king lan.* See PERIODICAL PUBLICATIONS: *Shanghai.*

側人明堂圖 *Ts'ih jin ming t'ang t'oo.* See 魏玉麟 WEI YUH-LIN.

七家詩輯註彙鈔 *Ts'ih kea she tseih choo wei ch'aou.* See 張熙宇 CHANG HE-YÜ.

七克真訓 *Ts'ih k'ih chin heun.* See 沙勿畧 SHA WUH-LEŎ.

—— See 七克 TS'IH K'IH.

則克錄 *Tsih k'ih luh.* See 則克 TSIH K'IH.

則古昔齋算學 *Tsih-koo-seih chai swan heŏ.* See 李善蘭 LE-SHEN-LAN.

七修類藁 *Ts'ih sew luy kaou.* See 郎仁寶 LANG JIN-PAOU

測地繪圖 *Ts'ih te hwuy t'oo.* See 富路瑪 FOO-LOO-MA.

測圓海鏡 *Ts'ih yuen hai king.* See 李冶 LE YAY.

清漢文海 *Ts'ing Han wăn hai.* See 爪爾佳巴尼渾 KWA-URH-KEA-PA-NE-HWĂN.

清河書畫舫 *Ts'ing ho shoo hwa fang.* See 張青父 CHANG TS'ING-FOO.

井礦工程 *Tsing hwang kung ch'ing.* See 白爾捺 PIH-URH-NA.

清涼山志 *Ts'ing leang shan che.* See 鎮澄 CHIN CH'ING.

清明掃墓之論 *Ts'ing-ming saou moo che lun.* See 尙德 SHANG-TIH.

清明掃墓論 *Ts'ing-ming saou moo lun.* See 胡德邁 HOO TIH-MAI.

青萍軒詩錄 *Ts'ing p'ing heen she luh.* See 薛福保 SEAY FUH-PAOU.

青萍軒文錄 *Ts'ing p'ing heen wăn luh.* See 薛福保 SEAY FUH-PAOU.

靖節先生集 *Tsing tsëě seen-săng tseih.* See 陶潛 T'AOU TS'EEN.

清字西廂記 *Ts'ing tsze se Seang ke.* See 西廂 SE SEANG.

清文指要 *Ts'ing wăn che yaou.* See 清文 TS'ING WĂN.

清文鑑 *Ts'ing wăn keen.* See 董明鐸 TUNG MING-TŎ.

清文啟蒙 *Ts'ing wăn k'e mung.* See 舞格 WOO KIH.

215

清文補彙 *Ts'ing wǎn poo wei.* See 宜興 E HING.

清文典要 *Ts'ing wǎn teen yaou.* See 蕭硯精 SEAOU YEN-TSING.

—— See 秋芳堂主人 Ts'EW-FANG T'ANG CHOO-JIN.

清文彙書 *Ts'ing wǎn wei shoo.* See 李延基 LE YEN-KE.

秦漢圖章 *Ts'in Han t'oo chang.* See 秦漢 TS'IN HAN.

進教要理問答 *Tsin keaou yaou le wǎn ta.* See 崇教者 Ts'UNG KEAOU CHAY.

晉書詳節 *Tsin shoo tseang tsëë.* See 呂祖謙 LEU TSOO-K'EEN.

坐花誌果 *Tso hwa che kwo.* See 汪道鼎 WANG TAOU-TING.

粗定各口章程 *Tsoo ting ko k'ow chang ch'ing.* See 各口章程 KO K'OW CHANG CH'ING.

楚辭 *Tsoo ts'ze.* See 屈原 K'EŬH YUEN.

左繡 *Tso sew.* See 左邱明 Tso K'EW-MING.

作印集字 *Tso yin tseĭh tsze.* See 作印 Tso YIN.

導主聖範 *Tsun choo shing fan.* See 主 CHOO.

總會記錄成章摘譯 *Tsung hwuy ke luh ch'ing chang chai yih.* See 蒲德立 P'OO-TIH-LEĬH.

宗鏡錄 *Tsung king luh.* See 智覺 CHE-KEŎ.

崇修精蘊 *Ts'ung sew tsing wǎn.* See 精蘊 TSING WǍN.

罪 *Tsuy.* See CHINESE UNION.

萃忠全傳 *Tsuy chung ts'euen chuen.* See 孫高亮 SUN KAOU-LEANG.

醉菩提全傳 *Tsuy P'oo-te ts'euen chuen.* See 醉菩提 TSUY P'OO-TE.

—— See 天花藏主人 T'EEN HWA-TS'ANG KEU-JIN.

字學舉隅 *Tsze heŏ keu yu.* See 黃虎癡 HWANG HOO-CH'I.

* —— See 桂龍光 KWEI LUNG-KWANG.

字學三種 *Tsze heŏ san chung.* See 王懿榮 WANG E-YUNG.

詞學全書 *Tsze heŏ ts'euen shoo.* See 查繼超 CH'A KE-CHAOU.

紫琅玕院遺稿 *Tsze lankan yuen e kaou.* See 陳湘鄉 CH'IN SEANG-HEANG.

字類標韻 *Tsze luy peaou yun.* See 字 TSZE.

—— See 維寧 WEI NING.

詞名集解 *Tsze ming tseĭh keae.* See 汪汲葵 WANG KE-K'WEI.

字部輯解 *Tsze poo tseĭh keae.* See 字部 TSZE POO.

字典彙選集成 *Tsze teen wei seuen tseĭh ch'ing.* See 黃少珢 HWANG SHAO-K'EUNG.

字彙 *Tsze wei.* See 梅膺祚 MEI YING-TSOO.

紫陽正誼兩書院課藝合選 *Tsze-yang Ching-e leang shoo yuen k'o e ho seuen.* See 紫陽 TSZE-YANG.

讀史方輿紀要 *T'uh she fang yu ke yaou.* See 顧祖禹 KOO TSOO-YU.

* 讀書樂 *Tuh shoo loh.* See 黃自元 HWANG TSZE-YUEN.

讀杜詩愚得 *Tuh Too she yu tih.* See 杜甫 TOO FOO.

東昌府志 *Tung-ch'ang foo che.* See 胡德琳 HOO TIH-LIN.

—— See 嵩山 SUNG SHAN.

同治上海縣志 *T'ung che Shanghai heen che.* See 俞樾 YU YUĔH.

童貞修規 *T'ung ching sew kwei.* See 童貞 T'UNG CHING.

通藝錄 *T'ung e luh.* See 程瑤田 CH'ING YAOU-T'EEN.

董方立算書 *Tung Fang-leĭh swan shoo.* See 董方立 TUNG FANG-LEĬH.

東華錄 *Tung hwa luh.* See 蔣良騏 TSEANG LEANG-K'E.

通鑑直解 *T'ung keen chih keae.* See 張居正 CHANG KEU-CHING.

通鑑綱目 *T'ung keen kang muh.* See 朱熹 CHOO HE.

通鑑紀事本末 *T'ung keen ke sze pun moh.* See 遠樞 YUEN CH'OO.

東閣散錄 *Tung ko san luh.* See 東閣 TUNG KO.

同館賦鈔 *T'ung kwan foo ch'aou.* See 同館 T'UNG KWAN.

東萊博議 *Tung-lai po e.* See 呂祖謙 LEU TSOO-K'EEN.

東萊先生東漢詳節 *Tung-lai seen săng tung Han tseang tsĕĕ.* See 呂祖謙 LEU TSOO-K'EEN.

童蒙先習 *T'ung mung seen seih.* See 童 T'UNG.

* —— See 童蒙 T'UNG MUNG.

童蒙語解 *T'ung mung yu keae.* See 童 T'UNG.

同門錄 *T'ung mun luh.* See 同門 T'UNG MUN.

東坡先生詩 *Tung-p'o Seen-sang she.* See 蘇軾 SOO SHIH.

東史會綱 *Tung să hoi kang.* See 東史 TUNG SĂ.

東西洋考每月統記傳 *Tung se yang k'aou mei yuĕ t'ung ke chuen.* See PERIODICAL PUBLICATIONS: *Singapore.*

通商章程 *T'ung shang chang ch'ing.* See 章程 CHANG CH'ING.

通商須知 *T'ung shang heu che.* See 郭瀰貴 KO LO-KWEI.

通商各關華洋貿易總冊 *T'ung shang ko kwan hwa yang hwŏ e tsung ts'ih.* See CHINA: *Inspectorate General of Customs.*

通商各關沿海沿江建置鐙塔鐙船鐙杆譽船浮椿總冊 *T'ung shang ko kwan yen hai yen keang keen che tăng t'a t'ăng ch'uen tăng kan king ch'uen fow chwang tsung ts'ih.* See CHINA: *Inspectorate General of Customs.*

通書 *T'ung shoo.* See 周濂溪 CHOW LEEN-K'E.

—— See 羅傳炳 LO CHUEN-PING.

通天曉 *T'ung t'een heaou.* See 王槤堂 WANG SEANG-T'ANG.

通文館志 *T'ung wăn kwan che.* See 金慶門 KIN K'ING-MUN.

同文玉海 *T'ung wăn yuh hai.* See 文 WĂN.

動物類編 *Tung wuh luy peen.* See 韋明珠 WEI MING-CHOO.

東遊入仙記出身傳 *Tung yew pa seen ke ch'uh shin chuen.* See 吳元泰 WOO YUEN-T'AI.

桐陰清話 *T'ung yin ts'ing hwa.* See 倪雲瀧 E YUN-KEU.

同音字彙 *T'ung yin tsze wei.* See 諸名家 CHOO MING-KEA.

遯窟讕言 *T'un k'uh lan yen.* See 王韜 WANG T'AOU.

對山書屋墨餘錄 *Tuy-shan shoo wuh mih yu luh.* See 毛對山 MAOU TUY-SHAN.

對數表 *Tuy shoo peaou.* See 穆尼閣 MUH-NE-KO.

段氏說文注訂 *Tw'an She Shwo wăn choo ting.* See 段大令 TW'AN TA-LING.

二程先生傳道粹言 *Urh Ch'ing seen săng chuen taou suy yen.* See 張栻 CHANG CH'IH.

二程全書 *Urh Ch'ing ts'euen shoo.* See 耙昀 KE YUN.

二倫行實圖 *Urh lun hing shih t'oo.* See 二倫 URH LUN.

耳食錄 *Urh shih luh.* See 樂運裳 LO LEEN-SHANG.

二十四轉輪 *Urh shih sze chuen lun.* See CHINESE DRAWINGS.

二十四孝 *Urh shih sze heaou.* See 孝 HEAOU.

二十四孝圖解 *Urh shih sze heaou t'oo keae.* See 二十四孝 URH SHIH SZE HEAOU.

二十四山秘訣 *Urh shih sze shan pi keue.* See 蔡廷猷 TS'AI T'ING YEW.

二十二史劄記 *Urh shih urh she cha ke.* See 趙翼 CHAOU YIH.

二十一史緯 *Urh shih yih she wei.* See 陳允錫 CHIN YUN-SEIH.

* 廿一史約編 *Urh shih yih she yo peen.* See 鄭芷畦 CHING CHE-CH'E.

二申野錄 *Urh shin yay luh.* See 孫之騄 SUN CHE-LUH.

Urh too Mei. See MEI.

爾雅 *Urh ya.* See 爾雅 URH YA.

爾 雅 註 疏 *Urh ya choo soo.* See 邢 昺 HING PING.

二 友 相 論 *Urh yew seang lun.* See 二 友 URH YEW.

二 約 釋 義 叢 書 *Urh yo shih e ts'ung shoo.* See 韋 廉 臣 WEI-LEEN-CH'IN.

文 昌 化 書 *Wăn ch'ang hwa shoo.* See 文 昌 帝 君 WĂN CH'ANG TE KEUN.

文 章 練 要 *Wăn chang leen yaou.* See 王 源 WANG YUEN.

文 昌 聖 典 內 函 *Wăn ch'ang shing teen nuy han.* See 文 昌 帝 君 WĂN-CH'ANG TE KEUN.

文 昌 帝 君 繪 像 寶 訓 *Wăn ch'ang te keun hwuy seang paou heun.* See 顏 正 YEN CHING.

文 職. 武 職 *Wăn chih. Woo chih.* See 文 職 WĂN CHIH.

文 法 初 階 *Wăn fa ch'oo keae.* See KWOK CHAN-SANG.

萬 法 歸 心 錄 *Wan fa kwei sin luh.* See 源 超 溟 YUEN CHAOU-MING.

萬 方 鍼 線 *Wan fang chin seen.* See 蔡 烈 先 TS'AI LĔĔ-SEEN.

文 房 肆 考 圖 說 *Wăn fang sze k'aou t'oo shwo.* See 唐 衡 銓 T'ANG HĂNG-TS'EUEN.

萬 福 條 同 *Wan fuh t'eaou t'ung.* See EPHEMERIDES.

王 長 次 兄 親 目 親 耳 共 証 福 音 書 *Wang chang ts'ze heung ts'in muh ts'in erh kung ching fuh yin shoo.* See 太 平 天 國 T'AIP'ING T'EEN KWO.

王 狀 元 集 百 家 註 分 類 東 坡 先 生 詩 *Wang Chwang yuen tseïh pih kea choo fun luy Tung-p'o Seen-săng she.* See 蘇 軾 SOO SHIH.

王 羲 之 筆 陳 圖 *Wang He che peïh ch'in t'oo.* See 王 羲 WANG HE.

王 嬌 鸞 百 年 長 恨 *Wang-keaou-lwan pih neen ch'ang han.* See 王 嬌 鸞 WANG-KEAOU-LWAN.

徃 生 拾 因 *Wang săng shih yin.* See 徃 生 WANG SĂNG.

王 大 娘 補 缸 *Wang ta neang poo kang.* See 王 大 娘 WANG TA NEANG.

王 陽 明 先 生 全 集 *Wang Yang-ming Seen săng ts'euen tseïh.* See 王 伯 安 WANG PIH-GAN.

文 獻 徵 存 錄 *Wăn heen ching ts'un luh.* See 錢 東 生 TS'EEN TUNG-SĂNG.

文 獻 通 考 *Wăn heen t'ung k'aou.* See 馬 端 臨 MA TWAN-LIN.

文 學 書 官 話 *Wăn heŏ shoo kwan hwa.* See 高 第 丕 KAOU TE-P'EI, and 張 儒 珍 CHANG JOO-CHIN.

文 公 先 生 資 治 通 鑑 綱 目 *Wăn kung seen săng tsze che t'ung keen kang muh.* See 朱 熹 CHOO HE.

萬 國 公 法 *Wan kwo kung fa.* See 惠 頓 HWUY-TUN.

萬 國 公 報 *Wan kwo kung paou.* See PERIODICAL PUBLICATIONS : *Shanghai.*

萬 國 通 鑑 *Wan kwo t'ung keen.* See SHEFFIELD (D. Z.).

文 廟 祀 典 考 *Wăn meaou sze teen k'aou.* See 龐 鍾 璐 P'ANG CHUNG-LOO.

晚 笑 堂 竹 莊 畫 傳 *Wan seaou t'ang Chuh-chwang hwa chuen.* See 竹 莊 CHUH-CHWANG.

* 晚 笑 堂 畫 傳 *Wan seaou t'ang hwa chuen.* See 竹 莊 CHUH CHWANG.

文 選 正 文 *Wăn seuen ching wăn.* See 蕭 統 SEAOU T'UNG.

文 選 對 策 *Wăn seuen tuy ts'ih.* See 劉 仁 初 LEW JIN-CH'OO.

文 書 封 *Wăn shoo fung.* See 文 書 封 WĂN SHOO FUNG.

文 書 字 數 *Wăn shoo tsze soo.* See 文 書 WĂN SHOO.

萬 壽 盛 典 *Wan show shing teen.* See 萬 壽 WAN SHOW.

文 帝 全 書 *Wăn te ts'euen shoo.* See 劉 體 恕 LEW T'E-SHOO.

—— See 文 昌 帝 君 WĂN CH'ANG TE KEUN.

萬 字 典 *Wan tsze teen.* See 萬 字 WAN TSZE.

WAN—YAN

萬 物 與 原 *Wan wuh chin yuen.* See 艾 儒 略 GAI JOO-LEŏ.

—— See 萬 物 WAN WUH.

偽 忠 王 親 筆 口 供 *Wei Chung wang ts'in peth k'ow hung.* See 忠 王 CHUNG WANG.

味 閒 堂 課 鈔 *Wei heen t'ang k'o ch'aou.* See 陶 然 T'AOU JEN.

彙 刻 書 目 合 編 *Wei kih shoo muh ho peen.* See CATALOGUES.

* 衛 生 要 術 *Wei săng yaou shuh.* See 潘 霨 偉 P'AN WEI-WEI.

微 積 溯 源 *Wei tseih soo yuen.* See 華 里 司 HWA-LE-SZE.

彙 集 雅 俗 通 十 五 音 *Wei tseih ya suh t'ung shih woo yin.* See 十 五 音 SHIH WOO YIN.

彙 纂 詩 法 度 針 *Wei tswan she fa too chin.* See 徐 勳 右 SEU JANG-YEW.

我 國 志 畧 *Wo-kwo che leŏ.* See 鶯 江 寄 迹 人 LOO-KEANG KE TSEIH JIN.

五 東 韻 府 *Woo ch'ay yun foo.* See 陳 藎 謨 CH'IN TSIN-MOO.

五 車 韻 瑞 *Woo ch'ay yun suy.* See 凌 以 棟 LING E-TUNG.

吳 中 平 寇 記 *Woo chung p'ing k'ow ke.* See 吳 WOO.

武 夷 山 *Woo-e shan.* See 張 廷 輝 CHANG T'ING-HWUY.

五 方 元 音 *Woo fang yuen yin.* See 樊 騰 鳳 FAN T'ĂNG-FUNG.

吾 學 錄 *Woo heŏ luh.* See 吳 榮 光 WOO YUNG-KWANG.

五 虎 平 南 後 傳 *Woo Hoo p'ing nan how chuen.* See 五 虎 WOO HOO.

五 虎 平 西 前 傳 *Woo Hoo p'ing se ts'een chuen.* See 五 虎 WOO HOO.

五 諫 夫 *Woo keen foo.* See 諫 KEEN.

吳 郡 圖 經 續 記 *Woo keun t'oo king suh ke.* See 朱 長 文 CHOO CH'ANG-WĂN.

五 經 鴻 裁 *Woo king hung ts'ai.* See 薛 慰 農 SËĔ WEI-NUNG.

五 經 句 解 *Woo king keu keae.* See 五 經 WOO KING.

五 經 古 人 典 林 *Woo king koo jin teen lin.* See 何 崍 靑 HO LAI-TS'ING.

五 經 典 林 *Woo king teen lin.* See 何 崍 靑 HO LAI-TS'ING.

五 經 讀 本 *Woo king tuh pun.* See 五 經 WOO KING.

五 老 集 *Woo laou tseih.* See 五 老 WOO LAOU.

武 畧 *Woo leŏ.* See 太 平 天 國 T'AIP'ING T'EEN KWO.

五 倫 行 實 圖 *Woo lun hing shih t'oo.* See 姜 渾 KEANG HWĂN.

五 美 綠 *Woo mei yuen.* See 五 美 WOO MEI.

無 名 淨 光 經 *Woo ming tsing kwang king.* See 無 名 WOO MING.

武 備 秘 書 *Woo pe pe shoo.* See 施 永 圖 SHE YUNG-T'OO.

五 百 家 注 音 辯 韓 昌 黎 先 生 全 集 *Woo pih kea choo yin pien Han Ch'ang-le Sien-săng ts'euen tseih.* See 韓 愈 HAN YU.

吳 詩 談 數 *Woo she t'an sow.* See 吳 梅 村 WOO MEI-TS'UN.

吳 詩 集 覽 *Woo she tseih lan.* See 吳 梅 村 WOO MEI-TS'UN.

* 無 師 初 學 英 文 字 *Woo sze ch'oo heŏ Ying wăn tsze.* See LEAMAN (CHARLES).

無 悉 解 齋 詩 稿 *Woo tai heae chai she k'aou.* See 梁 遠 文 LEANG YUEN-WĂN.

—— See 梁 萬 如 LEANG KO-JOO.

五 代 地 理 考 *Woo tai te le k'aou.* See 練 恕 LEEN SHOO.

五 燈 會 元 *Woo tăng hwuy yuen.* See 慧 明 HWUY-MING.

武 帝 寶 訓 像 註 *Woo te paou heun seang choo.* See 譚 心 翼 T'AN SIN-YIH.

武 定 府 志 *Woo-ting foo che.* See 胡 寶 琳 HOO PAOU-LIN.

揚 州 休 園 志 *Yang-chow heu yuen che.* See 鄭 慶 祐 CHING K'ING-HOO.

養晦堂詩集 *Yang hwei t'ang she tseih.* See
劉蓉霞 LEW JUNG-HEA.

養晦堂文集 *Yang hwei t'ang wăn tseih.* See
劉蓉霞 LEW JUNG-HEA.

楊家將演義 *Yang kea tseang yen e.* See
秦淮墨客 TS'IN HWAI MIH KIH.

瘍科臨證心得集 *Yang ko lin ching sin tih
tseih.* See 高錦庭 KAOU KIN-T'ING.

養生錄 *Yang săng luh.* See 施禹泉 SHE
YU-TS'EUEN.

楊升巷外集 *Yang Shing-gan wai tseih.* See
楊慎 YANG SHIN.

養心詩調叙 *Yang sin she teaou seu.* See
養心詩 YANG SIN SHE.

養心神詩 *Yang sin shin she.* See 神詩
SHIN SHE.

楊椒山先生家訓 *Yang Tseaou-shan seen
săng kea heun.* See 楊椒山 YANG TSEAOU-
SHAN.

洋錢新廳全法 *Yang ts'een sin ying ts'euen fa.*
See 洋錢 YANG TS'EEN.

楊園先生全集 *Yang yuen seen săng ts'euen
tseih.* See 張考夫 CHANG K'AOU-FOO.

養雲山館試帖注釋 *Yang yün shan kwan
shih t'ĕ̈ choo shih.* See 許球 HEU K'EW.

要理講論 *Yaou le keang lun.* See 鐸林 TO
LIN.

要理六端 *Yaou le lew twan.* See 要理
YAOU LE.

要理辯正邪自證 *Yaou le peen ching seay
tsze ching.* See 要理 YAOU LE.

冶金錄 *Yay kin luh.* See 阿發滿 AH-FA-
MWAN.

耶穌之寶訓 *Yay-soo che paou heun.* See
愛漢者 GAI-HAN-CHAY.

耶穌異教四牌 *Yay-soo chin keaou sze p'ai.*
See 董中和 TUNG CHUNG-HO.

耶穌巡徒養心日課 *Yay-soo heun t'oo yang
sin jih k'o.* See STOW (BARON).

耶穌合稿 *Yay-soo ho kaou.* See 慕維廉
MOO WEI-LEEN.

耶穌降生一千八百八十九年主日
瞻禮齋期日表 *Yay-soo keang săng yih
ts'een pa pih pa shih kew neen choo jih chen le
chai k'e jih peaou.* See EPHEMERIDES.

耶穌降世傳 *Yay-soo keang she chuen.* See
JESUS CHRIST.

—— See 耶穌 YAY-SOO.

耶穌教官話問答 *Yay-soo keaou kwan hwa
wăn ta.* See 耶穌教 YAY-SOO KEAOU.

耶穌教畧 *Yay-soo keaou leŏ.* See 耶穌
YAY-SOO.

耶穌教例言 *Yay-soo keaou le yen.* See
麥嘉締培端 MIH-KEA-TE PEI-TWAN.

—— See 培端 P'EITWAN.

耶穌教消罪集福眞言 *Yay-soo keaou
seaou tsuy tseih fuh chin yen.* See 耶穌教
YAY-SOO KEAOU.

耶穌教要旨 *Yay-soo keaou yaou che.* See
MCCARTEE (DIVIE BETHUNE).

—— See 耶穌教 YAY SOO KEAOU.

耶穌教要理大問答 *Yay-soo keaou yaou le
ta wăn ta.* See 耶穌教 YAY-SOO KEAOU.

耶穌教要理問答 *Yay-soo keaou yaou le wăn
ta.* See 耶穌教 YAY-SOO KEAOU.

耶穌論 *Yay-soo lun.* See 耶穌 YAY-SOO.

耶穌門徒金針 *Yay-soo mun t'oo kin chin.*
See 韋理哲 WEI LE-CHE.

耶穌比喻註說 *Yay-soo pe yu choo shwo.*
See 耶穌 YAY-SOO.

耶穌聖教禱告文 *Yay-soo shing keaou tao
kaou wăn.* See LITURGIES: ENGLAND,
Church of.

耶穌事蹟考 *Yay-soo sze tseih k'aou.* See
師多馬 SZE TOMA.

耶穌登山教象體註 *Yay-soo tăng shan
keaou chung t'e choo.* See GODDARD (JOSIAH).

耶穌言行綱目 *Yay-soo yen hing kang muh.*
See 慕維廉 MOO WEI-LEEN.

耶穌言行紀畧 *Yay-soo yen hing ke leŏ.* See
耶穌 YAY-SOO.

臙脂牡丹 *Yen chih mu tan.* See 王德寬 WANG TIH-K'WAN.

兗州府志 *Yen-chow Foo che.* See 兗州府 YEN-CHOW FOO.

咽喉脈證通論 *Yen how mih ching t'ung lun.* See 許槤 HEU LEEN.

揅經室集 *Yen king shih tseǐh.* See 阮元 YUEN YUEN.

眼科證治 *Yen ko ching che.* See NORRIS (W. F.) and OLIVER (C. A.).

延年要訣 *Yen neen yaou keuĕ.* See 馬信道 MA SIN-TAOU.

簷曝雜記 *Yen paou tsa ke.* See 趙翼 CHAOU YIH.

煙波釣叟歌 *Yen po teaou sow ko.* See 趙普 CHAOU P'OO.

鹽運司出入文書 *Yen yun sze ch'uh juh wǎn shoo.* See 鹽運司 YEN YUN SZE.

有正味齋駢體文 *Yew ching wei chai peen t'e wǎn.* See 吳錫麒 WOO SEĬH-K'E.

*有正味齋試帖詩註 *Yew ching wei chai she t'ĕĕ she choo.* See 吳錫麒 WOO SEĬH-K'E.

幼主詔書 *Yew choo chaou shoo.* See 太平天國 T'AIP'ING T'EEN KWO.

幼學句解 *Yew heŏ keu keae.* See 錢恕齊 TS'EEN SHOO-TS'E.

幼學須知句解 *Yew heŏ seu che keu keae.* See 程允升 CH'ING YUN-SHING.

幼學操身 *Yew heŏ ts'aou shin.* See BLAIKIE (WILLIAM).

尤悔菴全集 *Yew Hwuy-gan ts'euen tseǐh.* See 尤侗 YEW T'UNG.

猶太地理誌 *Yew-t'ai te le che.* See 紀好弼 KE HAOU-PEĬH.

猶太地理擇要 *Yew-t'ai te le tsih yaou.* See 紀好弼 KE HAOU-PEĬH.

柚堂筆談 *Yew t'ang peǐh t'an.* See 盛百二 SHING PIH-URH.

柚堂文存 *Yew t'ang wǎn ts'un.* See 盛百二 SHING PIH-URH.

幼童習字法 *Yew tung seǐh tsze fa.* See 幼童 YEW TUNG.

酉陽雜俎 *Yew-yang tsa tsoo.* See 叚成式 TW'AN CH'ING-SHIH.

Yiæ-su Sing-du siu-k'wu tsong-leng. See YIÆ-SU SING-DU.

益智書彙 *Yih che shoo wei.* See 益智 YIH CHE.

益智新錄 *Yih che sin luh.* See PERIODICAL PUBLICATIONS: *Shanghai.*

易經正文 *Yih king ching wǎn.* See 易經 YIH KING.

易經具詮 *Yih king chin ts'euen.* See 易經 YIH KING.

易經增訂旁訓 *Yih king tsǎng ting pang heun.* See 易經 YIH KING.

翼駉稗編 *Yih kung pai peen.* See 湯芷卿 T'ANG CHE-K'ING.

奕妙 *Yih meaou.* 施裴夏 SHE PEI-HEA.

一目了然 *Yih muh leaou jen.* See 一目 YIH MUH.

一本萬利 *Yih pun wan le.* See EPHEMERIDES.

譯書事畧 *Yih shoo sze leŏ.* See 傅蘭雅 FOO-LAN-YA.

域外叢書 *Yih wai ts'ung shoo.* See 王塰 WANG LEW.

陰騭文 *Yin chih wǎn.* See 文昌帝君 WǍN CH'ANG TE KEUN.

吟鳳閣 *Yin fung ko.* See 余笠湖 YU LEĬH-HOO.

營城揭要 *Ying ch'ing kĕĕ yaou.* See 儲意比 CHOO-E-PE.

應酬彙選新集 *Ying ch'ow wei seuen sin tseǐh.* See 陸九如 LUH KEW-JOO.

瀛寰瑣記 *Ying hwan so ke.* See 小吉羅庵主 SEAOU-KEĬH-LO GAN CHOO.

英華仙尼華四雜字文 *Ying Hwa Seen-ne-hwa-sze tsa tsze wǎn.* See 仙尼華四 SEEN-NE-HWA-SZE.

英華字典 *Ying Hwa tsze teen.* See LOBSCHEID (WILHELM).

英華譯字則列類 *Ying Hwa yih tsze tsih le luy.* See 英華譯字 YING HWA YIH TSZE.

英烈全傳 *Ying lëë ts'euen chuen.* See 徐文長 SEU WĂN-CHANG.

營壘圖說 *Ying luy t'oo shwo.* See 伯里牙芒 PIH-LE-YA-MANG.

英文舉隅 *Ying wăn keuh yu.* See 喀爾氏 KIH-URH-SHE.

英語指南 *Ying yu che nan.* See 黃履卿 HWANG LE-K'ING.

* 英語必讀 *Ying yu pe tuh.* See 黃履卿 HWANG LE-K'ING.

英語易讀 *Ying yu yih tuh.* See LO SING-LAN.

音漢清文鑑 *Yin 'Han Ts'ing wăn keen.* See 董明鐸 TUNG MING-TO.

引家當道 *Yin kea tang taou.* See 楊格非 YANG KIH-FEI.

蟫史 *Yin she.* See 磊砢山房主人 LUY-LO SHAN FANG CHOO JIN.

引道三章 *Yin taou san chang.* See 楊格非 YANG KIH-FEI.

尹文子 *Yin Wăn tsze.* See 尹文 YIN WĂN.

岳忠武王文集 *Yo chung woo wang wăn tseih.* See 岳飛 YO FEI.

約翰傳福音書 *Yo-han chuen fuh yin shoo.* See BIBLE: NEW TESTAMENT—*John, Gospel of.*

約色弗言行錄 *Yo-sih-fuh yen hing luh.* See 善德 SHEN-TIH.

約瑟聖蹟圖說 *Yo-sih shing tsih t'oo shwo.* See JOSEPH.

約瑟言行全傳 *Yo-sih yen hing ts'euen chuen.* See 約瑟 YO-SIH.

Yü-be væn-ts'æn zi-dzo-ts'ah zi. See VÆN-TS'ÆN.

諭札牌詳示鈔抄錄 *Yu cha p'ai tseang she yo ch'aou luh.* See 諭札 YU CHA.

諭旨 *Yu che.* See CHINA 光緒 KWANG-SEU, *Emperor.*

御製繙譯詩經 *Yu che fan yih she king.* See 乾隆 K'EEN-LUNG, *Emperor.*

御製繙譯四書 *Yu che fan yih sze shoo.* See 乾隆 K'EEN-LUNG, *Emperor.*

御製耕織圖 *Yu che kăng chih t'oo.* See 康熙 K'ANG-HE, *Emperor.*

御製律曆淵源 *Yu che leüh leih yuen yuen.* See 允祿 YUN LUH.

御製滿漢蒙古西番合璧大藏全咒 *Yu che Man Han Mung-koo Se-fan ho peih ta ts'ang ts'euen chow.* See 乾隆 K'EEN-LUNG, *Emperor.*

御製避暑山莊詩 *Yu che pe shoo shan chwang she.* See 康熙 K'ANG-HE, *Emperor.*

御製西域同文志 *Yu che se yih t'ung wăn che.* See 乾隆 K'EEN-LUNG, *Emperor.*

御製詩 *Yu che she.* See 詩 SHE.

御製盛京賦 *Yu che shing king foo.* See 乾隆 K'EEN-LUNG, *Emperor.*

御製四體清文鑑 *Yu che sze t'e Ts'ing wăn keen.* See 清文 TS'ING WĂN.

御製增訂清文鑑 *Yu che tsăng ting Ts'ing wăn keen.* See 乾隆 K'EEN-LUNG, *Emperor.*

御製千字文 *Yu che ts'een tsze wăn.* See 太平天國 T'AIP'ING T'EEN KWO.

御製文集 *Yu che wăn tseih.* See 洪武 HUNG-WOO, *Emperor.*

御製五體清文鑑 *Yu che woo t'e Ts'ing wăn keen.* See 清文 TS'ING WĂN.

御製玉斧珮詩 *Yu che yuh foo pei she.* See 玉斧珮詩 YUH FOO PEI SHE.

粵中見聞 *Yuĕ chung keen wăn.* See 范端昂 FAN TWAN-GAN.

粵匪起手根由 *Yuĕ fei k'e show kăn yew.* See 粵匪 YUĔ FEI.

粵海關比例 *Yuĕ hai kwan pe le.* See CANTON.

粵海關稅務文 *Yuĕ hai kwan shwuy woo wăn.* See CANTON.

粵海關外洋船牌 *Yuĕ hai kwan wai yang ch'uen p'ai.* See 恒 HĂNG.

越南遊記 *Yueh nan yew ke.* See 陳省堂 CH'IN SĂNG-T'ANG.

月令粹編 *Yuĕ ling suy peen.* See 秦嘉謨 TS'IN KEA-MOO.

元人百種曲 *Yuen jin pih chung k'euh.* See 臧晉叔 TSANG TSIN-SHUH.

YUE—YUN

元人雜劇 *Yuen jin tsa keĭh.* See 臧晉叔 TSANG TSIN-SHUH.

元人雜劇百種 *Yuen jin tsa keĭh pih chung.* See 臧晉叔 TSANG TSIN-SHUH.

元曲選 *Yuen keuh seuen.* See 臧晉叔 TSANG TSIN-SHUH.

元詩別裁集 *Yuen she pĕĕ ts'ai tseĭh.* See 張景星 CHANG KING-SING.

*圓天圖說 *Yuen t'een t'oo shwo.* See 李明徹 LE MING-CHE.

鉛字拼法集全 *Yuen tsze peen fa tseĭh ts'euen.* See MATEER (JULIA B.).

寓意草 *Yu e ts'aou.* See 喻嘉言 YU KEA-YEN.

閱微草堂筆記五種 *Yuĕ-wei-ts'aou T'ang peĭh ke woo chung.* See 閱微草堂 YUĔ-WEI-TS'AOU T'ANG.

粵音指南 *Yuĕ yin che nan.* See 粵音 YUĔ YIN.

御風要術 *Yu fung yaou shuh.* See 白爾特 PIH-URH-T'IH.

玉釧緣 *Yuh ch'uen yuen.* See 西湖居士 SE HOO KEU SZE.

玉嬌梨 *Yuh keaou le.* See 金聖歎 KIN SHING-T'AN.

玉嬌梨平山冷燕 *Yuh keaou le. P'ing shan lăng yen.* See 玉 YUH.

玉谿生詩詳註 *Yuh k'e săng she tseang choo.* See 李義山 LE E-SHAN.

玉谿生詩箋註 *Yuh k'e săng she tseen choo.* See 李義山 LE E-SHAN.

玉歷鈔傳警世 *Yuh leĭh ch'aou chuen king she.* See 江潮遠 KEANG CH'AO-YUEN.

—— See 陸喬木 LUH K'EAOU-MUH.

—— See 玉歷 YUH LEĬH.

玉樓春 *Yuh low ch'un.* See 白雲道人 PIH-YUN TAOU-JIN.

玉茗新詞四種 *Yuh ming sin ts'ze sze chung.* See 湯義仍 T'ANG E-JĂNG.

玉臺新詠箋註 *Yuh t'ai sin yung tseen choo.* See 徐陵孝 SEU LING-HEAOU.

玉堂楷則 *Yuh t'ang k'eae tsih.* See 陳閟 CH'IN MAI.

玉堂字彙 *Yuh t'ang tsze wei.* See 梅膺祚 MEI YING-TSOO.

玉堂芽 *Yuh t'ang ya.* See 孫顏 SUN YEN.

瑜伽集要施食壇儀應門 *Yu-kea tseĭh yaou she shih tan e ying mun.* See 靈操竹 LING TS'AOU CHUH.

漁磯漫鈔 *Yu ke man ch'aou.* See 雷琳 LUY LIN.

豫軍紀略 *Yu keun ke leŏ.* See 李鶴年 LE HO-NEEN.

漁古山房詩經體註 *Yu koo shan fang she king t'e choo.* See 高朝瓔 KAOU CH'AOU-YING.

禹貢會箋 *Yu kung hwuy tseen.* See 徐位山 SEU WEI-SHAN.

于公太保演義傳 *Yu kung t'ai paou yen e chuen.* See 高亮懷 KAOU LEANG-HWAI.

語錄彙集 *Yu luh wei tseĭh.* See 具亮 CHIN-LEANG.

餘墨偶談 *Yu mih gow t'an.* See 孫詩樵 SUN SHE-TS'EAOU.

韻法 *Yun fa.* See 梅膺祚 MEI YING-TSOO.

韻府羣玉原本 *Yun foo k'eun yuh yuen pun.* See 陰時夫 YIN SHE-FOO.

韻府萃昔 *Yun foo ts'uy yin.* See 青霏子 TS'ING FEI-TSZE.

庸閒齋筆記 *Yung heen chai peĭh ke.* See 陳子莊 CH'IN TSZE-CHWANG.

*永樂大典 *Yung-lo ta teen.* See 永樂 YUNG-LO.

甬報 *Yung paou.* See PERIODICAL PUBLICATIONS: *Ningpo.*

連規約指 *Yun kwei yo chih.* See 白起偉 PIH-K'E-TIH.

韻目表 *Yun muh peaou.* See 錢恂 TS'EEN SEUN.

雲南夷類圖 *Yunnan e luy t'oo.* See 禮鶱 LECHAI.

筠清館金石 *Yun ts'ing kwan kin shih.* See 吳榮光 WOO YUNG-KWANG.

韻 字 鑑 *Yun tsze keen.* See 韻字 YUN TSZE.

禹 碑 *Yu pei.* See 禹 YU.

御 批 歷 代 通 鑑 輯 覽 *Yu p'e leih tai t'ung keen tseih lan.* See 傅 恆 FOO HĂNG.

—— China. 乾隆 K'EEN-LUNG, *Emperor.*

諭 示 抄 錄 *Yu she ch'aou luh.* See 諭 示 YU-SHE.

御 題 棉 華 圖 *Yu t'e kin hwa t'oo.* See 方 觀 承 FANG KWAN-CH'ING.

御 定 奎 章 全 韻 *Yu ting kw'ei chang ts'euen yun.* See 奎 章 KW'EI CHANG.

御 定 陸 奏 約 選 *Yu ting luh tsow yo seuen.* See 陸 奏 LUH TSOW.

御 定 三 元 甲 子 萬 年 書 *Yu ting san yuen ke̍d tsze wan neen shoo.* See 三 元 SAN YUEN.

御 定 萬 年 書 *Yu ting wan seen shoo.* See EPHEMERIDES.

輿 圖 要 覽 *Yu t'oo yaou lan.* See 輿 圖 YU T'OO.

* 輿 轍 摭 要 *Yu tsai ts'o yaou.* See 輿 轍 YU TSAI.

—— See 輿 YU.

御 纂 醫 宗 金 鑑 *Yu tswan e tsung kin keen.* See 吳 謙 WOO KEEN.

御 纂 詩 義 折 中 *Yu tswan She e che chung.* See 詩 經 SHE KING.

漁 洋 山 人 古 詩 選 *Yu yang shan jin koo she seuen.* See 王 士 禎 WANG SZE-CHING.

語 言 自 邇 集 *Yü-yen Tsŭ-erh chi.* See WADE (Sir T. F.), K.C.B.

A Catalogue of Chinese Works in the Bodleian Library

博德利图书馆藏中文典籍目录

CATALOGUE OF CHINESE WORKS.

1 四書類典賦

Sze shoo luy tëen foo. A Cyclopædia of Biography and Antiquities to illustrate the Four Books. By Kan yü lin. Preface dated 1742. 12 vols. Reprinted, 1777.

2 初學玉壺冰

Ch'oo heŏ yü hoo ping. Essays by various authors on passages in the *Lun yü* of Confucius and on Mencius, with comment. 4 vols. 1765.

3 書經

Shoo-king. Book of History.

These annals were collected by Confucius in the 6th century B.C. They contain the history of China from the time of the Emperor Yaou, B.C. 2357 to B.C. 700, not long before the times of Confucius.

Comment by Ts'ae Ch'in, A.D. 1200; undertaken at the command of his teacher Choo he, who died the next year. Finished A.D. 1210. 4 vols. Printed A.D. 1819.

4 易經監本

Yih king këen pun. The Book of Changes. The strokes on which it is based are by Fu hi; the oldest text is by Wen wang, and a second text called *Twan.* Additions by Chow kung are called *Seang.* Afterwards follows a comment, *Chwen,* by Confucius.

3 vols. Text, 2 vols.; comment, 1 vol. Modern exposition by Choo he. Date, Kea k'ing; year, Mow yin, 1819.

5 禮記

Le ke. Book of Ceremonies. Confucius transmitted among the Five Classics a book of this name. In this book there are traces of the work of Han authors; yet it is recognised as one of the Thirteen Classics by the Sung school and the *literati* generally.

Comment by Ch'en kaou of the Choo he school. His Preface dated 1322. 10 vols. Reprinted, 1838.

6 詩經

She-king, sc. Book of Odes. Said to have been collected by Confucius, and arranged in chronological order by him. This copy is the one in public use, approved and annotated by Choo he. 4 vols. Reign of Kea k'ing. Mow yin.

7 春秋左傳

Ch'un Ts'iew Tso chwen. Spring and Autumn Annals by Confucius, with supplementary history by Tso k'ew ming. 10 vols. Printed, 1823.

8 春秌

Ch'un Ts'iew. The Spring and Autumn Annals by Confucius, with comment by Hoo ngan kwo of the Sung dynasty. 6 vols. 1782.

9 分韻

Fun yün. Canton Dialect Tonic Dictionary. By Wǎn e fung. Preface dated 1824. 4 vols. bound in two. 1833.

10 行遠集

Hing yuen tseih. Essays on passages in the Four Books by authors of the present dynasty. Compiled by Ho cho. 20 vols. Preface dated 1725.

11 初學小題登龍

Ch'oo heŏ siaou t'e tǎng lung. Examples of Essays to aid the young in ascending to the Dragon Gate. Essays by various authors. Compiler: T'ang k'ing sun. Preface dated 1774. 4 vols. Printed, 1828.

12 東晋志傳

Tung tsin che chwen. Historical Novel based on the history of the Eastern Tsin dynasty, A.D. 322 to A.D. 471.

Comment by Ch'in che hwŏ. 8 vols.

B

13 聖 諭 廣 訓

Shing yü kwang heün. Amplification of the Sacred Edict. Instructions in Mandarin to be read publicly on the 1st and 15th of each month to the soldiers and people. Amplification by Wang yow p'uh. Text by Emperor Kang he. Published in the reign of his son, 1724. 2 vols.

14 四 書 合 講

Sze shoo hŏ keang. The Four Books, or Smaller Classics, as determined by Choo he. With two commentaries on the text: the one, that of Choo he; the other, the *Hŏ keang*, published A.D. 1730, by order of the Emperor Yung ching. 6 vols. 1841.

15 小 學 體 註

Seaou heŏ t'e choo. Text of and comment on *Heaou king*, Book of Filial Piety; *Chung king*, Book of Fidelity to the Sovereign; *Seaou heŏ*, Moral Instructions for the Young. Preface by Choo he, A.D. 1190.

Chung king edited by Ma yung of the Heu han, and commented on by Ching heuen.

Heaou king republished with preface by the Emperor Heuen tsung of the T'ang dynasty. Commented on by Ch'in seuen.

Seaou heŏ commented on by Ch'in seuen. Preface by him, 1484.

4 vols. Soo chow.

16 古 文

Koo-wăn-seih-e. Specimens of Ancient and Modern Literary Composition. Compiled by Lin se chung.

These selected essays in the old style, from the most eminent writers, beginning with Tso kew ming and ending with the Ming dynasty, constitute a student's introduction to essay writing. 16 vols. Date of Preface, 1717.

17 尙 友 錄

Shang yew luh. Biographical Dictionary. The surnames occur in the order of the tonic dictionaries. 22 chaps. in 10 vols. Author: Liaou 廖 pin yü. 1611.

18 納 書 楹 曲 譜

Na shoo ying k'euh poo. Songs with the Music. A collection of K'euh or Ch'ü, with the native musical notation between the lines. 20 vols. Author: Ye hwae t'ing. Compiled, 1791.

19 性 命 圭 旨

Sing ming kwei che. Taouist work on the Connection of Alchemy and the Moral Philosophy of the Sung Dynasty. Several pictures of alchemists in vol. i. The author shews how the Confucian Chow tsze derived ideas from Taouist authors in forming his system of the world. He also amalgamates Buddhism with Taouism. In p. 1 in Pa. X, picture of Confucius, Buddha, and Laoutsze; Buddha is placed highest. 4 vols. Author: Yin chin jin. Preface of Yew t'ung, 1730.

20 詩 韻 含 英

She-yün han ying. Dictionary of Terms used in making Poetry. Arranged in the order of the tonic dictionaries. By Lew wăn wei. 4 vols. 1832.

21 爾 雅 正 文 直 音

Urh ya ching wăn chih yin. Text of the *Urh ya*, with the correct pronunciation. This dictionary of difficult and obsolete words in the older classics professes to be of the Chow dynasty. The sounds of the characters are given from Luh teih ming of the T'ang dynasty. 2 vols. Edited by Sun poo, 1787. Printed, 1838.

22 今 古 奇 觀

Kin koo k'é kwan. A Novel in colloquial style. Wonderful mirror of recent times and of antiquity. 10 vols. Reprinted, 1816.

23 子 不 語

Tsze puh yü. The Book of those things which Confucius did not discourse on. A book of marvels, consisting of strange stories. 8 vols. In 24 chapters. 1807.

24 飛 龍 傳

Fei lung chwen. History of the Flying Dragon. A novel. 16 vols. 1787.

25 列 國 志

Liĕ-kwŏ-che. A History, in nearly colloquial style, of the various Kingdoms into which China was divided under the Chow dynasty. It is a historical romance, beginning with Seuen wang, B.C. 700, and ending with Ts'in she hwang, B.C. 242. 24 vols. 1843.

26 四 家 詩 鈔

Sze kea she ch'aou. Selections from four poets of the present dynasty, viz. Woo mei ts'un, Yuen tsze ts'ae,

Chaou ngow pih, and Woo koo jin. The poems of each embrace two volumes. 8 vols. 1823.

27　四書正體

Sze shoo ching t'e. The Four Books, i. e. *Ta heŏ, Chung yung, Lun yü, Măng tsze.* With comments of Choo he. Bound in 6 vols. *Măng tsze* is placed by the binder before *Lun yü.* Wants the Prefaces.

28　百美新詠圖傳

Pih mei sin yung t'oo chwen. Poems on, likeuesses of, and notices respecting a hundred beautiful women. 4 vols. Preface dated 1786.

29　孔子家語

K'ung-tsze kea-yü. The Domestic Talk of Confucius. The book constitutes a sort of Memorabilia of what the sage thought and said on the subjects mentioned. No author's name.

Comment by Wang suh. Like the *Lun yü* and *Heaou king,* it is believed to have been made by his disciples from their recollections and the results of their inquiries. 2 vols. Printed, 1807.

30　朱子綱鑒

Choo tsze kang këen. Title in full : *Tsze che tung këen kang muh.* Abridgment of the Mirror of History.

Choo he based this work on the previous productions of Sze ma kwang and Hoo. He and they began with B. C. 402.

Kin jin shaou and Nan hëen prefixed the *Ts'een pëen,* vols. i–viii, from Fu he downwards.

Choo's Preface is dated 1173. The work was concluded to 1366 by subsequent writers. Preface of Emperor Hëen tsung, 1472.

Extensive comments throughout by various writers subsequent to Choo.

102 vols. Wanting vol. xxxvii. Printed, 1809.

31　綱鑑易知錄

Kang këen e che luh. By Woo cheng k'euen. An abridgment (with notes explaining difficulties) of *T'ung këen kang muh,* the larger work of Choo he, and continued to the end of the Ming dynasty. 40 vols. Author's preface dated 1711.

32　四書離句集註

Sze shoo le-keu tseih choo. The Four Books, with the clauses separated and comment. Explained by

Choo he. The clauses and sentences are separated by circles.

The Four Books are *Ta heŏ, Chung yung, Lun yü, Măng tsze.* The text is that in common use.

13 vols. Reign of Kea k'ing. Printed, 1819. Canton.

33　正音撮要

Ching yin tso yaou. Introduction to the Peking Dialect. By Kaou tsing t'ing, a Canton author.

4 vols. Vol. i. Edict to put down the use by officers of the Canton and Fu këen dialects. Classification of sounds. Conversations in the Peking dialect. Vols. ii, iii. Phrases in Peking dialect. Vol. iv. Peking sounds spelled for the learner. No date.

34　廣博物志

Kwang-pŏ-wuh-che, sc. An extended Account of the Realm of Nature. Author : Tung hea chow. Preface dated 1604.

Extracts from Confucian, Buddhist, and Taouist literature. Subjects : Astronomy, geography, legends of old China, biography, feats of heroes and sages, military art, music, dwellings, precious stones, clothing, implements, food, plants, and animals.

32 vols. Volume xi wanting. Printed, 1762.

35　正音彙編

Ching yin hwei pëen. Brief introduction to the Northern and Southern Mandarin Dialect. Author : Chang yü ch'ing. Preface dates 1786.

2 vols. bound together. Consists of classified phrases in the Peking dialect. They are occasionally explained, and their pronunciation is frequently given. Printed, 1821.

36　咬嚙吧總論

Kalapa (in Mandarin, *Kiaou lew pa*) *tsung lun.* Account of Java. In 16 chapters.

Belongs to a series called *T'ih seuen tsoh yaou.* Important Selections. Published at Batavia, about 1830.

1 vol. Author : Rev. W. H. Medhurst, formerly resident at Batavia and afterwards in China. He writes under the soubriquet *Shang teih chay,* Promoter of Virtue.

37　靖匪編

K'an tsing keaou fei shuh pëen. A detailed Account of the Trampling-out of the White Lily Rebellion. In 12 chapters. Chaps. 1–8. Affairs in Sze chwen. Chaps. 9, 10. Affairs in Shen si, Kan suh, Hoo kwang, and Ho nan. Chap. 11. Miscellaneous details. Chap. 12. Supplemental.

The White Lily sect dates from the Yuen dynasty. The rebellion began 1796, and was extirpated 1803.

2 vols. Author's Preface dated 1826. Printed at Peking.

38   廣 事 類 賦

Kwang she luy foo. Cyclopædia of all Matters arranged in Rhyme. Explications and examples throughout, in smaller type. First published in the Sung dynasty about A.D. 980, in 30 sections, by Wu shu, who assisted in making the works called *T'ae p'ing yü lan kwang ke* and *Wăn yuen ying hwa,* under the orders of T'ae tsung, second emperor of that line.

Reprinted about 1560. Increased to 40 sections, and again printed 1699 by Woo hwa, a descendant of the author. 12 vols. Printed, 1834.

39   笠 翁 全 集

Leih ung ts'euen tseih. Collected Essays, Poetry, and various short Pieces of Li yü. Full title: *Leih ung yih kea yen ts'euen tseih.* 16 vols. Published, 1693. A recent reprint.

40   四 書 或 問

Sze shoo hwŏ wăn. Questions on the Four Books. Author: Ch'in ts'iew yae.

10 vols. The 1st vol. contains questions on the *Ta heŏ,* Great Instructor; 2nd, on the *Chung yung,* Invariable Mean; 3rd, on the Discourses of Confucius: *Lun yü,* 3rd chapter to 8th; 4th, Mencius: chaps. 9, 10. Written, 1747.

41   莊 子 南 華 經 解

Chwang tsze Nan hwa king keae. Commentary on the *Nan hwa king* of Chwang tsze, the Taouist philosopher, about B.C. 400.

Comment by Seuen ying mow.

This copy is printed from the original blocks when much worn.

4 vols. Date of Preface, 1772.

42   粵 東 筆 記

Yuĕ-tung-peĭh-ke. Recollections of Canton (Province). Natural history of the province, its superstitions, customs, aboriginal inhabitants, traditions, and manufactures. 4 vols. Author: Le t'eaou yuen.

43   唐 詩 合 觧

T'ang-she hŏ keae. Selected Poetry of the T'ang Dynasty (the Augustan age of Chinese poetry). With commentary by Wang yaou k'eu of Soo chow. Date of Preface, 1733.

5 vols. The 5th volume is selected from older poetry and commented on by the same author.

44   楚 辭 新 註

Ch'oo ts'ze sin choo. New Commentary on the *Ch'oo ts'ze.* By K'euh foo, a writer of the present dynasty.

The poems *Ch'oo ts'ze* consist of *Le saou, Tëen wăn, Chaou hwun,* etc., and were written by K'euh yuen about B.C. 220. They occupy middle ground between the ancient odes (*She-king*) and the modern poetry. The author was a man of genius, celebrated for his patriotism. He committed suicide in a fit of political despair.

4 vols. Printed, 1842.

45   漁 洋 詩 話

Yü yang she hwa. Talk about Poetry. By Wang e shang of Tsenan. 2 vols. Dates in Prefaces, 1706, 1726. Printed, 1836.

46   奇 嶽 雲 詩

Ke yŏ yün she. Select Poems of Neĕ sien min, a writer of the 17th century. 2 vols. Preface of new editor dated 1804.

47   清 華 集

Tsing-hwa-tseih, sc. Collections of the Clear and Beautiful.

Elegant poems by prizemen and eminent candidates at the Metropolitan Doctor's Examination from 1762 to 1820 inclusive. Compiled by Tseang e pin, 1824.

4 vols. Printed, 1830.

48   衛 濟 餘 編

Wei tse yü pëen. Miscellaneous Chapters on Self-preservation. A medical work, with valetudinarian precepts on food, occupations, household goods, calamities, etc. By Wang seang tang.

5 vols. Vol. i contains the title, *Tung t'ëen heaou,* of a series of works, of which this is the first. Printed, 1817.

49   留 青 新 集

Lew ts'ing sin tseih. New Collection of Examples in all Kinds of Composition, by various authors.

Here are birth-day addresses, sacrificial prayers, proclamations, congratulatory compositions, addresses, poems, etc., suited to all the incidents of life. Compiled by Ch'in mei of Hang chow. Preface dated 1708. 20 vols.

50 三才圖會

San ts'ae t'oo hwei. Illustrated Encyclopædia, consisting of a collection of plates, maps, and diagrams, illustrating the three kingdoms of nature, viz. heaven, earth, and man, with descriptions of each.

Date, A.D. 1370. 23 vols. by Wang k'e. The rest by Wang sze e.

49 vols. Missing 11 vols. In all 60 vols. The volumes missing are 1 *a*, 2 *b*, 8 *h*, 14 *n*, 15 *o*, 40 *an*, 46 *at*, 51 *ay*, 54 *bb*, 56 *bd*, 60 *bh*. The Chinese manuscript numbering is erroneous.

51 幼學

Yow heŏ. Youthful Learniug. A school book teaching the elements of astronomy, geography, morals, government, official distinctions, ceremonies, medicine, literature, accomplishments, law, Buddhism, Taouism, natural history. Author: Ch'ing yün shing. 4 vols. Printed, 1796.

52 風雅大成

Fung ya ta ch'ing. Complete Collection of Elegant Seutences. They consist of sentences suitable for wooden tablets, upright or horizontal, hung up in houses, and adapted to the circumstances and rank of the persons to whom they are to be presented. Printed, 1834.

53 春秋大事表

Ch'un ts'iew ta she peaou. View of the Chief Matters in the *Ch'un ts'iew*, or Spring and Autumn Annals of Confucius, viz. the calendar, boundaries, names, cities, geography, government, ceremonies, noted persons, lost passages, quotations from the classics. Author: Koo tung kaou of the present dynasty.

20 vols. Wanting 7, 19, 20. Chapters wanting: first and second parts of chapter 7; whole of chapters 45–50; and the appendices. New edition. Printed, 1747. Commendatory poem by the Emperor K'cen lung prefixed, 1753.

54 紀效新書

Ke heaou sin shoo. By Ts'eih ke kwang of the Ming dynasty.

A collection of military precepts and discussions strung together for a new work. It was written at the time of the Japanese hostile descents, for the defence of the province of Che keang. In 6 volumes; the last 3 wanting, viz. chapters 10–18.

3 vols. New edition. No date.

55 練兵實紀

Leën ping shih ke. Detailed and Correct Accounts of Methods for Training Soldiers. By Ts'eih ke kwang of the Ming dynasty. Imperfect copy, probably 6 volumes when complete.

3 vols. *b, e, f.* Wanting first part of chapter 1; the whole of chapters 2, 3, 4; the whole of chapters 10 and what follow.

56 練兵實紀雜集

Leën ping shih ke tsa tseih. Supplement to *Leën ping shih ke.* It consists of miscellaneous notes on military training. By Ts'eih ke kwang of the Ming dynasty. 2 vols. 4 chapters bound in 2 vols.

57 篆字彙

Chwen tsze hwuy. Collection of Characters in the Ancient Form or *Chwen wǎn.* By Tung wei foo.

Arranged in the order of the radicals under twelve heads, two in each volume.

Chwen forms are given, from one to twenty-four in number, to each modern character.

6 vols. Date of Preface, 1692.

58 史記

She ke. Historical Records. By Sze Ma-tsëen. In 130 chapters. Preface of Chang show tseĕ, A.D. 726. Modern Prefaces by Seu foo yuen and Ch'in tsze lung, who have added a perpetual commentary from the best authors.

The History extends from the time of the Emperor Hwang-te, B.C. 2697, to the time of the author in the Han dynasty, 1st cent. B.C. He founded the historical method followed since his time. His repute rose high about four centuries after his death, aud his work has always continued a model in style.

26 vols. Sung keang.

59 翠微山房數學

Ts'uy wei shan fang shoo heŏ. The Mathematics of the House upon the Ts'uy wei Mountain. Published in the 25th and following years of Kea k'ing, A.D. 1820 to 1824, in 28 vols. By Chang-tso-nan of Kin hwa, near Hang chow.

This work is based on the translations of the Jesuits, and treats specially on the measurement of triangles and practical land-surveying, trigonometry and astronomical calculations. It reproduces European tables in trigouometry and astronomy as given in Imperial works. 28 vols.

C

60 厦 門 志

Hea mun che. Topography and History of Amoy. In 16 chapters. With notice of the subjugation of a rebel force in Formosa. 12 vols. Printed, 1840.

61 聊 齋 志 評 註

Leaou chae che p'ing choo. The Leaou chae History, with Comment. Author: P'oo sung ling. A collection of stories in elegant style and of most remarkable popularity. 16 vols. Printed, 1765. This edition printed 1843.

62 三 國 志

San kwŏ che. History of the Three Kingdoms. A historical romance. With notes by Kin jin juy, or Shing t'an, who dates his Preface 1645. The work is about 300 years older. 30 vols. No date.

63 山 海 經

Shan hae king. Book of the Mountains and Seas.

First mentioned in the *Han shoo* by Pan koo as consisting of 18 chapters. It was re-arranged by Kwo p'uh, a noted author of the Tsin dynasty, A.D. 260 to 416, in 22 chapters. It treats of fabulous creatures and things distributed geographically, and forms a characteristic example of the Han tendency to legendary lore.

The comments and plates in this edition, A.D. 1819, are taken from Chang hwuy kwan of the Leang dynasty, Woo shen hing of the Ming, and Ch'ae shaou ping, A.D. 1728, with others. 4 vols.

64 性 理 精 義

Sing le tsing e. Essential Principles of the Sing le Philosophy. Compiled by order of K'ang he, A.D. 1717, from the works of the Sung dynasty philosophers— Chow, Chang, Ch'ing, Choo, and others—upon cosmogony, natural philosophy, divination, ceremonies of social life, music, literature, moral nature of man, geography, geomancy, and politics.

Required to be studied in the examinations. An abridgment has been recently substituted. 4 vols.

65 關 帝 蹟 圖 誌

Kwan te tseih t'oo che. Plates and descriptions to illustrate the achievements and marvellous manifestations of the god Kwan.

Kwan yün chang, the Chinese god of war, was a loyal follower of Lew pei, made emperor in Western China, A.D. 221, and represented the Han imperial family which fell in A.D. 221, being in the absence of a direct heir as good a claimant to the throne on the ground of collateral descent as could then be found. Kwan was in the Sung dynasty made into a god, a thousand years after his death, to represent the principle of legitimacy and martial virtues.

5 vols. Preface dated 1693. Printed, 1822, at Shang hae.

66 搜 神 記

Show Shin ke. History of the Gods.

This work is registered in the Suy and T'ang dynastic histories as having 30 chapters. The original author, Yow kan paou, also called Ta leang kan paou, lived about A.D. 300, and some say left it in 20 chapters. Eight now remain. In the modern copies there are additions made in the How Wei, Sung, Ts'e, and T'ang dynasties, coming down to about A.D. 750.

3 vols. Printed, 1820.

67 萬 病 回 春

Wan ping hwuy ch'un. Cures for all Diseases.

Author: Kung t'ing heën yün lin. Preface dated A.D. 1614. He was a physician of the province of Keang Se. His MS. was published by a President of the Board of Punishments, whose Preface states the history and objects of the work.

8 vols. Printed, 1821.

68 三 國 志

San kwŏ che. History of the Three Kingdoms. A historical romance. With notes by Kin jin juy, or Shing t'an, who dates his Preface 1645. The work is about 300 years older. 20 small vols. Printed, 1820.

69 紅 樓 夢

Hung low mung. Dream of the Red Chamber. A novel of last century, written in the Peking dialect and extremely popular. Preface by Kaou ngŏh, dated 1778, when the book had been known upwards of twenty years. 20 vols. Printed, 1811.

70 南 史 演 義

Nan she yen e. Paraphrased Account of the *Nan she,* that is, the Histories of the Dynasties Sung, Ts'e, Leang, Ch'in, A.D. 286 to 584. Historical novel by Heu paou shen. 10 vols. Preface dated 1795.

71   續英烈傳

Suh ying leĕ chwen. Supplement to the Narrative of Heroes. Historical novel describing the foundation of the Ming dynasty. 5 vols. No dates or names.

72   肉蒲團

Jŭh p'o poo. Garden of Meat and Spinach. A novel. No date of composition or author's name. 4 vols. Reprinted, 1810.

73   水滸傳

Shuy hoo chwen. Narrative of the Water Bank. A celebrated novel by She nai ngan. The scene is laid in that period of the Sung dynasty when brigandage was rife in North-eastern China. The natives praise it as the best of all the novels for vivacity, variety, and unflagging interest. 20 vols. Preface to this edition dated 1733.

74   五鳳吟

Woo fung yin. Song of the Five Phœnixes. A novel. Scene laid in the 16th century. Style colloquial. Name of author and date of composition, with date and place of printing this edition, all wanting. 4 vols.

75   雙鳳奇緣

Shwang fung k'e yuen. Marvellous Connecting Fate of the Pair of Phœnixes. A novel. Scene laid in the Han dynasty. The story of the Chinese Princess Chaou kiün forms the staple. She was married to the Emperor of the Heung noo Tartars. 8 vols. Date of Preface, 1815. Reprinted, 1826.

76   度生公案

Too shăng kung an. A Case of Judicial Inquiry for the Saving of Life. A novel. 3 vols. Reprinted from a Soo chow copy, 1832.

77   龍圖公案

Lung t'oo kung an. A Criminal Case decided by Paou lung t'oo.

Paou lung t'oo was a celebrated judge of the Sung dynasty who acquired immense fame by his decisions. This novel illustrates his sagacity and integrity.

5 vols. Reprinted, 1770.

78   琵琶記

P'e pa ke. Tale of a Guitar. A novel by Kaou tung kea, styled 'the seventh of the novelists who were possessed of genius.' Written in the time of the Yuen dynasty (14th ceut.). Illustrations by Keae tsze yuen. 6 vols. Date of Preface, by Ch'eng she jen, 1736.

79   夜譚隨錄

Ye t'an suy luh. Consecutive Record of Nightly Talk. (Contains stories of foxes and other superstitions.) A novel by an author calling himself Chae yuen choo jen, and writing in the learned style. Preface by himself, dated 1792. 6 vols.

80   隨唐傳

Suy t'ang chwen. Record of the Dynasties Suy and T'ang. Historical novel in Mandarin of the times of Suy Yang te, A.D. 621, and T'aug Ming hwang, 745, and modelled on the San kwŏ che.

20 vols. Preface dated A.D. 1696. Original Preface dated 1509. Reprinted, 1803.

81   封神演義

Fung shin yen e. 'Creation' of Deities. A paraphrased account of those persons who are appointed to be worshipped as gods.

An account of heroes and genii at the close of the Shang dynasty and the early part of the Chow, about B.C. 1100.

A novel by Chung pih king. Date of Preface, A.D. 1696. 10 vols. Reprinted, 1814.

82   西晉志傳

Se tsin che chwen. Account of the Western Tsin Dynasty, A.D. 260 to 313. Historical novel. 4 vols.

83   五虎平西狄青前傳

Woo hoo p'ing se teih ts'ing ts'een chwen. Subjugation of the West (the Leaou kingdom) by the Five Tigers (five generals of the Sung emperor Jin tsung), with a particular account of Generalissimo Teih ts'ing. First Part. 14 vols. Amoy. Reprinted, 1830.

84   後宋慈雲走國全傳

How sung ts'ze yün tsow kwŏ ts'euen chwen. Complete Account of the Flight of Ts'ze yün (eldest son of the Emperor Shin tsung) of the Later Sung Dynasty. A novel, of which the scene is laid in the 11th century. 8 vols. Reprinted, 1837.

85   萬 花 樓

Wan hwa low. Gallery of Ten Thousand Flowers. A novel, whose scene is laid in the Sung dynasty, in the 11th and 12th centuries. It describes the actions of three celebrated men, Yang kea tseang, Paou lung t'oo, and Teih ts'ing. 14 vols. Reprinted, 1837.

86   小 紅 袍

Seaou Hung P'aou. The Small Red Gown. A novel, whose scene is laid in the reign of Wan leih, A.D. 1571 to 1619. 6 vols. Amoy. Reprinted, 1832.

87   大 紅 袍

Ta Hung P'aou. The Great Gown. A tale in Mandarin of the Ming period, describing the actions of Hae chung keae, in the reign of Kea tsing, A.D. 1520 to 1565. By Le ch'un fang.

10 vols. Recent Preface dated 1822. Reprinted, 1838.

88   說 呼 全 傳

Shwo hoo ts'euen chwen. Complete Account of the Hoo Family. A novel, of which the scene is laid in the time of Jin tsung of the Sung dynasty, in the 11th century.

6 vols. Preface dated 1779. Reprinted, 1805.

89   說 唐 演 傳

Shwo T'ang yen chwen. Paraphrased Account of the Rise of the T'ang Dynasty, A.D. 620 to 631, when the Emperor T'ae tsung mounted the throne.

Historical novel, the same as that elsewhere called *Shwo T'ang ts'euen chwen.*

14 vols. New edition. No date.

90   唐 前 後 傳

T'ang ts'een how chwen. Narrative, in two parts, of the Earlier T'ang Dynasty. A novel, whose scene is laid A.D. 654 to 699. Author: a native of Soo chow. 10 vols. Reprinted, 1795.

91   綠 牡 丹

Lüh maou tan. The Green Peony. A tale of the time of Loo ling wang, a prince of the T'ang imperial family (son of T'ae tsung, who died A.D. 654). 6 vols. Reprinted from a Soo chow copy, 1816.

92   西 漢 全 傳

Se Han ts'euen chwen. Complete Account of the Western Han Dynasty (during the reign of the founder). Historical novel, period B.C. 200 to 182.

The preface and illustrations have reference to the Eastern and Western Han together.

8 vols. No date. Editor: Chung pih king.

93   東 漢 全 傳

Tung Han ts'euen chwen. Complete Narrative of the Rise of the Eastern Han Dynasty. A novel, whose scene is laid in the time A.D. 5 to 226.

Preface and illustrations are given in *Se Han ts'euen chwen.* 5 vols.

94   金 石 緣

Kin shih yuen. The Fated Union of the Kin and Shih Families. A Soo chow tale of common life.

The illustrations, in conformity to custom on the stage, and in robing the images in Taouist temples, give the old costume.

6 vols. No names or dates.

95   嶺 南 逸 史

Ling nan yih she. A Passage of Irregular History belonging to the province Kwang tung. A novel, whose scene is laid A.D. 1571 to 1619. 5 vols. Preface dated 1794. Reprinted, 1801.

96   南 北 宋 傳

Nan-pih Sung chwen, sc. Colloquial History of the Southern and Northern Sung Dynasties, A.D. 903 to 1100. Edited by Chung pih king. 10 vols. Preface to the second half dated 1606.

97   十 二 樓

Shih urh low. The Twelve Galleries, or a Sequel to the work *Kin koo k'e kwan.* A novel. By Chung le juy shuy. 10 vols. Preface dated 1658.

98   三 唐 征 西

San T'ang ching se. Narrative of the Victorious Expedition, under the General Seĕ jin kwei, to West China in the Early T'ang Dynasty, in the 7th century after Christ.

Historical novel, illustrated; the first of three colloquial works on the T'ang period.

10 vols. Printed, 1839.

99　　征東傳

Ching tung chwen. Narrative of the Conquest of the East. Describes the actions of Seĕ jin kwei. A novel of the Tᶜang dynasty (7th cent.), by a modern author styling himself Joo lëen keu she of Soo chow. The second in a series of three novels on the Tᶜang period. 6 vols.

100　　平山冷燕

Pᶜing shan lăng yen. Solitary Swallow of the Flat Mountain. A novel by the fourth among the novelists accounted men of genius. It has been translated by S. Julien. 4 vols.

101　　好逑傳

Haou kᶜew chwen. The Fortunate Union. A novel of the Ming dynasty by the second of the novelists accounted men of genius. Translated by Sir J. Davis. Edited by Kin shing tᶜan. 6 vols.

102　　玉嬌梨

Yü keaou le. The Pear-tree of Pearly Elegance and Grace. A novel by the third of the novelists who are esteemed men of genius. Scene laid in the Ming dynasty (15th cent.). Translated by S. Julien. Edited by Kin shing tᶜan. 4 vols.

103　　雷峰塔

Lui fung tᶜa. Pagoda of Thunder Peak. A tale of the Mongol dynasty, A. D. 1100 to 1296. Scene laid at Hang chow, where this pagoda still stands. 5 vols. No date.

104　　西廂記

Se seang ke. Record of the West Chamber. A celebrated novel, arranged for singing. Profusely annotated and illustrated. The author was the sixth of those esteemed men of genius. Edited by Kin shing tᶜan. Preface by Wang po heun, 1729. 6 vols.

105　　花箋記

Hwa tsᶜeen ke. Record of the Elegant Memorial. Novel by the eighth of those writers of tales who are esteemed men of genius, with comment by Kin shing tᶜan. Much of it in the essay style, but the basis is colloquial. 2 vols.

106　　斬鬼傳

Chan kwei chwen. Narrative of the Beheading of the Demon. Novel by the ninth of the men of genius. Scene laid in the Tᶜang dynasty. 4 vols. Author's Preface dated 1660.

107　　殘唐五代

Tsᶜan Tᶜang Woo tae. The Fall of the Tᶜang Dynasty and the Rise of the Five Dynasties (How Leang, How Tᶜang, How Tsin, How Han, How Chow), A. D. 879 to 964.

Historical novel, based on the regular history of Ngow-yang-sew. By Lo pun. 6 vols.

108　　玉樓春

Yü low chᶜun. Spring at the Jade Gallery. A novel, of which the scene is laid in the Tᶜang dynasty (8th cent.), in the reign of the Emperor Tᶜae tsung. 4 vols. No dates.

109　　玉樓春

Yü low chᶜun. Spring at the Jade Gallery. A novel, of which the scene is laid in the Tᶜang dynasty (8th cent.). 4 vols. No dates. Duplicate copy.

110　　濃情快史

Nung tsᶜing kᶜwae she. A Lively Narrative of Generous Feelings. A novel, of which the scene is laid in the Tᶜang dynasty, in the time of the Emperor Tᶜae tsung, who died A. D. 654. 4 vols. No dates. Imperfect copy.

111　　笑林廣記

Seaou lin kwang ke. Broad Record of the Forest of Jests. Book of Jests, in twelve sections, such as the gynecaeum, Buddhist and Taouist priests, covetousness, slander, poverty, etc. 4 vols. Reprinted, 1829.

112　　百圭傳

Pih kwei chwen. Narrative of the White Sceptre. Novel by the tenth man of genius. By Tsuy seang chᶜwen. 4 vols. Reprinted, 1807.

113　　西遊記

Se yew ke. Record of Western Journeyings. A romance of Buddhist pilgrimage, based on the travels

D

of the chief personage, Heuen tsang, who in the 7th century visited India to obtain Sanskrit books.

20 vols. By Yew tung, A. D. 1696. Commented on by Kin shing t'an.

114   麟 兒 報

Lin urh paou. Announcement of the K'e lin.

The K'e lin is a fabulous stag that appears at the birth of celebrated persons. A novel in the Mandarin dialect.

4 vols. The second missing. No dates.

115   說 唐 全 傳

Shwŏ T'ang ts'euen chwen. A novel in the Mandarin dialect, describing the rise of the T'ang dynasty, and ending with the establishment of the empire under T'ae tsuug, A. D. 631. 14 vols. No date. Duplicate copy.

116   天 豹 圖 傳

T'ëen paou t'oo chwen. Narrative of the Heavenly Panther. A novel of the 15th century, with illustrations. 6 vols. Printed at Amoy, 1814.

117   火 滸 後 傳

Shuy hoo how chwen. Later Narrative of the River Bank. A novel, intended as a supplement to the *Shuy hoo*, or 'Tales of the Brigands in the Sung Dynasty.' 4 vols. Preface dated 1608.

118   高 厚 蒙 求

Kaou how mung k'ew. Inquiries for Young Persons into the Laws of Heaven and Earth.

An introduction to astronomy and the description of the earth. Vol. ii. Geography. Vol. iii. Dialing. Climates. Vol. iv. Mapping. Vol. v. Tables of the sun's shadow for various latitudes. By Chang chaou tseun.

5 vols. First volume wanting. Printed, vol. i, 1807; vol. ii, 1809; vol. iii, 1815; vol. iv, 1829.

119   高 厚 蒙 求

Kaou how mung k'ew. Instructions and Inquiries for Pupils in Astronomy and Geography, in five volumes.

This work treats on astronomy, mathematical geography, mapping, construction of dials and clocks, and tables of the sun's shadow for various latitudes in China at different times of the year.

5 vols. Sung keang, 1807 to 1829.

120   賢 文 全 註

Hĕen wăn ts'euen choo. Maxims of the Wise and Virtuous, with a comment throughout. A book of proverbial teaching for the young. 1 vol. Printed, 1855.

121   千 字 文 全 註

Ts'een tsze wăn ts'euen choo. The Thousand-character Classic, with comment throughout. Author: Chow hing sze of the Leang dynasty, A. D. 550. Comment by Tseang show ch'ing. 1 vol. Reprinted.

122   廣 新 聞

Kwang sin wăn. An Extended Collection of Marvellous Stories. A book of stories, chiefly Taouist. 4 vols. Preface dated 1792. No names.

123   幼 學 故 事

Yew heŏ koo she. Book of Facts for the Young.

Chapter 1. Astronomy, geography, calendar, government. 2. Relationships, marriage, clothing, food. 3. Going to law, houses, implements, worship, disease and death. 4. Literature, botany, zoology, visiting and invitation cards, funeral, sacrificial, and congratulation cards. By Ch'ing yun shing.

4 vols. New Preface by a recent editor, dated 1793.

124   平 猺 述 略

P'ing yaou shoo lio. Brief Account of the Subjugation of the Yaou Tribes in the reign of Taou kwang.

These aboriginal tribes reside in the mountains of Kwang se, Hoo nan, and Canton.

1 vol. Preface by the author, Chow ts'un e, 1833. Preface by Loo shan te, 1833. Printed, 1834.

125   大 字 通 書

Ta tsze t'ung shoo. Book of Luck and Guide to Astrology for 1847.

It includes the twenty-four examples of filial piety, a brief herbal for edible and medicinal plants, calendar of fasts and festivals in honour of divinities, pictures of the twenty-eight constellations personified, and a collection of charms for curing the sick.

1 vol. Printed by the Foo kwei t'ang, a native house at Canton, 1846, for the year 1847.

126   水 石 錄

Shuy shih luh. Record of Water and Stones. A novel by Le chun yung. 3 vols. Preface dated 1774.

127   天崇百篇

T'ëen ch'ung pih p'ëen. A Hundred Select Essays from the writings of Ming dynasty essayists. Compiler: Woo mow ching of Hae yen. 2 vols. Printed, 1786.

128   感應篇

Kan ying p'ëen. The Book of Retribution, falsely attributed to Laou tsze, founder of the Taouist religion. It contains—Exhortations to virtue and warnings of the effects of vice, and ascribes the retribution of all moral acts to Heaven and Earth governing by means of innumerable spiritual beings found everywhere.

This edition includes the *Sin king* (Heart Sutra); Choo foo tsze's instructions for ruling the house; the Sutra of Kwan yin, in three parts; *Woo seang chin king* of Tsze Yang chin jin; the moral discourses of Wăn ch'ang and Kwan te; and medical recipes for all diseases; published for the good of mankind by charitable persons, whose names (and the amounts of their subscriptions) are appended. 2 vols.

129   太上感應篇

T'ae shang kan ying p'ëen. Book of Retribution, wrongly ascribed to Laou tsze.

1 vol. First pages wanting and also at the end a large portion of the work.

Illustrated throughout.

Given to the Library by Rev. T. Morris, Fellow of Hertford College, 27th November, 1747.

130   陰隲文詩

Yin-chih wăn she. The *Yin-chih wăn* of Wăn ch'ang te keun put into verse, with the original text and notes. Published in the 15th year of Kea k'ing, A.D. 1810.

This is a celebrated essay exhorting the world to the practise of virtue, on the ground of favours to be received secretly from the gods as the consequence.

Wăn ch'ang, god of literature and name of a constellation which (or who) became incarnate B.C. 1157. Appointed to the rank of Te keun A.D. 1195. 1 vol.

131   三字經註

San tsze king choo. The Trimetrical Classic, with comment (by Ch'in chung ming).

The commentator is a native of Canton. The text is one of the earliest books used in Chinese education, and is a compendium of morals and history.

1 vol. Printed, Canton, 1838.

132   重校幾書排列集字

Chung keaou ke shoo p'ae leĕ tseih tsze. A List of Characters used in several Works carefully examined.

This is a list of 3221 characters cast by Dyer's process. 1 vol. Printed apparently at Hong kong.

133   遊陰司悔悟錄

Yew yin sze hwuy woo lŭh. Record of Repentance following on a Journey to the Judgment Court of the Dead.

The visit to Hades is a dream. The moral is to lead a serious Buddhist life, living on vegetable diet, reading prayers, and avoiding sins. A spirit clothed in white guides the author through the city of Hades. The book is in colloquial Chinese.

1 vol. Printed at Amoy, 1848.

134   皇朝武功紀盛

Hwang ch'aou woo kung ke shing. Illustrious Military Conquests of the Present Dynasty. By Chaou yih, Taou t'ae of Western Kwei chow. Written, 1792.

1 vol. Chap. 1. Conquest over Woo san kwei, Keng tsing chung, Shang che siu, three early rebels. 2. Conquest of Chun ko urh, i. e. Sungaria. 3. Birmah. 4. Conquest of the two regions on the south-west of China, called Kin ch'wen. Appendix. Conquest of Nepaul.

135   三字經

San tsze king. The Trimetrical Classic. A common day-school copy. 1 vol. No date.

136   寸知堂遺草

Ts'un che t'ang e ts'aou. Poems by Leang han. Edited by his nephew. Preface by his grandson, A.D. 1845. The poems were written as he travelled in the emperor's service. 1 vol. Printed, 1846.

137   論語

Lun yü. Discourses of Confucius and his Disciples. The third of the Four Books. Comment by Choo he.

A Japanese edition, with Japanese words interspersed on the right hand of the columns in the text and comment. 1 vol. Second volume wanting.

Bound with it is the Taouist work called

太上感應篇

T'ae shang kan ying p'ëen, or in Manchu *Tai shang ni*

hachabume harolara bithe. Book of Retribution. The Manchu is a translation from the Chinese original.
Peking. Printed, 1759.

138 解 元 三 字 經

Keae yuen san tsze-king. The Original Text of the Trimetrical Classic. Printed from the edition of the Kwŏ tsze kĕen.

A Chinese work, six centuries old, used as a first book in native schools. Its subject is morality and instruction in things suitable for the young, such as history and literature. Called Trimetrical, because each sentence has but three characters for facility in committing to memory. 1 vol.

139 雪 心 賦 正 解

Seuĕ sin foo ching keae. Plain Exposition of the *Seuĕ sin foo* (Antithetical Verses of the Snowy Heart).

The *Seuĕ sin foo* is a celebrated work on geomancy of the T'ang dynasty, A.D. 622 to 897. (It is the oldest work but two on the subject, and is important for tracing the history of the false science on which it treats.) Author: Puh ying tĕen of Chang kung. Exposition by Meng t'een k'e. Preface by Chang to, A.D. 1771. 3 vols.

140 辯 論 三 十 篇

Peĕn lun san shih p'eĕn. Discussions (on Geomancy) in Thirty Chapters. A supplemental volume to *Seuĕ sin foo*, by the commentator on that work, Meng haou t'een. 1 vol.

141 六 合 叢 談

Luh hŏ ts'ung t'an. 'A Collection of what is talked about in all Countries.' First number of the Shanghae Serial. Edited by A. Wylie, who writes the Preface. 1 vol. Printed, A.D. 1857, at Shanghae.

142 莫 往 臺 灣 歌

Mo wang T'ae wan ko. 'Don't go to Formosa.' Two popular songs in the Amoy dialect. The first in lines of four words each, and sixteen to a verse; the second and fourth lines rhyme. The second in lines of seven words each, which all rhyme. 1 vol.

143 花 會 新 歌

Hwa hwuy sin ko. New Song of the Flower Assemblies. In seven-word verses, with rhymes. Amoy dialect.

These fairs, partly for the worship of the gods and partly for holiday amusement, sprang up in the prosperous times of the last century, and are represented in this song as most injurious to morality, especially as promoting robbery.
1 vol. Printed, 1827.

144 神 姐 歌

Shin tseay ko. Song of (a Visit to) the Spiritual Sister.

The *Shin tseay*, Spiritual Sister, gives information and advice about the dead to those who come to consult her.

The style is a rhyming prose for chanting. 1 vol. Amoy.

145 荔 枝 記 陳 三 歌

Le che ke ch'in san ko. Song of Ch'in san of the Sign of the Lychee. A popular song, in lines of seven words rhyming. 1 vol. Amoy.

146 臺 灣 十 二 月 相 思 歌

T'ae wan shih urh yuĕ seang sze ko. Songs of the Twelve Months in Formosa, with the thoughts they inspire. The lines are of various lengths and frequent repetitions, and are adapted for singing rather than reading. 1 vol. New edition, Amoy.

147 鴉 片 歌

Ya p'eĕn ko. Song of Opium. An exhortation to abandon and avoid opium smoking from its ruinous effects. Amoy popular song. Irregular versification, with rhymes. 1 vol. New edition.

148 潘 必 正 陳 妙 常 情 詩

Fan peih ching, Ch'in meaou ch'ang ts'ing she. Song of the Feelings of (a Husband) Fan peih ching and (his Wife) Ch'in meaou ch'ang. Also styled a villager's ditty (*Ts'un ko*). Amoy popular song. 1 vol.

149 東 海 鯉 魚 歌

Tung hae le yü ko, or *Hae fan ko.* Song of the Carp of the Eastern Sea, or The Rebellion in the Sea. A story of the dragon king and various fishes. Amoy popular song. 1 vol. New edition.

150   英臺歌

Ying t'ae ko. Song of the Maiden Ying t'ae. Story of a Soo chow girl who was bent on the acquisition of learning. Amoy popular song.   1 vol.

151   新傳臺灣娘子歌

Sin ch'wen T'ae Wan neang tsze ko. New Song of the Wife of Formosa. Amoy popular song. Rhyming lines of seven words each.   1 vol. Printed, 1826.

152   臺灣陳辨歌

T'ae Wan ch'in pien ko. Song of Ch'in pien of Formosa. Amoy popular song. Rhyming lines all of seven words each.   1 vol. New edition.

153   臺灣十八闖歌

T'ae Wan shih pa ch'in ko. Song of the Eighteen Sudden Impulses. Amoy popular song. Lines of seven words with rhymes.   1 vol.

154   拔皎歌

Pă keaou ko. Song of Plucking the White. Amoy popular song. Rhyming lines of irregular length.   1 vol.

155   離某歌

Le mow ko. Song of one whose name was Le. Amoy popular song. Irregular verse with rhymes.   1 vol.

156   笑談俗語歌

Seaou t'an suh yü ko. Colloquial Jests, in rhyme, newly selected. Amoy street ditties.   1 vol. Printed, 1843.

157   十勸娘附落神歌

Shih k'euen neang foo lŏ shin ko. Ten Exhortations to the Female Sex, supplemented by the Song of the Descent of the Spirit. Amoy popular song.   1 vol. Printed, 1840.

158   王抄娘新歌

Wang ch'aou neang sin ko. New Song of Ch'aou neang, a Maiden of the Wang Family. Amoy popular song. Lines of seven words each in rhyme.   1 vol. Printed, 1826.

159   戲闖歌

He ch'in ko. Song of the Play. An exhortation not to go to see plays. Amoy street ditties.   1 vol.

160   姜女歌

Keang niü ko. Song of the Maiden Keang. Amoy popular song. Lines of seven words in rhyme.   1 vol.

161   筭法統宗

Swan fă t'ung tsung. A Complete Work on the Laws of Calculation. At the end it gives a list of fifty works on mathematics, published since A.D. 1085 (when block printing became common) and before A.D. 1277. The author gives only the names of such as he knew.

Author: Ch'ing joo sze. Preface by his friend, Woo ke show, dated A.D. 1593.   6 vols.   New edition.

162   簷曝雜記

Yen paou tsă ke. Miscellaneous Record of what is under the Eaves and in the Sunshine.

A miscellany by Chaou yih, a Ken jin (Master of Arts) of the year 1750. He wrote this work in 1810, to record the most remarkable things he had seen and heard of respecting the Mongols, Russia, the Lama religion, the Mahommedans, Birmah, etc.   2 vols.

163   新增聖書節解以弗所

New Commentary on the Sacred Scriptures. The Epistle to the Ephesians, with Annotations and Commentary by Dr. Milne. (The only part of the commentary completed. The author died soon after the publishing of this work.)   1 vol.   Malacca, 1825.

164   大全童子往來百家通

Ta ts'euen t'ung tsze wang lae pih kea t'ung. Japanese Manual of Useful Knowledge for Youths, including the history of writing and the mode of acquiring the art.   1 vol.

165   永代節用無盡藏

Yung tae tsëë yung woo tsin tsang. A Japanese Treasury of Useful Knowledge for Daily Reference. Profusely illustrated with maps and woodcuts, descriptive of the geography, imperial residences, cities,

E

Buddhist mythology, chronology, social life, industrial implements, etc., of the country.

1 vol.   Imperfect.

166   中 外 理 辨

Chung wae le pëen. A tract in the Shang hai dialect, containing a discussion on doctrine between a Christian and a follower of Confucius.   1 vol.   No date.

167   要 理 推 原

Yaou le t'ui yuen. Important Doctrines investigated to their Source. A tract by Rev. R. H. Cobbold, formerly of the Church Missionary Society at Ningpo. 1 vol.   1853.

168   國 色 天 香

Kwŏ sih t'ëen heang.   A novel, of which the scene is laid in the time of the Mongoliau conquest of China. It is written in the learned style, half in verse and half in prose. By Yang ch'un tsze.   5 vols.

169   約 翰 傳 福 音 書

Yoh han ch'wen fuh yin shoo.   Gospel of John, translated into the Fuh chow dialect.   By Dr. Weldon. 1 vol.

170   西 湖 佳 話

Se hoo kiai hwa.   Good Words on the West Lake.

The West Lake is the celebrated See hoo, near the city of Hang cheu. This book is a guide to it, and contains the legends attached to the various localities.

4 vols.   New edition, 1817.

171   秘 傳 花 鏡

Pe ch'wen hwa king.   The Secretly-communicated Mirror of Flowers. A Japanese edition of a Chinese treatise on horticulture and arboriculture, with a supplement on zoology. (Japanese words are interspersed to help in reading.)   By Ch'in haou tsze.   6 vols. Date of Preface, 1688.

172   四 書 姓 氏 題 文

Sze shoo sing she t'e wen.   Essays on Mottoes taken from the Four Books, with the names of the authors. By Chaou tang keih.   Preface dated 1775.

173   註 釋 紅 樓 夢 賦

Choo shih hung low meng foo.   The Dream of the Red Chamber versified in twenty cantos, with explanatory notes.   By Ch'en tsing she.   1 vol.   Written, 1809.   Printed, 1846.

174   六 經 圖 說

Luh king t'oo shwo.   Maps and Diagrams illustrative of the Classics.

Contents :—Map of the constellations.   Ancient Chinese geography, as shewn by a map for B.C. 1100, for B.C. 700, and for B.C. 300.   Succession of philosophers from Fu he to Choo he.   Genealogy of Confucius. Numerical diagrams.   Ancient temples and altars. Plan of the Palace.   Music.   Agriculture.

1 vol.   Title wanting.

175

Introduction to the Study of Old Chinese Writing, with Examples.   Wanting title and date.

176   大 日 本 輿 地 便 覽

Ta jih pen yü te pëen lan.   Japanese Atlas. It contains nearly 100 maps, representing all the territorial divisions of the empire.   By Chai t'eng keen.   2 vols. (Fifth year of Tien pau.)

177   唐 詩 排 律 金 針 定 法

T'ang she p'ae leuh kin chin ting fa.   Guide to the Versification of T'ang Poetry.   By Le wen lin.   2 vols. Preface dated 1749.

178   創 世 傳 註 釋

Ch'wang she ch'wen choo shih.   Commentary on the Book of Genesis.   By W. Dean, D.D., American Baptist Missionary.   1 vol.   Hong kong, 1850.

179   瀛 環 志 畧

Ying hwan che leŏ.   Brief Account of the Oceanic Circle, that is, an Abridged Treatise on Universal Geography.   By Seu Ke yu, late President of the Imperial College in Peking for foreign languages and sciences.   He gives rough maps, brief sketches of foreign history and information derived from personal acquaintance with Dr. Abeel, an American Missionary at Amoy.   6 vols.   1848.

180   十 五 音

Sip ngo yin. 'The Fifteen Sounds.' Native dictionary of the Amoy dialect.

In this dictionary the words of the language are

arranged according to the Amoy pronunciation and tones, with brief meanings.

6 vols.　Preface dated 1820.

181　　全體新論

Ts'euen t'e sin-lun.　A New Treatise on Anatomy and Physiology.　Illustrated with engravings.　By Benjamin Hobson, M.B., Canton.　Medical Missionary. 1 vol.　1850.

182　　全體新論

Ts'euen t'e sin-lun.　A Treatise on Anatomy and Physiology, in Chinese, with vocabulary, and illustrated with engravings.　By Benjamin Hobson, M.B.　1 vol. Shanghae, 1858.

183

Ya-su dao-li.　The Doctrines of Jesus, in the local dialect of Ningpo, printed in Roman type.　By Bishop (then Rev. W. A.) Russell, Ningpo.　Missionary of the Church Missionary Society.　1 vol.

184　日月刻度通書

Jih yuě k'ih too t'ung shoo.　Almanac for 1845, with the times of sunrise and sunset, and of the moon rising and setting.

Contains tracts on religion, geography, and astronomy, a Sunday calendar, tabular statement of the import of opium into China, and an urgent entreaty to avoid opium smoking.

1 vol.　1845.

185

Di-li-shu.　A Work on Geography.　In the dialect of Ningpo, and printed with Roman letters.　It was drawn up by the missionaries of the Church Missionary Society resident in Ningpo, and printed for the use of those few native Chinese who have learned the use of the Roman alphabet and also for the children in their schools.　Ningpo, 1852.

186　　天文畧論

T'een wăn leŏ lun.　The Outlines of Astronomy (with lithographed plates).　By Benjamin Hobson, M.B., Medical Missionary, Canton.　1 vol.　29th of Taou Kwang, 1849.

187　古今萬國綱鑑

Koo kin wan kwŏ kang këen.　The Ancient and

Modern History of all Nations.　By C. Gutzlaff.　1 vol. Singapore, 1838.

188　　聖會禱詞

Shing hwuy taou ts'ze.　The English Book of Common Prayer, translated in an abridged form into Chinese. By C. Gutzlaff.

189　改正日本輿地路程全圖

Kae ching Jih pen yü te loo ch'ing ts'euen t'oo.　Corrected Map of the whole Japanese Empire, with the principal roads.　A folded map, coloured.

190　耶穌教要理答問

Ye-su kiau-yau-li tă măn.　Catechism on the Chief Doctrines of the Religion of Jesus.　By Dr. Happer. 1 vol.　Canton, 1850.

191　　蹶張心法

Kwei-chang-sin-fă.　Treatise on the Construction and Use of the Cross-bow, the Sword, and the Spear.　By Ch'ing chung tow.

While fire-arms have become all-important in war, the author believes that the construction and use of the old arms must still be carefully attended to.

1 vol.　Illustrated with woodcuts.　1842.

192　　樂府菁華

Yo foo ts'ing hwa.　A Collection of Extracts from Plays, in six chapters.　1 vol.　Printed in 1608.

193　　新遺詔書

Sin e chaou shoo.　The Books of the New Testament. Translated by Dr. Morrison.　4 vols.　Printed at Malacca.

194　　新遺詔書

Sin e chaou shoo.　Translation in Chinese of the New Testament.　By C. Gutzlaff.　1 vol.　Hong kong, 1850.

195　　三字經

San tsze king.　The Three-character Classic.　A primary book in Christian theology for schools.　The lines consist of three words throughout.　1 vol.　Hong kong, 1843.

196   創 世 傳 註 釋

Ch'wang she ch'wen choo shih. Genesis with Explanatory Notes. By W. Dean, D.D. 1 vol. Hong kong, 1850.

197   太 平 條 規

T'ae p'ing t'eaou kwei. Rules to be Observed by the T'ae p'ing Soldiers and Officers. 1 vol. 1852.

198   幼 學 詩

Yow heŏ she. Instruction in Verse for the Young. A compendium of instruction in Christianity as held by the T'ae p'ing rebels, in lines of five words each. 1 vol. 1851.

199   太 平 救 世 歌

T'ae p'ing kew she ko. Song of the Salvation of the World by the (Founding of the) T'ae p'ing Dynasty. By Hung sew ts'euen. An address to the T'ae p'ing army precedes the song. 1 vol.

200 天 父 上 帝 言 題 皇 詔

T'ëen foo Shang Te yen t'e hwang chaou. A Poetical Composition by Hung sew ts'euen, the T'ae p'ing chief. It is an address to the people, bidding them rejoice in the favour of the Heavenly Father, and act virtuously in the hope of heaven. It contains conceits founded on the names of himself and Yang sew ts'ing, his principal follower. 1 vol. 1851.

201 舊 遺 詔 書 靡 西 五 經

Kew e chaou shoo Mose woo king. Five Books of Moses. Ningpo, 1846.

202   舊 遺 詔 書

Kew e chaou shoo. The Old Testament. This volume contains only the Pentateuch, consisting of

創 世 傳   出 麥 西

Genesis,   *Exodus,*

etc. etc. Ningpo Presbyterian Press. 1846.

203   以 賽 亞 天 啓 錄

E sae ya t'ëen k'e luh. The Book of the Prophet Isaiah. Translated by C. Gutzlaff. 1 vol. No date.

204   舊 遺 詔 聖 書

Kew e chaou shing shoo. The Holy Books of the Old Testament. Translated by C. Gutzlaff. 4 vols. Reprinted in Hong kong, 1850.

205 馬 太 傳 福 音 書

Ma t'ae ch'wen fuh yin shoo. Gospel according to St. Matthew. Singapore, 1836.

206 約 翰 傳 福 音 書

Yoh han ch'wen fuh yin shoo. The Gospel according to St. John, in Chinese. By Dr. Medhurst ? 1 vol. No date.

207 差 徒 保 羅 寄 哥 林 多 人 書

Ch'ai-t'oo Paou-lo ke Ko-lin-to jin shoo. The First and Second Epistles of St. Paul to the Corinthians. Translated into Chinese by W. H. Medhurst, D.D. 1 vol.

208 馬 太 傳 福 音 書 註 釋

Ma t'ae ch'wen fuh yin shoo choo shih. The Gospel according to Matthew, in Chinese, with Explanatory Notes. By W. Dean, D.D. 1 vol. Hong kong, 1848.

209   祈 禱 文 式

K'e taou wen shih. Translation into Chinese of the English Book of Common Prayer. By R. Morrison, D.D. 1 vol. 1828.

210   聖 會 禱 詞

Shing hwei taou ts'ze. The English Book of Common Prayer, translated into Chinese. By C. Gutzlaff. 1 vol. No date.

211 耶 穌 聖 教 洗 禮 規 式

Yay soo shing keaou se le kwei she. Order of Christian Baptism. From the Book of Common Prayer. 1 vol. St. Paul's College, Hong kong, 1851.

212   聖 會 禱 詞

Shing hwei taou ts'ze. The Book of Common Prayer (of the Church of England), translated into Chinese. By C. Gutzlaff. 1845-1848.

213   証 道 問 答

Ching taou wǎn ta. Catechism of the Evidences of

Christianity. Issued at St. Paul's College, Hong kong. 1 vol. 3 copies.

214 續纂省身神詩

Suh ts'wan sing shin shin she. A Supplemental Hymn Book for Devotional Use. Printed at Malacca, Anglo-Chinese College, 1835.

215 講法律以儆愚頑

Keang fa leuh yi king yü wan. Discourse on the Laws to Warn the Stupidly Obstinate. A tract consisting of a section of the Mandarin colloquial sacred edict of Kang he on public morals. Issued by St. Paul's College, Hong kong. 1 vol.

216 教條

Theological Lectures by C. Gutzlaff. On the chief doctrines of Christianity. 1 vol. Hong kong, 1848-1850.

217 贖罪之道傳

Shŭh tsuy che taou chwen. The Doctrine of the Remission of Sins illustrated in a Series of Conversations. By a Chinese convert. The scene is laid in the Ming dynasty. Published under the direction of Dr. Gutzlaff. 1 vol. 1836.

218 天鏡明鑑

T'ëen king ming këen. The Bright Mirror of Heavenly Revelation. A brief system of Scriptural theology. By W. Milne, D.D. 1 vol. Malacca, 1826.

219 眞神天皇十誡

Chin-shin t'ëen hwang shih keae. Sermons on the Ten Commandments of the True God. Dr. Milne (?). Malacca. First vol. wanting.

220 論靡西之來歷

Lun Mose che lae leih. Birth and Acts of Moses. A section of *Shing king she ke*, a work on Scripture History. 1 vol. Shang hae, 1846.

221 神道篇

Shin taou p'ëen. A Primary Book in Christian Theology for Schools. Each line consists of three characters. Probably by Rev. A. P. Happer. 1 vol. 1851.

222 家寶全集

Kea paou ts'euen tseih. Complete Family Treasure. A work in colloquial Chinese, consisting of moral instructions. It is in four parts:—

1. Eight vols. Happiness and old age the reward of virtue.
2. (Wanting.) Self-government and the regulation of the family.
3. Four vols. Watchfulness and intelligence.
4. Six vols. (First three wanting.) On pleasure.

By Shih ch'ing kin of Yang chow. Preface dated 1729. In 15 vols.

223 綠牡丹

Luh maou tan. The Green Peony. Scene laid in the time of the Emperor T'ae tsung, A.D. 631 to 654. 1 vol. Imperfect copy.

224 家寶初集

Kea paou ch'oo tseih. First Fasciculus of the Family Treasure. Seventh chapter. An odd vol.

225 荔鏡奇逢集

Le king k'e fung tseih. A novel, of which the scene is laid in Southern Fuh këen. Adapted for Tie chiu and Amoy readers. 2 vols. 1814.

226 遊江南傳

Yew keang nan chwen. Record of a Journey to Keang nan. This is a novel founded on the *incognito* journey of the Emperor Ching teih (about A.D. 1500) to the province of Keang nan. An odd vol. 1832.

227 妤逑傳

Haou k'ew chwen. The Fortunate Union. A popular novel. 5 vols. The first is wanting.

228 西遊記

Se yew ke. Record of Western Travels. A novel, founded on the journey of Heuen Tsang to India in the 7th century. Vol. the first.

229 綱鑑易知錄

Kang këen e che luh. Abridgment of the Mirror of History. An odd vol. It records the events of the first

F

two reigns of the Han dynasty, and contains the 9th, 10th, and 11th sections of the complete work. 1 vol.

230

Two rolls by a Chinese water-colour painter, representing a funeral procession :—Document of honour. Lanthorns bearing titles. Streamers. Cymbals. Tablet in shrine. Horn-blowers. Umbrella of state. Offering preceding portrait. Musicians. Portrait in shrine. Mourners in white. Buddhist priests. Coffin borne by eight. Eldest son and other mourners. Musicians. Mourners in white. Torch-bearers. Baskets of paper to burn. More Buddhist priests. The wife. Household furniture. Provisions. Representations of the judges of the dead. Lanthorns.

231　綱鑑甲子圖

Kang këen keă tsze t'oo. Chart of the Emperors of China. From B.C. 424 to A.D. 1705. Arranged in 36 columns of 60 squares each, a square representing a year. Mounted on Chinese yellow grass cloth. 1705.

232

A Chinese Marriage Procession, drawn in water-colours by a native artist.

233

A Chinese Drawing in ink of Buddhist Figures. About thirty monks and Arhats, old and young, are represented in the possession of happiness and victory. A roll.

234

Battle of the Gods. Painted in water-colours by a Chinese artist. The phœnix, dragon, lion, and various sea monsters spoken of in the animal fables of the Chinese are ridden upon by the combatants.

235　四書正文

Sze-shoo-ching-wăn. The Text of the Four Books, with marginal notes. Copied from the text printed in Peking with movable metallic types. The Four Books were fixed on in the Sung dynasty :—

1. The *Ta-heŏ*, i. e. The Great Instruction.
2. The *Chung-yung*, i. e. The Invariable Mean ; vol. i.
3. The *Shang-măng* and *Hea-măng*, i. e. Works of Mencius ; vols. ii, iii.
4. The *Shang Lun* and *Hea Lun*, i. e. Discourses of Confucius ; vols. iv, v.

5 vols. 1842.

236　意拾秘傳

E shih pe chwen. Esop's Fables. Translated into Chinese by Robert Thom. Four parts.

This copy contains 77 fables, beginning with the Wolf and the Lamb, and ending with the Thunny and Dolphin. Life of Esop and Preface in the fourth part. 4 vols. Canton, 1838.

237　英華通用雜話

Hwa ying t'ung yung tsă hwa. Chinese and English Vocabulary, by the late Robert Thom, Esq., H. B. M. Consul at Ningpo. First Part. The Second Part was never published. Canton, 1843.

238　聖經史記
**　　論若瑟之來歷**

Shing king she ke. Lun Jo sih che lae leih. History of Joseph. (Extracted from a larger work called) Sacred History. Translated by W. H. Medhurst, D.D. 1 vol. Bound with Thom's Chinese and English Vocabulary. Shanghai, 1846.

239　致富新書

Che foo sin shoo. New Work on Political Economy, by a Chinese Student, educated in English at the Morrison Institution, Hong kong. It is a translation of a small work on Political Economy by Dr. Vickars, U.S.A. 1 vol. Hong kong, 1847.

240　正音撮要

Ching yin tsŏ yaou. The Chinese Speaker, or Extracts from works written in the Mandarin Language as spoken at Peking. Part I. By Robert Thom, H.B.M. Consul at Ningpo. 1 vol. Part II never published. Ningpo, 1846.

241　幾何原本

Ke ho yuen pŭn. Euclid's Principles of Geometry. First six books. Translated into Chinese by Matteo Ricci and the Ming dynasty statesman Seu kwang k'e. First printed 1607. Seu adds in a prefatory note to this edition, that after Ricci's death in 1610, he went over the whole work again with two other European missionaries in preparing this edition. 4 vols. in MS.

242 農政全書

Nung ching ts'euen shoo. Complete Book on Agriculture. This copious work, by Seu kwang k'e, the translator of Euclid, and convert of Ricci, treats, in 60 chapters, of the works of 64 former writers on the subject, of land proprietorship, methods of cultivation, agricultural calendar, irrigation, European methods of irrigation, implements, grain, vegetables, flowers, fruit trees, production of silk, the mulberry, hemp, trees, domestic animals, and all kinds of edible plants. Preface dated 1639. 24 vols. Reprinted, 1843.

243 神仙通鑑

Shin sëen t'ung këen. Complete History of the Gods and Genii. By Seu taou. A mythological romance, introducing the most celebrated Buddhist and Taouist personages in a connected order. 22 vols. Preface dated 1678.

244 數理精蘊表

Shoo le tsing yün peaou. Tables contained in the work called *Shoo le tsing yün*, 'Profound Principles of Numbers.' The work itself is wanting.

These tables are logarithmic and trigonometrical. 8 vols. Published in the reign of Kang he.

245 歷象考成表

Leih sëang k'aou ch'ing peaou. Tables to the work *Leih sëang k'aou ch'ing*, 'Treatise on Astronomy.' The work itself is wanting.

Tables of the daily motion of the sun, moon, and planets, of refraction, and of the places of the fixed stars, are here found. From European tables. 8 vols. Published in the reign of Kang he.

246 歷象考成後編

Leih sëang k'aou ch'ing how pëen. Supplement to the work called *Leih sëang k'aou ch'ing*, 'Treatise on Astronomy.'

The European missionary who translated this work calls himself Tae tsin hëen. He was the first Jesuit at Peking who taught the astronomy of Kepler and Tycho Brahe. The work contains chapters on the ellipse and on eclipses, with solar and lunar tables.

The Emperor Yung ching authorised the preparation of the book in 1730. 7 vols. Printed, 1742.

247 周易注疏

Chow yih choo shoo. Book of Changes, with double comment. Wei comment by Wang pih. T'ang comment by K'ung ying ta. Sound and meaning of words fixed by Luh teih ming.

The 1st volume contains the title to thirteen works, of which this is the 1st, and which in the Sung dynasty received the name *Shih san king*, 'The Thirteen Classics,' and were then published with a continuous double comment. The present and twelve following it are copies from the edition recently published at Canton by the Judge and Commissioner of Salt, Chung k'ëen keün.

5 vols. Reprinted, Canton, 1871.

248 尚書注疏

Shang shoo choo shoo. Book of History, with double comment. Han comment by K'ung ngan kwŏ. T'ang comment by K'ung ying ta. Pronunciation and meaning of words fixed by Luh teih ming. 8 vols. Reprinted, Canton, 1871.

249 毛詩注疏

Maou she choo shoo. Book of Odes, with double comment. Han comment by Ching k'ang ch'ing. T'ang comment by K'ung ying ta. Pronunciation and meaning of words fixed by Luh teih ming. 14 vols. Reprinted, Canton, 1871.

250 禮記注疏

Le ke choo shoo. Book of Rites, with double comment. Han comment of Ching k'ang ch'ing. T'ang comment of K'ung ying ta. Pronunciation and meaning of words fixed by Luh teih ming. 20 vols. Reprinted, Canton, 1871.

251 周禮注疏

Chow le choo shoo. Ritual of Chow, with double comment. Han comment by Ching k'ang ch'ing. T'ang comment by Kea kung yen. Pronunciation fixed by Luh teih ming. 14 vols. Reprinted, Canton, 1871.

252 儀禮註疏

E le choo shoo. Book of Customs and Rites, with double comment. Han comment by Ching k'ang ch'ing. T'ang comment by Kea kung yen. Pronunciation and meaning of words fixed by Luh teih ming. 10 vols. Reprinted, Canton, 1871.

253 春秋左傳註疏

Ch'un ts'ew Tso chwen choo shoo. The Spring and Autumn Annals by Confucius, with the Supplemental History of Tso k'ew ming and a double comment. Tsin comment by Too yuen k'ae. T'ang comment by K'ung ying ta. Pronunciation and meaning of words fixed by Luh teih ming. 20 vols. Reprinted, Canton, 1871.

254 公羊註疏

Kung yang choo shoo. Supplemental History of K'ung yang to the Spring and Autumn Annals of Confucius, with double comment. Han comment by Ho hew. T'ang comment by some unknown scholar. Words pronounced aud explained by Luh teih ming. 8 vols. Reprinted, Canton, 1871.

255 穀粱註疏

Kuh leang choo shoo. Kuh leang's Supplemental History to the Spring and Autumn Annals of Confucius, with double comment. Tsin comment by Fan ning. T'ang comment by Yang she keuen. Sound and meaning of words fixed by Luh teih ming. 6 vols. Reprinted, Canton, 1871.

256 論語註疏

Lun yü choo shoo. Discourses of Confucius, with double comment. Wei comment by Ho yen. Sung comment by Hing ping. Sound and meaning of words settled by Luh teih ming. 4 vols. Reprinted, Canton, 1871.

257 孟子註疏

Măng tsze choo shoo. Works of Mencius, with double comment. Han comment by Chaou ke. Sung comment by Sun peih. 6 vols. Reprinted, Canton, 1871.

258 爾雅註疏

Urh ya choo shoo. The *Urh ya*, a Dictionary of Rare Words in the Classics, with double comment. Tsin comment by Kwo p'uh. Sung comment by Hing ping.

Spelling and meaning of words fixed by Luh teih ming. 4 vols. Reprinted, Canton, 1871.

259 孝經註疏

Heaou king choo shoo. Book of Filial Piety, with double comment. T'ang comment by the Emperor T'ang ming hwang. Sung comment by Hing ping. Sounds and meanings of words fixed by Luh teih ming. 1 vol. Reprinted, Canton, 1871.

260

Yue hae kwan shuy hwo hëang tsih le. A Catalogue in Chinese and Portuguese of Articles liable to Duty at the Canton Custom-house, with a short description of them and the duties chargeable. In 3 volumes.

261 醫學入門外集

E heŏ juh mun wae tseih. Introduction to Medicine. Second Part. Third and fifth chapters only. (From the library of Archbishop Laud, Chancellor of the University. Dated 1635.) 2 vols.

262

E heŏ juh mun wae tseih. Duplicate of 261.

263 醫方考

E fang k'aou. Inquiry into Medical Methods of Cure. By Woo kwun of Hwuy chow. Imperfect copy. 1 vol.

264 藥性雷公炮製

Yŏ sing luy kung p'aou che. A Medical Book, published under the direction of the Imperial Board of Physicians. 4 vols., containing chapters 1, 2, 4, 5, 7, 8. By Yü joo he. Presented by Owen Woodde, Dean of Armagh, and others. Printed a second time, 1588.

265

Yŏ sing luy kung p'aou che. Same work as the preceding (264). First volume only. Reprinted, 1532.

266 丹溪心法附餘

Tan he sin fă foo yü. Work on Medicine, in 24 chapters, and an introduction. Chapters 8, 9, 10, 12–17, 20, 21 are missing. By Fang kwang. 8 vols. Printed, 1535.

267

Tan he sin fǎ foo yü. Duplicate of the preceding (266). 3 vols. only, containing the introductory chapter and chapters 1, 5, 6, 7. Printed, 1535.

268 小兒良方

Seaou urh leang fang. Medical Prescriptions for Children's Diseases. An imperfect volume.

269 大明中興永曆二十五年大統曆

Ta ming chung hing yung leih urh shih woo nëen ta t'ung leih. Calendar for the 25th year of Yung leih of the Great Ming Dynasty.

Calendar for the year 1671. Yellow silk title-page. Published by the representative of the Ming dynasty in the 10th year of the Tartar Emperor K'ang he. Probably a calendar of the great rebel Woo san kwei. *Yung leih* is the title of the reign. *Ta t'ung* is the title of the calendar used in the Ming dynasty. Gift of H. Aldrich, Dean of Christ Church, 1671.

270

Ta ming chung hing yung leih urh shih woo nëen ta t'ung leih. Calendar of the descendant of the Ming Imperial Family for the year 1671. Duplicate copy. Presented by R. Boyle, 1671 (?).

271 萬斛明珠

Wan huh ming choo. Guide to Fortune-telling, Social Ceremonies, Official Ranks, the Calendar, Costumes of Various Nations, etc. The 4th, 5th, and 6th chapters only. 1 vol.

272 福曜翔世

Fuh yaou sëang she. Star of Happiness descending on the World. A calendar published at Canton for the 10th year of K'ang he, A.D. 1671. By Ch'in leang tseun. 1 vol. Canton, 1671.

273 都名所圖會

Too ming so t'oo hwuy. Views of Celebrated Places in Kioto, the capital of Japan and residence, till 1868, of the Mikado.

Brought from Japan by Thunberg, Professor at Upsal.

A written account of the book, translated from Swedish, is appended to this copy.

After the view of the palace follow Buddhist and Shinto temples, followed by the amusements of the people. 6 vols.

274 地理考索

Te le k'aou sǒ. Treatise on Geomancy. By Le kwang heüh. Teaches the principles of Chinese geomancy (Feng shuy), the use of the geomancer's compass, planetary influences, contour of the ground, and the influence of water. Only the first volume is here. Printed, 1803.

275

Hwa ying t'ung yung tsa hwa. Chinese and English Vocabulary. Part I. By R. Thom, H. B. M. Consul at Ningpo. Duplicate copy.

276 各國消息

Kǒ kwǒ seaou seih. News of all Nations. Two monthly numbers of a newspaper formerly published by Dr. Gutzlaff. 9th and 10th months of 1838. 2 vols. Lithographed at Canton, 1838.

277 法帖

Fǎ t'ëěh. Copies for Writing, from Wang he che. They consist of rubbings from stone inscriptions in the ordinary writing-hand and in the grass character or running-hand. The most famous is the *Lan t'ing seu* of Wang he che, the founder of modern writing, A.D. 350. See the sheet which begins 永和九年 on the second line from the right.

278

Map of China. Made in the reign of K'ang he, 1739. A rough and common map. One large sheet, mounted on cotton cloth. Cut on wood, 1739.

279

A Japanese Proclamation. This is a roll of thick mulberry-bark paper.

280 大方廣佛華嚴經

Ta fang kwang fuh hwa yen king. The *Hwa yen*

G

king. Translated by a Buddhist priest, named Jit'a-nanda, a native of Khoten. The 31st chapter only.

The introductory picture represents Buddha instructing his disciples. Engraved at the expense of a native of Shaou Hing, A.D. 1418. Printed, 1418. 1 vol.

281 大般若波羅蜜多經

Ta po jo po lo meih to king. Maha Pradjña Paramita Sutra. Translated by Heuen tsang, the traveller who visited India in the 7th century.

This edition was engraved at Peking, partly in A.D. 1560 and partly also in 1583, at the expense of the empress at that date. Imperfect copy of chapters 53 to 60. 10 vols. and fragments. Peking, 1583.

282 四書白文三卷

Sze shoo pĭh wăn san keuen. Third Chapter of the Text of the Four Books.

In this volume four copies of the third chapter of the *Lun yü* of Confucius are sewed together.

A specimen of the school books used at Peking in the Ming dynasty. 1 vol.

283 醫學入門內集

E heŏ juh mun nuy tseih. Introduction to Medicine. First Part. First volume only. Imperfect.

284 三字經

San tsze king. The Three-character Classic. A child's first book. Duplicate copy. 1 vol.

285

A Volume of Chinese Cards, containing: A list of presents, including a live cow and pig, with various provisions. A Hoppo's document to the English ship 'Flora,' to protect the merchants belonging to her from trouble on shore through interference of the military. There are also various documents in Arabic writing. 1 vol. Date 1686.

286 讀禮通考

Tuh le t'ung k'aou. Complete Introduction to the Study of the Ceremonial Codes. By Seu k'ëen, A.D. 1695. In 120 chapters. Full discussion of ancient and modern precedents in regard to mourning and burial. In 16 vols.

287 五禮通考

Woo le t'ung k'aou. Complete Review of the Five Classes of Ceremonies. By Ts'in hwuy t'ëen, A.D. 1762. In 262 chapters. A work on sacrifices and domestic and social usages, treated archæologically and historically. In 64 vols.

288 國史畧

Kwŏ she leŏ. Abridged History of Japan. By a Japanese author, Sung meaou. 5 vols.

289 聖蹟圖

Shing tseih t'oo. Drawings illustrative of the Life of the Sage.

In front of this pictorial life of Confucius is printed, as a preface, the *Shing t'oo tëen ke*, 'Record of the Hall of Holy Pictures.' In that hall, at the back of the temple of Confucius in K'euh foo, his native city, the 112 scenes of this collection are engraved on stones set up in the walls. 1 vol.

290 朱子家禮

Choo tsze kea le. Code of Family Ceremonies by Choo foo tsze. By Choo he, of the Sung dynasty. A guide for family use in regard to ceremonies on attaining manhood, marriage, funerals, and sacrifices. Preface by Wang këen, editor of this modern edition, dated A.D. 1701. 4 vols.

291 歷代帝王年表

Leih tae te wang nëen peaou. Chronological Tables of the Emperors and Kings. By Ts'e chaou nan, A.D. 1777. Printed, 1824. 4 vols.

292 皇朝輿地畧

Hwang ch'aou yü te leo. Abridged Geography of the Empire. With maps of the provinces, drawn by Yen teih che. Printed, 1831. Maps printed 1834. 1 vol.

293 天路歷程官話

T'ëen loo leih ch'ing kwan hwa. The Pilgrim's Progress in the Mandarin Tongue. Translated into Chinese by Rev. W. C. Burns, M.A., in 1864. 1 vol.

294 續天路歷程官話

Suh t'ëen loo leih ch'ing kwan hwa. Supplement to the Pilgrim's Progress in the Mandarin Tongue. Second Part of the Pilgrim's Progress. Translated by Rev. W. C. Burns, M.A., in 1865. 1 vol.

295 康熙字典

K'ang he tsze tëen. Dictionary of K'ang he. Preface dated 1717.

This dictionary is the most useful of recent lexicographical works, and is arranged according to radicals. This copy printed 1827. 40 vols.

296 正道啓蒙

Ch'ing taou k'e mung. Introduction to the Correct Doctrine. The 'Peep of Day,' translated into Chinese by Rev. W. C. Burns, M.A., in 1863. 1 vol.

297

Arigon soragagoli yin asagoho uchihu bichig. Catechism of Christian Doctrine. Translated into Mongolian in 1865 by J. Edkins and a Mongol scribe. 1 vol.

298 聖教問答

Shing keaou wăn tă. Catechism of Christian Doctrine in Chinese. Printed in Peking, 1868. 1 vol.

299

Ch'agan Dara Ehe Orosiba. Relation of the White Dara Ehe, i. e. Mother Dara. A Buddhist work in Mongolian. Printed in Peking.

A Catalogue of Japanese and Chinese Books and Manuscripts Lately Added to the Bodleian Library

博德利图书馆新入藏中、日文刻本与写本目录

A

CATALOGUE

OF

JAPANESE AND CHINESE

BOOKS AND MANUSCRIPTS

LATELY ADDED TO THE

BODLEIAN LIBRARY

PREPARED BY

BUNYIU NANJIO

PRIEST OF THE MONASTERY, EASTERN HONGWANZI, JAPAN

1. A COLLECTION MADE BY MR. A. WYLIE IN JAPAN, AND BOUGHT BY THE CURATORS OF THE BODLEIAN LIBRARY IN 1881.

2. A COLLECTION PRESENTED BY THE JAPANESE GOVERNMENT TO MR. S. AMOS.

3. A COLLECTION MADE BY PROFESSOR MAX MÜLLER, AND PRESENTED BY HIM TO THE BODLEIAN LIBRARY.

AT THE CLARENDON PRESS

MDCCCLXXXI

MR. WYLIE'S COLLECTION.

THERE are thirty-seven different works in this collection, which may be divided into the following eight classes :—

1. Chinese translations of the Sûtras and transliterations of the Dhâranîs and Mantras. Nos. 1–5 : 5 vols.
2. Chinese-Sanskrit-Japanese vocabularies. Nos. 6, 7 : 2 vols.
3. Works on the Siddha or the Sanskrit alphabet. Nos. 8–26 : 53 vols. (56 fasciculi).
4. Collection of the Vîgas or the mystical letters or syllables and of invocations. Nos. 27–32 : 9 vols.
5. Works on the Mudrâs or certain positions or intertwinings of the fingers during prayers, blessings, etc. Nos. 33, 34 : 3 vols.
6. A commentary on a Chinese work. No. 35 : 9 vols.
7. A collection of miscellaneous treatises. No. 36 : 10 vols.
8. An explanation of the Sanskrit text of the Pragñâpâramitâhridaya-sûtra. No. 37 : 1 vol.

NOTE—The pronunciation of the Chinese characters given in this list is chiefly that which is known in Japan as the Gŏ-ŏn (呉 音), or the sound of the Kingdom of Gŏ, i. e. Wu, one of the Three Kingdoms in China (A. D. 222–280)[1].

EXPLANATION OF TRANSLITERATION OF THE JAPANESE SOUNDS.

a	as in	father.	g	as j in	jag.
e	„	men.	k	as in	king.
i	„	pin.	k	as ch in	church.
o	„	long.	sh	as in	shall.
u	„	put.	ts	„	sits.
dz	„	adze.	z	as z in	azure.
g	„	gag.			

The sounds of the other consonants, viz. b, d, f, h, m, n, p, r, s, t, w, y, and z, do not differ from their common English sounds.

---

[1] Cf. Hepburn's Japanese-English and English-Japanese Dictionary, p. v; Wells Williams' Syllabic Dictionary of the Chinese Language, p. xxxv, col. 1.

A 2

CLASS I.

Chinese Translations of the Sûtras and Transliterations of the Dhâranîs and Mantras.

1   金 剛 般 若 經

Kon-gô-han-nya-kio, or the Va*grakkh*edikâpra*gñâ*-pâramitâ-sûtra[1]. Translated by Kumâra*ĝi*va, about A.D. 401. Published at Yedo (Tôkio) in 1851. The preface, dated 1756, was written by a Japanese priest named Menzan, the first editor of this Sûtra in a small size. Next to the preface, there is a Gâthâ, written on a tablet, with a lotus-leaf on the top, and the flower at the bottom, in the Chinese seal characters; the common style of the characters is as follows:—

無 上 甚 深 微 妙 法
百 千 萬 劫 難 遭 遇
我 今 見 聞 得 受 持
願 解 如 來 眞 實 義

'The highest and most deep and subtle law
 Is difficult to be met with in hundred-thousand-ten-
     thousand-Kalpas;
 (Which) I am now able to see and hear, receive
     and hold,
 (So that) I wish to understand the true meaning of
     the Tathâgata' (Buddha).

This Gâthâ is called the Kai-kio-ge, or the Gâthâ for opening a Sûtra, i.e. it is to be recited by a reader as a prayer, before he begins to read the Sûtra.

Kumâra*ĝi*va's version is divided into 32 parts, each having a different title. This division is said to have been made by the heir-apparent (died A.D. 531) of Wu-ti, the first Emperor of the Liang dynasty in China (reigned 502–549). (See a commentary on this version by two Chinese priests, of the Ming dynasty, compiled in A.D. 1378[2].)

After the version, there is a short Mantra which is followed by two Chinese stories, the one concerning the Mantra, and the other the Sûtra.

Throughout the whole book, some marks are added on both sides of columns, which are called Kun-ten, or the marks made in translating a Chinese composition,

to show the order in which the characters must be rendered to suit the Japanese idiom.

The Sanskrit text of the Va*grakkh*edikâ has been published in China (one copy of it is in the possession of Mr. Wylie), and in Tibet (see Catalogue of the Oriental MSS. of the Imperial Academy of Sciences at St. Petersburg). A critical edition of the text will be published by Professor Max Müller in the Anecdota Oxoniensia. See Nos. 54, 55.

2   觀 音 普 門 品

Kwannon (lit. Kwan-on)-fu-mon-bon, or the Avalokites*v*ara-samantamukhâdhyâya[1], the 25th (or 24th in the Sanskrit text) Chapter of the Saddharmapu*nd*arîka-sûtra[2]. The portion of prose was translated by Kumâra*ĝi*va (about 401); and that of Gâthâs, by G*ñâ*na-gupta and Dharmagupta, of the N. *K*eu dynasty (about 570). The latter portion is said to have been added to the former by Tsun-shih (*Z*unshiki, in Japanese), of the Sung dynasty (about 1000).

On the opposite side of the cover, there is a figure of Avalokites*v*ara, who sits on a rock, facing a waterfall (as generally understood). The version is divided into several parts, each having its descriptive title. Similar marks to those explained under No. 1 are given in this book throughout. At the end, there are six short Mantras.

This book was edited by a layman named Kumazawa Sôzayemon, of the province Musashi. The date of the publication is not mentioned.

3   增 補 諸 陀 羅 尼

Zô-ho-sho-da-ra-ni, or an increased collection of Dhâra*n*îs.

The editor's name and the date of the publication are not given. A transliteration in the Japanese Hiragana, or the cursive letters, is added on the right of the Chinese characters nearly through the whole book.

There is a list of contents on the opposite side of the cover, which is as follows:—

(1) 般 若 心 經 Han-nya-shin-gio, or the Ma-

---

[1] No. 10 of the Chinese Tripi*t*aka, in the India Office Library.
[2] No. 1615 of the Chinese Tripi*t*aka.

[1] No. 137 of the Chinese Tripi*t*aka. A French translation by Burnouf in Lotus de la Bonne Loi, pp. 261–268.
[2] No. 134 of the Chinese Tripi*t*aka.

hâpragñâpâramitâhridaya-sûtra[1], translated by Hiouen-thsang (Genzio, in Japanese), of the Thang dynasty (about 650). This Sûtra contains a short Mantra.

(2) 大 悲 咒 Dai-hi-shu, or the 'Mahâkârunikamantra.'

(3) 大 施 餓 鬼 Dai-se-ga-ki, or the 'Mahâdâna to the Pretas,' i. e. a collection of prayers and Mantras to be recited at the religious service in honour of the departed spirits (Ga-ki, lit. 'hungry demon').

(4) 尊 勝 陀 羅 尼 Son-shio-da-ra-ni, or the 'Sarvadurgatibuddhoshnîsha-dhâranî[2].'

(5) 消 災 陀 羅 尼 Shio-sai-da-ra-ni, or the 'Dhâranî of expelling a misfortune.'

(6) 佛 母 陀 羅 尼 Butsu-mo-da-ra-ni, or the 'Buddhamâtri-dhâranî.'

(7) 光 明 眞 言 Kô-mio-shin-gon, or the 'Prabhâmantra.'

(8) 隨 求 陀 羅 尼 Zui-gu-da-ra-ni, or the 'Yathâsaya-dhâranî.'

(9) 舍 利 禮 Sha-ri-rai, or a prayer for worshipping the Sarîra, or the relics of Sâkyamuni.

(10) 囘 向 Ye-kô, or a prayer.

(11) 十 三 佛 眞 言 Ziu-san-butsu-shin-gon, or the 'Mantras of 13 Buddhas,' who are as follow :—

(a) 不 動 Fu-dô, i. e. 'Akala' (a Mio-wô, lit. 'bright king,' i. e. Vidyâ-râga (?)).

(b) 釋 迦 Sha-ka, i. e. Sâkyamuni (Buddha).

(c) 文 殊 Mon-zu, i. e. Mañgusrî (Bodhisattva).

(d) 普 賢 Fu-gen, i. e. Samantabhadra (Bodhisattva).

(e) 地 藏 Gi-zô, i. e. Kshitigarbha (Bodhisattva).

(f) 彌 勒 Mi-roku, i. e. Maitreya (Bodhisattva).

(g) 藥 師 Yaku-shi, i. e. Bheshagyaguru (Buddha).

(h) 觀 音 Kwannon, i. e. Avalokitesvara (Bodhisattva).

(i) 勢 至 Sei-shi, i. e. Mahâsthânaprâpta (Bodhisattva).

(j) 彌 陀 Mi-da, i. e. Amitâyus or Amitâbha (Buddha).

(k) 阿 閦 A-shuku, i. e. Akshobhya (Buddha).

(l) 大 日 Dai-niki, i. e. Mahâvairokana (Buddha).

(m) 虛 空 藏 Ko-ku-zô, i. e. Âkâsagarbha (Bodhisattva).

Thus, there are in fact 5 Buddhas, 7 Bodhisattvas, and 1 Vidyârâga.

(12) 神 咒 Zin-shu, or the (three) spiritual Mantras. Written in the Sanskrit alphabet.

4   般 若 理 趣 經

Han-nya-ri-shu-kio, or the 'Pragñâpâramitâbuddhisûtra.' This is a Chapter of the 大 樂 金 剛 不 空 眞 實 三 昧 耶 經 or the 'Mahâsukhavagrâmoghasatyasamaya-sûtra[1],' translated by Amoghavagra (who died in A.D. 774), of the Thang dynasty. At the beginning and end of the book, some verses are added by the Japanese editor, whose name and the date of the publication are not mentioned.

5   佛 說 延 命 地 藏 經

Butsu-setsu-yen-mei-gi-zô-kio, or the 'Buddhavakanâyushvardha-Kshitigarbha-(bodhisattva)-sûtra.' Translated by the same as before. Published in Kioto in 1852. It contains the Chinese version, together with a transliteration in the Japanese Hiragana or the cursive letters on the right of columns, and the marks explained under No. 1, on the left.

On the opposite side of the cover, there is a figure of the Bodhisattva, who sits on the lotus seat, placed on a rock, having a staff, called Shaku-gio, the top of which is armed with (metal) rings[2], in the right hand, and a Mani in the left. A short Mantra is given above the figure.

---

[1] No. 20 of the Chinese Tripitaka. See below, No. 37.
[2] Nos. 348–352 etc. of the Chinese Tripitaka.

[1] No. 1034 of the Chinese Tripitaka.
[2] I. e. Khakkharam or Hikkala.—Eitel's Handbook, p. 56 a.
Cf. Professor Max Müller's Selected Essays, vol. ii. p. 370.

CLASS II.

CHINESE-SANSKRIT-JAPANESE VOCABULARIES.

6   梵唐千字文

Bon-tô-sen-zi-mon, or 'A thousand Sanskrit and Chinese words.' Published in Kioto in 1773. This is a Chinese vocabulary with Sanskrit equivalents and two transliterations, the one in Chinese, and the other in Japanese. There is a preface ascribed to I-tsing (Gizio, in Japanese), who left China for India in 671; in which preface he says that he arranged this vocabulary. There follows another preface, written by a Japanese priest named Zakumio in 1727, who was the first editor of this work in Japan. In his introduction he says, that 'it is stated in Annen's work that this vocabulary was first brought (from China) by Zikaku (who went to China in 838, and returned to Japan in 847).' This is the book which is mentioned by Professor Max Müller in his Selected Essays, vol. ii. pp. 367, 368. The original title of this vocabulary is 梵語千字文 Bon-go-sen-zi-mon, or 'A thousand Sanskrit words.'

7   梵語雜名

Bon-go-zatsu-mio, or a list of 'Miscellaneous Sanskrit names or words.' Published in 1732. This is a second Chinese-Sanskrit-Japanese vocabulary, being a copy of the same book which Dr. Edkins brought to Professor Max Müller some years ago, and is mentioned in the Selected Essays, vol. ii. p. 338. This was compiled by a priest of the country of Kwei-tsi (Kharakar, by Eitel—Handbook, p. 56 a), named Li-yen (Reigon, in Japanese); who seems to have lived in China in the period from A.D. 713 to 847. He had two official titles, viz. 1. 翻經大德 Hon-gio-tai-toku, or 'the great virtuous one (Bhadanta), who translates the Sûtras,' i. e. a translator; and 2. 翰林待詔 Kan-rin-tai-shio, or 'in the Han-lin (Kan-rin, in Japanese) waiting to be called.' It is said that there was an Institution called the Han-lin, founded about A.D. 713, under the Thang dynasty. Then, it is stated on the cover of this vocabulary that this was brought to Japan by Zikaku in 847. The Japanese editor Shingen gives a list of corrections of the text at the end of the book.

CLASS III.

WORKS ON THE SIDDHA OR THE SANSKRIT ALPHABET.

8   悉曇字母表

Shitsu-tan-zi-mo-hio, or 'a table of the mother letters or alphabet, the Siddha.'

Composed in verses without rhyme by a famous Chinese priest named Yi-hsing (Ikigio, in Japanese), of the Thang dynasty (who died in 717 or 727). He was not only a good Sanskrit scholar, but also 'deeply versed in the sciences of astronomy and mathematics, by the aid of which he reformed the Chinese calendar. Several works on the above-named sciences proceeded from his pen.'—Mayers' Chinese Reader's Manual, p. 277, No. 921.

Published in 1669 by a Japanese priest named Kiozen. This table gives a peculiar meaning of each of the Sanskrit letters. There are two appendices, namely:—

(1) 字母離分 Zi-mo-ri-bun, or 'an analysis of the alphabet,' which is however incomplete. This table again gives a meaning of each part of a letter, e. g. '⌒ heaven, 人 man, ノ earth, and 乚 direction=

忍 (荒), which has the meaning of freedom from birth and destruction or death.'

(2) 梵字悉曇字母弁釋義

Bon-zi-shitsu-tan-zi-mo-narabini-shaku-gi, or an explanation of the Sanskrit alphabet. Composed by Kukai (died 835), the founder of the Japanese Shingon sect, i. e. the Mantra school.

9   因亏字母表便覽

(Siddhâm) Zi-mo-hio-ben-ran, or 'a manual of the table of the alphabet, the Siddha.'

Published in Kioto in 1719. This is a commentary on the preceding table by Yi-hsing. But the compiler's name is not given.

10 a   悉曇字記

Shitsu-tan-zi-ki, or 'a record of the letters of the Siddha.' Composed by a Chinese priest named K'-kwang (Kikô, in Japanese), of the Thang dynasty, about 800. Published in 1669 by Kiozen. This record gives a table of the Devanâgari alphabet in a peculiar form, and a few rules on the formation of compound letters. The author, K'-kwang, was a disciple of Pragñâbodhi, of Southern India, who was a disciple of Pragñâkosha, i. e. another name of Amoghavagra (died 774). This work was first brought to Japan by Kukai in 806.

10 b   悉曇字記

This is a second copy of the same edition as before.

11   悉曇字記鈔

Shitsu-tan-zi-ki-shio, i. e. a commentary on the preceding work. 6 vols.: 6 fasciculi. Compiled by a Japanese priest named Yiukwai. The date of the publication is not mentioned, but there is a note at the end of the work, in which it is stated that this was collated with six or seven good copies by a priest named Unnô, together with more than ten friends, in 1669.

12   悉曇字記指南鈔玄談

Shitsu-tan-zi-ki-shi-nan-shio-gen-dan, i. e. an introduction to the following work. Composed by a Japanese priest named Zioten in 1696, and published in Kioto in 1697.

13   悉曇字記指南鈔

Shitsu-tan-zi-ki-shi-nan-shio, i. e. a commentary on No. 10. 3 vols.: 6 fasciculi. Compiled by the same priest, and published in the same year as the preceding.

14   因亏字記捷覽

(Siddhâm) Zi-ki-shio-ran. This is another commentary on No. 10. 2 vols.: 2 fasciculi. Compiled by a Japanese priest named Shiukwan in 1698, and published in 1699.

15   悉曇藏

Shitsu-tan-zô, lit. 'a treasure of the Siddha.' 8 vols.: 8 fasciculi. Published in 1672. This is a great work of a Japanese priest, of the Tendai sect, named Annen. It contains numerous extracts from the Chinese Tripitaka and some other books, under eight heads, concerning the Sanskrit alphabet. There is a preface by the author, which is dated 880. It is stated in a note at the end of the work, that in 1230 this work was copied by a priest in the monastery called Kôshiozi, on the Kôya mountain, in the province Kii; where the principal temple and monastery of the Shingon sect were erected by Kukai, the founder of the sect, in 816. They are still in existence.

16   悉曇十八章

Shitsu-tan-ziu-haki-shio, or 'the eighteen sections on the Siddha.' Composed by a Japanese priest named Yiusen in 1566, and published in 1645. It is a short manual of the Sanskrit alphabet.

17   悉曇愚鈔

Shitsu-tan-gu-shio, or 'humble notes on the Siddha.' 2 vols.: 2 fasciculi. Written by a Japanese priest named Kiozen in 1659, and published by him in 1668.

18   悉曇連聲集

Shitsu-tan-ren-shio-shiu, or 'a collection of the "joining sounds" (i. e. compound letters) of the Siddha.' Collected and explained by Kiozen in 1668, and probably published by him in the same year.

19   悉曇初心鈔

Shitsu-tan-sho-shin-shio, or 'notes on the Siddha for beginners.' Written by Kiozen in 1671, and probably published by him in the same year.

20   悉曇考覈鈔

Shitsu-tan-kô-kaku-shio. This is a commentary on the Siddha or the Sanskrit alphabet. 4 vols.: 4 fasciculi. Originally composed by a Japanese priest named Yiukwai, and compiled by his surviving disciple Riohen, and published in 1669.

21 a 囡否三審鈔

फ्ग्गी (Siddhâm) san-mitsu-shio, or 'the records of the three secrets (of body, speech, and mind) concerning the Siddha.' Collected by a Japanese priest named Ziogon in about 1682, and published in the same year. 8 vols.: 7 fasciculi, and an extra vol. (i. e. the 1st), which contains two prefaces, dated 1682 and 1684, that of the later date is given first, and also a table of contents. This is a work similar to No. 15, and several accounts concerning the Sanskrit alphabet are arranged under eight heads.

21 b 囡否三審鈔

This is a second copy of the same edition as before. 6 vols.: 7 fasciculi.

22 梵字悉曇章椎輪

Bon-zi-shitsu-tan-shio-tsui-rin. This is a commentary on 'the section on the Siddha,' compiled by a Japanese priest named Tôku in 1806, and published in the same year.

23 悉曇字記椎輪

Shitsu-tan-zi-ki-tsui-rin. This is a commentary on No. 10, compiled and published by the same as before.

24 梵字原圖

Bon-zi-gen-dzu, or 'a table of the origin of the Sanskrit alphabet.' Made by a Japanese named Matama, who seems not to have been a priest. The date is not mentioned.

25 悉曇摩多體文

Shitsu-tan-ma-ta-tai-mon. This is a table of the Sanskrit alphabet with a few notes. Made by a Japanese priest named Kwairei, and published in 1869.

26 七九略鈔底彦多

Shiki-ku-ryaku-shio-ki-gen-ta. This is a work on the Tiñanta (तिङन्त) or the verbs of the Sanskrit. 2 vols.: 2 fasciculi. Written and annotated by a Japanese priest named Gomio in 1765, according to the instruction of his teacher Ziun, a famous Siddha scholar. Published in 1800. It contains several extracts from the Chinese Tripitaka and some other works. This forms a part of a large collection entitled Bon-gaku-shin-rio, or a 'ferry-beam for the study of Sanskrit.' This collection is said to consist of about 1000 fasciculi, most of them are still in MSS. preserved in a monastery called Kôkizi, in the province Kawaki; in which monastery Ziun was the president.

CLASS IV.

COLLECTION OF THE VIGAS OR THE MYSTICAL LETTERS OR SYLLABLES AND OF INVOCATIONS.

27 種類集

Shu-rui-shiu, or 'a collection of the Vigas.' Published in 1667.

28 梵字

Bon-zi (lit. 'Brahma letters,' i. e. the Sanskrit letters). This is another collection of the Vigas. Written (and published) in 1669 by Kiozen.

29 a 種子集

Shu-zi-shiu, or 'a collection of the Vigas.' 2 vols.: 2 fasciculi. Written by Kiozen, and published in Kioto in 1670.

29 b 種子集

This is a copy of a later edition of the same work as before, published in 1682.

30 五佛種子

Go-butsu-shu-zi, or 'the Vigas of five Buddhas.' This is the handwriting, containing six syllables, of a priest named Kakugen, which name is seen in the lower seal at the end of the book. No date.

31 金剛界句義抄

Kon-gô-kai-ku-gi-shio, or a collection of invocations concerning a Mandala called the Vagra-dhâtu.

32 胎藏界句義抄

Tai-zô-kai-ku-gi-shio, or a collection of invocations concerning a Mandala called the Garbha-dhâtu. The above two works were published in 1684.

CLASS V.

WORKS ON THE MUDRÂS OR CERTAIN POSITIONS OR INTERTWININGS OF THE FINGERS.

33 千手觀音瑜伽玄秘略

Sen-zu-kwannon-yu-ga-gen-hi-ryaku. This is the latter portion of a work on the Mudrâs. Composed by a Japanese priest named *K*ishuku, and published in 1712.

34 四度印圖

Shi-do-in-dzu, or a table of the forms of the Mudrâs. 2 vols.: 2 fasciculi. Published in 1669.

CLASS VI.

35 住心品疏略解

*Z*iu-shin-bon-sho-ryaku-ge, or a commentary on a (Chinese) commentary on the First Chapter of the Mahâ-vairo*k*ana-sûtra[1]. 9 vols.: 8 fasciculi, and an extra vol. (i. e. the 1st) containing an introduction. Compiled by a Japanese priest named Miogoku, and published by his disciple Rentai in 1702. The original Chinese commentary was compiled by Yi-hsing (I*k*igio), of the Thang dynasty (see note under No. 8).

CLASS VII.

36 密嚴諸秘釋

Mitsu-gon-sho-hi-shaku. This is a collection of 49 miscellaneous treatises, some (if not all) of them written by a Japanese priest named Kakuban, who founded a new school of the Shingon sect in 1130. 10 vols.: 10 fasciculi. The name of the collector and the date of the publication are not mentioned.

CLASS VIII.

37 梵文般若心經釋

Bon-mon-han-nya-shin-gio-shaku, or an explanation of the Sanskrit text of the Prag*ñ*âpâramitâh*r*idaya-sûtra[2]. Explained by a Japanese priest named Hôgo, a disciple of *Z*iun. Published by his fellow-disciple Tenzu in 1807. It contains the text, and a transliteration and a literal translation, both in Chinese, and an explanation. This explanation is also written in Chinese, to which the marks before explained are added. In the explanation, an unsuccessful attempt is made to give a grammatical analysis of the text, in the same style as in a similar work of the same author on the Sukhâvativyûha (see Professor Max Müller's Selected Essays, vol. ii. p. 348). This work forms the 346th book (i. e. fasciculus) of that large collection called Bon-gaku-shin-rio, or a 'ferry-beam for the study of Sanskrit' (see note under No. 26).

---

[1] No. 530 of the Chinese Tripi*t*aka.   [2] See No. 3, 1.

B

MR. S. AMOS' COLLECTION.

A LIST OF FIVE CHINESE AND TWO JAPANESE LAW BOOKS, PRESENTED TO MR. S. AMOS
BY THE JAPANESE GOVERNMENT.

NOTE—The titles of the five Chinese works are written in this list as they are generally pronounced in Japan, and with the Pekingese pronunciation added in parentheses. Nos. 38–40 were published in Japan, 41, 42 in China. The difference between the Chinese and Japanese sounds of the same character shows the changes that have taken place in the pronunciation of Chinese. All other Chinese proper names in this list are written with the Pekingese pronunciation only.

38   唐 律 疏 議

Tô-ritsu-so-gi (Thang-lü-su-i), or 'a commentary on the law of the Thang dynasty' (A.D. 618–907). 14 vols.: 30 fasciculi. Published in Japan in 1805, with the marks of Japanese translation on the right of each column. The compilation of this commentary was finished in 653, under the reign of the Emperor Kaotsung, by *K*hang-sun Wu-ki[1] and 18 others. The law itself was written down in 12 fasciculi and 500 articles in the preceding reign of the Emperor Thai-tsung (627–649). There are two prefaces, dated 1327 and 1735 respectively; and that of the later date is given first.

39   唐 六 典

Tô-roku-ten (Thang-liu-tien)[2], lit. 'the Six Canons of Thang,' or the official book of the Thang dynasty

---

[1] Mayers' Chinese Reader's Manual, p. 12, No. 39 a.

[2] As to the origin of the term 'Liu-tien,' or the Six Canons, Mr. Suyematz Kenchio, in London, gave me an extract from an ancient Chinese classic entitled *K*eu-li(-*ku*-su), or 'the rites of the *K*eu dynasty (with a commentary,' fasc. 1, fol. 14 b); the book is in the possession of the Royal Asiatic Society, in London. A translation of this extract is as follows:—

'The duty of the prime minister is to control the (following) Six fundamental Canons, and help the sovereign to rule the country.

'1. *K*'-tien, or the Canon of Ruling or Governing, by which he regulates the country, rules official departments, and governs the people.

'2. Kiao-tien, or the Canon of Instruction, by which he tranquillizes the country, instructs official departments, and pacifies the people.

'3. Li-tien, or the Canon of Ceremony, by which he makes the country peaceful, controls officials, and harmonizes the people.

'4. *K*ǎng-tien, or the Canon of Administration, by which he subdues the country, corrects officials, and rules the people equitably.

'5. Hsing-tien, or the Canon of Punishment, by which he

(A.D. 618–907). It enumerates the principal and subordinate officers belonging not only to the Six Boards of the Central Administration[1], but also to various departments, and describes their duties. 8 vols.: 30 fasciculi. Published with marks similar to those in No. 38, in 1836, in 'Tôto,' lit. 'eastern capital,' i.e. one of the former common names of Yedo (now Tôkio), of Japan. The work is ascribed to the Emperor Hsüentsung (713–755); and the commentary on it was compiled by Li Lin-fu[2] and others. There is a preface, dated 1515, in which it is stated that this work was probably compiled by *K*ang *K*iu-ling[3] and others in the period Khai-yuen (713–741). An appendix is dated 1134.

40   明 律

Min-ritsu (Ming-lü), or 'the law of the Ming dynasty' (1368–1644). 9 vols.: 30 fasciculi of the statutes and 3 fasciculi of the by-laws. Published in Japan in the period Kioho (1716–1735), with the marks of Japanese translation on both sides of each column. This was compiled by a minister of state, Liu Wéi-*k*hien, and others in 1374, modifying the law of the Thang dynasty (618–907). It comprises 606 articles. There is an Imperial preface, dated 1397, by Thai-tsu, the founder of the Ming dynasty (reigned 1368–1398). This is one of the well-known Chinese law books in Japan.

---

judges the country, punishes or examines officials, and combines the people.

'6. Sh'-tien, or the Canon of Business, by which he makes the country rich, employs officials, and causes the people to get means of living.'

[1] Cf. Mayers' Chinese Reader's Manual, p. 326, No. 206.

[2] Mayers' Chinese Reader's Manual, p. 118, No. 356.

[3] Mayers' Chinese Reader's Manual, p. 6, No. 21.

41   大 清 會 典

Dai-Shin-ye-ten (Ta-Tshing-hwui-tien), or 'a compilation of the canons or statutes of the great Tshing dynasty' (i. e. the present dynasty of China, began 1644). 24 vols.: 100 fasciculi. Published in China, but the date is not given. The compilation was finished in 1690, by a prince and numerous officials. An Imperial preface is dated 1764.

42 大 清 律 例 刑 案 新 纂 集 成

Dai-Shin-ritsu-rei-kei-an-shin-san-shiu-sei(Ta-Tshing-lü-li-hsing-an-sin-tswan-tsi-*khăng*), or 'a new complete compilation of the laws or by-laws and law papers of the great Tshing dynasty.' 24 vols.: 40 fasciculi. Published in China in 1875. Originally compiled by Yao Yü-hsiang, and added to by Hu Yang-shan. At the beginning of this book, there are seven Imperial writings, either prefaces or commands, dated 1646, 1679, 1725 (bi), 1740, and 1799 respectively.

43   類 聚 三 代 格

Rui-zu-san-dai-kaku, or 'a classified collection or compilation of the laws or statutes of three reigns.' 16 vols. Published in Japan in the period Kôkwa (1844–1847) with the marks of the Japanese translation of a Chinese composition on both sides of each column. The date of publication is given on the opposite side of the cover of the first volume, but the present copy is evidently a later edition; because there is a note, dated 1852, at the end of the third volume. This is a useful compilation of three separate books of the old Japanese laws, the different subjects being arranged in proper order. The following are the titles, dates, and compilers of the three books :—

(1) 弘 仁 格 Kô-nin-kaku, or 'the law (compiled) in the period Kônin' (10th year=819), by a minister of state, Fugiwara Fuyutsugu, and others.

(2) 貞 觀 格 Gio-gwan-kaku, or 'the law (compiled) in the period Giogwan' (10th year=868), by a minister, Fugiwara Ugimuné, and others.

(3) 延 喜 格 Yen-gi-kaku, or 'the law (compiled) in the period Yengi' (7th year=907), by a minister of state, Fugiwara Tokihira, and others.

The present compilation seems not to be a very recent work, but the name of the compiler is not mentioned.

44   延 喜 式

Yen-gi-shiki, or 'ceremonial rules (compiled) in the period Yengi' (901–922). 50 vols.: 50 fasciculi. Published in Japan in 1723. This is a very well-known Japanese law book, which contains minute rules to be performed by the Court or the Government in honour of the Kami or deities and Confucius, and on other occasions. The compilation was first ordered by the Mikado Daigo (898–930) to his minister Fugiwara Tokihira and others in 905. But most of these compilers died in a few years, leaving their work unfinished. In 912, therefore, the Mikado again ordered his minister Fugiwara Tadahira, a younger brother of Tokihira, and others to continue the work. They finished their compilation in 927, the 5th year of the period Yenkio. It was first published in 1657, and was carefully revised in 1667; the present copy is a later edition of the text of 1667. The rules, contained in this book, are for the most part similar to those of the Thang dynasty of China. An appendix, dated 1648, is added by a famous Japanese Confucianist, Hayashi Dôshun (died 1657), who was the founder of the so-called orthodox school of Confucianism in Japan.

PROFESSOR MAX MÜLLER'S COLLECTION.

A LIST OF JAPANESE BOOKS AND MANUSCRIPTS ETC., PRESENTED TO THE BODLEIAN LIBRARY
BY PROFESSOR MAX MÜLLER.

45

A roll in a box. Sent to Professor Max Müller as a present in November 1880, by H. E. Iwakura Tomomi, Minister at the Japanese Government; who visited England some years ago as the chief Ambassador of the Mikado. This roll contains carefully executed fac-similes of three Sanskrit MSS., preserved in Japan. The following is a list of the three MSS. :—

(a) A palm-leaf MS., 4 pages, believed to be the writing of the venerable Ânanda; and given by Pragñatara, of the Nâlanda monastery of Central India, to Yen*k*in, the fifth chief priest of the Japanese Tendai sect. Yen*k*in went to China in A.D. 853, and returned to Japan in 858. He met the Indian priest in the former country, and learnt from him the 悉曇章 Shitsu-tan-shio, lit. 'a section on the Siddha or the Sanskrit alphabet.' He is now better known by his posthumous title 智證大師 *K*ishio Daishi, or 'a great teacher called *K*ishio;' which title is mentioned in a note appended to the facsimile. The Sanskrit text contains a Dhârani, but it is not complete; and the palm-leaves are much injured. It begins : Nama*h* sarvabud-dhabodhisattvebhya*h*, etc. The palm-leaves are said to be still preserved among the treasures of the monastery Rai*k*ôzi, near the Biwa lake, in the province Ômi.

(b) Another palm-leaf MS., 2 pages, believed to be the writing of the venerable Kâsyapa. Formerly pre-served among the treasures of the monastery Hôriuzi, in the province Yamato; but now belonging to the Imperial Japanese Court. The first page, which is wrongly put under the second, contains the greater part of the Pragñâpâramitâh*r*idaya-sûtra; and the second, the latter passages of this Sûtra, and the whole of the Ush*n*ishavigaya-dhârani, generally known in Japan as the Son-shio (lit. 'honourable-excellent')-dhârani, and a list of the Sanskrit alphabet. See Professor Max Müller's Selected Essays, vol. ii. pp. 368 and 370. See also No. 46 a; Nos. 61, 62, 63.

(c) The writing of Pragñatara, 2 pages. Brought to

Japan by his before-mentioned disciple *K*ishio Daishi, and now preserved in a certain building called Tôin, lit. 'Chinese temple,' within the monastery Onziozi, also called Miidera, near the Biwa lake. It contains some portions of short Mantras. See No. 46 e, 3.

46   阿叉羅帖

A-sha-ra-*gi*o, i. e. the folded book of the Akshara or syllables or letters. 5 vols.: the first four are the same size, the fifth longer. Sent to Professor Max Müller by Mr. Satow, Japanese Secretary to the British Legation at Tôkio (formerly called Yedo), in November 1880. It is a collection of facsimiles of some old San-skrit MSS. and the handwritings of many Buddhists (chiefly priests) of the three countries of India, China, and Japan. Most of the originals are said to exist in several temples or monasteries in Japan. The name of the editor and the date of the publication are not men-tioned in the book itself; but on the outside covering, there is a seal stamped, in which 16 Chinese characters are given, namely : 大日本伊勢國安濃郡洞津西來寺文庫 Dai Nippon, Ise(no)kuni, Ano-gôri, Hora(no)tsu, Sairaizi, bunko, i. e. 'the Library of the monastery Sairaizi, at Hora-no-tsu, in the district Ano, of the province Ise, of great Japan.' From this seal it appears that this book was either published by a priest of this monastery, or that this copy formerly belonged to the said library. There are facsimiles of four palm-leaf MSS. at the beginning of the first part, namely :—

(a) Pragñâpâramitâh*r*idaya-sûtra and Ush*n*ishavi-gaya-dhârani, the same as the second MS. in the roll. See Nos. 37, 45 b.

(b) MS. preserved in the monastery Kôkizi, in the province Kawa*k*i. See also No. 57.

(c) MS. preserved in the monastery Shioriozi, at Saga near Kioto.

(d) MS. preserved in the monastery (Tô) Shiodaizi, at Nara in the province Yamato.

(e) Then there follow the facsimiles of the writings of three Indian priests who lived in China under the Thang dynasty (A.D. 618–907); whose names are (1) Subhakarasimha (about 700), (2) Amoghavagra (died in 774), and (3) Pragñatara (about 850). See No. 45 c. The rest of the collection are specimens of the writings of Chinese and Japanese Buddhists. These writings contain Dhâranîs, Mantras, list of the Sanskrit alphabet, and some Chinese verses and treatises.

47 梵漢阿彌陀經

Bon-kan-a-mi-da-kio, lit. 'Sanskrit-Chinese Amitâbba-sûtra,' i. e. the smaller Sukhâvatîvyûha-mahâ-yâna-sûtra. 1 vol.: 36 leaves and a half, with a preface of 2 leaves. This is the book which Professor Max Müller mentions in his Selected Essays (vol. ii. p. 347). A plate given to face p. 342 in the same work is a facsimile of the first half of the sixth leaf of this book. It contains the Sanskrit text, with a Japanese transliteration in the Kata-kana or the side letters on the right of each syllable, and a literal Chinese translation on the left in each column. The preface is written in Chinese and dated 1773, by the Japanese editor Ziomio. The Sanskrit text with English translation and notes has been published by Professor Max Müller in the Journal of the Royal Asiatic Society, 1880.

48 景祐天竺字源

Kei-yiu-Ten-giku-zi-gen (King-yiu-Thien-ku-tsz'-yuen, in Pekiugese), or 'the source of Indian words (lit. letters, compiled) in the period King-yiu.' 2 vols.: 6 fasciculi. Compiled by an Indian priest, Fa-hu (Dharmagupta?), together with a Chinese priest, Wéi-tsing, in the second year of the King-yiu period (1035), under the reign of the Emperor Zǎn-tsung, of the Sung dynasty. A preface is given by this Emperor, who wrote it in the same year. (See Fo-tsu-thung-ki, fasc. 45, fol. 6 a.) This book is mentioned in the K'-yuen-fa-pao-kien-thung-tsun-lu, or the Catalogue of the Chinese Buddhist canon, compiled in the K'-yuen period (1285), fasc. 7, fol. 22 a. In the Imperial preface and the Catalogue, this work is said to be complete in seven fasciculi; but the seventh is wanting in the present copy. This copy is dated 1722, and is in the handwriting of Kwanshiki, a Japanese priest. The whole book contains every possible and impossible combination of the Devanâgari letters with a Chinese transliteration, and a peculiar meaning of certain syllables.

The above two books (Nos. 47 and 48) were sent to Professor Max Müller by a Japanese scholar, Shuntai Ishikawa: the former in December 1879, and the latter in February 1881.

49

A Japanese translation of the Sukhâvatîvyûha-mahâ-yâna-sûtra. Written in the Kata-kana or the side letters. 11 leaves and a half, with a preface and two comparative tables of the Devanâgari, English, and Japanese letters, 4 leaves. Made by Bunyiu Nanjio, depending on the English translation of Professor Max Müller.—Selected Essays, vol. ii. pp. 348–362.

50

The same translation as before, written in the Roman letter. 11 pages, with a preface of 3 pages.

The above two MSS. were presented to Professor Max Müller by his pupil Bunyiu Nanjio in April 1880.

51

A facsimile of the palm-leaf MS. of the monastery Kairiuwôzi ('Sâgaranâgarâgavihâra'), at Nara in the province Yamato. 6 lines on each side, in a peculiar Sanskrit alphabet. Made from the original by two Japanese Buddhist students, K. Kanematsu and Y. Ôta, at the Exhibition at Nara, in April 1880. Certain parts are worm-eaten; and those letters written with the red colour are said to be doubtful to the copyists. Transcribed by Bunyiu Nanjio in the Devanâgari alphabet. The same as No. 59.

52

A facsimile of the palm-leaf MS. of the monastery Kigenzi, at Ôsaka in the province Settsu. 4 lines on each side. Made from the original by Kanematsu and Ôta, at the Exhibition in the same city of Ôsaka, in April 1880. This MS. is said to have been brought from China to Japan by Kishio Daishi in 858, who was mentioned before at No. 45. Transcribed as before.

53

A facsimile of the palm-leaf MS. of the monastery Honsenzi in Ôsaka. Pâli, in Kamboga letters. A fragment of the Vesantara-sutta. Made by Kanematsu and Ôta, at the Exhibition in Ôsaka, in June 1880. A similar leaf is said to be kept in the monastery Saihôzi, at Fushimi near Kioto.

54

MS. of the Sanskrit text of the Vagrakkhedikâ-pragñâpâramitâ-sûtra. 3 vols. Copied by K. Kanematsu, in September 1880, in the monastery Kôkizi, from a large collection entitled Bon-gaku-shin-rio, or 'a ferry-beam for the study of Sanskrit.' The present copy contains the text, three translations and a transliteration, both in Chinese. One of the three translations is merely a literal rendering (written on the right of the text); while the other two are those by Kumâra-gîva (about 401) and Dharmagupta (about 600)—(written in parallel columns next to the transliteration, which is given on the left immediately after the text). The author of the transliteration and the literal translation is unknown at present. The original MS. of this copy forms the 320th fasciculus of the large collection, the Bon-gaku-shin-rio. The comparison of the text with the three Chinese translations is said to have been made by a Japanese priest, Hôzu or Kidô, a disciple of Ziun, in about 1847.

The above three facsimiles and one MS. were sent to Professor Max Müller by the Eastern Hongwanzi, the principal monastery of the Tôha or the Eastern party or sect of the Shinshu, in Kioto. The former three were received here in October 1880, and the last in February 1881.

55

MS. of the Vagrakkhedikâpragñâpâramitâ-sûtra. 1 vol. divided into 2 parts: leaves 24 and 33. This is another copy of the same text as before. This copy seems to have been made by Mr. Kaishin Kurehito, of the monastery Kôkizi, and sent to Professor Max Müller by Mr. Satow.

56   普 賢 行 願 讚

Fu-gen-gio-gwan-san, i.e. the Samantabhadrakaristotra, or the Samantabhadrapranidhâna. 1 vol.: 22 leaves. Copied by a Japanese priest, Kaigon Fugimura, of the monastery Nyogwanzi, in July 1880. Sent by Mr. Satow to Professor Max Müller. The Sanskrit text of this work is also found in—

(a) MS. of the Royal Asiatic Society, London (Hodgson Collection). No. 33. 7 leaves.

(b) A volume belonging to the Imperial Academy of Sciences at St. Petersburg. No. 576. 17 leaves. Block-printing; the pagination is written in the Chinese characters, so that it seems to have been published in Peking or somewhere else in China. It contains the Sanskrit text and a Tibetan transliteration and translation.

57

A facsimile of the palm-leaf MS. of the monastery Kôkizi. 4 lines on each side. Made from the original by Mr. Kaishin Kurehito, of the same monastery, in August 1880, at the request of Mr. Satow, and presented to Professor Max Müller. This MS. is the same as that which is mentioned under No. 46 b. Transcribed in the Devanâgarî by B. N.

58

A facsimile of the palm-leaf MS. of the monastery Zuisenzi, at Kioshi in the province Yamashiro. 4 lines, only one side. Made from another copy by Mr. Kaishin Kurehito, in August 1880, at the request of Mr. Satow, and sent to Professor Max Müller. Transcribed as before.

59

A facsimile of the palm-leaf MS. of the monastery Kairiuwôzi. 6 lines on each side. Made by Mr. Kaishin Kurehito, in September 1880, from an old copy by Ziun. This MS. is the same as that of No. 51.

The above two MSS. and three facsimiles were sent to Professor Max Müller from Japan by Mr. Satow, in December 1880 and in May 1881.

60

Three facsimiles of the palm-leaf MS. of the monastery Ki-on-in, in Kioto. Pâli. Sent to Professor Max Müller by H. E. Iwakura Tomomi, in December 1880.

61

Copy of Pragñâpâramitâhridaya-sûtra, made by Mr. Kaishin Kurehito for Mr. Satow, and sent to Professor Max Müller. Same as Nos. 45 b, 46 a.

62

Another copy of Pragñâpâramitâhridaya-sûtra and Sonshio-dhârani, presented by H. E. Iwakura Tomomi to Professor Max Müller.

63

A copy of the MSS. of four Sanskrit texts. Made by two Japanese Buddhist students, K. Kanematsu and Y. Ôta, in June and July 1880. Sent to Professor Max Müller by the Eastern Hongwanzi, in Kioto, in October 1880. The following is a list of the four texts:—

(a) The Pragñâpâramitâhridaya-sûtra, with a transliteration (black) and a literal translation (red), both in Chinese.

(b) The Ushnishavigaya-dhârani, with a transliteration and translation as before. Then there follows a list of the Sanskrit alphabet, with the heading of 'Siddham.'

The above two texts were copied from the original palm-leaf MS. (two pages), which formerly belonged to the Hôriuzi; so that these are the same as Nos. 45 b, 46 a, 61 (which contains only the first text), and 62. But the Chinese transliteration and translation seem to have been made by a Japanese priest, Ziogon, who lived about two centuries ago, and the writers of our copy used his copy of these texts as a guide, while they were making their own copy from the original palm-leaf MS. In that old copy they found the present Chinese transliteration and translation. (This account is given in a letter of the two copyists to me.—B. N.)

(c) The Son-shio-shio-shin-zu, or 'honourable-excellent-small-mind-dhârani.' Copied from the original MS., which is the handwriting of a Chinese priest, Kanshin, on a dark blue paper with silver paint (Kon-shi-gon-dei). He came to Japan in A.D. 753, and founded a sect called Ritsushu or the sect of Vinaya; which no longer exists independently, but is united with another sect. The original MS. is said to contain five Mantras and this Dhârani. It is in the possession of the monastery Tô-shiodaizi, founded by Kanshin, at Nara in the province Yamato.

(d) A longer Pragñâpâramitâhridaya-sûtra, with a translation of a priest of Kubhâ (Cabul), Pragña (about A.D. 800), of the Thang dynasty (618–907), and a transliteration, both in Chinese. Copied from another copy kept among the monastery, Hasedera, at Hase in the province Yamato. The original MS. or a copy was brought from China to Japan in the ninth century of the Christian era, by a Japanese priest, Yeun, a disciple of Kukai (died 835). It is said to have been preserved in the monastery Shiokiin, on the Kôya mountain in the province Kii. There are seven dates given at the end of the present copy, viz. A.D. 1110, 1694, 1713, 1716, 1741, 1768, 1880. In these periods, certain priests made a copy of this text: the present copy is the last of all. This text is found also in a Sanskrit book, printed in China, and belonging to Mr. Wylie, pp. 30–32.

64 　梵 語 通 例

Bon-go-tsû-rei, lit. 'Common examples of the Sanskrit words.' This is a third Chinese-Sanskrit (but no Japanese) vocabulary. 5 vols. Sent to Professor Max Müller by a Japanese scholar, Shuntai Ishikawa, in May 1881. It is a Japanese MS.; but neither name of the collector or copyist nor date of the collection or copy is mentioned. The words are gathered together under ten different subjects, taking from several Chinese books, and especially from those two Chinese-Sanskrit-Japanese vocabularies, as already mentioned in the list of Mr. Wylie's Collection, as Nos. 6 and 7. Under each word, a part of the title of a book from which it is taken is given. It may be curious to add here a list of the ten different subjects, which is as follows:—

(a) Heaven and earth.	Vol. i.
(b) Instruments and treasures.	
(c) Relations of life.	
(d) Members of body.	Vol. ii.
(e) Different kinds of beings, chiefly lower animals.	
(f) Light and colour.	
(g) Number and measure.	Vol. iii.
(h) Food and incense.	
(i) Plants.	
(j) Manners and accomplishments, or miscellany.	Vols. iv and v.

Thus it seems to be a very useful collection, but after all it proves the reverse; because the sources drawn upon in this vocabulary are not always quite correct.

THE END.